CATALYSIS IN CHEMISTRY
AND ENZYMOLOGY

CATALYSIS IN CHEMISTRY AND ENZYMOLOGY

WILLIAM P. JENCKS
Professor of Biochemistry
Brandeis University

McGRAW-HILL BOOK COMPANY

NEW YORK   ST. LOUIS   SAN FRANCISCO   LONDON
SYDNEY   TORONTO   MEXICO   PANAMA

547.139
J 51

CATALYSIS IN CHEMISTRY
AND ENZYMOLOGY

Library of Congress Catalog Card Number 68-31661

32305

1 2 3 4 5 6 7 8 9 0 M A M M 7 6 5 4 3 2 1 0 6 9

Dedicated to:
George Wald
Fritz Lipmann
R. B. Woodward
Frank Westheimer
N. O. Kaplan
each of whom made this
volume possible

Preface

Catalysis by an enzyme requires the specific binding of one or more substrate molecules to a catalytic site and a chemical interaction with this site, which may directly utilize the binding forces, to decrease the free energy of activation of the catalyzed reaction. The purpose of this volume is to bring together some of the facts and principles about reactions and interactions in aqueous solution which are pertinent to an understanding of mechanisms of catalysis in this extraordinary solvent. The discussion is limited almost entirely to homogeneous ionic reactions; there is little or no discussion of heterogeneous catalysis or of oxidation-reduction reactions. Although reference is made to some specific examples of enzymatic reactions, the emphasis is on basic principles rather than on the properties of particular enzymes, for the same reason that many investigators feel that an understanding of cancer is more likely to come from an understanding of the mechanism of replication and differentiation than from study of cancerous tissues. These principles are of interest in their own right for students and investigators who are concerned with the mechanism and catalysis of nonenzymatic reactions in aqueous solution. Not all of the material in this volume is directly applicable to enzymatic catalysis at this time, but it is a part of the framework and language which has developed from our increased understanding of the mechanisms of chemical reactions in recent years, and it should provide part of the framework and language for an understanding of enzymatic catalysis in future years. To paraphrase Hindemith at the end of his book "Traditional Harmony,"[1] a knowledge of the material in this book proves nothing about the creative abilities of the student who has attained it; on the other hand, an enzymologist, even a very gifted one, is no more than half grown and unskilled if he is not thoroughly familiar with this material.

This book is based on the material presented in a one-semester course on "The Chemistry of Enzyme Catalyzed Reactions"; it could be used as a text for either a one- or a two-semester course by appropriate selection of material. Courses in physical chemistry and advanced organic chemistry, taken previously or concurrently, are desirable as background for the course. The chapters on the mechanisms by which enzymes and other substances can bind small molecules in water follow the chapters on the mechanisms by which enzymes may cause rate accelerations once the substrate is bound. Some instructors may wish to reverse the order of presentation of these topics in a course; the author has utilized both orders. The course given by the author consists of two formal lectures a week and a third, less formal, hour in which the material in the chapter on "Practical Kinetics" and some examples of the application of kinetics to the solution of problems of reaction mechanisms are discussed with the class. The chapter entitled "Carbonyl- and Acyl-group Reactions" is a summary of the results of the application of techniques for the elucidation of reaction mechanism to a particular class of reactions. The material in this chapter is not intended for presentation in a course in the same manner as the rest of the book, but may be useful for reading, reference, and discussion.

This volume is not a comprehensive review or a reference work; it is, rather, a summary of those principles and facts which seem to the author to be best understood and more or less clearly demonstrated at the present time. A considerable fraction of the book, especially that which deals with various branches of physical chemistry, is concerned with subjects about which the author is by no

[1] Paul Hindemith, "Traditional Harmony," p. 118, Associated Music Publishers, Inc., New York, 1943.

means an authority. The reason for dealing with these subjects here is simply that no single source of this material is available for the student or investigator who is not an expert in the field, and it is frequently difficult to obtain a useful introduction to this material from the detailed and often controversial literature in these areas. The author has attempted to describe those facts and principles which have provided the framework for his own thinking in these areas and to identify those subjects about which there is no general agreement. The requirements of this approach and of space have necessarily led to the omission of many important contributions to the field, and the author, for reasons of convenience and familiarity, has utilized work from his own laboratory for illustrative purposes far more than is justified by its importance.

It is impossible to acknowledge individually the contributions to this volume of the many colleagues and coworkers who have made it possible by their discussions and helpful criticisms of the manuscript. It is, however, important to emphasize the obvious; the author alone is responsible for the opinions and the errors in the book. My only regret is that I did not have the courage to follow the suggestion of a student and entitle the book "The Joy of Catalysis" (or of another student, who suggested the inverse order). I am grateful to the copyright holders, particularly the American Chemical Society, for permission to reproduce figures from the literature.

William P. Jencks

Contents

part one

Mechanisms for Catalysis

The assumption of this new force is detrimental to the progress of science, since it appears to satisfy the human spirit, and thus provides a limit to further research.

—Liebig, on Berzelius' description of catalysis

This easy kind of physiological chemistry is created at the writing desk and is the more dangerous, the more genius goes into its execution.

—Berzelius, on Liebig's "Organic Chemistry in Its Application to Physiology and Pathology"

It is not generally appreciated how little is understood about the mechanism by which enzymes bring about their extraordinary and specific rate accelerations. Our optimism about this subject is the result of the very considerable progress that has been made in elucidating the chemical nature of enzymes and, in some cases, in elucidating the steps that take place during catalysis. But there are few instances in which we have even an elementary notion of what provides the driving force for the reduction in the free energy of activation, of the meaning of the remarkable specificity, or of the relationship between catalysis and specificity in enzyme catalyzed reactions. It is revealing, with respect to these questions and to the general question of the nature of progress in science, to see how far we have progressed in some areas, and how little in others, from the views expressed by Bayliss in his monograph on "The Nature of Enzyme Action," published in 1911[1]:

CATALYSTS ARE DEFINITE CHEMICAL COMPOUNDS

Attention must be called to one more point before passing on to the consideration of the special class of catalysts known as "enzymes"; in view of certain theories as to the nature of enzymes, it is important to notice that all the catalysts mentioned in this chapter are definite chemical individuals of known composition and properties. As yet this statement cannot be made of any enzyme. We are not, however, warranted in denying definite chemical constitution to this latter class of bodies, until it has been shown that bodies of known constitution may at one time possess the properties of enzymes and at another time, without any change in their chemical nature, be devoid of such properties.

—page 8

ENZYMES NOT PROTEINS

On the whole it appears that all enzymes have not the same chemical structure, a fact probable enough in itself. Some indeed seem to belong to a class of bodies as yet unknown in chemical science, but containing nitrogen and carbohydrate in their molecules. . . .

The purified enzymes referred to above were obtained in quite sufficiently concentrated solutions to give the typical protein reactions, if they were bodies of this nature. The statement made sometimes that enzymes can be detected by their action in solutions too weak to give the most delicate protein reaction, is therefore beside the point.

—page 29

[1] W. M. Bayliss, "The Nature of Enzyme Action," 2d ed., Longmans, Green & Co., Inc., New York, 1911.

ENZYMES AS PROPERTIES

When we consider the way in which definite chemical properties diminish more and more as the preparations are purified, we see a certain degree of justification for the view expressed by De Jager and by Arthus, *viz.*, that enzymes are not chemical individuals, but that various kinds of bodies may have conferred upon them properties which cause them to behave like enzymes; so that we have to deal with properties rather than substances. The action, it is stated, can even be exerted at a distance. The experiments brought forward in support of this view are by no means convincing. . . . A somewhat similar theory has been recently proposed by Barendrecht, according to which enzymes act as radioactive bodies, the chemical activities of enzymes being due to radiations.

—pages 30, 31

GENERAL CONCLUSIONS

A careful study of these enzymes shows that they obey the usual laws of catalytic phenomena. . . . Reasons are given for the belief that the "compound" of enzyme and substrate, generally regarded as the preliminary to action, is of the nature of a colloidal adsorption-compound. The existence of a relation of this kind explains the exponential form of the law correlating the concentration of enzyme (*sic*) with its activity.

—page 116

It is customary to divide the problem of the mechanism of enzyme action into two separate parts: specificity and rate acceleration. Considerations regarding specificity have usually been based on the "lock-and-key" theory, and it has been difficult to say more than what follows obviously from the structural complementarity of the substrate and enzyme active site proposed by this theory. However, specificity is an even more characteristic property of enzymes, compared with other catalysts, than is the catalytic rate acceleration itself, and it will be a recurring theme of this volume that these two properties are frequently interdependent and inseparable. This is obvious if one is dealing with dilute solutions of substrates, which are concentrated at the active site of the enzyme through specific binding in order that the catalytic process may take place. It is less obvious for substrates at a concentration sufficient to saturate the enzyme, but there is reason to believe that in this case also the specific interactions between enzyme and substrate, mediated by binding forces, constitute an integral part of the catalytic process.

It is difficult to make a quantitative estimate of the amount of the rate acceleration brought about by enzymes, compared with other catalysts or with the rates of nonenzymatic reactions in water. In many cases the nonenzymatic reaction does not proceed at a measurable rate in the absence of enzyme under the experimental conditions in which enzyme catalysis is observed. One can then only set a lower limit for the rate acceleration, as illustrated in Table II, Chap. 1. Furthermore, the enzymatic reaction usually follows a rate law altogether different from that of the nonenzymatic reaction; it is difficult to make a meaningful comparison between an enzymatic reaction that proceeds through a first-order breakdown of the enzyme-substrate complex at 10^{-7} M hydrogen ion concentration in a pH-independent reaction and an acid catalyzed breakdown of the same substrate which follows a second-order rate law. In other words, an enzymatic reaction is likely to proceed through a mechanism which is entirely different from that of the predominant nonenzymatic reaction. It is still certain that the enzyme causes a decrease in the free energy of activation because the free energy of activation for the mechanism utilized by the enzyme is usually so high in the absence of enzyme that it does not take place at a measurable rate; it is only difficult to estimate the amount of this decrease.

It is often asked whether an enzyme lowers the enthalpy or the entropy of activation of a reaction. It is difficult to formulate an answer to this question because of the same problems of comparing different rate laws and mechanisms and the further problem that the observed thermodynamic quantities are subject to perturbations caused by changes in the structure of solvent and enzyme and do not, in any case, provide a direct measure of the potential-energy surface which is traversed by the enzyme-substrate complex.

An estimate of the decrease in the enthalpy and free energy of activation can be made in the case of the hydrolysis of urea catalyzed by urease. The nonenzymatic hydrolysis takes place with a pH-independent first-order rate constant of 4.15×10^{-5} sec^{-1} at 100° and an energy of activation of 32.7 kcal/mole.[2] The hydrolysis of urea bound to urease in an enzyme-substrate complex takes place at 20.8° and pH 8.0 with a first-order rate constant of 3×10^4 sec^{-1} and an activation energy on the order of 11 kcal/mole,[3] some 22

[2] W. H. R. Shaw and D. G. Walker, *J. Am. Chem. Soc.* **80**, 5337 (1958).

[3] M. C. Wall and K. J. Laidler, *Arch. Biochem. Biophys.* **43**, 299 (1953). This rate constant is based on a molecular weight of 483,000. If, as seems probable, there is more than one active site in each enzyme molecule, the specific rate constant for each active site will be proportionally reduced.

kcal/mole less than that of the nonenzymatic reaction. The nonenzymatic rate extrapolated to 20.8° is 3×10^{-10} sec^{-1}, so that the enzyme accelerates the rate by a factor of about 10^{14}. This rate acceleration corresponds to a lowering of the free energy of activation by 19 kcal/mole. It is probable that the mechanisms of the enzymatic and nonenzymatic reactions are different, so that the rate increase compared with the (unobserved) nonenzymatic reaction proceeding through the same mechanism is probably larger than 10^{14}.

The problem of the mechanism of enzyme action may be approached in three ways: by theorizing, by examining the properties of enzymes, and by examining the nature of chemical reactions and their catalysis. The conclusions of pure theory have not advanced dramatically since the time of Bayliss, although theory and speculation have served as a stimulus to experimental work and are utilized generously in Chap. 5. It is clear that the eventual solution of the problem must come from the elucidation of the chemistry of enzymes and enzyme-substrate complexes. However, our knowledge of this chemistry at the present time does not often provide an insight into the driving force or detailed nature of the catalytic process in any quantitative manner, and the third approach would seem to be a necessary preliminary to an understanding of these questions. Certainly, in order to understand the mechanism of catalysis of an enzymatic reaction one would first like to understand the mechanism of the nonenzymatic reaction and the means by which this reaction can be accelerated. At the present time we are in the position of the drunk on his hands and knees under the corner street light who, when approached by a citizen asking his intentions, replies that he is looking for his keys here, rather than in the poorly illuminated center of the block where they were lost, because the light is better at the corner.

Four mechanisms by which an enzyme might be expected to bring about a rate acceleration are discussed in these chapters: approximation of the reactants, covalent catalysis, general acid-base catalysis, and the induction of distortion or strain in the substrate, the enzyme, or both. It will be apparent that it is not always possible to draw a sharp line between these mechanisms: certainly no single mechanism accounts for the catalytic activity of an enzyme. They are approached here with an emphasis on where the light is; i.e., the main emphasis is on nonenzymatic reactions, although enzymatic reactions and some simple theory are discussed in cases in which something is known about the driving force for the catalytic process or in which theory is applicable in a reasonably straightforward manner. The treatment of nonenzymatic reactions and, to an even greater extent, of enzymatic reactions, is necessarily empirical and qualitative, or semiquantitative at best. However, significant progress is being made in most of these areas, and the author is hopeful that it will not be many years before this progress is sufficient to make this volume obsolete.

1
Approximation[1]

The most obvious means by which an enzyme might increase the rate of a bimolecular reaction is simply to bring the reacting molecules together at the active site of the enzyme. The two most important questions with respect to this topic are, first, the magnitude of the rate enhancement which might be expected from such an approximation of the reactants, and, second, the mechanism by which this rate enhancement is brought about. The first question is best approached by examining the rate accelerations that are brought about when the reactants are brought together in model systems, either by being covalently linked in the same molecule or by some weak and reversible binding force, similar to the forces which bind substrates to enzymes. There is no very complete answer to the

[1] For further reading and examples of intramolecular catalysis, see T. C. Bruice and S. J. Benkovic, "Bioorganic Mechanisms," vol. 1, p. 119ff., W. A. Benjamin, Inc., New York, 1966; B. Capon, *Quart. Rev.* 18, 45 (1964).

second question at the present time, but it is possible to reach some
tentative conclusions about the factors which might be expected to
lead to rate enhancements in systems of this kind by the rather
empirical application of simple principles.

A. INTRAMOLECULAR REACTIONS
AND ANCHIMERIC ASSISTANCE

1. EXAMPLES

The most extensively studied model systems are those in which the
reactants have been incorporated through covalent bonds into the
same molecule by a chemist, i.e., an intramolecular reaction or one
in which a group adjacent to the reacting center provides "anchi-
meric assistance" to the reaction. Presumably an enzyme could
bring together reacting groups in a similar relationship by making
use of the binding forces between enzyme and substrate. In both
cases, the bringing together of the reactants from dilute solution
overcomes part of the free energy of activation of the reaction, and
it would be expected that such a concentration effect would be reflected in the entropy of activation.

It is often difficult to obtain a reliable estimate of the rate acceleration which occurs in an intramolecular or anchimerically assisted reaction because the corresponding intermolecular reaction may
not proceed at all, or the intermolecular reaction between the same
compounds may proceed by a different mechanism. It is probable
that some known intramolecular reactions exhibit larger rate accelerations than any described here, but have not been examined
quantitatively for this reason. Nevertheless, several dramatic examples of large rate enhancements are known. The hydrolysis of
tetramethylsuccinanilic acid[2] occurs with intramolecular assistance at
pH 5 with a half-time of 30 minutes, whereas the estimated half-
time for the hydrolysis of acetanilide at pH 5 is some 300 years;
this is a rate difference of 1.6×10^8 (equation 1). The tetramethyl

$$
\begin{array}{ccc}
\begin{array}{c}
\mathrm{H_3C} \quad \mathrm{O} \\
| \quad || \\
\mathrm{CH_3 - C - C - NHC_6H_5} \\
| \\
\mathrm{CH_3 - C - C - OH} \\
| \quad || \\
\mathrm{H_3C} \quad \mathrm{O}
\end{array}
& \longrightarrow &
\begin{array}{c}
\mathrm{H_3C} \quad \mathrm{O} \\
| \quad || \\
\mathrm{CH_3 - C - COH} \\
| \qquad\qquad + \mathrm{H_2NC_6H_5} \\
\mathrm{CH_3 - C - COH} \\
| \quad || \\
\mathrm{H_3C} \quad \mathrm{O}
\end{array}
\end{array}
$$

(1)

[2] T. Higuchi, L. Eberson, and A. K. Herd, *J. Am. Chem. Soc.* **88**, 3805 (1966).

compound itself undergoes hydrolysis 1,200 times faster than unsubstituted succinanilic acid, which shows that the methyl groups bring the reacting and catalyzing groups into a relationship with each other which is about 4 kcal further along the reaction coordinate compared with the unsubstituted compound. It is noteworthy that the difference in rates between the substituted and unsubstituted compounds is accompanied by a decrease of more than 6 kcal/mole in the *enthalpy* of activation of the reaction.

The o-carboxyphosphonate ester 1 undergoes hydrolysis with a half-time of 15 minutes in 30% dimethylsulfoxide at 36°, whereas the *para*-substituted ester 2 undergoes no detectable hydrolysis in 77,960 hours under the same conditions.[3] The rate increase caused

by the carboxyl group in the *ortho* position amounts to a factor of more than 7×10^7. If the *ortho* carboxyl group is esterified, the abnormal reactivity is lost. It has been suggested that this rate enhancement is caused by intramolecular catalysis of proton transfer,[3] but the large magnitude of the enhancement suggests that it may involve nucleophilic attack by the adjacent carboxyl group.

Acyl compounds undergo intramolecular transfer to adjacent hydroxyl groups in a base catalyzed reaction, which is much faster than hydrolysis or intermolecular alcoholysis. An example of some biochemical interest is the migration of an acetyl group between the 2′ and 3′ hydroxyl groups of the ribose moiety of O-acetyluridine, a model for aminoacylribonucleic acid (equation 2). This migration

$$\tag{2}$$

takes place in $0.1\,M$ phosphate buffer at 20° with a half-time of 7.5 seconds; this is 350,000 times faster than the intermolecular transfer to surrounding water molecules, which has a half-time of

[3] M. Gordon, V. A. Notaro, and C. E. Griffin, *J. Am. Chem. Soc.* **86**, 1898 (1964).

some 30 days under the same conditions.[4] This rate difference is undoubtedly caused in part by the greater ease of anion formation from the ribose hydroxyl group than from water, but the rate increase which results from the proximity of the neighboring hydroxyl group must still be large. The migration is even faster for the more reactive aminoacyl compounds, which accounts for the fact that it is not possible to isolate only a single isomer of aminoacyl-ribonucleic acid from a solution which has been exposed to neutral pH. A similar rate acceleration is found in the well known formation of cyclic phosphates from nucleoside phosphate diesters, which is catalyzed by base, acid, and ribonuclease.

In these examples the inter- and intramolecular reactions which are being compared are not strictly analogous, and it would be preferable to obtain a quantitative estimate of the rate acceleration which occurs in reactions in which the same reacting groups are involved in the intramolecular and intermolecular reactions. Such a comparison of the rates of intermolecular and intramolecular reactions of two reactants A and B is complicated by the fact that the rate of the intermolecular reaction will usually be bimolecular and follow equation 3 with a rate constant k_2, which may be expressed

$$\text{Rate} = k_2[\text{A}][\text{B}] \tag{3}$$

in units of M^{-1} sec^{-1}, while the intramolecular reaction will be monomolecular and follow equation 4 with a rate constant k_1, which

$$\text{Rate} = k_1[\widehat{\text{A B}}] \tag{4}$$

may be expressed in units of sec^{-1}. The ratio k_1/k_2 has the units of molarity and represents the molarity of one of the reactants which must be present to cause a smaller concentration of the second reactant to undergo reaction with a pseudo first-order rate constant equal to that at which the intramolecular reaction occurs. For example if this ratio is 5, the pseudo first-order rate constant for the reaction of a dilute solution of A with 5 M B will be equal to the first-order rate constant for the intramolecular reaction of $\widehat{\text{A B}}$. This ratio, then, may be regarded as an estimate of the "effective concentration" of B in the vicinity of A in the molecule $\widehat{\text{A B}}$; i.e., it is the average concentration of B in the vicinity of A in the molecule $\widehat{\text{A B}}$ if the rate acceleration is caused entirely by an increase in the local concentration of B.

[4] B. E. Griffin, M. Jarman, C. B. Reese, J. E. Sulston, and D. R. Trentham, *Biochemistry* **5**, 3638 (1966).

It should be noted that the numerical value of this factor depends on the concentration units in which the second-order rate constant is expressed, and the use of the molarity scale introduces an arbitrary factor into the comparison. It might be preferable for the purposes of such comparisons to express the concentration in the unitary or mole fraction scale. The second-order rate constant would then correspond to the pseudo first-order rate constant for the reaction of a small amount of A which is completely surrounded by molecules of B. If the rate constant for a corresponding intramolecular reaction were found to be much larger than this, it would mean that factors other than a simple local concentration effect would have to be invoked to explain the increase in the rate of the intramolecular reaction. We shall return to this point later.

The nucleophilic reactions of phenyl esters with amines and carboxylate ions provide good examples of comparisons of this kind. The second-order rate constant of 8×10^{-3} M^{-1} min^{-1} for the intermolecular aminolysis of phenyl acetate by trimethylamine at 20° (equation 5) may be compared with the first-order rate constant of 10 min^{-1} for the similar intramolecular reaction of phenyl γ-$(N,N$-dimethylamino)butyrate (equation 6).[5] The ratio of these two rate

$$H_3C-\underset{\underset{CH_3}{|}}{\overset{\overset{CH_3}{|}}{N}} \quad \underset{H_3C}{\overset{O}{\underset{}{\parallel}}}C\diagdown_{OC_6H_5} \longrightarrow H_3C-\overset{+}{\underset{\underset{CH_3}{|}}{\overset{\overset{CH_3}{|}}{N}}}-\overset{O}{\overset{\parallel}{C}}CH_3 + {}^-OC_6H_5 \qquad (5)$$

$$H_3C-\underset{\underset{H_2C}{}}{\overset{\overset{H_3C}{|}}{N}}\diagdown C\overset{O}{\underset{}{\parallel}}-OC_6H_5 \longrightarrow H_3C-\overset{+}{\underset{H_2C}{\overset{\overset{H_3C}{|}}{N}}}-\overset{O}{\overset{\parallel}{C}} + {}^-OC_6H_5 \qquad (6)$$

constants is 1250 M, which implies that the "effective concentration" of trialkylamine in the neighborhood of the acyl group in the intramolecular reaction is 1250 M. Since this is an unattainable concentration, the rapid rate of the intramolecular reaction must be ascribed to factors other than a local concentration effect. The enthalpies of activation of the intermolecular and intramolecular reactions are almost identical, 12.9 and 12.5 kcal/mole, respectively, so that it is the difference of 3.7 kcal/mole in the entropy term,

[5] T. C. Bruice and S. J. Benkovic, *J. Am. Chem. Soc.* 85, 1 (1963).

$T \Delta S$, of the two reactions that is responsible for the difference in reaction rates. The imidazole group can also act as an effective nucleophile in intramolecular reactions.[6]

A more complete examination of the effect of structure on reactivity may be made in a series of substituted phenyl succinates and glutarates.[7-10] The hydrolysis of these compounds proceeds by intramolecular nucleophilic attack of the carboxylate anion on the acyl group to expel phenolate ion and form the cyclic anhydride, which undergoes hydrolysis in a subsequent step (equation 7).

$$
\begin{array}{ccc}
\underset{\underset{\displaystyle C\text{--}OC_6H_4X}{\overset{\displaystyle O}{\|}}}{\overset{}{\Big(}}\underset{C}{\overset{}{\searrow}}O & \xrightarrow{\;-\,{}^-OC_6H_4X\;} & \underset{\underset{\displaystyle O}{\|}}{\overset{\overset{\displaystyle O}{\|}}{\Big(}}\begin{array}{c}C\\ C\end{array}O \quad \xrightarrow{\;H_2O\;} \quad \Big(\begin{array}{c}COH\\ COH\end{array}
\end{array}
$$

$$
\tag{7}
$$

In the faster reactions the accumulation of the intermediate anhydride can be detected. There is a progressive increase in rate as the structure is made more rigid or as *gem*-dimethyl substituents are added (Table I). Both of these structural changes will tend to keep the reacting groups in proximity by making it improbable or impossible for the molecule to take up a number of extended configurations which would not lead to reaction. This has led to the suggestion that the increases in reaction rate result from a decrease in the number of unreactive rotamer distributions which the molecule can assume.[8] In order to account for the 53,000-fold difference in the rates of reaction of the phenyl glutarate 3 and the bicyclic compound 7, this hypothesis requires that only 1/53,000 of the population of phenyl glutarate molecules exist in a conformation in which the acyl and carboxylate groups may undergo reaction.

Comparison of these rate constants for intramolecular reactions with rate constants for corresponding intermolecular reactions is complicated by the fact that the reaction of acetate with most phenyl acetates represents general base catalysis of hydrolysis, rather than a nucleophilic attack of the carboxylate group.[11] Since

[6] G. L. Schmir and T. C. Bruice, *J. Am. Chem. Soc.* **80**, 1173 (1958); T. C. Bruice and J. M. Sturtevant, *Ibid.* **81**, 2860 (1959).

[7] E. Gaetjens and H. Morawetz, *J. Am. Chem. Soc.* **82**, 5328 (1960).

[8] T. C. Bruice and U. K. Pandit, *J. Am. Chem. Soc.* **82**, 5858 (1960).

[9] T. C. Bruice and U. K. Pandit, *Proc. Natl. Acad. Sci. U.S.* **46**, 402 (1960).

[10] T. C. Bruice and W. C. Bradbury, *J. Am. Chem. Soc.* **87**, 4846 (1965).

[11] A. R. Butler and V. Gold, *J. Chem. Soc.* **1962**, 1334; D. G. Oakenfull, T. Riley, and V. Gold, *Chem. Commun.* **1966**, 385.

Table I Intramolecular reactions of monophenyl esters of dicarboxylic acid anions [8,9]

	Ester [a]	$\dfrac{k_{\text{hydrol}}}{k_{\text{hydrol}}(glutarate)}$
3	—COOR / —COO$^-$	1.0
4	Me, Me —COOR / —COO$^-$	20
5	—COOR / —COO$^-$	230
6	COOR / COO$^-$	10,000
7	—COOR / —COO$^-$ / O	53,000

[a] R = C_6H_5- or p-Br-C_6H_4-

the rate constants for the intermolecular nucleophilic reactions must therefore be slower than the observed rate constants, we can only set a lower limit for the increase in rate which is found in the intra-molecular reactions. Such a comparison indicates that the rates of the intramolecular reactions of p-nitrophenyl and phenyl glutarate correspond to intermolecular reactions of p-nitrophenyl and phenyl acetate with more than 30 M and 600 M acetate, respectively. If the comparison is carried on to the bicyclic compound V, the differ-ence is on the order of more than $600 \times 53{,}000 = 3 \times 10^7$ M. This corresponds to a difference of more than 10,000 cal/mole in the free energies of activation of the reactions. This large rate en-hancement is of the order of magnitude that one would like to have in a model for enzymatic catalysis.

Nucleophilic catalysis by a mechanism of this kind requires a good leaving group, such as a phenolate ion, in order that displacement by carboxylate ion may occur. Phthalate monoesters undergo hydrolysis with carboxylate participation when the pH of the leaving alcohol is less than 13.5; phthalate monoesters of less acidic alcohols undergo hydrolysis by a different mechanism with assistance from the free carboxyl group.[12]

It should be possible to obtain information about the differences between intramolecular and intermolecular reactions more directly by comparing systems at equilibrium, in which the structures of the reactants and products are known, rather than by comparing rate constants, in which the structure of the reactants must be compared with a transition state of unknown structure. There are surprisingly few reactions in aqueous solution for which sufficient data are available to make even a rough comparison of this kind. One comparison which is pertinent to reactions with intramolecular participation of carboxyl groups is the hydrolysis of acetic anhydride compared with that of succinic anhydride. The free energies of these equilibria of approximately $-15,700$ and -8300 cal/mole for acetic and succinic anhydride, respectively, differ by 7400 cal/mole, which is even larger than the differences in the free energies of the transition states of related intermolecular and intramolecular reactions.[13-15] The heat of hydrolysis of acetic anhydride is $-14,000$ cal/mole.[16,17] The heat of hydrolysis of succinic anhydride is $-11,200$ kcal/mole for the solid[16] and approximately -9000 kcal/mole in water.[15] Thus, a large part of the smaller free energy for the hydrolysis of the cyclic anhydride appears as a less favorable *enthalpy* of hydrolysis. The equilibrium constants for anhydride formation increase regularly with increasing methyl substitution in the succinic acid series, with values of 1.0, 6.0, 16.5, and 32×10^{-6} for unsubstituted, methyl-, 2,2-dimethyl-, and 2,3-*dl*-dimethylsuccinic acids, respectively.[15]

[12] A. Agren, U. Hedsten, and B. Jonsson, *Acta Chem. Scand.* **15**, 1532 (1961); L. Eberson, *Ibid.* **18**, 2015 (1964); J. W. Thanassi and T. C. Bruice, *J. Am. Chem. Soc.* **88**, 747 (1966).

[13] W. P. Jencks, F. Barley, R. Barnett, and M. Gilchrist, *J. Am. Chem. Soc.* **88**, 4464 (1966).

[14] T. Higuchi, T. Miki, A. C. Shah, and A. K. Herd, *J. Am. Chem. Soc.* **85**, 3655 (1963).

[15] T. Higuchi, L. Eberson, and J. D. McRae, *J. Am. Chem. Soc.* **89**, 3001 (1967).

[16] J. B. Conn, G. B. Kistiakowsky, R. M. Roberts, and E. A. Smith, *J. Am. Chem. Soc.* **64**, 1747 (1942).

[17] I. Wadsö, *Acta Chem. Scand.* **16**, 471, 479 (1962).

The intramolecular formation of the phenyl ester of equation 8 proceeds spontaneously, i.e., with a negative free energy,[18] whereas

$$(8)$$

the formation of phenyl acetate from acetic acid and phenol requires 7390 cal/mole.[19] The more favorable free energy of more than 7400 cal/mole for the intramolecular reaction is similar to the value above for intramolecular anhydride formation.

The equilibrium constants for the formation of 5-membered lactones from γ-hydroxybutyric acid and γ-hydroxyvaleric acid of 2.7 and 13.9 correspond to free energies of -600 and -1550 cal/mole, respectively, which may be compared with the corresponding value of $+1660$ cal/mole for the synthesis of ethyl acetate (based on a standard state of 1 M for acetic acid and ethanol).[19,20] The difference between these values is considerably smaller than the previous examples.

2. INTERPRETATION

In order that a reaction between two molecules in solution may occur, it is necessary that the two molecules encounter each other, assume a correct mutual orientation, undergo changes in solvation, overcome van der Waals repulsion, and undergo the changes in electron overlap which are required to reach the transition state. We would like to know how much each of these factors may contribute to the rate accelerations which are observed in intramolecular reactions; it would be expected that similar contributions would occur in enzymatic rate accelerations.

The maximum increase in encounter frequency from an increase in the local *concentration* of the reactants would be expected if a reactant were completely surrounded by molecules of a second reactant. As indicated above, this factor can be evaluated by using a unitary or mole fraction standard state, instead of a standard

[18] J. W. Thanassi and L. A. Cohen, *J. Am. Chem. Soc.* **89**, 5734 (1967).

[19] J. Gerstein and W. P. Jencks, *J. Am. Chem. Soc.* **86**, 4655 (1964).

[20] A. Kailan, *Z. Physik. Chem.* (*Leipzig*) **101**, 63 (1922).

state of 1 M, to express rate and equilibrium constants. For aqueous solutions, the factor is 55 M, which corresponds to about eight entropy units or 2400 cal/mole at 25°. This is close to the observed value for the difference in free energy between lactone formation and ester formation, based on a standard state of 1 M for the acid and alcohol. This suggests that the more favorable equilibrium constant for lactone formation can be accounted for by the increased effective local concentration of acid and alcohol in the hydroxyacid; i.e., the less favorable free energy for bimolecular ester formation simply reflects the entropy requirement for bringing together the reactants from a 1 M standard state. The rate increases in a number of intramolecular reactions, compared with their intermolecular counterparts, may be accounted for in the same way.

However, it is clear that the large rate and equilibrium constants for many intramolecular reactions, compared with their intermolecular counterparts, cannot be accounted for by a local concentration effect. The difference in the free energies for anhydride formation from succinic and acetic acids is some 3 times larger than expected from the concentration effect; the impossibility of accounting for this difference by a concentration effect is qualitatively obvious from the fact that there is no detectable amount of acetic anhydride in equilibrium with glacial acetic acid, whereas the concentration of succinic anhydride in equilibrium with succinic acid is small, but detectable, even in the presence of a large excess of water.[14] It is even more obvious that "effective concentrations" of amine and carboxylate ion of 1250 M and 3×10^7 M in the reactions of equations 6 and 7 cannot represent a simple concentration effect. Another explanation must be sought for rate enhancements in intramolecular reactions corresponding to an "effective concentration" of more than 55 M or decreases in free energy of activation of more than 2400 cal/mole. An observed entropy of activation for a bimolecular reaction in water should be increased by eight entropy units before comparison with a monomolecular reaction in order to correct for the arbitrary choice of the molar scale to express concentration units.

There are a few reactions in which a significant additional rate acceleration might be expected from favorable *orientation* or rotamer distribution of the reactants in an intramolecular reaction in which the reactants are fixed in a reactive position. The transfer of hydrogen atoms from hindered tri-t-butylphenol and related compounds to the corresponding oxygen radicals in carbon tetrachloride (equation 9) occurs with a $\Delta H^{\ddagger}$ of only 1 to 2 kcal/mole but with a

$$(9)$$

$\Delta S^{\ddagger}$ of about -40 entropy units (e.u.).[21] The principal barrier to reaction of these compounds ($k = 200\ M^{-1}\ \mathrm{sec}^{-1}$) is the unfavorable entropy term, which presumably arises in large part from the severe orientational and steric demands of the transition state for the highly hindered reactants. The reactions of many acyl compounds in water occur with large negative entropies of activation, which may be as large as -50 e.u. It is probable that this large entropy barrier to reaction results from a requirement for the orientation and electrostriction of a number of surrounding solvent molecules, some of which are acting as catalysts for proton transfer, rather than from a severe steric or orientation requirement for the nucleophile and the acyl compound. Acyl transfer reactions provide an especially favorable case for multifunctional catalysis in which a number of catalyst molecules are oriented correctly in the active site of an enzyme or synthetic catalyst, so that reaction can occur without the large entropy loss which is required for the orientation of individual catalyst molecules in solution. Ring closure reactions of flexible chain molecules have unfavorable entropies because of the loss of internal rotation upon ring closure, and similar unfavorable entropies are expected for the formation of transition states which require a similar loss of freedom of rotation. The entropy of cyclohexane is 21 units less than that of its open chain isomer, hexene-1, for example.[22] In the gas phase each internal rotation corresponds to 5 to 6 e.u., but the loss of entropy upon freezing such a rotation, and also upon loss of translational freedom, is much reduced in solution.[23]

For the great majority of reactions, it is unlikely that orientational requirements are so strict that induction of a favorable orientation will lead to a large rate acceleration. The probability factors of collision theory which are observed for many more or less "normal" reactions suggest that one in 10 or 100 collisions which occur with the necessary activation energy lead to reaction, a conclusion

[21] R. W. Kreilick and S. I. Weissman, *J. Am. Chem. Soc.* **88**, 2645 (1966).

[22] F. H. Westheimer and L. L. Ingraham, *J. Phys. Chem.* **60**, 1668 (1956).

[23] L. L. Schlager and F. A. Long, *Advan. Phys. Org. Chem.* **1**, 1 (1963).

which is in accord with chemical intuition and inspection of molecular models. In the author's opinion, the rate accelerations which are observed in some intramolecular reactions are too large to be explained by favorable orientation or rotamer distribution.

Koshland has approached this question for enzymatic reactions in a similar manner by calculating the amount that a reaction rate might be increased upon bringing the reacting molecules together, assuming that the concentration of the reactants at the active site of an enzyme is as high as it would be if the whole solution were composed of nothing but the reacting molecules; i.e., the concentrations of the reacting molecules A and B are taken as equal to those of pure A and pure B.[24] These concentrations are then assumed to exist at each enzyme active site in the solution (Fig. 1). This local concentration effect turns out to cause rather little rate enhance-

[24] D. E. Koshland, Jr., J. Cellular Comp. Physiol. 47, suppl. 1, 217 (1956).

[25] D. E. Koshland, Jr., J. Theoret. Biol. 2, 75 (1962).

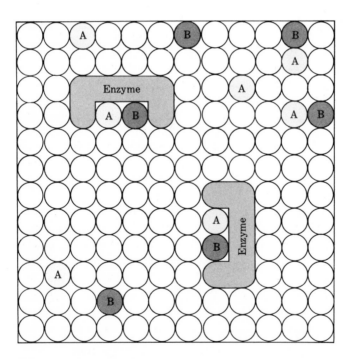

Fig. 1 Schematic representation of the concentration of the reacting molecules A and B from dilute solution at the active site of an enzyme.[25]

Table II   Comparison of observed rates of enzyme catalyzed reactions with those calculated from collision theory [24]

Enzyme	Substrate	$[Enzyme]$ equiv/liter	Observed V_O mole/liter/min	Observed V_E	V_E/V_O calculated from theory	$\dfrac{V_E/V_O \ observed}{V_E/V_O \ theory}$
Hexokinase	Glucose 0.003 M ATP 0.002 M	10^{-7}	$< 1 \times 10^{-13}$	1.3×10^{-3}	1.8	$> 7 \times 10^9$
Phosphorylase	Glucose-1- phosphate 0.016 M Glycogen 10^{-5} M	6×10^{-8}	$< 5 \times 10^{-15}$	1.6×10^{-3}	2.5	$> 1.4 \times 10^{11}$

ment, principally because the concentration of enzyme molecules and active sites in an enzyme-containing solution is ordinarily so small that no attainable local increase in the concentration of the reactants can lead to a very large increase in the rate of the overall reaction. Limiting values for some of these rates for the reactions catalyzed by hexokinase and phosphorylase are shown in Table II, in which V_O is an upper limit for the observed rate of the nonenzymatic reaction (based on the fact that no nonenzymatic reaction is observed over a period of time) and V_E is the observed rate of the enzymatic reaction. There is a discrepancy on the order of 10^9 to 10^{11} between the rates which are calculated from this concentration effect and the observed rates of the enzymatic reactions. This discrepancy sets a lower limit on the magnitude of the rate acceleration that must be explained by factors other than a simple concentration effect.

Somewhat larger accelerations may be obtained if it is assumed that the reacting molecules have to be in a particular position relative to each other in order to undergo reaction and that they bind to the active site of the enzyme in this favorable mutual orientation.[25] As indicated above, only a relatively small further rate increase would be expected from this orientation effect for most reactions.

As the number of molecules which must come together in order to bring about a reaction is increased, there is a corresponding increase in the rate acceleration which would be expected from this approximation effect. A reaction which involves two molecules of reactants and three catalysts would be fifth-order overall and would proceed according to the rate law of equation 10, in which S refers

$$\text{Rate} = k[S_1][S_2][Cat_1][Cat_2][Cat_3] \tag{10}$$

to a reactant and Cat to a catalyst. A rate acceleration of 10^{13} to

10^{17} might be expected if all five of these molecules were brought together at the active site of an enzyme.[25] This is a large factor, but it should be kept in mind that a nonenzymatic fifth-order reaction is ordinarily so slow that it is not observed at all, so that even such a large rate acceleration would not necessarily increase the rate to an observable level. Any comparison of rate constants for reactions of this kind must be made with careful attention to differences in reaction order, as indicated above for bimolecular and monomolecular reactions.

It is particularly difficult to account for rate accelerations of monomolecular reactions or reactions which involve water as a nucleophilic reagent by a concentration or orientation of the reactants at the active site of an enzyme. The concentration of water cannot be increased significantly above that present in the solvent, and it is difficult to imagine very severe orientation requirements for an attacking water molecule.

Changes in *solvation* may provide a significant rate-accelerating effect in both intramolecular and enzymatic reactions. In the attack of carboxylate ion on an ester, for example, it is necessary that the water molecules which solvate the charge on the carboxylate group be removed before the transition state is reached. Examination of molecular models indicates that the carboxylate group of the bicyclic ester 7 (Table I) cannot be solvated by water on the side which attacks the ester, so that there is no additional requirement for the loss of solvating water in this position in the intramolecular reaction. The fact that there is no very large difference in the pK values shows that there is not a large net difference in solvation energy in the ground state of the fast and slowly reacting esters, but there is an increase of about 0.5 unit in the pK of glutarate monoesters upon substitution of bulky *gem* substituents in the 3 position,[10] which could reflect a hindrance to solvation on one side of the carboxylate group.

Finally, there may be progress in overcoming *van der Waals repulsion* and in changing *electronic overlap* in the ground state of compounds which undergo rapid intramolecular reactions and in enzyme-substrate complexes. The large magnitude of the rate accelerations which are observed in intramolecular reactions suggests that effects of this kind will be required to account for the rapid rates of intramolecular and of enzymatic reactions. There is no sharp dividing line between such effects and those which have just been discussed, but the former may be classed as "strain or distortion" and will be discussed further in Chap. 5.

The experimental fact that rates are accelerated in intramolecular and enzymatic reactions may be depicted by a reaction-coordinate–transition-state diagram such as that of Fig. 2. The observed decrease in the free energy of activation may be interpreted as a movement of the reactants part way along the reaction coordinate toward the transition state which is brought about by the enzyme or by the chemist who links the reacting groups together in a single molecule. The detailed interpretation of such diagrams requires great care. The overall decrease in free energy of activation includes the bringing together of the reactants from dilute solution (which involves an arbitrary entropy term depending on the concentration of the solution), orientation of the reactants, desolvation, and the overcoming of the energy barrier to reaction. It should be noted that the binding forces between the enzyme and substrate as well as specific catalytic effects provide the driving force for this process.

3. ENTHALPIES AND ENTROPIES

Ideally, it should be possible to separate the contributions of concentration and orientation effects from those which result from partially overcoming the energy barrier to reaction in an intramolecular reaction because the former should appear as a more favorable entropy of activation and the latter as a more favorable enthalpy of activation for the intramolecular reaction. However, as it was pointed out above, the rapid rate of the intramolecular aminolysis of phenyl esters appears as a difference in the entropy

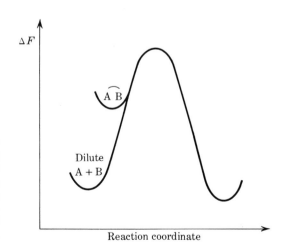

Fig. 2   Transition-state diagram to show how reacting molecules are brought part way along the reaction coordinate by being chemically linked to each other, as in an intramolecular reaction, or by being bound at the active site of an enzyme.

ΔF

A B

Dilute
A + B

Reaction coordinate

of activation, whereas the rapid rate of hydrolysis of tetramethyl-succinanilic acid with carboxyl group participation, compared with unsubstituted succinanilic acid, is accompanied by an *unfavorable* change in the entropy and a large lowering of the enthalpy of activation. Similarly, the increase in the rate of lactonization of 2-hydroxymethylbenzoic acids which is caused by *ortho* substituents may be explained by a forcing of the starting material into an average conformation in which the reacting groups are favorably oriented with respect to each other, but the rate increase is reflected entirely in the enthalpy, not the entropy, of activation.[26] The hexane-cyclohexane equilibrium in the gas phase is favored in the direction of the cyclic compound by the addition of methyl groups through *both* entropy and enthalpy effects. The enthalpy effect on this equilibrium has been attributed to the smaller increase in the number of *gauche* interactions upon ring formation from the sub-stituted hexane compared with unsubstituted hexane.[27] The more facile formation of succinic than of acetic anhydride is also in large part the consequence of a more favorable enthalpy of activation. It is apparent that the change from an intermolecular to an intramole-cular reaction is not manifested uniquely in either the entropy or enthalpy.

There is even some uncertainty as to the magnitude of the entropy difference to be expected upon bringing reacting molecules together. The equilibrium hydration of aldehydes may be regarded as a model for the bringing together of a water molecule and a carbonyl or acyl reactant in a transition state, but the entropy for this equilibrium is approximately -18 e.u.[23] This value is more negative than might have been expected, indicating that there is a considerably larger restriction to free movement of the aldehyde hydrate and its associated solvent molecules than in the starting materials. Bruice and Benkovic have shown that the entropies of activation of a number of nucleophilic reactions with phenyl esters bear a rather constant relationship to the order of the reaction, a relationship such that each increase in the order of the reaction is accompanied by a decrease of about 5 kcal/mole in the $T \Delta S^{\ddagger}$ term.[28] One example of this is the intramolecular compared with the intermolecular aminolysis of phenyl glutarates; others involve comparison of general base or acid catalyzed reactions with "un-catalyzed" reactions. However, it is difficult to make too detailed an interpretation of these results. The $\Delta H^{\ddagger}$ for the third-order

[26] J. F. Bunnett and C. F. Hauser, *J. Am. Chem. Soc.* **87**, 2214 (1965).

[27] N. L. Allinger and V. Zalkow, *J. Org. Chem.* **25**, 701 (1960).

[28] T. C. Bruice and S. J. Benkovic, *J. Am. Chem. Soc.* **86**, 418 (1964).

hydrazinolysis of phenyl acetate catalyzed by hydrazinium ion is about 1 kcal/mole. This is less than the $\Delta H^{\ddagger}$ of 3 to 4 kcal/mole for diffusion in water and suggests that some compensatory process must be taking place so that the intrinsic enthalpy of activation is masked by a secondary effect, such as a change in solvent structure, which causes compensating changes in enthalpy and entropy.

Thus, although favorable rates and equilibria in intramolecular reactions are often accompanied by more favorable entropies than are found for the corresponding intermolecular reactions, it does not yet seem possible to use thermodynamic activation parameters to provide a clear distinction among the possible mechanisms for the changes in the free energy of activation which are seen in these reactions. This is not unexpected since the observed thermodynamic activation parameters do not correspond directly to the differences in potential energies and entropies of the reactants and transition state. In aqueous solution, especially, the large effects of changes in solvent structure on these parameters, which may be accompanied by negligible changes in free energy, suggest that the free energy is often the most reliable indicator of the properties of a transition state. The problem of the interpretation of these thermodynamic parameters is discussed more fully in Chap. 5, Sec. F.

4. OTHER INTRAMOLECULAR REACTIONS

Comprehensive reviews of intramolecular reactions are available elsewhere,[1] and only a few more examples, which illustrate particular points of special interest, will be described here.

The ketone, o-isobutyrylbenzoic acid, undergoes enolization with intramolecular participation of the carboxylate group, probably by the mechanism shown in equation 11. The rate of this reaction

$$\tag{11}$$

is approximately the same as that which would be observed in the presence of 50 M carboxylate ion in an intermolecular reaction.[29] This rate acceleration is somewhat larger than that which is observed for the analogous enolization of pyruvate.[30]

[29] E. T. Harper and M. L. Bender, *J. Am. Chem. Soc.* **87**, 5625 (1965).

[30] W. J. Albery, R. P. Bell, and A. L. Powell, *Trans. Faraday Soc.* **61**, 1194 (1965).

Amide and peptide groups are active as nucleophilic agents on both the oxygen and nitrogen atoms in intramolecular reactions, although they have very little such activity in intermolecular reactions.[31-33] The reaction of the nitrogen atom usually takes place by a specific base catalyzed attack of the conjugate base of the amide to form an imide, which undergoes subsequent hydrolysis at a rate which may be either faster or slower than its rate of formation (equation 12). The rate of cleavage of certain β-benzyl esters of

$$\text{(12)}$$

aspartyl peptides to the imide is more than a million times faster than the rate of hydrolysis of analogous compound lacking an amide group, and the monomolecular rate constant for imide formation from O-acetylsalicylamide (equation 12) is considerably more than 60,000 times larger than the rate constant for the bimolecular reaction of an amide with phenyl acetate under the same conditions.[31, 33]

It is frequently difficult to distinguish between several possible kinetically equivalent mechanisms for an intramolecular reaction. For example, the facilitated hydrolysis of the anions of phenyl salicylate and phenyl p-nitrosalicylate could occur by attack of hydroxide ion, which is assisted by general acid catalysis by the neighboring hydroxyl group (8), or by attack of water, which is assisted by general base catalysis by the neighboring phenoxide anion (9).[34, 35] These two mechanisms follow the rate laws of equations 13 and 14, which are interconvertible by substitution of the

8   9

[31] S. A. Bernhard, A. Berger, J. H. Carter, E. Katchalski, M. Sela, and Y. Shalitin, J. Am. Chem. Soc. 84, 2421 (1962).

[32] J. A. Shafer and H. Morawetz, J. Org. Chem. 28, 1899 (1963).

[33] M. T. Behme and E. H. Cordes, J. Org. Chem. 29, 1255 (1964).

[34] M. L. Bender, F. J. Kézdy, and B. Zerner, J. Am. Chem. Soc. 85, 3017 (1963).

[35] B. Capon and B. C. Ghosh, J. Chem. Soc. 1966B, 472.

$$\text{Rate} = k[\text{Ester-OH}][\text{OH}^-] \tag{13}$$

$$\text{Rate} = k'[\text{Ester-O}^-][\text{HOH}] \tag{14}$$

appropriate equilibrium expressions for the ionization of the reactants and are kinetically indistinguishable because the stoichiometric
composition and charge of the transition states for the two mechanisms are the same. General acid and base catalysis of the breakdown of anionic and neutral tetrahedral addition compounds 10 and
11, respectively, are additional possible mechanisms which would

give the same rate law.

It is possible to make a choice between some of these mechanisms by examining the reaction of a nucleophile in which the ionic
form of the attacking reagent is less ambiguous than water, which
can react as either H_2O or OH^-. The facts that the reactions of
imidazole, azide ion, and sulfite ion with p-nitrophenyl salicylate
are not unusually fast and that the reaction of imidazole with phenyl
salicylate is not faster than with phenyl o-methoxybenzoate suggest
that the attack of the nucleophile (8) or the departure of the leaving
phenol (10) is not being facilitated by general acid catalysis in these
reactions because any such facilitation should cause an acceleration
of these nucleophilic reactions as well as hydrolysis. Base catalysis
of the attack of a protonated nucleophile (9) or of the breakdown of
a neutral addition intermediate (11), which would be expected to be
most significant for a nucleophile with at least one proton on the
attacking atom, is therefore the most reasonable mechanism. The
rate acceleration of the hydrolysis of p-nitrophenyl salicylate is only
about ninefold compared with p-nitrophenyl acetate, but the rate
acceleration with phenyl salicylate anion is about 50-fold compared
with phenyl o-methoxybenzoate. Catechol monobenzoate, which can
undergo hydrolysis by a similar mechanism (12), reacts several
hundred times faster than o-methoxyphenyl benzoate.

The same technique has been used to determine which ionic
species of aspirin (13) is the reactive species in the rapid carboxyl-
group-assisted reactions of this compound with nucleophiles.[36] For

[36] T. St. Pierre and W. P. Jencks, *J. Am. Chem. Soc.* **90**, 3817 (1968).

weakly basic tertiary amines and other compounds which must react in the basic form N, the reaction follows the rate law of equation 15

13

$$v = k_1 [\text{Asp-COOH}][\text{N}] + k_2 [\text{Asp-COO}^-][\text{N}] \tag{15}$$

with a somewhat larger contribution of the k_1 term, for assistance by the carboxylic acid group, compared with the k_2 term, for the anion. The k_2 term is important only for weakly basic nucleophiles with a hydrogen atom attached to the attacking nitrogen or oxygen atom. The magnitude of the observed rate enhancement for assistance by the carboxylic acid group (k_1) is insufficient to account for the well known rapid hydrolysis of aspirin anion[37] (see Fig. 12, Chap. 11) by the kinetically indistinguishable hydroxide ion catalyzed hydrolysis of the free acid. The rate increase of about two orders of magnitude for hydrolysis of the monoanion, compared with that for p-carboxyphenyl acetate monoanion, is in the range predicted from the rate increases observed with other weakly basic nucleophiles with a proton attached to the attacking atom (Fig. 3). The reactions of phenyl acetate with water and semicarbazide are subject to intermolecular general base catalysis by acetate ion, and the "effective concentration" of the carboxylate ion of aspirin for catalysis of the reactions of these nucleophiles is 23 to 28 M, after correction for the difference in basicity of the carboxylate groups of acetate and aspirin. The reactions of the two ionic species of aspirin with nucleophiles probably proceed with intramolecular general base and acid catalysis according to mechanisms 14 and 15 or 16, respectively.

14   15   16

---

[37] L. J. Edwards, *Trans. Faraday Soc.* **46**, 723 (1950); **48**, 696 (1952); E. R. Garrett. *J. Am. Chem. Soc.* **79**, 3401 (1957).

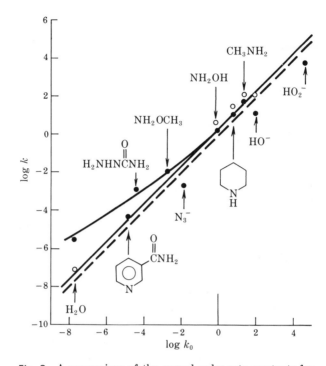

Fig. 3 A comparison of the second-order rate constants for the reactions of a series of nucleophilic reagents with phenyl acetate (k_0) with those for the reactions of the same compounds with p-carboxyphenyl acetate anion (open circles) and aspirin anion (closed circles). The dashed line represents $k = k_0$.

These mechanisms are supported by structure-reactivity correlations of the reactions of substituted aspirins and the rate constants for the reactions of aspirin with oxygen anions.[38]

If the hydrolysis of aspirin proceeded by direct nucleophilic attack of the carboxylate group on the phenyl ester to form an intermediate anhydride, it would be expected that some labeled oxygen would be incorporated into the carboxyl group of the salicylic acid product upon hydrolysis of the anhydride when the reaction is carried out in ^{18}O-labeled water (equation 16).[39] No such incorporation is observed for aspirin itself, indicating that the nucleophilic pathway is not important for the unsubstituted compound, but labeled oxygen is incorporated into the carboxyl group of 3,5-dinitroaspirin

[38] A. R. Fersht and A. J. Kirby, J. Am. Chem. Soc. 89, 4853, 4857, 5960, 5961 (1967) and personal communication.

[39] M. L. Bender, F. Chloupek, and M. C. Neveu, J. Am. Chem. Soc. 80, 5384 (1958).

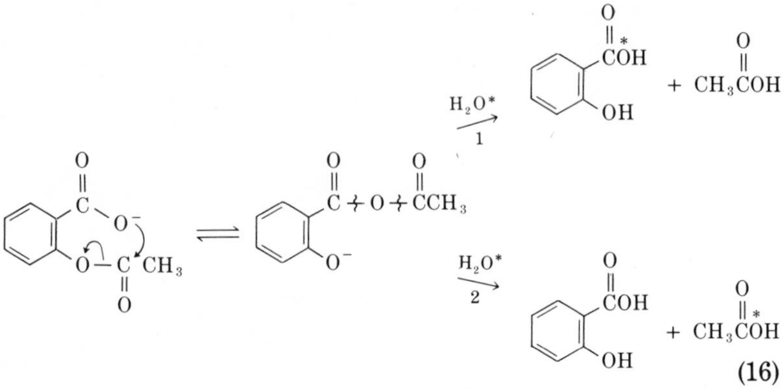

$$
\text{(16)}
$$

to an extent which indicates that the hydrolysis of this compound proceeds through an anhydride, with cleavage at the aromatic carbonyl-oxygen bond (pathway 1, equation 16) to an extent of 39%.[38] Thus, the hydrolysis of aspirin is similar to the intermolecular reactions of phenyl acetates in that the carboxylate group catalyzes the hydrolysis of esters with good leaving groups by direct nucleophilic attack, whereas catalysis of the hydrolysis of esters with poor leaving groups, which are too basic to be directly expelled by the carboxylate ion, involves general base catalysis of a nucleophilic reaction of water.[11]

The dianions of salicyl phosphate and other o-carboxyaryl phosphates undergo hydrolysis at a rate which is very fast relative to the p-substituted compounds, indicating that these reactions are also facilitated by the ortho carboxyl group. This facilitation could occur by intramolecular nucleophilic attack to give an acyl phosphate which subsequently undergoes hydrolysis (equation 17) or by intra-

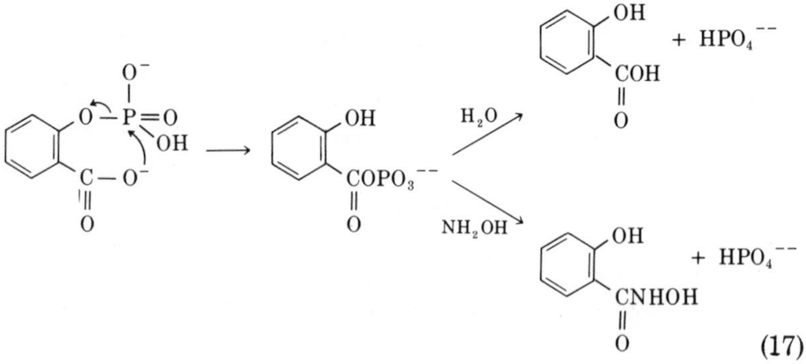

$$
\text{(17)}
$$

molecular general acid-base catalysis by a mechanism such as that shown in equation 18. The nucleophilic catalysis mechanism of

(18)

equation 17 may be tested by carrying out the reaction in the presence of compounds which would trap the intermediate acyl phosphate if it is formed. Acyl phosphates, including salicoyl phosphate, react readily with hydroxylamine to give the acylhydroxamic acid, but no hydroxamic acid is formed if the hydrolysis of salicyl phosphate is carried out in the presence of hydroxylamine.[40] The facilitation by the carboxyl group therefore must proceed by general acid-base catalysis according to a mechanism such as that of equation 18, which is analogous to that for the reactions of the acidic species of aspirin. The hydrolysis of salicyl sulfate probably proceeds by the same mechanism.[41]

Water is itself an effective acid and base catalyst and a good solvent for reactions with polar transition states. Consequently, rate accelerations by intramolecular general acid-base catalysis or internal solvation of the transition state are likely to be less dramatic in water than in other solvents, especially nonhydroxylic solvents, in which a much larger relative stabilization of the transition state may be brought about by such catalysis. There are a number of examples of catalysis of this kind in the literature of synthetic organic chemistry, but few of them have been examined quantitatively. One example which seems to represent both general acid and base catalysis is the solvolysis of a rigid 1,3-diaxialhydroxy-monoacetate in methanol, for which there is evidence for assistance to the reaction by a neighboring amine as well as by the hydroxyl group.[42] Comparison with the rates of methanolysis of structurally

[40] M. L. Bender and J. M. Lawlor, J. Am. Chem. Soc. 85, 3010 (1963).

[41] S. J. Benkovic, J. Am. Chem. Soc. 88, 5511 (1966).

[42] S. M. Kupchan, S. P. Eriksen, and M. Friedman, J. Am. Chem. Soc. 88, 343 (1966); S. M. Kupchan, S. P. Eriksen, and Y-T. S. Liang, Ibid., p. 347.

similar compounds which lack the neighboring hydroxyl and amine groups suggests that the hydroxyl group gives a 40-fold rate acceleration and the amino group an additional 25-fold rate acceleration, presumably by some form of general acid and general base catalysis, respectively.

The hydrolysis of a substituted phenyl ester by poly-5-(6)-vinylbenzimidazole in neutral and alkaline solution occurs at a rate which is some tenfold larger, per benzimidazole unit, than the hydrolysis catalyzed by benzimidazole monomers under the same conditions. This suggests that the benzimidazole groups in the polymer are facilitating each other's reactivity, probably by some form of polyfunctional catalysis.[43]

B. INDUCED APPROXIMATION

An enzyme brings reacting molecules together at the active site by the use of weak binding forces, and it is of interest to examine the behavior of model systems in which the reacting molecules are brought together in a similar manner.

Some of the more dramatic examples of this kind of behavior involve reactions of borate derivatives, since borate can reversibly form covalent adducts with hydroxylic compounds at a rate which is fast relative to the rates of many other reactions. In the presence of boric acid, phenol reacts with formaldehyde in benzene solution to give exclusively o-hydroxymethylphenol; under the same conditions in the absence of boric acid there is little or no formation of the *ortho* product.[44] The reaction must involve the rapid and reversible formation of a complex of phenol, borate, and formaldehede and could occur by the mechanism shown in equation 19, or, since reactions of

$$\tag{19}$$

carbonyl compounds almost always involve addition to the free carbonyl compound rather than displacement on a saturated carbon atom, by a mechanism similar to that shown in equation 20. Hy-

[43] C. G. Overberger, T. St. Pierre, and S. Yaroslavsky, *J. Am. Chem. Soc.* **87**, 4310 (1965).

[44] H. G. Peer, *Rec. Trav. Chim.* **79**, 825 (1960).

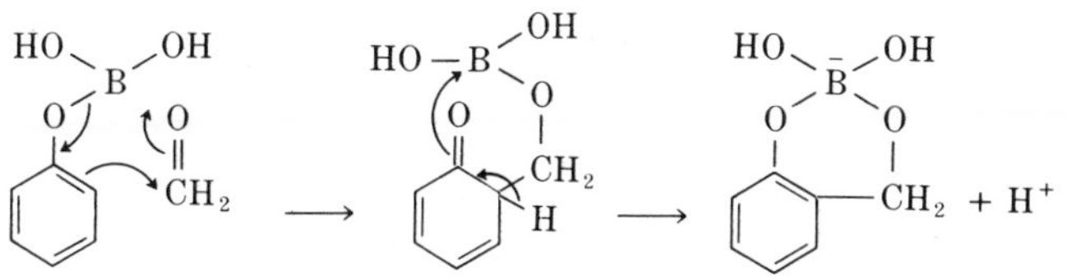

(20)

droxymethylation at the *ortho* position is also specifically catalyzed by metal hydroxides, such as $Cu(OH)_2$, which can presumably bring about the formation of a complex similar in structure to the borate complex. Catalysis does not occur in water, presumably because competition by water makes the equilibrium for complex formation too unfavorable to permit reaction.

The boron-containing compound **17** acts as a specific catalyst for the hydrolysis of chloroethanol to ethylene glycol in wet dimethyl-formamide; in the absence of the catalyst, cyclization takes place to give ethylene oxide in a specific base catalyzed reaction.[45] Experiments with a series of substituted chloroalochols have established that the chloride and hydroxyl groups must be *trans* and that the displacement of chloride ion occurs with inversion of configuration. This means that there must be a direct attack of oxygen on carbon to give the product, rather than a double displacement mechanism in which displacement by nitrogen is followed by displacement by water, with a second inversion of configuration. Again the specificity of the reaction requires that complex formation take place and suggests a mechanism such as that shown in equation 21.

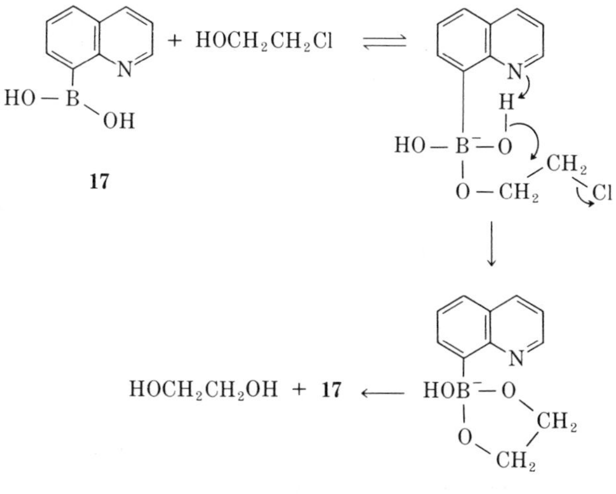

(21)

[45] R. L. Letsinger, S. Dandegaonker, W. J. Vullo, and J. D. Morrison, *J. Am. Chem. Soc.* **85**, 2223 (1963); R. L. Letsinger and J. D. Morrison, *Ibid.*, p. 2227.

Borate catalyzes the hydrolysis of phenyl salicylate in aqueous solution more than 100 times as rapidly as the hydrolysis of phenyl *o*-methoxybenzoate. Borate is known to form a complex with salicylic acid and with acetoacetate, in which it causes a shift in the equilibrium towards the complexed enolic form 18.[46] This suggests

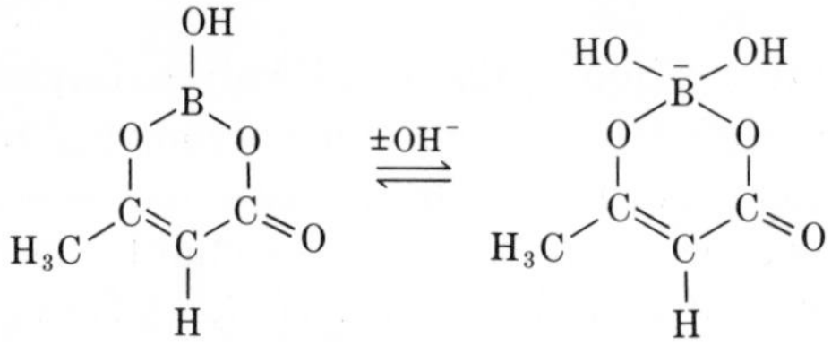

18

that it can stabilize the transition state for phenyl salicylate hydrolysis, which resembles a tetrahedral addition intermediate, by a mechanism such as that shown in equation 22. The dependence on pH

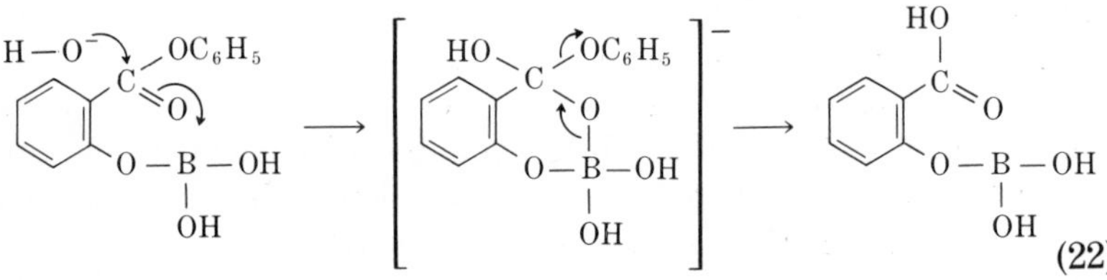

(22)

suggests that reactions with both water and hydroxide ion are facilitated by the borate catalyst.[35,47] Alternatively, borate may act as an intramolecular nucleophilic catalyst after addition to the phenolic hydroxyl group (equation 23).[48]

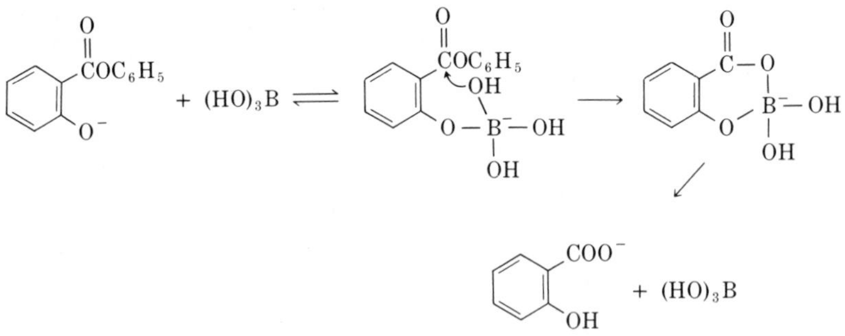

(23)

[46] S. Neece and I. Fridovich, *Arch. Biochem. Biophys.* **108**, 240 (1964).

[47] D. W. Tanner and T. C. Bruice, *J. Am. Chem. Soc.* **89**, 6954 (1967).

[48] R. Breslow, personal communication.

It has frequently been suggested that one role of metal ions in enzymatic reactions is to hold the substrates and the reactive groups on the active site of the enzyme in the proper steric relationships to each other. A probable example of the facilitation of a nonenzymatic acyl transfer reaction in aqueous solution by complex formation of the reactants with a metal ion is found in the reaction of the zinc complex of pyridine-2-aldoxime (**19**), with the acetoxyquinoline sulfonate **20**.[49] The ester **20** acylates **19**, which has a pK of 6.5, at about the same rate that it acylates the more basic uncomplexed oxime anion, which has a pK of 10. p-Nitrophenyl acetate acylates **19** at a rate which is about one-seventh that of the acylation of the uncomplexed oxime anion. The enhanced reactivity of the quinoline acetate with the zinc complex of pyridine-2-aldoxime is attributed to the formation of a mixed complex of **19** and **20**, which is stabilized by the interaction of the metal ion with the nitrogen atom of the quinoline acetate (equation 24).

$$(24)$$

The enzyme carbonic anhydrase catalyzes the hydration of aldehydes and esters as well as carbon dioxide and requires a metal ion, such as zinc, for activity. A model reaction for the enzyme is found in the zinc ion catalyzed hydration of pyridine-2-aldehyde, which takes place with a second-order rate constant 6.5×10^6 faster than that for the "water" reaction.[50] This rate increase is only tenfold less than that brought about by the enzyme. The reaction probably involves an approximation of zinc to the reacting center because zinc catalysis of the hydration of pyridine-4-aldehyde is 280 times less effective. The reaction could involve attack of water in the hydration shell of the zinc ion on the aldehyde or a polarization

[49] R. Breslow and D. Chipman, *J. Am. Chem. Soc.* **87**, 4195 (1965).

[50] Y. Pocker and J. E. Meany, *J. Am. Chem. Soc.* **89**, 631 (1967).

of the carbonyl group by the metal ion (e.g., mechanisms 21 and 22).

        21   22

     The hydrolysis of the p-nitrophenyl ester of leucine is catalyzed by 10^{-3} to 10^{-4} M benzaldehyde, which is a more effective catalyst than even imidazole.[51] Since the weakly basic benzaldehyde molecule is a poor nucleophile, it is probable that the reaction involves the addition of benzaldehyde to the amino group of the ester to form an amino alcohol; this makes possible an intramolecular attack of oxygen on the ester to form a lactone, which then undergoes rapid hydrolysis through an elimination reaction (equation 25). In this re-

$$(25)$$

action the combination of the catalyst with the reacting molecule not only converts an intermolecular into an intramolecular reaction, but brings about a change in the properties of the catalyst to convert it from an unreactive to a highly reactive nucleophile. A similar mechanism accounts for the rapid hydrolysis of o-formylbenzoate esters in the presence of morpholine (equation 26).[52] In this reaction the accumulation of the intermediate morpholine addition compound 23 may be detected spectrophotometrically. The

[51] B. Capon and R. Capon, *Chem. Commun.* **1965**, 502.

[52] M. L. Bender, J. A. Reinstein, M. S. Silver, and R. Mikulak, *J. Am. Chem. Soc.* **87**, 4545 (1965).

$$(26)$$

intermediate undergoes decomposition by pH-independent and base catalyzed pathways of uncertain mechanism. The hydrolysis of esters of *o*-formylbenzoate and a number of related compounds in the presence of alkali is also very rapid; the second-order rate constant for the hydrolysis of the *ortho* formyl compound of about 2,000 M^{-1} sec^{-1} may be compared with that of about 8×10^{-3} M^{-1} sec^{-1} for the *para* formyl ester. The rapid alkaline hydrolysis of the *ortho*-substituted compound may be attributed to addition of hydroxide ion to the carbonyl group to form a reactive addition compound adjacent to the ester, in a manner similar to that for the morpholine catalyzed reaction (equation 26).

1. ICE

It has occasionally been noticed by a number of investigators that compounds which are stable in aqueous solutions in the cold or even at room temperature undergo decomposition when they are stored in the frozen state, but no serious notice seems to have been taken of this interesting phenomenon until Grant et al. reported that penicillin undergoes decomposition in frozen solutions which contain imidazole buffers, but not in the same liquid solutions at higher temperature.[53] This report stimulated further work on this phenomenon by a number of investigators, and it was suggested that special modes of proton transfer in ice, approximation of reactants on the surface or within the crystal lattice, or concentration effects could be responsible for the rate increases which were observed in ice for several reactions.

[53] N. H. Grant, D. E. Clark, and H. E. Alburn, *J. Am. Chem. Soc.* 83, 4476 (1961).

The most definitive experiments in this area have been carried out by Pincock and coworkers, who investigated reactions which proceed by fairly well understood mechanisms in liquid water. The specific base catalyzed decomposition of 10^{-3} M ethylene chlorohydrin (chloroethanol) in the presence of 10^{-3} M base (equation 27) is

$$\text{CH}_2-\text{CH}_2 + \text{OH}^- \overset{\text{fast}}{\rightleftharpoons} \text{CH}_2-\text{CH}_2 \longrightarrow \text{CH}_2-\text{CH}_2 + \text{Cl}^- \tag{27}$$

accelerated up to 1,000-fold in ice, compared with the rate in water at the same temperature.[54] It was shown that this rate increase and other properties of the reaction in ice may be accounted for quantitatively by calculating the concentrations of the reactants in the liquid regions in ice by use of the known phase relationships of the system. Most foreign molecules cannot be incorporated into the ice lattice, and the rapid reaction in this case occurs in small "puddles" of liquid phase, in which the reactants are highly concentrated by the extraction of water into the surrounding ice in a manner quite analogous to the classical New England method of strengthening hard cider in the winter. The acceleration of the acid catalyzed mutarotation of glucose in ice may be explained in the same manner.[55] Although the possibility remains that there are more complicated mechanisms for rate acclerations in frozen solutions, and there are still some unexplained observations,[56] there is no proof for any such mechanisms at the present time; and it is clear that the phase relationships and concentration effects of frozen solutions must be quantitatively accounted for before more complex mechanisms can be established.

C. SPECIFICITY

There are a number of examples of model systems which exhibit a substrate specificity, which, while not as exacting as that exhibited by many enzyme systems, presumably involves similar characteristics.

If silica gels are formed in water in the presence of dyes of differing structure, it might be expected that the gel will form in a

[54] R. E. Pincock and T. E. Kiovsky, *J. Am. Chem. Soc.* 88, 4455 (1966).

[55] T. E. Kiovsky and R. E. Pincock, *J. Am. Chem. Soc.* 88, 4704 (1966).

[56] N. H. Grant, D. E. Clark, and H. E. Alburn, *J. Am. Chem. Soc.* 88, 4071 (1966).

Table III   Specific adsorption of dyes by silica gels [57]

| | Relative adsorption power for:[a] | | | |
Gel prepared with:	Methyl orange	Ethyl orange	Propyl orange	Butyl orange
Methyl orange	17	8	3	2
Ethyl orange	9	30	10	3
Propyl orange	7	22	30	25
Butyl orange	5	13	30	30

[a] 0.5×10^{-6} mole/kg of solution.

stereospecific manner around the dye molecules. After washing out of the dye, the gel might then specifically bind dye molecules of the same structure to this specific "site." Such a specific binding has been reported for dyes which differ in structure by as little as the addition of a methylene group.[57] The relative adsorptive powers of gels which were prepared in the presence of methyl, ethyl, propyl, and butyl orange toward these four dyes are shown in Table III. In each case, the gel exhibits a selectivity toward the dye in the presence of which it was prepared and a progressive decrease in adsorptive power toward dyes with larger or smaller alkyl groups.

The reaction of hydrogen cyanide with benzaldehyde in chloroform gives an optically active cyanohydrin of about 10% optical purity when it is carried out in the presence of an optically active alkaloid as catalyst.[58] Presumably the catalyst either interacts with HCN to remove a proton and give an ion pair which reacts preferentially with one side of benzaldehyde, or the protonated catalyst interacts with benzaldehyde stereospecifically in such a manner that the attack of cyanide ion on one side of the benzaldehyde is favored. Similar stereospecificity is observed in catalysis by optically active imine polymers.[59]

The acylation of a racemic alcohol in the presence of an alkaloid catalyst also gives a partially stereospecific product.[60] Tertiary amines act as nucleophilic catalysts for acylation by highly reactive acylating agents to form the cationic acylated tertiary amine as an intermediate. The stereospecificity of these reactions must then result from the preferential attack of one isomer of the alcohol on

[57] F. H. Dickey, *J. Phys. Chem.* **59**, 695 (1955).

[58] V. Prelog and M. Wilhelm, *Helv. Chim. Acta* **37**, 1634 (1954).

[59] S. Tsuboyama, *Bull. Chem. Soc. Japan* **35**, 1004 (1962); **38**, 354 (1965).

[60] R. Wegler, *Ann. Chem.* **506**, 77 (1933); R. Wegler and A. Rüber, *Ber.* **68B**, 1055 (1935); H. Pracejus, *Ann. Chem.* **634**, 9 (1960); C. W. Bird, *Tetrahedron* **18**, 1 (1962).

the optically active acylated catalyst (equation 27). The degree of

$$
RCX + N\overset{\cdot\cdot}{\underset{|}{\diagdown}} \longrightarrow RC\overset{O}{\overset{\|}{N}}\overset{+\cdot\cdot}{\underset{|}{\diagdown}} \overset{\overset{*}{ROH}}{\longrightarrow} RC\overset{O}{\overset{\|}{O}}R\,* \tag{27}
$$

stereospecificity is similar to that for cyanohydrin formation, but may increase at very low temperatures. In acylations by phenylmethylketene the stereospecificity is introduced into the acyl portion of the molecule by a stereospecific protonation in an analogous manner (equation 28).

$$
\overset{H_3C}{\underset{C_6H_5}{\diagdown}}C=C=O + N\overset{\cdot\cdot}{\underset{|}{\diagdown}} \longrightarrow \overset{H_3C}{\underset{C_6H_5}{\diagdown}}\overset{(-)}{C}\!\cdot\!\cdot\!\overset{\overset{(-)}{O}}{\underset{\underset{|}{N}^{+}}{C}} \overset{HA}{\longrightarrow} \overset{H_3C}{\underset{C_6H_5}{\diagdown}}\overset{H}{\underset{|}{C}}\!*\!-\!\overset{O}{\overset{\|}{C}}-\overset{+}{N}\overset{\cdot\cdot}{\underset{|}{\diagdown}}
$$

$$
\Big\downarrow R'OH
$$

$$
\overset{H_3C}{\underset{C_6H_5}{\diagdown}}\overset{H}{\underset{|}{C}}\!*\!-\!\overset{O}{\overset{\|}{C}}OR' \tag{28}
$$

Catalysis of the benzoin condensation by an optically active analog of thiamine (24) gives a low yield of a product from the mother liquor with an optical purity of 22%.[61] The stereospecificity is introduced during the addition of a carbanion to benzaldehyde in step 4 (equation 29).

The hydrolysis of the L isomer of N-methoxycarbonylphenylalanine p-nitrophenyl ester is favored by twofold over that of the D isomer in the presence of the catalyst thr–ala–ser–his–asp, in which all of the amino acids are in the L configuration.[62] The reaction involves nucleophilic attack of the imidazole group of histidine on the active ester.

One of the most interesting examples of stereospecificity in a model system is found in an oxidative activation of carboxylates (and probably phosphates) which accompanies the oxidation of sulfides to sulfoxides by iodine in aqueous solution near neutrality.[63] If the oxidation is catalyzed by phthalic acid, phthalic anhydride is

[61] J. C. Sheehan and D. H. Hunneman, J. Am. Chem. Soc. 88, 3666 (1966).

[62] J. C. Sheehan, G. B. Bennett, and J. A. Schneider, J. Am. Chem. Soc. 88, 3455 (1966).

[63] T. Higuchi and K-H. Gensch, J. Am. Chem. Soc. 88 3874 (1966); T. Higuchi, I. H. Pitman, and K-H. Gensch, Ibid. 88, 5676 (1966).

$$C_6H_5-\overset{*}{C}H-CH_2-\overset{+}{N}\diagup \quad \underset{1}{\overset{-H^+}{\longrightarrow}} \quad \cdots$$

24

$$\underset{2}{\Big\downarrow} +H^+$$

$$\overset{-H^+}{\underset{3}{\longleftarrow}} \qquad H-\overset{R^*}{\underset{C_6H_5}{\overset{|}{C}}}-\cdots \qquad \overset{HO}{\underset{C_6H_5}{}}$$

$$\underset{4}{\Big\downarrow} +H^+$$

$$C_6H_5-\overset{H}{\underset{H}{\overset{|}{\underset{C_6H_5}{C}}}}-\cdots \quad \underset{5}{\longrightarrow} \quad C_6H_5-\overset{HO}{\underset{H}{\overset{|}{C}}}-\overset{O}{\overset{\|}{C}}-C_6H_5 + 24 \qquad (29)$$

formed as an intermediate, presumably by the mechanism shown in equation 30. When benzylmethylsulfide is oxidized in the presence of

$$\cdots \qquad (30)$$

optically active 2-methyl-2-phenylsuccinate as catalyst, the product benzylmethylsulfoxide is optically active with an optical purity of 6%.

A somewhat different kind of specificity is observed with cyclodextrins, which can undergo reaction with compounds with which they can form more or less specific inclusion compounds. Cyclodextrins are phosphorylated by sym-dichlorophenylpyrophosphates in the presence of calcium ion at pH 12 at relative rates of 15, 100, and 31 for α, β, and γ cyclodextrins, respectively, which demonstrates a specificity with respect to the ring size of the cyclodextrin.[64] An

[64] N. Hennrich and F. Cramer, *J. Am. Chem. Soc.* 87, 1121 (1965).

even larger degree of specificity with respect to the substrate is manifested in the acylation of cyclohexaamylose by substituted phenyl acetates, in which the maximum relative rates of acylation are 13×10^{-2} compared with 0.075×10^{-2} sec^{-1} for the complexes with m- and p-t-butylphenyl acetates, respectively.[65] Presumably the $meta$-substituted ester fits into the cavity of the cyclodextrin in such a manner that the acyl group is brought into a favorable position for reaction with a hydroxyl group of the dextrin. It is noteworthy that the binding constants for the two esters are not very different. These reactions show saturation behavior with respect to the dextrin and the substrate with increasing concentration, as would be expected if complex formation occurred. It would be of interest to compare these rates of acylation within the complex with the bimolecular rates of acylation of a similar sugar in solution in order to obtain an estimate of the "effective concentration" of hydroxyl groups in the neighborhood of the reacting acyl group in the complex.

There are a number of other examples of reactions which exhibit rate acceleration or specificity resulting from electrostatic, hydrophobic, and charge transfer interactions between the reacting molecules and catalysts. Some of these will be described in the chapters in which these interactions are discussed.

D. HETEROGENEOUS CATALYSIS

The subject of heterogeneous catalysis is too large to be taken up here in any detail. The stereospecificity of these reactions which results from the mode of attachment of the substrate to the catalyst, the covalent bond formation between substrates and catalysts, and the requirements for a particular spacing between the atoms of the catalyst, which may induce strain and deformation upon binding of the substrate, are all pertinent to enzymatic catalysis, but the chemistry of catalysis by metals is different from that of the great majority of enzymatic reactions. A few examples of nonmetallic heterogeneous catalysis deserve brief mention, however.

Adenosine triphosphate is adsorbed upon solid calcium apatite and reacts with phosphate molecules in the crystal to give pyrophosphate, which is incorporated into the surface of the apatite crystal.[66] This reaction presumably involves an interaction of the phosphate groups of ATP with calcium ions on the crystal surface

[65] R. L. VanEtten, J. F. Sebastian, G. A. Clowes, and M. L. Bender, $J.~Am.~Chem.$ $Soc.$ **89**, 3242 (1967); R. L. VanEtten, G. A. Clowes, J. F. Sebastian, and M. L. Bender, $Ibid.$, p. 3253.

[66] S. M. Krane and M. J. Glimcher, $J.~Biol.~Chem.$ **237**, 2991 (1962).

which have positions open for such binding. This interaction may serve to approximate the reacting phosphate groups, to overcome electrostatic repulsion, to convert the ADP to a better leaving group, and, possibly, to facilitate the reaction by inducing strain in the bound ATP. It is of interest that barium apatite, although it binds ATP more strongly, is less reactive toward phosphorylation. This indicates that the interaction between the crystal and the nucleotide must be highly specific in order to give a reaction, and probably depends upon the spacing of the atoms in the crystal lattice of the apatite.

In the presence of charcoal, 3'-phosphoadenosine-5'-phosphosulfate (PAPS) transfers its sulfate group to a hydroxyl group of hexoseamine to give the 6-sulfate derivative.[67] The mechanism of this reaction, which proceeds in low yield, is unknown.

If tetraglycine methyl ester is heated in solution at 100° it undergoes intermolecular aminolysis to give chains of polyglycine; but if the solid is heated at the same temperature, an intermolecular alkylation takes place on the nitrogen atom to give a sarcosyl peptide.[68] Evidently the structural forces within the crystal favor alkylation relative to the acylation reaction.

The polymerization of olefins under the influence of metal catalysts can proceed with a high degree of specificity to give crystalline polymers in which the monomer units are all arranged in the same configuration.[69] This demands that there be a stereospecific interaction between the growing polymer, the catalyst, and the reacting monomer as the polymer is synthesized.

[67] J. B. Adams, *Biochim. Biophys. Acta* **62**, 17 (1962).

[68] L. A. Æ. Sluyterman and H. J. Veenendaal, *Rec. Trav. Chim.* **71**, 137 (1952); L. A. Æ. Sluyterman and M. Kooistra, *Ibid.*, p. 277.

[69] G. Natta, *J. Pol. Sci.* **34**, 21 (1959); *J. Inorg. Nucl. Chem.* **8**, 589 (1958).

2
Covalent Catalysis

A. INTRODUCTION

The discovery that certain enzymes react chemically with their substrates to form covalently bonded enzyme-substrate intermediates
has done more than anything else to dispel mysterious mechanisms
and vitalistic theories of enzyme action because it suggests that the
mechanism of enzyme action is not fundamentally different from that
of any other chemical reaction. In particular, the covalent nature of
many enzyme-substrate intermediates has made it possible to apply
to these reactions the techniques of physical organic chemistry and
other chemical approaches which have been successful in helping to
elucidate the mechanisms of nonenzymatic reactions. The rapid
progress in describing some enzymatic reactions in chemical terms
and in the application of these methods to enzymology has led to a
swing of the pendulum of opinion to an optimistic point at which
papers are beginning to appear entitled "The Mechanism of Action
of the Enzyme, ..." In spite of the many important advances which

have been made, it is important to keep firmly in mind that we do not in any case have a detailed or quantitative understanding of the mechanism and driving forces which account for the enormous specific rate accelerations which are brought about by enzymes and that, although there is no necessity to return to vitalism, there may still be important chemical principles involved in enzymatic catalysis about which we have little or no understanding at the present time.

Table I lists some of the enzymatic reactions for which there is evidence, of varying degrees of reliability, for the formation of covalent intermediate compounds from the enzyme and a part of the substrate(s). The best known examples are the proteases and esterases that catalyze the hydrolysis and transfer of acyl groups with the intermediate transfer of an acyl group to the hydroxyl or sulfhydryl group of a serine or cysteine residue on the enzyme. Glyceraldehyde-3-phosphate dehydrogenase catalyzes the oxidation of an aldehyde to an "energy-rich" thiol ester of a cysteine group at the active site; the acyl group may then be transferred to phosphate to preserve the energy-rich bond as an acyl phosphate. There is evidence for the formation of phosphoryl-enzymes with a covalent link to the hydroxyl group of a serine or the imidazole group of a histidine residue as intermediates in the action of several phosphate-transferring enzymes. Certain decarboxylases, aldolases, and pyridoxal phosphate enzymes form covalent intermediates in which the substrate is bound to the enzyme through a Schiff base (or, more properly, imine) linkage, which provides an electrophilic center to aid the catalytic process. In fact, the action of most coenzymes involves

Table I   Some enzymatic reactions

Enzyme class	*Reacting group*	*Covalent intermediate*
Chymotrypsin, trypsin, esterases, subtilisin, thrombin, elastase	OH (serine)	Acyl-serine
Papain, ficin, glyceraldehyde-3-phosphate dehydrogenase	SH (cysteine)	Acyl-cysteine
Alkaline phosphatase, phosphoglucomutase	OH (serine)	Phosphoserine
Succinic thiokinase, phosphoenol-pyruvate-hexose transphosphorylase	Imidazole (histidine)	Phosphoryl-imidazole
Aldolases, decarboxylases, pyridoxal phosphate enzymes	$>C=O$ and $>C=N-$ (lysine and substrate amino)	Schiff base

the intermediate formation of covalent bonds between a portion of the substrate and the coenzyme, and there is no fundamental difference between a situation in which the substrate reacts with a functional group which is covalently bound to the enzyme and a reaction with a coenzyme which is bound to the enzyme by noncovalent bonds.

The basic problem in covalent catalysis is to define the reason why it is advantageous for a reaction to proceed through a covalent intermediate with an enzyme or coenzyme rather than directly. In some cases, particularly in reactions which involve coenzymes, a reasonable answer may be given to this question, but in many others this is not yet possible, at least in a quantitative manner. Before approaching this question, however, we will consider the more immediate problem of the experimental demonstration that a covalent enzyme-substrate compound is formed as an intermediate in an enzyme catalyzed reaction.

B. EXPERIMENTAL EVIDENCE FOR COVALENT ENZYME-SUBSTRATE INTERMEDIATES

The following criteria provide proof that a particular covalent enzyme-substrate compound is formed as an intermediate in an enzymatic reaction:

1. *Isolation*. The isolation and chemical characterization of the intermediate that is formed from the reaction of the enzyme with a substrate.
2. *Kinetics*. The demonstration that the intermediate is formed and reacts further with rate constants which are adequate to account for the observed rate of the enzyme catalyzed reaction. It must be shown that this is the same intermediate that was characterized in (1), i.e., that migration or isomerization has not occurred during the isolation of the intermediate.
3. *Generalization*. It should be shown that the same intermediate is formed with one or more "normal" substrates. It is often possible to fulfill the first two of these criteria only with poor substrates, which react sufficiently slowly to make possible the isolation and kinetic study of stoichiometric amounts of the enzyme-substrate complex. The possibility must be considered that such substrates, which may be highly reactive chemically, react nonspecifically with the enzyme to form compounds which are not intermediates in the reactions of specific substrates.

There are few, if any, instances in which all of these criteria have been fulfilled for enzymatic reactions that do not involve rapidly dissociable coenzymes. It is particularly difficult to measure the rates of formation and further reaction of intermediates which are formed from normal substrates because these intermediates usually undergo reaction so rapidly that their detection with stoichiometric amounts of enzyme requires the use of special rapid-reaction techniques. The pioneering work in the application of such techniques to enzymatic reactions has now been carried out, however, and important further progress in this direction is to be expected in the near future. One of the earliest and clearest examples is the demonstration by the use of the stopped-flow technique that the reduction of lipoyl dehydrogenase by reduced lipoic acid to a colored intermediate, possibly a semiquinone, is the rate-determining step of the overall reduction of nicotinamide-adenine dinucleotide by this substrate and that the rate of formation of the intermediate is adequate to account for the rate of the overall catalyzed reaction; in the reverse direction, reduction of oxidized lipoic acid by the intermediate is the rate-determining step.[1] In the absence of direct proof for the intermediacy of covalent enzyme-substrate compounds, indirect criteria are generally used as suggestive evidence for their formation; some of these criteria are summarized here.

1. OBSERVATION OF THE FORMATION AND DISAPPEARANCE OF AN INTERMEDIATE

Hartley and Kilby showed that the hydrolysis of p-nitrophenyl acetate (PNPA) catalyzed by a large amount of chymotrypsin proceeds with an initial burst of p-nitrophenol release, followed by a slower steady-state release of this product (Fig. 1).[2] There are several possible explanations for such an initial rapid release of product upon mixing an enzyme and its substrate: (a) The enzyme may be subject to severe product inhibition, which leads to the formation of product from the enzyme-substrate-product complex at a new, reduced rate (k_1', equation 1) after an initial faster for-

$$E + S \rightleftharpoons ES \xrightarrow{k_1} E + P$$
$$\pm P \Big\|$$
$$ESP \xrightarrow{k_1'} EP + P \qquad (1)$$

[1] V. Massey, Q. H. Gibson, and C. Veeger, *Biochem. J.* **77**, 341 (1960).
[2] B. S. Hartley and B. A. Kilby, *Biochem. J.* **56**, 288 (1954).

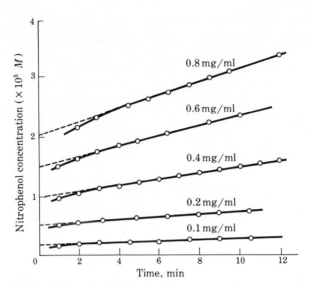

Fig. 1   The "initial burst" in the reaction of p-nitrophenyl acetate with a high concentration of chymotrypsin.[2]   The different lines are for different concentrations of chymotrypsin reacting with 5×10^{-4} M p-nitrophenyl acetate.

mation from the enzyme-substrate complex (k_1); (b) the presence of substrate may cause a time-dependent conformation change from an active form of the enzyme E, which is present initially, to a less active form E' (equation 2); or (c) the enzyme may react rapidly

$$
\begin{array}{ccc}
\text{E + S} \rightleftharpoons & \text{ES} \xrightarrow{k_1} & \text{E + P} \\
\text{slow} \Big\updownarrow & \Big\updownarrow \text{slow} & \\
\text{E' + S} \rightleftharpoons & \text{E'S} \xrightarrow{k_1'} & \text{E' + P}
\end{array}
\tag{2}
$$

with the substrate to release one product and form an intermediate composed of the enzyme and the remaining part of the substrate, which then undergoes a slower, steady-state decomposition, as shown for the chymotrypsin catalyzed hydrolysis of PNPA in equation 3.

$$
\text{E + PNPA} \underset{K_s}{\rightleftharpoons} \text{E} \cdot \text{PNPA} \xrightarrow[k_2]{\text{fast}} \underset{\substack{+ \\ \text{PNP}^-}}{\text{Ac}-\text{E}} \xrightarrow[k_3]{\text{slow}} \text{E + AcOH}
\tag{3}
$$

Situation b provides a possible explanation for the rapid initial burst of ATP hydrolysis which is observed with myosin ATPase.[3] Under some experimental conditions this burst corresponds to 1 mole of phosphate release for each mole of myosin. If situation b is the correct explanation for the burst, combination of the first mole of ATP with the enzyme must bring about a conformation change, perhaps concomitantly with hydrolysis, to the less active form of the enzyme E'. Such a change would be of particular significance for an enzyme which is involved in the conversion of chemical to mechanical energy in the process of muscle contraction.

The initial burst of p-nitrophenol formation in the reaction of chymotrypsin with PNPA also corresponds to 1 mole for each mole of enzyme. That this stoichiometry results from the more usual explanation c, with the release of one equivalent of p-nitrophenol as the enzyme reacts with PNPA to form an acyl-enzyme, is shown by the fact that the acyl-enzyme can be isolated from dilute acid solution, in which it is relatively stable, and thus can react with hydroxylamine and other acyl acceptors to give 1 mole of acylated acceptor. In fact, the trimethylacetyl-chymotrypsin intermediate has been crystallized.[4] This achievement is of particular significance when it is realized that only a few years previously the question of whether or not enzyme-substrate intermediates existed at all was a subject for active debate.

PNPA, although highly reactive chemically, is a poor substrate for chymotrypsin, so that a large amount of enzyme is used to study its hydrolysis. The detection of the initial burst is made possible by the presence of this high concentration of enzyme and by the relatively slow turnover of PNPA by the enzyme after the steady-state rate of hydrolysis has been attained. More recently, an initial burst has been demonstrated in the reaction of chymotrypsin with a specific substrate, the p-nitrophenyl ester of N-acetyl-L-tryptophan, by carrying out the reaction at pH 2 to 4. At this pH the rate of hydrolysis of even this specific substrate is slow enough to permit the use of a high concentration of enzyme with a low turnover rate of the substrate.[5]

With slowly reacting substrates, unfavorable reaction conditions, or apparatus to measure rapid reactions it may be possible to ob-

[3] L. Sartorelli, H. J. Fromm, R. W. Benson, and P. D. Boyer, *Biochemistry* **5**, 2877 (1966); H. Tokuyama, S. Kubo, and Y. Tonomura, *Biochem. Z.* **345**, 57 (1966) and references therein.

[4] C. E. McDonald and A. K. Balls, *J. Biol. Chem.* **227**, 727 (1957).

[5] F. J. Kézdy, G. E. Clement, and M. L. Bender, *J. Am. Chem. Soc.* **86**, 3690 (1964).

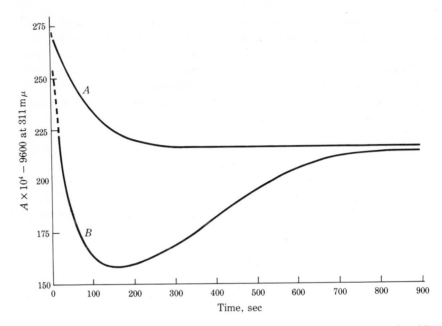

Fig. 2 The change in absorbance upon the reaction of N-acetyl-L-tryptophan (A) and N-acetyl-L-tryptophan methyl ester (B) with chymotrypsin at pH 2.42.[5]

serve the formation and decomposition of enzyme-substrate intermediates directly. For example the reaction of a small amount of N-acetyl-L-tryptophan methyl ester with chymotrypsin at pH 2.42 results in a small decrease and then an increase in absorbance at 242 mμ (Fig. 2).[5] The rate constant for this increase in absorbance is approximately the same as that for the maximal rate of hydrolysis of N-acetyl-L-tryptophan p-nitrophenyl ester under the same conditions. The rate constant for the latter reaction corresponds to the rate of deacylation of the acyl-enzyme (equation 3, k_3) because the acylation step with p-nitrophenyl esters is much faster than the deacylation step. The similarity of this rate constant to that obtained from the increase in absorbance in curve B of Fig. 2 suggests that the second part of curve B represents the deacylation of the same acyl-enzyme, which has been formed from the methyl ester. Curve A shows the same experiment with the free acid, N-acetyl-L-tryptophan. The spectral change observed with this compound could represent a spectral change associated with a substrate-induced conformation change of the enzyme or an acylation of the enzyme by the acid to form an equilibrium mixture of free and acylated enzyme. That the latter interpretation is correct is shown by the observation that the amount of the initial burst which is observed upon the addition of N-acetyl-L-tryptophan p-nitrophenyl ester and, hence, the amount of free enzyme which can be acylated, is reduced in the presence of this acid in a time-dependent process. By measuring the change in the amount of free enzyme at different concentrations of acid, an equilibrium constant for the formation of the acyl-enzyme from the free acid may be calculated. The rate of acyl-enzyme formation from the free acid corresponds approximately to the rate of ^{18}O exchange from water into N-acetyl-L-tryptophan at pH 7.9 (equation 4) if it is assumed that only the free-acid form of

$$RCOO^- + H_2O^* \rightleftharpoons RCOO^{*-} + H_2O \tag{4}$$

this compound is able to acylate the enzyme and if the appropriate corrections are made for the pH-dependence of enzyme activity and for the amount of free acid which exists at pH 7.9. Thus, even such an unreactive substrate as the carboxylate ion can react with chymotrypsin to give an acyl-enzyme intermediate by undergoing reaction in the form of the more reactive free acid. There are a number of less specific substrates, such as cinnamoyl, furoyl, and benzoyl derivatives, which react with chymotrypsin to give an acyl-enzyme and show larger spectral changes upon acylation and deacylation. These compounds have been useful for kinetic studies of the acylation and deacylation steps under conditions in which these steps are sufficiently slow for convenient measurement with ordinary spectrophotometers.[6,7]

The dye proflavin binds to the active site of chymotrypsin and undergoes a change in spectrum upon binding. Spectral shifts of this kind provide a useful tool for measuring the rate and equilibrium constants for the formation and decomposition of enzyme-substrate intermediates, when occupancy of the active site by substrate prevents binding of the dye.[8]

The principal experimental limitation to these techniques is the requirement for stoichiometric amounts of pure enzyme in order that the formation and decomposition of the intermediate may be observed directly. The following indirect methods may be utilized with catalytic quantities of enzyme and do not necessarily even require a pure enzyme, provided that any impurities do not affect the activity of the enzyme.

[6] M. L. Bender, G. R. Schonbaum, and B. Zerner, *J. Am. Chem. Soc.* 84, 2540, 2562 (1962).

[7] P. W. Inward and W. P. Jencks, *J. Biol. Chem.* 240, 1986 (1965); M. Caplow and W. P. Jencks, *Biochemistry* 1, 883 (1962).

[8] S. A. Bernhard and H. Gutfreund, *Proc. Natl. Acad. Sci. U.S.* 53, 1238 (1965).

Table II   Rates of reactions of esters of carbobenzoxyglycine at 25°[9]

Ester	Papain catalyzed, pH 6.8 K_m, $M \times 10^{-5}$	V_{max}, sec^{-1}	Nonenzymatic hydrolysis k_{OH^-}, $M^{-1} min^{-1}$
p-Nitrophenyl	0.93	2.73	6900
m-Nitrophenyl	1.89	2.18	4050
o-Nitrophenyl	15.2	2.14	3680
Phenyl	10.7	2.45	728
Ethyl	514	1.90	40.6

2. DECOMPOSITION AT THE SAME RATE OF A COMMON INTERMEDIATE FORMED FROM DIFFERENT SUBSTRATES

If esters with the same acyl group but with different leaving groups react rapidly with an enzyme to form an acyl-enzyme intermediate which then undergoes hydrolysis in a slow step, the maximum rate of hydrolysis of all of the esters will be the same because the rate-determining step of the reaction will be the hydrolysis of the same acyl-enzyme intermediate in each case (equation 5, k_3). An example

$$\text{Acyl}-\text{X}_a + \text{E} \underset{}{\overset{K_{sa}}{\rightleftharpoons}} \text{Acyl}-\text{X}_a \cdot \text{E}$$

$$\text{Acyl}-\text{X}_b + \text{E} \underset{}{\overset{K_{sb}}{\rightleftharpoons}} \text{Acyl}-\text{X}_b \cdot \text{E}$$

$$\text{Acyl}-\text{X}_c + \text{E} \underset{}{\overset{K_{sc}}{\rightleftharpoons}} \text{Acyl}-\text{X}_c \cdot \text{E}$$

$$\text{Acyl}-\text{X}_d + \text{E} \underset{}{\overset{K_{sd}}{\rightleftharpoons}} \text{Acyl}-\text{X}_d \cdot \text{E}$$

$$\begin{matrix} k_{2a} \\ k_{2b} \\ k_{2c} \\ k_{2d} \end{matrix} \quad \begin{matrix} \text{Acyl}-\text{E} \xrightarrow{k_3} \text{RCOO}^- + \text{E} \\ + \\ \text{X} \end{matrix}$$

$$(5)$$

of behavior of this kind for the hydrolysis of a series of esters of carbobenzoxyglycine catalyzed by papain is summarized in Table II. The similarity of the maximal rates of hydrolysis of the different esters suggests that the hydrolysis of a common carbobenzoxyglycyl-enzyme with the rate constant k_3 is the rate-determining step for the reaction of all of the esters and, consequently, that a common acyl-enzyme intermediate exists.[9]

As in most experiments of this kind, the maximal rates of hydrolysis of the different esters are not *exactly* the same. The

[9] J. F. Kirsch and M. Igelström, *Biochemistry* 5, 783 (1966).

following explanations should be considered to account for such differences:

a) **Experimental error.** The error of the rate measurements is not always reported, but when it is, it is frequently smaller than the observed differences in rate. This may reflect either undue confidence on the part of the investigators or a real difference in rate which requires explanation.

b) **Absence of a common intermediate, with coincidentally similar rates.** If the substrates are chemically similar, it would not be surprising if the enzyme catalyzed their hydrolysis by a direct attack of water at similar, but not quite identical, rates. This is unlikely for the particular case described here because of the large differences in the chemical reactivity of the different esters, which are manifested in their widely different rate constants for alkaline hydrolysis (k_{OH^-}, Table II).

c) **A rate-determining conformation change of the enzyme is rate-determining.** If such a conformation change is required for the reaction and is induced by the substrate, it is unlikely that it would occur at exactly the same rate but it might occur at similar rates with different substrates (Chap. 5, Sec. D).

d) **Different degrees of product inhibition by the different products.** This can be avoided by studying true initial rates and can be examined directly by adding product.

e) **Substrate inhibition.** While a large amount of inhibition by the binding of substrate to the acyl-enzyme would be apparent from the kinetics, a small amount of such inhibition might easily escape detection and lead to different apparent maximal rates of reaction.

f) **A diffusion-controlled step of the reaction is rate-determining.** An encounter with some component of the solvent or the movement of some group on the enzyme into the correct position may occur with a very large rate constant, but may still be rate-determining for even a relatively slow reaction if preceded by one or more unfavorable equilibrium steps. If a common step of this kind is rate-determining for different substrates, the same overall rate will be observed if the prior equilibrium steps have the same equilibrium constants for the different substrates.

g) Decomposition of the covalent enzyme-substrate intermediate is not entirely rate-determining. With a series of acyl donors with progressively poorer leaving groups, the rate of acylation will become progressively slower. When the rate of acylation approaches the rate of the deacylation step, it will become partially rate-determining and the observed maximal rate will decrease. With a very poor leaving group on the acylating agent, acylation will be entirely rate-determining and the observed rate will be much slower. This is the case, for example, with amides, which are hydrolyzed by chymotrypsin several orders of magnitude more slowly than esters of the same acyl compound. The slower rate for the ethyl ester in Table II may mean that acylation is becoming partly rate-determining in the papain catalyzed hydrolysis of this substrate.

Mechanisms which involve covalent enzyme-substrate intermediates, such as those of equations 3 or 5, provide a good example of the well known fact that the dissociation constant of the initial enzyme-substrate complex K_s is not necessarily equal to the Michaelis constant K_m. Equation 6 shows the relationship between

$$K_m = K_s \frac{k_3}{k_2 + k_3} \tag{6}$$

these constants for this system when the initial binding step is fast.[10] If acylation is rate-determining and deacylation is fast, $k_3 \gg k_2$, the equation reduces to $K_m = K_s$ and the observed Michaelis constant is equal to the dissociation constant. However, if deacylation is rate-determining, $k_3 \ll k_2$, all of the steps before and including the rate-determining deacylation must appear in the expression for the Michaelis constant, which reduces to $K_m = k_3 K_s / k_2$ under these conditions. If the actual dissociation constants K_s for a series of substrates are not very different and k_3 is constant, then the principal variable in the measured K_m will be the rate constant for the acylation step k_2, and the differences in this rate constant for the different esters will be the principal cause of the differences in the Michaelis constants. The Michaelis constants for the papain catalyzed hydrolysis of the series of carbobenzoxyglycine esters decrease inversely with the rate of the nonenzymatic reaction of these esters with hydroxide ion (Table II, Fig. 3). The point which falls below the line in the figure is for the sterically hindered o-nitrophenyl ester. This suggests that this situation may hold in

[10] H. Gutfreund and J. M. Sturtevant, *Biochem. J.* **63**, 656 (1956).

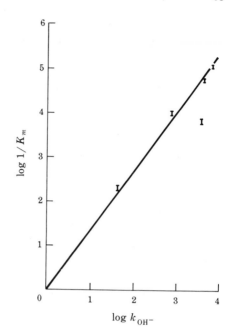

Fig. 3 The relationship between $1/K_m$ for the papain catalyzed hydrolysis and the rate of alkaline hydrolysis of a series of esters of carbobenzoxyglycine at 25°.[9]

this case; i.e., the decrease in the Michaelis constants as the leaving group becomes better simply reflects an increase in the reactivity of the ester, which is manifested in an increase in the rate of acylation k_2, as well as in the rate of alkaline hydrolysis k_{OH^-},

3. PARTITIONING OF THE INTERMEDIATE TO GIVE TWO PRODUCTS AT A CONSTANT TOTAL RATE

If the *formation* of the covalent intermediate is the rate-determining step of the reaction and this intermediate can react with two acceptors to give different products, then when the concentration of the acceptors is varied, the partitioning of the intermediate to products will change, but the sum of the rates of formation of the two products will be the same and will correspond to the rate of formation of the intermediate (equation 7).

$$A-B + E \underset{}{\overset{K_s}{\rightleftharpoons}} A-B \cdot E \xrightarrow[-A]{slow} B-E \overset{X}{\underset{Y}{<}} \begin{matrix} B-X + E \\ B-Y + E \end{matrix} \qquad (7)$$

There has been some question as to whether the chymotrypsin catalyzed hydrolysis of amides proceeds through an acyl-enzyme intermediate or through a direct attack of water or another acceptor on the amide which is bound to the active site of the enzyme. An attempt to resolve this question by the use of this criterion was made by examining the chymotrypsin catalyzed hydrolysis and hydroxylaminolysis of N-acetyltyrosine-p-nitroanilide in the presence of increasing concentrations of hydroxylamine (equation 8).[11] If

$$\text{Actyr}-\text{NA} + \text{Enz} \xrightarrow{-\text{NA}} \text{Actyr}-\text{Enz} \Big\langle \begin{array}{l} \xrightarrow{\text{H}_2\text{O}} \text{Actyr}-\text{OH} \\ \xrightarrow{\text{NH}_2\text{OH}} \text{Actyr}-\text{NHOH} \end{array} \tag{8}$$

the chymotrypsin catalyzed hydrolysis of amides and anilides proceeds through an acyl-enzyme intermediate, the formation of the intermediate is certainly the rate-determining step because the hydrolysis of esters of the same acyl compound proceeds much more rapidly. The finding that the overall reaction rate, as measured by the appearance of p-nitroaniline, shows little change in the presence of hydroxylamine, whereas nearly half of the product in the presence of $1.6\,M$ hydroxylamine is the hydroxamic acid, suggests that the reaction does proceed through a common acyl-enzyme intermediate. Unfortunately, Michaelis constants and maximal velocities were not determined, and the high concentration of hydroxylamine which is required to give significant amounts of hydroxamic acid might mask an increase in the overall rate by affecting either or both of these kinetic parameters. The interpretation is further complicated by the occurrence of enzyme catalyzed hydrolysis of the N-acetyltyrosine hydroxamic acid which is formed.

A special case of this situation is that in which one of the acceptors is the same as the leaving group A. In this case the reaction with this acceptor will regenerate starting material and will appear as an inhibition of the rate of formation of B–X in the presence of A (equation 9). An attempt was made to apply this criterion

$$\text{A}-\text{B} + \text{E} \longrightarrow \text{B}-\text{E} \Big\langle \begin{array}{l} \xrightarrow{\text{X}} \text{B}-\text{X} + \text{E} \\ \xrightarrow{\text{A}} \text{A}-\text{B} + \text{E} \end{array} \tag{9}$$

to the chymotrypsin catalyzed hydrolysis of N-acetyltyrosine hydroxamic acid by comparing the amount of inhibition of this reaction in the presence of hydroxylamine to the amount predicted from the

[11] T. Inagami and J. M. Sturtevant, *Biochem. Biophys. Res. Commun.* **14**, 69 (1964).

partitioning of the presumed intermediate acyl-enzyme to hydrolysis and hydroxylaminolysis products.[12] The partitioning of the presumed intermediate was determined by measuring the amounts of hydroxamic acid and free acid which are formed from acetyltyrosine ethyl ester in the presence of different concentrations of hydroxylamine (equation 10). The results of this experiment are not in good

$$
\begin{array}{c}
\text{Actyr} - \text{OEt} \\
\downarrow \\
\text{Actyr} - \text{Enz}
\end{array}
$$

$$
\pm \text{NH}_2\text{OH} \nearrow \qquad \nwarrow \pm \text{H}_2\text{O}
$$

$$
\text{Actyr} - \text{NHOH} \qquad \text{Actyr} - \text{OH} \tag{10}
$$

agreement with the acyl-enzyme mechanism, but complications arising from a dependence of the partitioning ratio on the concentration of enzyme prevent a rigorous interpretation of the results. More disturbing is the fact that the rate of the reaction in the lower part of equation 10 in the reverse direction, the synthesis of N-acetyltyrosine hydroxamic acid from the free acid in the presence of increasing concentrations of hydroxylamine, does not show the dependence on hydroxylamine concentration that would be expected from the relative rates of hydrolysis and hydroxylaminolysis of the presumed acyl-enzyme intermediate. At a high concentration of hydroxylamine, at which the intermediate breaks down mainly to give hydroxamic acid, the free-energy barrier for this step must be lower than that for the addition (and loss) of water. Consequently, the formation of the acyl-enzyme should be the rate-determining step of hydroxamic acid synthesis from the free acid, and the rate should become almost independent of hydroxylamine concentration. This does not occur. The results require either that some uncontrolled factor, such as a solvent effect, is perturbing the rates in such a way as to exactly cancel the expected leveling off of the rate with increasing hydroxylamine concentration or that this reaction does not occur through the ordinary acyl-enzyme mechanism.

A more complete examination of this situation can be carried out if the inhibiting molecule of A is isotopically labeled, so that the rate of the back-reaction of A with the intermediate may be determined directly and compared with the amount of inhibition of

[12] M. Caplow and W. P. Jencks, *J. Biol. Chem.* **239**, 1640 (1964).

the formation of B–X. Examples of this case will be described below in the section on exchange reactions.

4. PARTITIONING OF A COMMON INTERMEDIATE TO A CONSTANT RATIO OF TWO PRODUCTS

Regardless of which step is rate-determining, a common intermediate which is formed from several donor molecules must give the same ratio of products at a given concentration of acceptors X and Y (equation 11). This criterion for the formation of an intermediate

$$
\begin{array}{l}
A-B \\
C-B \\
D-B \\
E-B
\end{array}
\Biggr\}
E-B
\begin{array}{l}
\xrightarrow{X} B-X + E \\
\xrightarrow{Y} B-Y + E
\end{array}
\tag{11}
$$

requires the assumption that the enzyme would not catalyze the *direct* transfer of a group from different donor molecules to X and Y at a constant ratio of rates. It is, therefore, less exacting than the preceding two criteria, which require that molecules of varying intrinsic reactivity react directly at identical rates or at a constant sum of two rates if a common intermediate is formed. That is, a coincidental identity of rate *ratios* is more probable than a coincidental identity of absolute rates for different reactants.

This criterion has been applied to the chymotrypsin catalyzed reactions of a series of hippurate esters with hydroxylamine and water.[13] At a constant concentration of hydroxylamine, different esters, which react at widely different rates, give the same ratio of hydroxamic acid to free acid as products (Table III), suggesting that hydroxylamine and water are reacting with a common intermediate hippuryl-enzyme at a constant ratio of rates. The argument is strengthened by the demonstration that the ratio of hydrolysis to hydroxylaminolysis in the nonenzymatic reaction at pH 12 is different for the different esters (Table III), but it is difficult to rule out unequivocally the possibility that the enzyme could catalyze a direct attack of hydroxylamine and water on different hippurate esters at the same relative rates.

5. KINETICS

It is always depressing to realize that, in spite of the enormous amount of effort that has been expended in both theoretical and

[13] R. M. Epand and I. B. Wilson, *J. Biol. Chem.* **238**, 1718 (1963); **240**, 1104 (1965).

Table III   Ratio of hydrolysis to hydroxylaminolysis of different hippurate esters catalyzed by α-chymotrypsin in the presence of 0.1 M hydroxylamine[13]

| Hippurate ester | $\dfrac{Hydroxylaminolysis}{Hydrolysis}$ | |
	Enzymatic, pH 6.7	Nonenzymatic, pH 12
Methyl	0.37	0.99
Isopropyl	0.38	0.29
Homocholine	0.37	1.73
4-Pyridinylmethyl	0.37	3.03

experimental work on the subject, steady-state enzyme kinetics has seldom played a major role in elucidating the mechanism of action of an enzyme. The single example of steady-state kinetic behavior for any specific substrate which is directly interpretable in terms of mechanism is "ping-pong" or parallel-line kinetics, in double reciprocal plots of rate against substrate concentration. Such behavior suggests that the overall reaction proceeds through two half-reactions, with the intermediate formation of a complex or compound of the enzyme with the group which is being transferred (equation 12).[14] The kinetics of such a reaction follow equation 13. This equation

$$A\text{--}B + E \rightleftharpoons A\text{--}B \cdot E \rightleftharpoons B\text{--}E + A$$
$$B\text{--}E + X \rightleftharpoons X\text{--}B \cdot E \rightleftharpoons X\text{--}B + E \tag{12}$$

$$\frac{1}{v} = \frac{1}{V_{max}}\left(\frac{K_m AB}{[AB]} + \frac{K_m X}{[X]} + 1\right) \tag{13}$$

lacks the product terms of the form $K/[AB][X]$ which appear in the expressions for ternary complex and other mechanisms and which lead to intersecting lines on reciprocal plots. No kinetic test can prove a particular mechanism unequivocally because it is always possible that particular kinetic constants, such as those in a product term, are so small as to be undetectable; in this case there is the additional ambiguity that the same kinetic behavior may be obtained with a ternary complex mechanism in which the first step is slow

[14] R. A. Alberty, *Advan. Enzymol.* 17, 1 (1956); K. Dalziel, *Acta Chem. Scand.* 11, 1706 (1957); W. W. Cleland, *Biochim. Biophys. Acta* 67, 104, 173, 188 (1963).

and essentially irreversible.[14,15] Nevertheless, the observation of
"ping-pong" kinetics is perhaps the most useful of all kinetic results
in the study of enzyme reactions because it directly suggests a chemical reaction mechanism which may be tested experimentally.

The best known "ping-pong" group transfer enzymes are the
transaminases, in which the enzyme–B compound contains the ammonia which is being transferred in the form of the bound pyridoxamine phosphate coenzyme.[16] The same kinetic behavior is observed
with a number of flavin enzymes, in which hydrogen is being transferred as a part of the bound reduced coenzyme,[17] with nucleoside
diphosphokinase and phosphoglucomutase, which catalyze phosphate
transfer through an intermediate phosphoryl-enzyme,[18] and with
sucrose phosphorylase, which catalyzes glucose transfer through an
intermediate glucosyl-enzyme.[19] An example of parallel-line kinetics
is shown in Fig. 4 for succinyl CoA–acetoacetate coenzyme A transferase, which catalyzes the transfer of coenzyme A from one acyl
group to another through an enzyme–CoA intermediate according to
the mechanism of equation 14,[20] in which Succ and AcAc refer to
succinate and acetoacetate, respectively.

$$\text{SuccCoA} + \text{E} \;\rightleftharpoons\; \text{SuccCoA} \cdot \text{E} \;\rightleftharpoons\; \text{E–CoA} + \text{Succ}$$
$$\text{E–CoA} + \text{AcAc} \;\rightleftharpoons\; \text{AcAcCoA} \cdot \text{E} \;\rightleftharpoons\; \text{AcAcCoA} + \text{E}$$

$$(14)$$

The interpretation of reaction mechanisms of this kind follows
from the fact that they consist of two separable half-reactions, and
it is easy to see, at least qualitatively, why the lines in the reciprocal
plots do not intersect at a common maximal velocity. If the reaction
of equation 14, for example, is being examined at a suboptimal
concentration of succinyl CoA, then the first half-reaction will not
proceed at its maximal rate, and, no matter how much the rate of
the second reaction is increased by adding more acetoacetate, the
true maximal velocity of the overall reaction cannot be reached
because of the limiting rate of the first reaction. Similarly, if the

[15] H. J. Fromm and V. Zewe, *J. Biol. Chem.* **237**, 1661 (1962).

[16] S. F. Velick and J. Vavra, *J. Biol. Chem.* **237**, 2109 (1962).

[17] V. Massey and C. Veeger, *Ann. Rev. Biochem.* **32**, 579 (1963).

[18] W. J. Ray, Jr. and G. A. Roscelli, *J. Biol. Chem.* **239**, 1228 (1964); N. Mourad
and R. E. Parks, Jr., *Ibid.* **241**, 271 (1966).

[19] R. Silverstein, J. Voet, D. Reed, and R. H. Abeles, *J. Biol. Chem.* **242**, 1338
(1967).

[20] L. B. Hersh and W. P. Jencks, *J. Biol. Chem.* **242**, 3468, 3481 (1967).

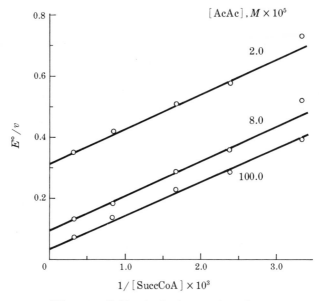

Fig. 4 "Ping-pong" kinetics in the reaction of acetoacetate with succinyl CoA catalyzed by CoA transferase.[20]

acetoacetate concentration is limiting, the true maximal velocity can never be reached by increasing the concentration of succinyl CoA because the rate will always be limited by the suboptimal rate of the second half-reaction.

The mechanisms of equations 12 and 14 are almost certainly oversimplified for reactions of this kind because they neglect binding of the leaving and acceptor molecules A and X; and the fact that the enzymes show some degree of specificity with respect to these molecules means that such binding sites must certainly exist. An expanded mechanism which includes such binding sites is shown in equation 15. It is one of the fortunate simplifications of kinetics

$$
\begin{aligned}
&\text{A--B} + \text{E} \;\rightleftharpoons\; \text{A--B} \cdot \text{E} \;\rightleftharpoons\; \text{B--E} \cdot \text{A} \;\rightleftharpoons\; \text{B--E} + \text{A} \\
&\text{B--E} + \text{X} \;\rightleftharpoons\; \text{B--E} \cdot \text{X} \;\rightleftharpoons\; \text{X--B} \cdot \text{E} \;\rightleftharpoons\; \text{X--B} + \text{E}
\end{aligned}
\tag{15}
$$

that the kinetic behavior of equation 15 is exactly the same as that of equations 12 and 14, although the detailed interpretation of the kinetic constants is somewhat different. However, the existence of binding sites means that the acceptor molecule X may bind prematurely to the free enzyme and interfere with the binding of A–B, to cause a form of substrate inhibition. Such behavior is frequently observed in this class of reaction and causes a deviation from the parallel-line behavior of reciprocal plots at high substrate concentrations.

In the absence of complicating factors, inhibition by the donor molecule A is competitive with respect to the acceptor molecule X, and is noncompetitive with respect to the group-donating molecule A–B. This behavior is observed for the inhibition of CoA transferase by succinate, for example, which is competitive with respect to acetoacetate and noncompetitive with respect to succinyl CoA (Fig. 5). In its simplest form, the inhibition may be regarded as a manifestation of the reverse operation of the first half-reaction. In the presence of succinate some of the enzyme–CoA intermediate which is formed from succinyl CoA will react with succinate to regenerate starting material and this back-reaction will compete with the normal reaction with acetoacetate to give products; i.e., acetoacetate and succinate are competing directly for reaction with the intermediate. The inhibition may be partly overcome by adding more succinyl CoA to increase the rate of the first half-reaction, but a certain fraction of the intermediate will always react with succinate to give starting material instead of products, so that the inhibition cannot be completely overcome by adding succinyl CoA and is noncompetitive with respect to this substrate. As in the case of the kinetics in the absence of inhibitor, this interpretation may be modified if there is significant binding of A or X under the conditions of the kinetic measurements.

A "ping-pong" mechanism leads to no less than four Haldane relationships, which relate the overall equilibrium constant of an enzyme catalyzed reaction to the observed kinetic constants.[21] Agreement of the kinetic constants with these four relationships provides further support for this type of mechanism.

6. EXCHANGE AND TRANSFER REACTIONS

It is frequently stated that the occurrence of enzyme catalyzed isotope exchange or group transfer reactions is evidence for the existence of a covalent enzyme-substrate intermediate. In the absence of further information there is no basis for such a conclusion. There is no reason to believe, a priori, that an enzyme is more

[21] C. P. Henson and W. W. Cleland, *Biochemistry* **3**, 338 (1964).

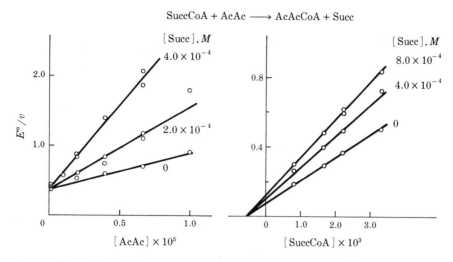

Fig. 5 Competitive inhibition by succinate with respect to acetoacetate and noncompetitive inhibition with respect to succinyl CoA of the reaction catalyzed by CoA transferase.[20]

likely to catalyze the transfer of B from A–B to X through an enzyme–B intermediate (equation 16) than by a direct displacement of

$$\boxed{\;A - B\;}\; \overset{\pm\,A}{\rightleftharpoons}\; \boxed{\;\underset{\text{enzyme}}{B}\;}\; \overset{\pm\,X}{\rightleftharpoons}\; \boxed{\;B - X\;} \qquad (16)$$

A by X (equation 17). Similarly the exchange of isotopically labeled A* into AB can occur either through an enzyme–B intermediate (equation 18) or by direct displacement (equation 19).

$$\boxed{A - B \quad X} \rightleftharpoons \boxed{A \quad B - X} \qquad (17)$$

$$\boxed{\;A - B\;} \overset{\pm\,A}{\rightleftharpoons} \boxed{\;B\;} \overset{\pm\,A^*}{\rightleftharpoons} \boxed{\;A^* - B\;} \qquad (18)$$

$$\boxed{A - B \quad A^*} \rightleftharpoons \boxed{A \quad B - A^*} \qquad (19)$$

Other criteria, however, may suggest the existence of an enzyme–B intermediate in such reactions. If it is assumed that the direct transfer of a saturated carbon atom from A to X must occur with inversion of configuration, the observation that a group transfer reaction takes place with retention of configuration suggests that the reaction occurs through a double replacement mechanism,

in which the enzyme replaces A with inversion to give enzyme–B and
X replaces the enzyme with a second inversion to give a product
with retention of configuration (equations 20 and 21). The transfer

$$A - B \overset{R_1}{\underset{R_3}{\overset{\cdot\cdot R_2}{\longleftarrow}}} Enz \rightleftharpoons \overset{R_1}{\underset{R_3}{R_2\cdot\cdot\overset{\,}{\underset{\,}{\diagdown}}}} B - Enz \tag{20}$$

$$X \overset{R_1}{\underset{R_3}{\longrightarrow}} R_2\cdot\cdot B - Enz \rightleftharpoons X - B \overset{R_1}{\underset{R_3}{\overset{\cdot\cdot R_2}{\diagdown}}} + Enz \tag{21}$$

of glucose between fructose and phosphate catalyzed by sucrose
phosphorylase occurs with retention of configuration, suggesting the
intermediate formation of a glucosyl-enzyme, and a number of related enzymes also catalyze the transfer of sugars with retention of
configuration.[22] The formation of a glucosyl-enzyme has recently
been substantiated by the isolation of this intermediate from the
reaction of sucrose phosphorylase with labeled sucrose.[23] It should
be noted that the term "replacement" in this context is not meant to
imply anything about chemical mechanism, but refers only to the
stereochemistry of the reaction; these reactions may well proceed
with the same stereospecificity through shielded carbonium ions,
rather than by S_N2 displacement.

In order that an exchange of A^* into A–B may occur by a
direct replacement, as shown in equation 19, it is necessary that A^*
fit into the site which is normally occupied by the acceptor X. If the
enzyme is nonspecific with respect to the acceptor or if there is no
site at all for the acceptor, this is possible and the occurrence of an
exchange reaction per se provides no evidence one way or another
as to whether the reaction proceeds through an enzyme–B intermediate. However, if the enzyme is highly specific with respect to the
acceptor X and if A is structurally different from X, it would not be
expected that A^* would fit into the acceptor site, and the occurrence
of an exchange reaction is evidence that the reaction proceeds through
an enzyme–B intermediate according to equation 18. Similar considerations apply to the specificity of transfer reactions.

These points are illustrated by the enzyme lysozyme, which
catalyzes the transfer of the C_1 carbon atom of glycoside substrates

---

[22] D. E. Koshland, Jr., in W. D. McElroy and B. Glass (eds.), "Mechanisms of
Enzyme Action," p. 608, Johns Hopkins Press, Baltimore, 1954.

[23] J. Voet and R. H. Abeles, *J. Biol. Chem.* **241**, 2731 (1966).

to water, alcohols, and sugars.[24] The fact that the products of the transfer reactions (to ROH) have the same β configuration as the starting material means that the reaction does not occur through a single S_N2 displacement with inversion of configuration; it must occur through a double replacement mechanism, a shielded carbonium ion, or a relatively improbable frontside displacement mechanism. The fact that specific sugar acceptors, such as N-acetylglucosamine, are some three orders of magnitude more effective as acceptors than water or simple alcohols means that acceptor molecules bind to a specific site. The leaving group A_1, which has a structure similar to that of the acceptor A_2, must have left this site in order that the binding of acceptor may occur, but the group that is being transferred remains in some activated state on the enzyme; i.e., there must be an intermediate (equation 22).

$$A_1{-}B \;\rightleftharpoons\; A_1\,B \;\underset{}{\overset{\pm A_1}{\rightleftharpoons}}\; B \;\underset{}{\overset{\pm A_2}{\rightleftharpoons}}\; A_2\,B \;\rightleftharpoons\; A_2{-}B \tag{22}$$

A different type of evidence for an enzyme–B intermediate may be obtained from a quantitative evaluation of the exchange reaction. If the concentration of the acceptor is increased so that B–X is being formed at a maximal rate, this rate will often be a measure of the rate of formation of the enzyme–B intermediate (equation 23). If

$$A{-}B + E \;\xrightarrow{-A}\; B{-}E \;\underset{A^*}{\overset{X}{\diagdown\!\!\!\diagup}}\; \begin{array}{l} B{-}X + E \\ A^*{-}B + E \end{array} \tag{23}$$

the maximal rate of the exchange reaction of A^* to give A^*–B is the same as the maximal rate of formation of B–X, this suggests that the rate of formation of a common enzyme–B intermediate is being measured in both cases. It would be an improbable coincidence for these rates to be the same in a simple direct displacement reaction, because it would not be expected that A^* and X would displace A at identical rates. An inequality of the rates of formation of B–X and A^*–B does not rule out an enzyme–B intermediate. If the desorption of B–X or A^*–B from the enzyme is slow, the two rates will not be equal and the maximal rate of formation of B–X may be less than the maximal rate of formation of enzyme–B if the leveling off of the rate at high X concentration is caused by saturation of a binding site for X, rather than by the rate-determining formation of enzyme–B.

[24] J. A. Rupley and V. Gates, *Proc. Natl. Acad. Sci. U.S.* **57**, 496 (1967); J. J. Pollock, D. M. Chipman, and N. Sharon, *Arch. Biochem. Biophys.* **120**, 235 (1967).

   An alternative but less probable mechanism which might account for the equality of maximal rates of formation of B–X and of exchange to give A*–B can be imagined without invoking an enzyme–B intermediate (equation 24). If the formation of the activated

$$
\begin{array}{ccccccc}
\mathrm{E + A - B} & \rightleftharpoons & \mathrm{E \cdot A - B} & \overset{slow}{\rightleftharpoons} & \mathrm{E' \cdot A - B} & \overset{\pm A,\ \pm X}{\rightleftharpoons} & \mathrm{E' \cdot X - B} \\
 & & \pm A^*,\ \pm A \big\updownarrow & & & & \big\updownarrow \\
\mathrm{E + A^* - B} & \rightleftharpoons & \mathrm{E \cdot A^* - B} & \rightleftharpoons & \mathrm{E' \cdot A^* - B} & & \mathrm{E \cdot X - B} \\
 & & & & & & \big\Updownarrow \\
 & & & & & & \mathrm{E + X - B} \qquad (24)
\end{array}
$$

intermediate $\mathrm{E' \cdot A{-}B}$ occurs in a slow intramolecular isomerization step (such as a substrate-induced change in enzyme conformation), this intermediate might then react with X and with A* to give product and exchange at equal maximal rates. However, the kinetic equation for this mechanism does not predict parallel line or "ping-pong" kinetics in double reciprocal plots of velocity against substrate concentration and predicts different inhibition behavior from that expected for a "ping-pong" mechanism.

   An example of the equivalence of maximal rates of exchange and of the overall reaction for the reaction catalyzed by CoA transferase in the presence of acetoacetyl CoA is shown in Table IV. The maximal rate of the reaction of the enzyme–CoA intermediate with acetoacetate to give exchange of acetoacetate into acetoacetyl CoA is the same as the maximal rate of its reaction with succinate to give succinyl CoA as product.

7. EXCHANGE AND INHIBITION

If the reaction is carried out in the presence of a "saturating" concentration of the acceptor X, so that every molecule of intermediate that is formed goes on to products, the rate of formation of products is usually a measure of the rate of formation of the intermediate E–B (equation 25). If the reaction is now inhibited by the addition

$$
\mathrm{A - B + E} \ \underset{slow}{\overset{-A}{\longrightarrow}} \ \mathrm{E - B} \ \begin{array}{l} \overset{fast}{\nearrow} \mathrm{X - B + E} \\ \overset{X}{} \\ \underset{A^*}{} \\ \underset{fast}{\searrow} \mathrm{A^* - B + E} \end{array} \qquad (25)
$$

of the first product A, the inhibition occurs because the intermediate reacts with A to regenerate starting material instead of with X to

Table IV Exchange of AcAc into AcAcCoA catalyzed by CoA transferase[20]

AcAc, M	AcAc exchange, mμmoles/min
4×10^{-4}	134
2×10^{-3}	193
1×10^{-2}	276
Extrapolated to ∞	280
Maximum rate of SuccCoA formation	260

give product, as described above. Now, the amount of inhibition under these conditions is equal to the amount of back-reaction of A with E–X to give starting material, and this is equal to the amount of incorporation of labeled A into starting material, if A is isotopically labeled. This provides a useful and sensitive criterion of mechanism because it is unlikely that the amount of exchange of A* into A–B would be equal to the amount of inhibition by A in a simple displacement mechanism. This is essentially the same situation as the partitioning of an intermediate to give two products at a constant total rate (equations 7 and 9), except that in this case one of the products is labeled starting material.

As described in the previous section, an inequality of the amount of inhibition and exchange does not rule out a common intermediate because the formation of such an intermediate is not necessarily the rate-determining step of the reaction.

This criterion has been used as evidence for the intermediate formation of a phosphoryl-enzyme in the reaction catalyzed by glucose-6-phosphatase, which is inhibited by glucose.[25] Under conditions in which the enzyme is apparently saturated with the normal acceptor molecule, water, the amount of inhibition by glucose is equal to the amount of labeled glucose incorporated into glucose-6-phosphate.

If the concentration of X is low, so that the rate of formation of X–B is less than the maximal possible rate of formation of the intermediate, there will be a piling up of the intermediate; i.e., the steady-state concentration of E–B will increase. If labeled A* is present, it will react with the intermediate to give starting materials and will reduce the formation of product B–X by reducing the

[25] L. F. Hass and W. L. Byrne, *J. Am. Chem. Soc.* **82**, 947 (1960).

steady-state concentration of the intermediate E–B. However, since the rate of formation of the intermediate under these conditions is more than is needed to account for the rate of formation of the product B–X, there will be relatively less inhibition than in the previous case and the amount of exchange of A* into A–B will be *larger* than the amount of inhibition. Under these conditions the first step may be regarded as a fast step, which is more or less at equilibrium, while the formation of product is the rate-determining step (equation 26). Thus, the first step can go back and forth

$$E + A-B \underset{\pm A}{\rightleftharpoons} E-B \underset{\pm A^*}{\rightleftharpoons} E + A^*-B \quad \text{fast}$$

$$\left\downarrow \begin{matrix} X \\ \text{slow} \end{matrix} \right.$$

$$E + BX \tag{26}$$

several times to give exchange, while relatively little product is formed in the second step. The limiting case of this situation, of course, is that in which no X is present and only the exchange reaction takes place.

Both types of behavior, at high and low concentrations of succinate as acceptor for the enzyme–CoA intermediate, have been observed for succinyl CoA–acetoacetate coenzyme A transferase.[20] At saturating concentrations of succinate and in the absence of acetoacetate, every molecule of enzyme–CoA that is formed from acetoacetyl CoA reacts with succinate to give succinyl CoA. In the presence of acetoacetate as inhibitor each molecule of the enzyme–CoA intermediate that reacts with acetoacetate cannot react with succinate, so that the amount of inhibition is equal to the amount of incorporation of acetoacetate into acetoacetyl CoA (Table V, first

Table V   Relationship of inhibition to acetoacetate exchange in the reaction AcAcCoA + succ $\longrightarrow$ SuccCoA + AcAc catalyzed by CoA transferase[20]

Inhibitor, AcAc	Succinate, M	SuccCoA formation, mμmoles/min	Inhibition, mμmoles/min	AcAc → AcAcCoA exchange, mμmoles/min	Exchange / Inhibition
−	0.014	213			
+	0.014	107	106	114	1.1
−	0.004	68			
+	0.004	29	39	165	4.2
−	0.0008	27			
+	0.0008	23	4	30	7.4

two rows). At low concentrations of succinate the rate of the first reaction, to give the enzyme–CoA intermediate, is faster than the rate of reaction of the intermediate with succinate, so that the amount of exchange of acetoacetate into acetoacetyl CoA becomes larger than the amount of inhibition of succinyl CoA formation (Table V).

C. NUCLEOPHILIC CATALYSIS

1. IMIDAZOLE AND ACYL TRANSFER

Nucleophilic catalysis of acyl transfer in a nonenzymatic reaction is illustrated by imidazole catalysis of the hydrolysis and transfer of the acetyl group of p-nitrophenyl acetate and related activated acyl compounds.[26,27] In order that such catalysis may occur, the acyl compound must be activated by a good leaving group that can be expelled by the attacking imidazole; i.e., it must have anhydride-like character. The reaction proceeds according to the mechanism shown in equation 27 with the intermediate formation of acetylimidazole, which may be recognized by its characteristic absorption at

$$(27)$$

245 mμ. In the absence of acyl acceptors other than water the observed reaction is hydrolysis, and the hydrolysis of the acylimidazole intermediate is the slow step of the overall reaction, as shown

[26] T. C. Bruice and G. L. Schmir, J. Am. Chem. Soc. 79, 1663 (1957); 80, 148 (1958); M. L. Bender and B. W. Turnquest, Ibid. 79, 1652, 1656 (1957); D. M. Brouwer, M. J. Vlugt, and E. Havinga, Proc. Koninkl. Ned. Akad. Wetenschap. (Amsterdam) B60, 275 (1957).

[27] W. P. Jencks and J. Carriuolo, J. Biol. Chem. 234, 1272, 1280, (1959); R. Wolfenden and W. P. Jencks, J. Am. Chem. Soc. 83, 4390 (1961).

by the fact that the intermediate accumulates. In the presence of other nucleophilic reagents such as thiols or amines, the observed reaction may be acyl transfer, rather than hydrolysis. The great selectivity of acyl-group transfer reactions makes possible the catalysis of such transfer reactions in the presence of a large molar excess of water; for example, transfer of the acyl group to a thiol, to give a thiol ester, occurs at a thiol concentration of 10^{-3} M, in preference to reaction with 55 M water, because of the high nucleophilic reactivity of thiols toward acyl compounds. In the presence of moderate concentrations of such reactive nucleophilic compounds the second step is fast and the attack of imidazole on the acyl compound becomes rate determining.

If N-methylimidazole is substituted for imidazole, the reactive acylimidazolium ion intermediate cannot lose a proton and either undergoes rapid hydrolysis or reacts with an acyl acceptor. The fact that the rates of acyl transfer reactions catalyzed by N-methylimidazole and imidazole are similar, and the fact that most acyl transfer reactions of acetylimidazole proceed by reaction of the nucleophilic reagent with protonated acetylimidazole, show that the active intermediate in the acyl transfer reaction is the acetylimidazolium ion and that free acetylimidazole is usually not on the direct reaction path.

Imidazole catalyzed acyl transfer reactions serve to illustrate the three essential requirements for effective nucleophilic catalysis.

1. The catalyst must have a higher nucleophilic reactivity than the final acyl-group acceptor under the conditions of the experiment.
2. The intermediate which is formed by reaction of the substrate with the catalyst must be more reactive than the substrate.
3. The intermediate must be thermodynamically less stable than the product, so that it does not accumulate instead of the final product.

The existence of all these properties in a catalyst is unusual and requires that the catalyst have special properties. Structural changes that favor requirement 1 will generally be unfavorable to requirement 2 and vice versa. For example, the addition of an electron-donating substituent to an amine or phenolate ion will increase its nucleophilic reactivity, but will decrease the reactivity of the acylated intermediate. Imidazole and N-methylimidazole possess several special properties which make them effective as nucleophilic catalysts. They are amines, and amines are, compared to their basicity, much more reactive than hydroxide ion. Furthermore, they are tertiary amines, which have a higher intrinsic nucleophilic reactivity than primary or secondary amines. The enchanced reactivity of tertiary amines is usually cancelled out by the increased steric hindrance in such amines, but in imidazoles the substituents on the nitrogen atom are held back in an aromatic 5-membered ring and cause relatively little steric hindrance. Imidazole has a pK of 7, so that it is the strongest base which can exist at neutral pH. A weaker base would have a smaller nucleophilic reactivity, whereas a stronger base would be more reactive in the form of the free base, but would be partly protonated at neutral pH and, hence, would react less rapidly at a given total concentration of amine.

The acetylimidazole intermediate has a high susceptibility to attack by nucleophilic reagents because it can easily be protonated to the reactive acetylimidazolium ion and because of its relatively small resonance stabilization compared with ordinary amides. The pK of acetylimidazolium ion is 3.6, compared with pK's near zero for ordinary amides. One reason for the high basicity of acetylimidazole is that protonation can occur on a different nitrogen atom than that to which the acyl group is attached without interfering with resonance (1), whereas protonation of an ordinary amide occurs on the oxygen atom and cannot occur on nitrogen without a large loss of resonance stablization (2). Futhermore, protonation on nitrogen activates

1   2

the leaving amine directly, whereas protonation on oxygen, although it facilitates the attack of a nucleophilic reagent, must be followed by proton transfer to nitrogen before the leaving amine can be expelled. However, the most important single factor which contributes to the reactivity of acetylimidazole and acetylimidazolium ion is the relatively small resonance stabilization of the starting material compared with ordinary amides. The lone pair electrons of the nitrogen atom which interact with the carbonyl group in ordinary amides (2) are in large part unavailable for such resonance in acetylimidazole because of their involvement in the π electron system of the aromatic ring (1).

Finally, the acetylimidazole intermediate, although it is rapidly formed from suitable acyl donors, is thermodynamically unstable compared with most other amides, esters, and thiol esters.[28] The free energy of hydrolysis of acetylimidazole at pH 7 is $-13,000$ cal/ mole and that of the acetylimidazolium ion is considerably more negative.

With all these desirable properties one might expect that the imidazole groups of histidine residues would be found to act as nucleophilic catalysts in the active sites of enzymes; indeed, the discovery of these model reactions and the requirement for a free imidazole group for the activity of chymotrypsin and related enzymes led to speculation that imidazole does fill such a catalytic role. Unfortunately, nucleophilic catalysis by chymotrypsin and related enzymes occurs with the intermediate formation of an ester, formed from the acyl group and the hydroxyl group of a serine residue, and there is no convincing evidence at the present time that imidazole acts as a nucleophilic catalyst in any enzymatic acyl transfer reaction. While this may at first sight seem surprising from a teleological point of view, it is understandable when it is recalled that imidazole is an effective nucleophilic catalyst only for reactions of highly activated acyl groups, from which the acylimidazole intermediate may be formed. Most biological acyl transfer reactions involve less activated acyl compounds, and in nonenzymatic reactions of such compounds, including an O-acetylserine model compound for the acyl-enzyme, imidazole acts as a general base rather than as a nucleophilic catalyst, as appears to be the case also in enzymatic reactions.[29, 30]

There is some evidence that imidazole acts as a nucleophilic catalyst in enzymes which catalyze phosphate transfer. Phosphorylimidazole derivatives have been isolated from hydrolysates of succinic thiokinase and of an enzyme which catalyzes phosphate transfer from phosphoenolpyruvate to hexose, after incubation of the enzyme with a phosphoryl donor.[31] However, imidazole is not an especially

---

[28] E. R. Stadtman, in W. D. McElroy and B. Glass (eds.), "Mechanisms of Enzyme Action," p. 581, Johns Hopkins Press, Baltimore, 1954; J. Gerstein and W. P. Jencks, *J. Am. Chem. Soc.* **86**, 4655 (1964).

[29] B. M. Anderson, E. H. Cordes, and W. P. Jencks, *J. Biol. Chem.* **236**, 455 (1961).

[30] W. P. Jencks and J. Carriuolo, *J. Am. Chem. Soc.* **83**, 1743 (1961).

[31] W. Kundig, S. Ghosh, and S. Roseman, *Proc. Natl. Acad. Sci. U.S.* **52**, 1067 (1964); G. Kreil and P. D. Boyer, *Biochem. Biophys. Res. Commun.* **16**, 551 (1964); R. A. Mitchell, L. G. Butler, and P. D. Boyer, *Ibid.*, p. 545.

good nucleophilic reagent toward monosubstituted phosphates in nonenzymatic reactions, and phosphorylimidazoles are not especially reactive compared with other phosphoramidates, probably because resonance stablization from the nitrogen atom is much less important in phosphates (3) than in acyl compounds.[32, 33]

$$^-O-\overset{\overset{\displaystyle O}{\|}}{\underset{\underset{\displaystyle ^-O}{|}}{P}}-N\overset{<}{}\quad\longleftrightarrow\quad{}^-O-\overset{\overset{\displaystyle ^-O}{|}}{\underset{\underset{\displaystyle ^-O}{|}}{\overset{+}{P}}}-N\overset{<}{}\quad\longleftrightarrow\quad{}^-O-\overset{\overset{\displaystyle ^-O}{|}}{\underset{\underset{\displaystyle ^-O}{|}}{P}}=\overset{+}{N}\overset{<}{}$$

3

2. NUCLEOPHILIC GROUPS IN ENZYMES

In other cases there are indications that the groups which have been identified as the active nucleophilic reagents in enzymatic reactions have properties which fit them for such a role. For example, the hydroxyl group of N-acetylserinamide, a model for the serine hydroxyl group of an enzyme, reacts with acyl compounds some three orders of magnitude faster than does water, in base catalyzed reactions near neutral pH.[29] This high reactivity is caused by the relative ease of ionization of this hydroxyl group (pK 13.6) to the reactive oxygen anion, compared with that of water (pK 15.7)[34] and by the abnormally low nucleophilic reactivity of hydroxide ion and other strongly basic alkoxide anions, which has not yet been satisfactorily explained.[35] The serine alkoxide ion is a stronger base than imidazole and can react with unactivated acyl compounds to give an acylated intermediate more readily than imidazole, so that it appears to be well suited for its role in the enzyme active site. The O-acylserine product of such reactions is a moderately reactive ester, although it is not more reactive than expected for an ester with electron-withdrawing substituents on the alcohol moiety.[29] In particular, it reacts with amines much more rapidly than does ethyl acetate, and its reactions with amines and with water are subject to general base catalysis by imidiazole, which is the probable mechanism of the catalytic action of the imidazole group in the enzymatic reactions. It is of interest that general base catalysis by imidazole of the attack of the hydroxyl group of N-acetylserinamide on acyl

[32] W. P. Jencks and M. Gilchrist, *J. Am. Chem. Soc.* 87, 3199 (1965), and references therein.

[33] A. J. Kirby and W. P. Jencks, *J. Am. Chem. Soc.* 87, 3209 (1965).

[34] T. C. Bruice, T. H. Fife, J. J. Bruno, and N. E. Brandon, *Biochemistry* 1, 7 (1962).

[35] W. P. Jencks and M. Gilchrist, *J. Am. Chem. Soc.* 84, 2910 (1962).

compounds has not been observed. It is important to keep in mind that the model reactions of serine and O-acylserine derivatives are many orders of magnitude slower than the enzymatic reactions, so that other factors must be invoked to explain the catalytic activity of the enzyme. The reactivity of acyl-chymotrypsins may be reversibly reduced to that of the model compounds if the acyl-enzyme is unfolded in 8 M urea; in fact, this is one of the pieces of evidence that the acyl-enzyme is an acylserine derivative.[6, 29]

The thiol group, which is the active nucleophilic reagent in papain and related enzymes, has a high intrinsic reactivity toward acyl compounds. This is caused in part by its relatively large acidity (pK_a about 9), which facilitates ionization to the reactive anionic form, and in part by a high nucleophilic reactivity of the anion itself, which is one to two orders of magnitude larger than that of "normal" nitrogen and oxygen compounds of comparable basicity.[36, 37] The thiol ester which is formed as the acylated intermediate has a reactivity toward hydroxide ion which is very similar to that of oxygen esters and is even less reactive than oxygen esters toward acid catalyzed hydrolysis.[38] However, thiol esters react readily with less basic nucleophilic reagents, such as amines, under conditions in which ordinary oxygen esters do not react.[39, 40]

3. CARBONYL TRANSFER REACTIONS

Nucleophilic catalysis at the *carbonyl* level of oxidation is illustrated by aniline catalysis of semicarbazone formation from benzaldehydes (equation 28).[41] The reaction proceeds through the intermediate

$$
\begin{array}{ccc}
\overset{\text{H}}{\underset{|}{\text{RC}}}=\text{O} + \text{H}_2\text{NNHCONH}_2 & \longrightarrow & \overset{\text{H}}{\underset{|}{\text{RC}}}=\text{NNHCONH}_2 \\
\searrow \text{C}_6\text{H}_5\text{NH}_2 & \nearrow \text{H}_2\text{NNHCONH}_2 & \\
& \overset{\text{H}}{\underset{|}{\text{RC}}}=\text{NC}_6\text{H}_5 \xrightarrow{\ \text{NH}_2\text{OH}\ } \overset{\text{H}}{\underset{|}{\text{RC}}}=\text{NOH} & \quad (28)
\end{array}
$$

formation of the Schiff base of aniline with the aldehyde. That the formation of the Schiff base is the rate-determining step is shown

[36] W. P. Jencks and J. Carriuolo, *J. Am. Chem. Soc.* **82**, 1778 (1960).

[37] J. W. Ogilvie, J. T. Tildon, and B. S. Strauch, *Biochemistry* **3**, 754 (1964).

[38] P. N. Rylander and D. S. Tarbell, *J. Am. Chem. Soc.* **72**, 3021 (1950); B. K. Morse and D. S. Tarbell, *Ibid.* **74**, 416 (1952).

[39] F. Lynen, E. Reichert, and L. Rueff, *Ann. Chem.* **574**, 1 (1951).

[40] K. A. Connors and M. L. Bender, *J. Org. Chem.* **26**, 2498 (1961).

[41] E. H. Cordes and W. P. Jencks, *J. Am. Chem. Soc.* **84**, 826 (1962).

by the fact that the rates of aniline catalyzed semicarbazone and oxime formation are the same in the presence of semicarbazide and hydroxylamine, respectively. Catalysis of these reactions occurs because the formation of the intermediate Schiff base with aniline is *kinetically* rapid but is *thermodynamically* unfavorable so that the intermediate does not accumulate, but instead reacts rapidly with the ultimate carbonyl-group acceptor to give products. Interference with resonance interaction of the nitrogen lone pair electrons with the phenyl group in the aniline Schiff base and the resonance interaction of the adjacent electron-donating group in the oxime and semicarbazone (4) would be expected to contribute to these

$$\overset{\frown}{R}\overset{}{C} = N \overset{\frown}{-} \overset{..}{X} - \quad \longleftrightarrow \quad R\overset{-}{C} - N = \overset{+}{X} -$$
$$\underset{H}{|} \qquad\qquad\qquad \underset{H}{|}$$

4

relative stabilities. The high reactivity of the Schiff base intermediate toward nucleophilic attack by the carbonyl-group acceptor is in large part a reflection of the ease of protonation of a Schiff base, which generally has a pK only some two to three units lower than that of the parent amine, compared with the original aldehyde, which has a pK of about -7. The ease of this protonation more than compensates for the fact that the protonated carbonyl group, once formed, would be expected to have a higher reactivity than the protonated Schiff base.

Enzyme catalyzed reactions of amino acids which involve pyridoxal phosphate as a coenzyme require the condensation of the amino acid and coenzyme to a Schiff base as the first step. The requirement that the rate of this step must be at least as fast as that of the subsequent steps means that catalysis by the enzyme is probably required for this step as well as for the more difficult steps which involve C—C and C—H bond cleavage.[42] It is, therefore, advantageous that pyridoxal phosphate generally exists in the form of a Schiff base with the amino group of a lysine residue at the active site of the enzyme, since a Schiff base would be expected to react with the amino acid in a trans-imination ("trans-Schiffization") reaction more rapidly than free pyridoxal phosphate. Amine catalysis of carbonyl-group transfer has been demonstrated in the nonenzymatic reaction of pyridoxal phosphate with semicarbazide and is

---

[42] E. H. Cordes and W. P. Jencks, *Biochemistry* **1**, 773 (1962); W. P. Jencks and E. Cordes, in E. E. Snell, P. M. Fasella, A. Braunstein, and A. Rossi Fanelli (eds.), "Proceedings of Symposium on Chemical and Biological Aspects of Pyridoxal Catalysis, Rome, 1962," p. 57, Pergamon Press, New York, 1963.

especially efficient with secondary amines, such as morpholine and proline, which can give highly reactive cationic imine intermediates (equation 29).[42]

$$\underset{\displaystyle \overset{\textstyle H}{|}}{RC}=O \ + \ HN\diagdown \ \ \rightleftharpoons \ \ \underset{\displaystyle \overset{\textstyle H}{|}}{RC}=\overset{+}{N}\diagdown \ \ \xrightarrow{R'\,NH_2} \ \ \underset{\displaystyle \overset{\textstyle H}{|}}{RC}=NR' \ + \ HN\diagdown \qquad (29)$$

An example of amine catalysis of carbon-carbon condensation is the reaction of piperonal with nitromethane catalyzed by n-butylammonium acetate (equations 30 and 31).[43] The rates of reactions 30 and 31 have been measured separately and account for the rate of

$$\underset{\displaystyle \overset{\textstyle H}{|}}{RC}=O \ + \ H_2NR' \ \rightleftharpoons \ \underset{\displaystyle \overset{\textstyle H}{|}}{RC}=NR' \ + \ H_2O \qquad\qquad\qquad (30)$$

$$\underset{\displaystyle \overset{\textstyle H}{|}}{RC}=NR' \ + \ CH_3NO_2 \ \rightleftharpoons \ \underset{\displaystyle \overset{\textstyle H\ \ H}{|\ \ \ |}}{RC}{\overset{+}{=}}NR' \ + \ \overset{(-)}{CH_2}{\cdots}\overset{(+)}{N}{\overset{\displaystyle O}{\underset{\displaystyle O}{\diagdown}}}_{(-)}$$

$$\Big\Vert$$

$$\underset{\displaystyle \overset{\textstyle H}{|}}{RC}=CHNO_2 \ + \ H_2NR' \ \rightleftharpoons \ \underset{\displaystyle \underset{\textstyle H_2N^+-R'}{|}}{\overset{\textstyle H}{\underset{\textstyle |}{RC}}}{\overset{(-)}{-}}CH{\cdots}\overset{(+)}{N}{\overset{\displaystyle O}{\underset{\displaystyle O}{\diagdown}}}_{(-)} \qquad (31)$$

the overall catalyzed reaction. The rate of the analogous ammonium acetate catalyzed condensation of vanillin with nitromethane is decreased by added acid or base under conditions in which the second step (equation 31) is largely rate-determining, which suggests that the transition state for this step has no net charge and probably involves either the attack of nitromethane anion on the protonated Schiff base or the deamination of the addition compound through a zwitterionic intermediate.[44]

4. *cis-trans* ISOMERIZATION

Nucleophilic catalysis provides an effective mechanism for catalysis of *cis-trans* isomerization. For example, catalysis by amines and alcohols of the isomerization of ethyl-*cis*-α-cyano-β-o-methoxyphenylacrylate involves addition of the catalyst to the double bond to form a saturated intermediate, which undergoes rotation and elimination of the attacking group to give a *trans* product (equation 32).[45] The relative rates of the reaction in benzene at 40° are 7.5,

[43] T. I. Crowell and D. W. Peck, *J. Am. Chem. Soc.* 75, 1075 (1953).

[44] T. I. Crowell and F. A. Ramirez, *J. Am. Chem. Soc.* 73, 2268 (1951).

[45] S. Patai and Z. Rappoport, *J. Chem. Soc.* 1962, 396; Z. Rappoport, C. Degani, and S. Patai, *Ibid.* 1963, 4513 and references therein.

$$\underset{\substack{\\ \text{Nuc}}}{\overset{R_1}{\underset{R_2}{\rangle}}C \overset{\curvearrowright}{=} \overset{\cdot}{C} \overset{R_3}{\underset{R_4}{\langle}}} \rightleftharpoons \left[\begin{array}{c} \overset{R_1}{\underset{+\text{Nuc}}{\underset{|}{R_2 - \overset{|}{C} - \bar{C}}}} \overset{R_3}{\underset{R_4}{\langle}} \\ \\ \updownarrow \pm H^+ \\ \\ R_2 - \overset{R_1}{\underset{+\text{Nuc}}{\underset{|}{C}}} - \overset{H}{\underset{R_4}{\underset{|}{C}}} - R_3 \end{array} \right] \rightleftharpoons \overset{R_1}{\underset{R_2}{\rangle}}C = C \overset{R_4}{\underset{\substack{+ \\ \text{Nuc}}}{\langle R_3}} \qquad (32)$$

0.106, and 0.0106 for catalysis by di-n-butylamine, tributylamine, and pyridine, which reflect the effects of steric hindrance and basicity in the catalyst molecules. The fact that tertiary amines are effective catalysts suggests that the reaction can proceed through the intermediate zwitterion without proton transfer to the anionic carbon atom, but it is probable that in other reactions in which the carbanion is less stable the intermediate is protonated before it undergoes rotation and elimination. The enzyme catalyzed isomerization of maleylpyruvate to fumarylpyruvate requires glutathione, and both the enzymatic and nonenzymatic reactions in the presence of glutathione proceed in deuterium oxide without incorporation of deuterium from the medium. It has been suggested that these reactions proceed through the addition of thiol anion to the double bond, according to the mechanism of equation 32, but without the addition of a proton to the intermediate carbanion.[46] Radical additions of iodide, thiols, and nitric oxide (NO) also cause isomerization. The isomerization of olefins catalyzed by these compounds proceeds by addition to give a radical intermediate, which undergoes rotation and elimination to give the isomerized product (equation 33). Depending on the

$$X \cdot + \overset{R_1}{\underset{R_2}{\rangle}}C = C \overset{R_3}{\underset{R_4}{\langle}} \underset{k_{-1}}{\overset{k_1}{\rightleftharpoons}} R_2 - \overset{R_1}{\underset{X}{\underset{|}{C}}} - \overset{\cdot}{C} \overset{R_3}{\underset{R_4}{\langle}} \underset{k_{-2}}{\overset{k_2}{\rightleftharpoons}} R_2 - \overset{R_1}{\underset{X}{\underset{|}{C}}} - \overset{\cdot}{C} \overset{R_4}{\underset{R_3}{\langle}}$$

$$k_3 \updownarrow k_{-3}$$

$$\overset{R_1}{\underset{R_2}{\rangle}}C = C \overset{R_4}{\underset{R_3}{\langle}} + X \cdot \qquad (33)$$

[46] L. Lack, *J. Biol. Chem.* **236**, 2835 (1961).

stability of the addition intermediate, either the addition or the rotation step can be rate-determining.[47]

5. PHOSPHATE TRANSFER

Nucleophilic catalysis of reactions of monosubstituted phosphates is much less dramatic than that of acyl compounds because of the relatively small differences in the susceptibility of such compounds to attack by different nucleophilic reagents and the lack of selectivity of the phosphorylated intermediate toward phosphoryl acceptors, which tends to make hydrolysis rather than phosphate transfer the predominant reaction. Nucleophilic catalysis by imidazole in enzymatic and nonenzymatic reactions has been mentioned in Sec. C, Part 1. Tertiary amines, such as pyridine and triethylenediamine, are moderately effective catalysts for hydrolysis and phosphate transfer from such activated phosphate compounds as acetyl phosphate and phosphoramidates.[32,48,49] The fact that the intermediate in the reaction of acetyl phosphate with triethylenediamine can be trapped in the presence of fluoride, to give fluorophosphate, shows that the reaction is indeed nucleophilic catalysis, rather than general base catalysis, and that nucleophilic catalysis of transfer as well as hydrolysis can occur if the acceptor molecule is a sufficiently strong nucleophile toward phosphate (equation 34).[49] The intermediate

$$
CH_3\overset{\overset{\displaystyle O}{\|}}{C}OPO_3^{--} + N\!\!<\; \rightarrow\; ^{--}O_3P\overset{+}{N}\!\!< \quad
\begin{array}{l} \overset{H_2O}{\nearrow}\;^{--}O_3POH + N\!\!< \\[2ex] \underset{F^-}{\searrow}\;^{--}O_3PF + N\!\!< \end{array}
\tag{34}
$$

phosphorylated tertiary amine is much more stable than the corresponding intermediate in acyl transfer reactions: phosphorylated 4-methylpyridine has a half-life of about 5 minutes at 25° and phosphorylated N-methylimidazole has a half-life of nearly 10 hours at 39°.[32] The corresponding acetylpyridinium and acetylimidazolium compounds have half-lives of less than 2 seconds and about 20 seconds, respectively. The fact that ordinary acyl amides are generally far more stable than phosphoramidates is, again, a consequence of the large amount of resonance stabilization of the acyl compounds. In phosphoramidates and either acylated or phosphorylated tertiary

[47] S. W. Benson, K. W. Egger, and D. M. Golden, *J. Am. Chem. Soc.* **87**, 468 (1965); K. W. Egger and S. W. Benson, *Ibid.*, p. 3314.

[48] J. H. Park and D. E. Koshland, Jr., *J. Biol. Chem.* **233**, 986 (1958).

[49] G. Di Sabato and W. P. Jencks, *J. Am. Chem. Soc.* **83**, 4393 (1961).

amines this resonance stabilization is either less important or impossible, and the compounds are correspondingly more reactive.

6. ALKYL TRANSFER

Nucleophilic catalysis at the *alkyl* level of oxidation is illustrated by iodide catalysis of the solvolysis of methyl bromide.[50] Again, the requirements for catalysis are that the catalyst be both an effective nucleophilic reagent and a good leaving group and that the intermediate be thermodynamically unstable relative to the product. Sulfite ion catalyzes the transfer of the activated methylenepyrimidine portion of thiamine, via an intermediate sulfonic acid, to a number of nitrogen bases.[51] This is the same reaction as is catalyzed by the enzyme thiaminase,[52] but almost nothing is known about the mechanism of action of thiaminase or any other alkyl-group transferring enzyme.

Since alkyl compounds have an intrinsically lower reactivity toward most nucleophilic reagents than acyl or carbonyl compounds of comparable structure, they require a greater degree of activation to react at reasonable rates in chemical and biochemical systems. In biological systems alkyl groups which are to be transferred are generally bound to an atom with an actual or potential positive charge, as in the sulfonium ion of S-adenosylmethionine (5), the thiazolium ion of thiamine (6), and (protonated) 5-methyltetrahydrofolic acid (7).

[50] E. A. Moelwyn-Hughes, *J. Chem. Soc.* **1938**, 779.

[51] T. Matsukawa and S. J. Yurugi, *J. Pharm. Soc. Japan* **71**, 1423 (1951); **72**, 33 (1952).

[52] A. Fujita, *Advan. Enzymol.* **15**, 389 (1954); R. H. Kenten, *Biochem. J.* **67**, 25 (1957); **69**, 439 (1958).

D. NUCLEOPHILIC REACTIVITY

An understanding of the factors which influence the nucleophilic reactivity of different compounds, particularly those which cause "abnormal" nucleophilic reactivity, provides an important probe into the detailed nature of the transition states of chemical reactions. In enzymatic reactions, although such a detailed examination is not yet possible, understanding of these factors should shed some light on the mechanisms by which the rates of nucleophilic reactions are increased by enzymes.

A nucleophilic reaction involves the donation of electrons from a nucleophile to a substrate, with the partial formation of a bond to the substrate in the transition state (equation 35). The most profit-

$$\text{N: + S} \rightleftharpoons \overset{\delta+ \quad \delta-}{\text{N} \cdots \text{S}} \tag{35}$$

able empirical approach to understanding the nature of this process is based on a comparison of the energy required to form the transition state from a series of different nucleophiles and substrates with the energy of other rate or equilibrium processes. To the extent that such a correlation holds, it may be inferred that the same factors are contributing to both processes and that the transition state resembles the model reaction. Correlations of this kind are usually made by comparisons of the free energies for different equilibrium and rate processes, which are proportional to the *logarithms* of the equilibrium or rate constants (equations 36 and 37). The

$$\Delta F = -RT \ln K \tag{36}$$

$$\Delta F^{\ddagger} = -RT \ln K^{\ddagger} = -RT \ln \frac{h}{k_B T} k \tag{37}$$

latter proportionality is defined by the transition-state theory of reaction rates according to equation 37, in which $K^{\ddagger}$ is the pseudo equilibrium constant for the formation of the transition state, h and k_B are Planck's and Boltzmann's constants, respectively, and k is an observed rate constant. The use of such *linear* (and nonlinear) *free-energy correlations* constitutes one of the most powerful tools for the elucidation of reaction mechanisms.

The simplest such correlation for nucleophilic reactions is a comparison of the rates of one reaction series with those of another. This may be described by the Swain-Scott equation 38:

$$\log \frac{k}{k_0} = sn \tag{38}$$

Table VI   Values   of   the   Swain-Scott   nucleophilic   reactivity
parameter, n[53]

Compound	n	$\log k/k_0$ for β-propiolactone
H_2O	0	0
CH_3COO^-	2.72	2.49
Cl^-	3.04	2.26
Br^-	3.89	2.77
N_3^-	4.00	
HO^-	4.20	(6.08)[a]
$C_6H_5NH_2$	4.49	
SCN^-	4.77	3.58
I^-	5.04	3.48
$S_2O_3^=$	6.36	5.28

[a]For attack at the acyl group.

in which k is the rate constant of a particular reaction in a series
under study, k_0 is the rate of a reference reaction in the same series,
s is a measure of the susceptibility of the substrate to the nucleophilic reactivity of the attacking reagent, and n is a measure of this
nucleophilic reactivity, determined in a reference reaction series to
which the reaction series under examination is being compared.[53]
Some values of n for different nucleophilic reagents, based mainly
on rate constants for attack at saturated carbon, and some values of
$\log k/k_0$ for nucleophilic displacement on the saturated carbon atom
of β-propiolactone are shown in Table VI.   The rates of reactions
which   have   transition   states   of   similar   structure   are   correlated
successfully by this equation, and the values of s and n for such reactions provide an indication of the nature of small differences, such
as in the amount of bond formation, in the transition states.   The
correlation is frequently found to fail if different types of reactions,
such as attack at saturated carbon and attack at a carbonyl group,
are compared.   Such a failure means that the nature of the transition states for the two types of reaction are fundamentally different.
The nature of the differences may often be inferred from the nature
of   the   deviations   with   different   types   of   nucleophilic   reagents.

1. BASICITY

The most obvious model reaction to correlate with the pseudo equilibrium for the attainment of the transition state of equation 35 is

[53] C. G. Swain and C. B. Scott, *J. Am. Chem. Soc.* **75**, 141 (1953).

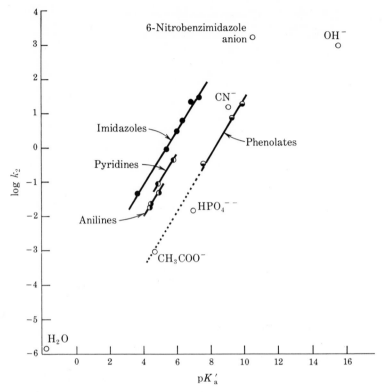

Fig. 6 The effect of basicity on the reactivity toward p-nitrophenyl acetate of imidazoles, pyridines, anilines, and oxygen anions in 28.5% ethanol at 30°.[54]

the equilibrium for the addition of a proton to the nucleophile (equation 39). Since basicity is a measure of the tendency of a compound

$$N: + H^+ \;\rightleftharpoons\; N^+\!\!-H \tag{39}$$

to donate a pair of electrons to a proton in a partly covalent, partly ionic, bond, with the development of positive charge on the base, one might expect to find a correlation of this process with the donation of electrons to a substrate in a transition state, with the development of a partial positive charge on the nucleophile. If the correlation is restricted to a limited range of reactivity and to structurally similar nucleophiles, there is a close correlation of nucleophilic reactivity with basicity for some reactions. Such a correlation is shown for the reaction of an ester, p-nitrophenyl acetate, with a series of imidazoles, pyridines, anilines, and anionic oxygen nucleophiles in Fig. 6. Over a restricted range of basicity there is a good correlation of basicity with nucleophilicity, but different classes of nucleophilic reagents follow different lines.[54] The slope of the lines may be expressed according to the Brønsted equation 40, which may

$$\log \frac{k}{k_0} = \beta pK + C \tag{40}$$

be applied to nucleophilic as well as to general acid-base catalyzed reactions. The slope of the lines β is 0.8 for these reactions, which shows that the dependency on basicity is large, that basicity is a good model for the transition state, and that there is a large amount of positive charge developed on the attacking nucleophile in the transition state. We might infer, then, that the transition state for these reactions looks something like 8. (This reaction is discussed in more detail in Chap. 10, Sec. B, Part 9).

$$
{}^+N \cdot\cdot \overset{\displaystyle O}{\overset{\|}{C}} \cdots {}^-OR
$$

8

In contrast to reactions with acyl compounds, the sensitivity of reactions of monosubstituted phosphate to the basicity of the nucleophilic reagent is very small. Correlations with basicity of the rate constants for the reaction of p-nitrophenyl phosphate dianion with different types of amines are shown in Fig. 7.[33] The rate constants for different classes of amines fall on different lines, depending on the steric demands and the degree of substitution at the nitrogen atom of the amine, but for a given class of amine the dependence on basicity is small, with a Brønsted slope of only about 0.2. This suggests that there is relatively little bond formation and development of positive charge on the attacking amine in these reactions. In fact, reactions of monosubstituted phosphates show little sensitivity to any change in the properties of the nucleophile, with the exception of steric effects. On the other hand, these reactions are extremely sensitive to the nature of the leaving group: the rates of hydrolysis of a series of phosphate dianions depend on the basicity of the leaving group with a slope β of -1.2 (Fig. 8), and a similar large sensitivity is seen for reactions which definitely involve the attack of a nucleophilic reagent.[32,33] These facts suggest that the transition

[54] T. C. Bruice and R. Lapinski, *J. Am. Chem. Soc.* **80**, 2265 (1958).

state for these reactions resembles **9**, in which there is a small

$$N \cdots P \cdots X^{(-)}$$

9

degree of bond formation by the attacking nucleophile, a large amount of breaking of the bond to the leaving group, and the principal driving force for the reaction comes from electron donation

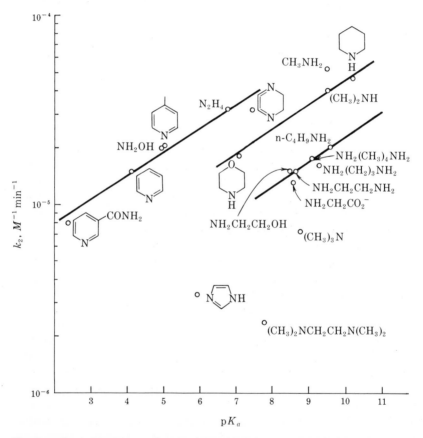

Fig. 7   Effect of basicity on the reactivity of amines toward p-nitrophenyl phosphate dianion at 39°. The values for diamines are corrected for statistical factors by halving the observed values for K_a and k_2.[33]

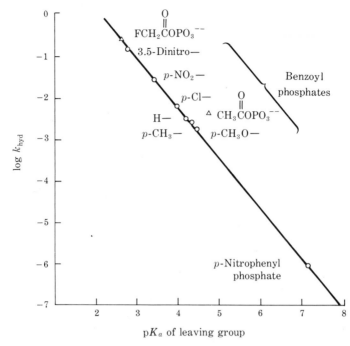

Fig. 8 Effect of the acidity of the leaving group on the rates of hydrolysis of acyl phosphate and p-nitrophenyl phosphate dianions.[33]

from the negative charges on the oxygen atoms to expel the leaving group. These reactions are similar to borderline carbonium ion reactions in carbon chemistry; the electron-deficient transition state **9** resembles the hypothetical electron-deficient monomeric metaphosphate monoanion **10**, which has been postulated as an intermediate in the hydrolysis of monosubstituted phosphates and is analogous to the carbonium ion **11** in carbon chemistry.

$$\left[\begin{array}{c} O \underset{P}{\overset{\cdots\cdots}{\Vert}} O \\ \Vert \\ O \end{array}\right]^{-} \qquad \left[\begin{array}{c} \diagdown C \diagup \\ \vert \end{array}\right]^{+}$$

    10   **11**

    If one considers reactions carried out at a particular pH (which is pertinent to enzymatic reactions at neutral pH), the nucleophilic reactivity of bases with pK's below the pH at which the experiment is carried out will decrease according to the Brønsted slope

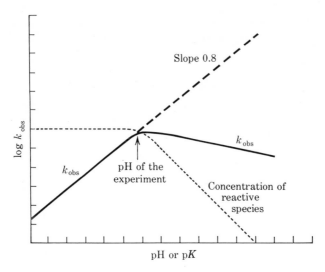

Fig. 9 A diagram to show how the reactivity of a nucleophile at a given pH depends on its basicity because of the increase in reactivity with increasing basicity and the decrease in the fraction of the nucleophile which is present as the reactive free base as the pK becomes larger than the pH at which the reaction is observed.

for the particular reaction, as shown in Fig. 9 for a β value of 0.8. The free-base form of nucleophilic reagents with pK's above the pH of the experiment will have a higher reactivity, but the concentration of the free base at a given total concentration of the nucleophile will be decreased because most of it will be protonated. The observed reactivity, then, will be the resultant of the Brønsted slope and the slope of -1.0 which describes the decrease in the fraction of the nucleophile present as the free base with increasing pH. For a β value of 0.8 the observed reactivity of strongly basic nucleophiles will decrease with increasing basicity with a slope of 0.2, as shown in the figure. For reactions with a smaller dependence on basicity the decrease will be correspondingly larger. An enzyme cannot cause a very large change in the reactivity of a group in its active site by changing its basicity, but the utilization of groups such as imidazole, which have pK's near the pH at which the enzyme acts, provides the maximum nucleophilicity with respect to basicity. The fact that the Brønsted plot is not linear, but levels off for strongly basic oxygen anion nucleophiles, means that at neutral pH the reactivity of such nucleophiles will be especially low. This is because for a given increase in basicity, which lowers the concentration of the reactive form at neutrality, there is no longer a compensating increase in reactivity. That is the reason that the serine oxygen anion is a much more effective nucleophile than the conjugate base of less acidic alcohols.[29,34,35]

2. POLARIZABILITY, OXIDATION–REDUCTION POTENTIAL, "SOFTNESS"

Examination of a wider series of reactions discloses that correlation of reaction rates with basicity is more the exception than the rule; in fact, many displacements at saturated centers show no detectable dependence on the basicity of the nucleophile over a very large range of reactivity.[55] These reactions are not similar to displacements on monosubstituted phosphates, which show little sensitivity to basicity or any other property except the steric demands of the nucleophile, but rather display a large sensitivity to the nature of the nucleophile, which must reflect some property other than basicity. A typical order of nucleophilic reactivity toward saturated carbon, for displacement on the β carbon atom of β-propiolactone, is shown in Table VI. Note that iodide is an order of magnitude more reactive than acetate ion, in spite of a basicity which is probably more than 10^{10} less than that of acetate. It is evident that the transition states for these reactions do not resemble those for reactions at the carbonyl group and do not resemble the model of the addition of a proton to the nucleophile. There has been a great deal of effort expended in attempts to find the factor or factors other than basicity which are correlated with nucleophilic reactivity in these reactions. The search has turned up a plethora of properties which show some such correlation and turn out to be more or less closely interrelated, but the fact that the search continues indicates that none of these correlations is entirely satisfactory and that we still do not have a detailed understanding of the problem.

It is not difficult to rationalize, at least after the fact, the difference in the nature of the transition states for reactions at saturated and unsaturated carbon atoms. At unsaturated carbon the orbital of the carbon atom which was initially utilized to form the π bond of the double bond can be made available for interaction with the attacking reagent, so that a large amount of bond formation may take place easily, and the attacking reagent will be close to the carbon atom in the transition state (12). This is one reason that displacements at unsaturated carbon (e.g., the hydrolysis of acyl chlorides and esters) generally take place through an addition-elimination mechanism much more easily than displacements at saturated

[55] R. E. Dessy, R. L. Pohl, and R. B. King, *J. Am. Chem. Soc.* 88, 5121 (1966).

carbon (e.g., alkyl halides, ethers). For reactions at saturated carbon, no extra obital is available and the carbon atom must become pentavalent in the transition state (13). The d orbitals of

12   13

carbon are too high in energy to provide much stabilization, so that the formation of the transition state must involve rehybridization of the s and p orbitals to interact with electrons from five atoms. Under these circumstances much less bond formation may take place than in attack at unsaturated carbon, and the nucleophilic reagent will be at a considerable distance from the carbon atom in the transition state. Another factor that will tend to keep the nucleophile at a distance is the larger number of substituents on the carbon atom than in attack at saturated carbon; a pentavalent transition state is likely to be seriously crowded (13). Since basicity involves bond formation at a short distance with the small proton, we should search for a model for the transition state for attack at saturated carbon which is a measure of the ability of the nucleophile to form a bond or a partial bond at a larger distance.

The most successful quantitative efforts in this direction have been the four-parameter equations of Edwards.[56] The first of these equations is:

$$\log \frac{k}{k_0} = \alpha E_n + \beta H \tag{41}$$

In this equation E_n is the oxidation potential of the nucleophile (equal to $E^0 + 2.60$),[57] H is the basicity of the nucleophile (equal to $pK_a + 1.74$),[57] and α and β are measures of the sensitivity of the substrate to these two parameters. The oxidation potential, defined by the half-reaction of equation 42,

$$2N \;\rightleftharpoons\; N_2^{++} + 2e \tag{42}$$

is a measure of the ability of the nucleophile to donate an electron to an electrode and is a quite different measure of electron-donating

[56] J. O. Edwards, *J. Am. Chem. Soc.* 76, 1540 (1954); 78, 1819 (1956).

[57] The constants 2.60 and 1.74 relate these quantities to water as a standard.

ability than is basicity. Equation 39 also involves the formation of a new bond between two molecules of oxidized nucleophile, so that E_n may also be a measure of the ability of the nucleophile to form a covalent bond.

The second Edwards equation is

$$\log \frac{k}{k_0} = AP + BH \tag{43}$$

Here P is the polarizability of the nucleophile, which may be determined from the molar refraction in uncomplicated cases, H is again a measure of basicity, and A and B are measures of the susceptibility of the substrate to these two parameters. The polarizability is a measure of the mobility of the electrons of the nucleophile and as such might be expected to be correlated with the ability of the nucleophile to interact with the substrate to form a partial bond at a considerable distance. A high polarizability will also facilitate approach of the nucleophile through the electron clouds of the surrounding atoms. These two equations are interrelated by the fact that the oxidation potential is itself related to the polarizability and, to a lesser extent, to the basicity according to the empirical equation 44, in which a and b are 3.60 and 0.062, respectively. The fact

$$E_n = aP + bH \tag{44}$$

that these two apparently different parameters are so related suggests that these correlations may be part of a more general correlation which involves still other properties.

The Edwards equations have been generally successful in correlating the reaction rates of nucleophiles with saturated carbon atoms and some other substrates. The small values of the β and B parameters which are required for such correlations reflect the small sensitivity of these reactions to basicity. In fact, a fairly good correlation may be made by ignoring the basicity contribution altogether; for such reactions the oxidation potential is directly related to the Swain-Scott nucleophilic constant n (Fig. 10). Unfortunately, there are serious practical and theoretical difficulties in the application of the Edwards equations to reactions of complicated molecules. In many cases the oxidation potential of such molecules is not known or may involve fragmentation or other more complex changes in structure than are likely to occur in a transition state. The polarizability that is of importance in the transition state is the polarizability in the direction and at the atom at which the new bond is

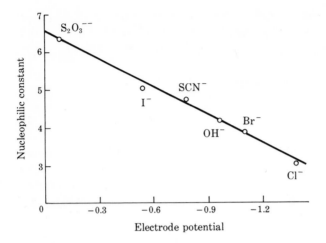

Fig. 10 The linear relationship between the nucleophilic constant of Swain and Scott and the electrode potential.[56]

being formed, not the overall polarizability of the molecule in all planes and over all the constituent atoms. This information is generally not available and is probably not determinable for any but the simplest molecules and ions.

The list of more or less interrelated properties that have been or might be utilized for correlations of nucleophilic reaction rates may be extended as follows:

1. Basicity
2. Oxidation potential
3. Polarizability
4. Ionization potential
5. Electronegativity
6. Energy of the highest filled molecular orbital
7. Covalent bond strength
8. Size

These properties are all measures of the ability of the nucleophile to donate electrons and/or to form a covalent bond with a substrate at a distance, and most of them have been proposed as parameters for the correlation of nucleophilic reactivity with varying degrees of success. It is clear that there are interrelationships among these properties, but it has been difficult to define these interrelationships quantitatively or to select a single parameter which provides a satis-

factory model for the transition state. Even such an unlikely parameter as the size of the nucleophilic atom is correlated with nucleophilic reactivity because larger atoms hold their outer electrons
relatively weakly, so that these electrons are polarizable and may
be easily donated to an electrode or to the diffuse orbital of a
transition state. This situation has led to the introduction of the
imprecise but useful term "softness," which describes the ability
of a molecule to interact effectively with other "soft" molecules or
transition states and is correlated with the properties in the above
list. "Softness" is contrasted with "hardness," which is the
ability of the molecule to interact with other "hard" molecules such
as the proton.[58]

The division of electron donors and acceptors into "hard" and
"soft" categories is an outgrowth of the earlier division of ligands
and metal ions into "A" and "B" classes.[59] Type A or "hard"
ligands have a concentrated negative charge which can interact
effectively with small metal ions which also have a concentrated
charge, such as Mg^{++}, Al^{3+} and the proton. The order of effectiveness is

$$F^- > Cl^- > Br^- > I^- \quad \text{and} \quad RO^- > RS^- \sim RSe^- \gtrsim RTe^-$$

which follows the order of basicity and of absolute nucleophilic
reactivity toward the carbonyl group. Type B or soft ligands are
large and polarizable and interact effectively with large metal ions
with a diffuse charge such as Cu^+, Pt^{++}, and Hg^{++}. The order of
effectiveness is

$$I^- > Br^- > Cl^- > F^- \quad \text{and} \quad RTe^- \sim RSe^- \sim RS^- \gg RO^-$$

Saturated carbon falls somewhere in the middle of this scale, with a
sensitivity to the "softness" of a nucleophile in the transition state
which is much larger than that of carbonyl carbon, but is smaller
than that of some metals. In general, hardness is associated with a
relatively large amount of ionic character and softness with a large
amount of covalent character in a bond or transition state. In addition, soft atoms with a high polarizability are stabilized in compounds or transition states by van der Waals or London force interactions with atoms other than those to which bond formation occurs
directly.

[58] R. G. Pearson, *J. Am. Chem. Soc.* 85, 3533 (1963); R. G. Pearson and J. Songstad,
Ibid. 89, 1827 (1967).

[59] S. Ahrland, J. Chatt, and N. R. Davies, *Quart. Rev. (London)* 12, 265 (1958).

The terms "hard" and "soft" have been criticized because of their imprecision and the difficulty of defining them quantitatively.[60] Nevertheless, such terms have a real value in a situation such as that which exists at present with respect to nucleophilic reactivity, in which the exact nature of the properties which determine reactivity is not understood and a general term is needed to describe a tendency toward a high nucleophilic reactivity which is different from that measured by basicity and which cannot be satisfactorily described by a single quantitative parameter.

One of the characteristics of many "soft" nucleophiles and ligands is the availability of unoccupied d or π orbitals with which an electron pair on the substrate or metal may interact by "back bonding" or "π bonding." Such back bonding of metals with carbon monoxide and sulfur is shown in 14 and 15. The same type

$$^{(+)}O \equiv C \overset{\frown}{-} M \longleftrightarrow O = C = \overset{(+)}{M} \qquad R-S-M \longleftrightarrow R-\overset{(-)}{S} = \overset{(+)}{M}$$

$$\textbf{14} \qquad\qquad\qquad\qquad\qquad\qquad \textbf{15}$$

of interaction is less firmly established as a contributing factor toward nucleophilic reactivity, but it provides an attractive explanation for the unexpected almost complete insensitivity toward basicity of the rate of attack of thiol anions on acetaldehyde (16).[61]

$$R-\overset{\overset{\textstyle (-)}{\textstyle O}}{\underset{\underset{\textstyle C}{\textstyle }}{S}} \longleftrightarrow R-\overset{(-)}{S}\overset{O}{\underset{\underset{\textstyle C}{\textstyle }}{|}}$$

$$\textbf{16}$$

Although the absolute nucleophilic reactivity of "soft" polarizable molecules toward carbonyl compounds is generally small because of the relatively small basicity of these molecules, transition states for carbonyl reactions do show some sensitivity to "softness," and deviations from the simple relationship of nucleophilicity to basicity alone for these reactions may frequently be attributed to softness or polarizability of the nucleophile. The nucleophilic reactivity of a series of compounds toward the ester, p-nitrophenyl acetate, is shown as a function of basicity in Fig. 11. This correlation does not

[60] C. K. Jørgensen, *Structure and Bonding* 1, 234 (1966); R. J. P. Williams and J. D. Hale, *Ibid.* 1, 249 (1966).

[61] G. E. Lienhard and W. P. Jencks, *J. Am. Chem. Soc.* 88, 3982 (1966).

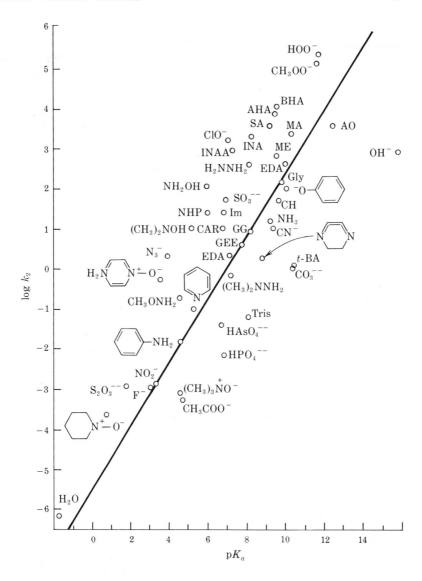

Fig. 11 Reactivity of a wide variety of different nucleophiles toward p-nitrophenyl acetate at 25° as a function of their basicity. Abbreviations: BHA, butyrohydroxamate; AHA, acetohydroxamate; INA, isonitrosoacetone; SA, salicylaldoxime; MA, mercaptoacetate; ME, mercaptoethanol; AO, acetone oxime; GLY, glycine; INAA, isonitrosoacetylacetone; EDA, ethylenediamine (free base and monocation); NHP, N-hydroxyphthalimide; IM, imidazole; CH, chloral hydrate anion (30°); CAR, carnosine; GG, glycylglycine; GEE, glycine ethyl ester; t-BA, t-butylamine.[36]

show the regularity of the data in Fig. 6 because of the inclusion of nucleophilic agents of widely varying structure. A straight line of slope 0.8 is drawn through the points for a number of simple primary amines which fit the line reasonably well. The positive deviations from this line and from similar correlations for other reactions of thiol, hydroperoxide, and azide anions and of unhindered tertiary amines may be attributed, at least in part, to the "softness" or polarizability of these reagents; conversely, the negative deviations of such oxygen anions as phosphate, carbonate, and acetate may reflect, in part, the relative "hardness" of these nucleophiles.

3. SOLVATION

Solvation is a quite different, but not unrelated, factor which can have an enormous influence on nucleophilic reactivity.[62] In water the order of nucleophilic reactivity for S_N2 displacement on methyl iodide is $I^- > Br^- > Cl^- > F^-$, but in the aprotic solvent dimethylformamide this sequence disappears and there is a trend in the opposite direction (Table VII).[63] Furthermore, the absolute rate of reaction of chloride ion is increased by a factor of 1.3×10^6 in dimethylformamide, as compared with water. An even more dramatic solvent effect is seen in the rate of the methoxide ion catalyzed exchange of protons adjacent to an activating cyano, ester, or amide group, which is increased by a factor of 10^9 in the aprotic solvent, dimethylsulfoxide, as compared with methanol.[64]

The solvation energy of ions upon transfer from the gas phase to water (-60 to -120 kcal/mole for the halide anions)[65] is orders of magnitude larger than the relatively small differences in the free energy of activation which are reflected in the differences in reaction rates of these ions. If an anion acts as a nucleophile to displace a leaving group or abstract a proton, it will lose most of its charge and solvation in the product of the reaction and will lose a significant fraction in the transition state as solvent molecules are removed to permit interaction with the substrate. The examples cited above show that these differences in solvation may be large enough to be of overriding importance in determining the rate of a nucleophilic reaction. A small anion with a high charge density, such as fluoride or methoxide, is much less stable in an aprotic

[62] A. J. Parker, *Adv. Phys. Org. Chem.* **5**, 173 (1967).

[63] A. J. Parker, *J. Chem. Soc.* **1961**, 1328.

[64] D. J. Cram, B. Rickborn, C. A Kingsbury, and P. Haberfield, *J. Am. Chem. Soc.* **83**, 3678 (1961); D. J. Cram, C. A. Kingsbury, and B. Rickborn, *Ibid.*, p. 3688.

[65] W. M. Latimer, K. S. Pitzer, and C. M. Slansky, *J. Chem. Phys.* **7**, 108 (1939).

Table VII   Rates of displacement reactions with methyl iodide[63]

Nucleophile	k_{MeI} in water	k_{MeI} in dimethylformamide
LiI	1.6×10^{-5}	
LiBr	0.18×10^{-5}	0.11
LiCl	0.010×10^{-5}	0.13
KF	0.007×10^{-5}	> 0.1

solvent than in water, in which the charge may be delocalized by hydrogen bonding to the solvent. It will, therefore, have an enhanced tendency to add a proton or enter a transition state, as manifested by an increased basicity and nucleophilicity, in the aprotic solvent, compared with a larger ion for which solvation effects are less important. A number of properties of ions, including solubility, basicity, and spectra, show a large dependence on the nature of the solvent for the same reason.[66]

Differences in the ground-state solvation of ions may be more clearly evaluated from equilibrium measurements of a system such as that of equation 45, in which the relative ability of different

$$X^- + RCH_2Br \rightleftharpoons RCH_2X + Br^- \qquad (45)$$

halide ions to displace bromide from a standard substrate are compared. The equilibrium constants for this reaction (Table VIII) show a change in the expected direction and a leveling effect in water compared with nitrobenzene, which may be attributed to the relatively larger destabilization of the smaller anions in nitrobenzene compared with water.[67] These differences in the free energies of ions in the ground state in different solvents may be obtained from several recent series of measurements and compilations; the differences in ground-state stabilities are large and correspond to differences in rate or equilibrium constants of up to 10^{17} if the differences disappear in the transition state or product of the reaction.[68] Al-

[66] A. J. Parker, *Quart. Rev.* (*London*) **16**, 163 (1962); *Advan. Org. Chem.* **5**, 1 (1965).

[67] A. J. Parker, *Proc. Chem. Soc.* **1961**, 371.

[68] R. Alexander, E. C. F. Ko, Y. C. Mac, and A. J. Parker, *J. Am. Chem. Soc.* **89**, 3703 (1967); R. Alexander and A. J. Parker, *Ibid.*, p. 5549; B. Case and R. Parsons, *Trans. Faraday Soc.* **63**, 1224 (1967); J. F. Coetzee and J. J. Campion, *J. Am. Chem. Soc.* **89**, 2517 (1967).

Table VIII   Equilibrium constants of the reaction $X^- +$
$RCH_2Br \rightleftharpoons RCH_2X + Br^-$ in nitrobenzene and in water[67]

	$C_4H_{11}Br$ *in* *nitrobenzene* (K)	CH_3Br *in* *water* (K)
X^-		
Cl^-	1.5×10^2	10
Br^-	1	1
I^-	2×10^{-2}	13

though the differences are especially marked for small anions, which are poorly solvated in aprotic solvents, differences among cations are also significant, and there is evidence for specific interactions of even very large ions with aprotic as well as protic solvents.[68, 69]

It is difficult to separate clearly the effects of solvation from the properties grouped together under the term "softness," since large, "soft" ions are the same ones which are easily able to lose their solvation and undergo reaction. Two facts are clear. First, ground-state solvation is of great importance in determining nucleophilic reactivity; second, it is certainly not the only factor which determines nucleophilic reactivity. The large differences in the *relative* nucleophilic reactivity of different compounds toward different substrates cannot be accounted for by differences in the solvation of the nucleophile. The solvation effect should be largely compensated for in correlations of nucleophilic reactivity against basicity because solvation of the anion must be lost upon adding a proton as well as upon forming a transition state. Positive deviations of uncharged nucleophiles and of thiol, hydroperoxide, and azide anions from such correlations suggest that there is an influence of polarizability or "softness," as well as basicity, upon reactivity. Such deviations are significant for reactions of carbonyl compounds, such as p-nitrophenyl acetate,[36] which show a large sensitivity to the basicity of the nucleophile. They are much larger for attack on saturated carbon, and the fact that the order of basicity is the *opposite* of the order of nucleophilic reactivity in water toward saturated carbon for F^-, Cl^-, Br^-, and I^-, although both of these properties should be influenced in the same direction by solvation of the anion, means that factors other than solvation must be of fundamental importance.

[69] H. L. Friedman, *J. Phys. Chem.* **71**, 1723 (1967).

The fact that changes in the nature of the solvent change the rates more than the equilibrium constants for the reactions of anions with carbonium ions means that specific interactions of the solvent with the transition state, which are different from those with the ground state, are important in these reactions. This behavior further suggests that solvent reorientation may contribute directly to the free-energy barrier for the activation process.[70]

For a given basicity, the order of nucleophilic reactivity of amines is quite generally $3° > 2° > 1° > NH_3$, but this order is often masked by the greater steric demands of the more substituted amines.[71] For the reaction with chloramine to give substituted hydrazines, which has relatively small steric requirements, the relative rates of reaction of trimethylamine, dimethylamine, methylamine, and ammonia are 1550:700:120:1,[72] and N-methylimidazole is twice as reactive as ammonia toward p-nitrophenyl acetate, in spite of the 100-fold greater basicity of the latter compound.

Especially strong solvation of the conjugate acid of a nucleophile will often give negative deviations from a correlation of nucleophilicity with basicity, and this probably accounts, in part, for the relatively low reactivity of primary amines and ammonia as compared with secondary and tertiary amines. As discussed in Chap. 3 in connection with the reactivity of such compounds in general acid-base catalysis, the increase in base strength caused by solvation of the cation will ordinarily be larger than the increase in reactivity caused by partial solvation of the developing positive charge in the transition state. If β is large, this will result in a negative deviation from a basicity-nucleophilicity plot. The deviations of these compounds may, therefore, be more appropriately described as being caused by their abnormal basicity than by their abnormal nucleophilic reactivity (cf. Fig. 6, Chap. 3).

If a charged group, such as a carboxylate anion, is poorly solvated in a hydrophobic region of the active site of an enzyme, its nucleophilic reactivity will be increased. However, the basicity of such a group will be correspondingly increased because destabilization of the anion by poor solvation will favor any process which decreases the charge on the anion. This effect presumably accounts for the pK values of up to 7 or more for "buried" carboxyl

[70] C. D. Ritchie, G. A. Skinner, and V. G. Badding, *J. Am. Chem. Soc.* **89**, 2063 (1967).

[71] H. K. Hall, Jr., *J. Org. Chem.* **29**, 3539 (1964).

[72] G. Yagil and M. Anbar, *J. Am. Chem. Soc.* **84**, 1797 (1962).

groups in enzymes and other proteins,[73] and, while it increases the nucleophilicity of these groups, it does not cause an increase in nucleophilicity relative to basicity. Large rate enhancements would not be expected from this effect, therefore, unless the nucleophile is protected against protonation by the solvent while remaining available for attack on the substrate. Such a situation is conceivable if the nucleophile is normally buried so as to be out of contact with any component of the solvent and the addition of substrate causes a conformation change so as to expose the nucleophile for attack on the substrate in a hydrophobic environment. This would constitute another example in which the binding forces between substrate and enzyme are utilized to change an equilibrium in a direction so as to facilitate the catalytic process with a corresponding decrease in the observed binding energy, as discussed for the induction of strain in Chap. 5. In general, if a rate increase is brought about by changing the nature of the "solvent" surrounding the substrate in the active site, this must result from a specific interaction with the substrate which utilizes the enzyme-substrate binding energy. For example, the rate of reaction of two oppositely charged reactants will be increased in a hydrophobic environment at an active site because the charged reactants will be destabilized by the nonpolar environment and this destabilization will be partly removed when the less charged transition state is reached (equation 46). The energy

$$\underset{E}{(+)} + \underset{}{(-)} + \underset{E}{\boxed{}} \rightleftharpoons \underset{E}{\boxed{(+)(-)}} \rightleftharpoons \underset{E}{\boxed{(\overset{\delta}{+})\cdot(\overset{\delta}{-})}} \qquad (46)$$

required to force the charged reactants into this reactive, unstable state must come from the binding energy of nonreacting portions of the substrates. Conversely, bringing two uncharged reactants close to charged groups on the enzyme, which will facilitate the attainment of a charged transition state by a microscopic solvent effect, will utilize binding energy to force the reacting groups of the substrates into this initially unfavorable environment.

4. STERIC HINDRANCE

Steric hindrance will obviously decrease the rate of nucleophilic reactions, but this does not require detailed comment here. The greater sensitivity of nucleophilic reactions to steric hindrance compared with that of general base catalyzed reactions is a useful experimental criterion to help in distinguishing these two mechanisms

[73] H. Susi, T. Zell, and S. N. Timasheff, *Arch. Biochem. Biophys.* 85, 437 (1959).

of catalysis. For example, 2,6-dimethylpyridines are more basic than pyridine, but are several orders of magnitude less reactive than pyridine in nucleophilic reactions. In general base catalyzed reactions they can be either more or less reactive than pyridine, depending on the sensitivity of the reaction to basicity and steric hindrance, but the differences are small compared with those for nucleophilic reactions.[74] The reduced steric demands around the nitrogen atom in the 3- and 4-membered rings of aziridine and azetidine presumably account, in large part, for the increased reactivity of these compounds toward phenyl acetate by a factor of about 10^2, compared with other amines of comparable basicity.[75]

5. ELECTROSTATIC EFFECTS

Electrostatic effects are small and variable in aqueous solution because of the exceptional charge-solvating ability of water. Qualitatively, the fact that phosphate esters require prolonged boiling in concentrated alkali for hydrolysis and that the acyl group of acetyl phosphate dianion is far more resistant than other acyl groups to attack by thiol anion suggests that the negative charges of ionized phosphates discourage attack by anionic nucleophilic agents.[76,49] The monocation of tetramethylethylenediamine reacts with p-nitrophenyl phosphate dianion with a rate constant of 1.9×10^{-5} M^{-1} min^{-1}, which is fourfold *larger* than the rate constant of 0.43×10^{-5} M^{-1} min^{-1} for the reaction of the free base, in spite of the fact that the monocation (pK 5.7) is 2,000 times less basic than the free base (pK 9.1).[33] At first glance this high reactivity might be attributed to intramolecular general acid catalysis by the proton on the second nitrogen atom of the monocation, according to a concerted, bifunctional mechanism such as 17. However, the monocation of triethyl-

17   18

[74] See, for example, Refs. 30 and 33 and F. Covitz and F. H. Westheimer, *J. Am. Chem. Soc.* **85**, 1773 (1963).

[75] L. R. Fedor, T. C. Bruice, K. L. Kirk, and J. Meinwald, *J. Am. Chem. Soc.* **88**, 108 (1966).

[76] J. Kumamoto, J. R. Cox, Jr., and F. H. Westheimer, *J. Am. Chem. Soc.* **78**, 4858 (1956).

enediamine (18, pK 3.6, $k = 2.5 \times 10^{-5}$ M^{-1} min^{-1}) is also more
reactive than would be expected for its basicity, and has a rate
constant approximately equal to that of the free base (pK 8.8,
$k = 6.2 \times 10^{-5}$ M^{-1} min^{-1}) if the later value is corrected by a factor
of 2 to allow for the fact that there are two reactive nitrogen atoms
in the free base. Concerted hydrogen bonding is not possible with
the monocation of this compound, so that the rapid rates of the
reactions with monocations may be attributed simply to a favorable
electrostatic interaction of the cationic nucleophile with the dianionic
substrate.

Not all reactions in which electrostatic effects are possible
show such effects. For example, there is no significant effect of the
charge of the nucleophile on reactivity toward the cation 1-(N,N-
dimethylcarbamoyl)-pyridinium chloride or the anion of o-nitrophenyl
hydrogen oxalate, as compared with uncharged esters such as p-
nitrophenyl acetate and ethyl o-nitrophenyl oxalate.[77,78] On the
other hand, electrostatic effects on the reaction rate of about one
order of magnitude are observed for the nucleophilic reactions of
anions with the acyl groups of 1-acetoxy-4-methoxypyridinium cation
and acetylsalicylate monoanion.[79]

6. RESONANCE STABILIZATION AND STRUCTURAL REARRANGEMENTS

Resonance stabilization and structural rearrangements may cause
different amounts of stabilization or destabilization of ground states,
transition states, and products and may, at least in theory, affect
nucleophilic reactivity in the same way that they affect the efficiency
of general acid-base catalysts, as described in Chap. 3 for general
acid-base catalysis by carbon acids. The effect of resonance stabilization of the basic form of a nucleophile, such as carbonate dianion,
will be to decrease the nucleophilic reactivity of the compound
because the resonance stabilization will be partly lost in the transition state. However, resonance stabilization of the base will also
decrease its basicity, and this effect will generally be larger than the
effect on nucleophilicity because resonance interaction with the
reacting atoms is almost completely lost in the equilibrium protonation process, but is only partly lost in a transition state. In a correlation of nucleophilicity with basicity, therefore, resonance stabilization can cause either positive or negative deviations from the Brøn-

[77] S. L. Johnson and K. A. Rumon, *J. Am. Chem. Soc.* **87**, 4782 (1965).

[78] T. C. Bruice and B. Holmquist, *J. Am. Chem. Soc.* **89**, 4028 (1967).

[79] W. P. Jencks and M. Gilchrist, *J. Am. Chem. Soc.* **90**, 2622 (1968); T. St. Pierre
and W. P. Jencks, *Ibid.*, p. 3817.

sted line depending on the slope of the line and the relative amounts of resonance stabilization in the base, acid, and transition state.

If a structural rearrangement of the nucleophile is required in order to reach the transition state, the nucleophilic reactivity may be decreased by an amount corresponding to the free energy required for this rearrangement.[80]   The fact that the development of resonance stabilization generally involves changes in bond lengths, bond angles, and hybridization ties this influence to the resonance effect.

The wide range of interpretations which becomes possible by invoking effects of this kind makes them attractive as explanations for unusual behavior of nucleophilic agents, but also makes a definitive demonstration of their importance difficult.   Although it is possible to explain isolated examples of unusual reactivity by such effects, their influence has not been shown clearly in a systematic study of a large series of nucleophiles and, in the opinion of the author, their importance in controlling nucleophilic reactivity has not yet been clearly defined.

7. BOND STRENGTH TO CARBON

It might be expected that compounds which exhibit an unusually strong affinity for carbon in equilibrium addition reactions (e.g., equation 47) should also exhibit a strong affinity in a transition state (equations 48 and 49), in which the bond to carbon is partly rather than completely formed, so as to form an unusually stable transition state and react at a rapid rate.   Comparisons of these two kinds of

$$HX + \;\;\diagdown \!\!\! C = O \; \rightleftharpoons \; X - \overset{|}{\underset{|}{C}} - OH \qquad\qquad (47)$$

$$HX + \;\;\diagup\!\!\!^{\diagdown}\!\! C = O \; \rightleftharpoons \; \overset{(+)}{HX} \cdots \overset{\diagdown}{\underset{\diagup}{C}} = O^{(-)} \qquad\qquad (48)$$

$$X^- + \;\;\diagup\!\!\!^{\diagdown}\!\! C = O \; \rightleftharpoons \; \overset{(-)}{X} \cdots \overset{\diagdown}{\underset{\diagup}{C}} = O^{(-)} \qquad\qquad (49)$$

stabilities may be made in various ways.   The affinity toward carbon of the basic species of the nucleophile may be defined as the "carbon basicity" (e.g., equation 50), which is analogous to hydrogen basicity (equation 51), or the *relative* affinities of the nucleophile

[80] J. Hine, *J. Org. Chem.* **31**, 1236 (1966).

$$X^- + \,{}^{\diagdown}_{\diagup}C = O \;\rightleftharpoons\; X - \overset{\displaystyle |}{\underset{\displaystyle |}{C}} - O^- \tag{50}$$

$$X^- + H^+ \;\rightleftharpoons\; X - H \tag{51}$$

toward carbon and hydrogen may be compared in equilibria such as that of equation 47.[67,81-83] Equation 47 involves the breaking of an X—H bond and the π bond of the carbonyl group and the formation of an X—C bond and an O—H bond. Since the energies of the carbonyl π bond and the O—H bond will not be very different for a series of different nucleophiles X—H, the equilibrium of equation 47 measures principally the difference in the X—H and X—C bond energies. The use of equilibria expressed according to equation 47 removes the contribution of those factors which are responsible for basicity toward the proton from the comparison, so that one might hope to correlate deviations from a plot of nucleophilic reactivity against basicity with differences in the relative affinities toward hydrogen and carbon, as measured by this equilibrium. Hydrogen basicity has almost no influence on affinity toward the carbonyl group as expressed by equation 47; the equilibrium constants for the addition of amines of comparable steric requirements are almost independent of basicity. For example, the equilibrium constants for the addition of formaldehyde to simple primary amines (pK 10 to 11) are not much larger than those for addition to urea and amides (pK 0 to 1), and the affinity of formaldehyde for a series of carbon acids is independent of their acidity over a range of basicity of 10^{11}.[82,84]

The correlation of transition-state stabilities with product stabilities holds for a limited number of reactions. The equilibrium constants for the addition of a series of nucleophiles to the carbonyl group of pyridine-4-aldehyde, expressed according to equation 47, are shown in Table IX.[85] These equilibria, which show trends similar to those of a number of related equilibria, show that the affinities of hydroxylamine, hydroperoxides, and thiols, and the

[81] J. Hine and R. D. Weimar, Jr., *J. Am. Chem. Soc.* **87**, 3387 (1965).

[82] R. G. Kallen and W. P. Jencks, *J. Biol. Chem.* **241**, 5864 (1966).

[83] W. P. Jencks, in S. G. Cohen, A. Streitwieser, Jr., and R. W. Taft (eds.), "Progress in Physical Organic Chemistry," vol. 2, p. 63, Interscience Publishers, Inc., New York, 1964.

[84] T. N. Hall, *J. Org. Chem.* **29**, 3587 (1964).

[85] E. Sander and W. P. Jencks, *J. Am. Chem. Soc.* **90**, 6154 (1968).

Table IX   Equilibrium constants for the addition of nucleophiles to pyridine-4-aldehyde[85]

	K, M^{-1}
Ethylamine	43
Hydroxylamine	1500
Semicarbazide	250
Water	0.023
Ethanol	0.27
Hydrogen peroxide	19.8
Acetohydroxamic acid	0.93
N-Hydroxypiperidine	$\leqslant 0.34$
Acetone oxime	0.80
β-Mercaptoethanol	193

greater affinity of simple alcohols than of water, parallel the unusually large nucleophilic reactivity of these compounds or their conjugate bases toward the ester p-nitrophenyl acetate (Fig. 11). On the other hand, hydroxamic acids and the hydroxyl group of hydroxylamines have similar or only slightly greater affinities for the carbonyl group as compared with simple alcohols, although these oxygen anions are several orders of magnitude more reactive toward p-nitrophenyl acetate than other oxygen anions of comparable basicity. Cyanide, which has an enormous affinity for the carbonyl group, is not an unusually effective nucleophile.[36, 54] It is apparent that even such an empirical correlation as this does not provide a complete parallelism with nucleophilic reactivity if a sufficient number of compounds is examined.

Similar conclusions may be drawn from equilibria, similar to that of equation 50, for the addition of nucleophiles to the cationic pyridine ring of diphosphopyridine nucleotide (equation 52). Thiol

$$X^- + \underset{R}{\overset{O}{\underset{\|}{\overset{}{\bigcirc}}}}\text{—CNH}_2 \rightleftharpoons \underset{R}{\overset{X\ \ H\ \ \overset{O}{\overset{\|}{}}}{\bigcirc}}\text{—CNH}_2 \qquad (52)$$

anions, hydroxylamine, and sulfite, which are highly effective nucleophiles, all add to the pyridine ring in the presence of a large molar excess of water, but cyanide, which is not an unusually good nucleophile, also adds readily.[86] The shape of the potential-energy curves for the formation and breaking of carbon-carbon bonds probably exhibits a curvature similar to that for carbon-hydrogen bonds such that in both of these processes transition-state stabilities are relatively less than ground-state stabilities, as compared with corresponding bonds with more electronegative elements. This may be, in part, a reflection of the greater degree of covalent character of bonds to carbon.

The reasons for the different ground-state and transition-state stabilities of other nucleophiles are not clear at the present time. There is a tendency for compounds with two electronegative atoms bound to carbon to show a special stability,[87] and the increase in the electrophilic character of the nucleophile which is brought about by an adjacent electronegative atom may enhance this effect. It has been suggested that this effect results from double-bond–no-bond resonance similar to that proposed for carbon-hydrogen hypercon-jugation, as shown in **19** for acetals. The acidity of fluorocarbons

$$R-O-\overset{|}{\underset{|}{C}}-O-R \longleftrightarrow R-\overset{+}{O}=\overset{|}{\underset{|}{C}}\ \ ^{-}O-R$$

19

has been attributed to a similar no-bond resonance (**20**). However,

$$-\overset{|}{\underset{|}{\overset{..}{C}}}-\overset{|}{\underset{|}{C}}-F \longleftrightarrow -\overset{|}{C}=\overset{|}{C}\ \ \bar{F}$$

20

this explanation has been brought into question by the observation that base catalyzed proton exchange at the bridgehead position of **21**, at which only polar effects can be operating, is even slightly

21

faster than in tris(trifluoromethyl)methane; it appears that the in-ductive effect of the fluorine atoms is sufficient to account for the

[86] J. Van Eys and N. O. Kaplan, *J. Biol. Chem.* **228**, 305 (1957).

[87] J. Hine, *J. Am. Chem. Soc.* **85**, 3239 (1963).

acidity of fluorocarbons.[88] Van der Waals–London dispersion interactions of the nonbonded electrons of the addends may contribute
to these special stabilities.

The order of reactivity of halide anions toward saturated carbon of $I^- > Br^- > Cl^-$ in water (Table VII) is not reflected in a
corresponding order of equilibrium affinity for saturated carbon,
which does not differ in any large or regular way for these anions
(Table VIII).[58,67] Therefore, a property which is manifested more
in the transition state than in equilibria, such as polarizability,
must be important in these reactions. It follows that a highly reactive nucleophile, such as iodide, will also be a good leaving group;
this is observed. A correlation of reactivity with equilibria does
appear if the comparison is made on the basis of the acids HI,
HBr, and HCl, but this reflects principally the low basicity of the
larger anions, such as I^-, and nucleophilic reactivity increases in
the opposite order to basicity in this series.

Fluoride ion, in spite of its low basicity and polarizability, is
an extremely effective nucleophile toward phosphate; it is one of
the few compounds which competes effectively with water for reaction with monosubstituted phosphates, and it is more reactive than
ethoxide, phenoxide, and thiophenoxide toward diisopropyl phos-
phorochloridate.[49,89,90] This high reactivity parallels the high thermodynamic stability of fluorophosphates and may reflect the occurrence of resonance according to 22[91] in the transition state as well as
in the products.

$$F - \overset{|}{\underset{|}{P}} - \quad \longleftrightarrow \quad \overset{(+)}{F} = \overset{|}{\underset{|}{P}} \overset{(-)}{-}$$

22

8. INTRAMOLECULAR GENERAL ACID CATALYSIS.

Intramolecular general acid catalysis has often been proposed as an
explanation for the special reactivity of nucleophilic agents which
contain an acidic group in an appropriate position relative to the
nucleophilic center. There are a number of examples of large rate
enhancements resulting from such assistance in nonaqueous solvents,

---

[88] A. Streitwieser, Jr. and D. Holtz, *J. Am. Chem. Soc.* **89**, 692 (1967); A. Streitwieser Jr., A. P. Marchand, and A. H. Pudjaatmaka, *Ibid.* p. 693.

[89] I. Dostrovsky and M. Halmann, *J. Chem. Soc.* **1953**, 508.

[90] W. P. Jencks and M. Gilchrist, *J. Am. Chem. Soc.* **87**, 3199 (1965).

[91] D. W. J. Cruickshank, *J. Chem. Soc.* **1961**, 5486.

in which catalysis or solvation by a third molecule would be necessary if intramolecular catalysis did not occur; however, in aqueous solution the ubiquitous and efficient water molecule is likely to be hydrogen bonded to the substrate even before the reaction takes place, and the number of instances in which an acidic group on the nucleophile has been shown to take the place of this water molecule and provide effective catalysis is small. Many of the proposals for mechanisms of this kind in aqueous solution have not withstood close examination, and the number which have not been subjected to close examination is even larger. For reactions in which intramolecular catalysis by a Brϕnsted acid, such as a hydroxyl group, is suspected, the most useful controls are examination of the reactivity of related compounds in which the acidic hydrogen has been replaced by an alkyl group and compounds in which the acidic group is located in a position from which it can exert polar substituent effects, but cannot participate as an intramolecular catalyst.

It has just been pointed out that the enhanced reactivity of diamine cations with p-nitrophenyl phosphate dianion, which might have been ascribed to intramolecular acid catalysis, can be shown to be an electrostatic effect by the examination of compounds in which intramolecular catalysis is sterically prohibited. Another example is the rapid reaction of hydroperoxide anion with p-nitrophenyl acetate in water. Intramolecular assistance by the hydroxyl group of the hydroperoxide molecule has frequently been proposed for reactions of this kind. The fact that methyl hydroperoxide ion is also highly reactive, only slightly less so than hydroperoxide itself, requires that some other explanation be sought for this reactivity, at least in the case of this reaction.[36, 79]

One of the few carefully studied reactions for which there is evidence for a rate enhancement in aqueous solution caused by internal general acid catalysis is the reaction of catechol monoanion with isopropyl methylphosphonofluoridate (Table X).[92] The rate enhancement of 12-fold above that predicted by the Brϕnsted plot which was established for the reaction of a number of simple *meta*- and *para*-substituted phenolate ions with this substrate, is probably significant but is certainly not extraordinary. No rate enhancement is caused by the p-hydroxy group of hydroquinone or by an o-methoxy group. Possible mechanisms for the catalysis include assistance to the attack of the phenolate anion by hydrogen bonding to

[92] J. Epstein, R. E. Plapinger, H. O. Michel, J. R. Cable, R. A. Stephani, R. J. Hester, C. Billington, Jr., and G. R. List, *J. Am. Chem. Soc.* **86**, 3075 (1964).

Table X   Rates of reaction of substituted phenolate ions with isopropyl methyl-phosphonofluoridate at 25°[92]

Substituent	pK_a[a]	$k_2,$ M^{-1} min^{-1}	Rate enhancement[b]
H	9.78	34	1
o-OH	9.60	369	12
o-OCH$_3$	9.85	11.3	0.27
p-OH	10.12	77	1.3
o-CH$_2\overset{+}{N}H_3$	8.89	59	5.1
m-CH$_2\overset{+}{N}H_3$	9.06	30.2	2.1
p-N(CH$_3$)$_3$$^+$	8.30	13.1	2.5

[a] Corrected for statistical effects.
[b] Compared with the expected reactivity based on the relationship log $k_2 = 0.589$ $pK_a -$ 4.172, which has been established for the reaction of meta- and para-substituted phenolates.

the phosphate oxygen (23), proton removal from an addition compound (24), and assistance to the departure of fluoride (25). The

23   24   25

fivefold rate enhancement caused by a protonated o-aminomethyl group might be attributed to a similar mechanism, but rate enhancements are also brought about by the same group in the meta position and by the p-trimethylammonium group, which suggests that it is instead an electrostatic effect. The positive charge in these molecules should have a larger effect on the ionization of the hydroxyl group to give a negative charge than on the stability of a transition state with only a partial negative charge on the phenolic oxygen atom, so that the high reactivity of these compounds may be more appropriately attributed to an "abnormally" low basicity than to an unusual reactivity.

The oxygen atom of hydroxylamine is a better nucleophile toward the acetyl group of phenyl acetates than the nitrogen atom[36,93] in spite of the fact that the nitrogen atom is more basic by

[93] W. P. Jencks, J. Am. Chem. Soc. 80, 4585 (1958).

a factor of at least 10^7. This extraordinary reactivity must almost
certainly mean that it is not the free hydroxyl group, but rather
the oxygen anion of the dipolar form of hydroxylamine (26) that is
the reactive nucleophilic species. The fact that hydroxylamine

$$H_2NOH \rightleftharpoons H_3{}^+N - O^-$$

26

(pK 6.0) is not very much more basic than trimethylamine-N-oxide
(pK 4.6) suggests that a significant amount of hydroxylamine normally exists in the dipolar form in aqueous solution. Although a
quantitative evaluation is not possible, the overall reactivity of hydroxylamine is some 300-fold larger than that of other amines of
comparable basicity, and the reactivity of the oxygen anion of the
dipolar form must be several orders of magnitude larger than that
of oxygen anions of comparable basicity. It is unlikely that this
dipolar ion has an unusual polarizability (hydroxylamine itself has a
normal polarizability), and it does not have a free electron pair on
the atom adjacent to the reacting oxygen atom. The most probable
mechanism for this rapid reaction is, therefore, one which involves
internal general acid-base catalysis, for example, 27 to 29. The

27   28   29

fact that alkylation of hydroxylamine takes place on the nitrogen
atom in preference to the oxygen atom provides a further indication
that the high reactivity of the oxygen atom towards acylating agents
involves general acid-base catalysis because such catalysis would
not be important for alkylation.

There is no reason that Lewis acids as well as Brønsted acids
could not provide assistance to the reaction of a nucleophile. Interaction of the electrons of the carbonyl oxygen atom with unoccupied
d orbitals of the chlorine atom of hypochlorite (30) or the antibonding
π orbitals of pyridine-N-oxide (31) provides a possible explanation
for the high reactivity of these compounds with p-nitrophenyl
acetate. Donor-acceptor interactions of this kind with the carbonyl

30   31

group are known to exist in solution and in the solid state (for example, in the bromine and iodine complexes of acetone and amides).[94,95]

Rate accelerations caused by catalyzing groups on the nucleophile are not different in principle from those which are caused by catalyzing groups on the substrate, which have been discussed in Chap. 1.

9. THE α EFFECT

It is frequently found that compounds which contain an electronegative atom with a free electron pair adjacent to the nucleophilic atom display an unusually high nucleophilic reactivity, which has been called the "α effect."[36,96,97] Compounds which exhibit an unusually large reactivity and which may belong to this class include hydroxylamine and hydrazine and the anions of hypochlorite, hydroxamic acids, oximes, hydroperoxides, nitrite, and sulfite. Some examples are evident in Fig. 11, page 91.

The α effect is not a single, distinct entity, and there are so many different factors influencing nucleophilic reactivity which are important in "α-effect" compounds that one is sometimes tempted

"α-effect" compounds

[94] O. Hassel and K. P. Strǿmme, *Acta Chem. Scand.* **13**, 275 (1959).

[95] R. S. Drago and B. B. Wayland, *J. Am. Chem. Soc.* **87**, 3571 (1965).

[96] A. L. Green, G. L. Sainsbury, B. Saville, and M. Stansfield, *J. Chem. Soc.* **1958**, 1583.

[97] J. O. Edwards and R. G. Pearson, *J. Am. Chem. Soc.* **84**, 16 (1962).

to doubt the usefulness of the term. The fact that the atom adjacent to the nucleophilic center usually has few or no substituents
means that steric hindrance will be relatively small in these compounds; the high reactivity of hydroperoxide anion may be ascribed
to its high polarizability; the reactivity of hypochlorite may be
ascribed to general (Lewis) acid catalysis by the chlorine atom;
and many "α-effect" compounds exhibit an unusual thermodynamic
stability toward carbon, although others do not.[36, 81, 85, 98] Nevertheless, it is often useful to have an inclusive term to describe effects
which are not completely understood, and it is probable that the
electronegative atom with its free electron pair in the α position
contributes directly to the enhanced nucleophilicity of some, if not
all, of these compounds.

The role most frequently proposed for this electron pair is that
it acts to increase nucleophilicity by increasing the effective electron
density at the reaction center. If one or two electrons are removed
from an atom Y to give a radical or an onium ion, this electron-
deficient species will be greatly stabilized by electron donation by
resonance from an adjacent free electron pair on $\ddot{X}$. One might
then argue that the partial removal of electrons from Y by donation
to a substrate in a transition state is a similar process which creates
an electron deficiency on Y, and that this electron deficiency can be
stabilized by electron donation from X in the same manner as with
radicals and onium ions (**32** to **34**); the result would be to increase

$$\ddot{X}-Y\cdot \longleftrightarrow \dot{X}-Y:$$
$$\textbf{32}$$

$$\ddot{X}-Y^+ \longleftrightarrow \overset{+}{X}=Y$$
$$\textbf{33}$$

$$\ddot{X}-\overset{(+)}{Y}\cdots\overset{\diagdown\diagup}{S}\cdots Z \longleftrightarrow \overset{+}{X}=Y\cdots\overset{\diagdown\diagup}{S}\cdots Z$$
$$\textbf{34}$$

the effective electron density on the substrate and, hence, the
nucleophilicity of X–Y.[97]

An apparent difficulty with this proposal is that it requires an
involvement of the nucleophilic atom Y with more bonds and electrons
than is normally possible without expansion of its valence shell.

---

[98] J. Gerstein and W. P. Jencks, *J. Am. Chem. Soc.* **86**, 4655 (1964).

The fact that Y can be a first-row element means that any such expansion which involves significant participation of d orbitals is unlikely. However, there is not an excessive number of electrons compared with the total number of available atomic orbitals in such a system, and if the p orbitals from each of the atoms involved undergo hybridization to molecular orbitals involving the complete system, it should be possible to obtain a stable system without the utilization of d orbitals. This is the same type of hybridization that is used to describe the covalent character of the hydrogen bond, the transition state for simple S_N2 substitution on carbon, and the formation of polyhalide complexes such as I—I—I^- without utilizing high-energy orbitals, although each of these situations involves bonding of the central atom to more than the usual number of atoms.[99,100] In these systems the central atom is bonded to the two outer atoms by a single bond involving two electrons. Another electron pair is in a nonbonding orbital involving only the two outer atoms, which results in a high charge density on these atoms, as shown for the triiodide ion in **35**. This is the desired situation for a

$$\overset{\delta-}{I}—I—\overset{\delta-}{I}$$

35

nucleophilic reaction, in which a high charge density on the substrate helps to expel the leaving group. Furthermore, even in the ground state the hydrogen peroxide molecule may be usefully regarded as a system of two oxygen atoms which are connected by multiple bonds similar to those of the oxygen molecule, with hydrogen atoms bonded to each of the two unpaired electrons which are in antibonding orbitals in the oxygen molecule.[101] This model may be regarded as a restatement in modern terms of the proposal that hydrogen peroxide has multiple-bond character between the oxygen atoms, which was put forward by Brühl in 1895 to explain the unusually high polarizability and molar refraction of hydrogen peroxide.[102] These examples suggest that the resulting high coordination number of the nucleophilic atom in "α-effect" compounds does not rule out

[99] R. E. Rundle, *Record Chem. Progr. Kresge-Hooker Sci. Lib.* **23**, 195 (1962).

[100] G. C. Pimentel and A. L. McClellan, "The Hydrogen Bond," p. 236, W. H. Freeman and Company, San Francisco, 1960.

[101] R. D. Spratley and G. C. Pimentel, *J. Am. Chem. Soc.* **88**, 2394 (1966).

[102] J. W. Brühl, *Chem. Ber.* **28**, 2847 (1895).

an energetically favorable participation of the electron pair on the adjacent atom in the transition state. The extra orbital which is available in unsaturated substrates may facilitate the formation of stable molecular orbitals, and it is in reactions of unsaturated substrates that most examples of the α effect have been observed.[103] Unfortunately, no quantitative treatment of this type of interaction has been reported. Alternatively, it is possible that the lone pair electrons of the α atom interact directly with the substrate or that the α effect has nothing to do with this free electron pair, but is instead a consequence of the electronegativity of the α atom.

It should be noted that factors which destabilize the starting material, such as unfavorable solvation or an energetically unfavorable interaction of the electron pairs on adjacent atoms, could cause an increase in nucleophilic reactivity if the destabilization were lost or decreased in the transition state, but should cause at least at large an increase in basicity, so that an increase in nucleophilic reactivity relative to basicity cannot easily be accounted for by such mechanisms.

The rate enhancements which are observed in the attack of nucleophiles on a saturated carbon atom adjacent to a carbonyl group may involve a similar type of interaction. The rapid rates of displacement reactions of α-haloketones have been ascribed to some sort of overlap of the attacking electron pair with the orbitals of the π electron system of the carbonyl group, which serves to lower the energy of the transition state.[104] The displacement of the dinitrophenolate ion from **36** at 0° occurs 9,000 times faster than from **37**, in which the direction of approach of the attacking

36   **37**

nucleophile precludes such an interaction with the carbonyl group.[105]

[103] M. J. Gregory and T. C. Bruice, *J. Am. Chem. Soc.* **89**, 4400 (1967).

[104] A. Streitwieser, Jr., "Solvolytic Displacement Reactions," p. 28, McGraw-Hill Book Company, New York, 1962.

[105] P. D. Bartlett and E. N. Trachtenberg, *J. Am. Chem. Soc.* **80**, 5808 (1958).

Such an interaction cannot directly increase the electron density at the reaction center, but may permit a degree of stabilization by providing additional electron overlap in the transition state (38).

$$O \overset{\diagdown}{\underset{X\cdots}{\diagup}} \overset{\diagup}{\underset{C\cdots Y}{C}} \quad \longleftrightarrow \quad {}^{(-)}O \overset{\diagdown}{\underset{X\cdots}{\diagup}} \overset{\diagup}{\underset{C\cdots Y}{C}}$$

38

This explanation is similar to that for the "α effect" in that it postulates stabilization of a transition state by the utilization of electrons and orbitals on adjacent atoms that would not be expected to participate in bonding according to classical valance bond concepts.

E. ELECTROPHILIC CATALYSIS

The "important" role of the catalyst in electrophilic covalent catalysis is to provide a driving force for a reaction by withdrawing electrons from the reaction center. The division between electrophilic and nucleophilic catalysis is by no means sharp, since a step which involves electrophilic catalysis is often preceded by a step in which the catalyst acts as a nucleophile in order to attach itself to the substrate (for example, equations 27 and 28). Furthermore, electrophilic catalysis of a reaction in one direction is likely to be nucleophilic catalysis in the other direction. A quite arbitrary division is made here, based on whether the step which seems to be most "important" for catalysis represents nucleophilic or electrophilic facilitation of the reaction in the direction in which it is usually written.

Electrophilic catalysis may be brought about by the proton, which may be donated from the solvent or from a general acid, by metal ions, and by combination with organic molecules which contain groups which can act as electron sinks. Catalysis by the proton in enzyme reactions usually involves general acid catalysis and is discussed in Chap. 3. Metal ion catalysis will not be discussed here in detail. The most important single mechanism of covalent electrophilic catalysis in enzyme reactions is that in which the substrate and catalyst combine to give a compound in which a cationic nitrogen atom acts as an electron sink or free nitrogen acts as the donor of an electron pair, as in the reactions of an enamine (39, 40). Although

39   40   41

nitrogen itself is not strongly electronegative, it can act as an effective electron sink in such reactions by virtue of the fact that it is
easily protonated and can form cationic unsaturated adducts easily.
The ease of formation of these charged compounds more than makes
up for the low electronegativity of nitrogen, so that nitrogen is
generally more effective as an electron sink than oxygen, which is
more electronegative but forms a cation at neutral pH with such
great difficulty as to be relatively inactive as an electron acceptor
by this mechanism. Conversely, the ease with which nitrogen can
donate an electron pair permits it to act as a sort of a low-energy
carbanion; the enamine can easily donate electrons to form a new
bond to a carbon atom (40), whereas the formation of a true carbanion (41) is a much higher energy process.

1. ATP AND METALS

An interesting example of electrophilic catalysis by metals is found
in the catalysis of the transfer of phosphate from ATP (adenosine
triphosphate) to water and other acceptors.[106] There are several
possible roles for the metal ion in reactions of this kind. (1) It can
shield the negative charges of the phosphate group which would
otherwise tend to repel the attack of the electron pair of a nucleophile, especially an anionic nucleophile. (2) It can increase the reactivity of the atom which is being attacked, by withdrawing
electrons. (3) It can make the leaving group a better leaving group.
(4) It can act as a bridging group between nucleophile and substrate.
(5) It can change the pK and reactivity of the nucleophile. (6)
Finally, it can, perhaps, change the geometric arrangement of the
substrate in such a manner as to facilitate the reaction. Metal ion
catalysis is, of course, important in many enzymatic reactions and
presumably involves the same factors; in addition, the metal may
be involved in the binding of the substrate to the enzyme in the
correct position. The introduction of electron-spin resonance and
nuclear magnetic resonance techniques as probes of the immediate

---

[106] J. M. Lowenstein, *Biochem. J.* **70**, 222 (1958); **75**, 269 (1960); *Biochim. Biophys.
Acta* **28**, 206 (1958); M. Tetas and J. M. Lowenstein, *Biochemistry* **2**, 350 (1963).

environment of the metal ion has made possible some discrimination among these possibilities in enzymatic as well as in nonenzymatic reactions.[107, 108]

Metal ion activation of ATP is of special interest in that it makes possible the nonenzymatic phosphorylation of anionic acceptors, such as phosphate (to give pyrophosphate) and acetate (to give acetyl phosphate, which is trapped with hydroxylamine as the hydroxamic acid), as well as hydrolysis. There are large differences in the effectiveness of different metal ions, which reflect differences in the solubilities of the metal complexes, in the affinities of the metal for ATP and for phosphate (metal binding to phosphate will decrease its nucleophilic reactivity), in the relative amounts of metal chelates of different structure and reactivity which are present at equilibrium, and in the catalytic effectiveness per se of the bound metal. The rate increases more rapidly than the first power of the metal ion concentration, and the reaction in the presence of divalent metals is further facilitated by monovalent cations such as potassium and, to a lesser extent, sodium. This suggests that a reactive complex which contains two metal ions and in which the charge of the ATP is almost completely shielded makes an important contribution to the observed catalysis. The rate of the hydrolysis reaction catalyzed by cupric ion shows a sharp maximum near pH 5, and other metals show characteristic, but less marked, variations in rate with pH.

The significance of these pH dependencies and the mechanisms of these interesting reactions have still not been worked out in detail. The special catalytic effectiveness of "soft" metals such as cupric ion, which have a strong affinity for nitrogen, suggests that chelation with the nitrogen atom of the adenine group gives an especially reactive metal-phosphate complex. The importance of this interaction with the adenine base is shown by the fact that the cupric ion catalyzed hydrolysis of ATP is some 20 times faster than that of γ-phenylpropyl triphosphate, in which such an interaction is not possible. Catalysis of phosphate hydrolysis and transfer reactions of this compound and of ATP by the "harder" metals, magnesium and calcium, occurs at very similar rates, indicating that interactions with the ring are not important for catalysis by these

[107] M. Cohn and T. R. Hughes, Jr., *J. Biol. Chem.* **237**, 176 (1962); H. Sternlicht, R. G. Shulman, and E. W. Anderson, *J. Chem. Phys.* **43**, 3123, 3133 (1965).

[108] W. J. O'Sullivan and M. Cohn, *J. Biol. Chem.* **241**, 3104 (1966) and references therein; A. S. Mildvan and M.C. Scrutton, *Biochemistry* **6**, 2978 (1967).

metals.[109]   A number of different structures for metal–ATP complexes are possible (42 to 45), and it should be kept in mind that the predominant species in solution may not be the reactive species and that different structures may be the most reactive for different reactions with different mechanisms. Nucleophilic attack on the terminal phosphate will be most facilitated by metal ion binding to that group, as in 42, 44, and 45, whereas departure of the leaving group will be most favored in a structure with metal binding to the proximal phosphates, as in 43 and 44. There is a considerable

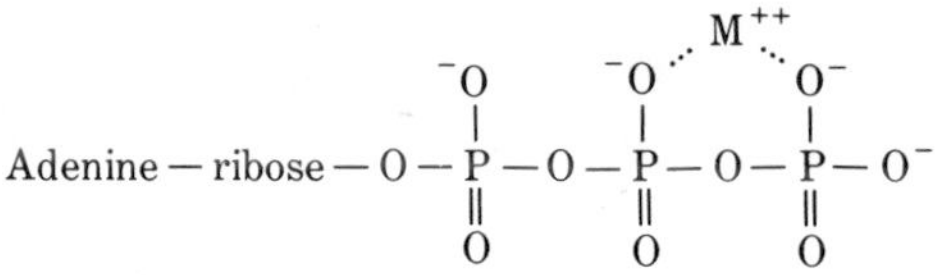

42

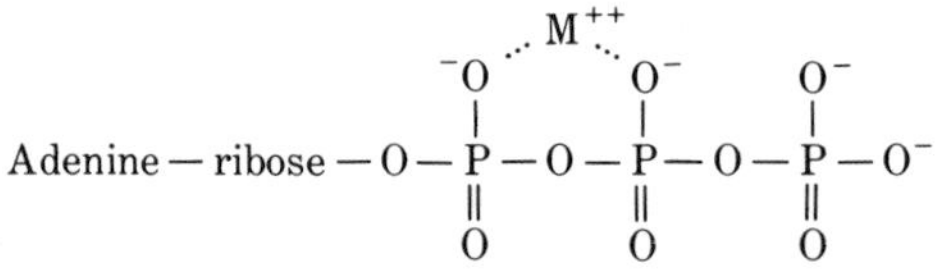

43

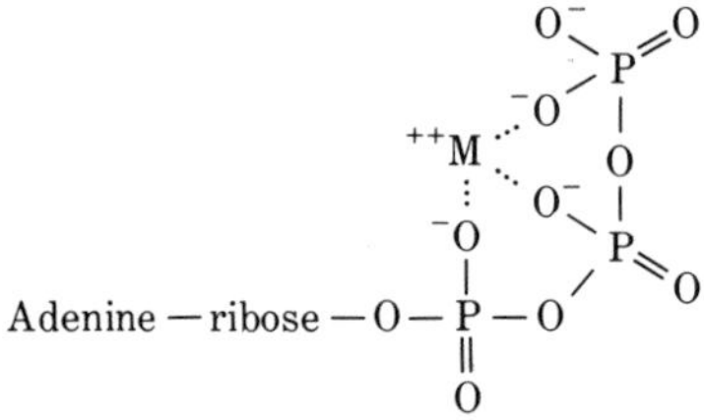

44 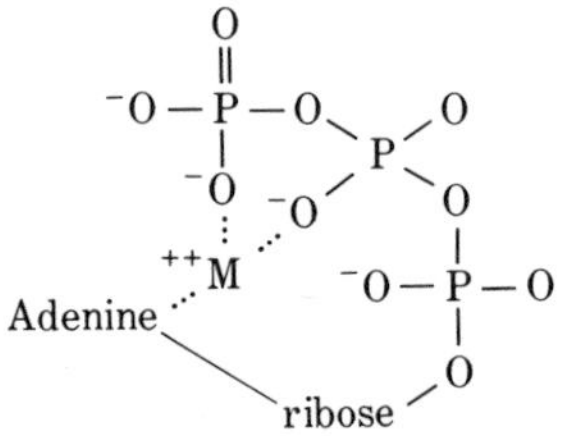   45

amount of evidence that the hydrolysis of monosubstituted phosphates can occur by an elimination mechanism to give metaphosphate monoanion as the initial product, which then undergoes rapid hydration to inorganic phosphate (equation 53),[110] and such a

[109] D. L. Miller and F. H. Westheimer, *J. Am. Chem. Soc.* 88, 1507, 1514 (1966).

[110] W. W. Butcher and F. H. Westheimer, *J. Am. Chem. Soc.* 77, 2420 (1955); C. A. Bunton, D. R. Llewellyn, K. G. Oldham, and C. A. Vernon, *J. Chem. Soc.* 1958, 3574; G. Di Sabato and W. P. Jencks, *J. Am. Chem. Soc.* 83, 4400 (1961); J. R. Cox, Jr. and O. B. Ramsay, *Chem. Rev.* 64, 317 (1964).

$$\overset{\curvearrowleft}{RO} \!\!-\!\! \underset{\underset{O}{\|}}{\overset{\overset{O\bar{\,}}{|}}{P}} \!-\! O^- \longrightarrow RO^- + \left[\underset{O}{\overset{O}{\underset{\diagdown}{\overset{\|}{P}}\diagup}} O \right]^- \overset{H_2O}{\longrightarrow} HO - \underset{\underset{O}{\|}}{\overset{\overset{O^-}{|}}{P}} - OH \tag{53}$$

mechanism would be facilitated by metal binding to the proximal phosphates (43) but hindered by binding to the terminal phosphates (42 and 45) of ATP. In enzyme reactions, the enzyme may facilitate the reaction and contribute to its specificity simply by favoring the binding of metal in the most favorable possible structure for the particular reaction which is being catalyzed.

There are many examples of metal ion catalysis of hydrolysis and transfer reactions of acyl compounds which presumably involve activation of the carbonyl group toward nucleophilic attack and binding to the leaving group to assist its expulsion. Direct evidence for the former type of activation has been obtained with Co^{III} complexes, which undergo exchange of ligands very slowly.[111] The Co(triethylenetetramine)$^{3+}$ group acts as both an activating group and a protecting group to catalyze the rapid condensation of two moles of glycine ethyl ester to glycylglycine ethyl ester. The immediate product of the reaction is the glycylglycine compound (47) with both an amine and a carbonyl group bound to cobalt. Compound 46, with similar carbonyl-group activation, reacts with glycine ethyl ester in less than 1 minute at 20° to give 47. These results suggest that the reaction sequence of equation 54 accounts for metal catalysis of this and related reactions.

$$(54)$$

[111] D. A. Buckingham, L. G. Marzilli, and A. M. Sargeson, *J. Am. Chem. Soc.* 89, 2772, 4539 (1967).

2. DECARBOXYLATION OF β-KETO ACIDS

The mechanistic requirement for decarboxylation is that the substrate contain an electrophilic center to accept the electron pair which must be donated by the carboxylate group to give a carbanion or carbanion-like product. In β-keto acids such as acetoacetate this role may be filled by the β-carbonyl group, which acts as an electron sink and gives an enolate anion as the product (equation 55).

$$
\begin{array}{c}
-\overset{\overset{\displaystyle O}{\|}}{C}-\overset{\displaystyle |}{\underset{\displaystyle |}{C}}-C\overset{\diagup O^-}{\diagdown_O} \xrightarrow{\ -CO_2\ }
\end{array}
\left[\ -\overset{\overset{\displaystyle O^{(-)}}{\|}}{C}=C\diagdown \ \right]
\begin{array}{c} \xrightarrow{\ H_2O\ } \\ \\ \xrightarrow{\ Br_2\ } \end{array}
\quad
\begin{array}{c}
-\overset{\overset{\displaystyle O}{\|\,|}}{C}CH \\ \\
-\overset{\overset{\displaystyle O}{\|\,|}}{C}CBr
\end{array}
$$

$$
\begin{array}{c}
\Big\updownarrow \pm H^+ \\[4pt]
-\overset{\overset{\displaystyle {}^+OH}{\|\,|}}{C}-\overset{\displaystyle |}{\underset{\displaystyle |}{C}}-C\overset{\diagup O^-}{\diagdown_O} \xrightarrow{\ -CO_2\ }
\end{array}
\left[\ -\overset{\overset{\displaystyle OH}{\big|}}{C}=C\diagdown \ \right]
\tag{55}
$$

The reaction can be facilitated by protonation of the carbonyl group to give a more active electron sink and the free enol as the product, although the low basicity of the carbonyl group provides a large energy barrier to this pathway. The transition state for the acid catalyzed mechanism has no net charge, so that the rate of the observed reaction according to this mechanism will be proportional to the concentration of uncharged acetoacetic acid (equation 56).

$$
v = k \left[\ \overset{\overset{\displaystyle HO^+}{\|\,|}}{CH_3CCCOO^-} \ \right] = k' \left[\ \overset{\overset{\displaystyle O}{\|\,|}}{CH_3CCCOOH} \ \right]
\tag{56}
$$

The small dependence of the rate on solvent polarity is consistent with a concerted mechanism is which the carboxyl group donates a proton to the carbonyl group (48).[112] However, since solvent effects provide evidence only for the *difference* in the polarity of the ground

$$
\begin{array}{c}
\overset{\displaystyle H}{\diagdown} \\
-\overset{\overset{\displaystyle O}{\|}}{C}\underset{\underset{\displaystyle |}{C}}{\diagup}\overset{O}{\diagdown}\,\overset{|}{C}=O
\end{array}
$$

48

and transition states, the small solvent effect does not in itself rule out a zwitterionic intermediate, but only shows that the polarity of the transition state is similar to that of the starting material. The

[112] F. H. Westheimer and W. A. Jones, *J. Am. Chem. Soc.* **63**, 3283 (1941).

occurrence of significant deuterium isotope effects is consistent with the concerted mechanism for some β-keto acids, but the isotope effect is variable with different compounds and solvents, and an appreciable isotope effect would be expected on the equilibrium constants for the formation of a dipolar intermediate.[113]

The mechanism is best studied with α,α-dimethylacetoacetic acid, which avoids the complication of enolization of the starting material. With this compound the rate of decarboxylation in the presence of bromine is equal to the rate of formation of the brominated ketone product, although the rate is independent of the concentration of bromine. This shows that the product enol may be trapped in a fast reaction with bromine (equation 55).[114]

The decarboxylation of α,α-dimethylacetoacetate is catalyzed by amines, with an order of effectiveness of $1° > 2° > 3°$ amines. Although the rate laws for the catalyzed reactions with aniline and o-chloroaniline contain several terms, some of which have not been adequately explained, both reactions show a pH-rate maximum caused by the presence of a term containing the elements of the free amine, the carboxylate anion, and a proton (equation 57). A reason-

$$v = k \, [\mathrm{RNH_2}] \left[\begin{array}{c} \mathrm{O} \\ \| \ | \\ -\mathrm{CCCOO}^- \\ | \end{array} \right] [\mathrm{H^+}] = k' \left[\begin{array}{c} \overset{+}{\mathrm{RNH}} \\ \| \ | \\ -\mathrm{C}-\mathrm{C}-\mathrm{COO}^- \\ | \end{array} \right] \tag{57}$$

able mechanism which is in accord with this rate law involves the formation of a Schiff base from the amine and the β-carbonyl group, protonation of the relatively basic nitrogen atom of the Schiff base to convert it to an effective electron sink, and decarboxylation (equation 58, k_2 and k_4).[114] An alternative mechanism

(58)

[113] C. G. Swain, R. F. W. Bader, R. M. Esteve, Jr., and R. N. Griffin *J. Am. Chem. Soc.* **83**, 1951 (1961); C. S. Tsai, *Can. J. Chem.* **45**, 873 (1967).

[114] K. J. Pedersen, *J. Phys. Chem.* **38**, 559 (1934); *J. Am. Chem. Soc.* **60**, 595 (1938).

involves only the formation of the protonated carbinolamine addition compound, which then undergoes concerted elimination and decarboxylation with expulsion of the amine (equation 58, k_3). There is some kinetic evidence favoring the latter mechanism for the aniline catalyzed decarboxylation of oxalacetate in water,[115] and the decarboxylation of cinnamic acid dibromides occurs by a concerted *trans* elimination in nonaqueous solvents (49).[116] However, the mechanism

49

is likely to be different with different reaction conditions and different substrates. The cinnamic acid dibromide reaction proceeds to a significant extent by a stepwise carbonium ion mechanism in water, in which an ionic mechanism is favored (equation 59).[116] The rate of

$$(59)$$

decarboxylation of oxalacetic acid in ethanol in the presence of amine is the same as the rate of formation of the Schiff base from the ethyl ester,[115] and the rate of the cyanomethylamine catalyzed decarboxylation of acetoacetate in aqueous solution is the same as the rate of reaction of ethyl acetoacetate with cyanomethylamine to give the Schiff base and enamine.[117] If, as seems probable, the rate-determining step in these reactions is the dehydration of the carbinolamine intermediate (k_2, equation 58), the equivalence of the rates of decarboxylation of the acid and of adduct formation with the ester suggests that these decarboxylation reactions proceed with rate-determining formation of the Schiff base. Concerted decarboxylation of the carbinolamine adduct should also be possible with tertiary amines; and, provided that steric factors are not responsible,

[115] R. W. Hay, *Australian J. Chem.* 18, 337 (1965).

[116] S. J. Cristol and W. P. Norris, *J. Am. Chem. Soc.* 75, 632, 2645 (1953); E. Grovenstein, Jr., and S. P. Theophilou, *Ibid.* 77, 3795 (1955); E. Grovenstein, Jr., and D. E. Lee, *Ibid.* 75, 2639 (1953).

[117] J. P. Guthrie and F. H. Westheimer, *Fed. Proc.* 26, 562 (1967).

the inactivity of tertiary amines as catalysts is further evidence against the concerted mechanism.

There is strong evidence that the enzymatic decarboxylation of acetoacetate proceeds with the intermediate formation of a Schiff base by a mechanism analogous to that of the nonenzymatic amine catalyzed reaction (equation 58).[118] In the presence of substrate the enzyme is irreversibly inhibited by reduction with borohydride, presumably because the intermediate Schiff base is reduced to give an unreactive amine (equation 60). Upon hydrolysis the N-isopropyl

$$\searrow C = \overset{+}{N} \diagdown \quad + \ BH_4^- \ \longrightarrow \quad -\overset{\overset{\displaystyle H}{|}}{\underset{|}{C}} - N \diagdown \qquad (60)$$

derivative of lysine can be isolated from the inhibited enzyme, which means that it is the Schiff base (or an enamine) containing the elements of acetone and the ϵ-amino group of a lysine residue of the enzyme that is reduced; evidently the decarboxylation step takes place rapidly, before reduction. If the acetoacetate is labeled with ^{18}O in the carbonyl group, the acetone product of the enzymatic reaction is free of ^{18}O. This is evidence for the formation of an intermediate in which this oxygen has been removed, as would be expected for the Schiff base mechanism, and argues against a mechanism in which there is a concerted elimination of amine from a carbinolamine intermediate (equation 58, k_3), which would not require the loss of this oxygen atom. Finally, in the presence of substrate the enzyme is inhibited by cyanide, which adds to the Schiff base to form a stable addition compound (equation 61).

$$\searrow C = \overset{+}{N} \diagdown \quad + \ CN^- \ \longrightarrow \quad -\overset{\overset{\displaystyle |}{|}}{\underset{\underset{\displaystyle CN}{|}}{C}} - N \diagdown \qquad (61)$$

The decarboxylation of dimethyloxalacetate is catalyzed by metals, such as Al^{3+} and Cu^{++}, which can chelate with the carboxylate and ketone groups, act as an electron sink for the decarboxylation process, and stabilize the product enolate ion (equation 62).[119]

$$(62)$$

[118] G. A. Hamilton and F. H. Westheimer, *J. Am. Chem. Soc.* **81**, 6332 (1959); S. Warren, B. Zerner, and F. H. Westheimer, *Biochemistry* **5**, 817 (1966).

[119] R. Steinberger and F. H. Westheimer, *J. Am. Chem. Soc.* **73**, 429 (1951).

No catalysis is seen with the monoethyl ester or with acetoacetate, which cannot undergo such chelation. An analogy to the enzymatic reaction in this reaction also is suggested by the fact that most enzymes which catalyze oxalacetate decarboxylation require a metal ion for activity. In the absence of a direct interaction with a metal, other enzymatic decarboxylations of oxalacetate involve donation of electrons to an electrophilic center, provided by the energy-rich pyrophosphate bond of pyrophosphate or a nucleoside triphosphate bound to a metal ion, to give phosphoenolpyruvate as the product (equation 63).

$$\text{(63)}$$

3. ALDOL CONDENSATIONS

There are two difficult steps in aldol condensations, and both of these must be catalyzed if the rate of an aldol condensation is to be greatly increased. First, the activated carbon atom which is to attack the carbonyl group must lose a proton to give the enolate ion or its equivalent, and second, the enol or enolate must form a new carbon-carbon bond with the acceptor carbonyl group (equation 64). Since the first of these steps is first order and the second is

$$\text{(64)}$$

second order with respect to the carbonyl compound, either of them may be rate-determining, depending on the reaction conditions; and indeed in the self-condensation of acetaldehyde there is a change from rate-determining enolization at high acetaldehyde and low base concentrations to rate-determining condensation at low acetaldehyde and high base concentrations.[120]

Enzymatic catalysis of aldol condensation may also be separated into its component steps. Native aldolase catalyzes the stereospeci-

---

[120] A. Broche and R. Gibert, *Bull. Soc. Chim. France* 1955, 131; R. P. Bell and P. T. McTigue, *J. Chem. Soc.* 1960, 2983.

fic removal of a proton from dihydroxyacetone phosphate, measured by tritium exchange with the solvent, at a more rapid rate than it catalyzes the overall reaction; i.e., the condensation step of equation 64 is largely rate-determining. However, if the enzyme is modified by treatment with carboxypeptidase, there is a specific decrease in the catalytic activity of the enzyme for the proton-removal step, so that this step becomes rate-determining, the rate of tritium exchange becomes small, a deuterium isotope effect on the rate of the overall reaction is observed with dihydroxyacetone, which contains deuterium in the position which undergoes proton removal, and there is observed a rapid exchange of the carbonyl component of the reaction, glyceraldehyde-3-phosphate, into hexose diphosphate (equation 64, step 2 fast).[121]

Amine catalysis of the dealdolization of diacetone alcohol, which is the aldol condensation of equation 64 in reverse, shows an order of effectiveness of $1° > 2° > 3°$ amines,[122] which is similar to that for amine catalysis of decarboxylation. The pH-dependence of the reaction shows that the rate is proportional to the concentration of free amine and free diacetone alcohol; i.e., the transition state has a net charge of zero and contains the elements of diacetone alcohol and an amine. Since the rate-determining step in dilute solution is probably carbon-carbon bond cleavage, these facts suggest that catalysis occurs by the mechanism of equation 65, pathway A, in

$$(65)$$

[121] I. A. Rose, *Brookhaven Symp. Biol.* **15**, 293 (1962).

[122] F. H. Westheimer and H. Cohen, *J. Am. Chem. Soc.* **60**, 90 (1938).

which primary and secondary amines react with the carbonyl group of the substrate to give a cationic Schiff base, which acts as an electron sink to accept electrons from the anion of the alcohol in the cleavage reaction. This is in accord with the transition state with no net charge required by the pH-dependence of the reaction (equation 66). The reaction does not exhibit large solvent effects,

$$v = k \left[HO - \overset{|}{\underset{|}{C}} - \overset{|}{\underset{|}{C}} - \overset{O}{\overset{\|}{C}} - \right] [R_2NH] = k' \left[^-O - \overset{|}{\underset{|}{C}} - \overset{|}{\underset{|}{C}} - \overset{|}{C} = \overset{+}{NR_2} \right] \tag{66}$$

which shows that the transition state has a polarity similar to that of the starting materials, but does not rule out a dipolar intermediate. As in amine catalyzed decarboxylation, it is possible that the cleavage reaction occurs at the carbinolamine stage with a concerted expulsion of the protonated amine (equation 65, pathway B)[123]; again the inefficiency of tertiary amines as catalysts is evidence against this mechanism (if it is not a steric effect). This mechanism and the analogous mechanism for amine catalyzed decarboxylation would require a concerted, termolecular attack of amine on an enol and of enol on a C=O group in the reverse direction.

The mechanism of amine catalyzed aldol condensation is presumably the same as that of the dealdolization reaction, but in reverse.[124] In the condensation direction the catalyst makes possible the formation of an enamine, which is essentially an easily formed carbanion in which the electron pair on the nitrogen atom provides the driving force for attack at the carbonyl group to form the new carbon-carbon bond (equation 65, pathway A in reverse). The details of the mechanism have still to be worked out; it is possible, for example, that one of the steps in the formation of the Schiff base may be rate-determining under some experimental conditions.

The second necessary step in aldol condensations and in most carboxylation-decarboxylation reactions is proton transfer to and from the carbon atom which reacts as a carbanion or carbanion-like species. This proton transfer usually occurs through a keto-enol tautomerization (equation 64, step 1), but it is greatly facilitated by amines which allow it to occur through an energetically more favorable imine-enamine tautomerization (equation 67). Amine cat-

[123] R. W. Hay and K. R. Tate, *Australian J. Chem.* **19**, 1651 (1966).

[124] T. S. Buiko, N. V. Volkova, and O. O. Yasnikov, *Ukr. Khim. Zh.* **29**(11), 1179 (1963) [*Chem. Abstr.* **70**, 3964b (1964)]; T. A. Spencer, H. S. Neel, T. W. Flechtner, and R. A. Zayle, *Tetrahedron Letters* **1965**, 3889.

alysis of this step may be examined conveniently either by following the rate of deuterium or tritium exchange or of iodination of the product enol or enamine. The enolization of acetone and isobutyraldehyde is catalyzed by amines through conventional general base catalysis of proton abstraction from the carbonyl compound, but, with primary and secondary amines and ammonia, there is also a rapid catalyzed reaction with a rate which is proportional to the concentration of protonated amine and is as much as 10^6 times faster than catalysis by carboxylic acids of comparable acidity.[125] The fact that the rate is proportional to the concentrations of the carbonyl compound and the protonated amine means that the transition state has a positive charge and contains the elements of the carbonyl compound, the amine, and a proton. The mechanism may then be formulated according to equation 67, which follows the rate law of

$$(67)$$

equation 68. This mechanism is further supported by the facts that

$$v = k \left[H - \overset{O}{\underset{|}{\overset{||}{C}}} - \overset{|}{\underset{|}{C}} - \right][H_2 \overset{+}{N}R_2] = k' \left[H - \overset{|}{\underset{|}{C}} - \overset{|}{C} = \overset{+}{N}R_2 \right]$$

$$(68)$$

[125] M. L. Bender and A. Williams, *J. Am. Chem. Soc.* **88**, 2502 (1966); J. Hine, B. C. Menon, J. H. Jensen, and J. Mulders, *Ibid.*, p. 3367; J. Hine, F. C. Kokesh, K. G. Hampton, and J. Mulders, *Ibid.* **89**, 1205 (1967).

under favorable conditions accumulation of the intermediate imine may be observed directly and that the catalyzed reaction is subject to further catalysis by conventional general bases to give a term in the rate law which involves the base and the cationic imine, as shown in equation 69. This term must represent general base

$$v = k \left[\mathrm{H} - \overset{|}{\underset{|}{\mathrm{C}}} - \overset{|}{\mathrm{C}} = \overset{+}{\mathrm{N}} \diagdown \right] [\mathrm{B}] \tag{69}$$

$$\mathrm{B} \overset{\frown}{} \mathrm{H} - \overset{\frown}{\underset{|}{\mathrm{C}}} - \overset{+}{\mathrm{C}} = \overset{+}{\mathrm{N}} \diagdown \;\; \rightleftharpoons \;\; \mathrm{B} - \overset{+}{\mathrm{H}} \; \overset{\frown}{\underset{|}{\mathrm{C}}} = \mathrm{C} - \overset{..}{\mathrm{N}} \diagdown \tag{70}$$

catalysis of the removal of a proton from the intermediate cationic Schiff base to give the enamine (equation 70). The rate expression of equation 68, then, represents a special case of equation 69, in which the base B is water. In the reaction of equation 67 the cationic imine acts as an electron sink to facilitate the removal of a proton in the same way that it acts to facilitate removal of carbon dioxide and a carbonyl compound in decarboxylation and dealdolization, respectively.

There is strong evidence suggesting that this type of amine catalysis is utilized in several enzymatic aldol condensations.[126,127] Borohydride reduction of the enzyme in the presence of the ketone which is to undergo enolization causes irreversible enzyme inactivation and gives a stable secondary amine derived from this compound and a lysine residue of the enzyme, presumably by reduction of the intermediate imine (equation 60) or enamine, as in the case of acetoacetate decarboxylase. Aldolase is also inhibited by cyanide in the presence of the dihydroxyacetone phosphate, presumably by the addition of cyanide to the intermediate imine (equation 61).[128] Finally, the ketone oxygen atom of 2-keto-3-deoxy-6-phosphogluconate is replaced by solvent oxygen upon cleavage of this substrate by its specific aldolase, as would be expected if an intermediate imine were formed.[129]

The synthesis of pyrrole from two molecules of δ-aminolevulinic acid probably occurs through a Schiff base intermediate of

[126] J. C. Speck, Jr., P. T. Rowley, and B. L. Horecker, *J. Am. Chem. Soc.* 85, 1012 (1963); B. L. Horecker, T. Cheng, E. Grazi, C. Y. Lai, P. Rowley, and O. Tchola, *Fed. Proc.* 21, 1023 (1962).

[127] J. M. Ingram and W. A. Wood, *J. Biol. Chem.* 241, 3256 (1966).

[128] D. J. Cash and I. B. Wilson, *J. Biol. Chem.* 241, 4290 (1966).

[129] I. A. Rose and E. L. O'Connell, *Arch. Biochem. Biophys.* 118, 758 (1967).

one molecule of substrate with the enzyme, which can be trapped by borohydride, followed by attack of the enamine intermediate on the carbonyl group of the second molecule of substrate, dehydration of the adduct, and, finally, a transimination ("trans-Schiffization") and deprotonation to give the pyrrole (equation 71).[130]

(71)

The consequences which can follow from the amine catalyzed removal of a proton are well illustrated by the rather complex reaction sequence for the enzyme catalyzed conversion of 2-keto-3-

[130] D. Shemin and D. L. Nandi, *Fed. Proc.* **26**, 390 (1967).

deoxy-L-arabonate to α-ketoglutarate semialdehyde (equation 72).[131]

$$
\begin{array}{ccc}
\begin{array}{c}
CO_2^- \\
| \\
C=O \\
| \\
CH_2 \\
| \\
HOCH \\
| \\
CH_2OH
\end{array}
&
\underset{1}{\overset{Enz-NH_3^+}{\rightleftharpoons}}
&
\begin{array}{c}
CO_2^- \\
| \\
C=\overset{+}{N}-Enz \\
\; | \;\; H \\
H-CH \\
| \\
HOCH \\
| \\
CH_2OH
\end{array}
\quad
\underset{2}{\overset{\pm H^+}{\rightleftharpoons}}
\quad
\begin{array}{c}
CO_2^- \\
| \\
C-\overset{..}{N}-Enz \\
\; \| \;\; H \\
CH \\
| \\
HO-CH \\
| \\
CH_2OH
\end{array}
\end{array}
$$

$\searrow 3$

$$
\begin{array}{c}
CO_2^- \\
| \\
C=\overset{+}{N}-Enz \\
\; | \;\; H \\
CH \\
\| \\
CH \\
| \\
H-COH \\
| \\
H
\end{array}
$$

$$
\begin{array}{ccc}
\begin{array}{c}
CO_2^- \\
| \\
C=O \\
| \\
HCH^* \\
| \\
H^*CH \\
| \\
C=O \\
H
\end{array}
&
\underset{6}{\overset{-Enz-NH_3^+}{\longleftarrow}}
&
\begin{array}{c}
CO_2^- \\
| \\
C=\overset{+}{N}-Enz \\
\; | \;\; H \\
HCH^* \\
| \\
H^*CH \\
| \\
C=O \\
H
\end{array}
\quad
\underset{5}{\overset{\overset{*}{H}_2O}{\longleftarrow}}
\quad
\begin{array}{c}
CO_2^- \\
| \\
C-N-Enz \\
\| \quad H \\
CH \\
| \\
CH \\
\| \\
COH \\
H
\end{array}
\end{array}
$$

$\nearrow 4$

$$\tag{72}$$

The occurrence of steps 1 and 2 through an enzyme-substrate-imine intermediate is suggested by the fact that the enzyme is irreversibly inactivated by sodium borohydride in the presence of substrate, accompanied by covalent binding of 1 mole of substrate to the enzyme, and by the enzyme catalyzed exchange of hydrogen atoms α to the carbonyl group of substrate analogs. Formation of the enamine (step 2) is followed by dehydration (step 3) and loss of a second hydrogen atom (step 4), also in amine activated steps. Finally, the intermediate adds two protons from the solvent stereospecifically to the 3 and 4 positions, to give an imine-aldehyde (step 5), and undergoes hydrolysis of the product (step 6).

The similarity in the mechanisms of catalysis of these reactions by amines suggests that an enzyme catalyzing one of them might also catalyze others. This has been found to be the case for the aldolase which splits 2-keto-3-deoxy-6-phosphogluconate to pyruvate and glyceraldehyde-3-phosphate.[127] In addition to catalyzing the

[131] D. Portsmouth, A. C. Stoolmiller, and R. H. Abeles, *J. Biol. Chem.* **242**, 2751 (1967).

aldol condensation, this enzyme catalyzes the *enolization* of pyruvate, as evidenced by a rapid exchange of hydrogen into the methyl group of pyruvate, and the *decarboxylation* of oxalacetate, which occurs at a rate 0.5% of that of the overall reaction. Further, it is of interest that this enzyme is irreversibly inhibited by bromopyruvate, which presumably adds to the enzyme to form an imine in the same way as pyruvate, but then inactivates the enzyme by alkylating a basic group in the active site, possibly the basic group that normally acts to remove a proton from pyruvate (equation 73).[132]

$$(73)$$

4. THIAMINE PYROPHOSPHATE[133]

Although many of the reactions catalyzed by thiamine pyrophosphate-requiring enzymes had already been observed in model systems, the mechanisms of these interesting reactions were elucidated only after Breslow's demonstration that thiazolium salts undergo rapid base catalyzed exchange of the hydrogen atom in the 2 position with the solvent, which demonstrated that this position is highly acidic and that the carbanion or ylid (50) is easily formed.[134] There

---

[132] H. P. Meloche, *Biochemistry* **6**, 2273 (1967).

[133] For a recent detailed review of thiamine and pyridoxal catalysis, see T. C. Bruice and S. J. Benkovic, "Bioorganic Mechanisms," vol. II, chap. 8, W. A. Benjamin, Inc., New York, 1966.

[134] R. Breslow, *J. Am. Chem. Soc.* **79**, 1762 (1957).

have been few detailed kinetic examinations of the model reactions,

$$\text{H}-\text{C} \underset{\text{S}}{\overset{+\text{N}}{\diagdown}} \quad + \quad \text{HO}^- \quad \rightleftharpoons \quad {}^-\text{C} \underset{\text{S}}{\overset{+\text{N}}{\diagdown}} \quad + \quad \text{HOH}$$

50

and an unequivocal demonstration that synthetic intermediates are active in enzymatic systems has not been possible in most cases because the rates of association and dissociation of thiamine pyrophosphate and its derivatives with the enzyme are generally slow relative to the turnover rate of the enzymatic reaction. Nevertheless, the intermediates do show activity in the presence of enzymes, and the mechanisms which have been proposed for these reactions are so elegant and reasonable that it is difficult to believe that they are not correct, at least in their essentials.

It would be difficult to imagine a better catalyst than thiamine pyrophosphate for the reactions which are catalyzed by this coenzyme. The center of catalytic activity in the molecule is the cationic nitrogen atom, which is joined to the carbon atom in the 2 position by a double bond. By its proximity to this atom, the cationic nitrogen provides electrostatic stabilization of the carbanion or ylid 50, which makes possible the facile removal of a proton, a carbonyl group, or an acyl group which is bonded to this position. The sp^2 hybridization of the carbon atom and other properties of the thiazolium ring provide additional factors favoring ionization. The remarkable feature of the catalytic activity of the molecule, however, is that the same cationic imine nitrogen atom can act as an electron sink to stabilize the development of negative charge on an *adjacent* carbon atom, bonded to the 2 position of the ring (51). This stabilization, which takes place by resonance interaction through the

$$\text{H}-\text{O}-\overset{-}{\text{C}}-\text{C} \underset{\text{S}}{\overset{+\text{N}}{\diagdown}} \quad \longleftrightarrow \quad \text{H}-\text{O}-\text{C}=\text{C} \underset{\text{S}}{\overset{\text{N}}{\diagdown}}$$

51

double bond to the nitrogen atom, makes possible decarboxylation, aldol condensation and cleavage, dehydration, and oxidation, all of which require the development of negative charge at this position.

The initial step of reactions which are catalyzed by thiamine pyrophosphate generally involves ionization of the thiamine to the

carbanion **50**, which adds to the carbonyl group of pyruvate or a
hydroxyketone (equation 74, steps 1 and 3). The interaction with

(74)

the thiamine ring makes possible the development of negative
charge on the carbon atom of the substrate which was formerly the
carbonyl group, so that decarboxylation or dealdolization takes
place readily (steps 2 and 4). The immediate product is the enamine
51, which upon protonation gives a substituted hydroxymethyl
derivative of thiamine (**52**). This is one of those key intermediates
that was thought at one time to be so unstable as to defy synthesis
and isolation. It later followed the history of many such intermediates in that not only was it found to be sufficiently stable for
isolation under the proper conditions, but it was also found to be
easily synthesized, which was accomplished simply by allowing the

thiazolium compound to undergo spontaneous addition to a concentrated solution of aldehyde in water. Furthermore, it is the form in which a large fraction of thiamine pyrophosphate exists *in vivo*. Synthetic intermediates of this type have been shown to be active in most thiamine pyrophosphate catalyzed enzymatic reactions, but, as mentioned previously, the slow rates of association and dissociation and, possibly, of ionization, of these coenzyme derivatives lead to rates of product formation from the synthetic intermediates which are much slower than the normal turnover rates of the enzyme. The activation which is brought about by combination with the thiazolium ring is shown by the fact that at pH 8 to 9 the proton of this substituted hydroxymethyl adduct exchanges with the protons of the medium through the reverse of step 5.[135] However, this exchange is slow, at least in the absence of enzyme, and it seems probable that in some cases the carbanion-enamine intermediate 51 undergoes further reaction directly, without protonation.

The carbon atom of the carbanion-enamine intermediate 51 reacts as a nucleophile with electrophilic acceptors. The stable intermediate 52, which results from attack on a proton, can undergo cleavage to give an aldehyde product; this is the mechanism of acetaldehyde formation from pyruvate (steps 5 and 6). Attack of 51 on a carbonyl group (equation 75), which is the reverse of the dealdolization reaction (equation 74, steps 4 and 3), gives a hydroxyketone product and is the mechanism of the reaction catalyzed by transketolase. Attack of this intermediate on an oxidizing agent (equation 76) results in the loss of the electron pair and the formation of an acyl-thiamine, which can in turn donate its acyl group to water to give the free acid or to an acyl acceptor, such as phosphate or a thiol, to preserve the energy-rich nature of the acyl-thiamine bond and give an acyl phosphate or thiol ester as product. These two processes are combined in a single overall reaction in the reaction of hydroxyethylthiamine pyrophosphate with oxidized lipoic acid to give the energy-rich thiol ester of reduced lipoic acid; it is not known whether this reaction occurs in one step, as shown in equation 77, or in two separate steps. Finally, if there is a hydroxyl group adjacent to the anionic carbon atom, this hydroxyl group may be expelled to give an enol, which rearranges to an acyl-thiamine and eventually gives acetyl phosphate as a product (equation 78). The overall reaction involves an internal oxidation-reduction of a hydroxyketone to an acetate, which is catalyzed by the enzyme phosphoketolase.

[135] J. J. Mieyal, R. G. Votaw, H. Z. Sable, and L. O. Krampitz, *Fed. Proc.* **26**, 344 (1967).

$$(75)$$

$$(76)$$

$$(77)$$

$$(78)$$

The cyanide catalyzed formation of ethyl acetate from the aldehyde **53** in ethanol[136] may be described by a mechanism similar to that proposed for the phosphoketolase reaction. The addition of

[136] V. Franzen and L. Fikentscher, *Ann. Chem.* **623**, 68 (1959).

cyanide gives the cyanohydrin which, like the corresponding thiazolium adduct, can give the stabilized anion 54 (equation 79). This

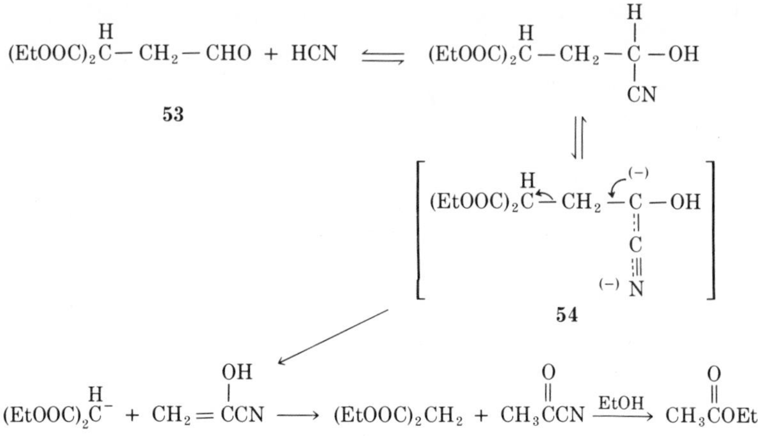

$$(EtOOC)_2\overset{H}{C}-CH_2-CHO + HCN \rightleftharpoons (EtOOC)_2\overset{H}{C}-CH_2-\underset{CN}{\overset{H}{\underset{|}{\overset{|}{C}}}}-OH$$

53

$$\left[(EtOOC)_2\overset{H}{C} \sim CH_2 - \underset{\underset{(-)\ N}{\overset{\text{:}|}{\overset{\text{C}}{\text{:}|}}}}{\overset{(-)}{C}}-OH \right]$$

54

$$(EtOOC)_2\overset{H}{C^-} + CH_2 = \overset{OH}{\underset{|}{C}}CN \longrightarrow (EtOOC)_2CH_2 + CH_3\overset{O}{\overset{\|}{C}}CN \xrightarrow{EtOH} CH_3\overset{O}{\overset{\|}{C}}OEt$$

$$(79)$$

anion eliminates the diethyl malonate anion to give the enol of an
acyl cyanide, which, after ketonization, reacts with the solvent to
give ethyl acetate.

The acyl-thiazolium 55 is another intermediate which was thought
to be extraordinarily unstable; however, it turns out to be stable
even in water if the hydroxide ion concentration is low.[137,138] It

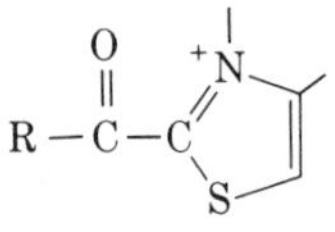

$$R-\overset{O}{\overset{\|}{C}}-\overset{+\overset{|}{N}}{C}\underset{S}{\diagdown}$$

55

provides a particularly direct illustration of the factors which determine whether an acyl transfer reaction may or may not take place.
Water, thiols, and phosphate all add to the carbonyl group of 2-
acetyl-3,4-dimethylthiazolium ion in aqueous solution to give easily
detectable amounts of the tetrahedral addition compounds that are
thought to be intermediates in acyl transfer reactions to these
nucleophilic reagents (equations 80 and 81). However, only the
water adduct undergoes decomposition to product in aqueous solution.

[137] G. E. Lienhard, *J. Am. Chem. Soc.* 88, 5642 (1966).

[138] T. C. Bruice and N. G. Kundu, *J. Am. Chem. Soc.* 88, 4097 (1966).

$$R-\overset{\overset{\displaystyle O}{\|}}{C}-\overset{\overset{\displaystyle +N}{|}}{C}\diagup_{S}\diagdown \quad \rightleftharpoons \quad R-\overset{\overset{\displaystyle \bar{O}}{|}}{\underset{\underset{\displaystyle H}{O}}{C}}-\overset{\overset{\displaystyle +N}{|}}{C}\diagup_{S}\diagdown \quad \longrightarrow \quad R-\overset{\overset{\displaystyle O}{\|}}{C}-OH \ + \ ^-\overset{\overset{\displaystyle +N}{|}}{C}\diagup_{S}\diagdown$$

$$B\frown H-\underset{H}{\overset{\displaystyle O}{|}}$$

(80)

$$R-\overset{\overset{\displaystyle O}{\|}}{C}-\overset{\overset{\displaystyle +N}{|}}{C}\diagup_{S}\diagdown \quad \rightleftharpoons \quad R-\overset{\overset{\displaystyle \bar{O}}{|}}{\underset{\underset{\displaystyle R'}{S}}{C}}-\overset{\overset{\displaystyle +N}{|}}{C}\diagup_{S}\diagdown \quad \nrightarrow \quad R-\overset{\overset{\displaystyle O}{\|}}{C}-S-R' + \ ^-\overset{\overset{\displaystyle +N}{|}}{C}\diagup_{S}\diagdown$$

$$R'-S^-$$

(81)

The addition of the less basic thiol and phosphate anions is always followed by expulsion of these relatively good leaving groups to give back starting materials, rather than expulsion of the thiazole ylid to give products. Only in the case of hydroxide ion addition can sufficient driving force be obtained by electron donation from the two oxygen atoms to expel the thiazole ylid and give products.[137] In solvents of low water content, in which hydrolysis does not provide such serious competition, acyl transfer to thiols is observed,[139] and the same type of reaction must occur in those enzymatic reactions which give thiol esters and acyl phosphates, rather than hydrolysis products, after oxidation of substituted hydroxymethylthiamines to the corresponding acyl-thiamines.

5. PYRIDOXAL[133]

The first step of reactions of amino acids catalyzed by pyridoxal and related compounds in both chemical and enzymatic systems is the combination of the amino acid with the carbonyl group of the catalyst to form a Schiff base, which may be recognized by its characteristic yellow color that corresponds to the second of two absorption maxima near 330 and 410 mμ. It has been generally assumed that the structure of this intermediate is that shown in **56**, and this structure is still frequently given. The products formed from the reaction of amines with 3-hydroxypyridine-4-aldehyde have a yellow color and an absorption spectrum similar to that of the pyridoxal–amino acid compounds, but if the phenolic hydrogen atom

[139] K. Daigo and L. J. Reed, *J. Am. Chem. Soc.* **84**, 659 (1962).

is replaced by a methyl group, the yellow color and 410-mμ absorption band disappear and the intensity of the absorption band near 330 mμ is increased.[140] This fact, together with the additional findings that the infrared absorption spectrum of these compounds resembles that of an amide rather than that of a simple imine[141] and that the proton of 58 in polar solvents is largely on the nitrogen rather than the oxygen atom (as shown by a splitting of the nuclear

magnetic resonance band of the hydrogen atom by spin coupling with the ^{15}N nitrogen atom[142]), provide strong evidence that in aqueous solutions these compounds exist partly in the form 57, which is responsible for the yellow color, and partly in form 56, which is responsible for the 330-mμ peak. Structure 57 may be regarded as a resonance hybrid between a dipolar cationic imine form (57, structure A), which is more stable in polar solvents, and an amide-quinoid form (57, structure B). It differs from 56 only in the transfer of the hydrogen-bonded proton from oxygen to nitrogen. Although it might appear that the resonance of the aromatic ring is lost in 57, structure B, this resonance is maintained through the contribution of form 57, structure A, and the stability of structure 57 is understandable when it is realized that it is really only a vinylogous amide, in which the carbonyl and nitrogen functions are separated by a

[140] D. Heinert and A. E. Martell, *J. Am. Chem. Soc.* 85, 183 (1963).

[141] D. Heinert and A. E. Martell, *J. Am. Chem. Soc.* 84, 3257 (1962).

[142] G. O. Dudek and E. P. Dudek, *Chem. Commun.* 1965, 464.

double bond and the typical amide resonance is maintained (59). Monoimines of β-diketones quite generally exist in this enamine

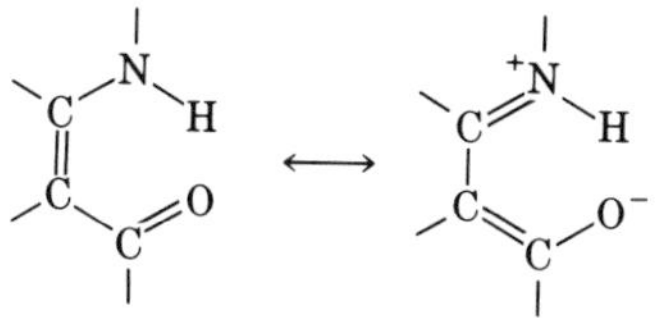

59

form, which corresponds to the enol form of the parent ketone and in which significant stabilization by resonance is possible. The fact that pyridoxal Schiff bases exhibit distinct absorption bands corresponding to structures **56** and **57** means that these compounds exist as a mixture of these two tautomers, rather than as the resonance hybrid **60**, in which the hydrogen atom is in a single potential well between the nitrogen and oxygen atoms and is itself involved in a semi-aromatic resonating system.[143] The fraction of the product in

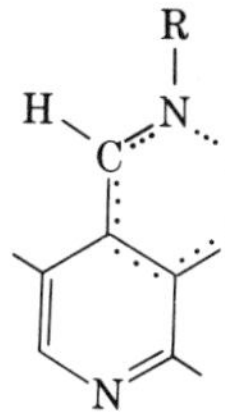

60

form **57** decreases if electron-withdrawing substituents are added to the amine to decrease its basicity and in the oxime only the short-wavelength absorption corresponding to form **56** is observed.

Although it is important to keep in mind that pyridoxal-amine derivatives exist in both of these structural forms, there is no large difference in the mechanistic conclusions to be drawn from the two different structures. The transmission of electron density into the ring can be written according to **61** for the classical structure and can involve electron shifts over the same pathway according to **62**, which utilizes the partial double-bond character of the quinoid-amine

[143] A. E. Martell, in E. E. Snell, P. M. Fasella, A. Braunstein, and A. Rossi Fanelli (eds.), "Chemical and Biological Aspects of Pyridoxal Catalysis," p. 13, Pergamon Press, New York, 1963.

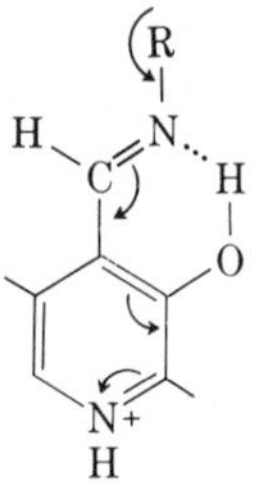

61 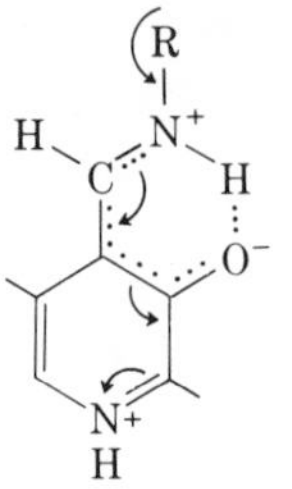   62

structure shown in **57**, structure B. There is a larger positive charge on the Schiff base nitrogen atom in **62** than in **61** and this provides an important additional driving force for electron withdrawal. The importance of this positive charge, which is stabilized by the partial negative charge of the phenolic oxygen atom, is suggested by the fact that the activity of pyridoxal analogs in nonenzymatic reactions is much reduced or eliminated if they do not have a hydroxyl group in the 3 position.[144]   The pK of the pyridine nitrogen atom of pyridoxal Schiff bases is about 5.9, so that an appreciable fraction will exist in form **62**, with a proton on this nitrogen atom, at neutrality.[145]   The dipolar form is even more stable in the case of pyridoxal itself, which has pK values of 4.2 and 8.7 for the loss of a proton from the phenolic hydroxyl group and pyridinium nitrogen atom, respectively; this reversal of the usual assignments for the pK's of such groups has been established unequivocally by spectrophotometric comparison with hydroxypyridine model compounds with methyl groups on the pyridine nitrogen and phenolic oxygen atoms, and reflects the large acid-strengthening effect of the pyridinium nitrogen on the phenolic ionization and the base-strengthening effect of the phenolate ion on the pyridine nitrogen.[146]

It has been said that God created an organism especially adapted to help the biologist find an answer to every question about the physiology of living systems; if this is so it must be concluded that pyridoxal phosphate was created to provide satisfaction and enlightenment to those enzymologists and chemists who enjoy push-

[144] J. W. Thanassi, A. R. Butler, and T. C. Bruice, *Biochemistry* **4**, 1463 (1965); D. S. Auld and T. C. Bruice, *J. Am. Chem. Soc.* **89**, 2083, 2090, 2098 (1967).

[145] D. E. Metzler, *J. Am. Chem. Soc.* **79**, 485 (1957).

[146] S. A. Harris, T. J. Webb, and K. Folkers, *J. Am. Chem. Soc.* **62**, 3198 (1940); D. E. Metzler and E. E. Snell, *Ibid.* **77**, 2431 (1955).

ing electrons, for no other coenzyme is involved in such a wide variety of reactions, in both enzyme and model systems, which can be reasonably interpreted in terms of the chemical properties of the coenzyme. Most of these reactions, which on the surface appear to be quite different, are made possible by a common structural feature. That is, electron withdrawal toward the cationic nitrogen atom of the imine and into the electron sink of the pyridoxal ring from the α carbon atom of the attached amino acid activates all three of the substituents on this carbon atom for reactions which require electron withdrawal from this atom (63, R$'$ = H, or, in some model compounds, R$'$ = alkyl). There are a few reactions which

R$-$C$-$COO$^-$ (structure 63)

63

require a similar activation of the β carbon atom by the imine nitrogen atom, but if these two principles are understood, nearly all of the reactions in which pyridoxal phosphate has been shown to participate directly may be explained. These explanations are, in the first instance, paper chemistry, but many of the reactions have been duplicated in model systems and the few detailed mechanistic studies which have been carried out support the mechanistic hypotheses which were first worked out in detail by Snell and by Braunstein and their coworkers.[147]

The three types of reactions which can result from electron withdrawal from the three substituents on the α carbon atom of the amino acid will be considered first.

a) **Proton removal from the α carbon atom.** The most important reaction is the removal of the proton from the α carbon atom to give

[147] E. E. Snell, *Vitamins and Hormones* **16**, 77 (1958); A. E. Braunstein in P. D. Boyer, H. Lardy, and K. Myrbäck (eds.), "The Enzymes," 2d ed., vol. II, p. 113, Academic Press, Inc., New York, 1960.

a stabilized intermediate (equation 82, **64**), which may be regarded

(82)

as the carbanion of an amino acid (**64**, structure A) or of a pyridoxamine Schiff base (**64**, structure B). The formation of this key
intermediate makes possible a series of further reactions. The
addition of a proton back to the same position of the amino acid,
but from the opposite side, leads to racemization. Addition of a
proton to the carbonyl carbon atom of the pyridoxal gives the Schiff
base of pyridoxamine and an α-keto acid, which then undergoes

hydrolysis (equation 82). The reverse of this process with a different α-keto acid regenerates pyridoxal and gives a new amino acid, so that the overall result of the operation of equation 82 in two directions is the transamination of α-amino and α-keto acids (equation 83).

$$
\begin{array}{c}
\text{H} \\
| \\
R_1 - C - COO^- \\
| \\
{}^+NH_3
\end{array}
+
\begin{array}{c}
R_2 - C - COO^- \\
|| \\
O
\end{array}
\rightleftharpoons
\begin{array}{c}
R_1 - C - COO^- \\
|| \\
O
\end{array}
+
\begin{array}{c}
\text{H} \\
| \\
R_2 - C - COO^- \\
| \\
{}^+NH_3
\end{array}
\qquad (83)
$$

If there is a good leaving group on the β carbon atom, the electron pair of the anionoid intermediate provides the driving force for the elimination of this group to give an unsaturated product **65**, which can then either undergo hydrolysis and rearrangement to give pyruvate or the addition of a new anion, $R'X^-$, by reversal

(84)

of the original cleavage reaction to give a new amino acid, $R'XCH_2$ $CH({}^+NH_3)COO^-$ (equation 84). This type of reaction, with oxygen, thiol, and indole groups as the leaving and attacking reagents, accounts for the pyridoxal catalyzed breakdown and interconversion of serine, threonine, serine and threonine phosphates, and cysteine, cystathionine, and tryptophan.

b) Electron withdrawal from the carboxylate group of the amino acid adduct. This results in decarboxylation with the formation of an analogous anion (**66**), which can add a proton either to the remaining portion of the amino acid to give a simple decarboxylation product (equation 85, pathway A) or to the pyridoxal to give a pyridoxamine derivative, which undergoes hydrolysis to pyridoxamine and an aldehyde or ketone (pathway B).

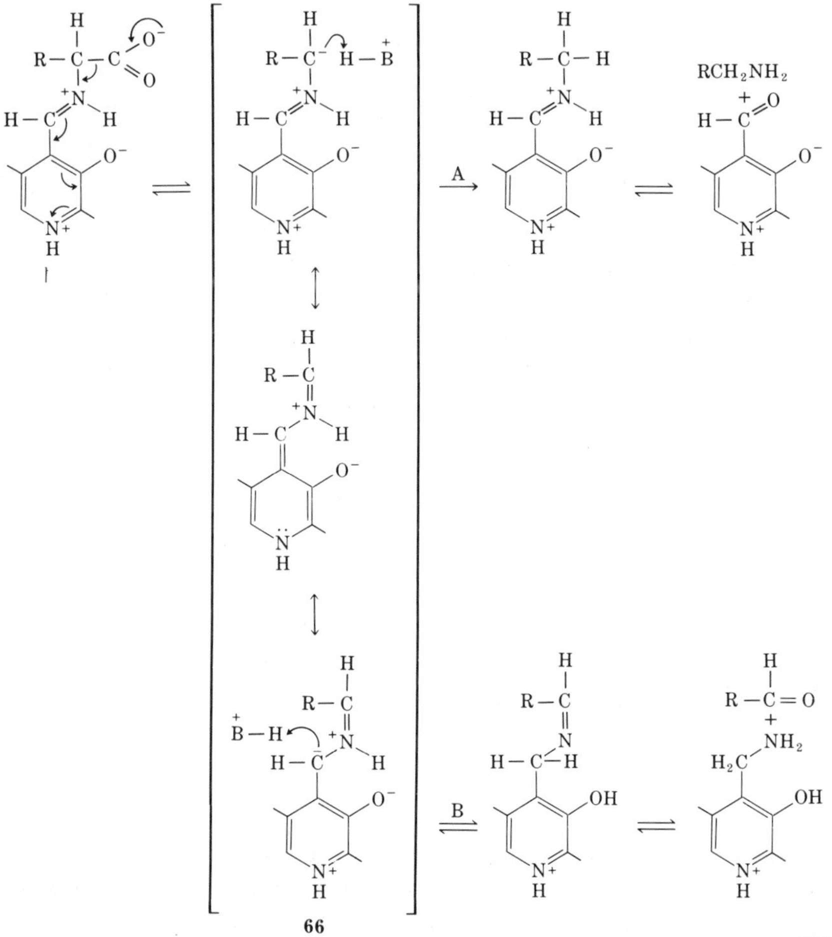

66

(85)

c)   **Electron removal from the side chain.**   Electron removal from the side chain of an appropriate amino acid, such as serine, results in an elimination reaction.   In the case of serine the initial products are formaldehyde and an anionoid intermediate, which undergoes proton addition at the α carbon atom to give glycine as the final product (equation 86).

(86)

Most of these enzymatic reactions requiring activation at the α carbon atom occur also in nonenzymatic reactions of pyridoxal derivatives with appropriate amino acids or keto acids in the presence of metal ions at elevated temperatures.[133,147] The metal ion may partially replace the function of the enzyme in bringing the reactants together in the proper position and providing an additional electrophilic center to assist electron withdrawal; however, it is not essential for the enzymatic reaction, since several purified pyridoxal phosphate requiring enzymes have been shown to be free of metals. Detailed kinetic studies of the mechanisms of these reactions in the absence of metal ions are only now beginning to appear. It has been shown that the transamination reaction is subject to general acid-base catalysis and follows a rate law such that either proton removal from the α carbon atom of the amino acid or proton addition to the carbonyl carbon atom of the pyridoxal is the rate-determining step, as shown in equation 82.[148,144] The former step must be rate-determining in the reaction with alanine, which shows an isotope effect with deuterated alanine.[144] The transamination of α-aminophenylacetic acid in the presence of pyridoxal and imidazole shows complex kinetics, with evidence for involvement of two molecules of imidazole as catalysts at low imidazole concentrations and for saturation with respect to imidazole, suggesting complex

[148] B. E. C. Banks, A. A. Diamantis, and C. A. Vernon, *J. Chem. Soc.* **1961**, 4235.

formation, at high concentrations.[149]   It is possible that this catalysis represents a concerted proton removal and addition, but reactions of this kind do not appear to be subject to concerted catalysis in simpler systems (cf. Chap. 3, Sec. D, Part 2), and it may be desirable to defer a definitive interpretation of the kinetics of this complex system.

Unequivocal identification of the key anionoid intermediate (64) has not yet been achieved, but there is evidence for its formation and accumulation in model systems in which amino acids containing strongly electron-withdrawing substituents react with pyridoxal derivatives. Aminomalonate and α-methylaminomalonate undergo decarboxylation in the presence of pyridoxal derivatives at physiological temperatures, presumably according to the mechanism of equation 85.[150,151]   Less expected is the finding that diethyl aminomalonate undergoes rapid hydrolysis and decarboxylation in the presence of 10^{-5} M pyridoxal phosphate at pH 6.[150]   The electron-withdrawing influence of the coenzyme evidently facilitates this reaction by assisting carbon-carbon bond cleavage either before (equation 87, pathway A) or after (equation 87, pathway B) hydrolysis of the ester, or by making possible the elimination of ethanol to give a ketene derivative, followed by addition of water and decarboxylation (equation 87, pathway C). Still another possible

$$(87)$$

[149] T. C. Bruice and R. M. Topping, *J. Am. Chem. Soc.* **85**, 1480, 1488 (1963).

[150] J. W. Thanassi and J. S. Fruton, *Biochemistry* **1**, 975 (1962).

[151] M. Matthew and A. Neuberger, *Biochem. J.* **87**, 601 (1963).

mechanism involves intramolecular attack of the aminoalcohol formed from pyridoxal and the aminoester on the acyl group, as described for the benzaldehyde catalyzed hydrolysis of leucine p-nitrophenyl ester in Chap. 1, Sec. B.

The most significant observation in this reaction, however, is that an intermediate with maximal absorption at 460 mμ is rapidly formed on mixing pyridoxal phosphate and diethyl aminomalonate; absorption maxima at this wavelength are not found in simple pyridoxal derivatives, and it is probable that this compound is, in fact, the key anionoid intermediate. This conclusion is strengthened by the finding that similar compounds with absorption maxima at 480 mμ in ethanol are formed from N-methylpyridoxal and diethyl aminomalonate, and are not discharged in base, but undergo reaction with aldehydes with the loss of the 480-mμ absorption band and, presumably, the formation of a hydroxymethyl addition compound (equation 88).[152] The adduct of aminomalonate and pyridoxal phos-

(88)

phate is known to undergo decarboxylation and addition to aldehydes to give α-amino-β-hydroxyacids, presumably through an analogous intermediate.[151] The conversion of alanine to pyruvate in the presence of N-methylpyridine-4-aldehyde cation proceeds through an intermediate with an absorption maximum at 500 mμ, which presumably has a similar structure.[153] Intermediates with absorption maxima near 500 mμ which have been detected in a number of enzyme reactions probably have this same anionoid structure.[154]

A few enzymatic reactions which require pyridoxal phosphate, such as β decarboxylation and γ elimination, call for activation at

[152] L. Schirch and R. A. Slotter, *Biochemistry* 5, 3175 (1966).

[153] J. R. Maley and T. C. Bruice, *J. Am. Chem. Soc.* 90, 2843 (1968).

[154] L. Schirch and W. T. Jenkins, *J. Biol. Chem.* 239, 3801 (1964); W. T. Jenkins and L. D'Ari, *Ibid.* 241, 2845 (1966); Y. Morino and E. E. Snell, *Ibid.* 242, 2800 (1967).

carbon atoms which are less directly linked to the pyridoxal ring than is the α carbon atom of an amino acid. The activating group in these reactions is presumably the protonated nitrogen atom of the Schiff base. After the removal of the proton on the α carbon atom, this group activates the β carbon atom for proton removal to give a β-carbanion-enamine intermediate (equation 89) according to a mechanism quite analogous to that for amine catalyzed aldol condensation. This intermediate provides the driving force for the elimination of a good leaving group from the γ carbon atom, as in cystathionine cleavage and phosphate elimination from phosphohomoserine in the course of threonine synthesis (equation 89). The

$$(89)$$

unsaturated elimination product can add a nucleophile to either position of the double bond or undergo hydrolysis and rearrangement in several steps. (It is instructive for the student to write out some of the several unproved but plausible mechanisms that can be written for these steps and for the final steps of the following reaction.) β Decarboxylation presumably occurs by a similar mechanism, in which the cationic nitrogen atom of the Schiff base activates the substrate for decarboxylation instead of for the loss of a proton (equation 90). These reactions have not yet been observed in model

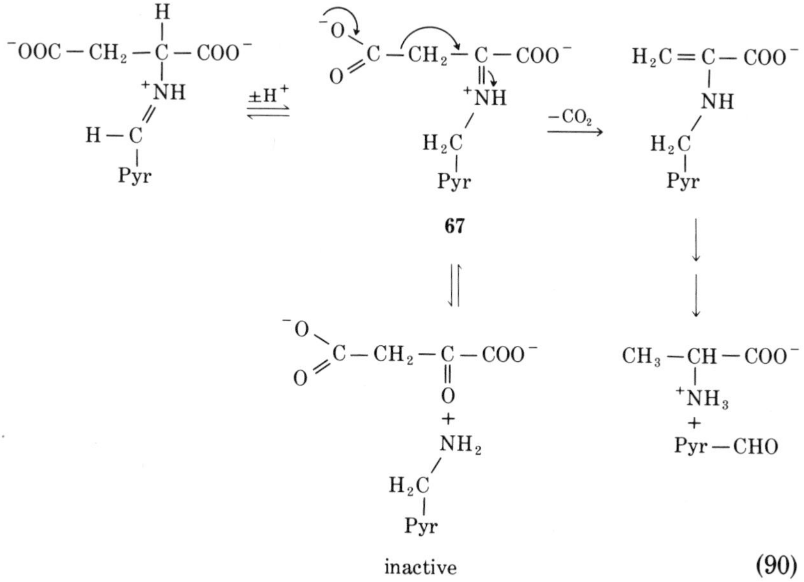

67

inactive   (90)

systems, presumably because other, simpler reactions occur more rapidly in the absence of the enzyme. It is of interest that the gradual loss of activity of aspartate β-decarboxylase in the absence of carbonyl compounds is caused by hydrolysis of the intermediate Schiff base **67** to pyridoxamine phosphate and an α-keto acid; in the absence of excess pyridoxal phosphate or a carbonyl compound to bring about its reconversion to the active pyridoxal form, the pyridoxamine form of the enzyme-coenzyme complex cannot catalyze further reaction of an amino acid.[155]

A different example of the interrelationships of these catalyzed mechanisms is found in the catalysis by serine transhydroxymethylase of a slow transamination of the D isomer of alanine to give

[155] A. Novogrodsky, J. S. Nishimura, and A. Meister, *J. Biol. Chem.* **238**, PC1903 (1963); **239**, 879 (1964).

pyruvate and pyridoxamine phosphate.[156]   Another example is found in the combined decarboxylation and transamination of α-dialkyl amino acids by a bacterial enzyme (equation 91).[157]   In this reaction

$$\underset{\underset{\textstyle +NH_3}{\textstyle |}}{\overset{\textstyle CH_3}{\overset{\textstyle |}{RCH_2-C-COO^-}}} + CH_3\overset{\textstyle O}{\overset{\textstyle \|}{C}}COO^- \longrightarrow \overset{\textstyle CH_3}{\overset{\textstyle |}{RCH_2-C}}=O + CO_2 + \underset{\underset{\textstyle +NH_3}{\textstyle |}}{\overset{\textstyle H}{\overset{\textstyle |}{CH_3C-COO^-}}} \quad (91)$$

the anionoid intermediate must be formed directly by the decarboxylation process, as in the analogous nonenzymatic half-reaction.[158] It is probable that the specificity of these enzymes with respect to which type of reaction is catalyzed depends in large part on the stereospecificity of substrate binding to the enzyme, which determines which bond cleavage can occur to give the anionoid intermediate.[159]

6. OTHER EXAMPLES

Several other reactions in which covalent combination with an electrophilic activator other than a proton brings about an increase in the leaving ability of a group are worth noting.   Trimethylamine-N-oxide in aqueous solution undergoes decomposition in the presence of sulfur dioxide, which can combine with the oxygen atom to give an adduct in which the oxygen atom of the N-oxide has been converted into a good leaving group.   This adduct can undergo elimination with the loss of a proton from a methyl group to give a cationic imine, which rapidly undergoes hydrolysis to formaldehyde and dimethylamine (equation 92).[160]   Since sulfite can lose water to

$$H_2C=\overset{+}{N}\overset{\textstyle CH_3}{\underset{\textstyle CH_3}{\big\langle}} + SO_3^{--} \xrightarrow{\ H_2O\ } HCHO + HN(CH_3)_2 + HSO_3^- \qquad (92)$$

[156] L. Schirch and W. T. Jenkins, *J. Biol. Chem.* **239**, 3797 (1964).

[157] H. G. Aaslestad and A. D. Larson, *J. Bacteriol.* **88**, 1296 (1964); G. B. Bailey and W. B. Dempsey, *Biochemistry* **6**, 1526 (1967).

[158] G. D. Kalyankar and E. E. Snell, *Biochemistry* **1**, 594 (1962).

[159] H. C. Dunathan, *Proc. Natl. Acad. Sci. U.S.* **55**, 712 (1966).

[160] H. Z. Lecher and W. B. Hardy, *J. Am. Chem. Soc.* **70**, 3789 (1948).

regenerate sulfur dioxide, the rate acceleration caused by this molecule is, at least in principle, a true catalysis.

The rate law for the bromination of anisole contains a term which is second order with respect to bromine.[161] This is evidence for catalysis of the reaction by a second mole of bromine, which can act by assisting the displacement of bromide ion in the initial attack step (equation 93, step 1) or, possibly, in an intermediate addition

$$(93)$$

compound (equation 93, step 2); in either case the assistance is made possible by the stability of the Br_3^- ion, which can subsequently decompose to regenerate Br_2.

The rate of hydrolysis of phosphoramidate is markedly increased in the presence of formaldehyde, which combines with the amino group of the substrate to give mono- and dihydroxymethyl adducts.[162] The rate law for the catalyzed hydrolysis contains terms first and second order with respect to formaldehyde and indicates that the transition state for the catalyzed reaction has a charge of -1 under most experimental conditions, so that the mechanism may be formulated as shown in equation 94. An additional rate accelera-

$$(94)$$

[161] P. B. D. De la Mare and J. H. Ridd, "Aromatic Substitution," p. 116, Academic Press, Inc., New York, 1959.

[162] W. P. Jencks and M. Gilchrist, *J. Am. Chem. Soc.* 86, 1410 (1964).

tion is caused by amines or ammonia, which can combine with formaldehyde and phosphoramidate to give an adduct with two positive charges in the leaving group (equation 95). The catalyzed

$$\text{HOCH}_2\overset{+}{\text{NH}}_2\text{R} \;\rightleftharpoons\; \text{H}_2\text{C}=\overset{+}{\text{N}}\text{HR} \xrightarrow{^{--}\text{O}_3\text{P}\overset{+}{\text{NH}}_3} \;^{--}\text{O}_3\text{P}\overset{\overset{\displaystyle \text{H}_2}{|}}{\text{N}}\text{CH}_2\overset{+}{\text{NH}}_2\text{R}$$

$$^{--}\text{O}_3\text{POH} + \text{H}_2\text{N}\text{CH}_2\overset{+}{\text{NH}}_2\text{R} \qquad\qquad\qquad (95)$$

pathways for this reaction are significant because of the very large sensitivity of monosubstituted phosphates to the nature of the leaving group. Conversion of the amino group of phosphoramidate to a better leaving group by reaction with formaldehyde or a formaldehyde-amine adduct causes a rate acceleration even if the protonated adduct is present only in low concentration. The reaction is a true catalysis, because the formaldehyde-containing products can break down to regenerate formaldehyde and, in addition, are themselves catalytically active.

A similar mechanism of catalysis apparently occurs in the enzyme catalyzed deamination of histidine[163] and reduction of D-proline.[164] In both of these reactions there is evidence for combination of the amino group of the substrate with a carbonyl group on the enzyme to make the amine a better leaving group either by protonation or by dehydration to the cationic Schiff base. In the histidase reaction the amine leaves in an elimination step to give an enzyme-amine intermediate, which can undergo exchange· with the unsaturated product, urocanic acid, to give labeled histidine more rapidly than it undergoes hydrolysis (equation 96).[165] In the reduc-

$$(96)$$

[163] T. A. Smith, F. H. Cordelle, and R. H. Abeles, *Arch. Biochem. Biophys.* **120**, 724 (1967).

[164] D. S. Hodgins and R. H. Abeles, *J. Biol. Chem.* **242**, 5158 (1967).

[165] A. Peterkofsky, *J. Biol. Chem.* **237**, 787 (1962).

tion of D-proline, combination with the carbonyl group makes the amine group more susceptible to reduction or displacement, as shown for a mechanism involving displacement of the amine by hydride ion in equation 97. The carbonyl group of proline reductase

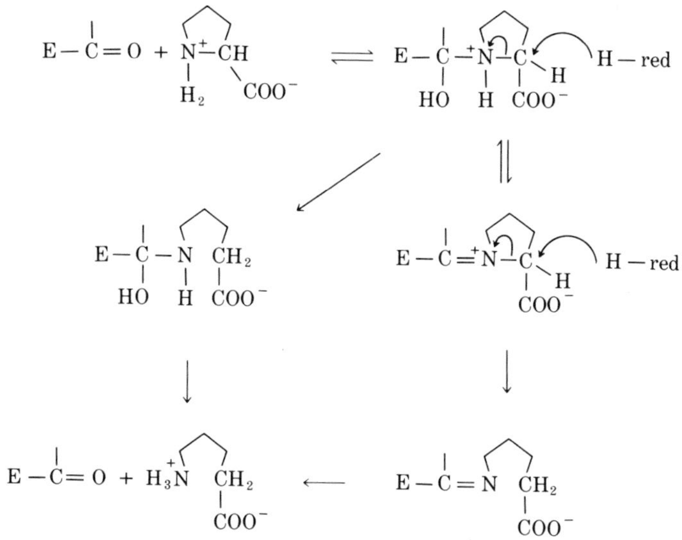

(97)

is the ketone group of a pyruvate molecule which is covalently bound to the enzyme. The enzyme is inactivated by carbonyl reagents and by sodium borohydride.[164]

Acylation or phosphorylation provides an effective mechanism by which the leaving ability of a hydroxyl group or oxygen anion may be increased sufficiently to make its displacement possible. Although this is usually an energy-requiring activation rather than a true catalysis, it can occur as a catalytic process, at least in principle, under conditions in which the hydroxyl compound is in reversible equilibrium with the acylating or phosphorylating agent. For example, trifluoroperoxyacetic acid, which is formed reversibly from trifluoroacetic acid and hydrogen peroxide, is an effective oxidizing agent for the hydroxylation of double bonds (equation 98)

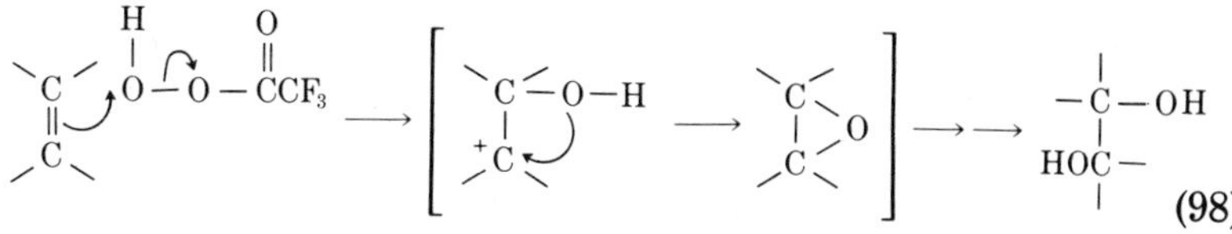

(98)

and for the oxidation of aniline to nitrobenzene under conditions in which hydrogen peroxide itself is unreactive.[166] Among the many enzymatic examples of this type of activation are the phosphorylation of the hydroxyl group of mevalonic acid pyrophosphate by ATP to provide a better leaving group in a subsequent decarboxylation step (equation 99)[167] and the acylation of the hydroxyl group of

$$\begin{array}{c}^-O\\ \diagdown\\ O^{\diagup}\end{array}\!C-\overset{|}{\underset{|}{C}}-\overset{|}{\underset{|}{C}}-OH \; + \; ATP \xrightarrow{-ADP} \begin{array}{c}^-O\\ \diagdown\\ O^{\diagup}\end{array}\!C-\overset{|}{\underset{|}{C}}-\overset{|}{\underset{|}{C}}-OPO_3^-H$$

$$\downarrow$$

$$\begin{array}{c}O\\ \parallel\\ C\\ \parallel\\ O\end{array} \; + \; \diagup\!\!\!\!\diagdown C=C \diagdown\!\!\!\!\diagup \; + \; HOPO_3^{--}$$

(99)

homoserine prior to its elimination in the pyridoxal phosphate catalyzed condensation of homoserine with cysteine to give cystathionine.[168] Simple displacements on saturated carbon are particularly difficult to catalyze, and it is of interest that in many enzymatic reactions of this kind, such as the condensation of isoprenoid units to precursors of cholesterol and other complex hydrocarbons, the synthesis of S-adenosylmethionine from methionine and ATP, and the synthesis of vitamin B_{12} coenzyme from a cobamide and ATP, the leaving hydroxyl group is incorporated into a pyrophosphate or triphosphate group. Polyphosphates are probably innately better leaving groups than inorganic phosphate and, in addition, are structurally well adapted for the attachment of metal ions and the induction of strain, which may provide further facilitation of the displacement reaction.

F. OXIDATIVE CATALYSIS

Oxidation may be defined, in a general sense, as a process which results in the removal of electrons from a molecule or atom. A reaction center which undergoes oxidation will, therefore, become more electrophilic, and reactions which require an electron deficiency at

---

[166] W. D. Emmons, *J. Am. Chem. Soc.* **76**, 3468, 3470 (1954); W. D. Emmons, A. S. Pagano, and J. P. Freeman, *Ibid.*, p. 3472.

[167] M. Lindberg, C. Yuan, A. DeWaard, and K. Bloch, *Biochemistry* **1**, 182 (1962).

[168] M. M. Kaplan and M. Flavin, *J. Biol. Chem.* **241**, 5781 (1966); J. Giovanelli and S. H. Mudd, *Biochem. Biophys. Res. Commun.* **25**, 366 (1966).

the reaction center should be facilitated by oxidation just as they are by Br∮nsted and Lewis acid catalysts (equations 100 and 101).

$$X - S:\frown H^+ \; \rightleftharpoons \; X - \overset{+}{S} - H \tag{100}$$

$$X - S:\frown \text{oxidant} \; \rightleftharpoons \; X - \overset{+}{S} + \text{reductant} \tag{101}$$

There are many examples of activation of this kind which are brought about by oxidation, but there are relatively few in which the activation is catalytic, although a reversible oxidation-reduction would seem to be a particularly attractive mechanism for temporarily causing a large change in electron density at a reaction center without requiring a large expenditure of energy or a localized increase in effective acidity.

The hypochlorite-induced hydrolysis of phosphoramidate is an example of catalysis by a reversible oxidative process in a nonenzymatic reaction.[162] In the presence of dilute hypochlorite at neutral or slightly acid pH the half-time for the hydrolysis of phosphoramidate is reduced from hours to a few seconds. The reaction proceeds through chlorination of the substrate to give the monochloro compound, which is stable at high pH, followed by addition of a second chlorine atom (equation 102). Dichloramine is a better leav-

$$^{--}O_3 PNH_2 + HOCl \longrightarrow {}^{--}O_3 PNHCl \xrightarrow{HOCl} O - \overset{\overset{\textstyle O}{\|}}{\underset{\textstyle O}{P}} - NCl_2$$

$$\left[\underset{O^{\cdots} P^{\cdots} O}{\overset{\overset{\textstyle O}{\|}}{}} \right]^- + HNCl_2 \xrightarrow{H_2O} H_2PO_4^- \tag{102}$$

ing group than the original ammonia, and the dichlorinated compound immediately breaks down to dichloramine and inorganic phosphate, perhaps through an elimination to give the monomeric metaphosphate monoanion as an intermediate. The process is catalytic because the chloramine product can chlorinate the starting material to induce further hydrolysis, although it does so less rapidly than does hypochlorite.

The utilization of a reversible oxidation-reduction to provide a low-energy pathway for a catalyzed reaction is known in several enzymatic reactions, but generally does not involve the direct activation of a leaving group. The reaction catalyzed by uridine diphosphate galactose-4-epimerase provides a straightforward example.[169] This enzyme contains a firmly bound molecule of nicotinamide adenine dinucleotide (NAD^+), and upon combination with the substrate, an absorption band at 345 mμ, characteristic of the reduced coenzyme, appears. The epimerization evidently involves oxidation at the 4 position followed by reduction from the other side of the carbonyl group (equation 103).

$$NAD^+ H \overset{\frown}{} \overset{|}{\underset{|}{C}} \overset{\frown}{-} OH \frown B \rightleftharpoons NADH \overset{\frown}{} \overset{\searrow}{} C = O \overset{+}{} HB \rightleftharpoons NAD^+ H \cdots \overset{|}{\underset{|}{C}} - OH$$

$$(103)$$

Several rearrangements of sugars are catalyzed by enzymes which require NAD^+ for activity, although the rearrangement does not involve a net oxidation of the substrate. In no case has the mechanism been proved, but it is probable that these related reactions involve a reversible oxidation of a hydroxyl group to a ketone so that a proton can be easily removed from the adjacent carbon atom to make possible an elimination or aldol condensation. One such reaction is the cyclization of glucose-6-phosphate to *myo*inositol-1-phosphate,[170] in which oxidation to a ketone at the 5 position would facilitate condensation of the 6-carbon atom with the carbonyl group at the 1 position to give ring closure in an aldol condensation (equation 104). The rearrangement and ring closure which occur in

$$(104)$$

the synthesis of 5-dehydroquinate can be reasonably formulated

[169] D. B. Wilson and D. S. Hogness, *J. Biol. Chem.* **239**, 2469 (1964).

[170] I. W. Chen and F. C. Charalampous, *J. Biol. Chem.* **241**, 2199 (1966); F. Eisenberg, Jr., *Ibid.* **242**, 1375 (1967); I. W. Chen and F. C. Charalampous, *Biochim. Biophys. Acta* **136**, 568 (1967).

according to equation 105 with oxidation of the 5 position to a ketone,

$$
\begin{array}{ll}
 & ^-OOC-\underset{|}{C}-OH \\
3 & CH_2 \\
4 & HOCH \qquad O \\
5 & HCOH \xrightarrow{NAD^+} \quad C=O \quad \longrightarrow \quad C=O \quad \longrightarrow \quad C=O \\
6 & HC \qquad\qquad H-COH \qquad \bar{C}-OH \qquad C-O-H \\
7 & CH_2OPO_3^{--} \qquad H_2COPO_3^{--} \quad H_2C-OPO_3^{--} \quad H_2C
\end{array}
$$

$$
^-OOC-C=O,\ CH_2,\ HOCH,\ C=O,\ C-O-H,\ H_2C
$$

$$\downarrow$$

(structures with HO, COO⁻, O=, OH, OH) $\xleftarrow{NADH}$ (structure with HO, COO⁻, O=, OH, O) (105)

followed by proton loss at the 6 position and elimination of phosphate at the 7 position to give an enol, which can easily add to the carbonyl group at the 2 position to give ring closure.[171] The rearrangement of a number of nucleoside diphosphate hexoses to 4-keto-6-deoxy derivatives[172,173] can be explained in a similar manner (equation 106).

$$
\begin{array}{ll}
 & R \\
4 & HCOH \qquad C=O \qquad C=O \qquad C=O \qquad C-O^- \\
5 & HCOH \xrightarrow{NAD^+} HCOH \longrightarrow \bar{C}OH \longrightarrow COH \xrightarrow{NADH} C-OH \\
6 & H_2COH \qquad H_2COH \qquad H_2C-OH \qquad H_2C \qquad CH_3
\end{array}
$$

$$
\begin{array}{l}
R \\
C=O \\
HCOH \\
CH_3
\end{array} \qquad (106)
$$

[171] P. R. Srinivasan, J. Rothschild, and D. B. Sprinson, *J. Biol. Chem.* **238**, 3176 (1963).

[172] A. D. Elbein and E. C. Heath, *J. Biol. Chem.* **240**, 1926 (1965); S. Matsuhashi, M. Matsuhashi, J. G. Brown, and J. L. Strominger, *Ibid.* **241**, 4283 (1966); A. E. Hey and A. D. Elbein, *Ibid.*, p. 5473; H. Nikaido and K. Nikaido, *Ibid.*, p. 1376. J. M. Gilbert, M. Matsuhashi, and J. Strominger, *J. Biol. Chem.* **240**, 1305 (1965).

[173] O. Gabriel and L. C. Lindquist, *J. Biol. Chem.* **243**, 1479 (1968); A. Melo, W. H. Elliott, and L. Glaser, *Ibid.*, p. 1467.

Oxidation to a ketone at the 4 position makes possible an elimination of water from the 5–6 positions, followed by reduction at the 6 position and ketonization of the enolate product. Labeled hydrogen in the 4 position of the substrate appears in the 6 position of the product and there is incorporation of labeled hydrogen from the solvent into the 5 position of the product, as would be expected for this mechanism.[173]

Reversible oxidation-reduction is such an attractive mechanism for providing a low-energy pathway for catalysis that the author would like to believe that a number of other enzymatic reactions will be found to occur through this mechanism.

G. OXIDATIVE ACTIVATION

Oxidation of an aldehyde requires the removal of hydrogen and two electrons from a carbon atom which already has a partial positive charge because of the dipole of the carbonyl group (equation 107).

$$\text{68} \tag{107}$$

Such an oxidation can be facilitated by the addition of a nucleophilic reagent to the carbonyl group, so that the electrons do not have to leave from a center which is already electrophilic. Addition of a nucleophile increases the driving force for the transfer of electrons to the oxidizing agent and, in addition, results in the formation of the acylated nucleophile as the immediate product. This is important to the economy of a living system because it results in the preservation of some of the free energy of the oxidative process in the form of an energy-rich bond in the product, which would be lost if the aldehyde were oxidized to the "low-energy" carboxylate ion. Furthermore, preservation of the acyl compound in an activated form facilitates attack of a reducing agent on the acyl group in the reverse reaction of equation 107; the unactivated carboxylate ion is not easily reduced.

In the presence of a suitable nucleophilic reagent, the involvement of the addition compound 68 rather than the free aldehyde in a number of chemical oxidations is suggested by the formation of the acylated nucleophile rather than the carboxylic acid as product. For example, the oxidation of aldehydes by bromine[174] and chromic acid[175] in the presence of alcohol and by another molecule of aldehyde in the Cannizzaro[176] and Tishchenko[177] reactions gives ester as product. The rate law for the Cannizzaro reaction in water contains terms both first and second order with respect to base (equation 108).[178] The second-order term reflects the increased driving force

$$R'CH + {}^-OR \rightleftharpoons R'-\overset{O}{\underset{OR}{\underset{|}{C}}}{-}H \quad \overset{O}{\underset{H}{\overset{||}{C}}}{\diagdown}_{R'} \xrightarrow{k_1} R'-\overset{O}{\overset{||}{C}}{-}OR + R'CH_2OH$$

$$\Big\Vert (R = H)$$

$$R'-\overset{O}{\underset{{}^-O}{\underset{|}{C}}}{-}H \quad \overset{O}{\underset{H}{\overset{||}{C}}}{\diagdown}_{R'} \xrightarrow{k_2} R'-COO^- + R'CH_2OH$$

$$(108)$$

for hydride transfer which is obtained by forming the dianion of the aldehyde hydrate (equation 108, k_2). In the case of the hemiacetal, which is formed by the addition of alcohol, only a single ionization is possible, and hydride transfer must occur from the monoanion to give the ester directly as product (equation 108, k_1). The Tishchenko reaction, the aluminum alkoxide catalyzed dismutation of an aldehyde into an alcohol and an ester, presumably proceeds by an intramolecular version of the same mechanism (equation 109).[179]

$$2RCHO + (R'O)_3Al \rightleftharpoons R-\overset{R'O \diagdown \ \diagup OR'}{\underset{R'O}{\underset{|}{\overset{Al}{\underset{O}{\overset{O}{\underset{|}{C}}}}}}}{-}H \quad \overset{O}{\underset{H}{\overset{||}{C}}}{\diagdown}_R \rightleftharpoons \overset{O}{\overset{||}{RCOR'}} + (R'O)_2AlOCH_2R$$

$$(109)$$

[174] I. R. L. Barker, W. G. Overend, and C. W. Rees, *J. Chem. Soc.* **1964**, 3254, 3263.

[175] J. C. Craig and E. C. Horning, *J. Org. Chem.* **25**, 2098 (1960).

[176] A. Lachman, *J. Am. Chem. Soc.* **45**, 2356 (1923).

[177] W. C. Child and H. Adkins, *J. Am. Chem. Soc.* **45**, 3013 (1923); **47**, 798 (1925).

[178] A. Eitel and G. Lock, *Monatsh. Chem.* **72**, 392 (1939).

[179] Y. Ogata, A. Kawasaki, and I. Kishi, *Tetrahedron* **23**, 825 (1967).

Examples of enzymatic oxidation of aldehydes to esters are found in the oxidation of sugar hemiacetals, which commonly give the lactone as the immediate product, and in the oxidation of formaldehyde and methanol to methyl formate catalyzed by liver alcohol dehydrogenase (equation 110).[180] The dehydrogenase evidently rec-

$$
H-\underset{\underset{OH}{|}}{\overset{\overset{H}{|}}{C}}-OH + HOCH_3 \;\rightleftharpoons\; H-\underset{\underset{OH}{|}}{\overset{\overset{H}{|}}{C}}-OCH_3 + H_2O \;\overset{NAD^+}{\rightleftharpoons}\; \overset{\overset{O}{\parallel}}{H}COCH_3 \tag{110}
$$

ognizes the hemiacetal as an alcohol and oxidizes it to the ester. The oxidation of hemithioacetals to "energy-rich" thiol esters, which is of greater biological significance, is facilitated by the strong tendency of the thiol group to add to carbonyl compounds. The reaction catalyzed by glyceraldehyde-3-phosphate dehydrogenase almost certainly involves the addition of the substrate to a sulfhydryl group in the active site of the enzyme to give a hemithioacetal, followed by hydride ion transfer to NAD^+ to give a thiol ester, and finally an acyl transfer to phosphate to give the acyl phosphate (equation 111).

$$\tag{111}$$

[180] R. H. Abeles and H. A. Lee, Jr., *J. Biol. Chem.* **235**, 1499 (1960).

An analog of the normal substrate, D-threose-2,4-diphosphate, is oxidized to a stable thiol ester-enzyme intermediate, which can be isolated and which reacts with hydroxylamine to give the hydroxamic acid, but which cannot react with phosphate to give an acyl phosphate, presumably because of the presence of two phosphate groups on the molecule.[181]

The enzyme glyoxalase I catalyzes the intramolecular oxidation-reduction of methylglyoxal in the presence of glutathione to give the thiol ester of lactic acid and glutathione (GSH, equation 112). Both

$$
\underset{\substack{\text{O}\\ \text{||}}}{\text{CH}_3\text{CCHO}} + \text{GSH} \;\underset{}{\overset{k_1}{\rightleftharpoons}}\; \underset{\substack{\text{O O}^-\\ \text{|| |}\\ \text{H}}}{\text{CH}_3\text{C}-\text{C}-\text{SG}} \;\overset{\text{glyoxylase I}}{\rightleftharpoons}\; \underset{\substack{\text{HO O}\\ \text{| ||}\\ \text{H}}}{\text{CH}_3-\text{C}-\text{CSG}} \tag{112}
$$

this reaction and the analogous hydroxide ion catalyzed internal dismutation of phenylglyoxal to mandelic acid (equation 113) proceed

$$
\underset{\substack{\text{O}\\ \text{||}}}{\text{C}_6\text{H}_5\text{CCHO}} + \text{OH}^- \;\rightleftharpoons\; \underset{\substack{\text{O O}^-\\ \text{|| |}\\ \text{H}}}{\text{C}_6\text{H}_5\text{C}-\text{C}-\text{OH}} \;\longrightarrow\; \underset{\substack{\text{HO O}\\ \text{| ||}\\ \text{H}}}{\text{C}_6\text{H}_5\text{C}-\text{C}-\text{O}^-} \tag{113}
$$

without exchange of the migrating hydrogen atom with the medium, which suggests that these reactions probably proceed by a hydride transfer mechanism.[182] Proof that the hemithioacetal is the true substrate for the enzymatic reaction comes from the demonstration that the observed rate becomes independent of the concentration of enzyme at high enzyme concentrations if the reaction is initiated by the addition of glutathione, but does not if the glutathione and methylglyoxal are incubated together before the addition of enzyme.[183] Under the former conditions the formation of the hemithioacetal from glutathione and methylglyoxal (k_1, equation 112) becomes rate-determining, so that an increase in enzyme concentration does not increase the rate.

In methanol or in water at pH 7.5 this reaction is catalyzed by dimethylcysteamine, but not by either trimethylamine or a thiol

[181] E. Racker, V. Klybas, and M. Schramm, *J. Biol. Chem.* **234**, 2510 (1959).

[182] V. Franzen, *Ber.* **89**, 1020 (1956); I. A. Rose, *Biochim. Biophys. Acta* **25**, 214 (1957); W. E. Doering, T. I. Taylor, and E. F. Schoenewaldt, *J. Am. Chem. Soc.* **70**, 455 (1948).

[183] E. E. Cliffe and S. G. Waley, *Biochem. J.* **79**, 475 (1961).

alone.[184] This model reaction also proceeds without exchange of hydrogen with the solvent, and it has been suggested that it proceeds with intramolecular facilitation of a hydride transfer, as shown in equation 114. A detailed kinetic examination of this interesting reaction would be of considerable interest.

$$
\begin{array}{c}
\text{O}\\
\parallel\\
\text{RCCHO} + \text{HS}\\
\mid\\
\text{CH}_2\\
\mid\\
\text{CH}_2\\
\mid\\
\text{NR}_2
\end{array}
\rightleftharpoons
\quad
\rightarrow
\quad
\begin{array}{c}
{}^-\text{O} \quad \text{O}\\
\mid \quad\; \parallel\\
\text{R}-\text{C}-\text{C}-\text{S}\\
\mid \quad\quad \mid\\
\text{H} \quad\quad \text{CH}_2\\
\mid\\
\text{CH}_2\\
\mid\\
\text{H}^+\text{NR}_2
\end{array}
$$

$$
\begin{array}{c}
\text{HO}\quad \text{O}\\
\mid\quad\; \parallel\\
\text{R}-\text{C}-\text{COR}' + \text{HS}\\
\mid\\
\text{H}\quad\quad \text{CH}_2\\
\mid\\
\text{CH}_2\\
\mid\\
\text{NR}_2
\end{array}
\qquad (114)
$$

The formation of an activated acyl group from an aldehyde in an internal oxidation-reduction reaction may also be brought about by cyanide ion, but probably occurs by a quite different mechanism (equation 115).[136] Addition of cyanide to the aldehyde to give the cyanohydrin makes possible the loss of a proton to give the reson-

$$
\begin{array}{c}
\text{O}\\
\parallel\\
\text{HCCH}=\text{CHCOO}^- + \text{HCN}
\end{array}
\rightleftharpoons
\begin{array}{c}
\text{H}\\
\mid\\
\text{HOC}-\text{CH}=\text{CHCOO}^-\\
\mid\\
\text{C}\\
\parallel\mid\\
\text{N}
\end{array}
$$

$$
\pm\text{H}^+ \Updownarrow
$$

$$
\left[
\begin{array}{c}
{}^{(-)}\quad\quad\; {}^{(-)}\\
\text{HOC} \cdots \text{CH} \cdots \text{CHCOO}^-\\
\vdots\mid\\
\text{C}\\
{}^{(-)}\;\vdots\parallel\\
\text{N}
\end{array}
\right] \quad \mathbf{69}
$$

$$
\text{HCN} + \text{HOOCCH}_2\text{CH}_2\text{COOH}
$$

$$
\Big\downarrow \text{H}^+
$$

$$
\text{HOH} \nwarrow
$$

$$
\begin{array}{c}
\text{O}\\
\parallel\\
\text{NC}-\text{C}-\text{CH}_2-\text{CH}_2\text{COO}^-
\end{array}
\longleftarrow
\begin{array}{c}
\text{HOC}=\text{CH}-\text{CH}_2\text{COO}^-\\
\mid\\
\text{C}\\
\parallel\mid\\
\text{N}
\end{array}
$$

$$
\text{ROH} \nearrow
$$

$$
\text{HCN} + \text{ROOCCH}_2\text{CH}_2\text{COOH} \qquad (115)
$$

[184] V. Franzen, *Ber.* **88**, 1361 (1955); **90**, 623 (1957).

ance-stabilized anion **69**. Proton addition at the carbon atom adjacent to the carboxylate group, followed by ketonization, gives an acylcyanide, a reactive acylating agent which reacts rapidly with water or alcohol to give the saturated acid or ester.

The oxidative activation of a carboxylic acid and probably also of phosphate by reaction with a sulfide in the presence of iodine has been described in Chap. 1, Sec. C.

One of the central problems in biochemistry at the present time is the mechanism by which the energy which is released in the reaction of a C—H bond with oxygen to give carbon dioxide and water is converted to the energy of the phosphoanhydride bond of ATP, the common currency of chemical energy transfer which is utilized for a wide variety of synthetic and metabolic functions. If this energy coupling occurs by a chemical mechanism (and it may not[185]) it could proceed directly by the oxidation of some easily formed, "low-energy," phosphate derivative to a "high-energy" form, which could then transfer phosphate to ADP to give ATP, or it could proceed by the oxidation of some other "low-energy" molecule to a high-energy form, which could give high-energy phosphate by a series of group transfer reactions. Several examples have just been described of the latter activation process, in which an energy-rich thiol ester is formed from the oxidation of an aldehyde. The thiol ester may react further to give an acyl phosphate and, eventually, ATP. This type of activation is responsible for the formation of high-energy phosphate bonds in "substrate level" phosphorylation, in which the metabolite which undergoes oxidation is itself converted to an activated product, but there is as yet no evidence that a similar process occurs in the multistep transfer of electrons between the substrate and oxygen that is responsible for the release of most of the energy in aerobic metabolism. Interest in this problem has stimulated a search for reactions in which the phosphate group is itself converted to an energy-rich form in an oxidative process that may be a model for a reaction which could take place with a naturally occurring coenzyme. Although there is as yet no proof that any such process is responsible for oxidative phosphorylation, some interesting chemistry and potentially useful synthetic methods have arisen from this work.

One of the simplest examples of phosphate activation by oxidation is the transfer of the phosphoryl group of phosphate thiol esters to water and other acceptors that is induced by oxidation with iodine (equation 116).[186] Similarly, the oxidation of phos-

[185] P. Mitchell, *Biol. Rev.* **41**, 445 (1966).

[186] T. Wieland and R. Lambert, *Ber.* **89**, 2476 (1956); S. Akerfeldt, *Acta Chem. Scand.* **14**, 1980 (1960).

$$O-\overset{\overset{\displaystyle --O}{|}}{\underset{\underset{\displaystyle O}{\|}}{P}}-SR + I_2 \longrightarrow O-\overset{\overset{\displaystyle --O}{|}}{\underset{\underset{\displaystyle O}{\|}}{\underset{+}{P}}}-\overset{\displaystyle I}{\underset{}{SR}} \xrightarrow{XH} O-\overset{\overset{\displaystyle --O}{|}}{\underset{\underset{\displaystyle O}{\|}}{P}}-X + ISR \xrightarrow{RS^-} RSSR + I^- \tag{116}$$

phorohydrazides results in the transfer of the phosphate group to acceptors, including alcohols to give esters and phosphates to give pyrophosphates, and illustrates the possible application of this type of activation to synthetic chemistry (equation 117).[187]

$$\underset{\underset{\displaystyle O}{\|}}{\overset{\overset{\displaystyle O^-}{|}}{ROPNHNH_2}} + \text{oxidant}$$

with products

$$\xrightarrow{R'OH} \underset{\underset{\displaystyle O}{\|}}{\overset{\overset{\displaystyle O^-}{|}}{ROPOR'}}$$

$$\xrightarrow{R'OPO_3H^-} \underset{\underset{\displaystyle O \; O}{\| \; \|}}{\overset{\overset{\displaystyle O^- O^-}{| \; |}}{ROPOPOR'}} \tag{117}$$

A great deal of interest has arisen from studies of the oxidation of hydroquinone phosphates, since the quinones vitamin K, vitamin E, and coenzyme Q can undergo reversible oxidation-reduction and may be involved in the electron-transfer pathway of oxidative phosphorylation. The oxidation of hydroquinone phosphates by any of a number of oxidizing agents results in the hydrolysis of the phosphate and, in solvents of low water content, in the transfer of the phosphoryl group to an acceptor, which may be another phosphate molecule, to give a phosphate anhydride as product.[188,189] The detailed mechanism of these reactions is not known, but the principle

$$\tag{118}$$

---

[187] D. M. Brown and N. K. Hamer, *J. Chem. Soc.* **1964**, 326.

[188] V. M. Clark, G. W. Kirby, and A. Todd, *Nature* **181**, 1650 (1958); T. Wieland and F. Pattermann, *Angew. Chem.* **70**, 313 (1958).

[189] V. M. Clark, D. W. Hutchinson, G. W. Kirby, and A. Todd. *J. Chem. Soc.* **1961**, 715; V. M. Clark, D. W. Hutchinson, and A. Todd, *Ibid.*, p. 722.

of the oxidative activation is illustrated in equation 118. The withdrawal of electrons from the phosphate-oxygen bond which is brought about by the oxidative process makes this oxygen a better leaving group and facilitates departure of the phosphate in either a bimolecular displacement reaction with the acceptor or in a monomolecular elimination to give the metaphosphate monoanion, which reacts with the acceptor in a second step. The solvent may play a direct role in these reactions: dimethylformamide, for example, acts as a carrier of activated phosphate in the form of a phosphoimidate, which reacts with the acceptor in a later step.[190] The attractiveness of these reactions as models has been somewhat diminished, but by no means eliminated, by the demonstration with oxygen-labeled water that only part of the oxidation-induced hydrolysis occurs with phosphate transfer to water; a major part occurs with C—O bond splitting and represents an activation of the quinone ring rather than of phosphate (equation 119).[191] In meth-

$$(119)$$

anol, in fact, the reaction gives the addition compound **70** (R = CH_3) as the principal product.[192]

An especially direct demonstration of the formation of activated phosphate by oxidation is the bromine oxidation of phosphite esters in pyridine to give diesters or pyrophosphates (equation 120).[193]

$$(120)$$

[190] J. S. Cohen and A. Lapidot, *J. Chem. Soc.* **1967C**, 1210.

[191] A. Lapidot and D. Samuel, *Biochim. Biophys. Acta* **65**, 164 (1962).

[192] W. Durckheimer and L. A. Cohen, *Biochemistry* **3**, 1948 (1964).

[193] G. M. Blackburn, J. S. Cohen, and Lord Todd, *J. Chem. Soc.* **1966C**, 239.

This reaction is analogous to the oxidation of aldehydes to activated acyl compounds, but probably occurs by a different mechanism, in which electron removal results in phosphate transfer to the solvent, to give a reactive phosphorylpyridinium intermediate, which is followed by transfer of phosphate to the phosphate acceptor. An analogous reaction of biological importance is the reversible oxidation of sulfite in the presence of ADP or AMP to give an energy-rich phosphate-sulfate anhydride (equation 121). A purified enzyme

$$
\begin{array}{ccc}
\mathrm{O} & \mathrm{O} \quad \mathrm{O}^{--} & \mathrm{O}^{-} \quad \mathrm{O}^{-} \\
| & \diagdown\diagup & | \quad | \\
\mathrm{RO}-\mathrm{P}-\mathrm{O}^{--} \frown \mathrm{S}\odot \frown \mathrm{ox} \;\rightleftharpoons\; \mathrm{RO}-\mathrm{P}-\mathrm{O}-\mathrm{S}-\mathrm{O}\;\odot\,\mathrm{red} \\
\parallel & | & \parallel \quad | \\
\mathrm{O} & \mathrm{O} & \mathrm{O} \quad \mathrm{O}
\end{array}
\tag{121}
$$

which catalyzes the reaction with AMP has been shown to contain flavin adenine dinucleotide, iron, and an essential sulfhydryl group.[194] This reaction is a particularly simple and straightforward example of oxidative activation in a biological system.

[194] H. D. Peck, Jr., T. E. Deacon, and J. T. Davidson, *Biochim. Biophys. Acta* **96**, 429 (1965).

3
General Acid-Base Catalysis[1]

A. EXPERIMENTAL MANIFESTATIONS

1. ACETYLIMIDAZOLE HYDROLYSIS

Most of us were brought up to expect that the rate of an acid or base catalyzed reaction should be independent of the concentration of buffer because the concentrations of hydrogen and hydroxyl ions do not change significantly as the buffer concentration is changed. It can come as a shock, then, to find that this is not always the case. For example, the rate of hydrolysis of acetylimidazole increases with increasing concentration of imidazole buffer (Fig. 1).[2] Since the pH does not change with buffer concentration, this means that a component of the buffer itself, either imidazole or imidazolium ion, must be accelerating the reaction. The fact that the catalysis

---

[1] For further reading see R. P. Bell, "The Proton in Chemistry," Cornell University Press, Ithaca, N. Y., 1959.

[2] W. P. Jencks and J. Carriuolo, *J. Biol. Chem.* **234**, 1272, 1280 (1959).

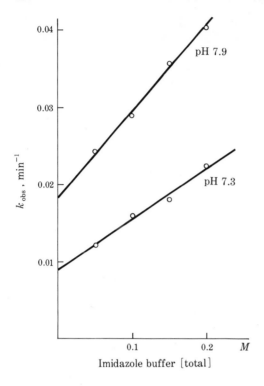

Fig 1. Catalysis of the hydrolysis of acetylimidazole by imidazole buffers at 25°; ionic strength maintained at 1.0 with potassium chloride.

is greater at higher pH values suggests that it is imidazole in the form of the free base that is the effective catalyst. The increased rate of hydrolysis cannot be caused by nucleophilic attack of imidazole because such a nucleophilic reaction would only regenerate acetylimidazole and would give no net reaction that could be observed in the absence of isotope labeling (equation 1).[3] Therefore, another mechanism of catalysis must be sought.

$$CH_3CN \diagdown N + N \diagdown NH \rightleftharpoons CH_3CN \diagdown N + N \diagdown NH \tag{1}$$

The two types of base catalysis which are observed experimentally are illustrated in Fig. 2. If catalysis is caused only by hydroxide ion, the rate is determined only by the pH and is independent of

[3] A mechanism in which imidazole adds to acetylimidazole to form a tetrahedral addition intermediate, followed by S_N2 displacement of imidazole by water, is unlikely in view of the fact that such addition compounds are almost always far less reactive toward nucleophilic attack than the unsaturated compounds from which they were formed.[2]

the concentration of buffer (Fig. 2a). This is *specific base catalysis.*
Reactions of this kind either involve hydroxide ion directly as a reactant or involve the conjugate base of one of the reactants, which
is formed in an amount proportional to the concentration of hydroxide ion in a rapid equilibrium step before the rate-determining
step. Other reactions are similar to the hydrolysis of acetylimidazole in that they increase in rate with increasing buffer concentration at constant pH and ionic strength, and show a larger increase
with the buffer which contains a larger amount of the basic component (Fig. 2b). Since the hydroxide ion concentration does not
change with increasing buffer concentration, this means that the
buffer itself, in this case the basic component of the buffer, is
catalyzing the reaction. This is *general base* catalysis; i.e., bases
other than hydroxide ion accelerate the reaction. The intercepts of
the lines in Fig. 2b at zero buffer concentration represent the hydroxide ion and solvent catalyzed portions of the reaction k_0, and
the slope of the plot against buffer concentration gives the apparent
rate constant of the buffer catalyzed reaction k_2'.

The way in which these slopes change as the composition of
the buffer changes shows whether the basic, the acidic, or both
components of the buffer are the active species for catalysis. In
Fig. 3 the lower line (circles) shows the way in which the apparent
second-order rate constants k_2' for imidazole catalysis of acetylimidazole hydrolysis change as the buffer composition is changed. The
intercept on the right ordinate is the rate constant k_B, for catalysis

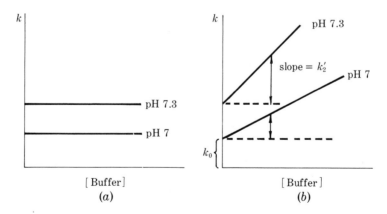

Fig 2. (a) Absence of the dependence of the rate on buffer concentration
in a specific base catalyzed reaction. (b) Dependence of the rate on buffer
concentration at constant pH values in a general base catalyzed reaction.

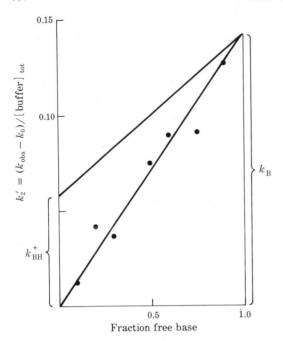

Fig 3. Dependence of the apparent catalytic constant for buffer catalysis k_2' on the composition of the buffer. Lower line: imidazole catalyzed hydrolysis of acetylimidazole, showing catalysis by the basic component of the buffer.[2] Upper line: behavior of a reaction which shows catalysis by both the basic (k_B) and acidic (k_{BH^+}) components of the buffer.

by the basic component of the buffer, while the intercept on the left ordinate is zero.[4] The upper line represents the behavior of a reaction which is subject to *both* general base and general acid catalysis by the buffer. Again the intercept on the right ordinate is the catalytic constant for general base catalysis, but the fact that the catalytic rate does not approach zero as the fraction of base in the buffer is decreased means that the acidic species of the buffer is also an active catalyst; the intercept on the left ordinate is the catalytic constant for this general acid catalysis, k_{BH^+}. The complete rate law for such a catalyzed reaction is

$$k_{obs} = k_{solv} + k_{H^+}[H^+] + k_{OH^-}[OH^-] + k_{BH^+}[BH^+] + k_B[B] \qquad (2)$$

[4]However, T. H. Fife [*J. Am. Chem. Soc.* **87**, 4597 (1965)] has shown that the hydrolysis of some acylimidazoles is subject to a relatively small amount of general acid catalysis by imidazolium ion.

with terms for catalysis by solvent, hydrogen ion, and hydroxide ion, as well as by the components of the buffer. The former terms may themselves represent general acid or base catalysis, in which the solvent, hydrogen ion, and hydroxide ion are acting as general acids or bases. If this is the case, equation 2 may be shortened to the form

$$k_{obs} = \Sigma_i k_{BH_i^+}[BH_i^{\cdot}] + \Sigma_j k_{B_j}[B_j] \qquad (3)$$

The importance of proton transfer steps in chemical and biochemical reactions is not always appreciated. Consider the hydrolysis of an acyl compound, such as acetylimidazole, at neutral pH (equation 4). In order that this reaction may take place, the

$$CH_3\overset{\overset{\displaystyle O}{\|}}{C}N\diagup N + H_2O \longrightarrow CH_3\overset{\overset{\displaystyle O}{\|}}{C}O^- + HN\overset{+}{\diagup}NH \qquad (4)$$

first requirement, and the one most often thought of by organic chemists, is that a carbon-nitrogen bond must be cleaved and a new carbon-oxygen bond formed. But the second requirement, which may be of equal or greater importance, is that the two protons which were originally on the water molecule be removed and that one or two protons be added to the imidazole molecule at some point in the course of the reaction. Facilitation of these proton transfers is the most important mechanism by which the rate of such a reaction may be increased in the chemistry laboratory and is almost certainly a major contributing mechanism in enzyme catalysis. The proton transfer steps have a small activation energy barrier in themselves, but they can add a large additional energy barrier to the overall reaction if the transition state requires the formation of unstable intermediates, such as the conjugate acids or bases of the reactants. The chemist is usually not too concerned about such an energy barrier, since it is no great problem to add hydroxide or hydrogen ions to the reaction mixture and drive the proton transfer steps in this manner. However, for an enzyme such a mechanism is not feasible. There is no obvious way in which an enzyme at neutral pH could increase the activity of hydrogen or hydroxide ions at its active site, so that it is important for an enzyme to be able to avoid the formation of such intermediates. The great importance of general acid or base catalysis for the mechanism of enzyme action is that it provides a means for achieving the same end result as does the intermediate formation of hydroxide or hydrogen ions, but avoids the formation of these unstable intermediates in solution.

One of several plausible mechanisms by which this could occur in the imidazole catalyzed hydrolysis of acetylimidazole is shown in equation 5. According to this mechanism, the general base catalyst

$$\text{HN} \overset{\frown}{\underset{}{N}} \overset{\frown}{\sim} \text{H} - \overset{\underset{H}{|}}{\text{O}} \quad \overset{\overset{O}{\underset{}{\parallel}}}{\underset{\underset{H_3C}{}}{\text{C}}} \overset{}{\underset{N \overset{}{\frown} N}{}} \longrightarrow \text{HN} \overset{+}{\underset{}{NH}} + \text{HOC} - \overset{\underset{CH_3}{|}}{N} \overset{\frown}{\underset{}{N}}$$

$$\downarrow$$

$$\text{products} \qquad (5)$$

removes a proton from the attacking water molecule to increase its nucleophilic reactivity without ever forming free hydroxide ion.

In addition to imidazole and its conjugate acid, there are a number of groups on the side chains of amino acids and coenzymes, such as carboxylate, sulfhydryl, ammonium, and phenolic hydroxyl groups, which are effective general acid or base catalysts and which are known to occur in the active sites of enzymes. Unfortunately, general acid-base catalysis in enzymatic catalysis is a subject about which it is far easier to speculate than to carry out definitive experiments. There are only a few enzymatic reactions in which the occurrence of general acid or base catalysis has been proved, a somewhat larger number in which there is suggestive evidence for such catalysis, and a very large number indeed in which such catalysis has been proposed and provides a reasonable and attractive mechanism for a rate acceleration in the absence of supporting evidence.

2. OTHER EXAMPLES

General base and acid catalysis of both chemical and enzymatic reactions is best known in reactions in which the proton transfer itself is the most important process which is occurring in the transition state. Most such reactions involve transfer of a proton to or from a carbon atom, in which the activation energy for proton transfer provides the largest energy barrier to the overall reaction. The classical example is the enolization of a ketone (equation 6).

$$\text{B} \overset{\frown}{\sim} \text{H} - \overset{|}{\underset{|}{C}} - \text{C} \overset{\nearrow O}{\underset{\searrow}{}} \quad \rightleftharpoons \quad \overset{+}{\text{BH}} \quad \overset{|}{\underset{}{C}} = \text{C} \overset{\nearrow \bar{O}}{\underset{\searrow}{}} \qquad (6)$$

General acid-base catalysis of reactions of this kind should be clearly distinguished from catalysis of acyl- and carbonyl-group reactions, such as acetylimidazole hydrolysis, in which the proton transfer does not provide the major energy barrier to reaction. In these reactions the catalyst assists the reaction by removing a proton from an attacking group or adding a proton to the carbonyl group or leaving group, and the principal energy barrier is provided by the making or breaking of bonds of heavy atoms to carbon, rather than the proton transfer itself.

General acid-base catalysis of the latter type is frequently observed in reactions which involve attack on an electrophilic center which is unsaturated or is a heavy atom with relatively low-energy d orbitals. Thus, the hydrolysis of the reactive cyclic phosphate triester, methyl ethylene phosphate,[5] and the methanolysis of aryloxytriphenylsilanes[6] are subject to general base catalysis, which might occur by the mechanisms of equations 7 and 8, respec-

$$\tag{7}$$

$$\tag{8}$$

tively. General base catalysis of displacement reactions at saturated carbon is generally not observed, presumably because these reactions are relatively insensitive to the basicity of the nucleophile, so that there is not a large stabilization of the transition state by the partial removal of a proton from the attacking nucleophile. An exception is the intramolecular general base catalyzed displacement of chloride from 4-chlorobutanol to give tetrahydrofuran (equation 9), which is catalyzed by borate, carbonate, and phenolate buffers

$$\tag{9}$$

[5] F. Covitz and F. H. Westheimer, *J. Am. Chem. Soc.* **85**, 1773 (1963).

[6] R. L. Schowen and K. S. Latham, Jr., *J. Am. Chem. Soc.* **89**, 4677 (1967).

as well as by hydroxide ion and water.[7,8] An unusual type of general base catalysis has been reported to occur in the reduction of riboflavin by dihydrolipoic acid.[9] A possible mechanism for this interesting reaction, which may be a model for the corresponding enzymatic reactions, is shown in equation 10.

$$B \frown H - S \; S - H \; \text{flavin} \longrightarrow BH^+ + S - S + \text{reduced flavin}$$

$$R \qquad\qquad\qquad\qquad\qquad R \tag{10}$$

B. THE BRØNSTED RELATIONSHIP

The efficiency of general base catalysts increases with increasing base strength of the catalyst, and the slope of a plot of log k_B against pK_a of a series of catalysts is a measure of the sensitivity of the reaction to the strength of the base catalyst. Such a plot for catalysis of the hydrolysis of ethyl dichloroacetate by a series of general base catalysts, including amines, carboxylate ions, and phosphate dianion,[10] is shown in Fig. 4. The slope of this plot is the Brønsted exponent β for general base catalysis, which is equal to 0.47 for this reaction. The fit of the points to the line is fairly typical of this type of correlation when different classes of catalysts are compared, and the largest deviations are found with bases of differing structure. The largest negative deviation in Fig. 4 is for aniline, which reflects the fact that the catalytic efficiency of primary amines is generally lower than that of secondary or tertiary amines. Because of these deviations, Brønsted slopes are best determined by comparing the catalytic activity of structurally similar compounds, which often give an excellent fit to a single line over a large range of basicity.

Logarithmic plots of the catalytic constants for catalysis by general acids against the pK_a of the catalyst exhibit a negative Brønsted slope α, which is a measure of the sensitivity of the reaction to the acid strength of general acid catalysts. These relationships are defined by the Brønsted equations

$$\log k_B = \log G_B + \beta(pK_a) \tag{11}$$

[7] C. G. Swain, D. A. Kuhn, and R. L. Schowen, J. Am. Chem. Soc. 87, 1553 (1965).
[8] W. P. Jencks, I. Givot, and A. Satterthwait, unpublished experiments.
[9] I. M. Gascoigne and G. K. Radda, Biochem. Biophys. Acta 131, 498 (1967).
[10] W. P. Jencks and J. Carriuolo, J. Am. Chem. Soc. 83, 1743 (1961).

for general base catalysis, and

$$\log k_{HA} = \log G_A - \alpha(pK_a) \tag{12}$$

for general acid catalysis, where G_A and G_B are constants for a particular reaction.

The line through the rate constants for catalysis by oxygen bases in Fig. 4 can be extrapolated to fit the rate constant for the "water" reaction of ethyl dichloroacetate. This point deserves special comment. In the first place, both the rate constant and the acidity constant for the water catalyzed reaction must be expressed in units comparable to those for the other catalysts in order to make a valid comparison. A correction is necessary because of the common convention that the standard-state activity or concentration of pure water is 1.0 instead of 55.5 M. The observed rate constant for the pH-independent water catalyzed reaction (k_{solv} of equation 2) must, therefore, be divided by 55.5 M before comparison with

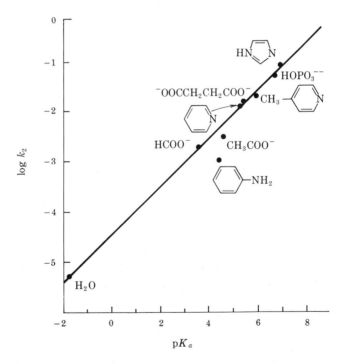

Fig 4. Brønsted plot of the catalytic constants for general base catalyzed hydrolysis of ethyl dichloroacetate.[10]

other catalytic constants. For the same reason, the pK of the solvated proton is taken as -1.74 instead of 0 in order to make allowance for the fact that the concentration of water, the conjugate base of this particular acid, is 55.5 M, rather than 1.0 M, the standard state of the conjugate base of other acids. Consider an acid HA, of pK = 0, the same as the formal pK of the solvated proton, and assume that its dissociation occurs according to equation 13, so that in the standard state at pH = 0 equal amounts of water and of the acid exist in the protonated form. Such an acid is

$$HA + H_2O \; \rightleftharpoons \; A^- + H_3O^+ \tag{13}$$

actually much weaker than the solvated proton because the acid exists one-half in the protonated form under conditions in which only one fifty-fifth as much of the water is protonated. The pK for the acidic dissociation of water to hydroxide ion at 25° is taken as 15.74, rather than 14, because the ion product of water of 10^{-14} is also based on a standard-state activity of 1.0 for pure water (equation 14), and this dissociation constant must be expressed according

$$K_w = [H^+][OH^-] = 10^{-14} \tag{14}$$

to the same convention as other acids before making comparisons (equation 15).

$$K_{HOH} = \frac{[H^+][OH^-]}{[H_2O]} = \frac{K_w}{[H_2O]} = \frac{10^{-14}}{55.5} = 10^{-15.74} \tag{15}$$

The satisfactory fit of the point for water on the Brønsted plot of Fig. 4 suggests that the behavior of water is similar to that of any other catalyst; i.e., the water reaction represents general base catalysis by the solvent water. On the other hand, the more basic nucleophiles ammonia, tris(hydroxymethyl) aminomethane and hydroxide ion show positive deviations from the Brønsted plots for general base catalysis of the hydrolysis of ethyl dichloroacetate and related esters. In the case of the nitrogen nucleophiles, the product of the reaction is the acylated nucleophile (in contrast to the more weakly basic aniline molecule, which increases the rate of ester disappearance by general base catalysis of hydrolysis without formation of the anilide). Thus, strongly basic nucleophiles which are able to displace the alkoxide ion leaving group react by nucleophilic attack rather than general base catalysis and, consequently, show a positive deviation from the Brønsted line for general base catalysis. The positive deviation for hydroxide ion, of just under two orders of magnitude for the ethyl dichloroacetate reaction, suggests that this reaction involves a direct nucleophilic attack of hydroxide ion on the ester rather than an attack of water catalyzed by hydroxide ion. Deviations of this kind are not uncommon for nucleophilic reactions. Their occurrence suggests that the attack of the conjugate base of a nucleophile is a different process from the hydroxide ion catalyzed attack of the free nucleophile and that a specific base catalyzed reaction can occur concurrently with a general base catalyzed process.

The special properties of water, the solvated proton and hydroxide ion, which arise from the fact that they are components of the solvent, and the difficulty of finding acids and bases with a comparable structure, mean that it is difficult to make quantitative correlations of the reactivity of these compounds. These catalysts frequently show a good fit to Brønsted plots based on other types of catalysts, but in many other cases they exhibit deviations for reasons which have not yet been firmly established.

1. STATISTICAL CORRECTIONS

The rate constants for general acid-base catalysis are usually corrected for statistical effects, which result from the fact that in some acids and bases there may be more than a single site which can donate or accept a proton.[11] The modified Brønsted expressions are given in equations 16 and 17, in which p is the number of equivalent

$$
\log \frac{k_{HA}}{p} = \log G_A - \alpha \left(pK_a + \log \frac{p}{q} \right) \tag{16}
$$

$$
\log \frac{k_B}{q} = \log G_B + \beta \left(pK_a + \log \frac{p}{q} \right) \tag{17}
$$

protons which can be transferred from the acid and q is the number of sites which can accept a proton in the base. Statistical corrections are nearly always made for compounds such as dicarboxylic acids, in which two different groups on the molecule can undergo acid dissociation or reaction. It is now generally agreed that a statistical

[11] (a) S. W. Benson, J. Am. Chem. Soc. **80**, 5151 (1958); (b) D. Bishop and K. J. Laidler, J. Chem. Phys. **42**, 1688 (1965); (c) R. P. Bell and P. G. Evans, Proc. Roy. Soc. (London) **291A**, 297 (1966).

correction should also be made for compounds such as the ammonium ion, in which several protons can be lost from the same atom, but most of the rate constants in the literature have not been subjected to such a correction. There is no certainty regarding the correction which should be made for the solvated proton, which certainly is bound tightly to a single water molecule to give H_3O^+, but is surrounded by three additional water molecules to give the species $H_9O_4^+$. No correction is ordinarily made for atoms which have several electron pairs which could accept a proton, such as an oxygen anion. Fortunately, the statistical correction is usually not large and the problem is not one of fundamental significance for the mechanism of acid-base catalysis. The data shown in Fig. 4 have not been corrected for statistical effects, but the overall fit of the points to the line is not greatly altered by such corrections.

Whether or not general acid or base catalysis can be detected experimentally depends on the value of the Brønsted slope, α or β, as well as on the strength and concentration of the acid or base. The experimental fact that general acid catalysis can be observed, for example, means that weak acid catalysts stabilize the transition state significantly as compared with the solvated proton, even though the solvated proton is a much stronger acid; i.e., the relatively low catalytic ability of a weak acid is more than compensated for by the fact that its concentration can be much larger than that of the solvated proton at a given pH value. This is a qualitative way of saying that general acid catalysis generally cannot be observed if the Brønsted slope α is 1.0 because if α does have this value the large catalytic effectiveness of the solvated proton will compensate for its low concentration and catalysis by other acids will be difficult or impossible to detect. Similarly, if $\alpha = 0$, there is no sensitivity to the acid strength of the catalyst and catalysis by added general acids will not be detectable because the reaction will be maximally catalyzed by the solvent, which is present in higher concentration than any added catalyst.

The situation is most readily demonstrated by a numerical example. Table I shows Bell's calculations of the fraction of the total reaction rate which is caused by catalysis by the solvated proton, by water, and by acetic acid in the presence of 0.1 M acetic acid $-0.1M$ sodium acetate buffer for reactions with α values of 0.1, 0.5, and 1.0.[12] It is evident that general acid catalysis by acetic acid will be detectable only at intermediate values of α. The same

---

[12] R. P. Bell, "Acid-Base Catalysis," p. 94, Oxford University Press, London, 1941.

Table I   Detection of general acid catalysis in the presence of a 0.1 M acetic acid-0.1 M sodium acetate buffer[12]

Brønsted α	Proportion of catalysis (in %) caused by		
	H^+	CH_3COOH	H_2O
0.1	0.002	2	98
0.5	3.6	96.4	0.01
1.0	99.8	0.2	5×10^{-12}

considerations hold for general base catalysis with respect to the value of β. The formation and breakdown of the hydrogen peroxide addition compound of p-chlorobenzaldehyde shows general acid catalysis by carboxylic acids in spite of the fact that α is equal or very close to 1.0. General acid catalysis is detectable in this reaction because the rate constant for catalysis by the proton falls below the Brønsted line for carboxylic acids.[13] It has sometimes been questioned whether there is a meaningful distinction between a specific acid catalyzed reaction and a general acid catalyzed reaction with an α value of 1.0. The fact that general acid catalysis by acids other than the solvated proton can be detected with an α value of 1.0 means that such a distinction is meaningful, although it may be difficult to make in practice.

2. DEVIATIONS FROM THE BRØNSTED RELATIONSHIP

The deviations of certain classes of catalyst from the Brønsted line established for a different class of catalyst may be large. Some examples of such deviations for general acid catalysis of the hydration of acetaldehyde are shown in Table II.[14] Acids in which the proton is bound to a carbon atom show negative deviations of between 10- and 100-fold as compared with a line based on the catalytic effectiveness of carboxylic acids, phenols, and some other acids, whereas oximes show positive deviations of about the same magnitude.

It is worthwhile to examine the possible explanations for such deviations because it is often just such irregularities that provide clues for the understanding of the mechanism involved. The Brønsted relationship compares the free energy of an equilibrium for

[13] E. Sander and W. P. Jencks, *J. Am. Chem. Soc.* **90,** 3817 (1968).

[14] R. P. Bell and W. C. E. Higginson, *Proc. Roy. Soc.* (*London*) **A197,** 141 (1949).

Table II   Deviation from the Brønsted relation in general acid catalysis of the dehydration of acetaldehyde hydrate[14]

	Logarithmic deviation		*Logarithmic deviation*
Nitromethane	−1.4	Acetoxime	+2.1
Nitroethane	−1.7	Acetophenone oxime	+1.4
Dimedone (1,3-diketo-5-dimethyl cyclohexane enol)	−1.1	Benzophenone oxime	+1.2
Benzoylacetate	−1.4		

complete proton transfer to the free energy of a transition state which involves partial proton transfer (equations 18 and 19). Deviations from the relationship mean that different effects which

$$B + HA \rightleftharpoons BH^+ + A^- \qquad (18)$$

$$S + HA \rightleftharpoons S \overset{\delta^+}{\cdots} H \overset{\delta^-}{\cdots} A \qquad (19)$$

influence these free energies do not do so with the same proportionality factor; i.e., the influence of some factor may be considered to be "abnormal" either on the pK of the catalyst or on the transition state of the reaction.

The explanation for the negative deviation exhibited by carbon acids follows most directly from the experimental fact that the rate of proton transfer from carbon acids is generally slow, whereas the rate of proton transfer from oxygen, nitrogen, and sulfur acids in the thermodynamically favorable direction is generally limited only by the rate of diffusion, so that the rate of the proton transfer process itself must be even faster than the diffusion-controlled rate. The situation is shown schematically in Fig. 5. Since the activation energy barrier for proton transfer from carbon acids is much larger than that for proton transfer from other acids, the energy of the carbon acid will be less favorable at any intermediate degree of proton transfer than that of an oxygen acid of comparable acidity. Consequently, the energy of the transition state for catalysis by a carbon acid must be higher than that for catalysis by an oxygen acid because general acid catalysis involves a partial proton transfer to the substrate.

Several explanations have been proposed for the slow proton transfer and inefficient general acid-base catalysis exhibited by

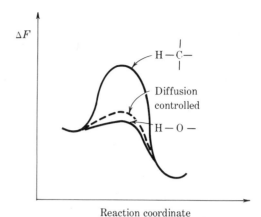

Fig 5. The energy barrier for the transfer of a proton bound to carbon is much larger than for one bound to oxygen. The barrier in the latter case is just that for diffusion, so the barrier for the proton transfer itself is even less than that for diffusion.

carbon acids.[14-17] The carbon-hydrogen bond has more covalent character than bonds between hydrogen and more electronegative elements, so that the slow proton transfer may be regarded as a reflection of the fact that it is generally more difficult to break covalent than electrostatic bonds. A closely related explanation is that hydrogen bonds involving carbon have only a small stability, largely because of the low electronegativity of carbon, so that it is difficult to form transition states for proton removal from carbon in which hydrogen bonding provides a stabilizing influence (1). A

$$\overset{\delta^+ \quad \delta^-}{B \cdots H \cdots X}$$

1

third explanation depends on the fact that the stability of most carbon acids, such as nitromethane, is made possible by resonance stabilization of the resulting anion, with most of the negative charge located on an electronegative atom rather than on carbon (equation 20). The development of this resonance requires considerable rear-

$$H_3CNO_2 \rightleftharpoons H^+ + \underset{H}{\overset{H}{\diagdown}} C \overset{(+)}{=\!=} N \overset{O^{(-)}}{\underset{O^{(-)}}{\diagup}} \tag{20}$$

[15] R. P. Bell, "The Proton in Chemistry," chap. X, p. 155, Cornell University Press, Ithaca, N.Y., 1959.

[16] M. Eigen, *Angew. Chem. Intern. Ed. Eng.* **3**, 1 (1964).

[17] J. Hine, *J. Org. Chem.* **31**, 1236 (1966).

rangement of structure and charge in both the ionizing acid and the solvent, and these rearrangements will contribute to the large free-energy barrier for proton removal. Support for this explanation is found in the fact that hydroxide ion removes a proton some two orders of magnitude faster from phenylacetylene, which undergoes little rearrangement upon ionization, than from nitroethane, in spite of the fact that phenylacetylene has been estimated to be 10^{11} less acidic than nitroethane.[17]

The abnormally high reactivity of oximes as general acid catalysts has been attributed to the small amount of structural reorganization that is required for the ionization of these compounds to an anion, in which most of the negative charge is on a single oxygen atom.[15] However, this explanation does not appear to be perfectly general. Different classes of acids exhibit different relative efficiencies for different types of reactions, and the deviations which might be predicted for oxygen acids which have a large amount of resonance stabilization of their conjugate base, such as nitrophenols, are not observed consistently.[14,18]

Differences in the *solvation* of acids, bases, and activated complexes are almost certainly an important cause of deviations from the Brønsted relationship, but the direction of such deviations depends on the relative solvation of the reactants and the activated complex and must be predicted with caution. An almost trivial solvation effect arises from a comparison of catalytic efficiencies in one solvent to acidities or basicities measured in another solvent, usually water. If the acidities of the different catalysts change by different amounts upon changing the solvent, deviations from the Brønsted relationship will, of course, be observed. This difficulty is easily avoided by the use of the same solvent for measurements of rates and acidities.

There is a large body of evidence which supports the conclusion that ammonium ions are stabilized by interaction of their hydrogen atoms with water (2), so that their acidity is decreased from what it would be in the absence of such stabilization.[1,19-21] A striking

[18] E. H. Cordes and W. P. Jencks, *J. Am. Chem. Soc.* **84**, 4319 (1962).

[19] A. F. Trotman-Dickenson, *J. Chem. Soc.* **1949**, 1293; H. K. Hall, Jr., *J. Am. Chem. Soc.* **79**, 5441 (1957); E. Folkers and O. Runquist, *J. Org. Chem.* **29**, 830 (1964); F. E. Condon, *J. Am. Chem. Soc.* **87**, 4481, 4485 (1965).

[20] T. C. Bissot, R. W. Parry, and D. H. Campbell, *J. Am. Chem. Soc.* **79**, 796 (1957); R. L. Hinman, *J. Org. Chem.* **23**, 1587 (1958).

[21] R. G. Kallen and W. P. Jencks, *J. Biol. Chem.* **241**, 5864 (1966).

$$
\begin{array}{c}
H{\diagdown}\underset{\vdots}{O}{\diagup}H \\[4pt]
\overset{+}{H} \\
RNH\cdots O{\diagup}^{H}_{\diagdown H} \\
\underset{\vdots}{H} \\
H{\diagup}\overset{O}{\diagdown}H
\end{array}
$$

2

example, which is difficult to account for by any other explanation, is found in the fact that methoxyammonium ion (pK_a 4.7) is 20 times stronger as an acid than hydroxylammonium ion (pK_a 6.0), presumably because the latter ion is subject to an extra stabilization by solvation of its hydroxyl group. Similar effects of methyl substitution are seen in hydrazine (pK_a 8.1) as compared with N,N-dimethylhydrazine (pK_a 7.2) and tetramethylhydrazine (pK_a 6.3) and have been invoked to explain the curious order of increasing and then decreasing basicity in the series ammonia, methylamine, dimethylamine, and trimethylamine. The same effect appears to be largely responsible for the decreased basicity of hydroxymethyl-amines compared with their parent amines (which makes possible the formol titration of amines), since the hydroxymethyl group itself has little inductive electron-withdrawing ability compared to hydrogen.[21] The effectiveness of ammonium ions and amines as general acid and base catalysts, then, should depend on the extent to which solvation effects of this kind have developed in the transition state as compared with the ammonium ion. As shown in Fig. 6, the result of extra stabilization of the ammonium ion through hy-

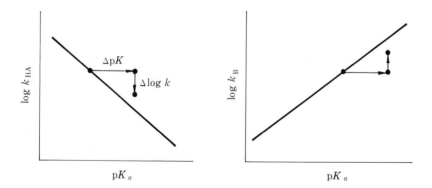

Fig 6. Brønsted plots for acid and base catalysis, showing how a factor affecting the strength of an acid, such as solvation, can cause deviations from the plot by changing the acidity and the catalytic effectiveness by different amounts.

drogen bonding to the solvent is to increase its pK compared with a similar ion without such solvation, and to cause a smaller decrease in its effectiveness as an acid catalyst and increase in its effectiveness as a base catalyst. Depending on the value of α or β and on the degree of solvation of the transition state, either a positive or a negative deviation from the Brønsted relation may result. The experimental finding that primary amines are less effective catalysts than tertiary amines of the same base strength for the decomposition of nitramide in water[22] suggests that relatively little solvation of the developing positive charge on the catalyst has developed in the transition state for this reaction.

The nature of deviations from the Brønsted relationship for different classes of general acid-base catalyzed reactions deserves more complete and systematic examination because these deviations may provide a method for approaching such difficult problems as the detailed structure of the transition state, the importance of "concerted" catalytic mechanisms, the extent to which the transferred proton is at the top of a potential barrier or in a potential well in the transition state, and the extent to which surrounding solvent molecules have been able to undergo rearrangement to provide favorable solvation for the transition state during the time in which the transition state is reached. Catalysts which undergo ionization by special mechanisms may be especially helpful in this regard if the factors which determine their catalytic efficiency can be evaluated. Boric and carbonic acids, for example, undergo acidic ionization predominantly by the addition of hydroxide ion, rather than by the loss of a proton (equations 21 and 22).[23] Carbon

$$\tag{21}$$

[22] R. P. Bell and G. L. Wilson, *Trans. Faraday Soc.* **46**, 407 (1950).

[23] J. O. Edwards, G. C. Morrison, V. F. Ross, and J. W. Schultz, *J. Am. Chem. Soc.* **77**, 266 (1955); R. P. Bell, R. B. Jones, and J. O. Edwards, as quoted in Bell and Evans[11c]; J. T. Edsall and J. Wyman, "Biophysical Chemistry," vol. 1, p. 588, Academic Press, Inc., New York, 1958.

$$
O=C=O \underset{\pm OH^-}{\rightleftharpoons} HO-\overset{\overset{\displaystyle O}{\|}}{C}-O^-
$$

$$
\Big\updownarrow \pm H_2O \qquad\qquad \diagup\!\!\diagup \pm H^+
$$

$$
HO-\overset{\overset{\displaystyle O}{\|}}{C}-OH \tag{22}
$$

dioxide in water is hydrated to only a small extent, so that the apparent pK of 6.4 for the dissociation of carbonic acid to bicarbonate ion is actually based on total carbonic acid plus dissolved carbon dioxide. The true pK for the dissociation of carbonic acid is 3.8. In other words, the observed equilibrium for the addition of a proton to bicarbonate ion is pulled by the dehydration of the carbonic acid product, so that bicarbonate appears to be a stronger base than it is in actuality. It would be expected that acids and bases of this kind would exhibit deviations from Brønsted plots which are based on their apparent rather than their true pK's but in fact deviations are seen in some reactions and not in others, for reasons which are not yet understood.

The possibility should, of course, be kept in mind that positive deviations from a Brønsted plot for general acid-base catalysis may be caused by a different mechanism of catalysis, such as nucleophilic or electrophilic catalysis. A number of examples of this type of catalysis have been described in the preceding chapter. The high catalytic activity for the hydration of carbon dioxide which has been reported for catalysts which can themselves undergo hydration and dehydration[24] could reflect a covalent reaction mechanism such as that shown in equation 23. There is convincing evidence for a mechanism of this kind in the hydration of carbon dioxide catalyzed

$$
\overset{\overset{\displaystyle O}{\|}}{\underset{\underset{\displaystyle O}{\|}}{C}} + HO\overset{|}{\underset{|}{C}}OH \rightleftharpoons HO\overset{\overset{\displaystyle O}{\|}}{C}-O-\overset{|}{\underset{|}{C}}-OH \rightleftharpoons HO\overset{\overset{\displaystyle O}{\|}}{C}-O^- + \overset{\overset{\displaystyle O}{\|}}{C}_{\diagup\diagdown} \tag{23}
$$

by carbonic anhydrase, in which a hydrated zinc ion is the catalytically active species (equation 24).[25] The hydrated zinc ion has a pK near neutrality, and the role of the metal cation appears to be to

[24] M. M. Sharma and P. V. Danckwerts, *Trans. Faraday Soc.* **59**, 386 (1963).
[25] J. E. Coleman, *J. Biol. Chem.* **242**, 5212 (1967).

$$O = C = O \quad \overset{O}{\underset{\overset{|}{\underset{-Zn-}{(+)OH}}}{\overset{\diagdown}{\underset{|}{C}}}} \quad \pm H_2O \quad \overset{(-)OH}{\underset{\overset{\vdots}{\underset{|}{-Zn-}}}{}} + \overset{O}{\underset{\overset{|}{OH}}{\overset{\diagdown}{\underset{}{C}}}} + H^+ \tag{24}$$

reduce the basicity of hydroxide ion to a point at which a high concentration of the nucleophile can exist at neutral pH or, conversely, to increase the basicity of water by replacing a proton with an electrostatic bond to a metal so that the oxygen atom becomes sufficiently basic to attack carbon dioxide (as well as other carbonyl compounds) at a rapid rate.

C. THE AMBIGUITY OF THE ASSIGNMENT OF THE SITE OF CATALYSIS

Consider the attack of water on an imine, such as a Schiff base or oxime, and the reverse reaction, which is the dehydration of the carbinolamine addition compound. These reactions are subject to general acid catalysis, and the first problem in determining the mechanism of catalysis is to decide at what site the catalyst is acting. As shown in equation 25, it might be acting to donate a

transition state

$$H^+ + O - \overset{|}{\underset{\underset{H}{|}}{C}} - NH + A^- \quad \underset{\rightleftharpoons}{\overset{fast}{\longrightarrow}} \quad \tag{25}$$

proton to the imine nitrogen atom, so as to increase the susceptibility of the imine to nucleophilic attack by water. The immediate product would then lose a proton in a fast step. Now once the mechanism of the forward reaction is decided, the mechanism of the reverse reaction is determined as well because both the forward and reverse reactions must pass through the same transition state, which is on the saddle point of the lowest energy pathway leading from reactants to products and back from products to reactants. This is in accord with the principle of microscopic reversibility. In this case, then, the reverse reaction would proceed through the addition of a proton to the carbinolamine oxygen atom in a rapid, reversible reaction, followed by the removal of a proton from the nitrogen atom by the conjugate base of the catalyst A⁻, to aid the expulsion of water (equation 25). In this and subsequent equations curved arrows are used to represent the formation and breaking of bonds in both the forward and reverse directions, on the left- and right-hand sides, respectively, of each equation. It is an almost (but not entirely) general fact that if a catalyst is acting to donate a proton in a given reaction when it proceeds in one direction, the conjugate base of the catalyst must act to remove that same proton in the reverse direction. In other words, a reaction that is subject to general acid catalysis in one direction is subject to specific acid catalysis (i.e., rapid proton transfer in a prior equilibrium step) and general base catalysis (by A⁻) in the reverse direction.

Now consider an alternative mechanism for the same reaction in which a proton is first added to the imine nitrogen atom in a fast equilibrium step, and the conjugate base of the catalyst A⁻ removes a proton from the attacking water molecule in order to make it a more effective nucleophilic reagent (equation 26). This

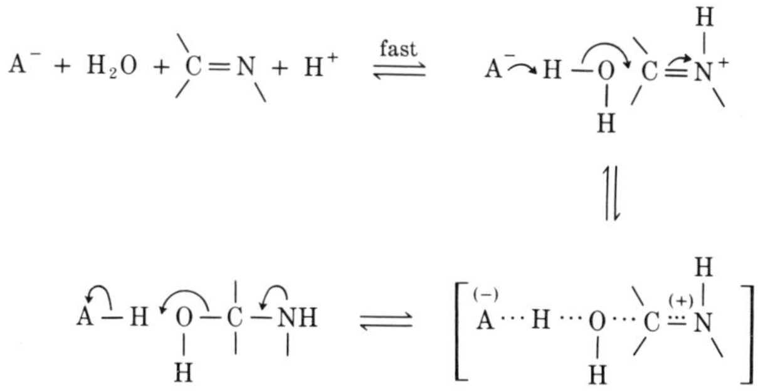

$$\tag{26}$$

amounts to specific acid catalysis–general base catalysis of the reaction in the forward direction. In the reverse direction the catalyst must act by donating a proton to the leaving hydroxyl group to partially convert it into a water molecule and increase its leaving ability. This is straightforward general acid catalysis.

These two mechanisms illustrate the ambiguity in assigning the site of catalysis in a general acid catalyzed reaction. This ambiguity is a problem in nearly all such reactions, and its resolution is one of the most important problems in the assignment of a mechanism to such a reaction. The same ambiguity exists in assigning mechanisms to enzyme catalyzed reactions, in which its resolution is even more difficult. In formal kinetic terms the ambiguity arises because both mechanisms exhibit the same rate law. This is easily shown algebraically. The rate law for reaction 25 is

$$v = k[\text{H}_2\text{O}][>\text{C}=\text{N}-][\text{HA}] \tag{27}$$

and that for reaction 26 is

$$v = k'[\text{H}_2\text{O}][>\text{C}=\overset{+}{\underset{\backslash}{\text{N}}}\text{H}][\text{A}^-] \tag{28}$$

The equilibrium constants for dissociation of the general acid and of the conjugate acid of the imine are

$$K_{\text{HA}} = \frac{[\text{H}^+][\text{A}^-]}{[\text{HA}]} \quad \text{and} \quad K_{\text{NH}^+} = \frac{[\text{H}^+][>\text{C}=\text{N}-]}{[>\text{C}=\overset{+}{\underset{\backslash}{\text{N}}}\text{H}]}$$

Substituting these into equation 28, one obtains

$$v = k'\frac{K_{\text{HA}}}{K_{\text{NH}^+}}[\text{H}_2\text{O}][>\text{C}=\text{N}-][\text{HA}] \tag{29}$$

which is identical to equation 27, except that $k = k'K_{\text{HA}}/K_{\text{NH}}^+$. Thus the two reactons follow identical rate laws and are indistinguishable by any ordinary kinetic test. There is a severe psychological barrier to the acceptance of this fact, but a firm understanding of it is essential for any considerations about the mechanism of chemical or enzymatic reactions in which this kind of ambiguity is possible.

The same ambiguity exists regarding general base catalysis. A reaction that is kinetically subject to general base catalysis may mechanistically be subject to true general base catalysis or to the kinetically indistinguishable specific base–general acid catalysis.

It may be noted here that there is a troublesome unresolved semantic problem regarding general acid and base catalysis. The phrase "general base catalysis" may refer, for example, to any one of the following.

1. The experimental observation that a reaction rate is accelerated by bases other than hydroxide ion. This could be caused by nucleophilic catalysis or by catalysis of proton transfer.

2. Catalysis of proton transfer by a buffer at a rate which is proportional to the concentration of the basic species of the buffer according to the rate law of equation 30. This could be true general base catalysis of proton transfer, or a combination of

$$v = k[HS][B] \tag{30}$$

the preequilibrium removal of a proton from the substrate (specific base catalysis) accompanied by general acid catalysis by the acidic species of the buffer. The latter reaction follows the rate law of equation 31, which is kinetically identical to

$$v = k'[S^-][HB^+] \tag{31}$$

that of equation 30, with $k = k' K_{HS}/K_{BH^+}$.

3. True general base catalysis in the mechanistic sense, in which the base is included in the transition state and acts to remove a proton when the reaction proceeds in a given direction.

There is no generally accepted way of distinguishing these meanings, so that it is important to explain which is meant when the terms are used.

It is perhaps worth explaining in more detail why the mechanisms of equations 25 and 26 are kinetically indistinguishable. First, one might hope to distinguish them by the pH-dependence of the rates. For simplicity we will assume that the fraction of the imine which is protonated in the range of pH under consideration is small. Then the pH-dependence of reaction 25 will be as shown in a logarithmic plot in Fig. 7 (solid line). The rate will be independent of pH in the range in which the catalyst is completely in the active form HA, and will decrease as it is converted to the inactive form A^-. The reason that reaction 26 will follow the same dependence on pH is as follows. In the low-pH region in which the rate is independent of pH an increase in pH of one unit, for example, will increase the concentration of the active form of the catalyst, A^-, tenfold (Fig. 7, dotted line), but will at the same time decrease the concentration of the active form of the substrate, $>C=\overset{+}{N}H$, tenfold (Fig. 7, dashed line). These effects will cancel each other out, so that the observed rate will be independent of pH. At high pH values the concentration of A^- will be independent of pH, but the concentration of $>C=\overset{+}{N}H$ will still decrease with increasing pH, so that the observed rate will decrease with increasing pH. Thus, the dependence on pH of the

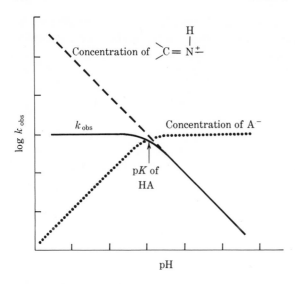

Fig 7.   Diagram to show why the dependence on pH of a reaction is the same if it involves general acid catalysis of the reaction of $>C=N-$ by HA or general base catalysis of the reaction of $>C=NH^+-$ by A^-.

two mechanisms is identical. The reader who feels uncertain about this conclusion should work out the analogous relationships for the mechanisms of the reverse reaction. The mechanisms also cannot be distinguished by differences in solvent effects, the effects of added salts, and other criteria of this kind. Although the effects of such changes on the concentrations of the various reactants and intermediates can be predicted, it can be shown in a manner analogous to that for the effect of pH that for a given polarity of the transition state, any differences in the effects on the intermediates cancels out and the same effect is predicted for both mechanisms.

The great utility of the transition-state treatment is that it enormously simplifies consideration of this kind of question, so that the correct answer can be seen at a glance. In terms of transition-state theory, the kinetics of a reaction determines the stoichiometric composition of the transition state. The kinetics, therefore, determines what atoms must be included and the net charge of the transition state, but gives no information on how the atoms or charges are arranged in the transition state. It is not possible to determine by ordinary kinetic techniques whether compounds which are in rapid equilibrium with the starting materials or products are true intermediates on the normal reaction path. It can immediately be seen that the transition states for the mechanisms of equations 25 and 26 have the same stoichiometric composition and charge and are, therefore, kinetically indistinguishable. Furthermore, if the transition states for reactions 25 and 26 have roughly the same polarity and charge distribution, one can immediately state that the mechanisms are indistinguishable by varying the solvent or added salts. Any such change may change the energy difference between the starting materials and the transition states, but the change will affect the stability of both transition states to a similar extent and, therefore, will affect the rate in a similar manner for both mechanisms.

Fortunately, there are techniques for resolving this ambiguity in some reactions. Four of these techniques are: (a) fixing the proton by complete protonation of the substrate; (b) examining a model compound in which an immobile substituent, such as a methyl group, is substituted for a proton; (c) showing that a particular mechanism requires an intermediate that is thermodynamically too unstable to permit the observed reaction rate; and (d) use of structure-reactivity correlations. These will be considered in turn with a few examples of their application; further examples are given in Chap. 10.

a) **Fixing the proton.** If the attack of water on an imine is studied at a pH at which the imine is already completely protonated, then the catalyst cannot be acting to donate a proton to the imine. If catalysis is observed under these conditions, therefore, it cannot occur according to the mechanism of equation 25, but is consistent with the mechanism of equation 26. It should be noted that the catalysis under these conditions will follow the rate law

$$v = k[\mathrm{H_2O}][>\mathrm{C}{=}\overset{+}{\mathrm{N}}\mathrm{H}][\mathrm{A}^-] \tag{32}$$

so that catalysis by the conjugate base of the catalyst will be observed. It has been shown above that this catalysis is kinetically the same as general acid catalysis of the reaction of the free imine (equation 28). This criterion is applicable to the hydrolysis of imines formed from aliphatic amines because such imines have pK values in the vicinity of 7 and are thus sufficiently basic to be examined at a pH at which they are completely protonated. The finding that the hydrolysis of benzylidene-1-1-dimethylethylamine (the imine of benzaldehyde and t-butylamine) is subject to catalysis by acetate ion at pH 4 to 5, under conditions in which it is completely protonated,[26] rules out the mechanism of equation 25 and supports that of equation 26.

The same principle may be applied to determining the mechanism of base catalysis by carrying out the reaction under conditions in which a dissociable proton has been completely removed from the substrate. For example, the reversible addition of acidic thiols to the carbonyl group of acetaldehyde is subject to general base catalysis and might, at first glance, be thought to proceed according to the mechanism of equation 33. In fact, it must proceed according

$$A^- \frown H \frown S \overset{\backslash}{\underset{R}{\diagup}} C = O \; \rightleftharpoons \; A - H \; S \overset{|}{\underset{R}{-}} \overset{|}{C} \frown O^- \; \overset{fast}{\rightleftharpoons} \; A^- + S \overset{|}{\underset{R}{-}} \overset{|}{C} - OH \tag{33}$$

to the kinetically equivalent mechanism of equation 34 because

$$RSH + \overset{\backslash}{\underset{\diagup}{C}} = O + A^- \; \overset{fast}{\rightleftharpoons} \; RS \frown \overset{\backslash}{C} = O \; H \frown A \; \rightleftharpoons \; RS \frown \overset{|}{C} \frown O - H \frown A^- \tag{34}$$

catalysis is observed under conditions in which the thiol is almost completely in the anionic form and no significant rate acceleration could result from partially removing a proton from the small remaining amount of free thiol.[27]

There are no reactions known in which a step that is thermodynamically easy, like the protonation of an imine of pK near 7 or the removal of a proton from an acidic thiol, has been shown to exhibit detectable general acid or base catalysis. One may make the tentative generalization that general acid or base catalysis occurs in such a way as to avoid the formation of the most unstable intermediates and transition states which resemble such intermediates in a reaction. In the mechanisms of equations 26 and 34, general acid-base catalysis avoids the formation of an unstable oxonium ion and alkoxide ion, respectively.

b) **Model Compounds** The problem with the proton is that it is mobile, and its position on one or another atom in the transition state cannot be decided from the rate law of a reaction. Now, if one substitutes a methyl group for the proton, the position of a group which differs only slightly from the proton in its polar character is

[26] E. H. Cordes and W. P. Jencks, *J. Am. Chem. Soc.* 85, 2843 (1963).
[27] R. Barnett and W. P. Jencks, *J. Am. Chem. Soc.* 89, 5963 (1967).

known, and from the observed behavior of this model compound the behavior of the corresponding protonic compound may be inferred. For example, the dehydration step in oxime formation is subject to general acid catalysis and could occur by the mechanisms of either equation 25 or equation 26 in the direction from right to left, as written. The mechanism of equation 25 requires that the conjugate base of the catalyst remove a proton from the nitrogen atom. Now, if a methyl group is substituted for the proton, the catalyst cannot remove it, so that if mechanism 25 is correct, no catalysis should be seen for the corresponding step of nitrone formation (equation 35) which is the same as that for oxime forma-

$$
\begin{array}{c}
 \text{H} \\
 | / \\
\text{A} \overset{\frown}{}\!\text{CH}_3\,\overset{\curvearrowright}{\text{N}} \!\overset{|}{-}\! \overset{\curvearrowright}{\text{C}} \!-\!\overset{/}{\text{O}}{}^{+} \\
 | | \backslash \\
 \text{OH} \text{H}
\end{array}
\tag{35}
$$

tion except for the methyl substitution. However, if catalysis of nitrone formation is seen, mechanism 25 is ruled out, and the mechanism of equations 26 and 36 is consistent with the experimental

$$
\begin{array}{c}
 \overset{\frown}{} | \\
\text{CH}_3 \overset{..}{\text{N}} \!\overset{|}{-}\! \text{C} \!-\!\overset{\curvearrowleft}{\text{O}} {}^{\backprime} \text{H} - \text{A} \\
 | | | \\
 \text{OH} \text{H}
\end{array}
\tag{36}
$$

results. As shown in Fig. 8 the dehydration step of nitrone formation from *p*-chlorobenzaldehyde shows catalysis by general acids and has a Brønsted slope of 0.77, which is the same as that for oxime formation.[28] Thus, it appears that these two reactions proceed by the same mechanism, which must be that of equation 26. The same principle has been used to determine the mechanism of catalysis of the attack of water on imines by examining the hydrolysis of benzhydrylidenedimethylammonium ion (3). This compound is a model for

$$
\begin{array}{c}
 \diagup\text{CH}_3 \\
\backslash \diagup \\
\text{C} =\!\!\overset{+}{\text{N}} \\
\diagup \backslash \\
 \text{CH}_3 \\
\textbf{3}
\end{array}
$$

[28] J. E. Reimann and W. P. Jencks, *J. Am. Chem. Soc.* **88**, 3973 (1966). The fact that catalysis is also observed in the reaction with methoxyamine suggests that catalysis does not involve the removal of a proton from the hydroxyl group of the hydroxylamine in nitrone formation.

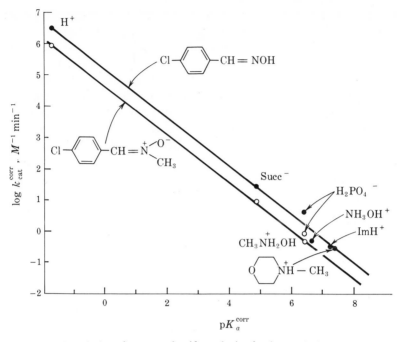

Fig 8.   Brønsted plots for general acid catalysis of oxime and nitrone formation.[28]

the conjugate acid of benzhydrylidenemethylamine, and the fact that similar catalysis is seen for both compounds rules out the mechanism of equation 25 and supports that of equation 26 for both reactions.[29]

  c) **Thermodynamically unstable intermediates and the diffusion-controlled limit.** A reaction mechanism which proceeds through an unstable intermediate may be ruled out if it can be shown that the intermediate would have to react with some other reactant in the solution at a rate which is greater than the diffusion-controlled limit in order to account for the observed overall rate of reaction. For example, general acid catalysis of the attack of semicarbazide on *p*-nitrobenzaldehyde could occur by proton donation to the carbonyl group (equation 37) or by general base catalysis of the

$$\overset{\frown}{A} - H \ \overset{\frown}{O} = \overset{/}{C} \overset{\frown}{\underset{\backslash}{H_2 NR}} \tag{37}$$

[29] K. Koehler, W. Sandstrom, and E. H. Cordes, *J. Am. Chem. Soc.* **86**, 2413 (1964).

attack of semicarbizide on the conjugate acid of p-nitrobenzaldehyde (equation 38). The kinetically indistinguishable rate laws for these

$$\begin{array}{c}\diagdown \\ \diagup\end{array} C=O \; + \; H^+ \; \overset{fast}{\rightleftharpoons} \; HO \overset{+}{=} C \begin{array}{c} H \\ | \\ N-H \frown A^- \\ | \\ R \end{array} \tag{38}$$

two reactions, for catalysis by the solvated proton, are

$$v = k\,[RNH_2]\,[> C = O]\,[H^+] \tag{39}$$

and

$$v = k'\,[RNH_2]\,[> C = \overset{+}{O}H] \; = \frac{k'}{K_A}\,[RNH_2]\,[> C = O]\,[H^+] \tag{40}$$

respectively, in which K_A is the dissociation constant for the conjugate acid of p-nitrobenzaldehyde (equation 41). Based on the H_0

$$K_A = \frac{[> C = O]\,[H^+]}{[> C = \overset{+}{O}H]} \tag{41}$$

scale of acidity, the value of K_A has been estimated spectrophotometrically[30] to be $10^{8.45}$. Since $k = 10^4$ M^{-2}sec^{-1} experimentally, k' would have to be 2.7×10^{12} M^{-1} sec^{-1} if mechanism 38 were correct. This is larger than the rate constant of 1.4×10^{11} M^{-1} sec^{-1} for the fastest known diffusion-controlled reaction in water, the reaction of the solvated proton with hydroxide ion.[31] This effectively rules out the conjugate acid of p-nitrobenzaldehyde as a free intermediate and suggests that the mechanism of equation 37 is correct for this reaction.[32] This calculation may be questioned because the H_0 scale of acidity may not hold exactly for benzaldehydes, but similar calculations for other reactions require even

[30] K. Yates and R. Stewart, *Can. J. Chem.* **37**, 664 (1959).

[31] M. Eigen and L. De Maeyer, *Z. Elektrochem.* **59**, 986 (1955).

[32] Actually, the reaction of equation 38 is a third-order reaction in which water acts as a general base catalyst. It is assumed here that the hydrogen of semicarbazide is hydrogen bonded to water and that the complex attacks the protonated aldehyde in a second-order reaction. If it is not hydrogen bonded, the situation would be even less favorable.

larger rate constants k' if they are to proceed through the conjugate acid of the aldehyde. For example, the acid catalyzed attack of tetrahydrofolic acid on formaldehyde would require a rate constant of 7.4×10^{15} M^{-1} sec^{-1} if it proceeded through this mechanism.[33] On the basis of the presently available evidence, the generalization that such conjugate acids are not involved as free intermediates in reactions of this kind appears to be warranted.

The possibility remains that the transition state of equation 38 can be reached by another path which does not involve the conjugate acid of the aldehyde as an intermediate, but this does not appear probable. The aldehyde could first form a weak complex with the nitrogen base, followed by reaction with the proton to give a pro-tonated intermediate and, finally, by conversion of the intermediate, to the transition state. However, the known equilibrium constants for the formation of such complexes of amines and carbonyl com-pounds are very small indeed even in nonaqueous solution,[34] and in any case would not be expected to cause a large increase in the basicity of the carbonyl group. The only remaining possibility would seem to be that this transition state is reached in a true termolecular reaction without the formation of such unstable inter-mediates. However, this requires that the molecule of acid which donates the proton to the carbonyl group be present in the transition state, which is the principal feature of the mechanism of equation 37, not equation 38.

The same argument may be applied to the rate constant of a reaction in the reverse direction. For example, the unfavorable equilibrium constant for the formation of an aniline anion (the pK_a of aniline is approximately 27)[35] requires that this unstable inter-mediate would have to react at a greater than diffusion-controlled rate to account for the calculated rate of the reaction of equation 42 (the breakdown of the tetrahedral addition intermediate in the hy-drolysis of the diphenylimidazolinium cation) in the reverse direc-tion.[36] A mechanism similar to that of equation 43, is, therefore, preferred for this reaction. It is probably another safe generaliza-tion to state that anions of ordinary amines are not involved as free intermediates in reactions which occur in aqueous solution; their

[33] R. G. Kallen and W. P. Jencks, *J. Biol. Chem.* **241**, 5851 (1966).

[34] O. H. Wheeler and E. M. Levy, *Can. J. Chem.* **37**, 1727 (1959); B. Becker and A. W. Davidson, *J. Am. Chem. Soc.* **85**, 159 (1963).

[35] D. Dolman and R. Stewart, *Can. J. Chem.* **45**, 911 (1967).

[36] D. R. Robinson and W. P. Jencks, *J. Am. Chem. Soc.* **89**, 7088 (1967).

$$
\begin{array}{c}
\text{H}_5\text{C}_6 \quad \quad \text{C}_6\text{H}_5 \\
\text{N} \quad \text{N} \\
\text{H} \quad \text{O} - \text{H} \cdots \text{B}
\end{array}
\quad \rightleftharpoons \quad
\begin{array}{c}
\text{H}_5\text{C}_6 \quad \quad \text{C}_6\text{H}_5 \\
\text{N} \quad \text{N} \\
\text{C} \\
\text{H} \quad \text{O} \cdots \text{H} - \overset{+}{\text{B}}
\end{array}
\tag{42}
$$

$$
\begin{array}{c}
\text{H}_5\text{C}_6 \quad \quad \text{C}_6\text{H}_5 \\
\text{N} \quad \text{N} \\
\text{H} \quad \text{O} - \text{H} - \overset{+}{\text{B}}
\end{array}
\quad \rightleftharpoons \quad
\begin{array}{c}
\text{H}_5\text{C}_6 \quad \quad \text{C}_6\text{H}_5 \\
\text{N} \quad \text{N} \\
\text{C} \\
\text{H} \quad \text{O} \quad \text{H} \cdots \text{B}
\end{array}
\tag{43}
$$

formation is frequently avoided by general acid-base catalysis.

This situation may be described in a different way by the statement that the free energy for the formation of an intermediate cannot be appreciably greater than the overall free energy of activation of the reaction (except in the case of chain reactions). The theoretical limit for the free energy of such an intermediate is some 5000 cal/mole less than the free energy of activation because the transition state has one more degree of freedom—along the reaction coordinate—than is allowed for in the calculation[37]; but this allowance is largely counterbalanced by the requirement of an additional free energy of activation for the formation and breakdown of the unstable intermediate. The latter quantity cannot be less than about 3000 cal/mole, the free energy of activation for a diffusion-controlled reaction.

d) **Structure-reactivity correlations and the Hammond postulate.** There is a widespread intuitive feeling that there should be a correlation between equilibrium and rate constants of reactions; that is, reactions which have a strong driving force thermodynamically will also proceed rapidly. A moment's consideration shows that no such correlation holds generally: the energetically favorable oxidation of organic compounds in the presence of air may not take place for years, while the energetically unfavorable hydration of carbon dioxide takes place in seconds. Nevertheless, there is certainly an element of truth in this intuitive feeling. This may be simply expressed in the statement that in the case of a reaction in which the transition state has structural features which are intermediate between those of the starting materials and products, factors which stabilize these features in the products will also stabilize them in the

[37] M. M. Kreevoy, in A. Weissberger (ed.), "Technique of Organic Chemistry," 2d ed., vol. VIII, part II, p. 1399, Interscience Publishers, Inc., New York, 1963.

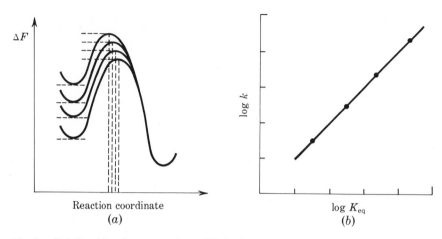

Fig 9. Relationship of rates and equilibria in the alkaline hydrolysis of esters. (*a*) Transition-state diagrams for a series of esters in which substituents with increasing electron-withdrawing ability are introduced into the alcohol moiety. (*b*) Linear free-energy relationship of rates and equilibria for the same series of esters.

transition state, relative to the starting materials, so that there will be a correlation of rates with overall equilibria. The fact that transition states frequently (but by no means always) do have some such resemblance to products accounts for the existence of such correlations within a given reaction series. The way in which a given structural change may have proportional effects on rates and equilibria is illustrated for ester saponification in Fig. 9*a*: as electron-withdrawing groups are introduced into the alcohol to make the overall reaction more favorable,[38] there is a parallel decrease in the energy of the transition state relative to the starting materials and an increase in the saponification rate. In this case, the effect of the electron-withdrawing substituents is perhaps best described as a destabilization of the starting material with respect to both the transition state and the products, owing to an energetically unfavorable interaction with the electronegative carbonyl group. This correlation may be shown directly in a logarithmic plot (Fig. 9*b*), which, since it correlates the free energy of activation with the free energy of the overall reaction, is another example of a linear free-energy relationship.

Another important consequence is evident from the (grossly exaggerated) transition-state diagrams of Fig. 9*a*. If it is assumed

[38] J. Gerstein and W. P. Jencks, *J. Am. Chem. Soc.* **86**, 4655 (1964).

that the shape of the energy curves does not vary greatly as the structure of the reactants is changed, then it is apparent that the transition state for the faster and thermodynamically more favored reaction will occur earlier along the reaction coordinate. In other words, in the faster reaction there will be less formation of the new bond and less breaking of the old bond than in the slower reaction; i.e., the transition state will resemble the starting materials more closely than the products. This principle is most obvious in the limiting case (Fig. 10); if there is almost no activation energy for a strongly exothermic reaction, the starting materials and transition states will be nearly identical. The existence of this sort of relationship has been noted many times,[39] but is most commonly referred to as the Hammond postulate.

Linear free-energy relationships may be correlated with each other, and certain correlations give what are essentially quantitative statements of the Hammond postulate.[40-42] The correlation which

[39] M. G. Evans and M. Polanyi, *Trans. Faraday Soc.* **34**, 11 (1938); J. E. Leffler, *Science* **117**, 340 (1953); G. S. Hammond, *J. Am. Chem. Soc.* **77**, 334 (1955).

[40] S. I. Miller, *J. Am. Chem. Soc.* **81**, 101 (1959); L. Wilputte-Steinert, P. J. C. Fierens, and H. Hannaert, *Bull. Soc. Chim. Belges* **64**, 628 (1955).

[41] J. Leffler and E. Grunwald, "Rates and Equilibria of Organic Reactions," John Wiley & Sons, Inc., New York, 1963.

[42] E. H. Cordes and W. P. Jencks, *J. Am. Chem. Soc.* **84**, 4319 (1962).

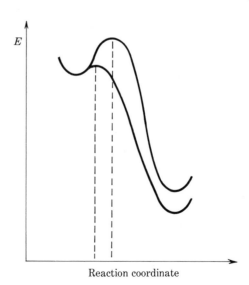

Fig 10. Energy profile to show how the transition state for a highly exothermic reaction occurs early along the reaction coordinate.

Reaction coordinate

is of interest here is that of the Brønsted relationship for general
acid catalysis (equation 44) with a relationship of the Swain-Scott

$$\log k_{i.j} = \log G_i{}^A - \alpha_i pK_{a.j} \tag{44}$$

type[43] for nucleophilic reactivity n and sensitivity to nucleophilic
attack s (equation 45). The subscripts in these equations refer to

$$\log k_{j.k} = \log k_{j.o} + n_k s_j \tag{45}$$

particular reactants or reaction series. Equations 44 and 45 may be
combined to give the relationships

$$pK_2 - pK_1 = c_2(s_2 - s_1) \tag{46}$$

and

$$n_k = c_2(\alpha_o - \alpha_k) \tag{47}$$

in which c_2 is a constant.[42,44] Equation 46 states, in accord with the
Hammond postulate, that as a substrate is made more reactive by
catalysis with a stronger acid (pK_2 decreases), its selectivity toward
the nucleophilic reactivity of the attacking reagent s_2 decreases.
For example, nucleophilic attack on a carbonyl group which is catalyzed by the solvated proton should be less selective with respect to
the nucleophile than reactions of the same carbonyl compound which
are catalyzed by water. Catalysis by a stronger acid decreases the
energy difference between the starting materials and the transition
state and thus, according to the Hammond postulate, makes the
transition state more closely resemble the starting materials and
occur earlier along the reaction coordinate. There will then be less
bond formation with the attacking nucleophilic reagent and, hence,
less selectivity with respect to the nucleophilic reagent. Equation
47 states the converse of this relationship, namely, that as the
nucleophilic reactivity of the attacking reagent n_k increases, the
reaction will show a smaller sensitivity to the strength of the acid
catalyst, i.e., a smaller value of α.

The analogous relationships for general base catalysis are
shown in equations 48 and 49. Equation 48 states that as the

[43] C. G. Swain and C. B. Scott, *J. Am. Chem. Soc.* **75**, 141 (1953).
[44] G. E. Lienhard and W. P. Jencks, *J. Am. Chem. Soc.* **88**, 3982 (1966).

catalyzing base becomes stronger, the selectivity toward the nucleophilic reagent will decrease. Equation 49 states that as the reactivity of the nucleophilic reagent becomes larger, the sensitivity of

$$pK_2 - pK_1 = c_5(s_1 - s_2) \tag{48}$$

$$n_i c_5 = \beta_o - \beta_i \tag{49}$$

the reaction to general base catalysis, as measured by the Brønsted β, will decrease. There are no assumptions in equations 46 to 49 beyond those of the original Brønsted and Swain-Scott relationships. However, the assumption that the sign of the constants c is positive relates the equations to the principle of the Hammond postulate and is in accord with experience. Equations 46 and 47 refer to true general acid catalysis, and not to its kinetic equivalent of specific acid–general base catalysis. Similarly, equations 48 and 49 refer to true general base catalysis, not specific base–general acid catalysis.

These relationships provide a means of resolving the kinetic ambiguity between general acid catalysis and specific acid–general base catalysis, since α for general acid catalysis is equal to $1 - \beta$ for the same series of catalysts if the reaction is actually specific acid–general base catalysis, and vice versa. This relationship may easily be demonstrated algebraically or by a numerical example. Thus, by determining in a series of related reactions whether α or β (that is, $1 - \alpha$) increases with decreasing nucleophilic reactivity of the attacking reagent, one can determine whether the reaction series follows equation 47 or equation 49, i.e., whether the observed catalysis is true general acid catalysis or specific acid–general base catalysis.

A series of values of α for attack of nucleophilic reagents of decreasing basicity and nucleophilic reactivity on acetaldehyde and benzaldehydes is shown in Table III.[13,26,27,42,44-52] It is apparent

[45] T. D. Stewart and H. P. Kung, *J. Am. Chem. Soc.* **55**, 4813 (1933).

[46] W. J. Svirbely and J. F. Roth, *J. Am. Chem. Soc.* **75**, 3106 (1953).

[47] T. D. Stewart and L. H. Donnally, *J. Am. Chem. Soc.* **54**, 2333, 3559 (1932).

[48] W. P. Jencks, *J. Am. Chem. Soc.* **81**, 475 (1959).

[49] L. do Amaral, W. A. Sandstrom, and E. H. Cordes, *J. Am. Chem. Soc.* **88**, 2225 (1966).

[50] E. H. Cordes and W. P. Jencks, *J. Am. Chem. Soc.* **84**, 832 (1962).

[51] J. B. Conant and P. D. Bartlett, *J. Am. Chem. Soc.* **54**, 2881 (1932).

[52] R. P. Bell, M. H. Rand, and K. M. A. Wynne-Jones, *Trans. Faraday Soc.* **52**, 1093 (1956).

Table III   Values of α for general acid catalysis of the addition of nucleophilic reagents to acetaldehyde and benzaldehydes

Nucleophile	pK_a	Aldehyde	α	Reference
HOO^-	11.6	ClC_6H_4CHO	0	13
RNH_2	~10	XC_6H_4CHO	0	26, 45
RS^-	~10	CH_3CHO	0	44
CN^-	9.4	Several	~0	46
$SO_3^=$	7.0	C_6H_5CHO	~0	47
NH_2OH	6.0	C_6H_5CHO	very small	48
$C_6H_5NHNH_2$	5.2	C_6H_5CHO	0.20	49
$XC_6H_4S^-$, CH_3COS^-	3-6	CH_3CHO	0.20	27
$C_6H_5NH_2$	4.6	ClC_6H_4CHO	0.25	50
$H_2NNHCONH_2$	3.7	C_6H_5CHO	0.25	42, 51
H_2NCONH_2	0.2	CH_3CHO	0.45	49
H_2O	-1.7	CH_3CHO	0.54	52
RSH	~-7	CH_3CHO	~0.7	44
$HOOH$	~-7	ClC_6H_4CHO	1.0	13

that the sensitivity to the strength of the catalyzing acid α increases
steadily as the nucleophilic strength of the attacking reagent decreases. This is as predicted for true general acid catalysis (equation 47) in the forward direction, which is equivalent to specific acid
catalysis–general base catalysis in the reverse direction. It is in the
opposite direction from that expected for specific acid–general base
catalysis (equation 49) in the forward direction, which is equivalent
to general acid catalysis in the reverse direction. Swain and
Worosz have reached the same conclusion for the attack of nitrogen
nucleophiles on the carbonyl group by application of two other
structure-reactivity relationships, the "reacting bond rule" and the
"solvation rule."[53]

The more limited data which are available for carbonyl addition
reactions that are subject to what appears kinetically as general
base catalysis in the forward direction suggest that this is true
general base catalysis for weakly acidic nucleophiles and not the
kinetically equivalent specific base–general acid catalysis.[54]

Other criteria may be helpful in distinguishing mechanisms
in special cases. For example, if it can be shown that the basic
species of a nucleophile attacks a carbonyl group without assistance

[53] C. G. Swain and J. C. Worosz, Tetrahedron Letters **36**, 3199 (1965).

[54] W. P. Jencks, Progr. Phys. Org. Chem. **2**, 63 (1964).

from general acid catalysis, then any observed general base catalysis of the attack of the conjugate acid of the nucleophile cannot be interpreted as general acid catalysis of attack of the basic species. A positive deviation of the rate constant for hydroxide ion catalysis from a Brønsted plot suggests that this term involves such a direct nucleophilic attack of the nucleophile, which is formed in a rapid prior equilibrium step (specific base catalysis). This criterion has been applied to the addition of hydrogen peroxide to aldehydes, for which the positive deviation of the hydroxide ion term has been interpreted as evidence for direct attack of the hydrogen peroxide anion[13] (Chap. 10, Sec. B, Part 2).

D. CONCERTED GENERAL ACID-BASE CATALYSIS, "ONE-ENCOUNTER" REACTIONS, AND PROTON EXCHANGE WITH SOLVENT

1. THE MUTAROTATION OF GLUCOSE

It has often been suggested that the extraordinary catalytic activity of enzymes might be the result of a concerted action of two or more general acid or base catalysts in the active site acting on different parts of the substrate. These speculations may, in large part, be traced back to Lowry,[55] who proposed that reactions which require both the removal and the addition of a proton, such as the mutarotation of glucose (equation 50), proceed by a concerted mechanism in

$$(50)$$

which catalysis of both of the proton transfers must occur in order for the reaction to take place (4). If an acid or base catalyst is not

4

added to the system, the solvent must play the role of proton ac-

[55] T. M. Lowry and I. J. Faulkner, *J. Chem. Soc.* **1925**, 2883; T. M. Lowry, *Ibid.* **1927**, 2554.

ceptor and donor. In support of this view it was shown that the mutarotation of glucose or tetramethylglucose proceeds very slowly or not at all in aprotic and weakly basic solvents, such as dry benzene, but is markedly accelerated by the addition of small quantities of water. In pure pyridine or cresol, there is no appreciable reaction, although each of these compounds is a catalyst of the reaction in water. However, if pyridine and cresol are mixed, so that both proton donors and acceptors are present in the solvent, the reaction proceeds rapidly.

Swain and Brown extended this approach with an examination of the kinetics of the mutarotation of tetramethylglucose in benzene, catalyzed by pyridine and phenol.[56] The reaction was found to be third order and to follow the rate law of equation 51. This rate law

$$v = k[\text{Glu}][\text{phenol}][\text{pyridine}] \tag{51}$$

indicates that both phenol and pyridine (or phenoxide and pyridinium ions) are required in the transition state and are presumably acting as an acid and a base *at the same time*. Reasoning that such catalysis should be even more effective in dilute solution if the acidic and basic groups were combined into the same catalyst molecule, they found that α-pyridone (α-hydroxypyridine) and benzoic acid are effective catalysts at low concentration, even though the catalyzing groups of these molecules are considerably weaker acids and bases than phenol and pyridine. A 0.05 M solution of α-pyridone was found to give a rate of mutarotation 50 times greater than equivalent concentrations of phenol and pyridine; in more dilute solutions the difference in rates is even more striking. A reasonable mechanism for this catalysis is shown in equation 52. "Push-pull" catal-

$$\tag{52}$$

ysis by the basic carbonyl group and the acidic N—H group facilitates cleavage of the hemiacetal to give the free aldehyde; the proton transfers take place in the reverse direction in the ring clo-

[56] C. G. Swain and J. F. Brown, Jr., *J. Am. Chem. Soc.* **74**, 2534, 2538 (1952).

sure reaction to give a mixture of the α and β forms of the sugar. In spite of the fact that α-pyridone exists predominantly in the pyridone, rather than the α-hydroxypyridine structure, the principle of microscopic reversibility requires that catalysis of the reverse reaction according to the mechanism of equation 52 must involve the α-hydroxypyridine tautomer. An equally plausible mechanism (originally proposed by Swain and Brown) involves catalysis by α-hydroxypyridine in the forward direction and by α-pyridone in the reverse direction (equation 53).

$$\tag{53}$$

The difficulties with this model reaction arise from the fact that it is carried out in benzene; no such special effectiveness of catalysts capable of concerted catalysis has been observed for the mutarotation of glucose in water. In benzene the experimental situation is set up to make the existence of such catalysis highly probable. The absence of effective acidic and basic groups in the solvent means that the proton transfers which are a necessary part of the reaction can take place only with great difficulty, and catalysts must be supplied in order to permit the reaction to occur at a reasonable rate. In water, the solvent itself is an effective proton donor and acceptor and no concerted catalysis is seen. An enzyme must catalyze a reaction faster than it occurs in water, and one could speculate with greater confidence about the possible role of concerted acid-base catalysis in enzymes if such catalysis could be shown to be effective in aqueous solution. The interpretation of such experiments is further confused by the extraordinary sensitivity of reactions in benzene solution to the presence of ions, which can stabilize polar transition states in this nonpolar solvent and which might be formed by the reaction of pyridine with phenol to give pyridinium phenoxide. Tetrabutylammonium phenoxide, which has no acidic proton, and other salts are effective catalysts of the mutarotation of tetramethylglucose in nonpolar solvents[57] and other

[57] Y. Pocker, *Chem. Ind.* (*London*) **1960**, 968; A. M. Eastham, E. L. Blackall, and G. A. Latremouille, *J. Am. Chem. Soc.* **77**, 2182 (1955); E. L. Blackall and A. M. Eastham, *Ibid.*, p. 2184.

reactions show rate accelerations of as much as 10^5 upon the addition of low concentrations of salts to nonpolar solvents.[58]

There have been many attempts to demonstrate the existence of concerted acid-base catalysis of reactions which involve the removal of protons from carbon. Such catalysis by separate molecules of acid and base for the enolization of a ketone would give a third-order term in the rate law of the form of equation 54. It

$$v = k[\text{HA}][\text{B}][\overset{|}{\underset{|\;|}{\text{HCC}}} = \text{O}] \tag{54}$$

would presumably involve proton donation to the carbonyl group by a general acid at the same time that a proton is removed from carbon by the base (5). Such a term has been detected in the rate law

$$B\frown H\overset{\curvearrowright}{-}\overset{|}{\underset{|}{C}}\overset{\curvearrowleft}{-}C\overset{O\cdots H-A}{\diagdown}$$

5

for catalysis of the enolization of acetone by acetic acid and sodium acetate,[59, 60] but for most such reactions this type of catalysis is either not observed or is not very important. The possibility exists that these terms in the rate law represent catalysis by a hydrogen-bonded acid-base pair, $A - H \cdots A^-$, rather than concerted acid-base catalysis.[59, 61] The analogous hydrogen-bonded species, $F - H - F^-$, is known to be an effective catalyst for the keto-enol interconversion of acetone.[62] However, the rate law for the ketonization of the enol of oxalacetate contains a product term of the form of equation 54, which is significant at low concentrations of phosphate, imidazole, and triethanolamine buffers.[63] The existence of a significant fraction of these buffers as hydrogen-bonded pairs is unlikely at the concentrations used in these experiments (0.1 to 0.2 M), so that a stronger case can be made for concerted catalysis in this reaction.

[58] S. Winstein, S. Smith, and D. Darwish, *J. Am. Chem. Soc.* **81**, 5511 (1959).

[59] H. M. Dawson and E. Spivey, *J. Chem. Soc.* **1930**, 2180.

[60] R. P. Bell and P. Jones, *J. Chem. Soc.* **1953**, 88.

[61] F. J. C. Rossotti, *Nature* **188**, 936 (1960).

[62] R. P. Bell and J. C. McCoubrey, *Proc. Roy. Soc. (London)* **234A**, 192 (1956).

[63] B. E. C. Banks, *J. Chem. Soc.* **1962**, 63.

2. BENZYLIDENEBENZYLAMINES

For many years one of the most convincing models for concerted general acid-base catalysis was the base catalyzed isomerization of substituted benzylidenebenzylamines (equation 55).[64] In this reac-

$$
\underset{1}{R_2 \backslash \overset{H}{\underset{*}{C}} / R_1} - N = C \overset{R_3}{\underset{R_4}{\diagdown}} \quad \overset{3}{\rightleftharpoons} \quad R_2 \backslash C = N - C \overset{H \quad R_3}{\underset{R_4}{\diagup}}
$$

$$
R_2 \backslash \overset{(-)}{C} \overset{(-)}{\cdots} N \overset{(-)}{\cdots} C / R_3 \atop R_1 \qquad R_4
$$

$$
\mathbf{6} \tag{55}
$$

tion racemization, incorporation of deuterium from the solvent, and the overall isomerization occur at the same rate in a solvent of 2:1 dioxane–EtOD. The equivalence of these rates rules out a mechanism which involves the *reversible* formation of the carbanion **6** because if reaction 1 proceeded more rapidly than reaction 2, racemization and hydrogen exchange would occur at a faster rate than the overall reaction. It was, therefore, suggested that the reaction proceeds in a concerted fashion according to reaction 3. However, it has recently been shown that this is incorrect, at least for the reaction shown in equation 56. This isomerization proceeds in the

$$
\underset{H}{\overset{C_6H_5}{\underset{|}{CH_3C}}} - N = CC_6H_4Cl \quad \overset{B}{\rightleftharpoons} \quad \underset{H}{\overset{C_6H_5}{\underset{|}{CH_3C}}} = N - \underset{H}{\overset{C_6H_4Cl}{\underset{|}{CC_6H_4Cl}}} \tag{56}
$$

forward direction without exchange of hydrogen with the solvent, but in the reverse direction hydrogen exchange occurs at a rate 10 to 20 times greater than that of the overall isomerization.[65] Thus, the reaction must proceed through a carbanion intermediate rather than by a concerted mechanism. The reason that no exchange or racemization of starting material is observed in the forward direc-

[64] R. P. Ossorio and E. D. Hughes, *J. Chem. Soc.* **1952**, 426.
[65] D. J. Cram and R. D. Guthrie, *J. Am. Chem. Soc.* **87**, 397 (1965); **88**, 5760 (1966).

tion is simply that reaction 2 of equation 55 is faster than reaction 1, so that the carbanion is more rapidly converted to product than it reverts to starting material.

3. PROTON EXCHANGE WITH THE SOLVENT

A most interesting finding in this reaction is that 38 to 50% of the proton transfers in the forward reaction occur without equilibration of the labeled protons with the solvent in t-butanol–t-butoxide. That is, in one-third to one-half of the reactions, the same proton is removed from one end of the molecule and added to the other, without exchange with the hydroxylic solvent. An even more striking example of the same phenomenon is found in the base catalyzed isomerization reaction shown in equation 57. In the

$$(57)$$

presence of deuterated triethylcarbinol as solvent, the proton transfer in this reaction proceeds 98% without exchange with solvent deuterons.[66] Even in the presence of 10% D_2O in tetrahydrofuran the reaction proceeds 34% without exchange with solvent. The proton must be picked up by a base at one end of the molecule and carried to the other end to react without exchange with solvent, and this mechanism must be preferred to the addition of a proton to the carbanion from the solvent at the other end. Cram[66] calls this a "conducted-tour" mechanism. Evidently, in these relatively nonpolar solvents the formation and movement of the initially formed ion pair to the other end of the molecule is preferred to a mechanism

[66] D. J. Cram, F. Willey, H. P. Fischer, H. M. Relles, and D. A. Scott, *J. Am. Chem. Soc.* 88, 2759 (1966).

which would require the development of a localized negative charge in a solvent molecule at the other end of the substrate molecule (equation 58).

$$ \text{(58)} $$

A somewhat analogous situation has been reported to occur in the reaction of benzoic anhydride with aniline.[67] If the reaction is carried out with anhydride which is labeled with ^{18}O only in the carbonyl group, it is found that the ^{18}O content of the benzanilide product requires that the oxygen atoms of the anhydride should have equilibrated with each other before the final product is formed. This result would be accounted for (equation 59) if the benzoate ion

$$ \text{(59)} $$

that is displaced from the anhydride can undergo equilibration of its oxygen atoms and attack the cationic intermediate, 7, to reform anhydride more rapidly than it can remove a proton from 7 to give the stable benzanilide product. This back-reaction would result in equilibration of the anhydride oxygen atoms. The equilibration is reported to occur in ether and in methanol as solvents. Although a control with ^{14}C-labeled benzoic acid was carried out to show that the equilibration was not caused by a direct attack of benzoate ion on the anhydride in ether, it would be desirable to carry out similar controls in other solvents.

It is clear that in some chemical reactions, especially in nonpolar solvents, the rate of equilibration of reacting protons with the solvent can be slow compared with the rate of other processes.

[67] D. B. Denney and M. A. Greenbaum, *J. Am. Chem. Soc.* **79**, 3701 (1957).

The same is true of enzymatic reactions. Phosphoglucose isomerase catalyzes a proton transfer from the 2 to the 1 carbon of the sugar to give fructose-6-phosphate. That it is indeed a proton that is being transferred is almost certain, because a labeled hydrogen atom in the 2 position undergoes partial exchange with solvent as it is being transferred to the 1 position. However, the fact that some transfer occurs *without* exchange with solvent means that the intermediate, in which the proton has presumably been transferred to a base in the active site of the enzyme (equation 60), can

$$
\begin{array}{c}
\left|\; -\text{B} \quad \overset{*}{\text{H}}-\overset{\displaystyle\overset{H}{|}}{\underset{\displaystyle\underset{C=O}{|}}{C}}-\text{OH} \;\right| \\[2em]
\Updownarrow \\[2em]
\end{array}
$$

$$
\left|\; -\text{B} \;\; \overset{\text{HC}^{\nearrow O}}{\underset{\overset{*}{\text{H}}-\text{COH}}{}} \;\right|
\;\rightleftharpoons\;
\left|\; -\overset{+}{\text{B}}-\overset{*}{\text{H}} \;\; \overset{\displaystyle\overset{H}{|}}{\underset{\displaystyle\underset{C-OH}{|}}{C}}-O^{-} \;\right|
\;\xrightarrow{\text{fast}}\;
\left|\; -\overset{+}{\text{B}}-\overset{*}{\text{H}} \;\; \overset{\displaystyle\overset{H}{|}}{\underset{\displaystyle\underset{C-O^{-}}{|}}{C}}-OH \;\right|
$$

$$
\Updownarrow \;\pm\overset{*}{\text{H}}{}^{+},\,\text{H}^{+}
$$

$$
\rightleftharpoons\;
\left|\; -\overset{+}{\text{B}}-\text{H} \;\; \overset{\displaystyle\overset{H}{|}}{\underset{\displaystyle\underset{C-OH}{|}}{C}}-O^{-} \;\right|
\;\rightleftharpoons \tag{60}
$$

donate a proton to the 1 position to give product at a rate comparable to the rate of equilibration of the proton with the solvent. The necessary proton transfers on the oxygen atoms can probably occur very rapidly, either with the aid of other acid-base catalysts on the enzyme or by a direct transfer. The ratio of the exchange with solvent to the transfer reaction increases with increasing temperature, showing that the former reaction has the larger temperature coefficient.[68]

In the case of the enzyme Δ^{5}-3-ketosteroid isomerase, which catalyzes a somewhat similar proton transfer, the transfer reaction

---

[68] I. A. Rose and E. L. O'Connell, *J. Biol. Chem.* **236**, 3086 (1961); I. A. Rose, *Brookhaven Symp. Biol.* **15**, 293 (1962).

is even faster as compared with exchange with solvent, so that very little dilution of labeled hydrogen with protons from the solvent occurs during the transfer reaction (equation 61).[69]

$$\tag{61}$$

4. DIFFUSION–CONTROLLED PROTON TRANSFERS

It was thought at one time that the absence of proton equilibration with the solvent in reactions which involve a hydrogen transfer meant that a hydride ion or a hydrogen atom rather than a proton was being transferred because a hydride ion or hydrogen atom would not be expected to equilibrate readily with the protons of water. It is now clear that this is not so, and, in retrospect, it is not surprising that proton transfers to the solvent should be relatively slow in many reactions. In order to consider this question it is necessary to outline in greater detail the properties of diffusion-controlled proton transfers between O, N, and S atoms.[16] The increase in our understanding of these important reactions has contributed greatly to our understanding of the mechanism of acid-base catalysis. The complete reaction is shown in equation 62, and a reaction-coordinate diagram is shown in Fig. 11. Let us as-

$$AH + B \underset{k_{-1}}{\overset{k_1}{\rightleftharpoons}} \left[AH \cdots B \underset{\text{fast}}{\overset{K'}{\rightleftharpoons}} A^- \cdots HB^+ \right] \underset{k_{-2}}{\overset{k_2}{\rightleftharpoons}} A^- + HB^+ \tag{62}$$

sume that HA is a stronger acid than HB^+ (the assignment of charges to the acid and base is arbitrary). In the forward direction the observed rate constant k_f, for nearly all such reactions, has been found to be near or equal to the diffusion-controlled limit, i.e., about $10^{10}\ M^{-1}\ sec^{-1}$. Thus, nearly every time a molecule of HA encounters B, proton transfer occurs; i.e., the rate constant for the proton transfer step itself is larger than that (k_{-1}) for the separation of AH $\cdots$ B, and the proton transfer is fast compared with the diffusion

[69]S-F. Wang, F. S. Kawahara, and P. Talalay, *J. Biol. Chem.* **238**, 576 (1963).

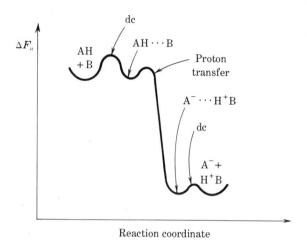

Fig 11. Reaction-coordinate diagram for a diffusion-controlled proton transfer from AH to B, assuming that AH is a stronger acid than BH^+.

step. In other words, the free-energy barrier for the proton transfer step is smaller than that for the diffusion-controlled step (Fig. 11).

The reverse reaction of A^- with $H\overset{+}{B}$ proceeds at an overall rate k_r which is less than diffusion-controlled. The rate of this step is fixed by the equilibrium constant of the overall reaction, and the rate constant of the forward reaction is readily calculated (equations 63 and 64). Although the rate constant for this reverse

$$K_{eq} = \frac{k_f}{k_r} \tag{63}$$

$$k_r = \frac{k_f}{K_{eq}} \tag{64}$$

reaction is much smaller than the diffusion-controlled limit, it is still useful for many purposes to regard the rate-determining step for this unfavorable proton transfer as a diffusion-controlled step, i.e., a diffusion-controlled separation of $AH \cdots B$. This is in accord with the principle of microscopic reversibility, which requires that the same step be rate-determining in both directions for a reaction at equilibrium. The reason that the overall rate of proton transfer from HB^+ to A^- is less than diffusion-controlled is that the diffusion-controlled step is preceded by an unfavorable equilibrium step, the transfer of a proton from HB^+ to A^-. After such a transfer occurs, the product $AH\cdots B$ will revert to $A^-\cdots HB^+$ many times before $AH \cdots B$ separates to give AH and B. In other words, the free-energy barrier for the separation of $AH\cdots B$ is larger than that for proton transfer within the complex, and this separation (k_{-1}) may be regarded as the rate-determining step (Fig. 11). The important point here is that even though the overall rate of this reverse reaction is much less than diffusion-controlled, the rate-limiting step does not involve proton transfer between BH^+ and A^-, and the properties of this limiting step will be determined by the *equilibrium* for the formation of $AH\cdots B$ from A^- and HB^+ and the rate of separation of this species. Since the rates of diffusion-controlled association and dissociation steps have little dependence on the acidity of the reactants, the rate of the reverse reaction is determined almost entirely by the equilibrium for the proton transfer step.

This is one of a number of instances in which a relatively slow observed rate constant reflects an unfavorable equilibrium process preceding a diffusion-controlled step. This situation is of great importance in consideration of reaction mechanisms because it means that the properties (such as isotope effects) of even rather slow reactions reflect an equilibrium and a diffusion-controlled process, rather than the making and breaking of covalent bonds in the rate-determining step.

Now suppose that in an enzyme catalyzed proton transfer reaction, such as that catalyzed by phosphoglucose isomerase or ketosteroid isomerase, it is the imidazole moiety of a histidine residue which acts as a base to remove the proton from carbon. Proton exchange requires proton transfer from the conjugate acid of imidazole to the solvent, which could occur by reaction with hydroxide ion or with water. The reaction with hydroxide ion (equation 65) proceeds in the direction favored by the equilibrium and

$$ImH^+ + OH^- \rightleftharpoons Im + H_2O \tag{65}$$

occurs with a rate constant corresponding to the diffusion-controlled limit of 2.3×10^{10} M^{-1} sec^{-1}. At pH 7, the activity of hydroxide ion is 10^{-7} M, so that the rate constant for proton transfer by this pathway would be 2.3×10^3 sec^{-1}. The reaction with water occurs with a rate constant which is below the diffusion-controlled limit because the equilibrium in this direction is unfavorable (equation 66). The rate constant for proton transfer in this direction may be easily

$$\text{ImH}^+ + \text{H}_2\text{O} \underset{k_r = 1.5 \times 10^{10}}{\overset{k_f = 1.5 \times 10^{3}}{\rightleftarrows}} \text{Im} + \text{H}_3\text{O}^+ \tag{66}$$

calculated to be 1.5×10^3 sec^{-1} from the overall dissociation constant of imidazolium ion of 10^{-7} and the diffusion-controlled rate constant of the reaction in the reverse direction of 1.5×10^{10} M^{-1} sec^{-1} (equations 63 and 66).[70] The rate of proton transfer would not be changed greatly by the substitution of another base for imidazole or by changing the pH a moderate amount from pH 7; the rates under these conditions may be calculated by the same procedure. Now rate constants on the order of 10^3 sec^{-1} for exchange of the proton with solvent are not very fast compared with the scale of rate constants for enzymatic catalysis. The turnover number of Δ^5-3-ketosteroid isomerase is 2.8×10^5 sec^{-1} at 25° and pH 7.0.[69] The individual steps in the catalytic process must occur at least as rapidly as this, so that the proton transfer steps within the enzyme-substrate complex occur more rapidly than exchange of the proton with solvent. Thus, it is not necessary to postulate any special shielding of the proton from the solvent in the active site in order to account for the observed absence of exchange. The turnover numbers of glucose phosphate isomerases[71] are in the range 2.5 to 6.0×10^2 sec^{-1}. This is of a similar order of magnitude to the expected rates of proton exchange, so that partial exchange with solvent in this reaction is not unexpected.

These reactions may be looked at in another way, as a competition for the proton between the solvent and the proton acceptor at the active site of the enzyme. Transfer to the solvent gives exchange, and transfer to the acceptor gives the net reaction. In both of the reactions described above the enzymatic reaction involves the donation of a proton to a carbanion. Proton transfers to strongly basic carbanions are known to occur rapidly and may even occur at a diffusion-controlled rate. The rate of proton transfer from an acid of pK 7 to the enolate of acetylacetone[16] is about 10^5 M^{-1} sec^{-1}, so that within the active site of an enzyme it would be expected that

[70] M. Eigen, G. G. Hammes, and K. Kustin, *J. Am. Chem. Soc.* **82**, 3482 (1960).

[71] A. Baich, R. G. Wolfe, and F. J. Reithel, *J. Biol. Chem.* **235**, 3130 (1960).

proton transfer to an enolate ion would compete effectively with proton exchange with water.

The activation energy for diffusion-controlled reactions is small, but the heats of dissociation of water and imidazolium ion are large, 13,520 and 7700 cal/mole, respectively.[72] The temperature coefficient of the reaction of imidazolium ion with hydroxide ion at pH 7 (equation 65) will be large because of the increase in hydroxide ion concentration with increasing temperature. The temperature coefficient for the water reaction (equation 66) will also be large because it is determined by the small temperature coefficient of the diffusion-controlled step, k_r of equation 66, and the large temperature coefficient of the equilibrium. Thus, it is reasonable that the proton exchange with solvent should increase more rapidly than the proton transfer reaction in the phosphoglucose isomerase reaction.[68]

5. ONE-ENCOUNTER AND CONCERTED MECHANISMS

The rates of proton equilibration with the solvent are also pertinent to the question of the site at which catalysis occurs and the "concerted" nature of the catalysis. Consider the possible mechanisms for the general acid catalyzed hydration of acetaldehyde or the very similar general acid catalyzed mutarotation of glucose. These reactions could occur by proton transfer to and from the carbonyl oxygen atom (equation 67) or by proton transfer from and to the

$$H-O^{\backslash}C=O^{\backslash}H-A \rightleftharpoons \overset{H}{\underset{R}{\overset{\backslash}{O^{+}}}}\!\!-C-O-H\!\frown\!A^{-}$$

$$\Big\| \text{fast}$$

$$H^+ + RO-C-OH + A^- \tag{67}$$

attacking and leaving ROH group (equation 68). We have already

$$A^- + HO + C=O + H^+ \overset{\text{fast}}{\rightleftharpoons} A\!\frown\!H-O^{\backslash}\ \ C=\overset{+}{O}H \rightleftharpoons AH^{\backslash}O\!-\!C\!-\!OH \tag{68}$$

pointed out that structure-reactivity correlations are consistent with

[72] J. T. Edsall and J. Wyman, "Biophysical Chemistry," pp. 452, 464, Academic Press, Inc., New York, 1958.

the first of these mechanisms. The second mechanism is rendered unlikely by comparison with the mechanism of acetal hydrolysis. The hydrolysis of nearly all acetals is subject to only *specific* acid catalysis; i.e., α is near or equal to 1.0 for this reaction.[73] Now this reaction (equation 69 in the reverse direction) is a model for

$$H-O-\overset{\backslash}{\underset{R}{\underset{/}{C}}}=\overset{+}{O}R' \;\rightleftharpoons\; H-\overset{+}{\underset{R}{O}}-\underset{|}{\overset{|}{C}}-OR' \;\rightleftharpoons\; H^{+} + \underset{R}{\overset{|}{O}}-\underset{|}{\overset{|}{C}}-OR' \tag{69}$$

acetaldehyde hydration or glucose mutarotation by the mechanism of equation 68; it differs from this mechanism only by the substitution of an alkyl group R' for the proton which is added in the fast equilibrium step. Therefore, if the latter reactions occurred by the mechanism of equation 68, they should exhibit α values near 1.0 and general acid catalysis should not be detectable. The fact that general acid catalysis is readily detectable for these reactions, with values of α equal to 0.54 and 0.4 for acetaldehyde hydration[14] and glucose mutarotation,[74] respectively, means that the hydration reactions do not resemble acetal hydrolysis. The mechanism of equations 68 and 69 is, therefore, improbable for aldehyde hydration.

However, a very simple calculation which has been carried out by Eigen[75] suggests that the mechanism of equation 67 cannot be correct in its simplest form. Equation 67 includes the conjugate acid of the aldehyde hydrate as an intermediate. In the case of the water catalyzed reaction, A^{-} is hydroxide ion and the reverse reaction requires the reaction of hydroxide ion with this unstable intermediate. Reasonable estimates of the pK of this intermediate indicate that it will be present in such low concentration that the rate constant for its reaction with hydroxide ion would have to be larger than the diffusion-controlled limit in order to account for the observed rate constant of the overall reaction in this direction. The possibility exists that the water catalyzed reaction actually represents base catalysis rather than acid catalysis, so that it would not be expected to proceed by the mechanism of reaction 67. However, the calculated rate constant for the hydroquinone catalyzed reaction in the reverse direction is very close to the diffusion-controlled limit. It would be expected that a Brønsted plot should level off as

[73] E. H. Cordes, *Progr. Phys. Org. Chem.* **4**, 1 (1967).

[74] R. P. Bell, "Acid-Base Catalysis," chap. 5, Oxford University Press, London, 1941.

[75] M. Eigen, *Discussions Faraday Soc.* **39**, 7 (1965).

it approaches the diffusion-controlled limit and the fact that no such leveling is observed for hydroquinone[14] is a further argument against the mechanism of equation 67.

Equation 68 includes the conjugate acid of the free aldehyde as an intermediate. According to most estimates of the acidity of this unstable species, the mechanism of equation 68 would require a still larger rate constant for the attack of water catalyzed by hydroxide ion or other A^- molecules in order to account for the observed reaction rate. The situation is similar to that described above for the acid catalyzed reaction of p-nitrobenzaldehyde with semicarbazide.

Thus, both of the possible mechanisms that we have postulated for this reaction are apparently ruled out. There are two different, but related, ways to avoid this apparent dilemma: "one-encounter" and "concerted" mechanisms of catalysis. According to both of these mechanisms, the same catalyst molecule acts as both the proton donor and acceptor in reactions similar to those of equations 67 and 68. The problem is to determine what is happening in the transition state and what provides the driving force for catalysis of the reaction.

Two one-encounter mechanisms may be written for acetaldehyde hydration, according to equations 70 and 71. These mechanisms

$$ \text{(70)} $$

$$ \text{(71)} $$

are perfectly analogous to those of equations 67 and 68, except that in each case the molecule of catalyst brings about a rapid, additional proton transfer step before or after the rate-determining step, but in the course of the same encounter with the reactants as that in which the rate-determining step occurs. Since no diffusion-controlled reaction of reactive intermediates with molecules outside the reaction "cage" is required, the diffusion-controlled limit is removed and only the rate of proton transfer within the reaction "cage," which is faster than diffusion-controlled, is required in these mechanisms. According to the mechanism of equation 70, in the forward direction the rate-determining step involves attack of a free hydroxyl group on the carbonyl group with assistance to the reaction by partial proton transfer from the catalyst to the carbonyl group in the transition state; this is followed by a fast proton transfer from the unstable oxonium ion intermediate of this mechanism to the conjugate base of the catalyst, followed by diffusion-controlled separation of the products. In the reverse direction, a fast proton donation by the catalyst is followed by a rate-determining breakdown of the unstable oxonium ion, with assistance by proton removal from the hydroxyl group by the conjugate base of the same molecule of catalyst. The mechanism of equation 71 in the forward direction involves a fast proton donation by the catalyst to give the conjugate acid of the carbonyl compound, followed by rate-determining attack of the hydroxyl group with assistance by partial transfer of the proton to the conjugate base of the same catalyst in the transition state. In the reverse direction, the catalyst assists the reaction by making possible a partial proton transfer to the leaving hydroxyl group in the transition state, after which there is a rapid proton transfer to the conjugate base of the catalyst, followed by diffusion apart of the reactants. (As usual in the consideration of such mechanisms, one or the other of the mechanisms is likely to appear more attractive, depending on which direction of the reaction is chosen to describe the mechanism. It is always important to consider a reaction mechanism in both directions in order to avoid this psychological hazard.)

Concerted mechanisms provide the other means of avoiding the difficulties of the stepwise mechanism of equations 67 and 68.[75] The term "concerted" has a number of quite different meanings, which will be considered in more detail later. For present purposes, "concerted" will be taken to mean that both protons are in different positions in the transition state compared with the starting materials as the result of an interaction with the catalyst, either directly or through one or more intervening water molecules. It is conceivable that a catalyst molecule could perturb the water molecules around the substrate in such a way as to facilitate both proton donation and removal at the same time (equation 72). However, it

$$
\begin{array}{ccc}
\overset{\displaystyle H}{\underset{\displaystyle |}{}} & & \overset{\displaystyle H}{\underset{\displaystyle |}{}} \\
A-H\cdots O-H & & A-H\cdots O\cdots H \\
\vdots \quad \quad O & \rightleftharpoons & | \quad | \\
H \quad \parallel & & H \quad O \\
| \quad C & & \vdots \quad | \\
R-O & & R-O-C-
\end{array}
\tag{72}
$$

is difficult to define the nature of the driving force for catalysis of this kind for the reaction in both directions. A more attractive concerted mechanism involves simultaneous proton donation and acceptance by a bifunctional catalyst containing both acidic and basic groups (equation 73). Again, one or more water molecules may be

$$\text{(73)}$$

interposed between the catalyst and the substrate. One might expect such catalysis to be most efficient if the acidic and basic groups are on different atoms of the catalyst but are connected by a system of bonds in such a way that the basicity of the base is increased as the proton is removed from the acid, as in phosphate monoanion or dianion. However, a single atom with several free electron pairs, such as the oxygen atom of a hydroxyl group, could act as both an electron donor and acceptor; an ammonium ion could not act as a bifunctional catalyst by this mechanism.

Although phosphate is slightly more effective than other catalysts of comparable acidity for the hydration of aldehydes, it is clear that there is not a large amount of additional stabilization of this or a large number of other reactions to be gained by bifunctional catalysis according to the mechanism of equation 73 in aqueous solution.[11c,13,76] There are several examples discussed in Chap. 2 in which it appears that concerted acid-base reactions are important in aqueous solution when the base is acting as a nucleophile, rather than as a catalyst for proton transfer. One of the few reactions in which concerted acid-base catalysis of proton transfer in aqueous solution gives a large rate acceleration is the hydrolysis of N-phenyliminolactones, studied by Cunningham and Schmir[77] (equation 74). In this reaction the product-determining step is faster than the rate-determining attack of water on the protonated iminolactone at

[76] G. E. Lienhard and F. H. Anderson, *J. Org. Chem.* **32**, 2229 (1967); Y. Pocker and J. E. Meany, *J. Phys. Chem.* **71**, 3113 (1967).

[77] B. A. Cunningham and G. L Schmir, *J. Am. Chem. Soc.* **88**, 551 (1966).

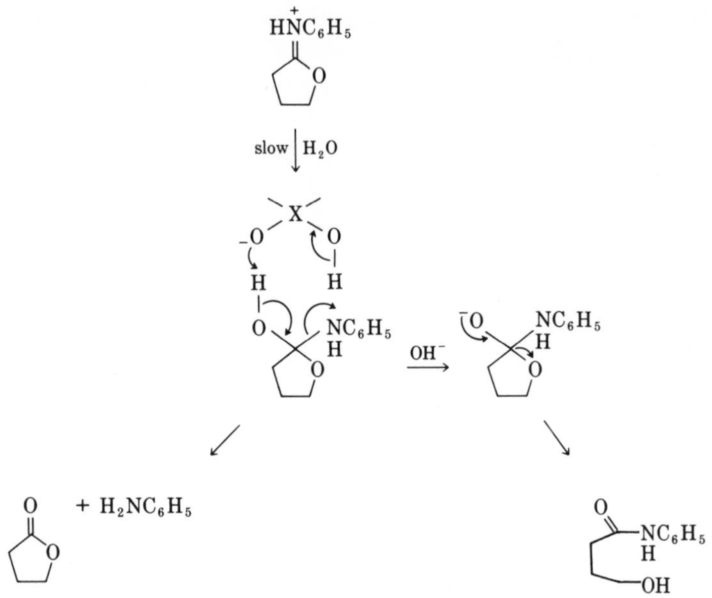

$$\overset{+}{H}NC_6H_5$$

slow $\Big|$ H_2O

OH^- →

O + $H_2NC_6H_5$

$$\begin{matrix} O \\ \diagdown \ \ NC_6H_5 \\ \ \ \ \ H \\ \diagdown OH \end{matrix}$$ (74)

pH values above 2, so that the ratio of lactone to anilide in the product is increased by increasing the acidity or the buffer concentration without changing the overall rate. These facts establish, first, that there must be an intermediate addition product and, second, that the breakdown of this intermediate to give lactone and aniline is catalyzed by buffers. The buffers which are effective in catalyzing breakdown in this direction are phosphate, acetic acid, and bicarbonate, which contain both acidic and basic groups, while buffers which contain only a single readily accessible catalytic group, such as imidazolium ion, p-nitrophenol, and tris(hydroxymethyl)aminomethane, are far less effective. For example, phosphate is 240 times more effective than imidazole buffer as a catalyst. It is noteworthy that the microscopic reverse of this reaction is the aminolysis of an ester by aniline, so that one might expect this reaction also to exhibit concerted general acid-base catalysis.

There are many reactions which are subject to acid or base catalysis, or to both acid and base catalysis, and which show well behaved Brønsted plots with no major deviations for different classes of catalysts. Since catalysts which have the special structural requirements for concerted acid-base catalysis should show large positive deviations if such catalysis were important, it appears that it is not important for many, and probably most, reactions of this kind.

The absence of a significant stabilization of the transition state by any sort of cyclic process is particularly clear in reactions such as nitrone and oxime formation,[28] in which substitution of a methyl group for one of the protons has almost no effect on the characteristics of the catalyzed reaction (Fig. 8). An important problem at the present time is to define the nature of the factors which determine whether or not bifunctional catalysis is important for reactions in aqueous solution. The postulation that concerted acid-base catalysis is responsible for large rate accelerations in enzyme catalyzed reactions, compared with the same reaction in water, remains only an attractive speculation in the absence of more complete experimental evidence in both chemical and enzyme catalyzed reactions.

E. ENZYMATIC REACTIONS

1. ACONITASE

For reactions which involve the removal of a proton from carbon, such as the isomerization of sugars[68] and steroids,[69] catalysis of the proton removal by a general base in the active site of the enzyme seems inescapable. In several instances, the maximal velocities of reactions of this kind show deuterium isotope effects in the range of $k_H/k_D = 2$-6, similar to those seen in analogous nonenzymatic reactions.

A particularly interesting enzymatic reaction of this kind is the aconitase catalyzed reversible isomerization of citrate to isocitrate. This reaction proceeds through a dehydration of citrate to *cis*-aconitate followed by hydration of the double bond in the opposite sense to give isocitrate, but *cis*-aconitate does not have to dissociate from the enzyme in the reaction sequence. If the reaction is carried out with 2-methyl-2-^{3}H-citrate as substrate in the presence of a high concentration of *cis*-aconitate, isocitrate labeled with tritium in the 3 position is formed as product.[78] This means that the methyl-*cis*-aconitate which is initially formed can diffuse off the enzyme and be replaced by unsubstituted *cis*-aconitate more rapidly than the tritium atom, which has been transferred to a general base on the enzyme, exchanges with the medium. The overall scheme for this reaction is shown in equation 75. There is no direct transfer of the

[78] I. A. Rose and E. L. O'Connell, *J. Biol.Chem.* **242**, 1870 (1967).

$$\text{Enz} + {}^3\text{H}^+$$

$$
\begin{array}{ccc}
2-{}^3\text{H}-citrate & \underset{\text{Enz}}{{}^3\text{H}} + cis\text{-aconitate} & 3-{}^3\text{H}-isocitrate \\[2mm]
\Big\updownarrow \pm\text{Enz} & \Big\updownarrow & \Big\updownarrow \pm\text{Enz} \\[2mm]
\underset{\text{Enz}}{2-{}^3\text{H}-citrate} \overset{\pm\text{OH}^-}{\rightleftharpoons} & \underset{\text{Enz}}{{}^3\text{H} \; cis\text{-aconitate}} \overset{\pm\text{OH}^-}{\rightleftharpoons} & \underset{\text{Enz}}{3-{}^3\text{H}-isocitrate}
\end{array}
\qquad (75)
$$

hydroxyl oxygen atom. The stereochemistry of the reaction requires that the proton add to different sides of the double bond of *cis*-aconitate to form the two products, so that the fact that intra-molecular transfer of tritium occurs suggests that the bound *cis*-aconitate can rotate while still attached to the enzyme, perhaps around a bound carboxylate group, without exchange of the proton with the solvent.

2. CHYMOTRYPSIN

In enzymatic reactions which involve proton transfer to or from oxygen, nitrogen, or sulfur, the occurrence of general acid-base catalysis is more difficult to prove. At the present time, the strong-est case for its occurrence in an enzymatic reaction can be made for chymotrypsin. It was noted in Chap. 2 that the hydrolysis by this enzyme of substrates which contain an activated acyl group proceeds by covalent catalysis, with the intermediate formation of an acyl-serine ester intermediate (equation 76). However, there is

$$
\underset{\text{RCX}}{\overset{\text{O}}{\underset{\|}{}}} + \text{HOSerEnz} \overset{\pm\text{XH}}{\rightleftharpoons} \underset{\text{RCOSerEnz}}{\overset{\text{O}}{\underset{\|}{}}} \overset{\text{H}_2\text{O}}{\longrightarrow} \underset{\text{RCO}^-}{\overset{\text{O}}{\underset{\|}{}}} + \text{HOSerEnz}
\qquad (76)
$$

also strong evidence that the imidazole group of a histidine residue in the active site is required for catalytic activity. The dependence on pH of the maximal velocity of both the acylation and deacylation steps indicates that activity is proportional to the fraction in the basic form of a group with a pK of about 7, in the range expected for an imidazole group. This alone does not prove than an imidazole group is involved in the active site; this apparent pK could repre-sent: (1) the ionization of some other group, the pK of which is perturbed by the protein; (2) an imidazole group which, upon protonation, forces the protein into a catalytically inactive conformation; or (3) a change in rate-determining step, rather than the ionization of any group. Stronger evidence for the involvement of an imidazole group comes from the fact that the enzyme is irreversibly inactivated upon alkylation of an imidazole group by a "Trojan horse" substrate analog, the chloroketone 8. This molecule resembles a normal substrate enough to bind to the active site—it is a

$$\text{(structure 8)}$$

8

competitive inhibitor over short time periods and other competitive inhibitors protect against irreversible inactivation by this compound—and then to react slowly but specifically with the imidazole group.[79] Since there is no evidence that this imidazole group acts as a nucleophilic catalyst, it has often been suggested that it acts as a general base catalyst to facilitate proton transfer. It is known that imidazole does act in this manner to catalyze the nonenzymatic hydrolysis of esters.[10,80,81] There are two types of evidence which provide some support for such a role for imidazole in the enzymatic reaction.

First, the solvent deuterium isotope effects, k_{H_2O}/k_{D_2O}, for the hydrolysis of the acyl-enzyme intermediates cinnamoyl-chymotrypsin and benzoyl-chymotrypsin are in the range of 2 to 4, which is similar to the isotope effects found for general base catalysis of the corresponding nonenzymatic reactions.[10,81-84] The difficulty in interpreting such isotope effects in enzymatic reactions arises from the possibility that they may be the result of a subtle, reversible change in conformation of the enzyme which is induced by the change in the solvent from water to deuterium oxide. Although the occurrence of a large or irreversible change in conformation has been ruled out,[84] the

[79] E. B. Ong, E. Shaw, and G. Schoellmann, *J. Am. Chem. Soc.* **86**, 1271 (1964).

[80] L. W. Cunningham, *Science* **125**, 1145 (1957).

[81] B. M. Anderson, E. H. Cordes, and W. P. Jencks, *J. Biol. Chem.* **236**, 455 (1961).

[82] W. P. Jencks and J. Carriuolo, *J. Am. Chem. Soc.* **83**, 1743 (1961).

[83] M. Caplow and W. P. Jencks, *Biochemistry* **1**, 883 (1962).

[84] M. L. Bender and G. A. Hamilton, *J. Am. Chem. Soc.* **84**, 2570 (1962); M. L. Bender, G. E. Clement, F. J. Kézdy, and H. d'A. Heck, *Ibid.* **86**, 3680 (1964).

possibility of the existence of such effects means that the occurrence of a solvent deuterium isotope effect must be taken as suggestive, rather than as conclusive evidence for the existence of general base catalysis in the enzymatic reaction.

The second type of evidence comes from a consideration of structure-reactivity correlations.[85] In the uncatalyzed (or water catalyzed) reactions of amines with esters, the rate of the reaction ordinarily displays a large sensitivity to the basicity of the amine, so that a plot of log k against pK has a slope of about 0.8. This is true of tertiary as well as of primary and secondary amines, which means that proton removal from the nucleophilic reagent is not very important in the transition state and that the effect of an electron-withdrawing substituent is to decrease nucleophilic reactivity by decreasing the electron density at the reacting site. On the other hand, the reaction of alcohols with esters at neutral pH displays the opposite sensitivity to substituents, showing an increased reactivity with increasing acidity of the alcohol. This is because it is the anion of the alcohol that is the reactive species, and the effect of an electron-withdrawing substituent in increasing the equilibrium concentration of the anion (equation 77) is more important than its

$$\text{ROH} \xrightleftharpoons{K_A} \text{RO}^- + \text{H}^+ \tag{77}$$

effect in decreasing the reactivity of that anion (equation 78). Thus,

$$\text{RO}^- + \underset{\substack{\parallel \\ \text{O}}}{\text{R'COR''}} \xrightarrow{k} \underset{\substack{\parallel \\ \text{O}}}{\text{R'COR}} + \text{R''O}^- \tag{78}$$

in a reaction in which there is no proton removal in the transition state, electron-withdrawing substituents decrease reactivity, whereas in a reaction with complete proton removal in the transition state they increase reactivity. It is reasonable to expect that in reactions with intermediate degrees of proton transfer in the transition state, they will have intermediate effects. Experimentally, it is found that for structurally related compounds the reactivity of *both* amines and alcohols with the acyl-enzyme intermediate, furoyl-chymotrypsin, shows little or no sensitivity to the basicity of the nucleophile. This means that there is little change in the charge on the attacking atom in the transition state for the enzymatic reaction and suggests that the proton is neither completely nor not at all transferred, but

[85] P. W. Inward and W. P. Jencks, *J. Biol. Chem.* **240**, 1986 (1965).

is partly transferred in the transition state, so that substituent effects on nucleophilic reactivity and on proton transfer effectively cancel each other out. This corresponds to general base catalysis.

A related argument based on structure-reactivity considerations may be used to approach the difficult question of determining the site at which the catalyst acts in the enzymatic reaction. The problem is essentially one of resolving the kinetic ambiguity of the two simplest mechanisms which are consistent with the experimental observation that the rate is proportional to the fraction of an imidazole group in the free base form. As has been discussed above for nonenzymatic reactions, this does *not* mean that imidazole is acting as a base to catalyze the reaction in both directions. The point is discussed in detail as an illustration of an important general problem, which is only now beginning to be seriously considered in the interpretation of enzymatic reaction mechanisms.

The rate law for the reaction of acyl-chymotrypsins with water or some other acceptor, HX, is

$$v = k \, [\overset{\text{O}}{\overset{\|}{\text{RCO}}} - \text{Ser} - \text{Enz} - \text{Im}] \, [\text{HX}]$$

$$= k \, \frac{K_{\text{ImH}^+}}{K_{\text{HX}}} \, [\overset{\text{O}}{\overset{\|}{\text{RCO}}} - \text{Ser} - \text{Enz} - \text{ImH}^+][\text{X}^-] \tag{79}$$

in which K_{ImH^+} and K_{HX} are the acid dissociation constants of the imidazolium group in the enzyme and HX, respectively. The rate law for the formation of the acyl enzyme from a substrate, RCOX, is

$$v = k' \, [\text{HOSer} - \text{Enz} - \text{Im}] \, [\overset{\text{O}}{\overset{\|}{\text{RCX}}}]$$

$$= k' \, \frac{K_{\text{ImH}^+}}{K_{\text{SerOH}}} \, [^-\text{OSer} - \text{Enz} - \text{ImH}^+][\overset{\text{O}}{\overset{\|}{\text{RCX}}}] \tag{80}$$

in which K_{SerOH} is the acid dissociation constant of the serine hydroxyl group in the active site of the enzyme. Suppose that the correct mechanism is the simplest possible one which utilizes these reactants. Then the deacylation reaction could occur by the mechanism of equation 81, in which imidazole acts as a general base to facilitate the removal of a proton from the attacking nucleophile, or by the mechanism of equation 82, in which the conjugate acid of imidazole

$$\text{(81)}$$

$$\text{(82)}$$

acts as a general acid to aid the departure of the serine oxygen atom and it is the conjugate base of the nucleophile X^- which attacks the ester. These two mechanisms correspond to the rate laws of equations 79 and 80 and are kinetically indistinguishable. The reason that the mechanism of equation 82 gives the same dependence of rate upon pH as that of equation 81 is that the effects of the decreasing concentration of imidazolium cation and the increasing concentration of the conjugate base of the nucleophile with increasing pH cancel each other out at high pH values, whereas at lower pH values the concentration of imidazolium ion is constant and the concentration of the conjugate base of the nucleophile increases to give the observed increase in rate with increasing pH. Note that the reverse of the mechanism of equation 81 involves the attack of serine alkoxide ion on the substrate, aided by general acid catalysis by imidazolium cation of the leaving of the group X^-. This must be the mechanism of the acylation step according to equation 81, in agreement with the principle of microscopic reversibility. Thus, if imidazole acts as a catalyst for proton removal in one direction, it must, in nearly all cases, act as a catalyst for proton donation in the reverse direction.

Similarly, the mechanism of equation 82 requires that in the reverse direction imidazole act as a general base catalyst to remove a proton from the serine hydroxyl group that attacks the substrate. Again, the existence of specific base plus general acid catalysis in one direction requires that the reaction be subject to general base catalysis in the other direction. The meaningful distinction between these two mechanisms is that equation 81 involves proton transfer to and from X as it leaves and attacks, while equation 82 involves proton transfer to and from the serine hydroxyl group as it leaves and attacks.

The principles which are important for the interpretation of nearly all reaction mechanisms, and which have already been discussed for a number of nonenzymatic reactions are, first, that a mechanism which proposes proton donation by a catalyst in one direction must, in nearly all cases, involve proton removal by the same catalyst in the reverse direction, and second, that the two or more kinetically equivalent mechanisms that can usually be written for such catalysis are, a priori, equally probable. These points may seen obvious when they are spelled out, but they are extraordinarily difficult to accept and apply in practice because the enzymologist will always be tempted to prefer the reaction mechanism that corresponds directly to the ionic species he has written in the rate law (for example, imidazole and the serine hydroxyl group, rather than imidazolium ion and the serine alkoxide ion).

The experimental finding that the reactivity of nucleophilic reagents with acyl-chymotrypsin is almost independent of the basicity of the nucleophile is consistent with the mechanism of equation 81, but is not easily explained by that of equation 82. According to the latter mechanism, the conjugate base of the nucleophile is the reacting species, without assistance by partial proton transfer. Such a mechanism requires ionization of the nucleophile before the rate-determining step and would almost certainly involve a change in the charge of the nucleophile in the transition state, compared with the starting materials. A mechanism involving attack or expulsion of free amine anions is unlikely, in any case, because these anions are thermodynamically too unstable to exist as free intermediates in moderately fast reactions in aqueous solution.

The maximal rate of hydrolysis of anilides by chymotrypsin generally[86] (but not always[87]) increases with electron-*donating* substituents in the aniline ring (Table IV). This suggests that proton donation to the leaving aniline, which is aided by electron donation, can facilitate the reaction more than the increase in the leaving ability of the aniline which is brought about by electron withdrawal. The change in rate is in the same direction, but is not as large as the increase in basicity of the anilines. This is also consistent with the mechanism of equation 81 (in the reverse direction) with a large degree of proton transfer to the aniline in the transition state, but is not easily explained by the mechanism of equation 82.

Protonation of the leaving group is also of primary importance in the nonenzymatic hydrolysis of anilides.[88] The rate of this reaction is almost independent of substituents ($\rho = 0.1$), but the exchange of labeled oxygen from $H_2{}^{18}O$ into the anilide is increased by electron-withdrawing substituents in the aniline. According to the mechanism of equation 83, this is interpretable in terms of a facilita-

$$
\overset{*}{HO^-} + RC\underset{\overset{\|}{O}}{\overset{}{}}-N\underset{\overset{|}{H}}{\overset{}{}}C_6H_4X \underset{k_{-1}}{\overset{k_1}{\rightleftharpoons}} R-\underset{\overset{|}{*OH}}{\overset{\overset{-O}{|}}{C}}-N\underset{\overset{|}{H}}{\overset{}{}}C_6H_4X
$$

$$
R-\underset{\overset{\pm}{*O}\ \ H}{\overset{\overset{-O}{|}}{C}}-\overset{+}{N}\underset{\overset{|}{H}}{\overset{}{}}C_6H_4X
$$

$$
\overset{*O}{HO^-} + RC\underset{\overset{\|}{}}{\overset{}{}}-N\underset{\overset{|}{H}}{\overset{}{}}C_6H_4X \underset{k_{-1}}{\overset{k_1}{\rightleftharpoons}} R-\underset{\overset{\pm}{*O}}{\overset{\overset{HO}{|}}{C}}-N\underset{\overset{|}{H}}{\overset{}{}}C_6H_4X
$$

$$
\downarrow k_2
$$

$$
R\overset{*}{CO O^-} + H_2NC_6H_4X \tag{83}
$$

[86] T. Inagami, S. S. York, and A. Patchornik, *J. Am. Chem. Soc.* 87, 126 (1965).

[87] H. F. Bundy and C. L. Moore, *Biochemistry* 5, 808 (1966).

[88] M. L. Bender and R. J. Thomas, *J. Am. Chem. Soc.* 83, 4183 (1961).

Table IV   Chymotrypsin catalyzed hydrolysis of substituted anilides of acetyltyrosine at pH 8.0[86]

Substituted aniline	$k_2 \times 10^2$, sec^{-1}	$K_m \times 10^4$, M	pK of aniline
m-Cl—	1.1	8.2	3.3
p-Cl—	1.4	6.7	3.8
m-CH$_3$O—	4.7	60	4.2
p-CH$_3$—	8.7	130	5.1
p-CH$_3$O—	21	120	5.3

tion of the first step by electron-withdrawing substituents, which gives an increased rate of ^{18}O exchange and an increased steady-state concentration of the tetrahedral addition intermediate, and an inhibition of the second step by such substituents because of an inhibition of the protonation of aniline which is required for aniline expulsion. Conversely, the effect of electron-donating substituents in aiding this protonation is sufficient to overcome the unfavorable effect of such substituents on the first step and accounts for the observed insensitivity of the overall rate to the nature of the substituent.

Catalysis by chymotrypsin undoubtedly involves rate-accelerating effects other than those indicated in equations 81 and 82, and the only justification for the above analysis of the reaction mechanism is that considerations of this kind provide a probe into the simpler aspects of the driving forces which are important in the bond-forming and bond-breaking steps. More complicated chemical mechanisms than those of equations 81 and 82 have frequently been proposed, in which *both* proton removal and donation in one step in one direction are catalyzed by imidazole; such mechanisms frequently include a tetrahedral addition compound as an intermediate.[89,90] There is no compelling experimental support for such mechanisms, but it is not unlikely that something of the kind occurs, as shown in equation 84. This is essentially the "one-encounter" mechanism already

(84)

[89] M. L. Bender and F. J. Kézdy, *J. Am. Chem. Soc.* **86**, 3704 (1964).

[90] T. C. Bruice, *Proc. Natl. Acad. Sci. U.S.* **47**, 1924 (1961).

described for the hydration of acetaldehyde. If a mechanism of this kind is correct, it is probable that one of the steps is of primary kinetic significance, and the discussion of the previous paragraphs refers to the identification and characterization of this step.

3. LYSOZYME

The lysozyme catalyzed hydrolysis of glycosides provides an instructive example of the difficulty of drawing sharp lines between different types of reaction mechanisms and mechanisms of catalysis. Analysis of the structure of lysozyme by x-ray diffraction and other evidence suggests that the hexose ring at which bond cleavage takes place is forced into a half-chair conformation adjacent to a carboxylic acid and a carboxylate group at the active site of this enzyme.[91, 92] The question is, how do those interactions lead to an acceleration of the rate of hydrolysis of the glycosidic bond?

Glycosides and other acetals provide a classical example of hydrolysis by an A1 mechanism, in which protonation of the substrate takes place in a fast, equilibrium step, followed by rate-determining loss of alcohol to give a (cyclic) oxonium-carbonium ion and a fast addition of water (equation 85).[73] There is a large body of

$$(85)$$

experimental data which indicates that this mechanism is followed for the great majority of such reactions but, as is the case for almost every classification of reaction mechanism, there is a gradual merging of mechanism into other categories for some compounds. Certain sugars, especially those with good leaving groups such as halide or substituted phenolate anions, undergo intramolecular displacement by hydroxyl, alkoxide, and amide groups attached to the sugar molecule and undergo intermolecular displacements in the presence of strong nucleophiles, such as thiol anions.[92-95] Some of these reactions appear to be straightforward S_N2 displacements,

[91] D. C. Phillips, *Proc. Natl. Acad. Sci. U.S.* 57, 484 (1967).

[92] C. A. Vernon, *Proc. Roy. Soc. (London)* 167B, 389 (1967).

[93] C. E. Ballou, *Advan. Carbohydrate Chem.* 9, 59 (1954).

[94] D. Piszkiewicz and T. C. Bruice, *J. Am. Chem. Soc.* 89, 6237 (1967).

[95] B. Capon and D. Thacker, *J. Am. Chem. Soc.* 87, 4199 (1965).

but others can be regarded as either an S_N2 displacement or as an assistance to ionization of the carbonium ion which is brought about by the negative charge and electrons of a properly located group without appreciable covalent bonding in the transition state.

A similar difficulty arises in the interpretation of the mechanism of acid catalysis. The hydrolysis of many acetals and glycosides has been shown to involve specific rather than general acid catalysis, but the rate of hydrolysis is accelerated by the presence of a neighboring carboxyl group,[96] and a weak general catalysis by formic acid has been reported for the hydrolysis of substituted 2-phenyl-4,4, 5,5-tetramethyl-1,3-dioxolanes (9).[97] The interpretation of the rate

$$XC_6H_4-\left\langle\begin{matrix}O-\\O-\end{matrix}\right.$$

9

increase brought about by a neighboring carboxyl group as general acid catalysis has been brought into question by the fact that the rates of a number of reactions of this kind can be satisfactorily accounted for in terms of the usual A1 mechanism, which proceeds at an enhanced rate because of the inductive effect of an adjacent carboxylate ion.[98] The two mechanisms follow the kinetically indistinguishable rate laws shown in equation 86. But this raises the

$$v = k\left[\begin{matrix}COOH\\ \\ C-O-C-\end{matrix}\right] = k'\left[\begin{matrix}COO^-\\ H\\ C-O^+-C-\end{matrix}\right] \tag{86}$$

question of whether these is a meaningful difference between a general acid catalyzed reaction, in which the carboxylic acid group donates a proton to facilitate formation of a carbonium ion, and a specific acid catalyzed reaction in which a carboxylate ion provides stabilization for a proton in essentially the same position on the leaving group (equation 87). The transition states are very similar,

[96] B. Capon, *Tetrahedron Letters* **14**, 911 (1963); B. Capon and M. C. Smith, *Chem. Comm.*, **1965**, 523.

[97] T. H. Fife, *J. Am. Chem. Soc.* **89**, 3228 (1967).

[98] T. C. Bruice and D. Piszkiewicz, *J. Am. Chem. Soc.* **89**, 3568 (1967).

$$
\begin{array}{c}
\begin{array}{c}
-C\!\!\begin{array}{c}{\nearrow O}\\{\searrow O}\end{array}\\
\mid\\
H\\
\vdots\\
-O\!\!\begin{array}{c}\\{\searrow}\end{array}\!\!C\!\!\begin{array}{c}{O-R}\\{\swarrow}\end{array}
\end{array}
\;\rightleftharpoons\;
\left[
\begin{array}{c}
-C\!\!\begin{array}{c}{\nearrow O}\\{\searrow O^{(-)}}\end{array}\\
\vdots\\
H\\
\mid {(+)}\\
-O^{(+)}\!\!\begin{array}{c}\\{\searrow}\end{array}\!\!C\!\!\begin{array}{c}{O-R}\\{\swarrow}\end{array}
\end{array}
\right]^{\ddagger}
\;\rightleftharpoons\;
\begin{array}{c}
-C\!\!\begin{array}{c}{\nearrow O}\\{\searrow O^{-}}\end{array}\\
\vdots\\
H\\
\mid {+}\\
-O\!\!\begin{array}{c}\\{\searrow}\end{array}\!\!C\!\!\begin{array}{c}{O^{+}\!-R}\\{\swarrow}\end{array}
\end{array}
\end{array}
$$

$$\downarrow$$

products   (87)

if not identical, for both of these mechanisms, and a more detailed understanding of the mechanism of acid catalysis will be required before a clear distinction can be made between them.

Both of these borderline areas of mechanism are pertinent to the interpretation of the mechanism of catalysis by lysozyme. The carboxylic acid group in the active site is expected to act by donating a proton to the leaving oxygen atom. This may be regarded as either general acid catalysis or as a stabilization of the protonated leaving group by a carboxylate ion. The carboxylate group in the active site presumably accelerates the reaction by providing electrostatic stabilization to the developing carbonium ion or by helping to displace the leaving group.[92] In this case, the former interpretation is favored by the fact that the arrangement of atoms on the enzyme surface prohibits an ordinary S_N2 displacement with a linear transition state. Forcing the substrate into a half-chair conformation provides additional stabilization for a developing carbonium ion. Nevertheless, it is difficult to draw a sharp line between a carbonium ion stabilized by an adjacent carboxylate group (10a, equation 88) and a strained bond between the 1 carbon of the sugar and the carboxyl group (10b). Perhaps the fact that the enzyme is catalytically active

$$
\underset{\textbf{10a}}{\overset{O}{\underset{}{\underset{}{RCO^{-}\cdots\overset{+}{\underset{}{C}}-}}}}
\;\rightleftharpoons\;
\underset{\textbf{10b}}{\overset{O}{\underset{}{\underset{}{RCO^{(-)}\cdots C^{(+)}-}}}}
\;\rightleftharpoons\;
\overset{O}{\underset{}{\underset{}{RCO-C-}}}
$$

$$\hspace{9cm}(88)$$

reflects a fine balance between these two extremes. A free carbonium ion intermediate would have too high an energy to permit the catalyzed reaction to take place at a reasonable rate, while the formation of a complete bond to the carboxyl group would provide an intermediate which is too stable to undergo rapid hydrolysis. By adjusting the distance and orientation between this carboxylate

group and the bound substrate, the enzyme can confound the acade-
mician who would like to place all reaction mechanisms into distinct
categories, but can achieve the balance between activation and
stabilization that is required for effective catalysis.

F. THE MECHANISM OF GENERAL ACID–BASE CATALYSIS

Just what does the catalyst do to accelerate a reaction which is
subject to general acid or base catalysis? And where is the proton
which is being transferred in the transition state for such catalysis?
These questions are relatively easy to answer in a general way,
but difficult to answer in detail and with clearcut experimental support.

First, it is important to reemphasize the distinction between
those reactions in which the proton transfer itself presents the major
energy barrier and those reactions in which proton transfer occurs,
but the major energy barrier is associated with some other part of
the reaction. The most familiar examples of the first class in both
chemistry and biochemistry involve the removal of a proton from a
carbon acid, as in the enolization of a ketone. The best-known examples of the second class are reactions of the carbonyl or imine
group and include the addition of water and nitrogen bases to carbonyl compounds, esters, and amides and many addition reactions to
Schiff bases.

1. PROTON TRANSFER TO AND FROM CARBON

The first class, in which the proton transfer itself presents the
major energy barrier, is in many respects easier to understand. It
is generally agreed that base catalysis of these reactions involves
the direct removal of a proton from carbon (equation 89), and it is

$$B \frown H - \overset{|}{\underset{|}{C}} - C \overset{\nearrow O}{\underset{\searrow}{}} \qquad (89)$$

probable that general acid catalysis actually involves general base
catalysis of the removal of a proton from the conjugate acid of the
substrate, rather than the kinetically equivalent simple general acid
catalysis (equations 90 and 91). Bell and coworkers have shown that

$$B \frown H - \overset{|}{\underset{|}{C}} - C \overset{\nearrow \overset{+}{O}H}{\underset{\searrow}{}} \qquad (90)$$

$$v = k[\text{H}^+\text{B}][\text{H}_3\text{CC} \!=\! \text{O}] = k'[\text{B}][\text{H}_3\text{CC} \!\overset{+}{=}\! \text{OH}] \tag{91}$$

as the carbon acid becomes less acidic and proton removal more difficult, the reaction shows an enhanced sensitivity to the base strength of the catalyst, i.e., an increased Brønsted slope β (Table V). This intuitively satisfying result is what one might expect from a consideration of the potential-energy curves for the reaction. According to the Hammond postulate the transition state for the more difficult reaction is reached further along the reaction coordinate, so that there is a relatively large amount of breaking of the carbon-hydrogen bond and bond formation to the base (Fig. 12). The large amount of bond formation to the base implies that the energy of the transition state will be highly sensitive to the basicity of the base, resulting in a large value of β.

Conversely, the rate constants for proton removal from acetylacetone show a decreasing dependence β upon the basicity of the base as the base becomes stronger.[16] This is in contrast to proton transfers between oxygen, nitrogen, and sulfur atoms, which occur with a much lower energy barrier and show the β values of 0 or 1.0

Table V   The effect of the acidity of the carbon acid on the sensitivity to general base catalysis β^a

Carbon acid	$\log k_A{}^b$	pK_s	β
CH_3COCH_3	-8.56	20.0	0.88
$\text{CH}_3\text{COCH}_2\text{CH}_2\text{COCH}_3$	-7.85	18.7	0.89
$\text{CH}_3\text{COCH}_2\text{Cl}$	-5.29	16.5	0.82
$\text{CH}_3\text{COCH}_2\text{Br}$	-5.03	16.1	0.82
$\text{CH}_3\text{COCHCl}_2$	-3.78	14.9	0.82
$\text{CH}_2\text{COCHCO}_2\text{C}_2\text{H}_5$ $\mid$ $\text{—(CH}_2)_3\text{—}$	-1.76	13.1	0.64
$\text{CH}_3\text{COCH}_2\text{CO}_2\text{C}_2\text{H}_5$	-1.06	10.5	0.59
$\text{CH}_2\text{COCHCO}_2\text{C}_2\text{H}_5$ $\mid$ $\text{—(CH}_2)_4\text{—}$	-0.60	10.0	0.58
$\text{CH}_3\text{COCH}_2\text{COC}_6\text{H}_5$	-0.45	9.7	0.52
$\text{CH}_3\text{COCH}_2\text{COCH}_3$	-0.24	9.3	0.48
$\text{CH}_3\text{COCHBrCOCH}_3$	$+0.26$	8.3	0.42

[a]R. P. Bell, "The Proton in Chemistry," p. 172, Cornell University Press, Ithaca, N.Y., 1959.
[b]For a base of pK 4.0, in M^{-1} sec^{-1}.

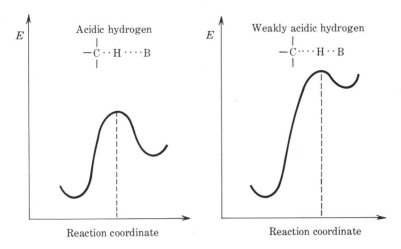

Fig 12. The transition state for the removal of a proton from a weakly acidic carbon acid occurs further along the reaction coordinate than that for proton removal from a stronger carbon acid.

expected for a simple diffusion-controlled reaction over a much larger range of basicity. It is also in contrast to the second class of reactions, discussed below, which frequently show little change in α or β over a large range of acidity or basicity.

2. PROTON TRANSFER TO AND FROM OXYGEN, NITROGEN, AND SULFUR

The difficulty in interpreting the detailed mechanism of the second class of reactions arises from the fact that the principal energy barrier for the reaction involves atoms different from those which are undergoing proton transfer, so that a complete description of the potential energy surface for a reaction such as the acid catalyzed addition of a nucleophile to a carbonyl group (equation 92) must

$$H-X \overset{\frown}{\underset{\smile}{}} C = \overset{\curvearrowright}{O} H \overset{\frown}{-} A \tag{92}$$

take account of the more or less simultaneous motions of five or more atoms, as well as changes in the surrounding solvent molecules. Physical chemists tend to throw up their hands in despair when confronted with such a problem, and any detailed consideration of the mechanism of this important class of reactions is certain to be oversimplified and qualitative at the present time. In considering the problem, one repeatedly runs up against the question of how much time is available, during the time that the transition state for the energetically most difficult part of the reaction is reached, for protons and solvent molecules to achieve low-energy equilibrium states. An answer to this question would help to resolve the essentially semantic and often repeated question of the extent to which these reactions are "concerted," but an unambiguous answer does not seem to be available at the present time.

The question of how long it takes for a reacting molecule or molecule pair to go from the ground to the transition state can be stated as follows: Is it more probable that the transition state will be reached by one of the very common small energy jumps suffered by one of the very few reacting species which has already almost attained the energy of the transition state, or that it is reached by a very rare large energy jump of one of the many reacting species which is at a low energy level (Fig. 13)? If the transition state is reached in a series of small energy jumps, the structure of the intermediate states will be different from that of the ground state, and it is likely that proton transfer can occur to give a system which is close to the most stable equilibrium position with respect to proton transfer in the transition state. If the transition state is reached rapidly, there may be insufficient time for proton transfer to occur unless the proton transfer is completely concerted with the remainder of the reaction. The rate at which proton transfer can occur within the reacting complex is not known exactly, but it is certainly faster than the rate of diffusion and is probably in the range of 10^{-11} to 10^{-13} seconds. The rate of reorganization of solvent

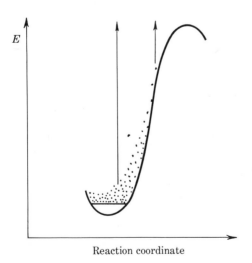

Reaction coordinate

Fig 13. Is it more probable that the transition state will be reached by a large energy jump from the many molecules of reactants in a low-energy state or by a small energy jump from one of the very few reacting molecules in a high-energy state?

molecules to provide optimal solvation is probably slightly slower than that of proton transfer.

In the absence of firm answers to these questions, we can only outline the possibilities at this time. It is convenient to do so in terms of a particular reaction, for which we will choose the general acid catalyzed addition of a nucleophilic reagent to the carbonyl group (equation 92).

a)   The first possibility is that the proton transfer itself is entirely rate-determining and the reaction is not concerted. The requirement for this case is that k_{-1} of equation 93 be larger than $k_2[HA]$, i.e.,

$$HX + {\overset{\diagdown}{\diagup}}C = O \underset{k_{-1}}{\overset{k_1}{\rightleftharpoons}} \overset{+}{HX} - \overset{|}{\underset{|}{C}} - O^- \xrightarrow[\text{slow}]{k_2[HA]} \overset{+}{HX} - \overset{|}{\underset{|}{C}} - OH$$

$$(93)$$

that the first step be at equilibrium. A somewhat analogous situation has been postulated for the hydrolysis of the monoanions of phosphate esters with very good leaving groups (equation 94).[99] Mechanisms of this kind require that the proton transfer step proceed at a

$$RO - \overset{\overset{\textstyle H}{\diagdown}{O}}{\underset{\overset{\|}{O}}{\underset{|}{P}}} - O^- \overset{\text{slow}}{\rightleftharpoons} RO - \overset{\overset{\textstyle +H \quad O^-}{|}}{\underset{\overset{\|}{O}}{\underset{|}{P}}} - O^- \longrightarrow ROH + \left[\overset{O}{\underset{O^{\diagup} \diagdown O}{P}} \right]^- \xrightarrow{H_2O} H_2PO_4^-$$

$$(94)$$

rate which is slower than the making or breaking of a covalent bond between two heavier atoms. This is not as improbable as it might seem because even though the rate constants for such proton transfers are at the diffusion-controlled limit, the rate in a given experimental situation may be relatively slow because of a low concentration of one of the reacting species or an unfavorable equilibrium step prior to proton transfer.

There are two experimental criteria for the recognition of a mechanism of this kind. First, the rate constant of the rate-determining step of the reaction in one direction or the other should be equal to the diffusion-controlled limit of about $10^{10} \ M^{-1} \ \text{sec}^{-1}$. It may not be possible to calculate this rate constant if the concentration of the species which reacts at a diffusion-controlled rate is unknown. This is likely to be the case, for example, for the break-

[99] A. J. Kirby and A. G. Varvoglis, *J. Am. Chem. Soc.* **89**, 415 (1967).

down of a tetrahedral addition intermediate in an acyl transfer reaction which occurs by a diffusion-controlled reaction with a molecule of acid or base in the solvent. Second, the value of α or β for such a reaction should be 0 or 1.0. If proton transfer is occurring in the direction favored by the equilibrium, the rate constant for proton transfer will be diffusion-controlled and will be independent of the acidity or basicity of the reacting species. If proton transfer is occurring in the unfavorable direction, the rate constant will be equal to approximately $10^{10}/K_{eq}$ (equation 64); i.e., the rate is directly dependent on the strength of the acid or base, so that α or β will be 1.0. A value of α or β of 0 or 1.0 ordinarily means that general acid-base catalysis will not be detectable, but such catalysis may be detectable in reactions of this kind because the slope of the Brønsted plot will change from 1.0 to 0 as the acidity and basicity of the catalysts change.[16] Such a break is likely to cause a negative deviation of the points for catalysis by the proton, water, or hydroxide ion, so that catalysis by other acids or bases becomes detectable.

A probable example of this situation is found in the general acid catalyzed S to N acetyl transfer reaction of S-acetylmercaptoethylamine, which shows a value of α experimentally indistinguishable from 0 for catalysis by carboxylic acids and phosphate monoanion.[100] There is other evidence that a proton transfer step must be rate-determining in this reaction (Chap. 10, Sec. B, Part 10). A possible explanation for the negative deviation of the catalytic constant for water in the general base catalyzed decomposition of the tetrahedral addition intermediate in formamidinium hydrolysis is that this reaction actually represents proton donation to the conjugate base of the intermediate and that the rate of reaction of the solvated proton has reached the diffusion-controlled limit (equation 95, $HA = H_3O^+$).[36]

$$(95)$$

The rate of the hydroxide ion catalyzed decomposition of hemithioacetals formed from acidic thiols is limited by the rate of diffusion of the reactants, but does not occur by the mechanism of equation 93. This reaction is subject to general base catalysis by weaker bases than hydroxide ion with a β value of 0.8. The fact

[100] R. Barnett and W. P. Jencks, *J. Am. Chem. Soc.* **90**, 4199 (1968).

that the value of β is 0.8 and not 1.0 means that proton transfer is not the only process which is occurring in the rate-determining step. The mechanism is formulated according to equation 96, in which the second step is a "concerted" general base catalyzed breakdown of

$$A^- + HO\overset{|}{\underset{|}{C}}SR \underset{k_{-1}}{\overset{k_1}{\rightleftharpoons}} \left[A^- \cdots HO\overset{|}{\underset{|}{C}}SR \right] \underset{k_{-2}}{\overset{k_2}{\rightleftharpoons}} AH + O = C\diagup + {}^-SR \qquad (96)$$

the hemithioacetal. The hydroxide ion catalyzed reaction with a rate constant at the diffusion-controlled limit represents a special case of this mechanism in which the diffusion together of the reactants (k_1) has become almost or completely rate-determining. Consequently, there is a leveling of the Brønsted plot at the diffusion-controlled limit, and the point for hydroxide ion exhibits a negative deviation from the line followed by other bases (Fig. 14). This reaction provides a clear example of a reaction in which the making and break-

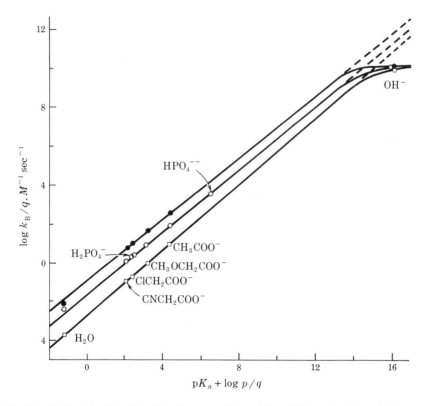

Fig 14. Brønsted plots for the decomposition of hemithioacetals formed from acetaldehyde and benzenethiol □ , thioacetic acid ○ , and p-nitrobenzenethiol ● at 25°.[27]

ing of covalent bonds to carbon can be faster than a diffusion-controlled step. The fact that the diffusion-controlled step is the slow step means that in the reverse, water catalyzed reaction (equation 96, $AH = H_2O$) the thiol anion will undergo reversible addition to the carbonyl group several times before the immediate product separates to give the hemithioacetal and hydroxide ion.[27]

b) The formation of the X—C bond is rate-determining, but the transition state is reached rapidly, so that the average position of the proton has not had time to adjust to the changing basicity of the carbonyl oxygen atom, and the catalyst aids the reaction by hydrogen bonding to the carbonyl group. This case is shown in equation 97, and the potential-energy curve for the proton as a function of its position between A^- and O is shown in Fig. 15a.

$$>C=O\cdots H-A \; \overset{K}{\rightleftharpoons} \; >C=\overset{+}{O}-H\cdots{}^-A$$

$$\qquad\quad \Big\downarrow k_1[\text{HX}] \qquad\qquad\qquad \Big\downarrow k_2[\text{HX}]$$

$$\qquad\quad \text{product} \qquad\qquad\qquad\quad \text{product}$$

$$\qquad\qquad (\text{I}) \qquad\qquad\qquad\qquad\quad (\text{II}) \qquad\qquad\qquad\qquad\qquad (97)$$

The hydrogen-bonded proton may be either closer to A^- (I) or to the carbonyl oxygen atom (II). Species I will react with the rate constant k_1, which will be larger than that for the free carbonyl compound. Species II will react with the very large rate constant

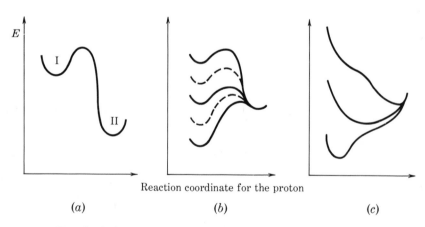

Reaction coordinate for the proton

(*a*)   (*b*)   (*c*)

Fig 15. Hypothetical energy diagrams for the movement of the *proton* during the course of the general acid catalyzed addition of HX to a carbonyl group.

k_2, but the amount of reaction which proceeds by this path may not be large because of the low concentration of II. The deuterium isotope effect and the Brønsted slope α for this reaction will be a function of the equilibrium constants for the formation of hydrogen-bonded complexes, the equilibrium constant K, and the relative magnitudes of k_1 and k_2. The transition state may be reached with the proton moving away from the carbonyl group

$$\overrightarrow{HX} \cdots > \overleftarrow{C} = \overrightarrow{O} \cdots \overrightarrow{H} - \overleftarrow{A}$$

or toward the carbonyl group

$$\overrightarrow{HX} \cdots > \overleftarrow{C} = \overrightarrow{O} \cdots \overleftarrow{H} - \overrightarrow{A}$$

The latter motion would be expected to provide a lower-energy transition state for attack on carbon, and to the extent that this is favored the reaction may be regarded as concerted.

c) The conversion of the reactants to the transition state is sufficiently slow relative to the rate of proton transfer that the positions of the double potential minima for the hydrogen-bonded proton change in the intermediate states between reactants, transition state, and products. Initially (Fig. 15b) the lowest-energy position for the proton is nearest to A^-, but as the reaction proceeds, the carbonyl oxygen atom increases in basicity, so that the energy for the proton bonded to this atom becomes equal to and finally more favorable than that for the proton bonded to A^-. The energy barrier to proton transfer, which is initially large, will decrease as the reaction proceeds and will be relatively small when the proton is transferred. Whether the proton jumps to the oxygen atom at the same instant that the transition state for X—C bond formation is reached is a moot point, but the fact that the proton immediately before the transition state is in a different position from its position in the starting materials means that the reaction is, in a sense, concerted. The fact that deuterium isotope effects for this type of reaction are often small means that in these cases the proton has not lost its zero-point energy in the transition state and suggests that the proton transfer process is not rate-determining in the usual sense; i.e., the proton does not have to be at the top of a potential barrier in the transition state.[7,101]

[101] C. A. Bunton and V. J. Shiner, Jr., *J. Am. Chem. Soc.* **83, 42**, 3207, 3214 (1961).

d) Again the rate of attainment of the transition state is slow relative to the rate of proton transfer, but in this case there is essentially no barrier for the transfer of the proton in the transition state. This would be the case if the hydrogen bond to the proton is sufficiently short and strong that there is only a single potential well for the proton or if proton transfer can occur with a high probability *through* a narrow potential barrier by tunneling.[102] The lowest-energy position for the proton between the donor and acceptor atoms may change progressively as the reaction proceeds, so that at no time does the proton cross a significant energy barrier (Fig. 15c).[103] As has been pointed out several times, the free energy of activation for proton transfer in a favorable direction is very small because proton transfer occurs faster than the rate of diffusion together of the reactants. A detailed calculation of the potential surface for the transfer of a proton from hydrochloric acid to ammonia suggests that there is no activation energy for this reaction.[104] There is a possible precedent for the concerted nature of reactions of this kind in the acid catalyzed transfer of a proton between phenol and water (equation 98).[105] The rate constant of 1.5

$$\tag{98}$$

$\times 10^7\ M^{-1}\ \mathrm{sec}^{-1}$ for this overall process and the thermodynamic instability of the conjugate acid of phenol (K_1) require that this conjugate acid cannot be an intermediate in the process because the further reaction to give products (k_2), even through an ultrafast proton transfer, would not be fast enough to account for the observed rate. The process must, therefore, be concerted, rather than stepwise, with some movement of the phenolic proton toward water before the addition of a second proton to phenol is complete.

[102] J. J. Weiss, *J. Chem. Phys.* **41**, 1120 (1964).

[103] M. M. Kreevoy, quoted in Cordes.[73]

[104] E. Clementi, *J. Chem. Phys.* **46**, 3851 (1967).

[105] E. Grunwald and M. S. Puar, *J. Phys. Chem.* **71**, 1842 (1967).

e) The transformation of starting materials to the transition state is sufficiently slow that diffusion of catalysts to the reacting molecules can occur. This is essentially a termolecular reaction, with the formation of stable intermediate complexes. The relatively long time required for diffusion of a catalyst to a reacting pair ($\approx 10^{-10}$ sec for $1 M$ solutions) would seem to make this unlikely as a mechanism for most reactions, but it cannot be ruled out as a possibility.

The mechanisms for general acid and base catalysis described in this chapter have generally been written as a direct interaction between the catalyst and substrate. Proton transfer reactions between small molecules in hydroxylic solvents occur either directly or through one or more intermediate solvent molecules (equation 99),

$$B \overset{+}{-} H \quad \underset{\underset{R}{|}}{O} - H \quad B \;\rightleftharpoons\; B \quad H - \underset{\underset{R}{|}}{O} \quad H \overset{+}{-} B \tag{99}$$

and it is probable that, at least in some reations, proton transfer in general acid-base catalysis takes place through intermediate solvent molecules.[106]

3. TRANSITION-STATE STABILIZATION BY GENERAL ACID-BASE CATALYSIS

Why does general acid or base catalysis lead to rate accelerations? It is an oversimplification to attribute such catalysis simply to the stabilization which results from hydrogen bonding in the transition state, although such hydrogen bonding is certainly involved. For general acid-base catalysis takes place through intermediate solvent stability of the transition state for the reaction in the absence of general catalysis, or with proton catalysis, to that of the transition state in the presence of a general acid catalyst. These transition states will, in general, differ by more than the presence or absence of hydrogen bonding because the extent to which other parts of the reaction have proceeded in the transition state will be influenced by the presence of the catalyst. The possible pathways for the dehydration of a carbinolamine and (in reverse) for the addition of water to an imine are shown in equation 100. The upper pathway

[106] E. Grunwald, A. Loewenstein, and S. Meiboom, *J. Chem. Phys.* **27**, 630, (1957); A. Loewenstein and S. Meiboom, *Ibid.*, p. 1067; W. P. Jencks and J. Carriuolo, *J. Am. Chem. Soc.* **82**, 675 (1960).

$$\left[\underset{>}{\overset{\delta+}{N}} \cdots \overset{|}{\underset{|}{C}} \cdots \overset{\delta-}{OH} \right]^{\ddagger} \rightleftharpoons \underset{>}{\overset{+}{N}} = C\overset{<}{} + {}^{-}OH$$

$$\underset{>}{N} - \overset{|}{\underset{|}{C}} - OH \overset{\pm HA}{\rightleftharpoons} \left[\underset{>}{\overset{\delta+}{N}} \cdots \overset{|}{\underset{|}{C}} \cdots \overset{}{\underset{|}{O}} \cdots H \cdots \overset{\delta-}{A} \right]^{\ddagger} \overset{\pm A^{-}}{\rightleftharpoons} \underset{>}{C} = \overset{+}{N}\overset{<}{} + H_2O$$

$$\pm H^{+}$$

$$\underset{>}{N} - \overset{|}{\underset{|}{C}} - \overset{+}{O} \overset{H}{\underset{H}{<}} \rightleftharpoons \left[\underset{>}{\overset{\delta+}{N}} \cdots \overset{|}{\underset{|}{C}} \cdots \overset{\delta+}{O} \overset{H}{\underset{H}{<}} \right]^{\ddagger}$$

$$\mathbf{11} \hspace{12cm} (100)$$

shows the uncatalyzed reaction, which requires the formation of the unstable OH^{-} ion as an intermediate. The lower pathway shows catalysis by hydrogen ion, which requires the formation of the unstable oxonium ion 11 (pK about -2) as an intermediate. At pH 7, the standard free energy of formation of either of these intermediates is in the range of 9,500 to 12,600 cal/mole, which is a large price to pay even for the formation of such reactive species. The middle pathway is for general acid catalysis and involves proton donation by the catalyst in the forward direction and proton removal by the conjugate base of the catalyst in the reverse direction. This pathway avoids the formation of both unstable intermediates, yet permits the reaction to proceed with the required proton transfers. The amount of stabilization of the transition state that is provided by general acid catalysis is the difference between the energy of the transition state for the middle pathway and that for the uncatalyzed upper or lower pathway. This stabilization is a complex resultant of the amount that carbon-oxygen bond formation and breakdown is stabilized by the presence of a proton, the amount of proton transfer in the transition state, and the strength of the acid catalyst. These quantitative relationships may be approached empirically by the use of structure-reactivity correlations, but no complete treatment of this complex situation is available at the present time.

In this connection it should be noted that the molecular interpretation of the Brønsted coefficient for this type of reaction is not simple. It is often assumed that the experimental meaning of the Brønsted coefficient—the relative stabilization of the transition state by acids of different strength—may be extrapolated to an interpretation of this quantity as a measure of the "amount" of proton transfer in the transition state. While the extrapolation is doubtless roughly correct, the multiplicity of factors that can affect the stability of the transition state suggest that too literal an interpretation should be avoided. Indeed, one might expect that there would be different amounts of proton transfer in the transition state for acids of different strengths (Fig. 16), in spite of the fact that the value of α for some reactions remains essentially constant over a wide range of acidity.[11c,107] The Brønsted exponent is best interpreted empirically as a measure of the extent to which substituents on an acid or base stabilize a transition state, compared with the extent that they stabilize the equilibrium for complete proton transfer. Since proton transfer causes a change in the charge of an acid or base, the Brønsted exponent is an approximate measure of the amount of change in the charge of the proton-donating or proton-accepting atom in the transition state.

Another reason why stabilization of the transition state is different from simple hydrogen bonding at equilibrium arises from the mode of formation of the transition state. The stability of an ordinary hydrogen bond is the difference between the free energy of the separated acid and base, acetic acid and sodium acetate, for example, and the free energy of the hydrogen-bonded pair. In water this stability is very small, and even the existence of hydrogen bonds between small solute molecules is in question. However, in reaching the transition state of the reaction shown in equation 100

[107] M. Caplow, personal communication.

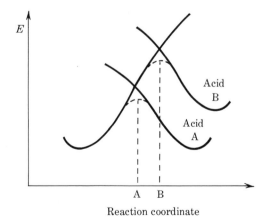

Fig 16. Diagram to show that the transition state for proton transfer might be expected to occur at different distances along the reaction coordinate for acids of different strength with little or no change in α.

Reaction coordinate

going from right to left, for example, we start with a water molecule which changes its acidity toward that of an oxonium ion as it
reaches the transition state. A large stabilization may result from
hydrogen bonding to such an acidic species, which would not be possible under equilibrium conditions in water. If movement of the proton occurs at the same time as the development of the transition
state, a large part of the stabilization may be regarded simply as
coming from the favorable net free energy of proton transfer from
the developing oxonium ion to the catalyzing base. Thus, the decrease in the energy of a transition state which results from general
acid catalysis may result from the proton transfer itself and be considerably greater than the energy of an ordinary intermolecular
hydrogen bond in water.

4
Isotope Effects[1]

A. INTRODUCTION AND THEORY

It is frequently observed that the rate of a reaction in which deuterium is being transferred is several times slower than that of the corresponding reaction in which hydrogen is transferred. For example, the rate-determining step of the bromination of acetone at all but very low concentrations of bromine is the base catalyzed removal of a proton to form the enolate ion, which reacts with bromine in a fast step (equation 1). This reaction and the directly

$$
\text{CH}_3\text{C} - \text{C} - \text{H} \cdots \text{B} \xrightarrow{\text{slow}} \text{CH}_3\text{C} = \text{CH}_2 + \overset{+}{\text{HB}} \xrightarrow[\text{Br}_2]{\text{fast}} \text{CH}_3\text{CCH}_2\text{Br} + \text{Br}^-
$$

$$(1)$$

[1] For further reading, see K. B. Wiberg, *Chem. Rev.* **55**, 713 (1955); L. Melander, "Isotope Effects on Reaction Rates," The Ronald Press Company, New York, 1960; R. P. Bell, "The Proton in Chemistry," chap. XI, Cornell University Press, Ithaca, N.Y., 1959; K. B. Wiberg, "Physical Organic Chemistry," pp. 351-364, John Wiley & Sons, Inc., New York, 1964.

measured exchange of the hydrogen atoms of acetone with the solvent are some six- to tenfold slower if deuterium is substituted for hydrogen.[2]

The deuterium (or tritium) isotope effect has most often been used as evidence for or against the occurrence of hydrogen transfer in the rate-determining step of a reaction, and has been ascribed to the difference in the zero-point energies of the stretching vibrations of bonds to hydrogen and deuterium. It has become increasingly evident that deuterium isotope effects are exceedingly useful in the diagnosis of reaction mechanism, but that the detailed interpretation of such effects is more complex than had generally been supposed and must be carried out with caution. Isotope effects with atoms other than hydrogen have been much less studied, because of the smaller differences in mass ratios and isotope effects, but they present a fertile field for further investigation of both chemical and enzymatic reaction mechanisms. The interpretation of isotope effects with these heavier atoms is often more straightforward than with hydrogen simply because the effects are so much smaller that they are not subjected to the same detailed and quantitative interpretations as are hydrogen isotope effects. For example, the isotopic composition of the carbon dioxide which is released initially in the manganese ion catalyzed decarboxylation of oxalacetate is enriched in the ^{12}C compound to an extent corresponding to an isotope effect $^{12}C/^{13}C$ of 1.06, but in the enzyme catalyzed decarboxylation there is no detectable isotope effect. This provides clear evidence that the rate-determining step of the nonenzymatic reaction involves decarboxylation, as expected (equation 2, step 1), but that in the enzymat-

$$\underset{\substack{\parallel \\ O}}{^-OOCCCH_2COO^-} \xrightarrow{\;1\;} \underset{\substack{\mid \\ OH}}{^-OOCC} = CH_2 + CO_2 \xrightarrow{\;2\;} \underset{\substack{\parallel \\ O}}{^-OOCCCH_3} \qquad (2)$$

ic reaction there is no cleavage of the carbon-carbon bond in the rate-determining step so that some other step, such as ketonization of the initial enol product to pyruvate (equation 2, step 2), must be rate-determining.[3]

Although many reactions exhibit "normal" kinetic deuterium isotope effects in the range k_H/k_D of about 6 to 10, as found for the enolization of acetone, any complete theory must explain kinetic and

[2] O. Reitz and J. Kopp, *Z. Physik. Chem.* **184A**, 429 (1939).

[3] S. Seltzer, G. A. Hamilton, and F. H. Westheimer, *J. Am. Chem. Soc.* **81**, 4018 (1959).

equilibrium deuterium isotope effects which encompass a far wider range and even a change in direction compared with those for acetone enolization. These include, on the one hand, reactions such as the removal of a proton from 2-nitropropane by 2,6-lutidine[4] with $k_H/k_D = 24$ and the abstraction of a hydrogen atom from methanol or acetate to form hydrogen gas[5] with $k_H/k_D = 20$–22. On the other hand, there are many reactions with small or inverse isotope effects, such as the proton exchange and racemization of certain carbon acids,[6] with k_H/k_D in the range 0.3 to 1.9, the general base catalyzed aminolysis of phenyl acetate by glycine,[7] with $k_{H_2O}/k_{D_2O} = 1.1$, and the acid catalyzed hydrolysis of sucrose,[8] with $k_{H_2O}/k_{D_2O} = 0.49$. In addition, many reactions show changes in rate upon isotopic substitution of atoms other than those which are being transferred. The interpretation of such secondary isotope effects has given rise to considerable controversy, but is now sufficiently well understood to be useful in the elucidation of reaction mechanisms.

A distinction should be made at the outset between isotope effects observed with hydrogen atoms which do not exchange readily with the medium, such as most carbon-hydrogen and boron-hydrogen compounds, and those observed with rapidly exchangeable hydrogen atoms bound to oxygen, nitrogen, or sulfur. If isotopic substitution is accomplished in the former class, the reaction of each isotopic species can be studied in both water and deuterium oxide. With the latter class, proton exchange with the solvent takes place rapidly, so that the nature of the atom which is being transferred is dependent on the composition of the solvent. The interpretation of an observed rate difference between reactions in water, deuterium oxide, and mixtures of these solvents must include isotope effects on the equilibrium distribution of hydrogen and deuterium atoms and differences in interactions with the solvent, as well as the kinetic isotope effect on the atom which is being transferred.

Although the detailed theoretical interpretation of the mechanism of primary deuterium isotope effects is a problem of great

[4] E. S. Lewis and L. H. Funderburk, *J. Am. Chem. Soc.* **89**, 2322 (1967); E. S. Lewis and J. K. Robinson, *Ibid.* **90**, 4337 (1968).

[5] M. Anbar and D. Meyerstein, *J. Phys. Chem.* **68**, 3184 (1964).

[6] D. J. Cram, D. A. Scott, and W. D. Nielsen, *J. Am. Chem. Soc.* **83**, 3696 (1961); W. T. Ford, E. W. Graham, and D. J. Cram, *Ibid.* **89**, 4661 (1967).

[7] W. P. Jencks and J. Carriuolo, *J. Am. Chem. Soc.* **82**, 675 (1960).

[8] Ph. Gross, H. Steiner, and H. Suess, *Trans. Faraday Soc.* **32**, 883 (1936).

complexity and considerable uncertainty,[9-11] many of the important aspects of the problem may be treated in a simplified and approximate manner with a precision which is adequate for most experimental work and which provides at least a qualitative insight into the mechanism of the observed effects. The most important reason for the existence of deuterium isotope effects is the difference in the zero-point energies of bonds to hydrogen and to deuterium and the experimental fact that such effects exist is a direct expression of the principles of quantum mechanics. According to quantum mechanics the energy levels of a hydrogen atom bound to a carbon atom, for example, are quantized, and the lowest energy state of a C—H bond with respect to C—H distance is not the lowest point on the potential energy curve for this system, but lies above this minimum by the amount of the zero-point energy (Fig. 1). The zero-point energy is equal to $\frac{1}{2}h\nu$ (where h is Planck's constant and ν is the frequency of the C—H vibration). From Hooke's law, ν is proportional to $1/\sqrt{\text{mass}}$, and the stretching frequencies of the C—H and C—D bonds are 2,900 and 2,100 cm^{-1}, which correspond to zero-point energies of 4.15 and 3.0 kcal/mole, respectively. It is the difference in mass between hydrogen and deuterium that is of primary importance in determining the difference in frequency of these vibrations because the atom to which hydrogen or deuterium is bonded is much heavier and remains almost fixed in the vibration.

[9] J. Bigeleisen, *J. Chem. Phys.* **17**, 675 (1949); J. Bigeleisen and M. Wolfsberg, *Advan. Chem. Phys.* **1**, 15 (1958).

[10] F. H. Westheimer, *Chem. Rev.* **61**, 265 (1961).

[11] L. Melander, "Isotope Effects on Reaction Rates," The Ronald Press Company, New York, 1960.

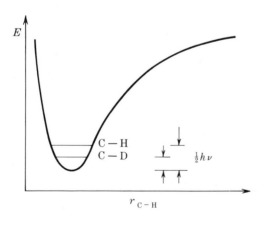

Fig 1.   The difference in the zero point energies of carbon-hydrogen and carbon-deuterium bonds.

If a hydrogen atom is transferred to an acceptor B, this stretching vibration is lost in the transition state when it is converted into a translation as the hydrogen atom moves toward the acceptor at the highest energy point of the energy profile (Fig. 2). Since the C—H and the C—D compound are reaching the same energy maximum but are starting from different zero-point energies, the difference between the amount of energy required to bring the two compounds to the transition state will be the difference in zero-point energies, $4.15 - 3.0 = 1.15$ kcal/mole. This corresponds to a difference in rate of sevenfold at room temperature. The corresponding stretching frequencies and zero-point energy differences for O—H and O—D correspond to a rate constant approximately tenfold larger for hydrogen than for deuterium.

This treatment takes into account only the loss of the stretching vibration and is no more than a crude approximation of any real situation. There may also be changes in the bending vibrations and, as discussed below, a new stretching vibration may appear in the transition state. Furthermore, it is an oversimplification to isolate the vibration to a single C—H bond in a polyatomic molecule. A given vibration is likely to be coupled, to a greater or lesser extent, to other vibrations, so that the change in frequency

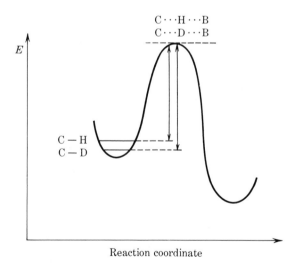

Reaction coordinate

Fig 2. In a reaction in which the zero-point energy is lost in the transition state, the difference in the rate of reaction of hydrogen and deuterium compounds should correspond to the difference in the zero-point energies of the bonds to these atoms in the ground state.

upon substitution of deuterium for hydrogen is not always predictable. Nevertheless, it is clear that the loss of the zero-point energy of the stretching vibration and the corresponding difference in the amounts of energy required to bring hydrogen and deuterium from the ground state to the transition state accounts for the largest part of the observed differences in the rates of transfer of hydrogen and deuterium in nearly all reactions which show significant kinetic deuterium isotope effects. The important point in the theoretical interpretation of isotope effects is that there is no difference in the potential-energy surfaces for compounds or reactions involving hydrogen and deuterium; the observed differences in rate and equilibrium constants arise from differences in the minimum energy levels, which arise from different vibrational frequencies of hydrogen and deuterium-containing molecules and transition states.

A useful qualitative generalization, which applies to secondary as well as to primary and equilibrium isotope effects, is that deuterium will tend to be concentrated (and deuterium-containing species will be relatively more stable) in those molecules and transition states in which it is in the narrowest potential well.[12] The zero-point energy may be regarded as an expression of the uncertainty principle and will be largest when the position of the atom in question is most certain, i.e., when it is restricted to a relatively narrow potential well and vibrates with a high frequency. The large zero-point energy of such an atom means that a large decrease in energy will be observed if deuterium is substituted for hydrogen.

The larger isotope effects that are observed with tritium are a simple consequence of the larger mass of this isotope and the resulting changes in frequencies and zero-point energies. If the mechanism of the isotope effect is similar to that for the hydrogen-deuterium isotope effect (i.e., if tunneling is not important), the differences in the loss of zero-point energies for hydrogen and tritium should be directly related to the masses of these atoms. The expected relationship of the isotope effects is given in equation 3.

$$\log \frac{k_H}{k_T} = 1.44 \log \frac{k_H}{k_D} \tag{3}$$

This relationship has been observed experimentally in several instances.[13]

[12] M. M. Kreevoy, *J. Chem. Ed.* **41**, 636 (1964).

[13] C. G. Swain, E. C. Stivers, J. F. Reuwer, Jr., and L. J. Schaad, *J. Am. Chem. Soc.* **80**, 5885 (1958).

Another important consequence of quantum mechanics, which follows from the uncertainty principle, is the possibility that hydrogen transfer may occur by *tunneling* through a narrow potential barrier rather than by passing over it.[14] The uncertainty principle does not permit an exact specification of the position of small particles, such as the electron. For particles with the mass of most atoms this uncertainty is insignificant, but for the relatively small proton it may be significant if the potential barrier for its transfer is not too thick. In other words, the uncertainty in the specification of the position of the proton is sufficiently large that there is a finite probability that a proton which is initially on one side of a thin potential barrier may at some later time be found on the other side, without having passed over the top of the barrier. Tunneling is of less importance for deuterium and tritium because of their larger mass. This difference in tunneling frequency will contribute to the observed isotope effect for hydrogen as compared with deuterium or tritium if tunneling is important. The large isotope effect of $k_H/k_D = 24.1$ for the removal of a proton from 2-nitropropane by the sterically hindered base 2,6-lutidine has been ascribed to tunneling; it may be compared with $k_H/k_D = 9.8$ for the corresponding reaction with pyridine.[4] The energy barrier for the former reaction will depend in large part upon the compressional energies of the atoms which provide the steric hindrance. These energies have a large dependence on distance, so that the energy barrier is likely to be thin and steep. This would be expected to favor tunneling. Furthermore, the difference in the apparent activation energy which is associated with the isotope effect of the 2,6-lutidine reactions is 3 kcal/mole, with a frequency factor ratio of 0.15. This difference in activation energy for hydrogen and deuterium transfer is much larger than can be accounted for by the difference in zero-point energies and is most easily explained by the occurrence of tunneling; the difference in frequency factor is an even stronger, although less obvious, indication of tunneling.[14] It is of interest that tunneling does not necessarily cause a deviation from equation 3, although it may do so. For example, the observed value of k_H/k_T of 79 for the ionization of 2-nitropropane by 2,4,6-trimethylpyridine is in good agreement with the value of 83 calculated from equation 3 and the deuterium isotope effect of 23 for this reaction.[4]

[14] R. P. Bell, "The Proton in Chemistry," p. 183, Cornell University Press, Ithaca, N.Y., 1959.

B. EQUILIBRIA IN WATER AND DEUTERIUM OXIDE

Reactions such as the hydrolysis of sucrose which are subject to specific acid catalysis proceed some two to three times faster in deuterium oxide than in water at a given acidity. This is a result of the fact that the acidity of many strong acids is decreased two to three times in deuterium oxide. A specific acid catalyzed reaction proceeds in two steps: (1) a rapid, equilibrium protonation of the substrate (equation 4), and (2) a reaction of the protonated substrate

$$S + H^+ \underset{\text{fast}}{\overset{K_{SH^+}}{\rightleftharpoons}} SH^+ \tag{4}$$

to give products (equation 5). If there is no proton transfer in the

$$SH^+ \underset{\text{slow}}{\overset{k_2}{\longrightarrow}} \text{products} \tag{5}$$

second step, the constant k_2 will be approximately the same in water and deuterium oxide. The difference in the overall rate occurs because the equilibrium concentration of the conjugate acid of the substrate is some 2 to 3 times higher in deuterium oxide than in water at a given acidity because SD^+ in D_2O is generally a weaker acid than SH^+ in H_2O.

The explanation for this difference in acid strengths that first comes to mind is that the dissociation of a proton (equation 6)

$$A—H \rightleftharpoons A^- + H^+ \tag{6}$$

involves a loss of the zero-point energy of A—H in a manner analogous to the loss of zero-point energy in a transition state for proton transfer, so that the larger loss of zero-point energy for the deutero acid A—D makes the dissociation of A—D more difficult than that of A—H. One would expect that the proton of stronger acids would be less tightly bonded and would have a smaller A—H stretching frequency than that of weaker acids. The difference in zero-point energies and the deuterium isotope effect for dissociation of a proton would, therefore, be smaller for stronger acids, and, indeed, a trend in this direction is observed experimentally (Fig. 3).[15, 16]

[15] C. K. Rule and V. K. La Mer, *J. Am. Chem. Soc.* **60**, 1974 (1938).

[16] R. P. Bell and A. T. Kuhn, *Trans. Faraday Soc.* **59**, 1789 (1963).

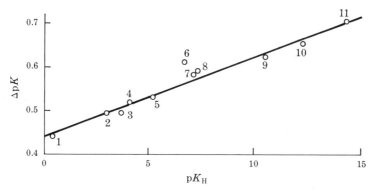

Fig 3. Isotope effect on the acidities of phenols and alcohols as a function of their acid strength pK_H.[16] Compounds: 1, picric acid; 2, 4-chloro-2,6-dinitrophenol; 3, 2,6-dinitrophenol; 4, 2,4-dinitrophenol; 5, 2,5-dinitrophenol; 6, 3,5-dinitrophenol; 7, p-nitrophenol; 8, o-nitrophenol; 9, hydroquinone; 10, 2,2′,2″-trifluoroethanol; 11, 2-chloroethanol.

There is a germ of truth in this explanation, but it is clear that it is not correct in its entirety because acids that are stronger than the solvated proton (such as the conjugate acid of sucrose) show a deuterium isotope effect in the same direction as weaker acids. The dissociation of an acid in water is more accurately written according to equation 7, in which the proton is donated to one or several water

$$A\text{—}H + H_2O \rightleftharpoons A^- + H_3O^+ \text{ (or } H_9O_4^+) \tag{7}$$

molecules upon dissociation. The solvated proton has a significant zero-point energy, and if the deuterium isotope effect were a function only of acid strength, it should change direction for acids which are stronger than H_3O^+ (or $H_9O_4^+$).

A more satisfactory approach is based upon a comparison of the observed or estimated stretching frequencies and zero-point energies of bonds to hydrogen in acids and in solvent molecules which are associated with the acid and its conjugate base, as described by Bunton and Shiner.[17] Since the vibration frequency and zero-point energy of a bond to deuterium bear a constant relationship to the corresponding bond to hydrogen, the isotope effect on the equilibrium constant of a reaction is a simple function of the difference between the sum of all of the vibration frequencies in the reactants $\Sigma\nu_H$ and in the products $\Sigma\nu'_H$, subject to the approximations mentioned above. This relationship is shown in equation 8.

[17] C. A. Bunton and V. J. Shiner, Jr., *J. Am. Chem. Soc.* **83**, 42 (1961).

$$\frac{K_{H_2O}}{K_{D_2O}} = \text{antilog} \frac{\Sigma \nu_H - \Sigma \nu'_H}{12.53T} \tag{8}$$

For many reactions there appears to be little change in the sum of the bending vibrations, so that the isotope effect is caused principally by changes in the stretching vibrations. The decrease in the A—H stretching frequency as the acid becomes stronger and the A—H bond becomes weaker accounts in part for the smaller difference in zero-point energy and deuterium isotope effect in the dissociation of stronger acids. However, these differences are not nearly large enough to account for the magnitude of the observed isotope effects, and in order to do so it is necessary to take into account the changes in the stretching frequencies of the solvent which result from hydrogen bonding to HA and to the conjugate base of the acid as shown in equation 9 (in which < represents a

$$\tag{9}$$

solvating water molecule). These frequencies are generally not known exactly, but they may be estimated with sufficient accuracy to permit an estimate of their influence on the isotope effect. Such estimates show the expected trend in isotope effect with acid strength and, except for the ionization of water, are in remarkably good agreement with the observed values for most acids (Table I).

The success of this treatment in accounting for the apparently anomalous position of the solvated proton itself is of particular importance. Most isotope effects involving the solvated proton are consistent with the hypothesis that this species exists in the form H_3O^+, although there are certainly more loosely bound surrounding water molecules which give species such as $H_9O_4{}^+$. The reaction of H_3O^+ with a base A^- (equation 9 in reverse) results in the loss of *three* stretching frequencies characteristic of an acid (about 2,900 cm^{-1}) and the gain of one characteristic of the acid HA, plus two of water (about 3,400 cm^{-1}). This situation and the associated changes in the frequencies of hydrogen-bonded water molecules mean that the transfer of a deuteron in D_3O^+ to a base A^- usually involves a smaller increase in total zero-point energy than the corresponding transfer of a proton from H_3O^+, regardless of whether HA is a weaker or stronger acid than H_3O^+.

Table I   Isotope effect of deuterium oxide solvent on the dissociation of weak acids[17]

Acid	pK_a	K_{H_2O}/K_{D_2O} (observed)	K_{H_2O}/K_{D_2O} (calculated)
Water	15.74	6.5	4.6
β-Trifluoroethanol	12.4	4.4	4.5
HCO_3^-	10.25	4.4	3.8
p-Nitrophenol	7.21	3.67	3.3
Acetic acid	4.74	3.33	3.1
Chloroacetic acid	2.76	2.76	2.8

The application of the Bunton and Shiner treatment to a particular reaction is often difficult because of our incomplete knowledge of the detailed nature of the hydrogen bonding between solutes and water. Furthermore, for some reactions it is not possible to neglect changes in bending vibrations. For example, it is necessary to include the changes in the bending frequencies of the O—H and S—H bonds in order to account for the K_{H_2O}/K_{D_2O} value of 0.44 for the addition of methoxyethanethiol to acetaldehyde (equation 10).[18] Nevertheless, this treatment accounts satisfactorily for the

$$RSH\ +\ >C=O\ \rightleftharpoons\ RS-\overset{|}{\underset{|}{C}}-OH$$

$$(10)$$

isotope effects on a number of equilibria and has also been applied with considerable success to a number of kinetic isotope effects.[19]

C. SECONDARY ISOTOPE EFFECTS[20]

Secondary isotope effects are caused by isotopic substitution of atoms which are not "reacting." For most reactions the distinction between primary and secondary isotope effects is clear, but it is sometimes difficult to decide whether an atom is "reacting" or not in the transition state. Ultimately, there is no sharp distinction between primary and secondary isotope effects because both are caused by changes in vibration frequencies and zero-point energies between ground states and transition states, and any atom which is involved in such a change is, in some sense, reacting. Secondary

[18] G. E. Lienhard and W. P. Jencks, J. Am. Chem. Soc. 88, 3982 (1966).

[19] C. A. Bunton and V. J. Shiner, Jr., J. Am. Chem. Soc. 83, 3207, 3214 (1961).

[20] E. A. Halevi, Progr. Phys. Org. Chem. 1, 109 (1963).

isotope effects are often further divided into such categories as "inductive," "steric," and "resonance" effects. These terms are useful for describing observed effects, but they do not have the same meaning as ordinary inductive, steric, and resonance effects, and it is important to keep in mind that they are ultimately caused by changes in vibrational frequencies rather than by changes in potential-energy surfaces.[20, 21] It is often convenient to say that changes in rates and equilibria behave "as if" isotopic substitution were giving rise to inductive, steric, and resonance effects.

1. FREQUENCY CHANGES OF BONDS TO NONREACTING ATOMS

In carbonium ion reactions, the reacting carbon atom undergoes a change from sp^3 to sp^2 hybridization, which is associated with changes in the vibration frequencies of bonds to neighboring atoms (equation 11). If these neighboring atoms are hydrogen or deute-

$$-\overset{|}{\underset{|}{C}}-X \;\rightleftharpoons\; \left[\overset{\delta^+}{-C}\overset{\delta^-}{\cdots}X \right] \;\rightleftharpoons\; -\overset{+}{C}\diagup \tag{11}$$

$$sp^3 \qquad\qquad \text{Intermediate} \qquad\qquad sp^2$$

rium, these frequency changes will give rise to a difference in the zero-point energies of the transition state and product and a secondary isotope effect. For example, the solvolysis of cyclopentyl tosylate-α-d is 15% slower than that of the hydrogen compound.[22] The change from sp^3 to sp^2 hybridization causes little change in the stretching and one of the bending frequencies, but is associated with a change in the other bending frequency from 1,340 to about 800 cm^{-1} in model compounds with sp^2 hybridization, such as aldehydes. Such a change would be expected to give an isotope effect of 1.38, and the observed isotope effect of 1.15 is thus explicable if there is a shift in this bending frequency part way toward that of a carbonium ion in the transition state. A somewhat larger isotope effect of $K_H/K_D = 1.29$ for deuterium substitution in the α position has been found for the *equilibrium* formation of a carbonium ion from benzhydrol (equation 12).[23] Kinetic isotope effects of this kind have now been observed in a number of chemical reactions and

[21] E. R. Thornton, *Ann. Rev. Phys. Chem.* **17**, 349 (1966).

[22] A. Streitwieser, Jr., R. H. Jagow, R. C. Fahey, and S. Suzuki, *J. Am. Chem. Soc.* **80**, 2326 (1958).

[23] M. M. Mocek and R. Stewart, *Can. J. Chem.* **41**, 1641 (1963).

$$
\begin{matrix} H \\ | \\ (C_6H_5)_2COH \end{matrix} + H^+ \; \rightleftharpoons \; \begin{matrix} H \\ | \\ (C_6H_5)_2C^+ \end{matrix} + H_2O \tag{12}
$$

deserve more attention as a probe for the nature of the rate-determining step in enzyme catalyzed reactions. The role of secondary isotope effects in modifying primary isotope effects will be described in Sec. D, Part 5.

2. INDUCTIVE EFFECTS

The substitution of deuterium for hydrogen in a nonreacting position very often results in a change in the chemical behavior of a molecule in the direction which would be expected if deuterium were slightly more electron-donating than hydrogen.[20] For example, the acid dissociation constant of phenol is 12% larger than that of phenol-d_5, and deuteroformic acid, DCOOH, is a weaker acid than formic acid, HCOOH, with a difference in pK of 0.035 units.[24] A more rigorous analysis of the isotope effect on formic acid ionization shows that the difference in pK is the result of a summation of small differences in a number of vibration frequencies of formic acid, deuteroformic acid, and their respective anions,[25] but for most practical purposes it appears to be legitimate to treat differences of this kind as a simple inductive substituent effect. The small differences in the dipole moments of hydrogen- and deuterium-containing compounds can also be regarded as a result of a greater electron-donating effect of deuterium, which may be ascribed to the shorter effective bond length of the C—D than of the C—H bond.[20]

3. HYPERCONJUGATION

Nuclear magnetic resonance spectroscopy of the ^{19}F nucleus in p-fluorotoluene provides a rather direct method for observing differences in the electronic environment of the fluorine atom. Such measurements with p-fluorotoluene and p-fluorotoluene-d_3 indicate a smaller electron donation from the deuterated than the normal methyl group. This is in the opposite direction from that expected from the electron-donating inductive effect of deuterium and is most easily interpreted as evidence for hyperconjugation from the *para* position, which is less significant for deuterium than for hydrogen

[24] R. P. Bell and W. B. T. Miller, *Trans. Faraday Soc.* **59**, 1147 (1963).

[25] R. P. Bell and J. E. Crooks, *Trans. Faraday Soc.* **58**, 1409 (1962).

because of the loss of zero-point energy which is implied by hyperconjugation (equation 13).[26] The change, although in the right

$$H-\underset{\underset{H}{|}}{\overset{\overset{H}{|}}{C}}\!\!-\!\!\langle\bigcirc\rangle\!\!-\!\!F \longleftrightarrow {}^+H\ \underset{\underset{H}{|}}{\overset{\overset{H}{|}}{C}}\!\!=\!\!\langle\bigcirc\rangle\!\!-\!\!F \tag{13}$$

direction, is smaller than might have been expected, but the fact
that no difference is observed upon deuterium substitution in the
meta position supports the conclusion that it is caused by hyperconjugation. The facts that methanol adds to acetone some 30%
less readily than to acetone-d_6 and that hydroxide ion attacks
ethyl acetate 10% more slowly than deuterated ethyl acetate might
also be explained in terms of hyperconjugative stabilization of the
starting materials (equations 14 and 15), which is more important

$$H-\underset{\underset{H}{|}}{\overset{\overset{H}{|}}{C}}\!-\!\overset{\overset{O}{\|}}{C}\!-\!\underset{\underset{H}{|}}{\overset{\overset{H}{|}}{C}}\!-\!H \longleftrightarrow H^+\ \underset{\underset{H}{|}}{\overset{\overset{H}{|}}{C}}\!=\!\overset{\overset{{}^-O}{|}}{C}\!-\!\underset{\underset{H}{|}}{\overset{\overset{H}{|}}{C}}\!-\!H \tag{14}$$

$$H-\underset{\underset{H}{|}}{\overset{\overset{H}{|}}{C}}\!-\!\overset{\overset{O}{\|}}{C}OEt \longleftrightarrow H^+\ \underset{\underset{H}{|}}{\overset{\overset{H}{|}}{C}}\!=\!\overset{\overset{O^-}{|}}{C}OEt \tag{15}$$

for the hydrogen than for the deuterium substituted compounds; but
the isotope effect in the latter reaction is complicated by an unusual
temperature dependence, and the situation is too complicated to
permit a firm conclusion at the present time.[27–29]

The strongest evidence for the importance of hyperconjugation
comes from the β-deuterium isotope effect on solvolysis. Substitution of deuterium for hydrogen at the β position causes a 16%
decrease in the rate of solvolysis of cyclopentyl tosylate, as would be
expected if hyperconjugation from this position provided significant
stabilization to the developing carbonium ion structure in the transition state (equation 16).[22] A similar effect ($k_H/k_D = 1.14$) on the

[26] D. D. Traficante and G. E. Maciel, *J. Am. Chem. Soc.* 87, 4917 (1965).

[27] J. M. Jones and M. L. Bender, *J. Am. Chem. Soc.* 82, 6322 (1960).

[28] M. L. Bender and M. S. Feng, *J. Am. Chem. Soc.* 82, 6318 (1960).

[29] E. A. Halevi and Z. Margolin, *Proc. Chem. Soc.* 1964, 174.

$$H - \underset{|}{\overset{|}{C}} - \underset{|}{\overset{|}{C}} \cdots \overset{(+)(-)}{X} \longleftrightarrow H^+ \quad \underset{|}{\overset{|}{C}} = \underset{|}{\overset{|}{C}} \cdots \overset{(-)}{X} \tag{16}$$

rate of solvolysis of the bicyclic compound 1 is seen upon deuterium substitution into the methylene group, but no rate decrease is

H $\longleftarrow k_H/k_D = 0.99$

HCCl

CH$_2$

H $\quad k_H/k_D = 1.14$

1

observed if the deuterium is substituted into the bridgehead position, from which hyperconjugation with its accompanying partial double-bond formation would not be expected to occur.[30]

4. STERIC EFFECTS

The lower zero-point energy of deuterium compared with hydrogen means that the average C—D bond length is slightly smaller than the average C—H bond length in the asymmetric potential well of the C—H or C—D bond. This results in a slightly smaller effective size of compounds or groups in which deuterium is substituted for hydrogen, but the differences are very small. The effective C—H bond length is about 0.005 Å longer than the C—D bond length, and benzene-d_6 is about 0.3% smaller than ordinary benzene.[31] The molar refraction, a measure of the polarizability, is 0.5% larger for benzene than for benzene-d_6.[32] A number of attempts to detect manifestations of steric effects as differences in reaction rate between hydrogen and deuterium substituted compounds have shown negligible rate differences, but significant differences have been found in a few reactions which have demanding steric requirements. For example, the racemization of 9,10-dihydro-4,5-dimethylphenanthrene (2) requires that the methyl groups slide past each other in a severely crowded transition state. The compound in which the methyl groups are substituted with deuterium

---

[30] V. J. Shiner, Jr., *J. Am. Chem. Soc.* **82**, 2655 (1960).

[31] L. S. Bartell and R. R. Roskos, *J. Chem. Phys.* **44**, 457 (1966).

[32] C. K. Ingold, C. G. Raisin, and C. L. Wilson, *J. Chem. Soc.* **1936**, 915.

undergoes racemization 13% faster than the corresponding hydrogen-containing compound.[33]

2

5. SOLVENT EFFECTS

In addition to solvent isotope effects that may be more or less rigorously ascribed to hydrogen bonding between solutes or transition states and the solvent, there are differences in solvation in water and deuterium oxide that cannot be directly assigned to hydrogen bonding to the solutes and are lumped together as "nonspecific solvent effects." It is not easy to make generalizations about these effects at the present time, other than that they are small, with a maximum of 30 to 40% in most instances, and are nearly always in the direction of a slower rate in deuterium oxide. The dielectric constants of water and deuterium oxide are almost identical, but it is generally agreed that deuterium oxide is appreciably more "structured" than water, as indicated, for example, by its 23% larger viscosity, so that solvent-solute interactions which depend on solvent structure would be expected to be different in the two solvents. Most ions, which are "structure-breaking," are slightly (about 40%) more soluble in water than deuterium oxide, whereas lithium fluoride, which is a "structure-forming" salt, is more soluble in deuterium oxide. The differences in enthalpy and entropy of solution and dilution of different salts are much larger than the differences in free energy, as would be expected if differences in effects on "solvent structure" are involved.[34-36] The similar free energies of transfer of a series of different chloride salts from water to deuterium oxide suggest that differences in the solvation of cations are small and that it is the solvation of anions

[33] K. Mislow, R. Graeve, A. J. Gordon, and G. H. Wahl, Jr., *J. Am. Chem. Soc.* **86**, 1733 (1964).

[34] C. G. Swain and R. F. W. Bader, *Tetrahedron Letters* **10**, 182 (1960).

[35] D. H. Davies and G. C. Benson, *Can. J. Chem.* **43**, 3100 (1965).

[36] Y-C.Wu and H. L. Friedman, *J. Phys. Chem.* **70**, 166 (1966).

that is different in the two solvents; this is what might be expected because anions interact more intimately than cations with protons or deuterions of water.[37]

The solvation of nonpolar solutes in the two solvents is more difficult to interpret. The greater solubilities in deuterium oxide of up to about 10% for several hydrocarbons and argon, which are thought to cause an increase in solvent structure upon solution, are in accord with the postulated increased "structure" of deuterium oxide.[38, 39] However, the solubilities of simple alkyl halides are similar or up to about 10% *smaller* in deuterium oxide than in water,[40] the solubility of iodine is some 20% smaller in deuterium oxide,[41] and estimates of the stability of the hydrophobic side chains of amino acids, after a correction for solvent effects on the charged groups on these molecules, suggest that the free energy of these nonpolar groups is also higher in deuterium oxide than in water.[38] Other factors than "solvent structure," such as differences in polarizability, must be invoked to account for these differences.

One would expect free-energy differences of this magnitude which are the result of "solvent effects" to affect reaction rates, depending on the extent to which the difference between the ground state and the transition state of the reaction resembles a structure-disrupting ion or a nonpolar molecule, but it is difficult to make generalizations about the size or even the direction of these effects without information about the solvent isotope effect on the stability of compounds which are suitable models for the ground and transition states of a given reaction.

D. THE MAGNITUDE OF KINETIC ISOTOPE EFFECTS

There are many reactions which involve proton transfer, but which do not show "normal" deuterium isotope effects in the range $k_H/k_D = 6$–10. The possibility of exceptionally large isotope effects if tunneling is important in the proton transfer, and the isotope

[37] P. Salomaa and V. Aalto, *Acta Chem. Scand.* **20**, 2035 (1966).

[38] G. C. Kresheck, H. Schneider, and H. A. Scheraga, *J. Phys. Chem.* **69**, 3132 (1965).

[39] A. Ben-Naim, *J. Chem. Phys.* **42**, 1512 (1965).

[40] C. G. Swain and E. R. Thornton, *J. Am. Chem. Soc.* **84**, 822 (1962); G. A. Clarke, T. R. Williams, and R. W. Taft, *Ibid.*, p. 2292.

[41] R. W. Ramette and R. W. Sandford, Jr., *J. Am. Chem. Soc.* **87**, 5001 (1965).

effects on equilibria for proton transfer which occur before the rate-determining step, have already been discussed. Some other explanations which have been proposed for "abnormal" isotope effects will be described in this section.

1. ASYMMETRIC TRANSITION STATES

It is sometimes suggested that the isotope effect in a proton transfer reaction may be small if there is either a small amount of bond breaking in the reactant or a large amount of bond making to the hydrogen acceptor, so that most of the zero-point energy of the stretching vibration of the bond to hydrogen in either the starting material or products is maintained in the transition state. For a linear, three-center reaction in which hydrogen transfer occurs in the rate-determining step, an explanation of this kind in its simplest form is not compatible with transition-state theory because one of the basic assumptions of this theory is that this stretching vibration no longer exists, as such, in the transition state, in which the hydrogen atom is at the top of a potential barrier and is undergoing translation toward the hydrogen acceptor (3). This imaginary

$$\overleftarrow{A}\cdots\overrightarrow{H}\cdots\overleftarrow{B}$$
3

vibration has no potential minimum and therefore has no zero-point energy. However, a more detailed examination of the situation suggests that there are ways in which significant zero-point energy may be maintained in the transition state, especially in reactions in which the transition state is highly asymmetric. [10, 11, 42-44]

For a linear transition state $A \cdots H \cdots B$ we can consider the possibility of the existence of both asymmetric and symmetric stretching vibrations. Although there is no zero-point energy from an asymmetric stretching vibration **3**, the symmetric vibration **4** can still exist in the transition state because it does not lead to either products or reactants. If the transition state is symmetrical, there

$$\overleftarrow{A}\cdots H \cdots\overrightarrow{B}$$
4

[42] J. Bigeleisen, *Pure Appl. Chem.* 8, 217 (1964).
[43] R. P. Bell, *Discussions Faraday Soc.* **39**, 16 (1966).
[44] R. A. M. O'Ferrall and J. Kouba, *J. Chem. Soc.* **1967B**, 985.

will be no motion of the hydrogen atom in this vibration, so that there will be no difference between the zero-point energies for hydrogen and deuterium in the transition state and a normal isotope effect should be observed. However, if the transition state is asymmetrical (5), the hydrogen atom may move in the transition

$$\overleftarrow{A} \cdots \overleftarrow{H} \cdots \overrightarrow{B}$$
5

state so that the zero-point energy is changed upon substitution of deuterium for hydrogen. To the extent that the difference in zero-point energy of the starting material is maintained in the transition state by this vibration, the observed isotope effect will be reduced from the theoretical maximum.[10]

Even this treatment is an oversimplification in some respects. There is a question about which force constants are appropriate to describe the symmetric stretching vibration in the transition state, and different theoretical treatments differ in their predictions of the extent to which the isotope effect is reduced in asymmetrical transition states, although there is general agreement that it is reduced significantly in at least the most asymmetric cases.[43-46] Furthermore, many, if not most, reactions do not occur through linear three-center transition states. In an elimination reaction, for example, the motions of at least five atoms are involved (6 and 7), and it is possible that a stretching vibration such as 7, which does not lead to reaction but is otherwise similar to the vibration which becomes

$$\overrightarrow{B} \cdots \overleftarrow{H} \cdots \overrightarrow{C} \cdots \overleftarrow{C} \cdots \overrightarrow{X}$$
6

$$\overrightarrow{B} \cdots \overleftarrow{H} \cdots C \cdots \overrightarrow{C} \cdots \overrightarrow{X}$$
7

the translation of the transition state 6, can result in the maintenance of significant zero-point energy. A similar situation may apply in proton abstraction reactions, such as the enolization of a ketone, in which a considerable amount of rehybridization, charge redistribu-

[45] W. J. Albery, *Trans. Faraday Soc.* **63**, 200 (1967).

[46] A. V. Willi and M. Wolfsberg, *Chem. Ind. (London)* **1964**, 2097.

tion, and movement of atoms takes place in the remainder of the molecule and must contribute to the energy and vibrations of the transition state (equation 17).

$$\text{B } + \text{ H}-\overset{\displaystyle |}{\underset{\displaystyle |}{\text{C}}}-\text{C}\underset{\diagdown}{\overset{\diagup O}{}} \;\rightleftharpoons\; \text{BH}^+ + \overset{\diagdown}{\underset{\diagup}{\text{C}}}=\text{C}\underset{\diagdown}{\overset{\diagup O^-}{}} \qquad (17)$$

Regardless of the theoretical interpretation, there are several experimental results which suggest that isotope effects are larger for symmetrical than for nonsymmetrical transition states. For example, the isotope effect for the chlorination of H_2CD_2, which is expected to have a symmetrical transition state, is 12.1, while that for toluene, which is expected to have an unsymmetrical transition state, is only 1.4.[47] Compilations of rate constants for the general acid catalyzed exchange of protons of aromatic compounds and the general base catalyzed removal of protons from carbon acids reveal a maximum in the isotope effect at a point at which the difference in pK between the catalyst and the substrate is close to zero.[48] While the correlations provide quantitative support for the view that isotope effects decrease with increasing asymmetry of the transition state, it is perhaps surprising that the transition state appears to be most nearly symmetrical for a ΔpK near zero, because of the difference in the shapes of the potential energy curves for C—H and O—H bonds. It has been suggested that as the activation energy of a reaction becomes small, the isotope effect also becomes small, but it is probable that this is not caused by the small activation energy, per se, so much as it is caused by the asymmetry of the transition state in many such reactions, which are usually strongly exothermic.[47, 49]

2. THE ROLE OF BENDING FREQUENCIES

It is often assumed that changes in the zero-point energies of bending frequencies are not significant in determining the magnitude of isotope effects, and, indeed, detailed calculations of the isotope effects expected for several relatively simple reactions have shown that there is a tendency for the contributions from changes in the

[47] K. B. Wiberg and E. L. Motell, *Tetrahedron Letters* **19**, 2009 (1963).

[48] R. P. Bell and D. M. Goodall, *Proc. Roy. Soc. (London)* **294A**, 273 (1966); J. L. Longridge and F. A. Long, *J. Am. Chem. Soc.* **89**, 1292 (1967).

[49] G. Chiltz, R. Eckling, P. Goldfinger, G. Huybrechts, H. S. Johnston, L. Meyers, and G. Verbeke, *J. Chem. Phys.* **38**, 1053 (1963).

bending frequencies to cancel out and not make a large contribution to the overall effect. In particular, there is a tendency for the effect of bending frequencies in the transition state to be canceled by the effect of tunneling on the isotope effect.[50] However, this is not likely to be so in all reactions, and it is probable that changes in the bending frequencies contribute to some unusually large or unusually small isotope effects.[44, 51, 52] A complete loss of the zero-point energies of both the stretching and bending frequencies of a bond to hydrogen in the transition state gives a calculated deuterium isotope effect as large as 17 to 48.[11, 47] Bending frequencies have more often been invoked to explain small isotope effects.[51, 52] They may be of importance in nonlinear transition states, as described below, but may also be of importance in linear transition states if a significant new bending vibration, with its accompanying zero-point energy, is developed in the transition state. The bending vibration of the bifluoride ion $F-H-F^-$ at 1,200 cm^{-1}, which is at a higher frequency than the symmetrical stretching vibration at 600 cm^{-1}, may be taken as a model for such a vibration in a transition state.

3. NONLINEAR TRANSITION STATES

The changes of vibration frequencies and zero-point energies which occur in reaching a nonlinear transition state, as in an intramolecular or cyclic reaction, are obviously different from those which occur with linear transition states, in which the loss of stretching vibrations is generally of primary importance. If there is only the loss of a bending frequency in the transition state, the isotope effect will be relatively small because of the smaller frequencies and zero-point energies of bending as compared with stretching vibrations. The magnitude of the isotope effects for such reactions is likely to be on the order of $k_H/k_D = 2$–3.[53–55] For example, the rate-determining step of the pinacol rearrangement of triphenylethylene glycol is the intramolecular shift of a hydride ion to the neighboring

[50] R. P. Bell, *Trans. Faraday Soc.* 57, 961 (1961).

[51] A. Streitwieser, Jr., R. G. Lawler, and C. Perrin, *J. Am. Chem. Soc.* 87, 5383 (1965).

[52] R. F. W. Bader, *Can. J. Chem.* 42, 1822 (1964).

[53] M. F. Hawthorne and E. S. Lewis, *J. Am. Chem. Soc.* 80, 4296 (1958).

[54] S. Winstein and J. Takahashi, *Tetrahedron Letters* 2, 316 (1958).

[55] C. J. Collins, W. T. Rainey, W. B. Smith, and I. A. Kaye, *J. Am. Chem. Soc.* 81, 460 (1959).

carbon atom (equation 18). The isotope effect for the reaction is

$$
\begin{array}{ccc}
\underset{\underset{H}{|}}{\overset{HO\quad OH}{\underset{|\quad|}{(C_6H_5)_2-C-C-C_6H_5}}} & \overset{H^+}{\rightleftharpoons} & (C_6H_5)_2-\overset{\overset{\displaystyle H\ \ H\ \ H}{\underset{\displaystyle +}{\diagdown\diagup}}}{\underset{}{C}}\!\!-\!\!\!-\overset{}{\underset{H}{C}}-C_6H_5 \\
& & \Updownarrow \\
\underset{\underset{H}{|}}{\overset{\overset{\displaystyle O}{\|}}{(C_6H_5)_2-C-CC_6H_5}} & \overset{slow}{\longleftarrow} & (C_6H_5)_2-\overset{+}{\underset{}{C}}-\overset{\overset{\displaystyle H}{|}}{\underset{\underset{H}{|}}{C}}-C_6H_5
\end{array}
$$

$$(18)$$

between 2.3 and 3.3 for a number of different catalysts.[55]

4. PROTON NOT AT AN ENERGY MAXIMUM IN THE TRANSITION STATE

Probably the most common reason for the occurrence of small or inverse isotop effects is the maintenance of zero-point energy because the proton is bonded to either product or reactant and is not undergoing translation at the saddle point of energy which represents the transition state; i.e., the transition state of the reaction is not the transition state for proton transfer. The most obvious example of this situation is a diffusion-controlled reaction, in which the diffusion or rotation of the reactants or products, rather than the proton transfer itself, is rate-determining. In such a situation the observed isotope effect will be only that of the diffusion or rotation process, plus effects on any equilibria that precede the rate-determining diffusion step. The identification of this situation is clear if the rate of reaction is equal to the maximum rate of a diffusion-controlled reaction of about $10^{10}\ M^{-1}\ sec^{-1}$. It is more difficult for slower reactions in which a rate-determining–diffusion-controlled step is preceded by one or more unfavorable equilibrium steps. As pointed out in Chap. 3, Sec. D, Part 4, a reaction which involves rate-determining encounter of two reactants in the direction favored by the overall equilibrium may be regarded as involving rate-determining separation of the same reactants in the opposite direction, in accord with the principle of microscopic reversibility. The observed rate in the unfavorable direction will be less than that of a diffusion-controlled reaction because the rate-determining step is preceded by an unfavorable equilibrium step; i.e., the reactive intermediate in this direction returns to starting materials more often than it diffuses apart to give products (equation 19; Fig. 11, Chap. 3). In this

$$AH + B \;\rightleftharpoons\; \left[AH \cdots B \;\underset{\text{fast}}{\overset{K}{\rightleftharpoons}}\; A^- \cdots \overset{+}{H}B \right] \;\underset{\text{dc}}{\rightleftharpoons}\; A^- + \overset{+}{H}B \tag{19}$$

situation, the observed isotope effect consists of the isotope effect on
the equilibrium prior to the rate-determining step and on the separation of the products, but does not involve a loss of zero-point
energy caused by breaking of an X—H bond in the transition state.
The isotope effect $k_H/k_D = 6.7$ for the transfer of a proton from
trimethylammonium ion to water in dilute acid[56] probably represents
an example of this situation. The isotope effect on the overall
equilibrium, $K_{(CH_3)_3NH^+}/K_{(CH_3)_3ND^+}$, is 5.0, and a similar value would
be expected for the equilibrium proton transfer within a hydrogen-
bonded complex, so that the overall isotope effect may be attributed
to the isotope effect on this equilibrium plus a small isotope effect
on the rate of separation of products.

The isotope effects on the rates of hydrogen exchange and
racemization of the carbon acid, 2-octyl phenyl sulfone, compared
with 2-octyl-3-d-phenyl sulfone, range from 0.3 to 1.9 in different
solvents.[6] The explanation proposed by Cram and coworkers[6] for
these surprising results describes essentially this same situation,
although it is expressed in somewhat different terms. The scheme
for the exchange reaction is shown in equation 20. The important

$$C-H + B \;\underset{k_{-1}}{\overset{k_1}{\rightleftharpoons}}\; \left[C^- \cdots H^+ B \right]$$

$$k_2 \Big\Updownarrow k_{-2}$$

$$C-D + B \;\underset{k'_{-1}}{\overset{k'}{\rightleftharpoons}}\; \left[C^- \cdots D^+ B \right] \tag{20}$$

point of Cram's proposal is that $k_{-1} > k_2$. In other words, the carbanion intermediate reacts faster with the proton which has just
left it than the proton can diffuse away or rotate so that it is replaced by a deuteron. In terms of the potential-energy diagram

[56] R. J. Day and C. N. Reilley, *J. Phys. Chem.* **71**, 1588 (1967). This reaction proceeds through an intermediate water molecule and in strong acid solution exchange
with the solvent is inhibited by back-reaction of a hydrogen-bonded water molecule
with a proton from the solvent; the description here applies only to the first proton
transfer step to water.

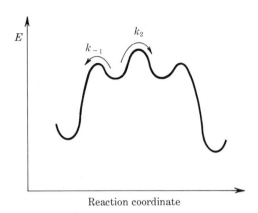

Fig 4. If $k_{-1} > k_2$, the rate-determining step of the reaction is that with the rate constant k_2.

(Fig. 4), this means that the energy barrier for diffusion away or exchange of the proton k_2 is larger than that for the back-reaction k_{-1}, so that the rate-determining step of the reaction is this exchange or diffusion step. The isotope effect of this reaction will be determined largely by the isotope effect on the equilibrium of the first step. A similar scheme can be visualized for the racemization reaction, in which the rate of return of the proton to the carbanion is faster than the rate of racemization, so that, again, the breaking of the carbon-hydrogen bond is not the rate-determining step.

A somewhat similar situation exists in the hydrogen atom transfer reactions between hindered phenols such as tri-t-butylphenol and tetra-t-butylindophenol and the corresponding oxyradicals. These exchange reactions take place at a relatively slow rate (ca. $10^2 M^{-1}$ sec^{-1} at 27° in carbon tetrachloride) but show a deuterium isotope effect of only about 2.0.[57] There is evidence from nuclear magnetic resonance spectra that a complex is formed as an intermediate in these reactions. The rate of breakdown of this complex is between 10^8 and 10^9 sec^{-1}, which suggests that the rate-determining step of the breakdown is partially or entirely a diffusion-controlled separation of the products. The reaction scheme may be formulated as shown in equation 21 (alternatively, the complex may be symmetrical). If the breakdown of the complex is partly or entirely diffusion-

$$ROH + \cdot OR \rightleftharpoons [ROH \cdots \dot{O}R \overset{\text{fast}}{\rightleftharpoons} R\dot{O} \cdots HOR] \rightleftharpoons RO \cdot + HOR \qquad (21)$$

[57] R. W. Kreilick and S. I. Weissman, *J. Am. Chem. Soc.* **88**, 2645 (1966).

controlled, the principle of microscopic reversibility indicates that its formation may also be regarded as being diffusion-controlled; the slow rate is a consequence of the fact that only a small fraction of the total reactants react at the diffusion-controlled rate. In other words, the slow rate of the overall reaction is caused by steric hindrance of the t-butyl groups, so that only a small fraction of the encounters occurs with precisely the correct orientation and geometry of the hindered reactants to permit complex formation to take place. This view is supported by the fact that the energy of activation for complex formation is only 1.2 to 2.1 kcal/mole, as expected for a diffusion-controlled reaction. The relatively slow rate is the result of an unfavorable entropy of activation of -38 to -43 e.u. If this interpretation is correct, this represents another example of a reaction which has the essential properties of a diffusion-controlled reaction in that making or breaking of covalent bonds in not occurring in the rate-determining step, but which occurs at a rate much slower than the limiting rate of a diffusion-controlled reaction.

There may also be included in this category the large group of reactions which involve a proton transfer between oxygen, nitrogen, or sulfur and a general acid or base catalyst, accompanying bond formation or breaking of heavier atoms. Most reactions of a carbonyl or acyl group are of this kind. Although the detailed nature of the catalysis of proton transfer in these reactions is not understood, it is probable that the proton is not at the top of a potential barrier in the transition state in spite of the fact that its position in the transition state is almost certainly different from its position in the reactants or products. These reactions commonly proceed some 2 to 3 times slower in deuterium oxide than in water[58] ($k_{H_2O}/k_{D_2O} = 3.0$ for general base catalysis by imidazole of the hydrolysis of ethyl chloroacetate[59]), but they may show larger isotope effects ($k_{H_2O}/k_{D_2O} = 4.0$ and 4.4 for the general acid and general base catalyzed reactions of morpholine with δ-thiolvalerolactone[60]), essentially no isotope effect ($k_{H_2O}/k_{D_2O} = 1.1$ for the general base catalyzed aminolysis of phenyl acetate by glycine[7]), or even an inverse isotope effect ($k_{H_3O}/k_{D_3O} = 0.59$ for the general acid catalyzed addition of methoxyethanethiol to acetaldehyde[18]). As discussed in Chap. 3, Sec. F, Part 2, it is probable that the proton is in a more or less stable potential well and can maintain a significant zero-point energy in the transition states of reactions of this kind.

[58] S. L. Johnson, *Advan. Phys. Org. Chem.* **5**, 237 (1967).

[59] W. P. Jencks and J. Carriuolo, *J. Am. Chem. Soc.* **83**, 1743 (1961).

[60] L. R. Fedor and T. C. Bruice, *J. Am. Chem. Soc.* **86**, 4117 (1964).

5. SECONDARY ISOTOPE EFFECTS

A normal primary isotope effect may be partially or completely masked by an inverse secondary solvent isotope effect, which is caused by changes in the frequencies and zero-point energies of hydrogen-bonded solute and solvent molecules that are not directly involved in the hydrogen transfer reaction.[19] The importance of such secondary effects, particularly for reactions which involve the solvated proton, has been clearly recognized only recently. Although the subject presents some difficulties of interpretation, at least the qualitative aspects of its experimental manifestations are clear once the basic principle is understood, and it is essential to understand this principle in order to interpret solvent deuterium isotope effects in aqueous solution.

The most direct qualitative and quantitative evidence for such secondary isotope effects comes from a comparison of the observed isotope effect on the rate constant with the amount of deuterium incorporated into the product from a mixed solvent in the addition of a proton to a nonexchangeable position on carbon.[61-63] For example, if the acid catalyzed decomposition of allylmercuric iodide (equation 22) is studied in mixtures of deuterium oxide and water, an isotope

$$H^+ + CH_2{=}CHCH_2HgI \longrightarrow CH_3CH{=}CH_2 + HgI^+ \tag{22}$$

effect $\varkappa_H/\varkappa_D = (RH/RD)_{prod} \times (D/H)_{solv}$ may be calculated from the relative amounts of hydrogen and deuterium incorporated into the product compared with the composition of the mixed solvent. For this reaction, this isotope effect is found to be 7.3, regardless of the composition of the solvent.[62] However, if the *rates* are measured at comparable acidities in pure water and deuterium oxide, the rate is found to be only 3.1 times faster in water than in deuterium oxide. Now, the relative amounts of incorporation of hydrogen and deuterium into the product is close to a true measure of the primary isotope effect because the average composition of the solvent is the same for hydrogen and deuterium incorporation in a given experiment. The rate measurements include this primary isotope effect, but also include the effect of the difference in solvent between water and deuterium oxide, i.e., a difference in the frequencies and zero-point

[61] A. J. Kresge, *Pure Appl. Chem.* 8, 243 (1964).

[62] M. M. Kreevoy, P. J. Steinwand, and W. V. Kayser, *J. Am. Chem. Soc.* 88, 124 (1966).

[63] V. Gold and M. A. Kessick, *J. Chem. Soc.* 1965, 6718.

energies of atoms other than those which are being transferred in the transition state.

The situation may be analyzed in greater detail as follows. Assume that the proton-donating species is H_3O^+ (or its isotopically substituted equivalent). The isotope effect which is determined from product composition $\varkappa_H/\varkappa_D$ is a measure of the difference between the isotopic composition of the solvent and the average isotopic composition of the reacting atom in the transition state (8 and 9, in which M is H or D, depending on the composition of the solvent).

$$
\begin{array}{cc}
\underset{\text{M}}{\overset{\text{M}}{\diagdown}}\!\!\!\!O\cdots\overset{+}{H}\cdots S & \underset{\text{M}}{\overset{\text{M}}{\diagdown}}\!\!\!\!O\cdots\overset{+}{D}\cdots S \\
8 & 9
\end{array}
$$

This, in turn, may be divided into two parts: the isotope fractionation between the solvent and the immediate proton donor, the conjugate acid of the substrate (for example, H_3O^+), and the fractionation between this acid and the transition state. Now, the latter term represents the primary isotope effect because the composition of the M atoms is the same for 8 and 9. The fractionation factor for the conjugate acid of water has been determined and, expressed in terms of equation 23, is very close to $l = 0.69$. (These determina-

$$
l = \frac{(\frac{1}{3}H_3O^+)(\frac{1}{2}D_2O)}{(\frac{1}{3}D_3O^+)(\frac{1}{2}H_2O)} \tag{23}
$$

tions[64] further suggest that so far as the distribution of isotopes is concerned, the solvated proton exists as the species H_3O^+; there is other evidence for the species $H_9O_4^+$, but the protons on the outer water molecules of $H_9O_4^+$ are isotopically equivalent to those of water.) Therefore, the true primary isotope effect $(k_H/k_D)_I$ is $7.3 \times 0.69 = 5.1$ for this reaction. This number reflects only the difference between the isotopic composition of the reacting acid, here assumed to be H_3O^+ or its equivalent, and the transition state. If there is a water molecule interposed between H_3O^+ and the substrate in the transition state, the isotopic composition of the proton donor initially would be expected to resemble water rather than H_3O^+, and correction by the fractionation factor l would not be necessary.

The observed ratio of the rate constants in pure water and deuterium oxide, k_{H_2O}/k_{D_2O}, is equal to $(k_H/k_D)_I(k_H/k_D)_{II}$, in

[64] A. J. Kresge and A. L. Allred, *J. Am. Chem. Soc.* **85**, 1541 (1963); V. Gold, *Proc. Chem. Soc.* **1963**, 141; K. Heinzinger and R. E. Weston, Jr., *J.Phys. Chem.* **68**, 744 (1964).

which $(k_H/k_D)_{II}$ is the secondary isotope effect. The secondary effect reflects differences in the frequencies and zero-point energies of the bonds to atoms which are not being transferred in the transition state, for example, the difference between the transition states **10** and **11**. These may be roughly calculated by the same procedure

10   **11**

as for equilibrium isotope effects. If **10** is taken as the correct model for the transition state, the experimental value of $(k_H/k_D)_{II}$ is $3.1/5.1 = 0.61$, which is close to the value estimated by the Bunton and Shiner method and to that observed for several other reactions which involve proton donation from the solvated proton in the transition state.

The secondary isotope effect provides a means of estimating the extent to which the proton-donating molecule resembles water or H_3O^+ in the transition state, i.e., of estimating the "amount" of proton transfer, the Brønsted α value.[61-63] If the nontransferring protons of the acid in the transition state resemble the starting material (**12**), there will be little proton transfer in the transition state, α will be small, and the absence of a change in structure between starting materials and transition state will result in the absence of a secondary isotope effect. If these protons resemble water (**13**),

12   **13**

there is a large amount of proton transfer in the transition state, α will be large, and the difference in the frequencies of these hydrogen-bonded protons in the starting materials and transition state will give a large secondary isotope effect, which will be similar to that for the equilibrium transfer of a proton from H_3O^+ to a base, as described above. This relationship is expressed quantitatively by equation 24, in which l is the fractionation factor defined in equa-

$$\alpha = \frac{\log (k_H/k_D)_{II}}{2 \log l} \tag{24}$$

tion 23. For the decomposition of allylmercuric iodide, the value of α calculated from equation 24 is 0.65.

Alternatively, the value of α may be obtained directly from the observed reaction rates in mixed water–deuterium oxide solvents according to equation 25, in which n is the atom fraction of deuter-

$$\frac{k_n}{k_{H_2O}} = \frac{(1 - n + nl^{1-\alpha})^2 (1 - n + nl^{1+2\alpha} k_{D_2O}/k_{H_2O})}{(1 - n + nl)^3} \tag{25}$$

ium in the mixed solvent.[61] Since the fractionation of isotope between solvent and the solvated proton, l, is known for such mixed solvents, it is possible to estimate how much the transition state resembles the solvated proton simply by determining the extent to which the isotope fractionation of the transition state resembles that of the solvated proton. If there is almost no proton transfer in the transition state, the transition state resembles the solvated proton, $\alpha = 0$, and the fractionation factor is equal to l. If there is complete proton transfer in the transition state, the proton donor resembles water in the transition state, $\alpha = 1.0$, and the fractionation factor for those protons which are not being transferred is 1.0. It has been shown that for the acid catalyzed decomposition of vinyl ethers and cyanoketene dimethylacetal the values of α obtained by fitting the rate constants in water–deuterium oxide mixtures to the curves predicted by equation 25 are in good agreement with values obtained directly from measurements of rate constants for catalysis by acids of differing strength.[65]

The magnitude of secondary isotope effects can be determined from a comparison of product compositions with rate measurements only when the proton is transferred to a site which does not undergo rapid exchange with the solvent. However, it is reasonable to expect that similar secondary effects occur in proton transfer reactions from the solvated proton to oxygen, nitrogen, and sulfur. The result of these secondary effects will be to decrease the magnitude of the isotope effects on the observed rate constants. For example

[65] P. Salomaa, A. Kankaanperä, and M. Lajunen, *Acta Chem. Scand.* **20**, 1790 (1966); A. J. Kresge and Y. Chiang, *J. Chem. Soc.* **1967B**, 58; V. Gold and D. C. A. Waterman, *Chem. Commun.* **1967**, 40.

there is an *inverse* isotope effect, $k_H/k_D = 0.7$ for ortho ester hydrolysis in spite of the fact that this reaction is subject to general acid catalysis.[66] Although other factors probably contribute to the low isotope effects in these reactions, the fact that the isotope effect for catalysis by the solvated proton is frequently found to be smaller than that for other acids in general acid catalyzed reactions undoubtedly reflects a significant secondary isotope effect.

The small isotope effect of 1.1 to 1.7 in the transfer of a proton to hydroxide ion from hydrogen-bonded dicarboxylic acid monoanions, such as dialkylsuccinic acid and cyclopropanedicarboxylic acid, has been ascribed to a masking by the secondary isotope effect of a primary effect which may be as large as 6.[67] An alternative explanation for the small isotope effect in this reaction is that the proton transfer is diffusion-controlled and that the relatively slow rate of proton transfer is accounted for by the fact that only a small fraction of the reacting acid is in the reactive form with a broken hydrogen bond (equation 26).

$$\tag{26}$$

The rates of reactions in which OD^- reacts as a nucleophile are usually some 20 to 40% higher than the corresponding reactions with OH^-; an extreme case is the base catalyzed elimination of trimethylamine from β-phenylethyltrimethylammonium ion, in which hydroxide ion acts as a nucleophile toward hydrogen and the ratio k_{OD^-}/k_{OH^-} is 1.79.[68] These differences can be explained, in large part, by changes in the $O-H$ frequencies of water molecules which are hydrogen-bonded to the hydroxide ion.[19]

[66] A. J. Kresge and R. J. Preto, *J. Am. Chem. Soc.* **87**, 4593 (1965).

[67] J. L. Haslam, E. M. Eyring, W. W. Epstein, R. P. Jensen, and C. W. Jaget, *J. Am. Chem. Soc.* **87**, 4247 (1965).

[68] L. J. Steffa and E. R. Thornton, *J. Am. Chem. Soc.* **89**, 6149 (1967).

E. SOME ELEMENTARY CONCLUSIONS REGARDING DEUTERIUM ISOTOPE EFFECTS IN CHEMICAL REACTIONS

It is evident that the situation is complicated and that the generalization that the presence or absence of proton transfer in the transition state is directly correlated with the presence or absence of a "normal" isotope effect does not hold on either theoretical or experimental grounds. It is quite generally true that the existence of a "normal" isotope effect is evidence for the occurrence of hydrogen transfer in the transition state if it can be shown that it is not caused by an isotope effect on the equilibrium constant of a step prior to the rate-determining step. The existence of smaller isotope effects means that there is a difference in the zero-point energy and in the position of hydrogen in the starting materials and the transition state. In several cases reasonable correlations have been made between the magnitude of isotope effects and the expected or observed changes in bond vibration frequencies and zero-point energies in the reactants, products, and transition state. The *absence* of an isotope effect does not rule out hydrogen transfer as an essential part of the mechanism of the reaction and does not even establish that hydrogen is not being transferred in the transition state. Reactions which are subject to specific acid catalysis exhibit inverse solvent deuterium isotope effects, but inverse isotope effects may also be observed in general acid catalyzed reactions. It is not yet possible to make a reliable estimate of the amount of proton transfer in the transition state from the magnitude of primary isotope effects, but there is evidence that some estimate of this kind may be made from an examination of secondary isotope effects in general acid catalyzed reactions which involve the solvated proton as a reactant.

There is no evidence that isotope effects can be useful in helping to distinguish between mechanisms which involve proton, hydrogen atom, or hydride ion transfer. The range of the observed magnitude of isotope effects for proton and hydrogen atom transfer is large, as illustrated by the examples given above, and shows no consistent difference between these two types of reaction. Hydride transfer reactions have been less extensively studied, but isotope effects ranging up to $k_H/k_D = 5$, for hydride transfer from cycloheptatriene to di-p-anisylphenylmethyl cation, have been reported.[69]

[69] L. McDonough and H. J. Dauben, Jr., cited by K. B. Wiberg and E. L. Motell in *Tetrahedron Letters* **19**, 2009 (1963).

It is also not possible to reach a simple conclusion about hydro-gen bonding in aqueous solution from isotope effects. The formation of hydrogen-bonded oligomers of imidazole in naphthalene solution is some 8% less for imidazole-d_1, which corresponds to a free-energy difference of 80 cal/mole and might suggest that hydrogen bonds are weakened upon deuterium substitution.[70] On the other hand the formation of hydrogen-bonded oligomers of hydrogen fluoride in the gas phase is favored by some 50 cal/mole upon substitution of deu-terium for hydrogen.[71] Indeed, the equilibrium constants for the formation of hydrogen-bonded complexes of phenol in carbon tetra-chloride have been reported to be both increased and decreased upon substitution of deuterium for hydrogen, depending on the nature of the proton acceptor.[72] None of these results is pertinent to the problem of deuterium isotope effects on the strength of hydrogen bonds in aqueous solution because the "making or breaking" of a hydrogen bond in aqueous solution does not involve the net formation or breaking of a hydrogen bond, but rather involves the replacement of hydrogen bonds in the reacting molecules by hydrogen bonds to the solvent (equation 27). Since there is no net change in the num-

$$A-H\cdots B + 2H_2O \rightleftharpoons A-H\cdots O\underset{H}{\overset{H}{\diagup}} + B\cdots H-O\underset{H}{\diagdown} \qquad (27)$$

ber of hydrogen bonds in this system, differences in the stability of hydrogen bonds in water and deuterium oxide will result only from small and unpredictable differences of the isotope effects on the strengths of the hydrogen bonds on the two sides of equation 27.

F. ISOTOPE EFFECTS IN ENZYMATIC REACTIONS

The isolated observation of a difference in the rate of an enzyme catalyzed reaction in water and deuterium oxide has no significance whatever with regard to mechanism. The elementary requirements for an interpretation of isotope effects in enzymatic reactions are: (1) a separation into effects on the maximal velocity and the K_m, with a further separation into effects on the mechanistically signifi-cant rate and equilibrium constants, if possible; (2) a distinction be-tween isotope effects involving hydrogen atoms which are non-

[70] A. Grimison, *J. Phys. Chem.* **67**, 962 (1963).

[71] R. W. Long, J. H. Hildebrand, and W. E. Morrell, *J. Am. Chem. Soc.* **65**, 182 (1943).

[72] S. Singh and C. N. R. Rao, *Can. J. Chem.* **44**, 2611 (1966).

exchangeable or rapidly exchangeable with the solvent; and (3) for experiments in deuterium oxide solutions, an evaluation of the effect of this solvent on the dependence of the maximal rate and Michaelis constant on acidity. Isotope effects on the transfer of nonexchangeable hydrogen atoms, which are usually bound to carbon, are relatively easy to interpret because they can be studied in a constant solvent, whereas protons bound to oxygen, nitrogen, or sulfur will almost always exchange with the solvent in diffusion-controlled reactions which are faster than the time of measurement of the reaction, so that deuterium isotope effects in such reactions must be studied in deuterium oxide as solvent, with the consequent difficulties of interpretation which are introduced by interactions with the solvent.

1. ISOTOPE EFFECTS ON V_{max}

The maximal velocity of most enzymatic reactions includes the rate constant for the covalent change which is taking place, so that an isotope effect on the reaction rate may be interpreted directly in terms of the mechanism. The absence of an isotope effect on the maximal velocity of a hydrogen transfer reaction may be the result of one of the reasons for a small isotope effect which have been described above for chemical reactions or may occur if the dissociation of product from the enzyme is the rate-determining step, as in the case of certain nicotinamide adenine dinucleotide linked dehydrogenases. The presence of a "normal" isotope effect in a reaction which involves the transfer of a nonexchangeable hydrogen atom is strong evidence that the maximal velocity is, in fact, a measure of the rate of the step in which covalent change takes place.

The majority of the isotope effects in enzymatic reactions which have been studied so far are "abnormal" and difficult to interpret. An unusually "normal" and straightforward result has been found with cytochrome b_5 reductase, a flavin enzyme which catalyzes the reduction of cytochrome b_5 and other electron acceptors by NADH.[73] The reaction involves the intermediate reduction of the enzyme (equations 28 and 29), which has been shown directly to

$$NADH + Enz \;\rightleftharpoons\; Enz-H + NA\overset{+}{D} \tag{28}$$

$$Enz-H + Acc_{ox} \;\rightleftharpoons\; Enz + Acc_{red} \tag{29}$$

[73] P. Strittmatter, J. Biol. Chem. **237**, 3250 (1962).

exhibit an isotope effect, but it is more conveniently studied with ferricyanide as an electron acceptor. Substitution of deuterium into the 4 position of NADH has no effect on the Michaelis constants, but decreases the maximal velocity of the reaction 3.7-fold for NADH and 10.4- and 8.7-fold for acetylpyridine and pyridine aldehyde anallogs of the coenzyme, respectively, if the deuterium is substituted for the hydrogen atom on the side of the ring which undergoes transfer. Substitution of the other hydrogen atom in the 4 position by deuterium gives no significant isotope effect. Two facts which have not yet been explained for this relatively "normal" enzyme are the differences in isotope effects which are exhibited by the different coenzyme analogs and the fact that the deuterium does not exchange with solvent even over long periods of time, although it might have been expected that it would be transferred to a nitrogen atom of enzyme-bound flavin and should then exchange rapidly with the solvent.

Isotope effects on enzymatic reactions which are carried out in deuterium oxide as solvent cannot be interpreted rigorously, although inferences can be drawn with varying degrees of confidence from sufficiently detailed studies. It is first necessary to determine the extent to which an observed isotope effect reflects changes in the ionization behavior of the active form of the enzyme or substrate in deuterium oxide. The acidity of deuterium oxide solutions can be measured conveniently with ordinary glass electrodes by adding 0.40 to the observed reading of a pH meter which has been calibrated with standard buffers in aqueous solution.[74] It is desirable to check this relationship with a given measuring system by comparing the pH meter readings obtained with 0.001 M HCl in water and 0.001 M DCl in deuterium oxide. The difference in the ionization constants of the substrate in water and deuterium oxide may be measured directly, but the corresponding differences in the active form of the enzyme must be inferred either from the dependence of the activity on pH (pD) or from isotope effects on the acidity of the ionizing groups which are known to affect enzymatic activity. A compilation of isotope effects on the ionization of a number of different types of ionizing groups is given in Bunton and Shiner.[16] Most acids are about three- to fivefold weaker in deuterium oxide than in water, which corresponds to a pK difference of 0.5 to 0.7 units.

The behavior of the citrate condensing enzyme in water and deuterium oxide provides an instructive illustration of the dependence

---

[74] P. K. Glasoe and F. A. Long, *J. Phys. Chem.* **64**, 188 (1960).

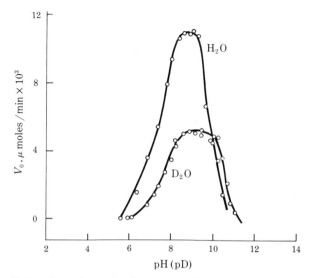

Fig 5. Dependence on pH and pD of the maximal rate of the reaction catalyzed by the citrate condensing enzyme in water and deuterium oxide.[75]

on pH of the isotope effect (Fig. 5).[75] The difference in the dependence of the rate on acidity in the two solvents leads to a variation in the isotope effect from a maximum value of 3.5 to an inverse isotope effect in the most alkaline solutions examined. It is evident that a rate determination at a single pH (pD) value could not be interpreted meaningfully. The observed dependence of the rate on acidity in the two solvents probably reflects both the isotope effect on the ionization of the active form of the enzyme and an isotope effect on the rate of reaction of the active ionic species of the enzyme. It is of interest that there is a large isotope effect on the Michaelis constant for acetyl coenzyme A in this reaction, which varies from 6.3 to 0.8 with changing acidity.

The most serious uncertainty in the interpretation of isotope effects of enzymatic reactions in deuterium oxide arises from the possibility that the solvent change from water to deuterium oxide changes the conformation of the enzyme, by changing the properties of hydrogen bonds, hydrophobic bonds, or other factors. These effects are individually small, but may be amplified with an enzyme which exists in a delicate balance between conformations of differing

[75] G. W. Kosicki and P. A. Srere, *J. Biol. Chem.* **236**, 2566 (1961).

activity. There is direct evidence that this solvent change can affect enzyme conformation in the fact that the "melting temperature" of ribonuclease is 4° higher in deuterium oxide than in water.[76] In addition, it has been shown by the temperature-jump technique that the *rate* of an intramolecular isomerization of ribonuclease, which probably involves a proton transfer, is 4 to 6 times slower in deuterium oxide than in water.[77] The twofold *faster* hydrolysis of *p*-nitrophenyl propionate catalyzed by carbonic anhydrase in deuterium oxide than in water[78] may represent such a conformation change.

Some of the reasons that the stability of different enzyme conformations would be expected to be different in water and deuterium oxide solutions have already been discussed; a further difference which may be significant is that the length of hydrogen bonds is changed significantly upon deuterium substitution. For example, crystallographic studies have shown that the O—H—O distance of oxalic acid dihydrate is increased by some 0.04 Å upon substitution of deuterium for hydrogen.[79] If the structure of the active site requires a precise fit to the substrate of the side chains of amino acids at different positions in a helix, significant differences in this fit might occur if the lengths of several hydrogen bonds were changed by deuterium substitution.

It is important to keep in mind that the very large isotope effect for tritium may result in a strong discrimination against tritium in competitive incorporation experiments, which may lead to incorrect conclusions regarding the source of a given hydrogen atom. If the conversion of *O*-phospho-L-homoserine to threonine, catalyzed by threonine synthetase with pyridoxal phosphate as coenzyme, is carried out in 100% deuterium oxide, one atom of deuterium is incorporated into the γ position (as well as into the α position) of the product (equation 30). However, if the reaction is carried out in

$$^{--}O_3POCH_2CH_2\overset{H}{\underset{NH_3^+}{\overset{|}{C}}}COO^- \xrightarrow{\overset{*}{H}_2O} CH_3-\overset{H}{\underset{HO}{\overset{|}{C}}}-\overset{H^*}{\underset{NH_3^+}{\overset{|}{C}}}COO^- \qquad (30)$$

[76] J. Hermans, Jr. and H. A. Scheraga, *Biochim. Biophys. Acta* **36**, 534 (1959).

[77] R. E. Cathou and G. G. Hammes, *J. Am. Chem. Soc.* **87**, 4674 (1965); T. C. French and G. G. Hammes, *Ibid.*, p. 4669.

[78] Y. Pocker and D. R. Storm, *Biochemistry* **7**, 1202 (1968). This isotope effect, which is observed in a plateau region of the pH-rate profile, cannot be accounted for by a greater nucleophilic reactivity of OD^- than of OH^- because at a given pH (pD) the concentration of OD^- will be 6.5 times smaller than that of OH^- (Table I).

[79] K. J. Gallagher, in D. Hadzi (ed.), "Hydrogen Bonding," p. 45, Pergamon Press, New York, 1959.

water containing trace quantities of tritium, the incorporation of tritium into the γ position amounts to only about 2% of that which would be expected if there were no isotope effect.[80] This isotope effect of about 50 is large, but is not abnormal for tritium. Isotope discrimination in tritium-incorporation experiments may be reduced by carrying out the experiment with deuterium oxide as solvent, in which discrimination will only result from the smaller T/D isotope effect.

This reaction represents one of a number of instances in which it is important to make a careful distinction between experiments which are carried out in pure deuterium oxide or with a substrate which is completely labeled with deuterium, and experiments carried out with mixtures or trace quantities of isotopically labeled reactants or solvent. In the former case, all the reaction has to proceed with the isotopically substituted compound, and conclusions may be drawn directly from the results of rate measurements with labeled and unlabeled substrates. In the latter case the equilibrium or steady-state concentration of a reactive isotopically labeled intermediate may change in a complex manner, depending on the kinetics of the reaction, and a detailed kinetic analysis may be required to interpret correctly the magnitude of the isotope effect. Measurements of rates and of product distributions in enzymatic reactions which are examined in water–deuterium oxide mixtures are likely to give different results because of secondary isotope effects, as described in Sec. D, Part 5, for nonenzymatic reactions.

2. ISOTOPE EFFECTS ON THE MICHAELIS CONSTANT

If the Michaelis constant were only a simple binding constant and if isotope effects were caused only by the complete loss of zero-point energy of a stretching vibration to a reacting atom in a transition state, it might be expected that there would be no isotope effect on Michaelis constants. Since neither of these assumptions is correct, it should not be surprising that the existence of isotope effects on Michaelis constants is more the rule than the exception, as in the case of the citrate condensing enzyme. It is of interest that there is a large but unexplained difference (up to 30%) in the adsorption of the different hydrogen isotopes on charcoal.[81] Some possible reasons for isotope effects on Michaelis constants follow.

[80] M. M. Kaplan and M. Flavin, *J. Biol. Chem.* **240**, 3928 (1965).
[81] P. M. S. Jones and C. G. Hutcheson, *Nature* **213**, 490 (1967).

a) **The inclusion of significant kinetic terms in the Michaelis constant.**
Even for the simple formulation of an enzymatic reaction of equation
31, the Michaelis constant includes the rate constant k_2 as well as

$$E + S \underset{k_{-1}}{\overset{k_1}{\rightleftharpoons}} ES \xrightarrow{k_2} E + products$$

$$K_m = \frac{k_{-1}}{k_1} + \frac{k_2}{k_1} \tag{31}$$

the dissociation constant k_{-1}/k_1, and the Michaelis constants for
more complicated mechanisms will generally also include kinetic constants. If these kinetic constants are large enough that they cannot
be neglected in the expression for the Michaelis constant (i.e., unless
$k_2 \ll k_{-1}$ in equation 31), an isotope effect on the kinetic constant
k_2 will appear in the Michaelis constant. Such isotope effects on the
Michaelis constants of compounds with the deuterium in a nonexchangeable position may be helpful in interpreting the kinetic significance of the Michaelis constant.

b) **Experiments in deuterium oxide as solvent.** The difficulties of
interpretation of such experiments have been discussed above. In
particular, effects of deuterium oxide on the pK of the substrate or
the form of the enzyme that is active in binding substrate, as well
as effects on enzyme conformation, are likely to affect the Michaelis
constant. In addition, "nonspecific" solvent effects of deuterium
oxide on the activity coefficient of the substrate and/or the active
site of the enzyme (as manifested, for example, in differing solubilities of the substrate in water and deuterium oxide) may give rise
to solvent isotope effects of up to 30 to 40% on the Michaelis constant.

c) **Steric effects.** It is possible that the small difference in the
effective radii of hydrogen and deuterium could result in differences
in binding from purely steric effects. Not enough is known about
the force constants and possible rigidity of the active sites of enzymes
to be able to conclude with any certainty whether or not this effect
may be significant, but the fact that steric isotope effects are generally seen only in nonenzymatic reactions with extremely severe
steric requirements and the probability that there is at least a small
degree of flexibility in the active site of enzymes makes it probable
that the very small steric differences between hydrogen- and deuterium-containing molecules would not result in a detectable effect
on the binding constant.

d) **Polarizability**. The slightly greater polarizability of bonds to hydrogen compared with those to deuterium could lead to a slightly smaller binding of the deuterated compound, but the expected size of these effects would be even less than that of steric effects and is well within the experimental error of most determinations of binding constants.

e) **Strain**. If the formation of the enzyme-substrate complex involves the utilization of binding forces to force the substrate to resemble the transition state, the resulting change in the frequencies and zero-point energies of bonds to hydrogen should give rise to an isotope effect on the binding constant of the substrate. In other words, a reaction such as the removal of a proton may have already proceeded to some extent in the Michaelis complex (Chap. 5). Such an isotope effect would be, in fact, evidence for the induction of strain in the enzyme-substrate complex if one could be certain that it is not caused by the presence of significant kinetic terms in the Michaelis constant or by steric effects.

5
Strain, Distortion, and Conformation Change[1]

Although there is no doubt that approximation, covalent catalysis, and general acid-base catalysis are involved in many enzymatic reactions, the available estimates of the rate accelerations to be expected from these factors make it doubtful that they can account for all of the extraordinary *specific* rate enhancements that are brought about by enzymes. One is, therefore, led to search for other factors which may be involved. Before invoking speculative mechanisms of catalysis for which there is no chemical basis or

---

[1] For additional reading see R. Lumry, in P. D. Boyer, H. Lardy, and K. Myrbäck (eds.), "The Enzymes," 2d ed., vol. 1, p. 157, Academic Press Inc., New York, 1959; K. U. Linderstrom-Lang and J. A. Schellman, *Ibid.*, pp. 443, 466; G. G. Hammes, *Nature* **204**, 342 (1964); I. B. Wilson, in M. Florkin and E. H. Stotz (eds.), "Comprehensive Biochemistry," vol. 12, p. 285, Elsevier Publishing Company, Amsterdam, 1964; W. P. Jencks, in N. O. Kaplan and E. P. Kennedy (eds.), "Current Aspects of Biochemical Energetics," p. 273, Academic Press Inc., New York, 1966; R. Lumry and R. Biltonen in S. Timasheff and G. D. Fasman (eds.), "Biological Macromolecules," vol. 2, chap. 1, Marcel Dekker, Inc., New York, 1969.

precedent at the present time, it is worthwhile to reexamine a venerable hypothesis for enzyme catalysis; that is, the induction of strain in the substrate, the enzyme, or both plays a significant role in bringing about the observed specific rate acceleration. It is apparent that this process is closely related to the conformation changes in enzymes which have been observed in the presence of substrates, activators, and inhibitors and which are important in providing control and specificity for enzymatic catalysis, as described in the "allosteric" and "induced-fit" hypotheses.

The main reason that more attention has not been paid to the strain-distortion hypothesis is that it is difficult to devise experimental tests for its evaluation. It is even difficult to speculate profitably about it, once the possibility of its existence has been stated. At the present time there is no experimental evidence which proves unequivocally that strain and distortion play a major role in enzymatic catalysis, but we will argue that, at least according to their broadest definition, these factors almost certainly contribute to the catalysis brought about by enzymes. The two most important theoretical considerations that suggest that the strain-distortion hypothesis should be taken seriously are, first, the difficulty of accounting satisfactorily for enzymatic catalysis of certain reactions by other known mechanisms and, second, the fact that enzyme specificity is frequently manifested in the maximal rates of reaction rather than, as might have been expected, in the binding of substrates to the enzyme. In addition, one would like to find an explanation for the fact that enzymes are large molecules with a definite structure that must be maintained intact in order that catalytic activity may occur.

A. CATALYSIS OF DISPLACEMENT REACTIONS

The simplest reactions are the hardest to account for by the previously discussed mechanisms of catalysis. Bimolecular displacement reactions in which general acid-base catalysis would give little advantage or is not possible are especially troublesome in this respect. These include, for example, the formation of trigonelline from S-adenosylmethionine[2] (equation 1) and the transfer of a methyl

$$\tag{1}$$

[2] J. G. Joshi and P. Handler, *J. Biol. Chem.* **235**, 2981 (1960).

group from S-adenosylmethionine to the thioether group of methionine to form a new sulfonium ion[3] (equation 2). Rate acceleration

$$R_2\diagdown \overset{+}{\underset{\underset{R_1}{|}}{S}}\diagup CH_3 + \underset{\underset{R_2}{|}}{S}\diagup CH_3 \longrightarrow R_2\diagdown \underset{\underset{R_1}{|}}{S} + H_3C\diagdown \overset{+}{\underset{\underset{R_2}{|}}{S}}\diagup CH_3 \tag{2}$$

by the induction of strain is a logical mechanism to enhance the rate of such reactions. The simplest way this could occur is by a simple compression of the nucleophilic reactant against the methyl-group donor in such a way as to partially overcome the van der Waals repulsion energy of the reacting atoms that provides much of the energy barrier for the reaction, but we shall see that other mechanisms of catalysis, which might be included in a broad definition of "strain," are also possible.

In fact, one can argue in the following way that for many reversible reactions the induction of strain in the enzyme-substrate complex *must* occur and is likely to accelerate the reaction in at least one direction. Suppose that in the case of a methyl-group transfer reaction from a sulfonium ion, the substrates fit perfectly into a rigid active site, with an internuclear distance d between the nucleophile and the carbon atom of the methyl group determined by the sum of the van der Waals radii of the reacting atoms (Fig. 1). Now, the products cannot fit perfectly into the same active site as the substrates. In the products the methyl group has moved closer to the nucleophile to which it has been transferred, and the distance d has been replaced by d', the internuclear distance in the product. The enzyme-product complex, then, is destabilized by steric hindrance to the methyl group in its new position, which is caused by interference by the groups shown with heavy shading in the figure, and has lost the binding energy of the methyl group at its normal position in the active site. Now, the consequence of this situation is that the products could bind more tightly if they were distorted in such a way that they more closely resembled the substrates, so that the binding forces to the enzyme will provide a driving force for such a distortion to resemble the substrate. Thus, upon binding of product there will be a tendency for the methyl group to move away from the nitrogen atom toward the thioether. This will facilitate the reaction in the reverse direction. Conversely, if the active site were to fit the products perfectly, there would be an imperfect fit for the starting materials and this would provide a driving force

[3] R. C. Greene and N. B. Davis, *Biochim. Biophys. Acta* **43**, 360 (1960).

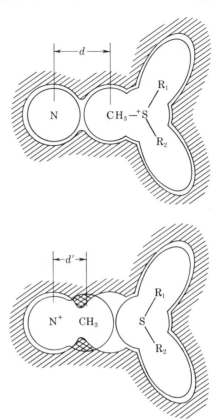

Fig 1. Diagram to show that if the active site of an enzyme has a structure which provides an optimum fit for substrates (a nucleophile and a sulfonium ion), it will not have an optimum fit (i.e., there will be a tendency toward the induction of strain or distortion) for the products, because of differences in bond lengths, bond angles, and charge.

to distort the starting materials to resemble the products. If the active site were intermediate in structure, both the starting materials and the products would be distorted and the rate of the reaction would be accelerated in both directions.

Moving one reacting atom toward another and pushing reacting molecules together is not the only way that strain and distortion, in the broadest sense, can accelerate the reaction. Almost any characteristic of the active site which is optimal for binding a product will be less satisfactory for binding a substrate and may, therefore, force the bound substrate to resemble the product with a consequent increase in reaction rate. For example, if the bond angle of R_1— S—R_2 is different in the sulfonium ion starting material and the thioether product, binding of one or the other compound must induce strain which will facilitate conversion to the compound which fits the active site best. An appropriately located negative charge in a hydrophobic environment will facilitate binding of a pyridinium or

sulfonium ion product, but will provide an energetically unfavorable
situation adjacent to the uncharged pyridine or thioether starting
material; this will provide a driving force for relief of this destabilization by transfer of the methyl group to the acceptor with the development of a positive charge. If the active site is not rigid, but
requires energy for distortion to fit the product, then this energy
will tend to force a return of the active site to its original structure
and will be available to facilitate the reaction in a similar manner.

   This argument may be generalized as follows: a single structure of the active site ordinarily cannot provide an optimum fit for
both the substrates and the products of a reaction. The difference
in the structures of the reactants and the products and a resistance
to change in the structure of the active site will cause the binding
energy of the substrates to appear as strain energy for the products
and vice versa. The most desirable situation, from the point of view
of accelerating the rate of reaction of the enzyme-substrate complex,
is that in which the active site is constructed so as to have a maximum affinity for the *transition state*. The induction of strain in the
enzyme-substrate complex involves the overcoming of part of the
energetic and entropic barrier to reaction by bringing the substrate
part way along the reaction coordinate toward the transition state
and thus decreasing the observed free energy of activation (Fig. 2.[4])

---

[4] It may be difficult to compare the energy barriers of the catalyzed and uncatalyzed reactions because the catalyzed reaction may proceed by a different mechanism
and follow a rate law with a different order. However, the experimental fact that
catalysis is observed means that the free energy of activation in the presence of the
catalyst under a given set of experimental conditions is less than that for the same
mechanism or for any other mechanism in the absence of the catalyst.

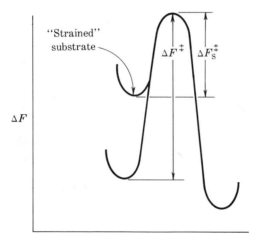

"Strained" substrate — $\Delta F^{\ddagger}$ $\Delta F_S^{\ddagger}$

ΔF

Fig 2. Diagrammatic representation of the induction of strain
or distortion in a substrate to
bring it part way along the reaction coordinate to the transition state.

A dramatic illustration of the induction of strain in the product of a reaction which is bound to a site which fits the starting material is found in the visual pigment, iodopsin. The photoisomerization of the 11-*cis* to the all-*trans* isomer of retinal (vitamin A aldehyde), which is bound to a specific site on a protein in iodopsin and the related carotenoid-protein, rhodopsin,[5] is an early step in the visual process. If the photoisomerization of the 11-*cis* retinal of iodopsin is carried out at $-195°$ and the system is warmed to $-100°$, the initially formed all-*trans* retinal rapidly isomerizes back to the 11-*cis* form to regenerate native iodopsin. Since the binding site for retinal in the starting material fits the 11-*cis* isomer, not the all-*trans*, the interaction of this site with the *trans* isomer after photoisomerization induces strain and reduces the activation energy for conversion of the *trans* to the 11-*cis* structure. The induction of distortion also provides an attractive explanation for the unusual spectral properties of the visual pigments, lobster shell pigments, and other native carotenoid-proteins, which cannot be adequately accounted for by other mechanisms.[6]

In order to lower activation energy by mechanisms of this kind, it is necessary to utilize some other energy. A maximum affinity of an enzyme active site for the transition state requires that there be a less than maximum affinity for the substrate and products. The strain energy which is induced in the substrate is paid for by a reduction in binding energy, so that the observed binding of substrate will be less than the maximum which would be possible if all available binding forces were utilized to bind the substrate to a site which provided an optimal fit for the substrate.

The concept that the active site lowers the free energy of activation by providing maximal binding for the transition state encompasses more than in usually included in the terms "strain" or "distortion," but no sharp line can be drawn between the different categories, and all of them utilize potential binding energy to the substrate to decrease the free energy of activation. Thus, the electrostatic destabilization of a pyridine or thioether by a negative charge can only occur if these groups are forced into apposition with the negative charge by binding forces to the rest of the molecule. Even the usual type of strain is not easily separable from an induced orientation of reacting groups; a given molecule spends different fractions of its time in different conformations, depending on the energies and entropies of each conformation, and a binding to the

---

[5] T. Yoshizawa and G. Wald, *Nature* **214**, 566 (1967).

[6] T. Yoshizawa and G. Wald, *Nature* **197**, 1279 (1963); M. Buchwald and W. P. Jencks, *Biochemistry* **7**, 844 (1968).

active site in one of these conformations which most easily leads to the formation of the transition state is paid for in a less favorable free energy of binding. It is only the improbability of reaching this particular conformation without such binding that leads to the rate acceleration, and it is not of great importance whether this improbability derives from an unfavorable entropy or enthalpy of the particular structure. Optimal binding of the transition state may even by utilized to describe the rate acceleration which results from the approximation of two reactants from dilute solution at the active site.

   If complementarity between the active site and the transition state contributes significantly to enzymatic catalysis, it should be possible to synthesize an enzyme by constructing such an active site. One way to do this is to prepare an antibody to a haptenic group which resembles the transition state of a given reaction. The combining sites of such antibodies should be complementary to the transition state and should cause an acceleration by forcing bound substrates to resemble the transition state.

B. MANIFESTATION OF ENZYMATIC SPECIFICITY IN MAXIMUM VELOCITIES

One of the general problems in enzymology is the question of why the specificity of enzymatic reactions is often manifested at high substrate concentrations at which the enzyme is saturated with substrate, i.e., in maximal velocities. It might have been expected that specificity would be manifested in the binding of substrates, so that a poor substrate would be bound weakly to the active site, but that once bound it would react normally. The "lock-and-key" model is adequate to explain the exclusion of large substrates from the active site and the poor binding of small substrates, but does not explain the specificity with respect to the rate constant for the catalytic step that is a characteristic property of enzymes. The problem is most serious for small substrates that should be able to bind to the active site in such a way as to undergo reaction, although they may not bind firmly. For example, the enzyme hexokinase catalyzes the transfer of a phosphate group from ATP to water as well as to the hydroxyl group of the specific acceptor, glucose, but the rate of the reaction with water is only 5×10^{-6} times as fast as the rate with glucose.[7] Water must certainly be able to penetrate to the active

---

[7] K. A. Trayser and S. P. Colowick, *Arch. Biochem. Biophys.* **94,** 161 (1961).

Table I   Hydrolysis of peptides by pepsin at
pH 4.0[8]

Peptide[a]	K_m, mM	k_{cat}, sec^{-1}
Cbz-Gly-His-Phe-Phe-OEt	0.80	2.43
Cbz-His-Phe-Trp-OEt	0.23	0.51
Cbz-His-Phe-Phe-OEt	0.18	0.31
Cbz-His-Phe-Tyr-OEt	0.23	0.16
Cbz-His-Tyr-Phe-OMe	0.68	0.013
Cbz-His-Tyr-Tyr-OEt	0.24	0.0094
Cbz-His-Phe-Leu-OMe	0.56	0.0025

[a]Cbz = carbobenzyloxy; Gly = glycine; His =
histidine; Phe = phenylalanine; Trp = tryptophan; Leu = leucine; Tyr = tyrosine.

site, so that it is necessary to find an explanation for its low reactivity in spite of its presence at the active site. Many other group transfer enzymes effectively catalyze transfer to specific hydroxylic acceptors, but catalyze little or no transfer of the group to water.

One of many examples of the manifestation of enzyme specificity in maximal reaction rates, rather than binding constants, is found in the hydrolysis of the central peptide bond of a series of synthetic substrates by pepsin (Table I).[8] These peptides undergo hydrolysis with a range of maximal velocities of 1,000-fold, although the Michaelis constant, which includes and is probably equal to the dissociation constant for the enzyme-substrate complex, varies over a range of only 4-fold. There are three possible explanations for this kind of behavior: induced fit, nonproductive binding, and rate acceleration by the induction of strain. It will be apparent that it is not always possible to draw a sharp line between these categories.

1. THE INDUCED-FIT THEORY

According to the induced-fit theory as propounded by Koshland,[9,10] the catalytic groups at the active site of the free enzyme are not in positions in which they can exert effective catalytic activity. When a good substrate is bound to the enzyme, the binding forces between

[8]K. Inouye and J. S. Fruton, *Biochemistry* 6, 1765 (1967).

[9]D. E. Koshland, Jr., *Proc. Natl. Acad. Sci. U.S.* 44, 98 (1958).

[10]D. E. Koshland, Jr., *Advan. Enzymol.* 22, 45 (1960); D. E. Koshland, Jr., and K. E. Neet, *Ann. Rev. Biochem.* 37, 359 (1968).

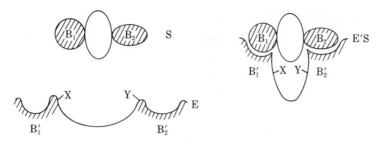

Fig 3. The induced-fit mechanism, in which binding of substrate through groups B_1 and B_2 causes a change in the conformation of the enzyme so that the groups X and Y in the active site, which are required for catalysis, are properly positioned relative to the substrate.[1]

the enzyme and the substrate are utilized to force the enzyme into an energetically less favorable, but catalytically active, conformation (Fig. 3). A poor substrate may bind to the active site, but will not have the necessary structural features to force such a conformation change of the enzyme to the active form, and, consequently, will not undergo reaction.

An induced fit provides specificity and control for an enzymatic reaction, but it does not involve a direct utilization of the binding forces to reduce the activation energy of the reaction. The equilibria and relative free energies of this situation are expressed by equation 3, in which E is the inactive form of the free enzyme and

$$
\begin{array}{ccc}
\mathrm{E} + \mathrm{S} & \xrightleftharpoons{K_1} & \mathrm{ES} \\[4pt]
K_4 \big\updownarrow & & \big\updownarrow K_2 \\[4pt]
\mathrm{E'} + \mathrm{S} & \xrightleftharpoons{K_3} & \mathrm{E'S} \longrightarrow \text{products}
\end{array}
\qquad (3)
$$

$E'S$ is the modified active enzyme bound to substrate. Since E is the energetically favored form of the free enzyme (the free enzyme is catalytically inactive) and $E'S$ is the favored form of the enzyme-substrate complex (the enzyme-substrate complex is catalytically active), the binding forces between the enzyme and the substrate must provide the driving force for the energetically unfavorable conversion of E to E'. The observed binding energy of the substrate (to give $E'S$) must be reduced by an equivalent amount. The overall free energy of substrate binding is $\Delta F_4 + \Delta F_3$ (in which the subscripts refer to the numbered reactions in equation 3), and this must always be less favorable than ΔF_3 alone (the energy of substrate binding to an active site which it fits most favorably) by an amount equal to ΔF_4 because ΔF_4 is positive.

Thus, the results of the induced fit are (1) the observed binding constant is decreased compared with the value it would have if the active site fit the substrate perfectly and no conformation change were required and (2) the maximal velocity of the reaction is optimal for a specific substrate which can utilize specific binding forces to force a conformation change. The ultimate result of the process is that substrate specificity is manifested at high rather than at low substrate concentrations. If the binding energy were not utilized to cause an induced fit, it could be used to give a tighter binding and, consequently, a more effective enzyme activity with specific substrates in dilute solution.

This theory is particularly attractive in providing an explanation for the inactivity of enzymes with small substrates such as water, which lack the necessary groups to provide the binding energy that is required to change the enzyme to an active conformation. It is still surprising that such a mechanism can work efficiently enough to cause the large rate differences which are observed. For example, in order to account for the rate difference of 5×10^{-6} between water and glucose in the hexokinase reaction, the concentration of active enzyme E' in the absence of specific inducing forces must be some 5×10^{-6} that of the inactive enzyme. The binding of glucose must cause a conversion of the enzyme to the active form, which requires over 7 kcal of free energy. This energy must be subtracted from the potential binding energy of glucose (which would be available at an active site that provided an optimal interaction without requiring a conformation change) to give the observed binding energy. This is a large price to pay for specificity, and an even larger price is required for greater degrees of specificity, but from a teleological point of view it may be a necessary price in order to avoid wasteful hydrolysis of ATP. Other theories do not avoid similar energetic problems any more successfully.

2. THE NONPRODUCTIVE-BINDING HYPOTHESIS[11-16]

According to the nonproductive-binding hypothesis, it is the substrate rather than the enzyme that is in a catalytically inactive posi-

[11] S. A. Bernhard and H. Gutfreund, *Proc. Intern. Symp. Enzyme Chem. Tokyo Kyoto* 1958, 124.

[12] S. A. Bernhard, *J. Cellular Comp. Physiol.* 54, (Suppl. 1), 256 (1959).

[13] T. Spencer and J. M. Sturtevant, *J. Am. Chem. Soc.* 81, 1874 (1959).

[14] G. E. Hein and C. Niemann, *J. Am. Chem. Soc.* 84, 4495 (1962).

[15] C. Niemann, *Science* 143, 1287 (1964).

[16] C. L. Hamilton, C. Niemann, and G. S. Hammond, *Proc. Natl. Acad. Sci. U.S.* 55, 664 (1966).

tion in the case of a poor substrate. Suppose that a good specific substrate has several binding sites which are complementary to sites on the enzyme, so that the substrate can bind only in one active position (Fig. 4). A poor substrate which lacks one or more of these binding groups or has incorrectly located groups may bind correctly, but also may bind incorrectly to give catalytically inactive enzyme-substrate complexes (Fig. 4). The observed maximum velocity V_{obs} for the poor substrates is, therefore, less than the maximum velocity for productively bound substrate V_p by a factor corresponding to

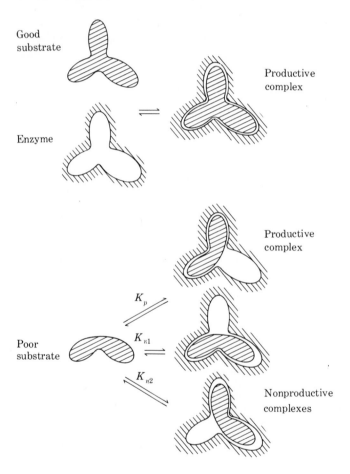

Fig 4. Productive and nonproductive binding of good and poor substrates.

the fraction of the substrate which is bound productively (equation 4). Similarly, the observed *binding* constant K_{obs} is larger than the

$$V_{obs} = V_p \frac{K_p}{K_p + K_{n1} + K_{n2} + \ldots + K_{nx}}$$

(4)

binding constant for productive binding K_p because it includes all possible modes of binding—productive and nonproductive (equation 5). If nonproductive binding predominates, the binding constant for

$$K_{obs} = K_p + K_{n1} + K_{n2} + \cdots + K_{nx}$$

(5)

productive binding may be so small as to make no significant contribution to the observed binding constant.

This theory has been applied most extensively to reactions catalyzed by chymotrypsin. For substrates of the type $R_1 CONHCHR_2 COR_3$ it is postulated that there are sites ρ_1, ρ_2, and ρ_3 on the enzyme which interact with R_1, R_2, and R_3, respectively. In the case of a good substrate there is correct matching of the groups on the substrate with the enzyme sites, but for a poor substrate there will be incorrect matching, which gives nonproductive binding. The theory is capable of giving a consistent picture of many of the catalytic properties of this enzyme.[14-16] The well known fact that derivatives of D amino acids are hydrolyzed very slowly or not at all by chymotrypsin, although their binding constants are very similar to those of the corresponding L substrates, is probably a consequence of nonproductive binding. It is of interest that acyl-enzyme intermediates formed from D substrates undergo hydrolysis even more slowly than intermediates of nonspecific substrates, such as acetyl- or acetylglycyl-chymotrypsin, and that the faster the intermediate formed from the normal L substrate undergoes hydrolysis, the *slower* is the hydrolysis of the D substrate.[17] Presumably the nonspecific substrate can exist in a number of positions on the active site, only a few of which lead to hydrolysis. A highly specific L substrate is bound correctly and undergoes hydrolysis rapidly, whereas the corresponding D substrate is bound incorrectly so that it is almost never in the correct position to undergo hydrolysis. Alternatively, since it is difficult to explain the very low rate of hydrolysis of the acetyl enzyme simply in terms of the improbability that it should take up a confor-

[17] D. W. Ingles and J. R. Knowles, *Biochem. J.* **104**, 369 (1967).

mation which leads to hydrolysis, the specific L substrate may cause a conformation change of the enzyme which facilitates hydrolysis by positioning catalytic groups correctly or inducing strain, whereas the D substrate causes a conformation change which hinders the reaction.

If it is desired to explain the low reactivity of water in the hexokinase reaction by the nonproductive-binding theory, it is necessary to assume that water binds incorrectly some 2×10^5 times more often than it binds correctly. This is difficult to understand in view of the much smaller orientational requirements for most chemical reactions. There must be a free-energy barrier of more than 7 kcal/mole for the correct binding of the hydroxylic substrate, and the binding energy of glucose must be sufficient to overcome this barrier. This seems an unusually large barrier if binding is perfectly random and suggests that there would have to be some specific steric or conformational interference to the correct binding of water.

3. THE STRAIN OR DISTORTION THEORY

According to the strain or distortion theory, the binding forces between the substrate and the enzyme are directly utilized to induce strain or distortion, which facilitates the reaction. If the active site of the enzyme is rigid, this means that the substrate is subjected to distortion in such a way that its structure must approach the transition state of the reaction in order that it may undergo binding, and the binding forces provide the driving force which allows the substrate to bind in the distorted configuration. This is shown in equation 6, in which S is the normal substrate, S' is the distorted sub-

$$
E + S \xrightleftharpoons{K_1} ES'
$$
$$
K_2 \diagdown \quad \pm E \quad \diagup K_3
$$
$$
S'
$$

(6)

strate, and E is the enzyme, which can bind only the distorted substrate. The observed binding energy ΔF_1 is the algebraic sum of the energy required to distort the substrate ΔF_2 and the binding energy of the distorted substrate ΔF_3. The same binding forces would be available to bind the substrate if it could be bound to the enzyme in an undistorted form. Therefore, the observed binding energy is less than the maximum binding energy which would be observed in the absence of strain or distortion by the amount of energy required to cause the distortion ΔF_2. Thus, an increase in reaction rate has been bought at the expense of a decrease in binding.

If the enzyme is conformationally mobile, but the substrate is relatively rigid, the situation may be described by the same equation as for the induced-fit theory (equation 3). The most stable state of the enzyme is one which does not fit the substrate optimally, but is more nearly complementary to the transition state. In order that substrate binding may take place, the enzyme must undergo an energetically unfavorable deformation. The tendency of the enzyme to return to its original, low-energy state will provide a driving force to force the substrate into a structure resembling the transition state. A schematic and unrealistic picture of how this could occur is shown, for purposes of illustration, in Fig. 5. Here, the tendency of the distorted enzyme E′ to return to its undeformed state E facilitates the reaction by simply helping to pull apart the bonds of the substrate. As in the induced-fit case, the observed binding energy of the substrate is smaller than that which would be available for a perfect fit to an optimum, undeformed active site by the amount of energy which is required to distort the enzyme. The difference between the induced-fit theory and this version of the strain theory is that according to the induced-fit theory the binding energy is utilized to bring catalytic groups into their proper position relative to a good substrate to provide specificity at high substrate concentrations, whereas according to the strain theory the binding energy is utilized

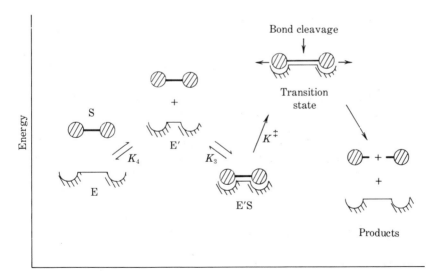

Fig 5. Scheme to show how a substrate-induced conformation change in an enzyme may be utilized to facilitate reaction of the substrate by simply helping to pull it apart.[1]

directly to decrease the free energy of activation of the reaction, as well as to provide specificity at high substrate concentrations.

In fact, neither of these descriptions of the strain hypothesis corresponds to reality because neither the enzyme nor the substrate is a rigid molecule. In a real system *both* the enzyme and the substrate would be expected to undergo distortion, and the observed effect would be intermediate between the two limiting cases described above. The enzyme, in particular, is likely to have a high degree of flexibility with respect to certain motions because of the weakness of the individual bonds which determine its conformation. This raises the question of whether the distortion energies which could be brought to bear by a protein are sufficient to cause a significant rate acceleration, for certainly many types of side-chain motion would not be expected to have large force constants. The types of protein-induced distortion which are easiest to visualize involve compression and changes of bond angles. For example, one can imagine grooves in the enzyme surface which lead to distortion of bond angles, or a requirement for bending around an interfering central atom to form hydrophobic or other bonds on either side of this atom. The distortion of a residue which involves the breaking of an α helix or other cooperative structural unit of the protein, or which leads to the formation of an unoccupied hole, would be expected to require a significant amount of energy. In fact, the distortion hypothesis provides a rationale for the fact that enzymes are much larger molecules than would be expected to be necessary to carry the required catalytic groups at the active site because an intact three-dimensional structure of some size and rigidity is required to provide the fit and force constants which are required for the induction of strain.

In terms of the strain theory, the greater activity of hexokinase toward glucose compared with water would be caused by the utilization of the specific binding forces to the glucose molecule to induce strain or distortion in the enzyme-substrate complex to facilitate phosphate transfer from ATP. Water, without such specific binding, cannot facilitate the reaction in this manner and reacts more slowly.

C. SOME APPLICATIONS OF THE STRAIN THEORY

1. ESTERASE AND CHYMOTRYPSIN

There are many experimental observations which can be satisfyingly explained in terms of the strain theory, although none of them constitute unequivocal proof of the theory. One of the most interesting is Hofstee's finding that the maximal rate of hydrolysis of substituted phenyl esters, $CH_2(CH_2)_n COOC_6H_4COO^-$, by liver esterase and chymotrypsin increases with increasing chain length of the acyl portion.[18] Within certain limits, this occurs with relatively little change in the value of the Michaelis constant. Thus, a lengthening of the hydrocarbon chain, which has little effect on the chemical reactivity of the esters and would be expected to give only a tighter binding, results in an increase in the rate of attack at the acyl group in the enzymatic reaction. In terms of the strain theory[19] this suggests that the energy of interaction of the hydrocarbon chain with the protein is utilized to induce strain in the enzyme-substrate complex, as shown schematically in Fig. 6. Suppose that a short-chain substrate has a certain binding energy ΔF_A. A longer-chain substrate would have an additional binding energy ΔF_B from hydrophobic bonding to the hydrocarbon chain. If this energy is utilized to induce strain energy ΔF_{B_S}, and decrease the free energy of activation, it will not appear in the observed binding constant; and if ΔF_B equals ΔF_{B_S}, the observed binding energy will be the same as that of the shorter-chain substrate ΔF_A. For a still longer chain, a larger binding energy ΔF_C can be converted to a larger strain energy ΔF_{C_S} to give a further increase in reaction rate. The observed rate in-

[18] B. H. J. Hofstee, *Biochim. Biophys. Acta* **24**, 211 (1957); **32**, 182 (1959); *J. Biol. Chem.* **207**, 219 (1954).

[19] R. Lumry, in P. D. Boyer, H. Lardy, and K. Myrbäck (eds.), "The Enzymes," vol. 1, p. 157, Academic Press Inc., New York, 1959.

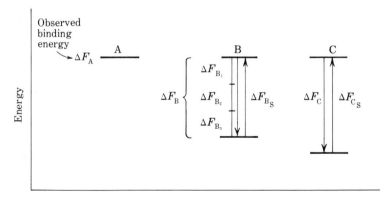

Fig 6. Scheme to show how enzyme-substrate binding forces may be utilized to induce strain in the enzyme-substrate complex.

crease with increasing chain length is of the magnitude which would be expected if the hydrophobic binding energy of each additional methylene group were utilized directly to decrease the free energy of activation rather than to increase binding. If these observations are to be explained in terms of the induced-fit theory, it must be postulated that the increase in chain length results in a progressively better fit of the catalytic groups around the acyl group of the substrate. The nonproductive-binding theory requires that the smaller substrate bind incorrectly and that a progressively larger fraction of the substrate bind in a productive mode with increasing chain length.

Cane and Wetlaufer have recently shown that the rates of deacylation of a series of acyl-chymotrypsins, $CH_3(CH_2)_nCO-Enz$, also increase with increasing chain length of the acyl group. The decrease of 1.6 kcal/mole in the free energy of activation between the two- and six-carbon compounds which is reflected in this rate increase represents a small difference between an *increase* of 10.1 kcal/mole in the enthalpy and a decrease of 11.7 kcal/mole in the contribution of the entropy term to the activation barrier.[20] These changes are too large to be easily explained by any process which does not involve a change in the conformation of the enzyme, probably accompanied by changes in solvent structure which cause mutually compensatory changes in enthalpy and entropy. The decrease in the free energy of activation induced by the longer-chain substrate could represent either an induced fit of the catalytic groups or a strain-distortion mechanism. The much larger differences between the rates of the deacylation step for certain specific and nonspecific substrates are associated with very little difference in the enthalpy, but with a large difference in the entropy of activation.[21] Cane and Wetlaufer's findings suggest that the apparent absence of an enthalpy difference for the specific substrates could easily result from a masking of an enzyme-mediated decrease in the enthalpy of activation by an endothermic conformation change in the presence of the specific substrates.

2. TRYPSIN

A different type of evidence for a role of the nonreacting portion of a substrate in the catalytic process is found in the sevenfold in-

---

[20] W. P. Cane and D. Wetlaufer, *Abstr. Am. Chem. Soc.* 152d *Ann. Meeting* **1966**, 110C.

[21] M. L. Bender, F. J. Kézdy, and C. R. Gunter, *J. Am. Chem. Soc.* **86**, 3714 (1964).

crease in the rate of hydrolysis of acetylglycine ethyl ester by trypsin, which occurs in the presence of methylguanidinium ion. Normal, specific substrates for trypsin contain a cationic group which
presumably interacts with an anionic site on the enzyme, as shown
in 1 for benzoylarginine ethyl ester. Acetylglycine ethyl ester, a
smaller, uncharged substrate, cannot interact with this anionic site
and undergoes hydrolysis some 10^3 times more slowly than the
specific substrate, but if a methylguanidinium group is placed in
this site (2), a small fraction of the normal activity is regained. This

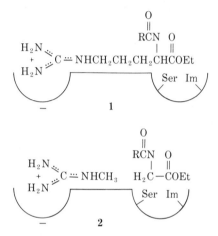

result and similar results which have been observed for a number of
other enzymes suggest that the portion of the normal substrate
which is responsible for specificity interacts with the enzyme to cause
a change in the geometry of the system which either orients catalytic
groups correctly relative to the substrate or induces strain in the
reacting bonds. It is of interest that methylguanidinium ion also
causes a sixfold increase in the rate of alkylation by iodoacetamide
of the imidazole group in the active site of trypsin.[22]

3. 2-KETO-3-DEOXY-6-PHOSPHOGLUCONIC ALDOLASE

This enzyme provides another example in which enzyme activity is
dependent on the presence of a group, in this case a phosphate
ester, which is some distance from the reacting atoms.[23] The enzyme catalyzes the reaction of the dephospho substrate 4 more than
10,000 times less effectively than that of the normal substrate 3.

[22] T. Inagami, *J. Biol. Chem.* **240**, PC3453 (1965).

[23] J. M. Ingram and W. A. Wood, *J. Biol. Chem.* **241**, 3256 (1966).

It might be expected that the dephospho compound would be able to undergo binding in a correct orientation because of the several possible specific sites for interaction on the sugar molecule. This expectation is supported by the fact that it reacts with the enzyme at low concentration to form a covalent bond by imine formation at the active site, which is presumably the first step in the normal catalytic

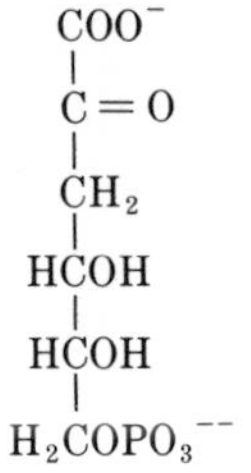

$$
\begin{array}{cc}
COO^- & COO^- \\
| & | \\
C=O & C=O \\
| & | \\
CH_2 & CH_2 \\
| & | \\
HCOH & HCOH \\
| & | \\
HCOH & HCOH \\
| & | \\
H_2COPO_3{}^{--} & H_2COH
\end{array}
$$

$$
\qquad 3 \qquad\qquad 4
$$

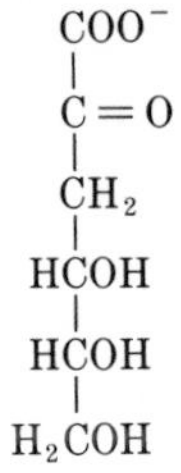

process. The requirement of the phosphate group for activity is most readily interpreted if this group acts as a "handle" to bring about the induction of strain in the enzyme-substrate complex, although less satisfying interpretations in terms of the induced-fit or nonproductive-binding hypotheses are possible.

4. INHIBITION BY TRANSITION-STATE ANALOGS

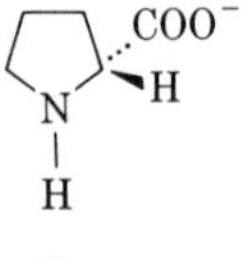

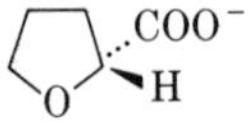

Since the hypothesis that the substrate is distorted to resemble the transition state at the expense of its binding energy is equivalent to the statement that the transition state is bound to the active site more tightly than the substrate, compounds which resemble the transition state should also be bound more tightly than the substrate. There are several indications that this may be so. Proline racemase is inhibited by pyrrole-2-carboxylic acid (5) at a concentration 160 times less than that of proline (6). Furan-2-carboxylic acid (7) and thiophene-2-carboxylic acid (8) are also potent inhibitors, but tetrahydrofuran-2-carboxylic acid (9), which more closely resembles proline, is not. The transition state for the proline racemase reaction almost certainly approaches sp^2 hybridization of the α carbon atom and is more planar than the starting material, with its tetrahedral carbon atom, so that the strong inhibition by planar aromatic molecules is in accord with what might be expected if the enzyme distorts the substrate toward a planar transition state.[24] A 160-fold difference in binding corresponds to 3000 cal/mole of free energy, which could be utilized to distort the substrate.

Similar behavior is exhibited by the enzyme Δ^5-3-ketosteroid isomerase, which presumably catalyzes the attainment of a near-planar transition state during the removal of a proton from the 4 position of its substrate, Δ^5-androstene-3,17-dione, 10. This enzyme is strongly inhibited by the planar molecule, 17-β-dihydro-equilenin, 11, with a K_i value of 6.3×10^{-6} M, which is much smaller

10   11

than the K_m value of 3.2×10^{-4} M for the substrate. Furthermore, substrates which undergo isomerization with maximal reaction rates smaller than that for 10 exhibit approximately tenfold *smaller* values of K_m.[25] The strong inhibition by 11 and by related inhibitors may, then, reflect their resemblance to the near-planar transition state and the larger K_m value for 10 than for less effective substrates may reflect a larger conversion of binding into strain energy in the case of 10, provided that the order of K_m values does, in fact, reflect the relative binding abilities of the substrates.

5. ACTIVATION BY CO-SUBSTRATES

For multisubstrate enzymes it might be expected that the effective structure of the active site would depend on the presence of the substrate, so that the reactivity of one substrate would depend on the presence of another even if there is no covalent reaction between the two substrates. There are many examples of enzymes which show a requirement for the presence of all or several of the substrates in order to exhibit activity in partial or exchange reactions. If this represents a mechanism for the manifestation of enzyme specificity, the induction of either strain or an induced fit by the presence of a

---

[24] G. Cardinale and R. Abeles, personal communication (1965).
[25] S. Wang, F. S. Kawahara, and P. Talalay, *J. Biol. Chem.* 238, 576 (1963).

second substrate might be expected to increase the reactivity of the first substrate toward small, abnormal reactants as well as toward the normal reactant. A possible example of this behavior is found in the enzyme luciferase, which normally catalyzes the displacement of pyrophosphate (PP) from ATP by the carboxyl group of luciferin (L) to give luciferyl–AMP and the reverse displacement of luciferin from luciferyl–AMP by pyrophosphate to give ATP and luciferin (equation 7). In the absence of pyrophosphate-containing compounds

$$\text{ATP} + \text{L}-\text{COOH} \underset{}{\overset{\pm\,\text{Enz}}{\rightleftharpoons}} \underset{\text{Enz}}{\underline{\text{AMP}-\overset{\overset{\text{activated}}{\overset{\text{L}}{|}}}{\text{CO}}\cdots\text{PP}}} \overset{\pm\,\text{PP}}{\lll}$$

$$\underset{\text{Enz}}{\overset{\overset{\text{stable}}{\overset{\text{L}}{|}}}{\text{AMP}-\text{CO}}}$$

$$\text{L}-\text{COOH} + \text{AMP} \xleftarrow[\substack{\pm\,\text{Enz,}\\ \text{ATP}}]{\text{H}_2\text{O}} \underset{\text{Enz}}{\underline{\text{AMP}-\overset{\overset{\text{L}}{|}}{\text{CO}}\cdots\text{ATP}}} \overset{}{\underset{\pm\,\text{ATP}}{\nearrow}}$$

$$(7)$$

the enzyme-bound luciferyl–AMP is quite stable, but in the presence of either pyrophosphate or ATP it becomes reactive and reacts to give ATP with the former compound, but to undergo hydrolysis in the presence of the latter.[26] Thus, an ATPase activity is observed in the presence of ATP, which may be due to an activation of the substrate toward the attack of water by this pyrophosphate-containing molecule. According to the strain hypothesis, the presence of a pyrophosphate group introduces strain into the luciferyl–AMP–enzyme complex to facilitate its reaction with any available acceptor. An analogous interpretation may be made for the hydrolysis of valyl–AMP by isoleucyl–RNA synthetase, which is activated by the presence of transfer RNA which contains isoleucine-specific chains.[27]

6. LYSOZYME

Speculations about these subjects have been brought into direct contact with reality by the x-ray crystallographic determination of the structure of lysozyme and lysozyme-inhibitor complexes.[28] Lysozyme catalyzes the cleavage of the N-acetylmuramyl bonds of an alternat-

[26] M. DeLuca and W. D. McElroy, *Biochem. Biophys. Res. Commun.* 18, 836 (1965).

[27] A. T. Norris and P. Berg, *Proc. Natl. Acad. Sci. U.S.* 52, 330 (1964).

[28] C. C. F. Blake, L. N. Johnson, G. A. Mair, A. C. T. North, D. C. Phillips, and V. R. Sarma, *Proc. Roy. Soc.* (*London*) 167, 378 (1967B); D. C. Phillips, *Proc. Natl. Acad. Sci. U.S.* 57, 484 (1967).

ing N-acetylglucosamine-N-acetylmuramic acid copolymer found in the cell walls of bacteria, but also cleaves oligosaccharides with the same alternating structure and even polymers composed only of N-acetylglucosamine. The x-ray studies suggest that the substrate binding region of the enzyme consists of a cleft which can interact with six hexose residues; the six subsites are designated A to F (12).

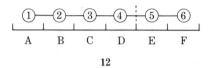

12

The hexasaccharide of N-acetylglucosamine is cleaved between residues 4 and 5, suggesting that the enzyme catalyzes cleavage at the C-1 carbon atom of the hexose group which is bound to the D subsite.

Measurements of the dissociation constants and Michaelis constants of N-acetylglucosamine oligosaccharides indicate that there is an increased binding as the number of hexose residues is increased from one to three, but no significant increase in binding as the chain length is increased further.[29] However, the *rate* of cleavage increases sharply with this further increase in chain length; the hexamer reacts some 30,000 times faster than the monomer in spite of its similar binding constant.[30] This is the situation which is expected for nonproductive binding (equations 4 and 5) and is in accord with the x-ray model; the short oligosaccharides bind primarily to sites A to C, which are nonproductive, rather than to site D. The larger substrates are forced to bind to sites D and E and undergo cleavage. The absence of an increase in binding energy with increasing chain length suggests that little or no net binding energy is made available by interaction with the D and E sites, so that unless binding takes place to other sites with the longer-chain substrate, binding will not take place productively at the active site. As indicated by equations 4 and 5, the observed maximum velocity of the short substrates represents a large rate constant for reaction of the very small fraction of the substrate that is bound productively to sites D and E; the observed binding constant represents the sum of the binding constants to the nonproductive sites, with a negligible contribution of the constant for weak binding at the active site.

The difficulty of attaching substrate productively to the active site is shown more directly by measurements of the binding constants

[29] J. A. Rupley, L. Butler, M. Gerring, F. J. Hartdegen, and R. Pecoraro, *Proc. Natl. Acad. Sci. U.S.* **57**, 1088 (1967).
[30] J. A. Rupley and V. Gates, *Proc. Natl. Acad. Sci. U.S.* **57**, 496 (1967).

for oligosaccharides with the alternating N-acetylglucosamine (G)–
N-acetylmuramic acid (M) structure.[31] With these substrates there
is an increase in binding with increasing chain length, as observed
for the N-acetylglucosamine polymers, up to three hexose units, but
the addition of a fourth residue to G–M–G to give G–M–G–M results
in a *decrease* in binding energy of 2.9 kcal/mole. This unfavorable
binding energy to the D subsite means that the undeformed hexose
residue does not fit into this subsite favorably, so that binding in this
position occurs only if the hexose is forced into the site by the energetically favorable binding of the adjacent hexose residues.

These facts are understandable in terms of the crystallographic
model and the chemistry of the catalyzed reaction. As described in
Chap. 3, Sec. E, Part 3, cleavage at the C-1 carbon atom of the
hexose bound to the D subsite probably occurs with assistance by a
carboxylate group and a carboxylic acid group at the active site of
the enzyme, through a transition state that has some of the character
of a carbonium ion. The occurrence of transfer reactions to specific
acceptor molecules with overall retention of configuration at the
C-1 carbon suggests that this transition state leads to an intermediate of similar structure, with a lifetime long enough for the
leaving group on site E to diffuse away and be replaced by a molecule of acceptor.[30,32] The carbonium-ion-like transition state requires a distortion of the hexose ring from a chair (13) toward a
half-chair (14) conformation, in order to obtain resonance stabilization from the neighboring oxygen atom. The x-ray data and the
results described above suggest that the enzyme decreases the energy required to reach this transition state by forcing the hexose
ring in the D subsite toward the half-chair conformation. This rep-

13   14

resents a conversion of binding energy into strain or distortion energy to lower the activation energy and may be summarized by the
statement that the active site binds the half-chair transition state
more tightly than it binds the substrate.

The possibility that strain may alter the reactivity of groups in

[31] D. M. Chipman, V. Grisaro, and N. Sharon, *J. Biol. Chem.* **242,** 4388 (1967).
    [32] J. J. Pollock, D. M. Chipman, and N. Sharon, *Arch. Biochem. Biophys.* **120,** 235
(1967); *Biochem. Biophys. Res. Commun.* **28,** 779 (1967).

the enzyme, especially metal complexes, has been pointed out by Williams.[33] The effective basicity, acidity, or oxidation-reduction potential of reacting groups may be altered by the steric requirements of the protein in such a way as to increase their reactivity, and the unusual spectra of many metalloproteins provide support for the occurrence of such alterations.

7. CHEMICAL REACTIONS

There are, of course, many examples of chemical reactions in which strain causes increases in reaction rate, and in some of these the rate enhancement is of the large magnitude that is required to account for enzymatic catalysis. One of the best examples is the alkaline hydrolysis of ethylene phosphate (15) compared with that of the structurally similar compound, dimethyl phosphate (16).[34-36] Hydrol-

$$
\begin{array}{cc}
\underset{\overset{|}{CH_2}-\overset{|}{CH_2}}{\overset{O}{\underset{O}{>}}P\overset{O}{\underset{O}{<}}} & \underset{\overset{|}{CH_3}\quad\overset{|}{CH_3}}{\overset{O}{\underset{O}{>}}P\overset{O}{\underset{O}{<}}}
\end{array}
$$

$$
\quad\quad 15 \quad\quad\quad\quad\quad 16
$$

ysis of the cyclic compound with P—O cleavage occurs at least 10^8 times faster than the same reaction in the noncyclic compound. This rate difference must reflect some distortion or destabilization brought about by the ring structure in 15 which forces the starting material part way towards the structure of the transition state. It is of interest that although strain must be relieved in the transition state, relief of ring strain does not determine the nature of the product because the hydrolysis of 5-membered cyclic triesters near neutrality gives the cyclic as well as the open chain diester product.[37] This means that the strain introduced by the 5-membered ring does not represent a simple pulling apart of the atoms in the ring which facilitates ring opening. The rapid acid catalyzed exchange of labeled oxygen from water into ethylene phosphate without ring opening is another expression of this same situation.[35] If an enzyme could induce a similar specific destabilization of a phosphate ester or other

[33] R. J. P. Williams, *Protides Biol. Fluids Proc. Colloq.* 14, 25 (1966).

[34] J. Kumamoto, J. R. Cox, Jr., and F. H. Westheimer, *J. Am. Chem. Soc.* 78, 4858 (1956).

[35] P. C. Haake and F. H. Westheimer, *J. Am. Chem. Soc.* 83, 1102 (1961).

[36] E. T. Kaiser, M. Panar, and F. H. Westheimer, *J. Am. Chem. Soc.* 85, 602 (1963).

[37] F. Covitz and F. H. Westheimer, *J. Am. Chem. Soc.* 85, 1773 (1963); F. Ramirez, O. P. Madan, N. B. Desai, S. Meyerson, and E. M. Banas, *Ibid.*, p. 2681.

substrate relative to the transition state for its reaction, a large fraction of the rate acceleration brought about by enzymes would be accounted for.

Another example is the rate increase by a factor of nearly 10^4 for the displacement of the thiol group in the strained trimethylene disulfide ring (equation 8) compared with the corresponding reaction of the open chain disulfide (equation 9). It is of interest that most of

$$C_4H_9S^- \curvearrowright S-S \longrightarrow C_4H_9S-S \quad S^- \tag{8}$$

$$C_4H_9S^- \curvearrowright S-S \longrightarrow C_4H_9S-S + {}^-SC_4H_9 \tag{9}$$
$$\overset{|}{H_9C_4} \quad \overset{\backslash}{C_4H_9} \qquad \qquad \overset{|}{C_4H_9}$$

this rate increase appears to be a reflection of a more favorable *entropy* of activation for the reaction of the cyclic compound, although the data are not conclusive.[38]

A somewhat different type of steric acceleration may be brought about by a bulky group which forces reacting groups into a reactive conformation. For example, the decomposition of *t*-butyl-*N*-nitrocarbonate occurs 10^3 times faster than the *n*-butyl compound. The bulky *t*-butyl group destabilizes the ground state by interfering with the nitro and carbomethoxy groups (equation 10). The relief

$$
\begin{array}{ccc}
\underset{R}{\overset{O\searrow N\swarrow O}{\underset{|}{N}}}\!\!-\!\!C\!\!\overset{\nearrow O}{\underset{|}{O-R'}}
&\rightleftharpoons&
\underset{R}{\overset{O\searrow N\swarrow O}{\underset{|}{N}}}\!\!-\!\!C\!\!\overset{\cdots O}{\searrow O-R'}
&\longrightarrow&
\left[\underset{R}{\overset{O\searrow\overset{+}{N}-O}{\underset{|}{N}}}\!\!-\!\!\overset{|}{C}\!\overset{O^-}{\underset{OR'}{\cdots}}\right]
\end{array}
$$

$$\downarrow$$

$$\text{products} \tag{10}$$

of this destabilization in the transition state leads to the rate acceleration, which appears entirely as a decrease of 5.4 kcal/mole in the *enthalpy* of activation.[39] There is no sharp line between this type of rate acceleration and that caused by approximation, as described in Chap. 1.

Examples of nonenzymatic reactions in solution in which reaction rates are accelerated by the induction of strain in the substrate upon binding to a catalyst are far less common. Catalysis of the racemization of the optically active molecules 1,1'-binaphthyl (17)

[38] A. Fava, A. Iliceto, and E. Camera, *J. Am. Chem. Soc.* **79**, 833 (1957).

[39] E. H. White and L. A. Dolak, *J. Am. Chem. Soc.* **88**, 3790 (1966).

and 9,10-dihydro-3,4;5,6-dibenzophenanthrene (18) by trinitrofluor-
enone (19) provides a simple and straightforward example, although

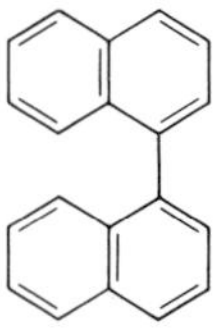

17 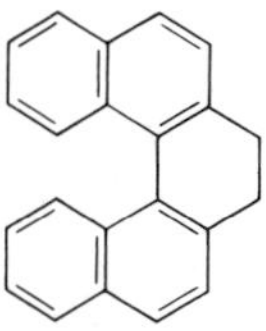　　　　　　18 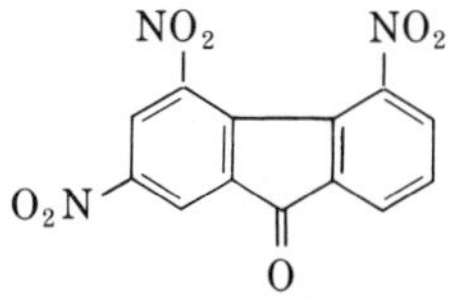　　　　　　　　19

the maximum observed rate increase is only twofold.[40]　Complex
formation between the asymmetrical substrate and the planar catalyst favors the formation of the planar transition state which is required for racemization.

A more complicated example which may represent a similar
type of catalysis is found in the catalysis of the *cis-trans* isomerization of the water-soluble azo dye chrysophenine (20) by certain
proteins.[41]　The rate of isomerization shows a specific acceleration

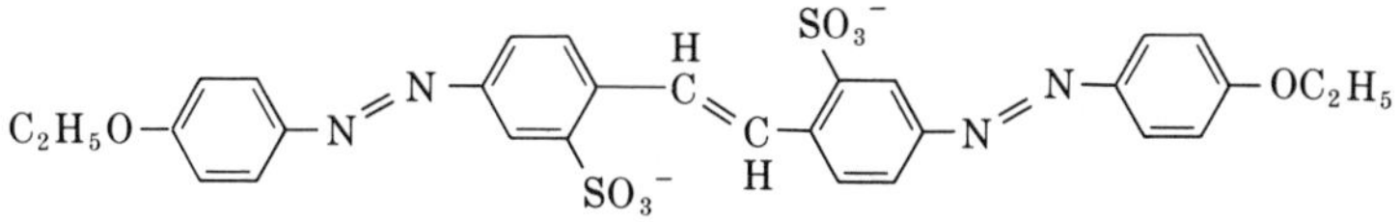

20

by a factor of up to 30- to 80-fold in the presence of serum albumin
and β-lactoglobulin.　These rate accelerations cannot easily be explained as solvent effects, and small molecules which correspond to
the functional groups of the side chains of the protein do not have
appreciable catalytic activity.　The catalyzed reaction shows a
maximum rate in the region of pH in which the proteins are known
to undergo conformation changes, suggesting that a conformation
change may take place upon adsorption of the dye which results in
the induction of strain and an increase in the reactivity of the bound
dye.

It is very probable that the induction of strain is significant in
heterogeneous catalysis and in reactions involving solids and polymers.　For example, trioxane crystals in the presence of formaldehyde vapor undergo polymerization to a polyoxymethylene polymer
in which the chains are aligned parallel to the sixfold axis of symmetry of the parent crystal, whereas no reaction is observed with

[40] A. K. Colter and L. M. Clemens, *J. Am. Chem. Soc.* 87, 847 (1965).

[41] R. Lovrien and T. Linn, *Biochemistry* 6, 2281 (1967).

tetroxane.[42] Since tetroxane, with a strained 8-membered ring, is expected to be inherently more reactive than trioxane, the crystal structure must impart an enhanced reactivity to the latter compound, as well as an ordering of the product. The mechanical distortion of polymers gives rise to strain and bond breaking, which leads to an increased reactivity. The stretching of rubber, for example, causes an enhanced rate of reaction with ozone, which presumably reacts with those bonds which are strained or completely broken to free radicals upon mechanical deformation.[43]

D. RATES OF CONFORMATION CHANGE

A change in conformation of the enzyme is required as part of the induced-fit mechanism and may occur in the strain mechanism, so that it is pertinent to ask what are the time relationships between such conformation changes and the catalytic process itself. Certainly, small changes in the position of residues near the active site would be expected to occur very rapidly, and the helix-coil transition of a large polymer, polyglutamate, also occurs very rapidly.[44,45] On the other hand, major changes in the structure of proteins, which are large enough to detect by physical methods, commonly occur over seconds to hours, presumably because the rate-determining step, which is itself fast, is preceded by unfavorable prior equilibrium steps. Such relatively slow conformation changes could not occur with each catalytic turnover of the enzyme and could only be significant in maintaining control of enzyme activity, as in the induced-fit mechanism.

Although it is difficult to detect small conformation changes by ordinary physical measurements, evidence for the induction of such changes by substrates has now been obtained in a number of instances. It is inherently reasonable that the interaction of two nonrigid molecules in solution would lead to reciprocal conformation changes in both—in fact it would be extraordinary if this did not occur—and the important questions at the present time are concerned less with the existence of these changes than with their nature, their rate, and the role they play in enzymatic catalysis.

[42] H. W. Kohlschütter, *Ann. Chem.* **482**, 75 (1930); H. W. Kohlschütter and L. Sprenger, *Z. Physik. Chem. Abstr.* **B16**, 284 (1932); cf. H. Morawetz, *Science* **152**, 705 (1966).

[43] J. E. Leffler and E. Grunwald, "Rates and Equilibria of Organic Reactions," p. 408, John Wiley & Sons, Inc., New York, 1963.

[44] J. J. Burke, G. G. Hammes, and T. B. Lewis, *J. Chem. Phys.* **42**, 3520 (1965).

[45] G. Schwarz, *J. Mol. Biol.* **11**, 64 (1965).

A simple and direct method for the detection of a substrate-dependent conformation change is the demonstration that a substrate causes an *increase* in the rate of reaction of the protein with an added compound, such as a sulfhydryl reagent or a proteolytic enzyme, which cannot be attributed to an electrostatic effect. Another particularly simple and often neglected means of demonstrating such changes is to take advantage of the slow rate of many conformation changes and show that the substrate-dependent activation of the enzyme requires a measurable period of time, i.e., that there is a lag in the attainment of maximum activity. It is difficult to account for such a lag by any mechanism except a change in enzyme conformation or a chemical reaction with the enzyme which occurs with a rate constant smaller than the rate constant for the turnover of substrate by the enzyme. The existence of such slow conformation changes introduces a serious complication into the study of enzyme kinetics by rapid mixing techniques because the state of the substrate-free enzyme may be different from that of the enzyme in the presence of substrate, and the interconversion of these forms may be slow relative to the maximum rate of turnover of the substrate.

An example of a substrate activation which is dependent on both time and temperature is found in the glutamic dehydrogenase of a *Neurospora* mutant studied by Fincham.[46] Another is the induction period in the oxidation of pyruvate by DPNH catalyzed by a D lactate dehydrogenase from *Escherichia coli*; this induction period, which must represent a slow conformation change, is abolished by prior incubation with pyruvate. It does not represent a change in the state of association of the enzyme because the rate of change of enzyme activity is independent of enzyme concentration and the molecular weight of the enzyme in very dilute solution is not changed in the presence of pyruvate.[47] There are many other examples of measurably slow, substrate-dependent changes in enzyme activity.[48]

Very recently it has become possible to follow the physical properties of proteins with techniques, such as the temperature-jump method, which operate on a time scale similar to that of the catalytic turnover of substrate by the enzyme, so that it should be possible to determine directly the relationship of the rates of sub-

[46] J. R. S. Fincham, *Biochem. J.* **65**, 721 (1957).

[47] E. M. Tarmy and N. O. Kaplan, *J. Biol Chem.*, **243**, 2579, 2587 (1968).

[48] S. Grisolia, *Physiol. Rev.* **44**, 657 (1964); A. Worcel, D. S. Goldman, and W. W. Cleland, *J. Biol. Chem.* **240**, 3399 (1965); E. B. Kearney, *Ibid.*, **229**, 363 (1957); T. K. Sundaram and J. R. S. Fincham, *J. Mol. Biol.* **10**, 423 (1964); J. H. Wang, M. L. Shonka, and D. J. Graves, *Biochemistry* **4**, 2296 (1965).

strate-dependent conformation changes to the rate of substrate turn-over. There is already some evidence available for the occurrence of isomerizations in enzymes and enzyme-substrate complexes which may represent conformation changes of this kind.[49-52] The rate of the monomolecular isomerization of glyceraldehyde-3-phosphate dehydrogenase is on the order of sec^{-1}, which is too slow to occur with each turnover of substrate and must represent a control phenomenon.[53] X-ray structural analyses of lysozyme,[28] chymotrypsin,[54] and carboxypeptidase[55] have provided direct evidence for changes in the conformation of the enzyme upon interaction with substrates or inhibitors. Hemoglobin, although it is not an enzyme, provides an instructive example of the application of all these techniques to demonstrate the conformation change that takes place in this protein upon combination with oxygen.[56]

In many instances conformation changes in proteins are associated with subunit dissociation or association. It is unlikely that such dissociations occur rapidly enough to be significant in individual turnovers of substrate molecules, so that their role is expected to be in control of activity. The question of whether all such dissociations are associated with changes in the conformation of the individual subunits has not been definitely answered, but it is probable that in most instances dissociation is brought about by such changes, and it would be surprising if such a major structural reorganization could take place without an accompanying conformation change within the subunits. In the case of the alkaline phosphatase from *E. coli* it has been demonstrated directly that a time-dependent conformation change must take place in acid-dissociated subunits before reassociation to the native enzyme can occur.[57]

The interesting possibility exists that the conformation change of the enzyme may be partially or entirely rate-determining for the

[49] G. G. Hammes and P. Fasella, *J. Am. Chem. Soc.* **84**, 4644 (1962).

[50] T. C. French and G. G. Hammes, *J. Am. Chem. Soc.* **87**, 4669 (1965); R. C. Cathou and G. G. Hammes, *Ibid.*, p. 4674.

[51] B. H. Havsteen, *J. Biol. Chem.* **242**, 769 (1967).

[52] J. E. Erman and G. G. Hammes, *J. Am. Chem. Soc.* **88**, 5607, 5614 (1966).

[53] K. Kirschner, M. Eigen, R. Bittman, and B. Voigt, *Proc. Natl. Acad. Sci. U.S.* **56**, 1661 (1966).

[54] P. B. Sigler, B. A. Jeffery, B. W. Matthews, and D. M. Blow, *J. Mol. Biol.* **15**, 175 (1966).

[55] T. A. Steitz, M. L. Ludwig, F. A. Quiocho, and W. N. Lipscomb, *J. Biol. Chem.* **242**, 4662 (1967).

[56] E. Antonini, *Science* **158**, 1417 (1967).

[57] J. A. Reynolds and M. J. Schlesinger, *Biochemistry* **6**, 3552 (1967).

catalyzed reaction.[49] This would be of special importance if it occurred at the same rate for different substrates[58] because the finding of identical rates of reaction of different substrates is often used as evidence for the existence of a common covalent enzyme-substrate intermediate, as in the case of a series of different esters of the same acyl group hydrolyzed by chymotrypsin or papain (Chap. 2, Sec. B, Part 2).

If the conformation change and the bond breaking are synchronous (equation 11), it is improbable that identical rates would be

$$E + S \rightleftharpoons ES \xrightarrow{\text{rds}} E'P \qquad (11)$$

observed because the observed energy barrier would be the sum of the barriers for the conformation change and for bond breaking. Since the latter would be different for different substrates, the observed rate should also be different. However, if the substrate binds only to the form E and a transformation to form E' is a necessary step preliminary to bond cleavage (equation 12), the making

$$
\begin{array}{ccc}
E + S & \rightleftharpoons & ES \\
\Updownarrow & & \Updownarrow \\
E' & & E'S \longrightarrow \text{products}
\end{array} \qquad (12)
$$

and breaking of covalent bonds is not necessarily involved in the rate-determining step. If the conformation change is induced by the binding forces of the substrate, as in the induced-fit or strain mechanisms, the inducing forces would not be the same for different substrates, and it is unlikely, but not impossible, that identical rates would be observed for different substrates. If the conformation change is spontaneous and occurs in the presence or absence of substrate, it could not provide much driving force for the induction of strain, but could result in a change to the catalytically active conformation of the enzyme. Such a change could occur at a rate which is independent of the nature of the substrate. It is of interest in this connection that the maximal rate constants for the reaction of related substrates, which are thought to give a common covalent intermediate, are often not exactly identical. Such small differences, which appear to be beyond the experimental error of the rate determinations, are seen with papain and acetylcholinesterase, for example.[59] This might occur if the breakdown of the common cova-

[58] J. F. Kirsch and E. Katchalski, *Biochemistry* **4**, 884 (1965).

[59] J. F. Kirsch and M. Igelstrøm, *Biochemistry* **5**, 783 (1966); R. M. Krupka, *Ibid.*, **3**, 1749 (1964).

lent intermediate were not entirely rate-determining, so that its formation made a significant contribution to the observed maximal rate, or if a conformation change, rather than the breakdown of the intermediate, were rate-determining. .

E. REVERSIBILITY

It is important to keep in mind that an enzyme must catalyze a reaction in both directions and that some mechanisms, such as a simple pulling apart of the substrate, account for catalysis in only one direction. The requirement for a strain or distortion mechanism that will accelerate the reaction in both directions is that it will force *both* the starting materials and the products to resemble the transition state. For nucleophilic reactions and the hydrolysis of esters and other acyl compounds, for example, this could involve a distortion of the acyl compound with its sp^2 carbonyl carbon atom out of planarity and toward the tetrahedral structure of the intermediate addition compound, with its central sp^3 carbon atom.

The relationship between the kinetic parameters for the enzymatic reaction of equation 13 in the forward and reverse directions

$$\text{E} + \text{S} \underset{K_S}{\rightleftharpoons} \text{ES} \overset{k_f}{\underset{k_s}{\rightleftharpoons}} \text{EP} \overset{K_P}{\rightleftharpoons} \text{E} + \text{P}$$

(13)

is given by the Haldane relation (equation 14) in which K_S and K_P

$$K_{eq} = \frac{[\text{P}]}{[\text{S}]} = \frac{1}{K_S} \frac{k_f}{k_r} K_P$$

(14)

are dissociation constants for the enzyme-substrate and the enzyme-product complexes, respectively. There are a number of instances in which enzymes appear to catalyze reactions much more efficiently in one direction than the other. This is not a violation of the principle of microscopic reversibility, since the conditions under which the measurements are made are different for the two directions; under equilibrium conditions the enzyme would give equal catalysis in both directions. In order to satisfy the Haldane relation, a ratio of rate constants k_f/k_r, which is different from K_{eq}, must be accounted for by a difference between the values of K_S and K_P. For example, if the catalysis of a reaction in the forward direction is much larger than that in the reverse direction (under conditions in which the enzyme is saturated with substrate or product for the measurements of initial rates in each direction), the dissociation constant K_S must be much larger than K_P. Such a small value of K_P is often manifested as a severe product inhibition of the reaction in the forward direction.

According to the strain and the induced-fit models, binding forces are utilized to cause an increase in maximal velocity. According to these models, then, this "one-way" catalysis could be explained if the conversion of binding to strain energy or the positioning of catalytic groups were more important in the forward than in the reverse direction, so that K_S and k_f are relatively large compared with K_P and k_r. This behavior is especially likely, according to the strain model, if the active site resembles the substrate or product more than the transition state. For example, if the active site is complementary to the product, it will cause a conversion of binding energy to a rate increase for the substrate by forcing it to resemble the product, but the product will bind tightly without being subject to a rate acceleration.

An example of "one-way" catalysis is found in the methionine activating enzyme, the first step of which (equation 15) is almost ir-

$$\text{ATP} + \text{S}\overset{\text{CH}_3}{\underset{\text{R}}{<}} \rightleftharpoons \text{Adenosine} - \overset{+}{\text{S}}\overset{\text{CH}_3}{\underset{\text{R}}{<}} \cdots \text{PPP} \cdots \text{Enz} \longrightarrow \text{PP} + \text{P} + \text{Enz} \quad (15)$$

reversible.[60] In this case the Haldane relation is satisfied by a very tight binding of the product, inorganic triphosphate, which is estimated to have a binding energy in excess of -9.4 kcal/mole. A similar binding energy must be available for the triphosphate group of ATP, and the faster rate in the forward direction would be accounted for if part of this binding energy were converted into strain energy. The considerable magnitude of this binding energy serves as a reminder that, although the individual forces are weak, the sum of the binding forces between enzyme and substrate is frequently large enough to lead to significant rate acceleration if it is converted into strain energy.

F. ENTROPY, ENTHALPY, AND FREE ENERGY

On theoretical grounds it would be expected that the induction of strain, by bending or stretching bonds or compressing atoms, would affect the heat of activation of a reaction. The attainment of the proper orientation of enzyme and substrate relative to each other, as envisioned in the induced-fit and nonproductive-binding hypotheses, implies an ordered state of minimum randomness and would be expected to be an entropic phenomenon. However, there are several reasons why it is difficult or impossible to draw a clear dividing line

[60] S. H. Mudd and J. D. Mann, *J. Biol. Chem.* **238**, 2164 (1963).

between these effects from experimental measurements of entropies and enthalpies of activation. The subject is worthy of discussion because of a widespread impression that the measured heat of a reaction or its heat of activation gives a more fundamental insight into the mechanism and, particularly, the nature of the substituent effects, than do the corresponding free-energy parameters.

In order to interpret polar effects of substituents, steric and resonance effects, strain, and related influences on a reaction, one would like to know the effects of these factors on the potential energies of the reactants, the various possible transition states, and the products. The first problem is that the experimentally determined heat or heat of activation of a reaction is not a direct measure of the desired potential energy because it includes terms involving the partition functions and will be significantly different from the potential energy at any temperature above absolute zero at which the vibrational and rotational energies are significant. In fact, the measured ΔH or $\Delta H^{\ddagger}$ is no better and may be a worse measure of the desired potential energy differences compared with the ΔF or $\Delta F^{\ddagger}$, that is obtained directly from the experimental equilibrium or rate constant.[61]

The second problem, which is especially important for reactions in aqueous solution, is that a major contribution to the observed thermodynamic quantities is made by solvation effects, and it is necessary to correct for these before conclusions can be drawn about the internal energies of the reaction. For example, one might expect that the inductive and resonance effects of substituents on the ionization of phenols and carboxylic acids would be manifested in the energies of the acid and anion, but the differences in acidity of the members of these series are determined to a much greater extent by the entropies than by the heats of ionization.[62] This is evident from the data for substituted benzoic acids shown in Table II. The same phenomenon is observed for the rate constants of reactions of phenol derivatives; the differences in the rates of alkaline hydrolysis of substituted phenyl acetates in water are caused principally by differences in the *entropy* of activation.[63] The importance of the solvent in determining thermodynamic activation parameters is shown by the fact that in 60% acetone-water the differences in the rates of hydrolysis of the same esters depend

[61] L. P. Hammett, "Physical-Organic Chemistry," pp. 76, 118, McGraw-Hill Book Company, New York, 1940.

[62] D. T. Y. Chen and K. J. Laidler, *Trans. Faraday Soc.* 58, 480 (1962); L. Eberson and I. Wadsö, *Acta Chem. Scand.* 17, 1552 (1963).

[63] T. C. Bruice and S. J. Benkovic, *J. Am. Chem. Soc.* 85, 1 (1963).

Table II   Ionization of substituted benzoic acids, $X\!\!-\!\!\bigcirc\!\!-COOH$, in water at 25°[a]

X	pK	$\Delta F°$	$\Delta H°$	$T\Delta S°$
p-OH	4.582	−0.24	+0.65	+0.89
H	4.213	−0.75	+0.53	+1.28
p-Br	4.002	−1.03	+0.22	+1.25
p-Cl	3.986	−1.06	+0.34	+1.40
m-Cl	3.827	−1.27	−0.07	+1.20
m-Br	3.809	−1.30	+0.05	+1.35
m-CN	3.598	−1.58	+0.07	+1.65
p-CN	3.551	−1.65	+0.14	+1.79
p-NO$_2$	3.442	−1.80	+0.14	+1.94

[a] G. Briegleb and A. Bieber, Z. Elektrochem. **55**, 250 (1951).

almost entirely upon differences in the *enthalpy* of activation.[64] One reason that the polar effects of substituents appear in the entropy of reaction is that the dielectric constant, which determines the transmission of an electrostatic influence from the substituent to the reaction center, depends on the temperature and this dependence appears in the entropy of the reaction. This situation, which is a sort of solvent effect, accounts for a large part of the effect of substituents on the thermodynamics of the ionization of substituted benzoic acids.[65]

Consider, as an example, the fact that the acid strength of p-nitrophenol is some 15 times greater than that of m-nitrophenol, although the heats of ionization are identical; the difference appears entirely in the entropies. This situation is understandable if one considers the solvation energies as well as the internal energies of the reaction, as described by Hepler.[66] The observed difference in the free energies of ionization, $\Delta\Delta F_{obs}$, is composed of the differences in the enthalpy and entropy between the acids and the anions ($\Delta\Delta H_{int}$, $\Delta\Delta S_{int}$) and the corresponding quantities resulting from interaction of the reactants and products with the solvent ($\Delta\Delta H_{solv}$, $\Delta\Delta S_{solv}$), as shown in equation 16. For a comparison of members of a structurally related series the difference in the internal en-

$$\Delta\Delta F_{obs} = \Delta\Delta H_{int} - T\,\Delta\Delta S_{int} + \Delta\Delta H_{solv} - T\,\Delta\Delta S_{solv} \qquad (16)$$

tropy of ionization, $\Delta\Delta S_{int}$, is so small that it ordinarily may be neglected because the change in the amount of order in the reactants

[64] E. Tommila and C. N. Hinshelwood, *J. Chem. Soc.* **1938**, 1801.

[65] L. P. Hammett,[61] page 83.

[66] L. G. Hepler, *J. Am. Chem. Soc.* 85, 3089 (1963); H. C. Ko, W. F. O'Hara, T. Hu, and L. G. Hepler, *Ibid.*, 86, 1003 (1964).

and products is relatively constant throughout such a series.[66,67] This leaves equation 17. Now, there is reason to expect that the

$$\Delta\Delta F_{obs} = \Delta\Delta H_{int} + \Delta\Delta H_{solv} - T\Delta\Delta S_{solv} \qquad (17)$$

solvation terms, $\Delta\Delta H_{solv}$ and $T\Delta\Delta S_{solv}$, will vary in such a way that they will partially or completely cancel each other out at the temperatures at which most experimental measurements are made. This follows both from theories of solution and from experimental measurements in a large number of different systems. In the case of the substituted nitrophenols, for example, the reason for the greater acidity of the *para* isomer is believed to be the greater resonance stabilization of the anion by the *para* than by the *meta* nitro group. The charge density on the phenolic oxygen atom of the anion, therefore, will be greater for the *meta*-substituted compound. This higher charge density will cause a stronger interaction with solvating water molecules than in the case of the *para* isomer (more negative ΔH_{solv}), but this stronger interaction will also lead to a higher degree of orientation of the water molecules around the negative charge (more negative ΔS_{solv}), which will tend to cancel out the change in the enthalpy term. This type of compensation appears to be a widespread phenomenon, so that enthalpies and entropies of solvation can show very large changes indeed, with very little effect on the free energies of solvation. To the extent that this cancellation is complete, and it appears to be nearly complete in these ionization processes at ordinary temperatures, we are left with the conclusion that the observed differences in the free energy are a rather good measure of the differences in the internal enthalpy of the reaction (equation 18). This conclusion is fully in

$$\Delta\Delta F_{obs} = \Delta\Delta H_{int} \qquad (18)$$

accord with what would be expected from chemical intuition and from somewhat different theoretical approaches in a great many reaction series, in which the effects of substituents are better correlated with the observed free energies (i.e., log K or log k) than with the enthalpies of reaction.[68,69] In fact, enthalpy and, particularly, entropy, determinations are most useful in providing an indication of the differences in solvation of the reactants, transition state, and products of the reaction; they do not provide a reliable guide to dif-

[67] K. S. Pitzer, *J. Am. Chem. Soc.* **59**, 2365 (1937).

[68] C. D. Ritchie and W. F. Sager, *Progr. Phys. Org. Chem.* **2**, 323 (1964).

[69] R. P. Bell, "The Proton in Chemistry," chap. 5, Cornell University Press, Ithaca, N. Y., 1959.

ferences in internal structure and stability or to the potential energies of these species.

It would be expected that in order to take substrate molecules
from dilute solution and transfer them to the active site of the enzyme in a state which resembles the transition state of the reaction,
both enthalpy and entropy changes are required. These will not be
easily separable, even theoretically, because the attainment of productive binding with a proper alignment and order of both the enzyme and the substrate will almost certainly require some bending
and compression of bonds and atoms, i.e., a change in enthalpy, and
the occurrence of strain or distortion is unlikely to occur without an
accompanying entropic contribution from restriction of motion. Thus,
one can think of both "entropic strain" and "enthalpic strain" but,
as in the analysis of approximation effects (Chap. 1), the difference
is usually difficult to define clearly on the basis of experimentally
determined thermodynamic quantities.

G. OSCILLATING ENZYMES

Suppose that an enzyme can exist in two states: state E', in which
it induces strain in a substrate to facilitate conversion to product,
and state E, in which it induces strain in the product to convert it
back to substrate. A system of this kind is shown schematically in
Fig. 7. Now, if there were a mechanism by which the enzyme

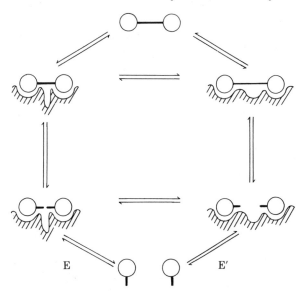

Fig 7. Catalysis of bond formation and cleavage by an
oscillating enzyme.[1]

could be forced into the states E and E′ in a cyclic manner with sufficient driving force, it could catalyze the reaction in both directions. In the system shown in Fig. 7 this would involve a pulling apart of the substrate and a pushing together of the products. A mechanism of this kind could avoid the limitation of previously discussed mechanisms, that is, that the enzyme must force both the substrate and products to resemble the same transition state; in such an oscillating mechanism the substrate can be forced toward a transition state which resembles the product and the products into a transition state which resembles the substrate. A serious theoretical objection to such a mechanism is that it would constitute a violation of microscopic reversibility because different pathways would be followed for the forward and reverse reactions.

Another serious conceptual problem with oscillating enzyme mechanisms of this kind is the definition of the force which would cause the enzyme to oscillate between the two conformations with sufficient driving force to carry the substrate along and cause it to undergo reaction. It is difficult to conceive of a spring-like oscillation of a protein molecule that would be set in motion by thermal energy and would not be damped out by random internal vibrations and encounters with solvent molecules. Such oscillations would require a mechanism for the focusing or coordinating of thermal energy in a cooperative manner which has not yet been clearly envisioned. It might be suggested that the binding forces to the substrate could be used to force the enzyme into the conformation E′ and the binding forces to the product to force it into the conformation E, but the difference in the structure of the substrate and product is ordinarily not sufficient to provide much driving force for two such different changes.

One mechanism by which it appears to be possible to obtain catalysis in one direction by an oscillation mechanism involves the binding of an activator A to the ES complex to facilitate the reaction by the induction of a conformation change to E′S (equation 19).

$$E + S \rightleftharpoons ES \overset{\pm A}{\rightleftharpoons} ESA$$
$$\updownarrow \qquad\qquad \updownarrow \qquad\qquad \updownarrow$$
$$E' + S \rightleftharpoons E'S \rightleftharpoons E'SA \rightleftharpoons E'PA \rightleftharpoons E + P + A \qquad\qquad (19)$$

In this mechanism the binding energy of the activator molecule provides the driving force for the conformation change. It is necessary that the activator bind only to the ES complex, in a compulsory, ordered mechanism. There is no violation of microscopic reversibility here, but effective catalysis by an oscillation mechanism in the reverse direction would require a different activator, which would induce a different conformation change.

H. CONTROL MECHANISMS AND ALLOSTERIC ENZYMES[70]

A detailed discussion of the role of conformation changes in the *regulation* of enzyme activity is beyond the scope of this volume, and only a few aspects of this subject will be mentioned here. Enzymes frequently show inhibition or activation in the presence of physiological concentrations of metabolites which are precursors or products in the metabolic pathway of which the enzyme is a part. This behavior is important in the regulation of the activity of enzymes in such a way that concentrations of metabolites may be maintained at physiological levels. This control of activity may be mediated by changes in enzyme conformation caused by activators, inhibitors, or the substrate itself, and often involves interactions between subunits of the enzyme. Two aspects of this subject are of particular importance: the cooperative nature of the interactions and the control of activity through binding of a molecule to a site other than the active site. Changes in enzyme activity which fall in this category are frequently called "allosteric" effects, but the use of this term is, unfortunately, not restricted to a single definition.

Cooperative interactions are often manifested in the well known sigmoidal curves relating enzyme activity to the concentration of a substrate or activator. The fact that the initial slope of such a curve is concave upward means that the rate is proportional to more than the first power of the substrate or activator concentration; i.e., two or more molecules must bind to the enzyme to give maximal activity. This means that binding to separate sites has more than an additive effect and requires that there be some interaction of the binding sites with each other. The different binding sites are usually on different subunits of the enzyme, so that this interaction represents an interaction of the subunits with each other. The interaction can cause a change in either the maximal velocity, the binding of substrate to the enzyme, or both, and it is not always immediately apparent from the kinetics of the reaction which of these is the case. Mathematical models of varying degrees of complexity have been developed to explain this type of behav-

[70] D. E. Atkinson, *Ann. Rev. Biochem.* **35,** 85 (1966); E. R. Stadtman, *Advan. Enzymol.* **28,** 41 (1966); D. E. Koshland, Jr., and K. E. Neet, *Ann. Rev. Biochem.* **37,** 359 (1968).

ior.[71,72] However, the number of variables in these models is so large that it is difficult or impossible to distinguish among them from the kinetics of a given reaction, and the mechanism of these effects can usually be approached more successfully by examination of the physical and chemical properties of the system. Aspartate transcarbamylase, for example, has been shown by physical studies to consist of two catalytically active subunits which can be separated from four smaller inhibitory subunits. The inhibitory subunits can bind inhibitor molecules even after they are separated from the catalytic subunits.[73]

The enzyme xanthosine 5'-phosphate aminase illustrates some of the characteristics of regulatory behavior which may result from binding to a site other than the active site. This enzyme is subject to noncompetitive inhibition by the antibiotic psicofuranine, which is structurally related to regulatory metabolites for this system. As in the case of many enzymes of this kind, the inhibitory activity can be lost upon the addition of compounds which would be expected to alter the structure of the protein, such as urea and sulfhydryl reagents, and by photooxidation in the presence of methylene blue. This occurs without destruction of the catalytic ability and suggests that the site for inhibition is different from the catalytic site. Treatment of the enzyme with mercaptoethanol results in a partial desensitization toward inhibition, although the desensitized enzyme still binds inhibitor. This leads to the further conclusion that there is a requirement for a region of intact protein structure between the catalytic and regulatory sites through which the regulatory effect may be mediated. Sedimentation of the enzyme in a sucrose gradient provides no indication of a role of dissociation into subunits in causing these changes.[74]

[71] J. Monod, J.-P. Changeux, and F. Jacob, *J. Mol. Biol.* **6**, 306 (1963).

[72] D. E. Koshland, Jr., G. Némethy, and D. Filmer, *Biochemistry* **5**, 365 (1966).

[73] J. C. Gerhart and A. B. Pardee, *Fed. Proc.* **23**, 727 (1964); J. C. Gerhart and H. K. Schachman, *Biochemistry* **4**, 1054 (1965).

[74] H. Kuramitsu and H. S. Moyed, *J. Biol. Chem.* **241**, 1596 (1966).

part two

Forces in
Aqueous Solution

It is not generally appreciated how little is known either experimentally or theoretically about the forces which exist between solute molecules in aqueous solution. Some understanding of the nature and strength of these forces is of fundamental importance for an understanding of the mechanism of reactions which take place between molecules in water and is of particular importance for reactions in which interactions between the reactants at points other than the reacting atoms lead to rate accelerations. In enzyme catalyzed reactions these forces provide the handles through which enzymes exert their specific catalytic activity by providing the energy for binding of substrates and, in all probability, by providing a significant part of the energy for overcoming the free-energy barrier of activation of the catalyzed reaction.

The most important characteristic of all intermolecular forces in aqueous solution is that these forces are more dependent on the properties of this extraordinary solvent than on the nature and strength of the intermolecular forces themselves. The interaction of water with ions, dipoles, and hydrogen-bond acceptors or donors is so strong as to cause a leveling or disappearance of most of the forces which would cause a strong intermolecular interaction in a vacuum or a nonpolar solvent. Thus, most intermolecular forces in aqueous solution represent a small difference between large numbers, that is, the difference between the energy of interaction of two molecules A and B with each other and the energy of their interaction with water (equation 1). In fact, the most important noncova-

$$A \cdots B + H_2O \cdots H_2O \; \rightleftharpoons \; A \cdots H_2O + B \cdots H_2O \tag{1}$$

lent intermolecular forces in water are almost certainly a consequence of the strong interaction of the water molecules with each other, rather than of a direct interaction of the solute molecules with each other. The large cohesive energy density of water which results from the large number of hydrogen bonds per unit of volume of this solvent makes it difficult to pull water molecules apart in order to insert a weakly interacting molecule into the solution. It is, therefore, the relatively nonpolar molecules which have the *smallest* tendency to form intermolecular bonds in a vacuum and cannot interact strongly with water that are squeezed out of an aqueous solution and forced to interact with each other. This paradoxical type of interaction is rather like phlogiston—it is the absence of a potent factor which leads to the observed effect.

6
Hydrogen Bonds[1]

A. EVIDENCE FOR HYDROGEN BONDING IN AQUEOUS SOLUTION

1. RATE ACCELERATIONS

Several examples of reactions in aqueous solution for which there is evidence that hydrogen bonding causes rate accelerations have been described in the chapters on approximation, covalent catalysis, and general acid-base catalysis. The amount of stabilization of a transition state that may be made available by such hydrogen bonding is moderate but real and is considerably larger than the stabilization of most ground-state complexes by hydrogen bonding in aqueous solution, presumably because the basicity or acidity of a transition state can be much larger than that which can exist in ground states at equilibrium (Chap. 3).

[1] For further reading see G. C. Pimentel and A. L. McClellan, "The Hydrogen Bond," W. H. Freeman and Company, San Francisco, 1960.

It has frequently been suggested that hydrogen bonding is responsible for the rapid reactions of acyl groups in acylated derivatives of ribose such as 2'(3')-aminoacyl–RNA, a system of particular interest to biochemists. Examination of the rates of hydrolysis and hydroxylaminolysis of model compounds bearing an acylated hydroxyl group on a 5-membered ring has shown that there is a definite rate-accelerating effect of either a *cis* or a *trans* hydroxyl group adjacent to the acyl group, but that this effect is not large, usually near one order of magnitude, and that a significant part of the enhanced reactivity of acylated ribose derivatives may be attributed simply to the inductive effects of the adjacent hydroxyl group and the ring oxygen atom.[2] Furthermore, although these compounds are "energy-rich" with a free energy of hydrolysis comparable to that of the terminal phosphate group of ATP, their high group potential at neutral pH is a general property of esters and is not significantly higher than that of other esters without an adjacent ribose hydroxyl group.[3] A contribution of hydrogen bonding to the increased reaction rates of these compounds could be brought about by hydrogen bonding to either the carbonyl or the ether oxygen atoms of the ester, and infrared examination of *cis*-and *trans*-cyclopentanediolmonoacetates shows that *both* of these types of hydrogen bonding (in carbon tetrachloride) are associated with rate enhancements (in water) (Table I).[4] The observed rate enhancement of 15-to 30-fold which is caused by an adjacent hydroxyl group includes a factor of 3 from the inductive effect, which is seen in the compound with an adjacent methoxy group, and a further factor of 5 to 10 which is specific to the hydroxyl group and has been called an "internal solvation effect."[4] This enhancement presumably involves hydrogen bonding to an oxygen atom of the ester in the transition state by the adjacent hydroxyl group instead of by a molecule of solvent water, an interpretation which is supported by the relatively favorable entropy of activation for the hydrolysis of the compounds with an adjacent hydroxyl group (Table I).

2. INTERMOLECULAR, MONOFUNCTIONAL HYDROGEN BONDS

The strongest known hydrogen bond is that in the $(F-H-F)^-$ ion. The formation of this bond by the addition of hydrogen fluoride to a fluoride salt, which is accompanied by little change in the crystal

[2] H. G. Zachau and W. Karau, *Ber.* **93**, 1830 (1960).

[3] P. Berg, F. H. Bergmann, E. J. Ofengand, and M. Dieckmann, *J. Biol. Chem.* **236**, 1726 (1961); W. P. Jencks, S. Cordes, and J. Carriuolo, *Ibid.* **235**, 3608 (1960).

[4] T. C. Bruice and T. H. Fife, *J. Am. Chem. Soc.* **84**, 1973 (1962).

Table I Effect of adjacent hydroxyl groups on the rates of hydrolysis of acetate esters[4]

Ester		$k_{OH}-73°,$ M^{-1} min^{-1}	$T \Delta S,$ kcal/mole
OAc (cyclopentyl)		9.3	−10.7
H ⋯OAc ⋯H OCH$_3$	trans	31.6	−9.2
H ⋯OAc ⋯H OH	trans	174	−6.3 (hydrogen bond to $C=O$ in CCl_4)
H ⋯OAc ⋯OH H	cis	309	−2.7 (hydrogen bond to $C-O-C$ in CCl_4)

lattice structure, is exothermic to the extent of -37 kcal/mole (equation 1).[5] A more usual energy for hydrogen-bond formation in

$$(CH_3)_4N^+F^-(s) + HF(g) \longrightarrow (CH_3)_4N^+FHF^-(s) \qquad (1)$$

nonpolar solvents or the solid state is on the order of -5 to -10 kcal/mole.

Water acts as both a hydrogen donor and acceptor, so that the formation of intermolecular hydrogen bonds between two solute molecules in water requires that hydrogen bonds of each of these molecules to water be broken (equation 2); the stability of any such

$$A-H\cdots OH_2 + B\cdots HOH \rightleftharpoons A-H\cdots B + HOH\cdots OH_2 \qquad (2)$$

hydrogen bond, therefore, depends only on the *differences* in the stabilities of the bonds on the two sides of equation 2, not on the absolute strength of the bond in $A-H\cdots B$. Although it is frequently suggested that hydrogen bonds provide an important driving force for intermolecular association in water, there is little experimental

[5] S. A. Harrell and D. H. McDaniel, *J. Am. Chem. Soc.* **86**, 4497 (1964).

data to provide quantitative support for such suggestions and, in fact, the *only* case in which there is direct evidence for the spontaneous formation of a monofunctional intermolecular hydrogen bond in aqueous solution is that of the bifluoride ion. Even this bond has only a small fraction of the strength in water that it has in the solid state. The nuclear magnetic resonance absorption of the fluoride ion in water exhibits a shift upon the addition of acid as the $(F-H-F)^-$ ion is formed. From the dependence of this shift upon the concentrations of the reactants an equilibrium constant, $K = [FHF^-]/[HF][F^-]$, of about $4\ M^{-1}$ for the formation of the hydrogen bond in the presence of $0.25\,M$ salt may be calculated.[6] Similar values have been obtained from potentiometric titrations of hydrogen fluoride at different concentrations,[7] but the latter values are, in themselves, less convincing because of the problems of correcting for specific activity coefficient effects in such titrations. The leveling effect of water as a solvent is dramatically illustrated by the fact that an equilibrium constant of $4\ M^{-1}$ corresponds to a free energy of association of only -0.8 kcal/mole, compared with the heat of formation of this hydrogen bond of -37 kcal/mole in the solid state. It is unlikely that entropy changes account for more than a very small fraction of this difference. There is indirect evidence for the formation of the analogous hydrogen-bonded species $(H_2PO_4-H-O_4PH_2)^-$ and $(IO_3-H-O_3I)^-$ in water, with formation constants of $3\,M^{-1}$ and $4\,M^{-1}$, respectively.[8]

Since hydrogen bonds are strengthened by increasing acidity of the hydrogen donor and increasing basicity of the hydrogen acceptor, the most favorable situation for hydrogen-bond formation should exist in a conjugate acid-base pair, such as acetic acid–acetate ion, which have the maximum possible acidity and basicity relative to each other (1). It has been suggested that the small deviations

$$
\begin{array}{ccc}
O & & O \\
\parallel & & \parallel \\
RCO^{\cdots} & H- & OCR
\end{array}
$$

1

from the theoretical titration curves which are observed in the acetic acid–acetate system with increasing concentration are the result of

[6] R. Haque and L. W. Reeves, *J. Am. Chem. Soc.* **89**, 250 (1967); K. Schaumberg and C. Deverell, *Ibid.* **90**, 2495 (1968).

[7] H. H. Broene and T. De Vries, *J. Am. Chem. Soc.* **69**, 1644 (1947).

[8] M. Selvaratnam and M. Spiro, *Trans. Faraday Soc.* **61**, 360 (1965); A. D. Pethybridge and J. E. Prue, *Ibid.* **63**, 2019 (1967).

such association, but the association constant of 0.1 M^{-1} indicates that this hydrogen bond, if it exists at all, is even weaker than that of the hydrogen fluoride system in water.[9]   It is difficult or impossible to distinguish such a weak association from salt or activity coefficient effects on titration behavior, and there are other difficulties in interpretation in such systems.[10]   Furthermore, the association, if it does exist, may be the result of hydrophobic bonding rather than of hydrogen bonding, since the apparent association constants increase as the size of the hydrocarbon chain is progressively increased from formate.[11]

3. INTRAMOLECULAR HYDROGEN BONDS

The evidence is much stronger for the existence of *intramolecular* carboxylic acid–carboxylate hydrogen bonds in water. There is a large entropic advantage for such hydrogen bonding because it does not require the bringing together of separate molecules from the solution. In fact, the existence of intramolecular hydrogen bonds does not show that carboxylic acid–carboxylate hydrogen bonds have an appreciable intrinsic stability in water, because they are found only in molecules with a structure such that there is almost no alternative to hydrogen bonding; if no hydrogen bond were formed, the carboxylate group would be forced into an energetically unfavorable position relative to the carboxylic acid group, with a close apposition of the negative charge of the anion and the negative end of the carbonyl dipole of the acid (for example, 2).

2

The existence of intramolecular hydrogen bonds was first inferred from the special stability of the monoanions of dicarboxylic acids in which such hydrogen bonding is possible. This stabilization is manifested in a larger acid dissociation constant K_1 of the free acid to form the monoanion and a smaller dissociation constant K_2 of the

[9] D. L. Martin and F. J. C. Rossotti, *Proc. Chem. Soc.* **1959**, 60.

[10] I. Danielsson and T. Suominen, *Acta Chem. Scand.* **17**, 979 (1963); H. N. Farrer and F. J. C. Rossotti, *Ibid.* p. 1824.

[11] E. E. Schrier, M. Pottle, and H. A. Scheraga, *J. Am. Chem. Soc.* **86**, 3444 (1964).

monoanion to the dianion, compared with acids in which hydrogen bonding is not possible. This leads to a larger difference, ΔpK, between pK_1 and pK_2 for dicarboxylic acids in which hydrogen bonding is possible. These differences are evident in the dissociation constants for maleic acid compared to fumaric acid (equation 3).

pK 3.03, 4.54   1.91   6.33

ΔpK 1.5   4.4

Fumaric acid   Maleic acid   (3)

However, such a treatment is a serious oversimplification because it neglects electrostatic interactions between the carboxyl groups: the energetically unfavorable interaction of the two adjacent negative charges in the dianion, which will be more important for maleic than for fumaric acid, and the several ion-dipole and dipole-dipole interactions in the other reactants. The magnitudes of these electrostatic effects are difficult to evaluate because of uncertainty regarding the microscopic dielectric constant in the region around and between the carboxyl groups. Westheimer and Kirkwood approached this problem by assuming that the acid exists in a cavity with a low dielectric constant of about 2.0, similar to that of a hydrocarbon, which is surrounded by solvent with a normal dielectric constant.[12] The change in pK caused by the electrostatic interaction can then be treated in terms of an "effective" dielectric constant D_E, which is based on the model and an assumed geometry of the cavity according to equations 4 and 5 for charge-charge and

$$\Delta pK = \frac{e^2}{2.303 D_E R k T}$$

(4)

$$\Delta pK = \frac{e\mu \cos \zeta}{2.303 D_E R^2 k T}$$

(5)

[12] J. G. Kirkwood and F. H. Westheimer, *J. Chem. Phys.* **6**, 506, (1938); F. H. Westheimer and J.G. Kirkwood, *Ibid.*, p. 513.

charge-dipole interactions, respectively. In equation 5, μ is the dipole moment of the dipole and ζ is the angle between the axis of the dipole and the line joining it to the charge. Tanford has pointed out that this model is very sensitive to the depth of the charge and dipole within the cavity and has found that calculations of the electrostatic interactions for a considerable number of ionizing groups are consistent with the assumption that charges are 1.0 Å and dipoles are 1.5 Å below the surface of the cavity.[13]

These models obviously do not correspond closely to the physical reality of a complex situation; the "effective dielectric constant" and "depth within the cavity" are semiempirical ways of dealing with the problems of the microscopic dielectric constant, dielectric saturation, the distance of closest approach of solvent molecules, and other variables. Nevertheless, they do provide self-consistent estimates of electrostatic effects on the ionization constants of a number of ionizing groups which are not hydrogen-bonded and should give at least a rough estimate of the electrostatic contribution to the ΔpK which is observed in dicarboxylic acids which are capable of hydrogen bonding. Such estimates suggest that the electrostatic effect can account for a major part or all of the abnormality in the dissociation constants of maleic compared to fumaric acid and of a number of other dicarboxylic acids.[14,15] The uncertainties in the calculations do not permit the definite conclusion that hydrogen bonding is not significant, but they do require that a different type of evidence be obtained if the occurrence of hydrogen bonding is to be established in these compounds.

Much larger values of ΔpK are observed for carboxylic acids with bulky substituents which force the carboxyl groups into close relationship with each other: the pK values of *racemic* 2,3-di-t-butylsuccinic acid are 2.20 and 10.25, giving the very large ΔpK value of 8.[16] The large ΔpK in these acids may be attributed either to the formation of a strong hydrogen bond in the monoanion, which is favored by the large substituents, or to a particularly unfavorable electrostatic interaction of the two adjacent negative charges in the dianion, which may be enhanced by interference of the substituents with solvation.

A simpler and more empirical approach is to compare the pK value of a dicarboxylic acid in which intramolecular hydrogen bond-

[13] C. Tanford, *J. Am. Chem. Soc.* **79**, 5348 (1957).

[14] F. H. Westheimer and M. W. Shookhoff, *J. Am. Chem. Soc.* **61**, 555 (1939).

[15] R. E. Dodd, R. E. Miller, and W. F. K. Wynne-Jones, *J. Chem. Soc.* **1961**, 2790.

[16] P. K. Glasoe and L. Eberson, *J. Phys. Chem.* **68**, 1560 (1964).

ing is suspected with that of the corresponding monoester (equation 6).[17] The polar effects of a hydrogen atom in the diacid and of an

$$\tag{6}$$

alkyl group in the monoester are not significantly different, so that any special stabilization of the monoanion of the diacid caused by hydrogen bonding should be apparent in a lower pK_1 of the diacid compared with the monoester after a correction of the ionization constant of the diacid by a statistical factor of two (there are two equivalent groups in the acid which can ionize and only one in the ester). The difference in the pK's of maleic acid (pK 1.91) and its monoester (pK 3.08) corresponds to about a 14-fold difference in ionization constants, of which 7-fold might therefore be attributed to stabilization of the acid monoanion by hydrogen bonding. This effect is probably real, but it is not large.

The existence of a cyclic hydrogen bond in dicarboxylic acid monoanions of suitable structure, such as maleate, is further suggested by the observation that upon ionization of such dicarboxylic acids to the monoanion there is a *downfield* chemical shift of the nuclear magnetic resonance absorption band of the skeletal protons, in contrast to the *upfield* shift that is normally observed for the protons on the α and β carbon atoms of carboxylic acids which cannot undergo hydrogen bonding, such as fumarate.[18] The theoretical interpretation of this shift is not yet certain.

Formation of a carboxylic acid–carboxylate hydrogen bond should decrease the bond length of the carbonyl group in the carboxylate ion by making it resemble a carboxylic acid and should increase the bond length of the carbonyl group of the carboxylic acid by making it resemble a carboxylate ion (equation 7). These shifts

[17] F. H. Westheimer and O. T. Benfey, *J. Am. Chem. Soc.* **78**, 5309 (1956).

[18] B. L. Silver, Z. Luz, S. Peller, and J. Reuben, *J. Phys. Chem.* **70**, 1435 (1966).

$$
\underset{RC \rightleftharpoons O}{\overset{O}{\Vert}} \;\; + \;\; H-O-\underset{}{\overset{O}{\overset{\Vert}{C}}}R \;\; \rightleftharpoons \;\; RC \text{---} O \cdots H-O-\underset{}{\overset{\delta^{-}O}{\overset{|}{C}}}R \qquad (7)
$$

should be apparent in the stretching frequencies of these groups in the infrared region. Infrared spectra in deuterium oxide solution of acids which might be expected to undergo intramolecular hydrogen bonding have given suggestive, but not altogether consistent, evidence for such hydrogen bonding.[15,19,20] The carboxylic acid group of di-n-propylmalonate monoanion shows the expected shift to lower frequency compared with malonate monoanion, suggesting the occurrence of hydrogen bonding in the former compound, but maleate monoanion shows a small shift in the opposite direction compared with fumarate (Table II). There is no increase in the carboxylate frequency of di-n-propylmalonate compared with malonate, but there is a large shift in salicylate compared with benzoate, in the direction expected for hydrogen bonding in the former compound. Larger differences are observed if the *changes* in frequency which occur upon ionization of the neighboring carboxylic acid group in a given compound are compared.[20] However, the interpretation of these differences as evidence for hydrogen bonding is not unequivocal, and the changes in the carboxylate frequency appear to be less a reflection of an abnormal frequency in the monoanion than in the dianion, which might be the result of an electrostatic interaction.

The most convincing evidence for the existence of intramolecular hydrogen bonds comes from measurements of the rates of proton

[19] L. Eberson, *Acta Chem. Scand.* **13**, 224 (1959).

[20] D. Chapman, D. R. Lloyd, and R. H. Prince, *J. Chem. Soc.* **1964**, 550.

Table II Infrared carbonyl stretching frequencies of carboxylic acid monoanions in deuterium oxide solution[20]

Monoanion	ν —COOH, cm^{-1}	ν^{asym} —COO$^-$, cm^{-1}
Maleate	1,698	1,570
Fumarate	1,690	1,577
Malonate	1,698	1,588
Di-n-propylmalonate	1,677	1,586
Salicylate		1,621
Benzoate		1,553

removal by hydroxide ion from hydrogen-bonded carboxylic acids.[21,22] The rate constants for proton abstraction from benzoic and acetic acids of 3.5×10^{10} and 4.5×10^{10} M^{-1} sec^{-1}, respectively, are at the diffusion-controlled limit and are independent of the acidity of the acid. In contrast, the rate constants for proton abstraction from di-n-propylmalonate and maleate monoanions and from the salicylate group of a dye molecule are 5.3×10^7, 7.4×10^8, and 1.4×10^7 M^{-1} sec^{-1}, respectively.[21] The rate constants for a larger series of monanions vary inversely as the ratio of the two acid dissociation constants K_1/K_2.[22] The reduction of several orders of magnitude of these rates below the diffusion-controlled value which is observed for other acids means that some factor must be interfering with the reaction and it is difficult to attribute this to any cause other than internal hydrogen bonding, which decreases the availability of the proton for reaction with hydroxide ion.

An example of the ability of hydroxylic solvents to break a hydrogen bond even in a case which one might expect to be unusually favorable for hydrogen-bond formation is found in salicylaldehyde and o-hydroxybenzophenones.[23] Benzaldehydes and benzophenones ordinarily exhibit a phosphoresence by emission of light from a triplet state. In nonpolar solvents the presence of an *ortho* hydroxyl group results in the disappearance of this phosphoresence because of rapid quenching of the excited triplet state by the hydrogen-bonded proton. The addition of a hydroxylic solvent such as ethanol causes a return of the normal phosphoresence, presumably because intermolecular hydrogen bonding to this solvent breaks up the intramolecular hydrogen bond to the carbonyl group (equation 8).

$$\tag{8}$$

4. PROTEINS, PEPTIDES, AND UREA

The most significant hydrogen bond which is involved in the maintainance of protein structure is that between amide groups in the

[21] M. Eigen and W. Kruse, *Z. Naturforsch.* **18b**, 857 (1963).

[22] J. L. Haslam, E. M. Eyring, W. W. Epstein, R. P. Jensen, and C. W. Jaget, *J. Am. Chem. Soc.* **87**, 4247 (1965).

[23] A. A. Lamola and L. J. Sharp, *J. Phys. Chem.* **70**, 2634 (1966).

α helix and other regular protein structures (3), and it would be of

$$H-N \overset{\underset{|}{R'}}{\diagup} C=O \cdots H-N \overset{\overset{R}{|}}{\diagup} C=O$$
$$\qquad\qquad\qquad\qquad\qquad\underset{R'}{|}$$

3

considerable interest to know whether such interamide hydrogen bonds have sufficient stability in water to provide a significant driving force toward the formation of these structures. It has been pointed out in Sec. A, Part 2, that, with the exception of special cases such as the bifluoride ion, monofunctional hydrogen bonds between small molecules have little or no stability in aqueous solution. This generalization holds also for bonds between amides. The occurrence of intermolecular hydrogen bonding between molecules of N-methylacetamide in carbon tetrachloride solution is shown by the change in the overtone N—H stretching frequency of the amide from the higher-frequency absorption band of the monomer to the broad, lower-frequency band of the hydrogen-bonded dimer or polymer which occurs as the concentration of amide is increased from 0.01 to 1.0 M in this solvent (Fig. 1).[24] In dioxane solution the oxygen atoms of the solvent compete with the amide carbonyl groups as hydrogen acceptors, and in this solvent it is necessary to increase the amide concentration to 3 M to obtain the absorption band of the aggregated form. In water, which competes as both a hydrogen donor and acceptor, the absorption band of the aggregate does not appear so long as there is water present to interact with the amide; the intermolecularly hydrogen-bonded species is formed only in almost pure N-methylacetamide, as the concentration of amide becomes larger than the concentration of water (Fig. 1). These results suggest that hydrogen bonds between individual amide molecules do not have appreciable stability in aqueous solution. The change in the activity coefficient of urea in concentrated solution may be interpreted in terms of the formation of a hydrogen-bonded urea dimer,[25] but similar near-infared studies of urea and of δ-valerolactam, both of which might be expected to form a cyclic

[24] I. M. Klotz, and J. S. Franzen, *J. Am. Chem. Soc.* **84**, 3461 (1962).

[25] J. A. Schellman, *Compt. Rend. Trav. Lab. Carlsberg* **29**, 223 (1955).

dimer **(4)**, do not provide evidence for the formation of stable hydrogen-bonded complexes of this kind in water.[24, 26]

4

[26] H. Susi, S. N. Timasheff, and J. S. Ard, *J. Biol. Chem.* **239**, 3051 (1964).

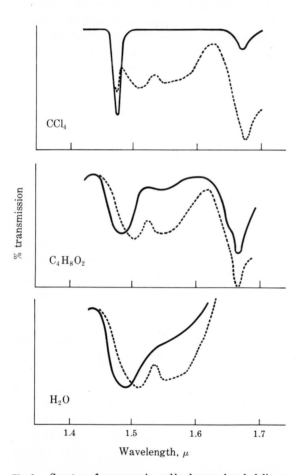

Fig 1. Spectra of monomeric and hydrogen-bonded dimers or aggregates of *N*-methylacetamide in the near-infrared region in carbon tetrachloride, dioxane, and water solution. Solute concentrations in CCl_4: ———— , 0.01 M; ····, 1 M; in dioxane: ———— 0.2 M; ···· 3 M; and in water: ———— 7 M; ···· 12.5 M.[24]

After the realization that there is no firm evidence to support the previously widely accepted hypotheses that interamide hydrogen bonds provide the stabilization energy which is responsible for the maintenance of the native structure of proteins and that denaturing agents like urea and guanidine hydrochloride cause denaturation by competing with the normal hydrogen-bonding partner to form hydrogen bonds between the denaturing agent and the peptide chain,[27] the pendulum of opinion has swung rather sharply to a point at which it is frequently suggested that such hydrogen bonding does not provide a significant driving force for the maintenance of protein structure in aqueous solution or for the denaturation of proteins by urea or guanidine. This view received some further support when it became apparent that urea and guanidine increase the solubility (i.e., lower the activity coefficient) of nonpolar molecules and should, therefore, promote denaturation by facilitating the exposure to the solvent of the hydrophobic groups which are normally in the interior of the protein.[28-30]

The pendulum is now beginning to swing back to a more central position, although it has by no means come to rest. In the first place, there is no doubt that interpeptide hydrogen bonds do exist in α-helical and β structures in the interior of proteins, even if they do not provide a large driving force for the formation of such structures. At the very least, the formation of hydrogen bonds represents the most stable arrangement for amide groups in the interior of a protein under conditions in which they cannot be exposed to water. Furthermore, the interaction of denaturing agents with model peptides and amino acids and with many (not all) proteins requires the presence of free hydrogen atoms on the nitrogen atoms of the denaturing agent.[31-33] Urea and guanidine hydrochloride cause a large increase in the solubility of acetyltetraglycine ethyl ester (ATGEE) in water (Fig. 2). This means that solutions of these

$$\underset{\text{ATGEE}}{CH_3\overset{O}{\overset{\|}{C}}NHCH_2\overset{O}{\overset{\|}{C}}NHCH_2\overset{O}{\overset{\|}{C}}NHCH_2\overset{O}{\overset{\|}{C}}NHCH_2\overset{O}{\overset{\|}{C}}OC_2H_5}$$

[27] A. E. Mirsky and L. Pauling, *Proc. Natl. Acad. Sci. U.S.* **22**, 439 (1936).

[28] W. Kauzmann, *Advan. Protein Chem.* **14**, 1 (1959).

[29] D. B. Wetlaufer, S. K. Malik, L. Stoller, and R. L. Coffin, *J. Am. Chem. Soc.* **86**, 508 (1964); P. L. Whitney and C. Tanford, *J. Biol. Chem.* **237**, PC1735 (1962).

[30] Y. Nozaki and C. Tanford, *J. Biol. Chem.* **238**, 4074 (1963).

[31] J. P. Greenstein, *J. Biol. Chem.* **125**, 501 (1938); **128**, 233 (1939); J. P. Greenstein and J. Edsall, *Ibid.* **133**, 397 (1940).

[32] J. A. Gordon and W. P. Jencks, *Biochemistry* **2**, 47 (1963).

[33] D. R. Robinson and W. P. Jencks, *J. Am. Chem. Soc.* **87**, 2462 (1965).

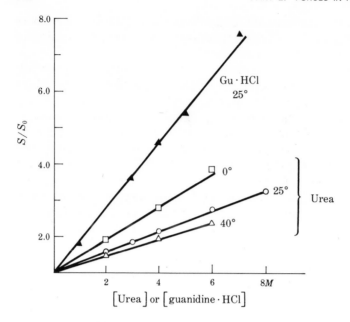

Fig 2.   Solubility of acetyltetraglycine ethyl ester in aqueous urea solutions at 0, 25, and 40° and in guanidine hydrochloride solutions at 25°.[33]

denaturing agents have an energetically favorable interaction with this compound, which is a model for the amide groups of a peptide chain.   They would, therefore, be expected to promote protein denaturation by a similar interaction with the amide groups of a protein. This effect is reduced if the hydrogen atoms of the denaturing agent are replaced with alkyl groups, and tetramethylurea and tetramethylguanidine hydrochloride cause a *decrease* in the solubility of ATGEE. The interaction with the peptide is not a "hydrophobic" effect because alkyl substitution causes an increase in the solubilization of nonpolar solutes by urea and guanidine hydrochloride.[33]   The same requirement for free hydrogen atoms is seen in the denaturation of bovine serum albumin by denaturing agents of this kind.[32]   This requirement for free hydrogen atoms is most easily explained by an interaction of the denaturing agent with peptide groups through hydrogen bonds.

These results suggest that, although monofunctional hydrogen bonds have no significant stability in aqueous solution, polyfunctional hydrogen bonding may contribute significantly to the driving force for intermolecular interaction in water.   One of the possible structures for hydrogen bonding of urea and guanidine hydrochloride with the carbonyl groups of a polypeptide is shown in **5**. The situa-

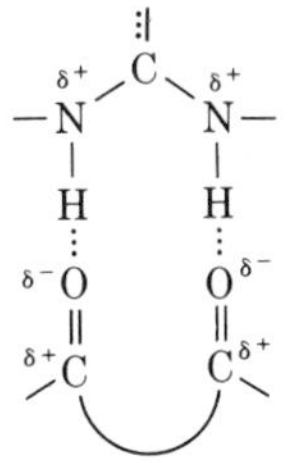

5

tion is analogous to the binding of metals to chelating agents; although a magnesium-acetate complex has negligible stability in
aqueous solution, the complex of magnesium ion with ethylenediaminetetraacetate, in which four acetate ions have been brought
together in a single molecule, is very stable.

The binding of sugars to proteins may also be interpreted in
terms of a polyfunctional hydrogen bonding in aqueous solution.
Hydrophobic bonding may contribute to the stability of such binding,
but the high solubility of many sugars in water suggests that this
binding is not caused entirely by hydrophobic interaction. A large
part of the (unitary) free energy of interaction of lactose with an
antibody, amounting to some -8 kcal/mole may, therefore, be attributed to polyfunctional hydrogen bonding to the hydroxyl groups
on the sugar.[34] The free energy of binding of tri-N-acetylglucos-
amine to lysozyme is -7.2 kcal/mole, and, if it is assumed that approximately half of this is the result of hydrogen bonding, an average value of -0.8 kcal/mole may be estimated for each of the hydrogen bonds to the protein that has been observed by x-ray structural analysis of this enzyme.[35]

One striking piece of evidence that the interaction of urea with
a protein can involve a large free energy of binding is the observation that the ureido group of biotin contributes a factor of 10^7 to
10^8, i.e., more than 10 kcal, to the binding of biotin to avidin and

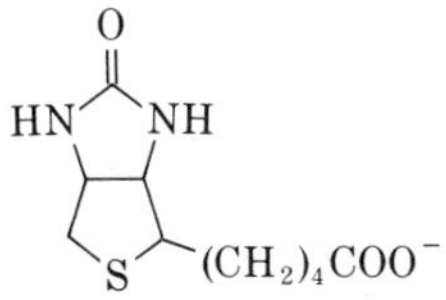

Biotin

[34] F. Karush, *Advan. Immunol.* **2**, 1 (1962).

[35] J. A. Rupley, L. Butler, M. Gerring, F. J. Hartdegen, and R. Pecoraro, *Proc. Natl. Acad. Sci. U.S.* **57**, 1088 (1967).

that ethyleneurea and urea bind to avidin with association constants of $10^2 - 10^3$.[36] This strong interaction is difficult to explain in terms of what is known about interaction energies in aqueous solution, but hydrogen bonding of the ureido group to suitably oriented groups on the protein must almost certainly be involved.

B. PROPERTIES OF THE HYDROGEN BOND

For many purposes it is useful to consider the hydrogen bond as an intermediate stage in the transfer of a proton from an acid to a base (equation 9). An acid can interact with a base in such a manner

$$A-H + :B$$

$$\overset{\delta^-}{A}\!-\!\!-\!\overset{\delta^+}{H}\cdots:B$$

$$\overset{(-)}{A}:\cdots H\!-\!\!-\!\overset{(+)}{B}$$

$$A^- + H\overset{+}{-}B \tag{9}$$

that a partial bond is formed between the proton and the base with a resulting stretching and weakening of the A—H bond. If the base B is sufficiently strong relative to A$^-$ (the charges in equation 9 are arbitrary), the stable position of the proton will be closer to B and a weak hydrogen bond will remain to A$^-$. Complete transfer and separation of the molecules gives A$^-$ and BH$^+$. From this point of view it is clear that the strength of a hydrogen bond will increase with the acidity (proton-donating power) of the proton donor and with the basicity (proton-accepting power) of the proton acceptor.

This expectation is fulfilled in practice if the compounds under consideration are structurally similar or if the correlation is extended over such a large range that deviations become less noticeable; it does not hold with precision for comparisons of different classes of compounds, particularly if the proton donor or acceptor atom is changed. There is a progressive increase in the length of the O—D bond, as measured by the O—D stretching frequency in the infra-red, when CH_3OD forms a hydrogen bond with a series of bases of increasing basicity, and this increase is approximately proportional to the pK of the base over more than 20 powers of 10 in basicity (Fig. 3).[37, 38] However, a closer examination of any part of this curve reveals compounds of similar basicity but different structure which

[36] N. M. Green, *Biochem. J.* **89**, 599 (1963).

[37] W. Gordy and S. C. Stanford, *J. Chem. Phys.* **9**, 204 (1961).

[38] E. M. Arnett, *Progr. Phys. Org. Chem.* **1**, 223 (1963).

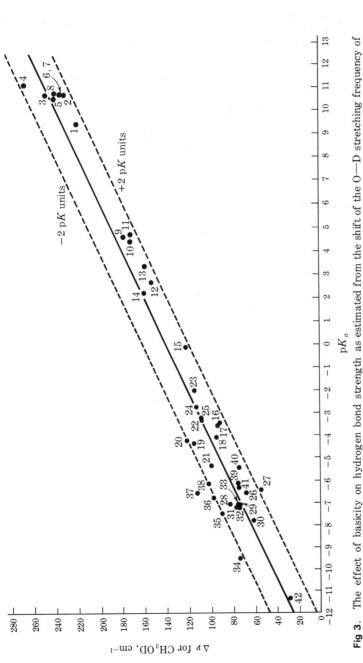

Fig 3. The effect of basicity on hydrogen bond strength as estimated from the shift of the O—D stretching frequency of CH₃OD upon hydrogen bonding to different bases.[38] (1) Benzylamine; (2) *n*-butylamine; (3) *n*-propylamine; (4) diethylamine; (5) *iso*-butylamine; (6) *n*-amylamine; (7) *iso*-amylamine; (8) cyclohexylamine; (9) aniline; (10) *o*-toluidine; (11) *m*-toluidine; (12) *o*-chloroaniline; (13) *m*-chloroaniline; (14) methyl anthranilate; (15) *N,N*-dimethylacetamide; (16) methyl *n*-butyl ether; (17) diethyl ether; (18) ethyl *n*-butyl ether; (19) di-*n*-propyl ether; (20) di-*iso*-propyl ether; (21) di-*n*-butyl ether; (22) ethylene glycol dimethyl ether; (23) tetrahydrofuran; (24) tetrahydropyran; (25) dioxane; (26) anisole; (27) phenetole; (28) *m*-methylbenzaldehyde; (29) benzaldehyde; (30) methyl benzoate; (31) acetone; (32) methyl ethyl ketone; (33) methyl *tert*-butyl ketone; (34) cyclobutanone; (35) cyclopentanone; (36) cyclohexanone; (37) cycloheptanone; (38) cyclooctanone; (39) acetophenone; (40) *p*-methyl acetophenone; (41) *n*-butyrophenone; (42) nitrobenzene.

show differences in their hydrogen-bonding ability, as measured by this criterion. A separate correlation line is required for substituted pyridines, for example, which cause a larger shift in the O—D frequency for a given basicity than do aliphatic amines.[39]

A closer correlation may be found between the stretching frequency of the O—H bond and the *enthalpy* of formation of hydrogen bonds, even if different classes of proton acceptors are compared.[39,40] This relationship is known as *Badger's rule*. The better agreement of correlations of stretching frequency with the enthalpy than with the pK (a measure of free energy) suggests that deviations in the latter correlation reflect differences in the entropy of hydrogen-bond formation, as might be expected for different classes of compounds.

The results of a number of direct measurements of the free energy of hydrogen-bond formation have become available in the past few years. A typical correlation of substituent effects on the stability of hydrogen bonds between a series of substituted pyridines and phenols in carbon tetrachloride solution is shown in Fig. 4. As

[39] M. Tamres, S. Searles, E. M. Leighly, and D. W. Mohrman, *J. Am. Chem. Soc.* **76**, 3983 (1954).

[40] T. D. Epley and R. S. Drago, *J. Am. Chem. Soc.* **89**, 5770 (1967).

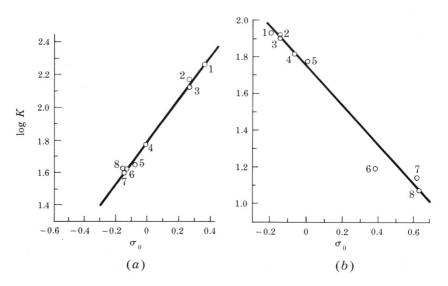

Fig 4. The effect of substituents in the phenol (*a*) and in the pyridine (*b*) on the equilibrium constant for hydrogen-bond formation between phenols and pyridines in carbon tetrachloride.[41] In (*a*) the substituents are (1) m-Cl, (2) p-I, (3) p-Cl, (4) H, (5) m-CH$_3$, (6) p-CH$_3$O, (7) p-t-butyl, (8) p-CH$_3$; in (*b*): (1) 4-t-butyl, (2) 4-CH$_3$, (3) 4-C$_2$H$_5$, (4) 3-CH$_3$, (5) H, (6) 3-Br, (7) 3-CN, (8) 4-CN.

would be expected, electron-donating substituents in the pyridine and electron-withdrawing substituents in the phenol increase the stability of the hydrogen bond, and plots of log K against the σ values of the substituents give ρ values of -1.0 and 1.14, respectively.[41]

One of the factors which may cause a deviation from the relationship of hydrogen-bond strength to acidity and basicity is the polarizability, covalent bond-forming ability, or "softness" of the donor and acceptor molecules. Although the relationship of these properties to hydrogen-bond strength is by no means settled, an empirical correlation of the strength of donor-acceptor interactions based on a division into "electrostatic" and "covalent" contributions to the enthalpy of complex formation suggests that hydrogen bonds formed by phenol have a considerably larger amount of covalent character than those formed from aliphatic alcohols or hydrogen fluoride.[42] Since the stability of an intermolecular hydrogen bond in water depends on the small differences between the stabilities of the hydrogen bonds to the solvent and to the partner of the hydrogen-bonded pair, special effects of this kind which influence these differences should be of great importance in determining whether or not such bonds can provide a significant driving force for intermolecular association in water. Unfortunately, there is too little experimental information available at the present time to make possible any generalizations about the stabilities of intermolecular hydrogen bonds in water, other than that they are small.

The potential-energy diagram as a function of the A—H distance for a hydrogen bond of the type described in equation 9 is shown in Fig. 5a. This is a "double-potential-well" system, with energy minima corresponding to unsymmetrical hydrogen bonds in which the proton is close to either A or B. The dashed line shows the potential curve for the proton of A—H in the absence of B. The addition of the base lowers the energy of the system and provides a stable energy minimum for the proton at a slightly greater A—H distance than in free A—H, in addition to providing a new minimum corresponding to $A^- \cdots H—B^+$. Now, if A and B are moved close together and the hydrogen bond becomes stronger, the separation between the two energy minima will be decreased, and a point should be reached at which the proton will be distributed between the positions near to A and to B over a time scale which is short relative to the time scale of a molecular vibration, either

[41] J. Rubin and G. S. Panson, *J. Phys. Chem.* **69**, 3089 (**1965**); J. Rubin, B. Z. Senkowski, and G. S. Panson, *Ibid.* **68**, 1601 (1964).

[42] R. S. Drago and B. B. Wayland, *J. Am. Chem. Soc.* **87**, 3571 (1965).

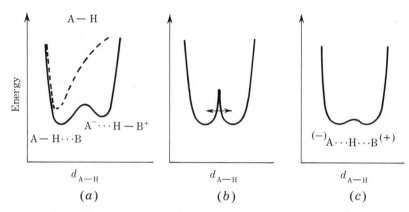

Fig 5. Potential-energy diagrams as a function of A—H distance for A—H (dashed line), a double-potential-well A—H···B hydrogen-bonded system (a), a system with rapid proton transfer by tunneling through the barrier separating two potential wells (b), and a strong, single-potential-well hydrogen bond (c).

through tunneling between the two potential wells, or through a lowering of the energy barrier between the two positions to an insignificant level (Figs. 5b and 5c). In other words the proton may exist somewhere between A and B in what is essentially a single potential well of a more or less symmetrical hydrogen bond. Under these circumstances one can no longer speak of a proton which is bonded to A and hydrogen-bonded to B; there is bonding to both A and B, and the normal infrared stretching frequency corresponding to the A—H bond will no longer be detectable. Furthermore, if A and B are the same, as in a bond formed from two carboxylate groups and a proton, the two carboxylate groups may lose their individuality, so that it would no longer be possible to detect separate absorptions corresponding to hydrogen-bonded RCOOH and RCOO⁻, for example.

    There is a great deal of evidence that supports the broad outlines of the scheme described in the preceding paragraph, but the details remain to be demonstrated. Except for the bifluoride ion, there is not even general agreement at this time on the question of whether or not a symmetrical, single-potential-well hydrogen bond exists. It is certain that the physical properties of strong hydrogen bonds are qualitatively different from those of ordinary hydrogen bonds and that the proton is not localized on one or the other of the donor atoms for an appreciable length of time; what is not certain is whether the proton is completely delocalized in a single potential well or whether it jumps back and forth at an extremely rapid rate between the two donor atoms and two potential wells. The most significant evidence bearing on these questions has been obtained from infrared and visible spectroscopy and from x-ray and neutron-diffraction measurements.

It is clear that the free-energy barrier for the transfer of a proton across an asymmetric hydrogen bond is small. Since the rate of proton transfer from an acid to a base in the direction favored by the equilibrium is diffusion-controlled, the free-energy barrier for the proton transfer itself must be less than for the diffusion process; transfer may occur rapidly across a narrow energy barrier by tunneling.[43] Furthermore, detailed calculations of the potential energy surfaces for the transfer of a proton from hydrochloric acid to ammonia reveal no energy barrier for this reaction.[44]

The strongest candidate for a symmetrical, single-potential-well hydrogen bond is the extremely strong bond of the $(F-H-F)^-$ ion, with an $F \cdots F$ distance of only 2.26 Å. The normal $H-F$ stretching frequency has disappeared in the infrared spectra of salts of this compound and is replaced by absorption bands at 1,450 and 600 cm^{-1}, which have been assigned to asymmetrical and symmetrical stretching frequencies, respectively, and a band at 1,225 cm^{-1}, assigned to the bending vibration of a symmetrical system in which the proton is in a single potential well midway between the two fluorine atoms; this interpretation is supported by the results of heat capacity and neutron diffraction measurements on these compounds.[45]

Solid hydrogen-bonded complexes, such as mixed salts of carboxylic acids and carboxylate ions, fall into two classes by several different physical criteria. The first class shows evidence by infrared spectroscopy and by x-ray and neutron diffraction that the carboxyl and carboxylate groups have, on the whole, maintained their identity, although their structure may be perturbed by hydrogen bonding, and that the proton exists nearer to one or the other of the atoms to which it is bonded. There does not appear to be much question that these systems represent double-potential-well hydrogen bonds, although the detailed properties of the potential energy curves are still controversial. The second class of solid complexes exhibits many of the properties which would be expected of a symmetrical, single-potential-well system. Neutron-diffraction measure-

[43] M. Eigen, *Angew. Chem. Intern. Ed.* **3**, 1 (1964); E. Grunwald, *Progr. Phys. Org. Chem.* **3**, 317 (1965).

[44] E. Clementi, *J. Chem. Phys.* **46**, 3851 (1967).

[45] K. S. Pitzer and E. F. Westrum, *J. Chem. Phys.* **15**, 526 (1947); B. L. McGaw and J. A. Ibers, *Ibid.* **39**, 2677 (1963); G. L. Coté and H. W. Thompson, *Proc. Roy. Soc. (London)* **210A**, 206 (1951); J. A. Ibers, *J. Chem. Phys.* **41**, 25 (1964).

ments of the potassium salt of the phenylacetic acid–phenylacetate system at low temperature have shown that, within the rather fine limit of resolution of this technique, the proton is located midway between the two oxygen atoms, apparently in a symmetrical hydrogen bond.[46] X-ray investigation of a number of salts of this type, such as the potassium trifluoroacetate-trifluoroacetic acid complex with an $O \cdots O$ distance of 2.435 Å, shows that the two carboxyl groups have become equivalent, with bond distances intermediate between those of a carboxylic acid and a carboxylate ion. This must mean either that the system is symmetrical (6) or that the proton can jump back and forth between the two carboxyl groups in such a

$$
\begin{array}{ccc}
O & & O \\
\parallel \;\;{\scriptstyle(-)}\;\;{\scriptstyle(+)}\;\;{\scriptstyle(-)} & \parallel \\
-C-O\cdots H\cdots O-C-
\end{array}
$$

6

manner that the two groups give a single structure on x-ray analysis. Such compounds are to be contrasted with representatives of the first class of complex, such as the potassium glyoxylate–glyoxylic acid system with an $O \cdots O$ distance of 2.53 Å, in which the two carboxyl groups are clearly different.[47]

The infrared spectra of a number of crystalline compounds of this kind and of maleate monoanion show no absorption in the region in which the O—H stretching vibration is normally found, but show a broad, strong absorption near or below 1,600 cm^{-1}, similar to that of the bifluoride ion. This must represent a very great stretching indeed of the normal O—H bond or, more probably, either an $[O \cdots H \cdots O]^{-}$ system in which the proton is located somewhere near the center of the bond or a double-potential-well system in which the proton moves back and forth between the two potential wells at a rate comparable to the frequency of an O—H stretching vibration, so that no such vibration can exist.[48, 49] In some cases the characteristic infrared absorption bands of the carboxylic acid and carboxylate anion groups have disappeared, suggesting that the carboxyl and carboxylate groups have merged into a single species with an absorption band at an intermediate position.[50] In solution

[46]G. E. Bacon and N. A. Curry, *Acta Cryst.* **10**, 524 (1957); **13**, 717 (1960).

[47]L. Golič and J. C. Speakman, *J. Chem. Soc.* **1965**, 2521, 2530; H. N. Shrivastava and J. C. Speakman, *Ibid.* **1961**, 1151; J. C. Speakman and H. H. Mills, *Ibid.*, p. 1164.

[48]R. Blinc, D. Hadži, and A. Novak, *Z. Elektrochem.* **64**, 567 (1960); R. Blinc and D. Hadži, *Spectrochim. Acta* **16**, 853 (1960).

[49]H. M. E. Cardwell, J. D. Dunitz, and L. E. Orgel, *J. Chem. Soc.* **1953**, 3740.

[50]D. Hadži and H. Marciszewski, *Chem. Commun.* **1967**, 2.

separate carboxyl and carboxylate absorptions are usually found and
the hydrogen bond is clearly not symmetrical[20]; however, in other
systems the disappearance or shift to very low frequencies of the
A—H stretching absorption is maintained in solution.[51-53]

The relationship between the basicity and acidity of the hydrogen-bonded partners and the character of the bond is evident in the
behavior of a series of substituted pyridine–benzoic acid hydrogen
bonds in the solid state and in acetonitrile solution.[51] If one starts
with a weakly acidic carboxylic acid, the infrared spectrum of the
carboxylic acid group is evident; and as the acidity of the carboxylic
acid is increased, there is a discontinuous change to the spectrum of
the carboxylate ion as the position of the potential curve for the
system is shifted, so that the proton is more stable in the potential
well corresponding to the pyridinium-carboxylate structure (equation
10). Thus, for most of the hydrogen-bonded pairs the proton exists

$$X{-}\underset{}{\bigcirc}{-}N\cdots H{-}O{-}\overset{\overset{O}{\|}}{C}{-}\bigcirc{-}Y \;\rightleftharpoons\; X{-}\bigcirc{-}\overset{+}{N}{-}H\cdots{}^{-}O{-}\overset{\overset{O}{\|}}{C}{-}\bigcirc{-}Y \tag{10}$$

predominantly in one or the other of the minima of a double-potential
system. At a ΔpK near the critical point at which the change in
structure occurs, neither a normal N—H nor O—H stretching
absorption is found above 1,700 cm^{-1} in some complexes, suggesting
that the proton is in a single potential well or transfers very rapidly
between the two bases; however, there does not appear to be a
continuous change through intermediate structures of the carboxyl
group in these complexes, such as might be expected for a truly
symmetrical hydrogen bond.

C. MODELS FOR THE HYDROGEN BOND

In considering the nature of the forces which provide stability to a
hydrogen bond it is customary to make a distinction between "electrostatic" and "covalent" theories of the hydrogen bond.[1] At the
outset it should be realized that there is no clearcut distinction between these approaches; covalent bonding is an expression of electrostatic forces, and the fundamental wave equations for bond formation do not contain separate terms for the "electrostatic" and
"covalent" contributions to the bond. Nevertheless, for descriptive

[51] S. L. Johnson and K. A. Rumon, *J. Phys. Chem.* **69**, 74 (1965).

[52] D. Hadži and N. Kobilarov, *J. Chem. Soc.* **1966A**, 439.

[53] J. M. Williams and M. Kreevoy, *J. Am. Chem. Soc.* **89**, 5499 (1967).

purposes it is useful to emphasize one or the other of these two contributions, and this approach will be followed here.

According to the electrostatic model, the stability of the hydrogen bond is brought about by an energetically favorable interaction between the partial positive charge of the proton and the negative charge of the acceptor atom or dipole (7). This type of interaction

$$\overset{\delta^+}{A-H}\cdots\overset{\delta^-}{B}$$

7

probably provides the greatest part of the interaction energy for hydrogen bonds with relatively long $A \cdots B$ distances. The energy will be maximal when the hydrogen bond is linear, but it will not be sharply decreased by moderate degrees of bending of the bond, and, contrary to some statements, there are a number of examples of stable hydrogen bonds in cyclic systems in which the hydrogen bond is almost certainly nonlinear, including the 5-membered ring hydrogen bonds of 1,2-diols, hydroxamic acids, and 2-substituted phenols such as halophenols (8–10).

8   9   10

The most serious objections to a purely electrostatic model of the hydrogen bond are that this model does not account for the unusually strong intensity of the hydrogen-bonded A—H stretching frequency in the infrared and that there is a poor correlation between the dipole moment of a series of acceptor molecules, B, and the strength of the hydrogen bonds formed by such molecules. Trimethylamine, with the small dipole moment of $0.7D$, forms strong hydrogen bonds; whereas acetonitrile, with the much larger dipole moment of $3.44D$, forms only very weak hydrogen bonds.[1,54] These objections have led to attempts to describe the "covalent" contribution to the hydrogen bond in terms of resonance and molecular orbital descriptions of covalent bonding.

According to the resonance picture, the hydrogen bond may be regarded as a hybrid which owes its stability to the following contributing structures:

ψ_a A—H   B
ψ_b A⁻ H⁺ ···· B ionic
ψ_c A⁻ H ——⁺B covalent
ψ_d A⁺ H⁻ ···· B ionic
ψ_e A   H⁻   ⁺B covalent

The wave equation of the hydrogen-bonded system is based on the contributions of these structures according to equation 11, in which

$$\Psi = a\psi_a + b\psi_b + c\psi_c + d\psi_d + e\psi_e \qquad (11)$$

the coefficients a, b, c,... represent the contributions of each structure to the overall system. Theoretical calculations suggest that the covalent contributing structures (especially c, in which there is a covalent interaction between H and B) are significant, although not dominant, for long hydrogen bonds and make a progressively larger contribution to the stability of the bond as the A···B distance becomes shorter.[55] However, calculations of this kind are still far from exact, even for simple systems.[56]

Molecular orbital theory provides an alternative description of the covalent contribution to the hydrogen bond which the author finds particularly satisfying. One of the problems of a hydrogen bond is that it requires that the hydrogen atom, which has only the single $1s$ orbital available for bond formation, exceeds its normal coordination number and interact with two atoms. In the resonance model this is explained by "no-bond" resonance among structures a, c, and e. The molecular orbital model provides a reasonable explanation of the bonding, which is essentially the same as that for the formation of donor-acceptor or charge transfer complexes and for the pentavalent transition state of S_N2 substitution at carbon, without invoking high-energy orbitals.[1] According to this model the molecular orbitals of the system are constructed from the available atomic orbitals: the two orbitals (usually p orbitals), which each contain a free electron pair in isolated A⁻ and B, and the $1s$ orbital of the hydrogen atom. These may be combined to form three mole-

[54] C. A. Coulson, *Research (London)* **10**, 149 (1957).

[55] C. A. Coulson and U. Danielsson, *Arkiv Fysik* **8**, 239 (1954); H. Tsubomura, *Bull. Chem. Soc. Japan* **27**, 445 (1954).

[56] H. C. Bowen and J. W. Linnett, *J. Chem. Soc.* **1966A**, 1675.

cular orbitals, a bonding orbital Ψ_1, a nonbonding orbital Ψ_2, and an antibonding orbital Ψ_3, as follows:

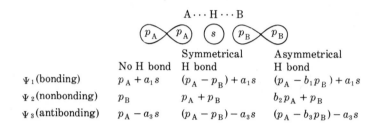

	No H bond	Symmetrical H bond	Asymmetrical H bond
Ψ_1 (bonding)	$p_A + a_1 s$	$(p_A - p_B) + a_1 s$	$(p_A - b_1 p_B) + a_1 s$
Ψ_2 (nonbonding)	p_B	$p_A + p_B$	$b_2 p_A + p_B$
Ψ_3 (antibonding)	$p_A - a_3 s$	$(p_A - p_B) - a_3 s$	$(p_A - b_3 p_B) - a_3 s$

In the starting materials, A—H and B, with no hydrogen bond, the bonding molecular orbital of the A—H bond is composed of the p orbital of A and the s orbital of H and contains one pair of bonding electrons. Another electron pair is in the p orbital of B, where it does not participate in bonding. The coefficients a and b in these expressions describe the amount of the contribution of each atomic orbital to the molecular orbital. Now if A—H and B are brought together to form a symmetrical hydrogen bond, a bonding orbital involving all three atoms may be constructed from the two p and one s orbitals and will contain one electron pair. (The signs in these expressions refer to the symmetry of the system and not to the amount of the contribution of each orbital.) The second electron pair will be in a nonbonding orbital which is composed of the p orbitals of A and B and does not involve the hydrogen atom at all. There will also be an antibonding orbital composed of all three atomic orbitals, which will be unoccupied.

In an unsymmetrical hydrogen bond the situation will be essentially the same, except that the contributions of the various orbitals will be asymmetrical, as indicated by the coefficients a and b.

The important point in this model is that it is possible to construct a three-atom, two-electron bond, which provides stability to the system without violating the Pauli exclusion principle. This bond may be regarded as electron deficient compared with a normal two-atom, two-electron bond, and, as would be expected for such a bond, the A—H distance is increased over that of the normal A—H covalent bond. The electrons in the nonbonding orbital composed of the p orbitals of A and B will be localized on A and B, so that the system will gain stability as A and B become more electronegative and more easily able to accommodate these electrons.

The covalent contribution is expected to be most important for short, exceptionally stable, hydrogen bonds. It will provide maximum stabilization when the bond is linear, but will withstand a moderate degree of nonlinearity without disappearance of the stabilization energy.

It has often been suggested that there is some "aromatic" character to cyclic hydrogen-bonded systems in which resonance structures involving the hydrogen bond can be written, such as enols of β-diketones (**11**) and sugar osazones (**12**). It is clear from the

existence of two ultraviolet absorption spectra corresponding to each of the two tautomers that in some systems in which such resonance structures can be written, such as the Schiff bases of pyridoxal phosphate and related compounds (Chap. 2, Sec. E, Part 5), no such resonance occurs and the proton is located asymmetrically, nearer to one or the other of the two basic atoms to which it is bound. Nuclear magnetic resonance spectra of compounds of this class generally show only a single hydrogen absorption, but this would be expected whether or not the compound has aromatic character because intramolecular proton transfer is generally fast relative to the time scale of nmr spectroscopy, so that only a single proton signal is detected for rapidly equilibrating tautomers. The position of the ultraviolet absorption maximum of enolic β-diketones has been interpreted as evidence for an asymmetric hydrogen bond, and some such enols

show two infrared bands, which may represent the carbonyl stretching vibrations of the two tautomers **11A** and **11B**. However, other
compounds of this type show only a single, intense, broad infrared
absorption band near 1,600 cm^{-1}, which is a considerably lower frequency than normal for the carbonyl stretching band, and do not
show an O—H stretching band in the normal region. This suggests
that there is a large amount of single-bond character in the carbonyl
group and that the interconversion of forms **11A** and **11B** may take
place more rapidly than the time scale of the vibrations of these
groups; i.e., the compounds may exist as a single, strongly hydrogen-
bonded resonance hybrid.[57] Indeed, if one accepts the evidence for
the existence of symmetical hydrogen bonds and either the resonance
or the molecular orbital model for the covalent character of the bond
between hydrogen and its two neighboring atoms, there would seem
to be no reason why covalent interaction of the hydrogen atom with
both donor atoms could not constitute a part of a cyclic system with
the properties ordinarily ascribed to aromatic molecules. Further
experimental work will be required to resolve this interesting question.

[57] R. D. Cambell and H. M. Gilow, *J. Am. Chem. Soc.* **82**, 5426 (1960); S. Forsén, *Acta Chem. Scand.* **18**, 1208 (1964); D. W. Barnum, *J. Inorg. Nuc. Chem.* **21**, 221 (1961).

7
Electrostatic Interactions

It is certain that interactions between charged groups contribute to the *specificity* of enzyme-substrate binding. The extent to which electrostatic attraction can provide the *driving force* for intermolecular interactions and the theoretical basis for understanding the strength and the specificity of ionic interactions in aqueous solution are less certain. There is an extensive literature on the theory of ionic interactions, but in the absence of an understanding of the detailed structure of water and of the microscopic nature of ion-water and ion-ion interactions in water the available theories cannot claim to provide a general quantitative description of such interactions. The approach in this section is an empirical one, based upon a description of some manifestations of these interactions and proceeding to some rather phenomenological attempts to correlate and begin to explain them. The reader is referred elsewhere for

351

more detailed theoretical and experimental approaches to the problem of electrostatic interactions in water.[1]

A. MANIFESTATIONS

1. ION BINDING

The binding of the positively charged group of acetylcholine and of related substrates and inhibitors to the anionic site of the enzyme acetylcholinesterase (1) provides a typical example of the action of electrostatic forces in enzyme-substrate interactions.[2] The substrate dimethylaminoethyl acetate (2) is similar to acetylcholine, except

that a methyl group is replaced by a dissociable hydrogen atom so that at high pH values the substrate is converted to the uncharged free amine form. The activity of this substrate relative to that of acetylcholine decreases by a factor of 3 as the pH is increased and the positive charge is lost. Similarly, the Michaelis constant for the uncharged substrate isoamyl acetate (3) is eightfold larger than that

for protonated dimethylaminoethyl acetate. A detailed kinetic study

---

[1] H. S. Harned and B. B. Owen, "The Physical Chemistry of Electrolytic Solutions," 3d ed., Reinhold Publishing Corporation, New York, 1958; R. A. Robinson and R. H. Stokes, "Electrolyte Solutions," Academic Press Inc., New York, 1955; J. T. Edsall and J. Wyman, "Biophysical Chemistry," vol. 1, Academic Press Inc., New York, 1958; R. W. Gurney, "Ionic Processes in Solution," McGraw-Hill Book Company, New York, 1953.

[2] I. B. Wilson, in P. D. Boyer, H. Lardy, and K. Myrbäck (eds.), "The Enzymes," vol. 4, p. 501, Academic Press Inc., New York, 1960; I. B. Wilson and F. Bergmann, *J. Biol. Chem.* **185**, 479 (1950).

would be required to determine whether these differences are caused by differences in binding or in the rate of acylation of the enzyme by the substrate, but in either case they show that the presence of a positive charge increases the enzyme-substrate interaction by a small but definite factor. Similarily, the inhibition of acetylcholinesterase by the quaternary ammonium compound neostigmine (4) is independent of pH, whereas inhibition by the tertiary amine physostigmine (5) decreases by a factor of 16 as the positive charge is lost;

4   5

the binding of the cationic inhibitor dimethylaminoethanol (6) to the enzyme is 30 times stronger than that of the uncharged inhibitor isoamyl alcohol (7). Thus, it appears that the contribution of electro-

6   7

static forces to the interaction energy of the rather well shielded charge of a quaternary ammonium ion with the anionic site of this enzyme is on the order of 1 to 2 kcal/mole ($\Delta F = -RT \ln 3$–30). We shall see later that it is doubtful whether even this relatively small energy represents a simple electrostatic attraction, in view of the small electrostatic interaction energies for tetraalkylammonium ions in water. The binding may be caused by forces other than simple electrostatic interaction and the negative charge on the anionic site may only serve to align the substrate properly in the active site and to provide specificity by making the binding of neutral or anionic substrates energetically unfavorable. The dependence on pH of the inhibition by alkylammonium cations suggests that a carboxylate group provides the anionic site on the enzyme.[3]

The interaction of *monoanions* with enzymes and other proteins

[3] R. M. Krupka, *Biochemistry* 5, 1988 (1966).

often involves much larger binding energies.[4-8] Acetoacetate decarboxylase is inhibited by anions with an order of inhibitory effec-
tiveness of $SCN^- > ClO_4^- > I^- > NO_3^- > ClO_3^- > Br^- > Cl^- > BrO_3^- > F^- \sim IO_3^-$ (HSO_3^- and Cl_3CCOO^- show effects which appear to be
specific for this enzyme and are omitted from this list) and a range
of dissociation constants from 1.1×10^{-4} to 0.10 M, corresponding to
free energies of binding in the range of -1 to -5 kcal/mole (Table
I). It is of interest that the thermodynamic parameters for inhibition
by these ions show an enormous range of variation with values of ΔH
ranging from -28 kcal/mole for SCN^- to $+1$ kcal/ mole for IO_3^-
and values of ΔS from -74 e.u. for SCN^- to $+8$ e.u. for IO_3^-. Thus
the observed relatively small differences in the free energy of binding reflect a not quite complete cancellation of much larger changes
in the enthalpy and entropy terms. This is another example of a
situation in which much larger changes in entropy and enthalpy
than would be expected from a direct interaction are mutually compensatory and accompany relatively small changes in free energy.
The large entropy changes presumably reflect changes in the structure of the solvent, the enzyme, or both, which can take place in
such a way as to give compensating enthalpy changes; for example,
an entropically unfavorable increase in water structure may be accompanied by an energetically favorable increase in hydrogen bonding with very little change in free energy.

A very similar order is found for the binding of anions to other
proteins, such as wool and bovine serum albumin, and for binding
to anion exchange resins, such as the tetraalkylammonium resin
Dowex 2 (Table I). This binding can also be strong: the binding
constants to the high-affinity site of bovine serum mercaptalbumin
for chloride, thiocyanate, and trichloroacetate ions are 2,400, 24,000
and 120,000 M^{-1}, respectively, which correspond to free energies of
binding of -5 to -7 kcal/mole.[9]

The striking characteristic of the binding order in these systems
is its relationship to ion size and charge density, especially in the

[4] I. Fridovich, *J. Biol. Chem.* **238**, 592 (1963).

[5] J. Steinhardt, C. H. Fugitt, and M. Harris, *J. Res. Natl. Bur. Std.* **28**, 201
(1942).

[6] S. Peterson, *Ann. N.Y. Acad. Sci.* **57**, 144 (1954); H. P. Gregor, J. Belle, and
R. A. Marcus, *J. Am. Chem. Soc.* **77**, 2713 (1955).

[7] J. Bello, H. C. A. Reise, and J. R. Vinograd, *J. Phys. Chem.* **60**, 1299 (1956);
P. H. von Hippel and K -Y. Wong, *Biochemistry* **1**, 664 (1962).

[8] D. Robinson and W. P. Jencks, *J. Am. Chem. Soc.* **87**, 2462, 2470 (1965).

[9] G. Scatchard and E. S. Black, *J. Phys. Chem.* **53**, 88 (1949); G. Scatchard, Y. V.
Wu, and A. L. Shen, *J. Am. Chem. Soc.* **81**, 6104 (1959).

Table I   The interaction of anions with proteins, an anion exchange resin, and acetyl-tetraglycine ethyl ester (ATGEE), listed in order of decreasing strength of interaction

	50% inhibition of acetoacetate decarboxylase[a] M	Affinity for wool at 0° $\log K^{b}$	Affinity for Dowex 2 K^{c}	Change in the melting point of 5% gelatin gels in 1 M salt $°C^{d}$	Interaction with ATGEE k_s^{e}
Picrate		3.86			
ClO_4^-	0.0007		32		-0.33
SCN^-	0.001		19	-14.4	-0.25
Cl_3CCOO^-	0.33	1.16	18	-17.7	-0.27
p-Tos$^-$		1.04	14	-14.9^{f}	-0.31
I^-	0.001		8-13	-14.4	-0.23
Br^-	0.01	0.69	3.4	-7.6	0
NO_3^-	0.013	0.89	3.3	-8.1	-0.08
Cl^-	0.05	0.43	1.0	-2.4	$+0.05$
BrO_3^-	0.076		1.0		$+0.09$
$H_2PO_4^-$		0.12	0.34		$+0.36$
CH_3COO^-			0.17		$+0.23$
F^-	0.10		0.10	$+4.1$	$+0.23^{g}$

[a] Reference 4.

[b] Affinity constants for wool in acid solution (Ref. 5).

[c] Affinity relative to that of Cl$^-$ (Ref. 6).

[d] Sodium salts (Ref.7). The melting point in water was 30.4°.

[e] Salting-out constant for the sodium salt (Ref. 8).

[f] Benzenesulfonate.

[g] Potassium salt.

halide series. The order of binding $I^- > Br^- > Cl^-$ is the *opposite* of that which would be expected if electrostatic interaction between the anion and the cationic binding site were the only factor to be considered. The relationship to ion size is not a general one, however, and many large anions, such as phosphate and acetate, bind very weakly.

The most direct indication of the strength of interionic interactions should be the equilibrium constants for the formation of ion pairs in aqueous solution, but such ion pairs of monovalent ions have little stability. Measurement of the equilibrium constants for weak association presents a difficult experimental problem, but it appears certain that the association constants for the formation of ion pairs from ordinary singly charged ions are near to or less than 1.0 M^{-1} and are not much larger than would be expected for random encounter of the solvated ions.[10] Even if one of the ions is divalent, the association constants are not large, but larger values are observed if both ions are divalent. Some representative values are 9 M^{-1} for $K^+ \cdot SO_4^=$, 5 M^{-1} for $Na^+ \cdot SO_4^=$, 190 M^{-1} for $Ca^{++} \cdot SO_4^=$ and 140 M^{-1} for $Mg^{++} \cdot SO_4^=$.[11]

The influence of charge-charge interactions on the rates of nucleophilic reactions of diamine monocations with p-nitrophenyl phosphate dianion is small (Chap. 2, Sec. D, Part 5), and the effects of such interactions on the rates of other reactions are usually less than an order of magnitude. More significant electrostatic effects may be observed if one of the reactants is a polyelectrolyte, as in the reactions of partially protonated polyvinylpyridine and polyvinyl-imidazoles with anionic substrates.[12, 13] Poly(4)vinylpyridine is a somewhat less effective catalyst (based on the activity per pyridine residue) for the hydrolysis of the neutral substrate 2,4-dinitrophenyl acetate (8) than is monomeric 4-methylpyridine, presumably because the accessibility of the nucleophilic pyridine nitrogen atoms is decreased in the polymer. However, toward the anionic substrate 3-nitro-4-acetoxybenzenesulfonate (9) the polymer is far more reactive

8   9

than the monomer and shows a maximal reaction rate at an intermediate degree of ionization, at which it is partly in the free base and partly in the cationic form (Fig. 1, line 2). If a comparison is made between this maximal rate and the rate expected at the same pH for the reaction with an uncharged substrate of comparable reactivity (based on the rate observed with the uncharged polymer at

[10] R. L. Kay, *J. Am. Chem. Soc.* **82**, 2099 (1960); R. M. Fuoss and K-L. Hsia, *Proc. Natl. Acad. Sci. U.S.* **57**, 1550 (1967).

[11] T. O. Denney and C. B. Monk, *Trans. Faraday Soc.* **47**, 992 (1951).

[12] R. L. Letsinger and T. J. Savereide, *J. Am. Chem. Soc.* **84**, 114, 3122 (1962).

[13] C. G. Overberger, T. St. Pierre, N. Vorchheimer, and S. Yaroslovsky, *J. Am. Chem. Soc.* **85**, 3514 (1963).

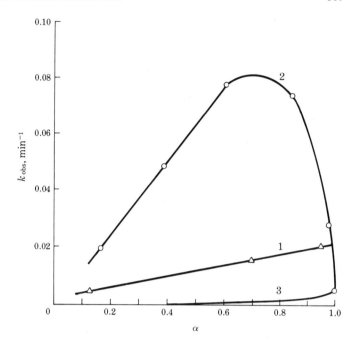

Fig 1. Catalysis of the hydrolysis of 3-nitro-4-acetoxybenzenesulfonate (9) by poly(4)vinylpyridine.[12] (1) 0.016 M 4-methylpyridine. (2) Poly(4)vinylpyridine, containing 0.01 M pyridine units. (3) Calculated line for the polymer reaction, based on the pH-dependence observed for the reaction with dinitrophenyl acetate (8).

high pH and the pH-dependence for the reaction of the polymer with 2,4-dinitrophenyl acetate, shown as curve 3 of Fig. 1), there is found a rate increase of 80-fold, which may be ascribed to electrostatic interaction of the cationic polymer with the anionic substrate. This interaction presumably involves a binding of the substrate and an increase in its effective concentration in the vicinity of the reactive pyridine groups. The maximum rate is observed with the partially neutralized polymer because both the cationic groups, for binding, and the uncharged pyridine residues, for nucleophilic attack on the substrate, are required for maximum catalytic activity.[12]

The electrostatic effect can give rise to large rate accelerations in dilute solutions if *both* the substrate and catalyst are polyelectrolytes. For example, the rate of hydrolysis of starch which contains protonated diethylaminoethyl groups is more than 500 times faster in the presence of polystyrenesulfonic acid than in a hydrochloric acid solution of comparable acidity. The mechanism of this rate acceleration leads to a degree of specificity: the hydrolysis products of the polymer catalyzed reaction consist of larger oligosaccharides than are obtained from the reaction catalyzed by mineral acid, and the size increases with decreasing amine substitution on the substrate.[14]

Electrostatic effects may also cause rate accelerations of reactions which take place on the surface of charged micelles; some examples are described in Chap. 8.

Salt effects on the rates of reaction of charged reactants can usually be accounted for adequately by the Debye-Hückel theory at low salt concentrations, but in the presence of more concentrated salts the effects frequently appear to be a function of the particular salt that is added, rather than of the ionic strength of the solution. These specific salt effects presumably reflect a direct interaction of a counter-ion with charged reactants, transition states, or both, and may be regarded in the same way as other direct ionic interactions.[15]

2. CONCENTRATED SALT SOLUTIONS

The interactions between ions which have been described so far take place at relatively low concentrations of salts, usually below 0.1 M. A quite different but not altogether unrelated series of salt effects is observed with both neutral and charged substances in more concentrated aqueous solutions of salts, on the order of 1 M. With some degree of overlap for borderline cases and a few inevitable exceptions the effects of concentrated salt solutions on proteins may be divided into two classes, within each of which there is a characteristic order of effectivenesss (Table II). Salts which contain sulfate, phosphate, citrate, acetate, or fluoride tend to precipitate proteins and protect proteins against denaturation and dissociation; whereas salts which contain thiocyanate, iodide, perchlorate, lithium, calcium, or barium tend to dissolve, denature, and dissociate proteins.[8,16] The addition of an aromatic group, particularly one with nitro substituents, tends to shift a salt into the second category. The order of effectiveness of salts with respect to these phenomena follows the Hofmeister or lyotropic series, which was originally based on the relative effectiveness of different salts in causing the

[14] T. J. Painter, *J. Chem. Soc.* **1962**, 3932.

[15] A. R. Olson and T. R. Simonson, *J. Chem. Phys.* **17**, 1167 (1949); C. W. Davies, in G. Porter (ed.), "Progress in Reaction Kinetics," vol. 1, p. 161, Pergamon Press, New York; S. Marburg and W. P. Jencks, *J. Am. Chem. Soc.* **84**, 232 (1962); M. R. Kershaw and J. E. Prue, *Trans. Faraday Soc.* **63**, 1198 (1967).

[16] P. H. von Hippel and K-Y. Wong, *Science* **145**, 577 (1964).

Table II   Effects of concentrated salt solutions on proteins

Solubility[17]

$\xleftarrow{\text{Precipitates}}$	$\xrightarrow{\text{Dissolves}}$
$Citrate^{3-} > SO_4^{2-} \sim HPO_4^{2-} > AcO^- >$ $Cl^- > NO_3^-$	Br^-, I^-

Denaturation

$\xleftarrow{\text{Inhibits}}$	$\xrightarrow{\text{Increases}}$

Edestin[19]
$\quad Fe(CN)_6^{4-} > citrate^{3-} > SO_4^{2-} > AcO^- >$ $NO_3^- < Br^- < I^- < salicylate^-$
$\quad Cl^-$

Ovalbumin[20]
$\quad SO_4^{2-} > HPO_4^{2-}, AcO^-, Cl^-$ $NO_3^- < I^- < SCN^- < O_2N-\!\!\left\langle\!\!\bigcirc\!\!\right\rangle\!\!-O^-$

Collagen, gelatin[7]
$\quad SO_4^{2-}, AcO^-, F^-,$ $Cl^-, Me_3CCOO^- < Br^-, NO_3^- <$
$\quad (CH_3)_4N^+$ $\quad CF_3COO^- < I^-, SCN^-, C_6H_5SO_3^-,$
$\quad\quad CCl_3COO^- < salicylate^- <$
$\quad\quad diiodosalicylate^-$
$\quad\quad NH_4^+ \sim Rb^+ \sim K^+ \sim Na^+ \sim Cs^+ < Li^+ <$
$\quad\quad Mg^{2+} < Ca^{2+} < Ba^{2+}$

Ribonuclease[16]
$\left\{\begin{matrix} HPO_4^{2-} \\ \\ H_2PO_4^- \end{matrix}\right\} > SO_4^{2-} > Cl^-$ $Br^- < ClO_4^- < SCN^-$
$(CH_3)_4N^+ \sim NH_4^+ \sim K^+ \sim Na^+ < Li^+$

DNA[24]
$Cl^-, Br^- < CH_3COO^- < I^- < ClO_4^-$
$\quad < SCN^- < CCl_3COO^-$
$(CH_3)_4N^+ \sim K^+ \sim Na^+ \sim Li^+$

Aggregation and Polymerization

$\xleftarrow{\text{Association}}$	$\xrightarrow{\text{Dissociation}}$

Glutamic dehydrogenase[21] $Cl^- < ClO_4^- < I^- < SCN^-$
F-actin $\rightleftharpoons$ G-actin[22]
$\quad SO_4^{--}, F^-$ $Cl^- < NO_3^- < Br^- < Cl_3CCOO^- \sim ClO_4^- <$
$\quad I^- < SCN^-$
$\quad K^+ < Na^+ \sim Rb^+ \sim Cs^+ \sim (CH_3)_4N^+ <$
$\quad\quad NH_4^+ \sim Li^+ \sim (C_2H_5)_4N^+$

precipitation of proteins and is followed for a wide variety of phenomena which take place in aqueous salt solutions.[17 , 18] For anions it
is essentially the same as that for anion binding to proteins and ion
exchange resins, suggesting that there is some relationship of the
effects observed in concentrated and in dilute salt solutions.

The effects of salts on protein denaturation are clearly illustrated in Fig. 2, which shows the concentration of urea which is required to initiate the denaturation of edestin in the presence of different salts. Salts which are effective in salting out proteins, such
as salts of citrate, sulfate, acetate, and chloride, protect against
urea denaturation, whereas salts which tend to dissolve proteins,
such as sodium iodide, barium chloride, guanidine hydrochloride, and
sodium salicylate, potentiate urea denaturation and are themselves
effective denaturing agents at higher concentrations.[19] More recent

[17] F. Hofmeister, *Arch. Exptl. Pathol. Pharmakol.* **24**, 247 (1888); J. W.McBain, "Colloid Science," chap. 9, Reinhold Publishing Corporation, New York, 1950.
[18] A. Voet, *Trans. Faraday Soc.* **32**, 1301 (1936); *Chem. Rev.* **20**, 169 (1937).
[19] N. F. Burk, *J. Phys. Chem.* **47**, 104 (1943).

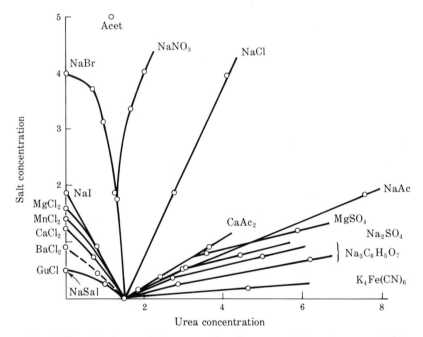

Fig 2. Effect of salts on the concentration of urea required to denature edestin, as measured by the exposure of sulfhydryl groups.[19]

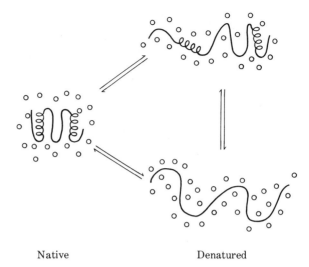

Native   Denatured

Fig 3. Schematic diagram of the equilibrium between a native globular protein in aqueous solution and two different denatured forms of the protein, showing increased exposure to the solvent upon denaturation of groups which are shielded from the solvent in the native protein.[8]

measurements reveal a very similar order for the effectiveness of salts in changing the melting temperature of gelatin gels (Table I), for the denaturation of other proteins,[16, 20] for the inhibition of a number of enzymes, presumably by disrupting their noncovalent structure,[23] and even for the denaturation of deoxyribonucleic acid (DNA).[24] The limited amount of available evidence suggests a similar order for the salt-induced disaggregation and dissociation of proteins.[21, 22] The depolymerization of F-actin to G-actin is induced by salts which cause protein denaturation at higher concentrations and is inhibited by sulfate and fluoride ions.[22]

All these changes in the physical state of proteins involve a change in the degree of exposure of the protein to the solvent. Denaturation ordinarily involves an unfolding of the protein so that the groups which are in the interior of the native protein become exposed to the solvent (Fig. 3). Areas on the surface of the protein monomer

[20] R. B. Simpson and W. Kauzmann, *J. Am. Chem. Soc.* **75**, 5139 (1953).
[21] J. Wolff, *J. Biol. Chem.* **237**, 230 (1962).
[22] B. Nagy and W. P. Jencks, *J. Am. Chem. Soc.* **87**, 2480 (1965).
[23] J. C. Warren, L. Stowring, and M. F. Morales, *J. Biol. Chem.* **241**, 309 (1966).
[24] K. Hamaguchi and E. P. Geiduschek, *J. Am. Chem. Soc.* **84**, 1329 (1962).

or subunit must become less available to the solvent upon aggregation to a polymer or upon precipitation. Thus, salt solutions with
which the interior (for denaturation) or surface areas (for aggregation and precipitation) can interact favorably will tend to favor the
exposure of these areas to the solvent. Formally, the equilibrium
for denaturation may be described according to equation 1, in which

$$K = \frac{a_D}{a_N} = \frac{C_D f_D}{C_N f_N}$$

(1)

C, a, and f refer to concentration, activity, and activity coefficient,
and the subscripts D and N refer to denatured and native protein,
respectively. If the activity coefficients are defined as 1.0 for dilute
solutions in water, an increase in the ratio of the concentration of
denatured to native protein can occur if the activity coefficient of
the native protein is increased or, as is usually the case, if the activity coefficient of the denatured protein is decreased. Since the
exterior of the protein is exposed to the solvent in both the native
and denatured states, denaturation must, therefore, involve a decrease in the activity coefficient of the interior residues of the protein
which become exposed to the solvent upon denaturation. Depolymerization and dissolving of a protein may be considered in a similar
manner with reference to those surface areas of the protein which
become exposed to the solvent in these processes. For precipitation,
however, there is the complicating factor that the composition of the
solid phase may not remain constant. For example, precipitation by
trichloroacetate and perchlorate in acid solution probably involves
binding of these anions to the cationic protein, which reduces the
charge of the protein and results in the precipitation of a protein-
salt complex. As long as the composition of the two phases or states
remains constant, then, the problem of accounting for salt-induced
denaturation, precipitation, and aggregation may be reduced to the
problem of determining which residues of the protein undergo changes
in their activity coefficients (or solubility) in the presence of a given
salt.

The precipitation of proteins by concentrated salts is a rather
complicated special case of the general phenomenon of salting out,
for which there is a great deal of experimental data available, based
largely on solubility measurements.[25] Since the activity of a pure
solid or liquid phase is constant, the activity of the same material

[25] F. A. Long and W. F. McDevit, *Chem. Rev.* **51**, 119 (1952).

in a saturated solution which is in equilibrium with the solid or
liquid must also be constant, and any variation in the concentration
of the saturated solute, i.e., in its solubility, which is brought about
by changing the nature of the solvent, can be described as a change
in the activity coefficient of the solute according to equation 2. The

$$a_{\text{solid}} = a_{\text{solute}} = f_{\text{solute}}\, C_{\text{solute}} = \text{constant} \tag{2}$$

activity coefficient of benzene is plotted logarithmically as a function
of the concentration of a number of salts in Fig. 4. It is found experimentally that many salts change the logarithm of the solubility

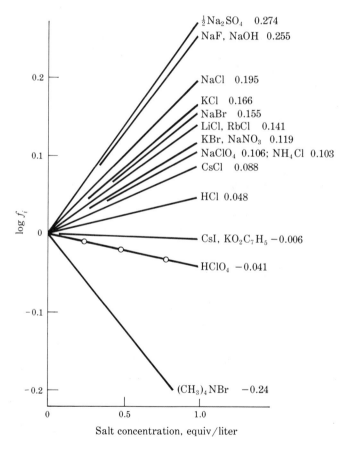

Fig 4. Effects of salts on the activity coefficient of benzene at
25°.[25] The numbers are k_s values (equation 3).

and activity coefficient of the solute in a linear manner as the salt concentration is increased, i.e., they affect the free energy of solution linearly. This relationship is expressed by the Setschenow equation 3, in which S_0 and f_0 refer to solubility and activity coeffici-

$$\log \frac{S_0}{S} = \log \frac{f}{f_0} = k_s \, C_{\text{salt}} \tag{3}$$

ents, respectively, in water, and k_s, the salting-out constant, is a measure of the sensitivity of the activity coefficient of the solute toward a particular salt. The sign of k_s is positive if the activity coefficient is increased and the solubility decreased and is negative if the activity coefficient is decreased and the solubility increased by the salt. It is remarkable that this equation frequently holds to salt concentrations of 1 M or more, in spite of the theoretical complexity of concentrated salt solutions, and that the same relationship is obeyed accurately for even such complicated solutes as proteins.[26] Simple nonpolar molecules such as benzene are salted out by nearly all salts, with an order of effectiveness which approximately follows the Hofmeister series, but are salted in by a few salts, such as tetramethylammonium bromide (Fig. 4). As the solute becomes larger, the value of k_s becomes larger. As it becomes more polar, there is a tendency for all the k_s values to shift in a negative direction; i.e., there is a downward movement of the fan-shaped array of lines in Fig. 4. If the solute contains acidic or basic groups which can undergo specific interactions with the salt solution, there may be alterations in this characteristic order of salt effectiveness.[25]

B. EXPLANATIONS

1. DIRECT IONIC INTERACTIONS

At first sight the order of the strength of electrostatic interactions in water, which generally shows little dependence on the size of the ion or is greater for large ions such as iodide, perchlorate, and tetraalkylammonium than for small ions such as chloride, fluoride, and sodium, appears to follow no sensible pattern according to simple electrostatic theory. Small cations such as lithium and sodium carry a rather firmly bound sheath of water of hydration around them, so

---

[26] A. A. Green, *J. Biol. Chem.* **93**, 495 (1931).

that it is customary to apply electrostatic theory to these ions based on an adjustable hydrated ionic radius, rather than the radius of the bare ion in the crystal. The smaller ion with a higher charge density will have a larger hydration sheath, so that hydration will tend to cause a leveling out of differences in electrostatic interactions. There is no doubt regarding the existence and importance of this layer of tightly bound water, but theories which base calculations of electrostatic interaction energies on a "hydrated ionic radius" must face the fact that different types of experimental measurements give very different numbers of bound water molecules for a given ion, although there is generally agreement as to the *order* of increasing hydration for different ions.[27-29] This is hardly surprising, because hydration is not an all-or-none phenomenon; the nature of "hydration" varies continuously between extremes and may involve several quite different phenomena. At one extreme is the Cr^{3+} ion, which binds water so tightly that its rate of exchange with the medium is slow enough to be easily measured. On the other hand, the iodide ion is certainly stabilized by water, as indicated by its large hydration energy upon transfer from the gas phase to water, but it does not bind water sufficiently tightly to form a distinct hydration layer, according to most methods of measurement. Still another type of "hydration" is found around very large ions in which the charge is well shielded from the solvent, such as the larger tetraalkylammonium ions; these ions behave as if they were surrounded by water molecules with a greater degree of order than those in the bulk solvent. Different experimental techniques probe different consequences of the "hydration layer" and so give different results. It is particularly difficult to account for the behavior of the halide ions on the basis of a "hydration layer" because anions are larger than cations of comparable atomic number and most methods of measurement indicate that there is no firmly bound hydration shell surrounding halides larger than fluoride.

In spite of the difficulties of quantitation, electrostatic interactions illustrate particularly clearly the overriding importance of the solvent in determining the behavior of molecules in aqueous solution. Consider, for example, the formation of an ion pair in water. The starting point for most calculations of electrostatic interaction energy is the ion in the gas phase (Fig. 5). The exact magnitude of the energy of solvation or hydration of individual ions is a matter of

[27] E. Glueckauf, *Trans. Faraday Soc.* **60**, 1637 (1964).
[28] D. W. McCall and D. C. Douglass, *J. Phys. Chem.* **69**, 2001 (1965).
[29] B. E. Conway, *Ann. Rev. Phys. Chem.* **17**, 481 (1966).

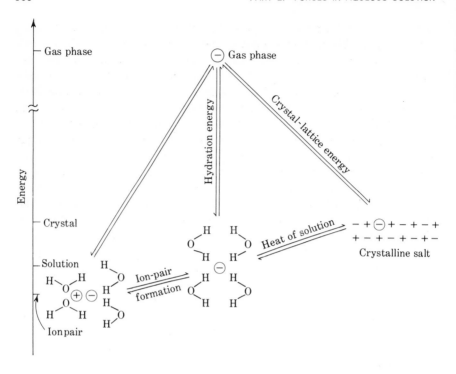

Fig 5. Diagram to show how the energy of ion-pair formation and heat of solution of an ion depend on the small differences between the hydration energies and crystal lattice energies of the various species. The differences in the energies of the ion in the crystal, solution, and ion pair are exaggerated.

some dispute, but it is certainly on the order of -50 to -200 kcal/mole. This may be contrasted with the free energy of ion-pair formation from monovalent ions in water of less than 1 kcal/mole, which is orders of magnitude smaller. The energy of solution of an ion from the crystal phase into water is also orders of magnitude smaller than the heat of hydration. Thus, the energy of an ionic interaction in water depends on the small difference between the amount of stabilization of a gas-phase ion when it interacts with the dipoles of water and when it interacts with the charge of another ion in water, which may or may not lose some of its surrounding water in order to form an ion pair. These relationships are illustrated for a hypothetical ion in Fig. 5, in which the differences in the energies of the ion in the crystal, solution, and ion pair have been greatly exaggerated. If the dependence of these energies on the radii of cations and anions were known exactly, it would be possible to predict the interaction energies of ions in water. The theory of ionic interactions in water is not yet sufficiently advanced to make possible the calculation of these small energy *differences* from first principles. The several different types of interaction energies and the specific geometrical factors involved in ion-water, ion-ion, and ion-dipole interactions interfere with the application of the usual electrostatic equations to the short distances between the reacting atoms and molecules. The following semiempirical and semiquantitative description of these processes may help to orient the reader with respect to the nature of the problem.

The situation is well illustrated by salt solubilities, which present a simpler and more clearly defined problem than the formation of ion pairs. The solubility of a salt depends on the difference between the stability of the ions in the crystal lattice and in water, i.e., on the difference between the crystal lattice free energies and the free energies of hydration of the ions. The crystal lattice energies of uni-univalent salts are dependent on the *sum* of the radii r_1 and r_2 of the constituent ions, and follow the empirical equation 4.[30] The

$$\Delta H^{\circ}_{298} \text{ (lattice)} = \frac{600}{r_1 + r_2} \left(1 - \frac{0.4}{r_1 + r_2}\right) \tag{4}$$

exact dependence of electrostatic free energies of hydration on ionic radius is not generally agreed upon,[31] but it certainly involves the ionic radii of the individual ions plus a constant (equation 5). In

$$\Delta F_{\text{el}} = -\frac{C}{r + a} \tag{5}$$

fact, the energy of interaction of an ion with water is determined by the strength of a number of different forces, including van der Waals, ion-dipole, and quadrupole interactions, which have different dependencies on the ionic radius; these dependencies average out in such a way that differences in hydration energy exhibit an approximate dependence on $(r + \alpha)^{-3}$, in which α is taken as the effective radius of the water molecule, 1.38 Å.[32] The crystal lattice energies for a series of salts and the hydration energies for individual ions,

[30] H. F. Halliwell and S. C. Nyburg, *J. Chem. Soc.* **1960**, 4603.

[31] G. H. Nancollas, "Interactions in Electrolyte Solutions," p. 118, Elsevier Publishing Company, Amsterdam, 1966.

[32] A. D. Buckingham, *Discussions Faraday Soc.* **24**, 151 (1957); H. F. Halliwell and S. C. Nyburg, *Trans. Faraday Soc.* **59**, 1126 (1963).

based on a value of -261 kcal/mole for the proton, are shown in Fig. 6. The solid line for the crystal lattice energies is calculated from equation 4. The heat of solution of any salt is determined by the *difference* between these curves, and the relative heats are a function of the small differences in the shapes of the individual curves. Thus if one takes a moderately large cation, such as cesium or tetramethylammonium ion, and varies the nature of the anion in the series I^-, Br^-, Cl^-, F^-, the hydration energy changes in a favorable direction more rapidly than the crystal lattice energy because a given change in r_2 will cause a smaller percentage change of the sum of the ionic radii $r_1 + r_2$ than of r_2 itself or of $r_2 + a$. The insolubility of salts of large anions and cations such as potassium perchlorate and cyclohexylammonium phosphates might, therefore, be regarded more properly as a reflection of the relatively small hydration energies of these ions than of any special stability of the crystal state; the hydration energies of the ions of such salts are simply insufficient to pull them out of the crystal lattice into solution.

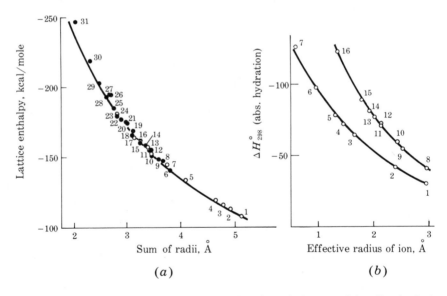

Fig 6. (a) Crystal lattice enthalpies as a function of the sum of the effective ionic radii for uni-univalent salts at 25°. (1) NMe_4I; (2) NMe_4Br; (3) NMe_4Cl; (4) CsI_3; (5) $CsClO_4$; (6) CsI; (7) CsN_3; (8) CsBr; (9) $KClO_4$; (10) KI; (11) $KBrF_4$; (12) CsCl; (13) KN_3; (14) $NaClO_4$; (15) KCN; (16) KBr; (17) $NaBF_4$; (18) NaI; (19) KCl; (20) CsF; (21) NaN_3; (22) NaBr; (23) LiI; (24) $LiBrF_4$; (25) NaCl; (26) LiN_3; (27) KF; (28) LiBr; (29) LiCl; (30) NaF; (31) LiF. (b) Absolute enthalpies of hydration for univalent ions at 25°. (1) NMe_4^+; (2) PhN_2^+; (3) Cs^+; (4) Rb^+; (5) K^+; (6) Na^+; (7) Li^+; (8) I_3^-; (9) $Ph \cdot SO_3^-$; (10) ClO_4^-; (11) I^-; (12) BF_4^-; (13) N_3^-; (14) Br^-, CN^-; (15) Cl^-; (16) F^-.[30]

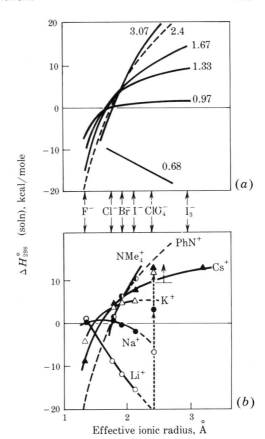

Fig 7. The heats of solution of salts of a series of cations with anions of increasing ionic radius (a) calculated from the differences between the hydration and crystal lattice energies and (b) experimental values at 25°. The broken line refers to values estimated for benzenediazonium salts. The numbers in (a) refer to the radius of the cation. The lower line in the figure represents the anomalous enthalpies of solution of perchlorate salts.[30]

A different situation obtains if a small cation, such as lithium, is examined with the same series of anions. With a *small* value of r_1, a change in r_2 in the series I^-, Br^-, Cl^-, F^- causes a larger change in the crystal lattice energy than in the hydration energy, so that lithium fluoride, for example, is relatively more stable in the crystal lattice than in water and therefore exhibits a smaller solubility than lithium chloride. The situation is illustrated in Fig. 7. When corrections are made for differences in entropy, this treatment successfully describes the solubilities of salts made up of ions of different radius.[30] Alternatively, the solubilities of salts may be considered as a function of the *sum* and the *ratio* of the radii of the two ions. The dependence of the crystal lattice and hydration energies on these quantities are such that the differences between these two energies are much more sensitive to the ratio than to the sum of the radii, and salts with a large difference between the radii of the two ions will be more soluble than those with similar radii.[33]

Ion-pair formation in water may be considered in a similar manner, although a quantitative treatment is more difficult. One of the principal difficulties is the fact that ion pairs exist in a series of different structures, including "intimate" and "solvent-separated" ion pairs (equation 6), and it is difficult to distinguish among these

$$Mg^{++}_{solv} + SO_4^{=}{}_{solv} \rightleftharpoons (Mg^{++} \cdot \overset{H}{O}H \cdot SO_4^{=})_{solv} \rightleftharpoons (Mg^{++} \cdot SO_4^{=})_{solv} \qquad (6)$$

forms in both experimental and theoretical approaches to the problem. The measurement of relaxation effects by sound absorption in such systems provides rather direct evidence for the existence of at least two such species of ion pairs of 2:2 electrolytes and provides a method for the quantitative measurement of the rates of interconversion of these species.[34]

Following Bjerrum, classical treatments of the energy of interaction of ions in ion pairs are based on the first principles of electrostatic theory, and the energy of interaction is calculated from the dielectric constant and the reciprocal of the ionic radii. Since the energy of ion-pair formation in water represents such a small difference between large numbers, it is not surprising that it is difficult to apply such treatments to ionic interactions in water. In fact, the tendency of large ions to undergo ion-pair formation in aqueous solution is frequently equal to or greater than that of small ions,[35] and the Bjerrum relationship is honored more in the breach than the observance unless adjustable parameters, such as effective ionic radii or regions of dielectric saturation, are introduced to improve the results. For example, conductance and activity-coefficient measurements suggest that ion-pair formation occurs to a significant extent in solutions of tetrabutylammonium iodide in water, whereas there is less or no ion-pair formation in solutions of tetramethylammonium iodide and tetrabutylammonium chloride.[36] The energy of interaction of two ions is reciprocally proportional to the sum of the effective radii r_1 and r_2 so that, as in the case of crystal

[33] H. L. Friedman, *J. Am. Chem. Soc.* **74**, 5 (1952).

[34] M. Eigen, *Discussions Faraday Soc.* **24**, 25 (1957); G. Atkinson and S. K. Kor, *J. Phys. Chem.* **71**, 673 (1967).

[35] C. W. Davies, "Ion Association," p. 77, Butterworth & Co. (Publishers), Ltd., London, 1962.

[36] R. M. Diamond, *J. Phys. Chem.* **67**, 2513 (1963); D. F. Evans and R. L. Kay, *Ibid.* **70**, 366 (1966).

lattice energies, a change in r_2 in a series of anions with a constant cation of radius r_1 may have either a larger or a smaller effect on the energy of ion-pair formation than on the hydration energy, depending on the size of r_1. For *large* cations, such as the alkylammonium groups of ion-exchange resins, the increase in the strength of the cation-anion interaction will increase more slowly as the anion becomes smaller in the series I^-, Br^-, Cl^-, F^- than will the strength of the water-anion interaction. Therefore, the stronger binding of large as compared with small ions to ion-exchange resins may be regarded in large part as simply an expression of the fact that large ions such as iodide interact weakly with water so that they can easily lose some of their water of solvation to interact with an ion exchanger, whereas small ions such as fluoride are so strongly solvated by water that they interact weakly with the ion exchanger.

In the case of polyatomic ions such as phosphate, perchlorate, and acetate, the strength of the interaction with water will be determined largely by the charge density on the individual oxygen atoms.

$$HO-\underset{\underset{OH}{|}}{\overset{\overset{O^{\delta-}}{|}}{P}}-O^{\delta-} \qquad O^{\delta-}\underset{\underset{O^{\delta-}}{|}}{\overset{\overset{O^{\delta-}}{|}}{Cl}}-O^{\delta-}$$

Thus, the negative charge of phosphate and acetate monoanions is distributed over two oxygen atoms, whereas that of perchlorate is distributed over four oxygen atoms, so that the weaker interaction of perchlorate with water permits a relatively stronger interaction with an ion-exchange resin.[37] High charge density also leads to a large basicity, and the most basic anions are least likely to leave an aqueous environment to interact with an ion-exchange resin. The same principles may be applied to ion-pair formation.[38] For *small* ions with a high charge density the energy of ion-ion interaction will change more rapidly with changing ionic radius than will the hydration energy, so that the tendency for ion-pair formation will increase with decreasing ionic radius. Thus, the stabilities of hydroxide complexes increase in the order $K^+ < Na^+ < Li^+ < Ba^{++} < Sr^{++} < Ca^{++} < Mg^{++} < La^{3+}$. This is one of the few examples in which a simple quantitative relationship is found between ionic radius, charge density, and ion-pair stability in water.[35] Strongly basic oxygen anions, including hydroxide and carboxylate, tend to follow this order of

[37] D. C. Whitney and R. M. Diamond, *J. Inorg. Nucl. Chem.* **24**, 1405 (1962).
[38] D. R. Rosseinsky, *J. Chem. Soc.* 1962 785.

cation affinity, and it is probable that direct ion pairing, without intervening water molecules, occurs in ion pairs of these salts.

The same general approach, based on the concept of *anionic field strength*, has been utilized by Eisenman to explain the orders of affinity of different glass electrodes for cations and has been extended to a number of chemical and biological systems, including ion-exchange resins, ion-pair formation, and interaction with membranes.[39] A scale of relative interaction energies of different cations with anions of varying field strength may be set up empirically for halide salts by comparing free energies of hydration with free energies of formation of alkali halide crystals. The result is similar to that of Fig. 7 and shows that for large anions, such as iodide, the interaction strength decreases in the order $Cs^+ > Rb^+ > K^+ > Na^+ > Li^+$, whereas for small anions, such as fluoride, the corresponding order is $Li^+ > Na^+ > K^+ > Rb^+ > Cs^+$. At intermediate field strengths intermediate orders are found which agree with those observed for glass electrode specificity. Similar comparisons based on the energies of a diatomic molecular gas of the alkali halide, on the activity coefficients of concentrated aqueous solutions of alkali halides, and on calculated electrostatic interaction energies as a function of ionic radii give essentially the same result. Basicity, the energy of interaction with a proton, may be considered as a special case of ion interaction and ligands with a high basicity, such as OH^-, also have a high anionic field strength and interact preferentially with other small cations such as Li^+ and Na^+.

The importance of the hydration energy of an ion, in its broadest sense, and its dependence on charge density has been realized for many years with reference to the Hofmeister or lyotropic series of ions. This order holds for a great many physical, chemical, and biological effects of ions in water and is itself correlated with ion hydration energy.[17, 18] The problem at the present time is to put these concepts into more quantitative terms and to obtain a clearer understanding of the detailed structure and electrostatic interaction energies of water molecules in the vicinity of ions of differing size and structure.

The tendency of combining groups to bind to an ion in dilute solution will be greatly increased if two or more such groups are immobilized in a larger structure, such as a macromolecule or chelat-

---

[39] G. Eisenman, in A. Kleinzeller and A. Kotyk (eds.), "Membrane Transport and Metabolism," p. 163, Czechoslovak Academy of Sciences, Prague, 1961; in C. N. Reilley (ed.), "Advances in Analytical Chemistry and Instrumentation," vol. 4, p. 213, John Wiley & Sons, Inc., New York, 1965; *Biophys. J.* 2, Pt. 2, 259 (1962).

ing agent. The combination of an ion with one or more ligands involves a restriction to the motion of the interacting molecules, which is manifested as a negative entropy of combination. If the change in this restriction to motion is made smaller by tying together the combining groups into a single molecule in the starting material, less entropy will be lost upon combination with the ion and the formation of a complex will be favored. This is the basis of chelation. It is illustrated by the exchange of ethylenediamine for methylamine molecules in the coordination shell of cadmium ion (equation 7). This process takes place spontaneously with a ΔF

$$Cd(NH_3)_n^{++} + H_2NCH_2CH_2NH_2 \rightleftharpoons (NH_3)_{n-2} Cd\left[\begin{array}{c} \overset{H_2}{N} \\ \underset{H_2}{N} \end{array}\right]^{++} + 2NH_3 \tag{7}$$

of -1.3 kcal/mole and a positive ΔS of 4.4 e.u. when the equilibrium is expressed on the usual molar scale because the decrease in entropy which is required to fix one ethylenediamine molecule is less than that required to fix two methylamine molecules into the coordination shell of the ion when all reactants and products are in a standard state of 1 M.

Much of the "driving force" for chelation arises from the completely arbitrary use of 1 M as the standard state for the expression of equilibrium constants. The contribution of this arbitrary entropy of concentration term to complex formation may be avoided by taking mole fraction 1.0 instead of 1 M as the standard state. If the equilibrium constant for the reaction of equation 6 is expressed on the mole fraction rather than the molar scale, the free energy of the reaction changes to the *positive* value of 1.0 kcal/mole and ΔS changes to -3.5 entropy units. One might say that a cadmium ion which is completely surrounded by methylamine or ethylenediamine molecules at mole fraction 1.0 would not enjoy the entropic advantage upon combination with the latter which provides the driving force for chelation in dilute solution.[40] Similarly, the affinity of magnesium ion for individual acetate ions is barely measureable, but the affinity toward the four carboxylate groups of ethylenediaminetetraacetate is large in dilute solution. The chelating agent provides a high local concentration of combining groups to overcome the low

[40] A. W. Adamson, *J. Am. Chem. Soc.* **76**, 1578 (1954); R. W. Parry, in J. C. Bailar, Jr. (ed.), "The Chemistry of the Coordination Compounds," p. 220, Reinhold Publishing Corporation, New York, 1956.

affinity for the individual groups and thereby overcomes the unfavorable entropy of concentration which would be required to bring together four acetate ions from dilute solution to the solvation shell of the magnesium ion. Alternatively, this problem may be approached by estimating the translational entropy that is lost upon complex formation, which is more unfavorable for monofunctional ligands than for a chelating agent, and correcting for the loss of rotational entropy which occurs when a flexible chelating agent binds to a metal.[41] The conclusions of this approach are similar to those just described; the chelate effect for a 5-membered ring near room temperature is close to $-RT \ln 55.5$, which is equivalent to about 2 to 3 kcal/mole, or about 8 to 11 entropy units.

In view of the small free energies of interaction which are observed for monovalent ions in aqueous solution, it is probable that the strong interactions which are found with some proteins are made possible by (1) a chelation effect of this kind, (2) nonelectrostatic binding energy for uncharged groups attached to the ion, or (3) a charged site which is fixed in a poor ion-solvating environment on the protein, so that there is an especially strong driving force for partial charge neutralization upon combination with an oppositely charged ion.

It is frequently suggested that nonelectrostatic attraction from hydrophobic or van der Waals-London dispersion forces provides the driving force for the binding of large ions to polymers. Such forces are certainly of overriding importance if a large hydrophobic group is attached asymmetrically to the charged group, as in a detergent. However, in the case of symmetrical ions it is difficult or impossible to find an experimental basis with which to evaluate the importance of this type of interaction, or to separate its influence from the electrostatic and solvation effects which have been discussed above and which certainly play an important role in determining the strength of the interaction. Although some ions which interact strongly are large and polarizable, such as iodide and perchlorate, other ions of similar size and polarizability, such as phosphate and acetate, interact weakly so that specific effects, such as fit and orientation of the polarizability, must be invoked if these forces are to make an important contribution to the binding energy.

An order very similar to that for binding to macromolecules and ion exchangers is found for the exclusion of ions from the surface of water, a phenomenon which cannot involve hydrophobic bonds or van der Waals interactions. The surface tension is a measure of the cohesive energy of a solution, and substances which increase the

[41] F. H. Westheimer and L. L. Ingraham, *J. Phys. Chem.* **60**, 1668 (1956).

cohesive energy, including most salts, increase the surface tension and are excluded from the surface layer, whereas substances which decrease the average cohesive energy, such as alcohols, decrease the surface tension and are concentrated on the surface. The reason for the exclusion of hydrated salts is clear—the ion cannot be fully hydrated if it is in the surface layer—and the effect of salts on the surface tension is very nearly the same for all salts of strongly hydrated ions, which are almost completely excluded from the surface. These ions include all of the simple alkali cations Na^+, K^+, Rb^+, and Cs^+, as well as $NH_4{}^+$, and strongly hydrated anions such as F^- and OH^-. However, larger anions are much more weakly hydrated and can enter the surface layer without a large loss of hydration energy. Consequently, there are large differences in the effects of salts of such ions on the surface tension, and the order of exclusion from the surface of $F^- > OH^- > Cl^- > BrO_3{}^- > Br^- > NO_3{}^- > I^- > ClO_4{}^- > SCN^-$ is very similar to that for the other phenomena which have been described above.[42] If the ion is sufficiently large and poorly solvated, it should be concentrated at the surface and cause a *decrease* in surface tension; this is the case for salts of the $PF_6{}^-$ ion. As might be expected, very much the same order is found for other phenomena which involve a transfer of ions from the midst of an aqueous solution to interaction with some inert material at a surface; this applies to the accumulation of ions at the metal-water interface of mercury and other electrodes, which can cause the generation of an electrical potential,[43] to interfaces between water and nonpolar organic liquids,[44] and to the salting out of nonpolar solutes.

2. CONCENTRATED SALT SOLUTIONS

a) **Salting out** According to classical electrostatic theory, the salting out of nonpolar organic molecules is a consequence of the less favorable electrostatic stabilization of salts in solvents of low dielectric constant. This important relationship is described quantitatively by equation 8, in which f_1 and f_2 are the activity coefficients and n_1

$$\frac{\delta \ln f_2}{\delta n_1} = \frac{\delta \ln f_1}{\delta n_2} \tag{8}$$

[42] A. Frumkin, *Z. Physik. Chem. (Leipzig)* **109**, 34 (1924); A. Frumkin, S. Reichstein, and R. Kulvarskaja, *Kolloid-Z.* **40** 9 (1926); J. E. B. Randles, *Discussions Faraday Soc.* **24**, 194 (1957); A. W. Evans, *Trans. Faraday Soc.* **33**, 794 (1937).

[43] M. A. V. Devanathan and B. V. K. S. R. A. Tilak, *Chem. Rev.* **65**, 635 (1965); D. C. Grahame, *Ibid.* **41**, 441 (1947).

[44] A. W. Evans, *Trans. Faraday Soc.* **33**, 794 (1937).

Table III Salting out of benzene[25, 45]

Salt	Observed	k_s Calc. Debye	k_s Calc. Kirkwood	Calculated internal pressure, equation 9, × 0.3	$V_s - \bar{V}_s{}^0$
Na_2SO_4	+0.55			0.58	53
NaOH	0.26			0.26	22.3
NaF	0.25	0.13	0.13	0.21	18.6
NaCl	0.20	0.13	0.13	0.16	12.8
KCl	0.17			0.12	10.3
CsCl	0.09	0.12	0.11	0.10	8.7
LiCl	0.14	0.13	0.14	0.12	10.4
$NaClO_4$	0.11			0.08	
NaBr	0.16			0.14	13.6
NaI	0.10	0.12	0.12	0.08	
NH_4Cl	0.10	0.12	0.11	0.10	9.0
$(CH_3)_4NBr$	−0.10	0.11	0.09	−0.11	−10
$(C_2H_5)_4NBr$	−0.25			−0.26	−23
$(C_3H_7)_4NBr$	−0.41			−0.37	−32

and n_2 are the amounts of two substances which might be added to water. This reciprocal relationship states that the destabilization of a salt in aqueous solution by the addition of an organic substance requires that the addition of a salt will cause destabilization of the organic solute, i.e., an increase in its activity coefficient and a decrease in its solubility. This equation holds regardless of the mechanism of the stabilization or destabilization.

Electrostatic theories of salting out based on the dielectric constant of the solution have been developed by Debye, Kirkwood, and others. The dielectric constant must certainly influence solubility behavior, but the macroscopic dielectric constant is a poor indicator of the ion-solvating ability of solvents over more than a very limited range of variation. Theories of this kind fail seriously in that they do not account for the large differences in the salting-out effectiveness of different salts, nor do they account for the fact that nonpolar solutes may be salted in by certain salts (Fig. 4). The observed salting-out constants for benzene are compared with those calculated by the Debye theory and by Kirkwood's modification of this theory in Table III; it is evident that these theories predict little difference between different salts and, in particular,

[45] N. C. Deno and C. H. Spink, *J. Phys. Chem.* **67**, 1347 (1963).

predict that tetramethylammonium bromide will behave similarly to other salts instead of salting in benzene.[25,45] The electrostatic theories may be improved by the inclusion of additional terms, such as an allowance for the sheath of strongly oriented molecules of water of hydration around small, highly charged ions from which organic solutes are completely excluded[46] or an estimated strength of the van der Waals–London interaction between the salt and the solute, but the modifications do not remove these difficulties if a sufficiently large series of salts is examined. A more successful approach might be based on the *observed* stabilities of ions in different solvents and water-solvent mixtures as measured by the Grunwald-Winstein Y values[47] or Kosower's Z values,[48] but such an approach would be essentially a restatement of the relationship of equation 8 and would not provide direct insight into the mechanism of the ion-solvent-solute interaction.

A much more successful semiemprical treatment of salting out is based on the effects of salts on the cohesive energy density or internal pressure of water.[25,45,49] The insertion of a nonpolar molecule into water may be divided into, first, the pulling apart of the water molecules to make a hole into which the solute can fit and, second, the insertion of the solute into the hole. In the case of a nonpolar solute which does not interact strongly with water the greater part of the free-energy requirement for this process may be ultimately ascribed to the decrease in the mutual interaction of water molecules in the first step. This provides the principal reason for the low solubility of organic molecules in water when the solute is not sufficiently polar to provide a compensating, favorable interaction with water in the second step (see Chap. 8). Now, the addition of any material which will increase the average cohesive energy of interaction among the water molecules will make it more difficult to separate the water molecules and dissolve the solute, whereas the addition of a substance, such as an alcohol, which will decrease the average mutual attraction of the water molecules will facilitate these processes. Most salts increase the average strength of mutual interaction and cohesive energy density of an aqueous solution. This is evidenced experimentally as an electrostriction and increase in surface tension and, according to this model, should

[46] B. E. Conway, J. E. Desnoyers, and A. C. Smith, *Phil. Trans. Roy. Soc.(London)* **A256**, 389 (1964).

[47] E. Grunwald and S. Winstein, *J. Am. Chem. Soc.* **70**, 841 (1948).

[48] E. M. Kosower, *J. Am. Chem. Soc.* **80**, 3253 (1958).

[49] W. F. McDevitt and F. A. Long, *J. Am. Chem. Soc.* **74**, 1773 (1952).

cause a salting out of solutes which do not themselves interact strongly with water. The salting out of a nonpolar solute may be regarded as simply a squeezing out caused by the electrostriction and increased average strength of the mutual interaction of the solvent molecules in the presence of salt.

The cohesive energy of a solution may be expressed in terms of its internal pressure, and the contribution of this effect to salting out may be evaluated by relating the change in internal pressure caused by electrostriction to the salting-out constant according to equation 9 in which $\bar{V}_i^0$ and $\bar{V}_s^0$ are the partial molar volumes of the

$$k_s = \frac{\bar{V}_i^0 (V_s - \bar{V}_s^0)}{2.3 \beta_0 RT} \tag{9}$$

solute and the salt, respectively, V_s is the molar volume of the "liquid" salt, and β_0 is the compressibility of water. These parameters are all readily available except for V_s, but this quantity can be estimated with reasonable certainty from compressibility measurements and other sources.

This relationship is successful in accounting for the order of effectiveness of different salts in salting-out benzene, and, after correction by a factor of about 3, for which an explanation is available,[49] gives a remarkably good quantitative correlation with the k_s values of a series of salts for the salting out of benzene (Table III). A sufficiently large ion will have a charge density at its surface which is less than that of the water dipole, so that salts of such ions will interact less strongly with water molecules than do water molecules with each other and will cause a *decrease* in the cohesive energy density and internal pressure of the solution. The addition of such a salt should, therefore, make it easier to dissolve a nonpolar solute in water. The greatest success of the internal-pressure theory is that it predicts the salting in of benzene by tetramethylammonium bromide, which has a *positive* volume of solution (i.e., $V_s - \bar{V}_s^0$ is negative, Table III). In addition, the relationship accounts reasonably well for the increase in the magnitude of salting-out constants with increasing volume of the solute and even for the pronounced salting in of benzene by larger tetraalkylammonium ions, up to tetrapropylammonium bromide.[45]

b) **Macromolecules** The changes in the physical state of macromolecules which take place in the presence of concentrated salt solutions depend in large part on the changes in the activity coefficients of those portions of the macromolecule which change their degree of exposure to the solvent during the change in state, so that the explanation for the effects of concentrated salt solutions on the physical state of macromolecules resolves itself largely into the problem of defining the nature of these activity-coefficient effects (equation 1). For proteins and nucleic acids the important structural components which are likely to undergo a change in activity coefficient in the presence of salts are the charged groups, the hydrophobic or nonpolar groups, such as aliphatic and aromatic side chains of amino acid residues and the bases of nucleic acids, and the backbone structure, i.e., the peptide chain of proteins and the phosphate diester chain of polynucleotides.

Direct electrostatic interactions with *charged groups* are important at low salt concentrations, but usually are much less important at high salt concentrations, at which the simple Debye-Hückel theory can no longer be applied to the energy of interaction of charged groups with salts. Protein denaturation at high and low pH is caused in large part by the mutual repulsion of charged groups of the same sign and is decreased in the presence of dilute solutions of salts, which serve to shield the charges. Similarly, the high charge density of the double helix of DNA is responsible for a breakdown of the helix and denaturation because of electrostatic repulsion at low salt concentrations. The dissociation of polymers into subunits in the presence of salts may be caused by electrostatic interaction of the salt with charged groups which help to hold the polymer together; a possible example is the dissociation of hemoglobin into subunits in the presence of calcium chloride.[50]

However, the available evidence suggests that charged groups are generally of minor importance in accounting for the effects of concentrated salt solutions on the denaturation and precipitation of proteins near neutral pH. The *absolute* solubility of a protein, such as carboxyhemoglobin, changes with pH because the protein has a minimum solubility when its net charge is near zero. However, the effect of concentrated salt solutions on this solubility, as measured by the k_s value for salting out, appears to be independent of the pH and the charge on the protein.[26] This is shown for the salting out of carboxyhemoglobin by phosphate in Fig. 8; the k_s values, determined by the slopes of the salting-out curves, are the same over the pH range from 6.05 to 7.43, which extends above and below the pH of minimum solubility and over which the absolute solubility varies by nearly tenfold. (Unfortunately, this experiment was carried out

[50] E. Antonini, J. Wyman, E. Bucci, C. Fronticelli, and A. Rossi-Fanelli, *J. Mol. Biol.* **4**, 368 (1962); K. Kawahara, A. G. Kirshner, and C. Tanford, *Biochemistry* **4**, 1203 (1965).

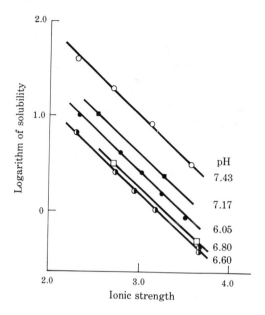

Fig 8. Salting out of carboxy-hemoglobin by phosphate, based on the ionic strength of the solution, at pH values both above and below the pH of minimum solubility of carboxyhemoglobin.[26]

with phosphate, which undergoes ionization in the pH region of interest; the salting out is therefore based on total ionic strength rather than salt concentration.)

That interactions with charged groups are not required to explain the effects of concentrated salt solutions on protein denaturation is most dramatically demonstrated in the melting of gelatin gels, a form of denaturation. The effect of concentrated salt solutions on the melting temperature of gelatin is unaltered if the pH is changed from neutrality to pH 2 or pH 11.7, at which the carboxylate and ammonium groups, respectively, have been converted to the uncharged form. Furthermore, the removal of charged groups by acetylation of the amino groups, esterification of the carboxylate groups, and nitration of the majority of the guanidinium groups has no significant effect on the change in the melting temperature induced by salt.[7] Even in the case of the DNA helix with its high anionic charge density, the denaturation caused by concentrated salt solutions is dependent more on the nature of the anion than the cation of the salt and can be accounted for by an effect of the salt on the uncharged bases rather than on the charges of the polymer.[24,51] It is apparent that the interaction of concentrated salt solutions with uncharged constituents of polymers is able to cause changes in the physical state of the polymer. It is not surprising that interactions

[51] D. R. Robinson and M. E. Grant, *J. Biol. Chem.* **241**, 4030 (1966).

with the charged groups are of little importance in protein denaturation at neutral pH because the charged groups are normally in contact with the solvent on the exterior of the native protein, so that they can interact with salts in a similar way in both the native and denatured states. Consequently, it would not be expected that a stronger interaction with one or the other of these states should affect the equilibrium for a change in state.

To the extent that *nonpolar* groups of polymers are on the surface or become exposed to the solution in the course of a change in state, the effects of salts on the activity coefficients of such groups must affect the equilibrium for the change in state. The large body of data for the effects of salts on simple organic model compounds, such as benzene (Fig. 4), makes it possible to predict the relative effectiveness of different salts if salt effects on nonpolar groups are important: salts which strongly salt out nonpolar compounds, such as sulfates and fluorides, should oppose a change in state in which nonpolar groups become exposed and salts which salt in nonpolar compounds, such as tetramethylammonium bromide, should favor such a change. Although effects of this kind must exist and certainly contribute to the effect of concentrated salt solutions on protein denaturation in particular, the available evidence suggests that for most proteins this is not the most important influence of salts. The tetramethylammonium ion does not exhibit a large effect on most proteins, for example, and the sodium and potassium salts of I^-, NO_3^-, and ClO_4^- and the chlorides of Ba^{++}, Ca^{++}, and Mg^{++} cause denaturation and solubilization of many proteins but salt *out* benzene and other nonpolar compounds. Furthermore, it is frequently found that the effects of salts on proteins are insensitive to the nature of the cation in the series Na^+, K^+, Cs^+, Rb^+, whereas the activity coefficients of simple nonpolar molecules show large differences with these different cations.

There is much closer correlation between the effects of concentrated salt solutions on proteins and on the solubility and activity coefficient of acetyltetraglycine ethyl ester (ATGEE), a model compound composed largely of amide groups (Tables I and II).[8] This

$$CH_3\overset{O}{\underset{H}{\overset{\|}{C}}}NCH_2\overset{O}{\underset{H}{\overset{\|}{C}}}NCH_2\overset{O}{\underset{H}{\overset{\|}{C}}}NCH_2\overset{O}{\underset{H}{\overset{\|}{C}}}NCH_2\overset{O}{\overset{\|}{C}}OC_2H_5$$

ATGEE

suggests that the effects of concentrated salts on proteins are exerted largely through their stabilizing or destabilizing effect on *amide groups*, which undergo a change in their degree of exposure to the solvent when the protein undergoes a change in physical state.

Those salts which tend to denature, dissolve, and dissociate proteins, such as LiBr, NaI, NaSCN, $CaCl_2$, guanidine hydrochloride, and lithium diiodosalicylate, increase the solubility of this model polyamide and should, therefore, favor any change in state of the protein which leads to a greater exposure of amide groups to the solvent. Conversely, salts which protect against denaturation and which precipitate and aggregate proteins, such as sulfates, phosphates, acetates, fluorides, and citrates, decrease the solubility of ATGEE and will tend to force amide groups out of contact with the solvent. More formally, the former group of salts will decrease the activity coefficient of amide groups which are in contact with the solvent and thus, according to equation 1, will increase the concentration of unfolded or exposed protein in which such contact occurs; the second group of salts will have the opposite effect. Although there is some variation in the direction of the effect of borderline salts, depending on the structure of a given protein (possibly because of a differing importance of interactions with hydrophobic and charged residues), the direction of the effects which are observed with the extreme members of the group is constant for a large number of proteins. Furthermore, the behavior of the model amide agrees with that of proteins for those salts which have opposite effects on the amide and on nonpolar compounds and in the relative insensitivity to the nature of the cation in the series Na^+, K^+, Cs^+, $(CH_3)_4 N^+$. It is premature to attempt detailed quantitative comparisons, but it is of interest that the salting-out constants k_s, for ATGEE are about one-fifth as large as those for hemoglobin, so that one might say that the salting out of hemoglobin could be accounted for if salt were excluded from the immediate environment of the equivalent of five molecules of ATGEE when a molecule of hemoglobin is transferred from solution to the solid state. This does not appear to be an unreasonable figure; much of the exterior of a crystallized protein is still surrounded by solvent molecules, and the activity-coefficient effect that leads to precipitation must involve those regions of the surface which are adjacent to other molecules and are not exposed to salt and solvent in the crystal.

The denaturation of DNA by concentrated solutions of salts, which follows an order of salt effectiveness similar to that for proteins, can be accounted for in an analogous way by the effects of salts on the activity coefficients of the nucleotide bases, which become more exposed to the solvent in denatured than in native DNA.[51] This is less surprising when it is realized that the heterocyclic bases of DNA have large dipoles and are composed largely of carbonyl groups adjacent to nitrogen atoms; in fact, they have the properties of cyclic amides.

The detailed or "microscopic" mechanism of the effects of concentrated salt solutions on proteins, peptides, nucleic acids, and other polar solutes is less certain. Salting out of these compounds and their constituents is presumably mediated by the same mechanism as the salting out of less polar compounds. The values of k_s for a polar solute of a given volume are smaller than for a nonpolar solute because there is a more favorable interaction of the polar solute with the solution; if the polarity is sufficient, salting in is observed. The internal-pressure theory appears to offer the most satisfactory explanation at the present time for the salting *out* of both polar and nonpolar solutes.

The salting in which is observed with model amides, nucleic acid bases, and polymers is most easily accounted for by a direct interaction between the dipoles of these compounds and the solvent ions, but the nature of this interaction is not well defined and this explanation has not been rigorously proved. For weak ion-dipole interactions of this kind it is difficult to draw a sharp line between a stoichiometric ion-dipole complex and the clustering of ions in the neighborhood of the dipole that must follow from the observed activity-coefficient effects and the reciprocal relationship of equation 8. Some support for the existence of a direct ion-dipole interaction comes from the close correlation between the effects of anions on the peptide ATGEE and their affinity for ion-exchange resins or for binding to charged groups at low concentration (Table I); in all these situations it appears that the large and less strongly solvated ions are most easily able to lose enough solvating water to interact effectively with a charge or dipole of relatively low field strength. The solute molecule might be regarded as the occupant of a solvent cavity, so that those ions which can most easily approach a surface (as indicated by their effect on surface tension) will be concentrated at the surface of this cavity to interact with the solute dipoles within.

Further support for the direct-interaction model comes from an examination of the effect of salts on the merocyanine dye **10**, which may be regarded as a vinylogous amide (**11a** and **11b**) in which the

$$CH_3N \bigcirc = C - C = \bigcirc = O \quad \longleftrightarrow \quad CH_3^+N \bigcirc - C = C - \bigcirc - O^-$$

10

$$\begin{array}{cc} \overset{O}{\underset{\parallel}{}} & \overset{O}{\underset{\parallel}{}} \\ {>}N - C{\diagdown} & {>}N - (C{=}C)_n - C{\diagdown} \end{array}$$

11a   11b

nitrogen atom and carbonyl group of the amide are separated by a system of double bonds through which the normal amide resonance can occur. The change in the visible absorption spectrum of this dye in the presence of concentrated salt solutions exhibits an isosbestic point rather than a continuous shift of the absorption maximum as the salt concentration is increased. This fact and the fact that with several salts the change in spectrum follows the concentration dependence expected for a simple association reaction with an association constant on the order of $1.0\ M^{-1}$ suggest that an ion-dipole complex is formed between the dye and one of the ions of the salt. This complexation does not account for all the effect of salts on the solubility and activity coefficient of the dye, but it does suggest that direct interaction constitutes an important part of the observed salt effects.[52]

It is frequently concluded that the demonstration that an ion or some other small molecule causes a change in state of a macromolecule by interacting with some group on the macromolecule means that interactions of that group with similar groups contribute to the stability of the macromolecule in its original state. This conclusion is fallacious. The situation may be described by the imperfect analogy of the "fishhook rule": the demonstration that a protein could be pulled apart by attaching fishhooks to each end and pulling them apart does not prove that the protein is held together with fishhooks.

It is particularly tempting to ignore this rule in the case of ionic interactions and conclude, for example, that charged groups provide the driving force for protein association if a protein can be dissociated by the addition of a salt. Suppose that the charged groups in the polymer are adjacent to peptide dipoles and that the free energy for their transfer to water is zero, or even negative (Fig. 9). Alternatively, they may form an ion pair in the polymer, but this ion pair may contribute no stabilization to the polymer— uni-univalent ion pairs are known to have little stability in water. In either case, the addition of a salt which does interact favorably with the charged groups will favor exposure of the group to the solvent and tend to dissociate the polymer, although the charged groups do not contribute to the stability of the polymer. It is known that large anions bind tightly to certain proteins, so dissociation by this mechanism is feasible. Furthermore, salts may exert their effects on uncharged groups. For example, hemoglobin is dissociated from a tetramer to a dimer in the presence of salts, and it might be thought that this is because the tetramer is held together by ionic interactions which are broken by added salts. However, the order of effectiveness of different salts is similar to that

[52] J. Davidson and W. P. Jencks, *J. Am. Chem. Soc.* (to be published).

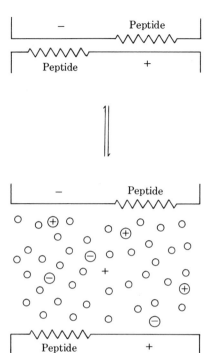

Fig 9. Diagram to show how an energetically favorable interaction of an aqueous salt solution with charged groups can provide a driving force for exposure of these groups to the solvent and denaturation of the protein when the charged groups do not contribute directly to the stability of the native protein.

for interaction with the peptide ATGEE, and dissociation could be brought about partly or entirely by an interaction of salts with amide groups between the subunits, without invoking charged groups.[50,53] The same point may be made for the depolymerization of F-actin.[22]

Analogous situations with other components of macromolecules, such as hydrophobic groups, are equally or more probable. All that can be concluded from the demonstration that a particular type of interaction causes a change in the physical state of a macromolecule is that the groups on the macromolecule which undergo the interaction undergo a change in their degree of exposure to the solvent when the physical change takes place and that they are *available* for maintaining the structure of the particular physical state of the macromolecule in which they are less exposed to the solvent.

c) **Water "structure."** A complete theory of the effects of salts on water and on water-solute interactions will relate the changes in enthalpy, entropy, volume, dielectric constant, and water "structure"

[53] G. Guidotti, *J. Biol. Chem.* **242**, 3685 (1967).

to the phenomenon under discussion and will provide a more detailed picture of the solution than is provided by such semiempirical approaches as the cohesive-energy-density–internal pressure treatment. Although beginnings have been made, the author is not convinced that detailed treatments of this kind are adequate to account for the properties of aqueous solutions at the present time, although they are of great value as stimuli to thinking about the role of these factors. After the electrostatic treatments, the most frequently discussed aspect of the interaction of salts and water is the effect of salts on water "structure."[54–57] The addition of any solute to water is very likely to be accompanied by changes in one or several of the parameters which have been utilized as indicators of the degree of water structure, and it is tempting to correlate these changes with other effects of the salts on the solution. These structural changes will certainly be included in a complete theory of salting out, for example, but the assumption that there is a cause-and-effect relationship between structural changes and salting out is not always accompanied by a detailed and critical description of the relationship of the change in structure to the observed change in the free energy of the solvent-solute interaction. Explanations based on water structure are not even always internally consistent with respect to the direction of the effect which is ascribed to an increase or decrease in structure.

At this point some comment should be made about the effects of salts on the "structure" of water. The strong directional interaction of water molecules with each other makes it certain that the mutual orientation of water molecules in liquid water is far from random, and many of the properties of water can be described by a model in which the orienting effects of water molecules on each other are considered in terms of a kind of structure, perhaps a number of "flickering clusters" of water molecules.[55,57] Such oriented regions of hydrogen-bonded molecules will have some of the properties of one or another form of ice, although it is unlikely that they represent regions with the structure of ordinary ice.

The introduction of an ion, with its surrounding electric field, will change this state of affairs, although the ways in which the changes take place are not simple. It has already been pointed out

[54] J. D. Bernal and R. H. Fowler, *J. Chem. Phys.* **1**, 515 (1933).

[55] H. S. Frank and M. W. Evans, *J. Chem. Phys.* **13**, 507 (1945); H. S. Frank and W-Y. Wein, *Discussions Faraday Soc.* **24**, 133 (1957).

[56] R. W. Gurney, "Ionic Processes in Solution," McGraw-Hill Book Company, New York, 1953.

[57] J. L. Kavanau, "Water and Solute-Water Interactions," Holden-Day, Inc., San Francisco, 1964.

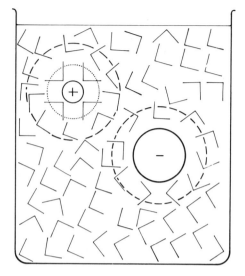

Fig 10. Effect of ions on the structure of water, after Frank et al.[55] The water molecules within the dotted line are in the immediate hydration shell of the ion, those within the dashed line are in a region of increased disorder produced by the ion, and some of those in the bulk solvent are oriented into "flickering clusters."

that a small, highly charged ion will orient the immediately adjacent water molecules into a firm hydration sphere, which will remain with the ion for an appreciable time and will have properties which are quite different from those of the bulk water molecules (Fig. 10, area inside the dotted circle). These water molecules constitute the immediate hydration shell of the ion and define the hydrated radius and hydration number, although these quantities vary over a wide range depending on the method used for their estimation.[27-29] These molecules may certainly be regarded as more "structured" than the bulk molecules of liquid water. Outside this firm hydration shell or immediately adjacent to the surface of larger ions the electrical field will not be strong enough to bind water molecules in a hydration shell, but will be strong enough to compete effectively with the dipole-dipole forces which provide some orientation and structure to the molecules of liquid water. The influence of this force is comparable to the effect of introducing the Beatles into the Boston Symphony Orchestra: the different types of forces compete with each other and the result is an increase in the disorder and entropy of the system (Fig. 10, area inside the dashed circles). In a still larger ion, in which the charge is effectively shielded from the solvent by bulky hydrocarbon substituents, the charge density at the surface is so low as to have no significant influence on the solvent, and the ion will behave in almost the same way as the comparable hydrocarbon, to restrict the motion and increase the structure of surrounding water molecules as described in the following chapter.

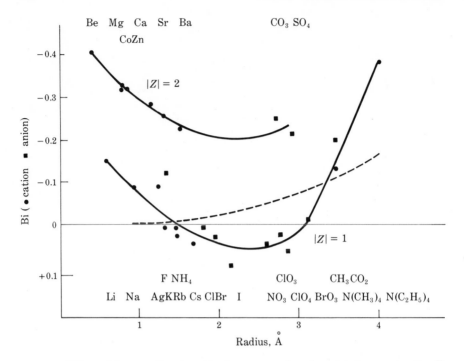

Fig 11. Effect of ions on the viscosity of water as a function of their crystal radius.[58] These B values are based on the fluidity, which is the reciprocal of the viscosity.

Thus, there are at least two types of "structure-forming" ions: small ions with a high charge density that orient surrounding water molecules by a strong electrostatic interaction, and very large ions which may orient surrounding water molecules because their electric field is too weak to have a significant influence on the solvent. For this reason a number of the parameters which measure water "structure" show maximal values for the smallest and largest ions, surrounding a minimum for the "structure-breaking" ions of intermediate size. An example of this behavior is found in the effect of ions on the viscosity of water (Fig. 11).[58] Keeping in mind the different reasons for the structure-forming effects of very large and very small ions, it is not surprising that the effects of these ions on other properties of aqueous solutions often cannot be accounted for solely in terms of their effect on water structure.

Some of the most easily visualized parameters which are thought to be measures of water "structure" are the viscosity, entropy, rate of self-diffusion, and dielectric relaxation time of

[58] R. J. Podolsky, *J. Am. Chem. Soc.* **80**, 4442 (1958).

water. The effect of ions and nonpolar solutes on the dielectric relaxation time of water is discussed in the following chapter. The effect of ions on the viscosity of water may be considered at three different levels of sophistication: effects on the viscosity itself (or on its reciprocal, the fluidity); effects on the viscosity B coefficient from the Jones-Dole equation 10, which separates out the relatively

$$\eta = \eta_0 \ (1 + A \ \sqrt{c} + Bc) \tag{10}$$

small influence of interionic electrostatic forces on the viscosity in the term containing the A coefficient; and effects on the temperature coefficient of the viscosity, which takes into account the increased "structure" of water at low temperatures (if there is more structure at a given temperature, a structure-breaking ion should have an increased effect on the viscosity).[56,59] As with other parameters, there is some disagreement among the conclusions from these parameters for borderline cases, but there is little question about the order of different ions or about the direction of the effect of the extremes. If a division of the effect of a salt into the effects of its constituent ions is made on the basis of some assumption regarding the relative effectiveness of anions and cations of a given size, a series of individual ion effects on water structure may be compiled, as shown for the effect of alkali and halide ions on the viscosity B coefficient in Table IV.[28,56,60] The smallest ions, lithium and fluo-

[59] R. L. Kay, T. Vituccio, C. Zawoyski, and D. F. Evans, *J. Phys. Chem.* **70**, 2336 (1966).

[60] E. R. Nightingale, Jr., *J. Phys. Chem.* **66**, 894 (1962).

Table IV   Effect of ions on water structure[28,56,60]

Ion	Viscosity B coefficient	Unitary partial molal entropy, e.u.	Self-diffusion of water
Li^+	+0.15	−8.8	−0.11
Na^+	+0.08	+0.5	−0.08
K^+	−0.01	10.7	0
Cs^+	−0.05	18.3	−0.01
$(CH_3)_4N^+$	+0.14		
$(C_2H_5)_4N^+$	+0.39		
$(C_3H_7)_4N^+$	+1.09		
$(C_4H_9)_4N^+$	+1.40		
F^-	+0.10		−0.11
Cl^-	−0.01	11.0	0
Br^-	−0.04	17.1	0.07
I^-	−0.08	22.8	0.08

ride, are structure-forming by virtue of their strong electrostatic orientation of surrounding water molecules, while the large cesium, bromide, and iodide ions are structure-breaking. Still larger ions, such as tetraethylammonium, are structure-making according to the various viscosity criteria.[59,60]

The disorder-producing effect of an ion should be manifested directly in its entropy of solution. In making comparisons of entropy values, there is a problem of choosing the proper units in order to ensure that the comparison is based on comparable standard states. A comparison of unitary partial molal entropies, which is most satisfactory in this respect, reveals the same order for the effects of ions on water structure as are reached from the viscosity B coefficient (Table IV).[56] The effects of salts on the self-diffusion coefficient of water lead to very similar conclusions and, in fact, are closely correlated with effects on the fluidity (the reciprocal of the viscosity).[28,61]

To return to the question of the extent to which an effect such as salting out may be directly ascribed to the influence of salts on the structure of water, it is important to emphasize the importance of demonstrating a self-consistent cause-and-effect relationship between such phenomena which holds for a wide range of salts and of avoiding the temptation to construct an "explanation" based on a *post facto* rationalization which can easily be constructed for almost any system with a limited series of salts. For example, the smaller salting-out effect of large anions as compared with small anions might be ascribed to the structure-breaking effect of the larger ions, which would disrupt the water structure and make it easier to insert a solute than in the presence of a comparable concentration of a small, structure-forming ion. But one might equally well argue that the salting-in effect of large tetraalkylammonium ions, such as the tetraethylammonium ion, results from the increase in water structure caused by these ions. The increase in water structure in the presence of a large ion or upon the addition of a relatively nonpolar material such as an alcohol or dioxane should make it easier to form a shell of structured water around the solute, which might be shared with the structured layer around the ion or the organic component of the solvent. But this explanation proposes an effect of water structure which is opposite to that of the preceding explanation and also faces some difficulty in the case of the tetramethylammonium ion. The tetramethylammonium ion is structure-breaking, at least

[61] J. H. Wang, *J. Phys. Chem.* **58**, 686 (1954).

according to some criteria,[59, 62] but has a salting-in effect on benzene which is only slightly smaller than that of the larger tetraalkylammonium ions (Table III, Fig. 4).

The ease with which mutually compensating changes in energy and entropy may occur with little change in the free energy of an aqueous solution makes it probable that changes in water structure may occur as a *secondary* change following some more fundamental change in the nature of the solution. The first problem in understanding the nature of the effects of ions on the behavior of solutes in water is to define the nature of the changes which are manifested most directly in the free energy of the system. Both the smaller salting-out effect of the structure-breaking iodide and perchlorate compared with fluoride and chloride ions and the salting-in effect of both large and small tetraalkylammonium ions may be accounted for in terms of the effect of these ions on the cohesive energy density or internal pressure of the solution without reference to water-structure effects (Table III). Similarly, the correlations of changes in water structure with the effects of concentrated salt solutions on proteins and peptides, which may be observed with a limited series of salts, tend to break down if a large series of salts is examined, suggesting that there is not a simple cause-and-effect relationship between these phenomena; less detailed but more successful explanations of these effects may be developed from the known effects of concentrated salt solutions on compounds which are models for the component parts of the macromolecule.[8, 63]

Further examples of mutually compensating changes in the entropy and enthalpy of aqueous solutions may be found in the behavior of thermodynamic parameters and activity coefficients of salt solutions. Tetrapropyl- and tetrabutylammonium chloride show large, mutually compensatory excess enthalpy and entropy terms with increasing concentrations, with little change in free energy.[64] The escaping tendency of water from 1 M solutions of NaCl, NaBr, and NaI is almost identical, as shown by the activity of water in these solutions of 0.967, 0.966, and 0.965, respectively, yet the structure of water is very different in these three solutions, as measured by a number of different parameters. If each ion affects the structure and entropy of only six water molecules, $^{12}/_{55}$ of the water

[62] G. E. Boyd, J. W. Chase, and F. Vaslow, *J. Phys. Chem.* **71**, 573 (1967); R. H. Wood and H. L. Anderson, *Ibid.*, p. 1871.

[63] W. P. Jencks, *Fed. Proc.* **24**, S-50 (1965).

[64] S. Lindenbaum, *J. Phys. Chem.* **70**, 814 (1966).

molecules are influenced by the salt, and a change in the free energy
of water would occur unless the entropy changes are offset by
compensating enthalpy changes. The similar free energies of water
in the three solutions probably represent a cancellation of the favorable enthalpy change which occurs when water molecules become
oriented in such a way as to undergo maximal hydrogen bonding by
the unfavorable entropy change arising from the restriction to free
movement which is demanded by this hydrogen bonding.

8
Hydrophobic Forces

When a molecule with a charge, a dipole, or a group which can act as a donor or acceptor of protons or electrons binds to another small molecule or a protein in aqueous solution, one's first reaction is to ascribe the driving force for the interaction to electrostatic, hydrogen-bond, or charge transfer forces. However, the strong charge-solvating and hydrogen-bonding ability of water and the weakness of ordinary charge transfer interactions in the ground state tends to reduce or eliminate the possibility of obtaining large binding energies from these forces (Chaps. 6, 7, and 9). In order to explain the large binding energies which are found in enzyme-substrate interactions and in the binding of other small molecules to proteins, it is frequently necessary to invoke some further mechanism of interaction which we will tentatively label a "hydrophobic bond," for want of a better name. "Hydrophobic forces" are probably the most important single factor providing the driving force for noncovalent intermolecular interactions in aqueous solution. The free energies for the

binding of substrates and inhibitors to the active sites of enzymes
are often of the order of -10 kcal/mole or more, only a small fraction of which can be attributed to other types of attractive interactions. The strength and specificity of the binding of small molecules
to proteins is seen particularly clearly in the interaction of haptens
with antibodies, for which the principal driving force is usually some
sort of hydrophobic bonding. The free energy of binding of ϵ-dini-
trophenyllysine to its specific antibody, which is almost all accounted
for by interaction with the dinitrophenyl group, is approximately
-12 kcal/mole, and the binding energies for small haptens of low
polarity are generally on the order of -5 to -10 kcal/mole.[1,2]

The terms "hydrophobic bond," "apolar bond," and "nonpolar
bond" may be misleading because they do not refer to a chemical
bonding, in the ordinary sense, between the interacting molecules.
Furthermore, many of the interactions to which these terms are applied involve molecules which have an appreciable solubility in water
and which contain strongly polar groups, such as hydroxyl, carbonyl,
and nitro substituents. However, other terms which have been suggested are even less satisfactory because they imply a specific mechanism for the interactions. From a phenomenological point of view,
hydrophobic bonding may be broadly defined as an interaction of
molecules with each other which is stronger than the interaction of
the separate molecules with water and which cannot be accounted
for by covalent, electrostatic, hydrogen-bond, or charge transfer
forces. No mechanism for the interaction is implied by this definition.

Examples of interactions which fall into this general class will
be described in the first part of this chapter, with little or no discussion of the possible mechanisms of interaction. In the second part
an elementary and qualitative attempt will be made to relate some
of these phenomena to the properties of water and to discuss the
perennial question of whether such interactions in aqueous solution
are better described in terms of a positive attraction between the
solute molecules or a negative interaction with the solvent. In the
latter section, the term "hydrophobic" will be applied in a more restricted sense to describe interactions resulting from the strong cohesive energy of hydrogen-bonded water molecules, which forces less
polar molecules to interact with each other regardless of whether or

[1] F. Karush, *Advan. Immunol.* **2**, 1 (1962).
[2] H. N. Eisen and G. W. Siskind, *Biochemistry* **3**, 996 (1964).

not there is a net attractive force between them. If the interaction is accompanied by a decrease in entropy and an increase in solvent "structure," it conforms to the classical model of the hydrophobic bond, but it will be suggested that the changes in solvent structure are secondary and that the mechanism of the interaction is fundamentally similar whether or not such changes occur.

A. EXAMPLES

1. INTERACTIONS OF IONS

It is frequently found that large ions interact strongly with each other in aqueous solution, whereas smaller ions with similar charged groups interact weakly or not at all. This binding may be divided into two distinct, but not unrelated classes. The first class consists of large, symmetrical ions in which the charge is shielded from water and the ion interacts more strongly with another ion than with water, as discussed in the previous chapter. The second class comprises ions in which the charge is attached to a hydrophobic group and the interaction of this hydrophobic group with a macromolecule or another ion provides the driving force for binding. Examples of the second class are found in dyes and ionic detergents, which bind to hydrophobic sites on proteins and may cause denaturation by solubilizing the hydrophobic interior of the protein. The binding of a series of substituted anions of related structure to proteins increases with increasing size of the substituents with little regard to inductive effects,[3] and it is commonly found that charged dyes which can undergo some sort of hydrophobic interaction bind stoichiometrically to oppositely charged groups on proteins, although small ions show little or no binding under the same conditions.

One of the few examples of this type of interaction with simple molecules which is susceptible to a more or less quantitative evaluation is the ion pairing of a series of sulfonates and alkylammonium ions, as determined by conductivity measurements (Table I). Ion pairs formed from the relatively large benzenesulfonate and trimethylbutylammonium ions have little or no stability in water, but ion-pair formation becomes detectable if a hydrocarbon chain or azobenzene group is added to one or the other of the ions and a very stable ion pair with a dissociation constant corresponding to a

---

[3] J. Steinhardt, C. H. Fugitt, and M. Harris, *J. Res. Natl. Bur. Std.* **26**, 293 (1941); **28**, 201 (1942).

Table I   Equilibrium constants[4] for ion-pair formation in water at 25°

Anion	Cation	K_{assoc}, liters/g-ion	$-\Delta F^{\circ}_{assoc}$, kcal/mole
$C_6H_5SO_3^-$	Me_3N^+-n-Bu	< 3	< 1
$C_6H_5SO_3^-$	$Me_3N^+C_{10}H_{21}$	7.1	1.8
$C_{12}H_9N_2SO_3^{-\,a}$	Me_3N^+-n-Bu	5.5	1.7
$C_{12}H_9N_2SO_3^{-\,a}$	$Me_3N^+C_{10}H_{21}$	42,000	8.4

[a] Azobenzene-4-sulfonate-.

free energy of binding of -8.4 kcal/mole is formed between azo-benzene-4-sulfonate and decyltrimethylammonium ion.[4]   The formation of this ion pair may be attributed either to hydrophobic interaction between the nonpolar groups or, conceivably, to a direct electrostatic interaction between the charges in a medium of low dielectric constant provided by the shielding hydrocarbon groups.

It is well known that many dyes exhibit deviations from Beer's law at low concentrations in water because of dimerization or aggregation to a series of large polymers; if there is interaction between their π electron systems, the dyes may show large spectral shifts (metachromasia) upon aggregation.[5]   It is noteworthy (1) that this aggregation may take place with cationic dyes, such as the cyanines, in spite of their mutual electrostatic repulsion, (2) that aggregation of neutral or charged dyes is generally eliminated or greatly reduced in nonaqueous solvents, such as ethanol, and (3) that the value of ΔH for dye aggregation is negative.[6]   The low dye concentrations at which association takes place reflect large free energies of interaction; values of ΔF of -10 kcal/mole are not uncommon.[7]

2. NUCLEIC ACID BASES

In spite of their large dipole moments, nucleic acid bases are hydrophobic in the sense that their solubility in water is generally small (i.e., their interaction with each other in the solid phase is strong relative to their interaction with water) and is increased by the addition to water of compounds such as alcohols, which increase the

[4] A. Packter and M. Donbrow, *Proc. Chem. Soc.* **1962**, 220.

[5] W. West and B. H. Carroll in T. H. James (ed.), "The Theory of the Photographic Process," 3d ed., p. 233, The MacMillan Company, New York, 1966.

[6] E. Rabinowitch and L. F. Epstein, *J. Am. Chem. Soc.* **63**, 69 (1941).

[7] Y. Tanizaki, T. Hoshi, and N. Ando, *Bull. Chem. Soc. Japan* **38**, 264 (1965).

solubility of hydrophobic compounds in water. The solubility of
adenine in water increases with increasing hydrocarbon substitution
on added alcohols, amides, ureas, and carbamates, and the increasing solubilizing effectiveness is paralleled by an increasing effectiveness of the compound as a denaturing agent for DNA (deoxyribonucleic acid).[8] This is one of several lines of evidence showing that
one of the factors which can cause denaturation of DNA is a change
in the nature of the solvent such that the solvent interacts more
favorably with the nucleic acid bases which undergo an increase in
the amount of their exposure to the solvent upon denaturation; this
is manifested experimentally by an increased solubility and decreased
activity coefficient of nucleic acid bases in such solvents.

The solubility of nucleic acid bases is also increased in the presence of other nucleic acid bases (Fig. 1). The decrease in the activ-

[8] L. Levine, J. A. Gordon, and W. P. Jencks, *Biochemistry* **2**, 168 (1963).

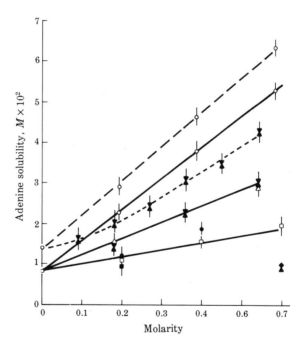

Fig 1. The solubility of adenine in the presence of
purine, O; uridine, ✗; cytidine, △; pyrimidine, □; phenol,
●; cyclohexanol, ■; urea, ▲; and adonitol, ◆, at 25.5°
(solid lines) and 38° (dashed lines).[9]

ity coefficient of a given base as its concentration is increased suggests that energetically favorable interactions may occur between molecules of the same base as well as different bases.[9] The fact that these solubilization and activity-coefficient effects are significant at relatively low base concentrations, on the order of 0.1 M in favorable cases, suggests that they are caused by a direct interaction of base molecules with each other, rather than by a nonspecific effect on the solvent. The observation of shifts in the nuclear magnetic resonance spectra of the ring protons of the bases with increasing concentration provides stronger evidence that direct association is responsible for these changes in activity coefficients.[10] Association constants calculated from solubility and activity-coefficient measurements, such as those shown in Fig. 1, also account successfully for the concentration dependence of the shifts in nuclear magnetic resonance spectra. The association constants are not large—approximately 5 M^{-1} for adenine-cytidine interaction and 1 M^{-1} for thymidine-uridine interaction—but they do indicate that the base molecules have a strong preference for other base molecules compared with water molecules, which are present in great excess at a concentration of 55 M. The unfavorable entropy for the association of individual molecules from dilute solution will be much reduced for bases which are tied together with a covalently bonded backbone in a nucleic acid chain, so that it is almost certain that the same mechanism which is responsible for the interaction of individual base molecules is the primary factor responsible for the stability of single- and double-stranded polynucleotide helices in aqueous solution. Since the detailed mechanism of this interaction has not been established beyond question, it is appropriate to refer to the forces involved by the noncommittal term "stacking interaction."

There is no evidence that the small driving force which can be obtained from hydrogen bonding in aqueous solution makes a major contribution to the stability of native nucleic acids, and, indeed, it has been shown that the stability of single-chain polycytidylate helices is unchanged in the presence of formaldehyde, which combines with the nucleotide bases and would be expected to reduce or eliminate any stabilization by intermolecular hydrogen bonding.[11] The primary role of hydrogen bonding in polynucleotides appears to be

[9] P. O. P. Ts'o, I. S. Melvin, and A. C. Olson, *J. Am. Chem. Soc.* **85**, 1289 (1963).

[10] S. I. Chan, M. P. Schweizer, P.O.P. Ts'o, and G. K. Helkamp, *J. Am. Chem. Soc.* **86**, 4182 (1964).

[11] G. D. Fasman, C. Lindblow, and L. Grossman, *Biochemistry* **3**, 1015 (1964).

that of providing specificity by determining which base-base inter-actions are sterically permitted and energetically least unfavorable in the double helical structure which is held together by "stacking interactions."

3. EFFECTS ON REACTION RATES

There are a few examples of rate accelerations in simple reactions which are caused by approximation of the reactants through hydro-phobic interactions. The catalytic activity of β-phenylpropionic acid in the general acid catalyzed enolization of benzoylacetone (1) is some threefold larger than expected from the activity of smaller acids of comparable acidity, although the catalytic activity of this

1

acid for the enolization of acetylacetone is normal. It is of interest that this enhanced catalytic activity was attributed by Bell and co-workers in 1949 to an approximation of the catalyst and substrate which is brought about primarily by a squeezing out of these hydro-phobic molecules from a solution of strongly interacting water mole-cules into a single cavity; i.e., the interaction is a consequence of the mutual attraction of the solvent molecules rather than an at-traction of the solute molecules.[12,13]

A somewhat similar phenomenon is seen in the acceleration of the alkaline hydrolysis of methyl naphthoate by large cations, such as tetrabutylammonium ion, which presumably interact with the substrate and facilitate reaction with the hydroxide anion; the ad-dition of large anions, such as tetraphenylboron or hydrocarbons, causes a decrease in rate. This interaction was attributed to van der Waals–London dispersion forces between the ion and the substrate.[14]

A more striking rate enhancement brought about by hydro-phobic interaction is found in a comparison of the rates of aminolysis of the p-nitrophenyl esters of acetate and decanoate by ethylamine and decylamine.[15] After correction for hydrolysis and for a 30-fold

[12] R. P. Bell, E. Gelles, and E. Möller, Proc. Roy. Soc. (London) 198A, 308 (1949).
[13] J. A. V. Butler, Trans. Faraday Soc. 33, 229 (1937).
[14] E. F. J. Duynstee and E. Grunwald, Tetrahedron 21, 2401 (1965).
[15] J. R. Knowles and C. A. Parsons, Chem. Commun. 1967, 755.

decrease in the reactivity of the longer-chain ester compared with the acetate, based on the rate of reaction with ethylamine and presumably caused by steric hindrance, there is a rate enhancement of approximately 100-fold in the reaction of decylamine with the decanoate ester which must be ascribed to an approximation of the reactants caused by hydrophobic interaction of the hydrocarbon chains. The rate enhancements are not the result of micelle formation because they are first order with respect to amine concentration and are observed with amine concentrations well below the critical micelle concentration.

It is much more common for binding to an added molecule to cause a rate *decrease*. One of the most striking examples is the inhibition of the hydrolysis of benzocaine [ethyl *p*-aminobenzoate (2)] by caffeine (3). The ester and inhibitor undergo association in

$$H_2N-\underset{}{\bigcirc}-\overset{\overset{\displaystyle O}{\|}}{C}OCH_2CH_3$$

2   **3**

water with an association constant of approximately 60 M^{-1}, and the decreasing hydrolysis rate in the presence of added caffeine follows the concentration of free ester closely, suggesting that the rate of hydrolysis of the complex is negligible compared with that of the free ester.[16]

4. ESTIMATION OF THE MAGNITUDE OF HYDROPHOBIC FORCES

The simplest and most direct model for hydrophobic bonding is the transfer of a compound from solution in water to another phase, which may be either the pure liquid compound or some other nonaqueous phase. The free energy of this transfer, calculated from the partition coefficients between the two phases or, in the case of a liquid, from the solubility, provides at least a rough estimate of the free energy to be expected for a hydrophobic interaction of the compound. Thus the binding of a series of hydrocarbons to serum al-

---

[16] T. Higuchi and L. Lachman, *J. Am. Pharm. Assoc.* **44**, 521 (1955).

bumin and of a different series of hydrocarbon inhibitors to the active site of chymotrypsin is in each case inversely correlated with the solubilities of the hydrocarbons in water.[17,18] Logarithmic plots of the solubility against the binding energy indicate that a change in structure changes the binding energy to serum albumin about half as much as it changes the solubility, whereas it has almost equal effects on the inhibitory potency and solubility in the case of the chymotrypsin inhibitors. This might be taken, rather crudely, as an indication that the binding behaves as if the environment of one half of the hydrocarbon molecule were changed from water to one resembling that of the pure hydrocarbon upon binding to albumin, while the other half remains exposed to water; in the chymotrypsin case the behavior resembles that which would be expected if the inhibitor were completely transferred to a nonaqueous phase.

There is a large amount of data available on the free energies of transfer of small molecules from water to nonaqueous phases such as isobutanol, hexane, ether, and benzene.[19] A hydrophobic binding parameter π, which is a measure of the possible hydrophobic binding energy of a given compound comparable to the σ parameter for polar effects, has been defined and is based on partition coefficients between water and octanol.[20] The slope of a logarithmic plot of binding constants against this parameter for a series of compounds is a measure of the extent to which the binding process resembles transfer from water to octanol; the slope of such a plot for binding to hemoglobin, for example, is 0.7.

Several different types of measurements suggest that, on the average, the free energy $-\Delta F$ which may be obtained by the transfer of a linear hydrocarbon chain from water to a nonpolar solvent increases by approximately 0.8 kcal/mole for each methylene group which is added to the chain. This number is based on the solubilities in water of alcohols, hydrocarbons, and fatty acids, equilibria for the formation of nonionic micelles and the dimerization of fatty acid anions; it shows remarkably little variation for chain lengths up to

[17] M. R. V. Sahyun, *Nature* **209**, 613 (1966).

[18] A. J. Hymes, D. A. Robinson, and W. J. Canady, *J. Biol. Chem.* **240**, 134 (1965).

[19] K. B. Sandell, *Monatsh. Chem.* **89**, 36 (1958); R. Collander, *Acta Chem. Scand.* **4**, 1085 (1950).

[20] K. Kiehs, C. Hansch, and L. Moore, *Biochemistry* **5**, 2602 (1966); C. Hansch, K. Kiehs, and G. L. Lawrence, *J. Am. Chem. Soc.* **87**, 5770 (1965); C. Hansch, E. W. Deutsch, and R. N. Smith, *Ibid.*, p. 2738.

12, and in some cases 16, carbon atoms.[21-23] (However, a recent study of the solubilities of aliphatic hydrocarbons suggests that these compounds do not exhibit such a constant increment at long chain lengths.[24]) The free energy of transfer of a benzene molecule from water to benzene is about -5 kcal/mole, and a comparable driving force is presumably available for the transfer of a benzene group from water to a hydrophobic region in a protein.

Data of this kind may also be used to estimate the contribution of hydrophobic forces to the stabilization energy of a macromolecule. Based on the assumption that the interior of a protein molecule is less hydrophobic than a pure hydrocarbon or long-chain alcohol and, on the average, resembles ethanol, Tanford has utilized the free energies of transfer of amino acid side chains from ethanol to water to estimate the contribution of hydrophobic forces to the stability of globular proteins.[25] Based on this model, the potential free energy of binding is increased by some 0.7 kcal/mole for each additional methylene group and by 2 kcal/mole for a benzene or indole ring.

An increase in the solubility of one compound upon the addition of another compound to the solvent may be interpreted either in terms of a nonspecific activity coefficient effect or the formation of a complex between the two compounds. A compilation of equilibrium constants for complex formation, many of which were obtained from solubility measurements at sufficiently low concentrations that large activity coefficient effects are unlikely, provides a valuable source for estimates of the magnitude of interaction energies that may be expected with a number of different classes of compounds.[26]

The binding of a series of simple aromatic molecules to polyvinylpyrrolidone (**4**), a water-soluble polymer with a hydrocarbon

$$\left[\begin{array}{c} -CH_2CH_2- \\ | \\ \langle N \rangle \!\!=\!\! O \end{array} \right]_n$$

4

[21] L. Benjamin, *J. Phys. Chem.* **68**, 3575 (1964).

[22] I. D. Robb, *Australian J. Chem.* **19**, 2281 (1966); C. McAuliffe, *J. Phys. Chem.* **70**, 1270 (1966); P. Mukerjee, *Ibid.* **69**, 2821 (1965).

[23] J. M. Corkill, J. F. Goodman, and J. R. Tate, *Trans. Faraday Soc.* **60**, 996 (1964).

[24] F. Franks, *Nature* **210**, 87 (1966).

[25] C. Tanford, *J. Am. Chem. Soc.* **84**, 4240 (1962).

[26] T. Higuchi and K. Connors in C. N. Reilley (ed.), "Advances in Analytical Chemistry and Instrumentation," vol. 4, p. 117, Interscience Publishers, Inc., New York, 1965.

backbone and cyclic tertiary amide groups in the side chains, is one of the few examples of the binding of simple molecules to polymers of known structure in aqueous solution that provides a model for the binding of small molecules to proteins (Table II).[27] The concentration dependence of the binding behaves as if there were one binding site for approximately each 10 pyrrolidone residues and the free energy of binding is about -1 to -2 kcal/mole for an aromatic ring, with some increased binding if polar substituents are added. The principal driving force for the binding is the positive change in entropy upon combination of the small molecule with the polymer, which is sufficient to overcome the positive enthalpy change observed with some compounds and the negative entropy change that might be expected from the contraction of the polymer. The polymer undergoes a contraction upon binding of uncharged small molecules, as measured by light scattering and a decrease in viscosity. This might be regarded as a model for the change of conformation of a protein upon binding a small molecule.

5. MICELLES

Micelles provide the best known and most extensively studied example of the operation of hydrophobic forces in aqueous solution, and much of the contemporary discussion of these forces follows closely the earlier description of micelles by colloid chemists.[28] The structure of micelles is determined by the tendency of the hydrophobic portion of the constituent detergent molecules to undergo aggregation so as to have the smallest possible contact with water

[27] P. Molyneux and H. P. Frank, *J. Am. Chem. Soc.* **83**, 3169, 3175 (1961).

[28] See, for example, H. G. B. DeJong in H. R. Kruyt, (ed.), "Colloid Science," vol. 2, p. 309, Elsevier Publishing Company, Amsterdam, 1949.

Table II Binding of small molecules to polyvinylpyrrolidine in water at 30°[27]

Compound	K_{assoc}, M^{-1}	ΔF, kcal/mole	ΔS_u, e.u.	ΔH, kcal/mole
Benzene	3.5	-1.1	$+18$	2.4
Benzoic acid	3.0	-2.1	$+12$	-1.0
Phenol	14.5	-1.6	$+15$	0.5
2-Naphthol	120	-2.9	$+12$	-1.7

and of the hydrophilic portions, which may be either charged or uncharged, to remain at the surface in contact with the aqueous phase. The addition of compounds which increase the solubility of nonpolar compounds in water, such as alcohols, will tend to destroy the micelle by making the exposure of the hydrophobic regions to the solvent energetically more favorable; this will be manifested as an increase in the critical micelle concentration in the presence of such compounds. In the case of ionic micelles the addition of such compounds will generally destabilize the high charge density at the surface of the micelle, which provides a further driving force for the breaking up of the micelle. Because of the perturbing influence of these charged groups, it is easier to draw unambiguous conclusions from examination of the behavior of nonionic than of ionic detergents.

The structure and properties of micelles provide a remarkably close analogy to those of globular proteins, including enzymes. The elucidation of the structure of several globular proteins by x-ray diffraction has shown that there is a strong tendency for hydrophobic amino acid side chains to be buried in the interior, away from the aqueous solvent, and for charged and other hydrophilic groups to be located at the surface in contact with the solvent.[29] The addition of an organic substance to a protein solution will increase the tendency of the hydrophobic groups to become exposed to the solvent, just as in the case of a micelle, and this decrease in the free energy of transfer of the group to the solvent provides the principal driving force for protein denaturation by alcohols, acetone, and related compounds. The temperature dependence and thermodynamic parameters for the denaturation of ribonuclease in ethanol-water mixtures are similar to those for the solution of nonpolar molecules.[30] (It is of interest that at low temperature and low alcohol concentration there is a *decrease* in protein denaturation which parallels a decrease in the solubility of argon under the same conditions; this may reflect a competition between ethanol and nonpolar groups for a limited number of interstitial sites in the solvent.)

It has been pointed out in Chap. 6 that protein denaturation by urea and guanidine hydrochloride involves an energetically favorable interaction of these compounds with amide and peptide groups, which is decreased upon the substitution of alkyl groups for the hydrogen

---

[29] J. C. Kendrew, *Brookhaven Symp. Biol.* **15**, 216 (1962); M. F. Perutz, *J. Mol. Biol.* **13**, 646 (1965).
[30] J. F. Brandts and L. Hunt, *J. Am. Chem. Soc.* **89**, 4826 (1967).

atoms of these denaturing agents. However, urea and guanidine hydrochloride also contribute to the denaturation of proteins through a "hydrophobic" mechanism by favoring the exposure of nonpolar groups to the solvent.[31] This is shown by their solubilizing effect on hydrocarbons and on the hydrophobic side chains of amino acids and by the destabilizing effect of urea on both ionic and nonionic micelles.[32,33] These two different mechanisms of action are responsible for the wide effectiveness of these compounds as denaturing agents for different types of macromolecules. They may be differentiated by an examination of the effect of alkyl substitution upon the denaturing activity of ureas and guanidine hydrochlorides because alkyl substitution increases the effectiveness of these compounds in solubilizing nonpolar molecules, as well as nucleic acid bases.[8,34,35]

The analogy between micelles and proteins may be carried further in that for certain reactions micelles exhibit a catalytic activity which has several of the characteristics of enzyme catalysis. In most such systems the catalyst is a micelle composed of an ionic detergent which concentrates the substrate on the surface and causes rate acceleration if the transition state of the reaction has a charge opposite to that of the micelle.[36,37] If the transition state has no net charge or the same charge a rate retardation is usually observed because concentration of the reactants in the micelle reduces their contact with water; consequently, reactions in which water is a reactant or provides effective solvation for a polar transition state are inhibited. The dielectric constant at the surface of dodecylpyridinium iodide micelles has been estimated to be approximately 36 from the absorption maximum of the pyridinium iodide charge transfer absorption band in such micelles.[38]

The acceleration of the base catalyzed hydrolysis of p-nitrophenyl esters of acetic and hexanoic acid by cetyltrimethylammonium bromide provides a good example of this type of catalysis (Fig. 2).[37]

[31] W. Kauzmann, *Advan. Protein Chem.* **14**, 1 (1959).

[32] Y. Nozaki and C. Tanford, *J. Biol. Chem.* **238**, 4074 (1963); D. B. Wetlaufer, S. K. Malik, L. Stoller, and R. L. Coffin, *J. Am. Chem. Soc.* **86**, 508 (1964).

[33] M. J. Schick, *J. Phys. Chem.* **68**, 3585 (1964); W. Bruning and A. Holtzer, *J. Am. Chem. Soc.* **83**, 4865 (1961); P. Mukerjee and A. Ray, *J. Phys. Chem.* **67**, 190 (1963).

[34] J. A. Gordon and W. P. Jencks, *Biochemistry* **2**, 47 (1963).

[35] D. R. Robinson and W. P. Jencks, *J. Am. Chem. Soc.* **87**, 2462 (1965).

[36] E. F. J. Duynstee and E. Grunwald, *J. Am. Chem. Soc.* **81**, 4540, 4542 (1959).

[37] M. T. A. Behme, J. G. Fullington, R. Noel, and E. H. Cordes, *J. Am. Chem. Soc.* **87**, 266 (1965).

[38] P. Mukerjee and A. Ray, *J. Phys. Chem.* **70**, 2144 (1966).

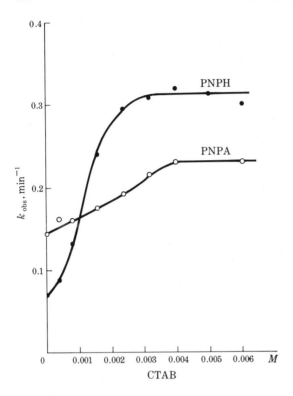

Fig 2. Acceleration of the hydrolysis of p-nitrophenyl
acetate (O) and p-nitrophenyl hexanoate (●) by the
cationic detergent cetyltrimethylammonium bromide
(CTAB) at pH 10.07 and 25°.[37]

At a constant pH of 10.07 the rate of hydrolysis of both these substrates is increased by the addition of detergent, but the increase is
larger for the substrate with the longer hydrocarbon chain, which
interacts more strongly with the detergent micelle through hydrophobic forces. As the catalyst concentration is increased, there is
a saturation with respect to the catalytic activity when the catalyst
is present in excess; a similar saturation is observed when the substrate concentration is increased in the presence of a limiting concentration of catalyst. Similar rate accelerations are observed for
the reactions of esters with the anions of amino acids in the presence
of cetyltrimethylammonium bromide. The rate increases which are
found in such systems are generally not large; the maximum rate
increase for the (acid catalyzed) hydrolysis of methyl orthobenzoate
in the presence of sodium lauryl sulfate at pH 4.76 is 85-fold.[37]

An example of a rate acceleration in which both reactants are incorporated into the micelle by hydrophobic forces is found in the acylation of the benzylamine derivative 5 by the ester 6, which

$$(CH_3)_3 \overset{+}{N} - \langle \rangle - CH_2NH(CH_2)_9CH_3$$

5

$$^-O_3S - \langle \rangle \underset{NO_2}{-} OC(CH_2)_6CH_3$$

6

shows a sharp increase in rate as the concentration of 5 is increased to its critical micelle concentration.[39]

The high density of positive charge at the surface of the cetyltrimethylammonium bromide micelle will stabilize negatively charged ions and transition states, so that the observed rate acceleration in a reaction of this kind might be regarded as the result of an increased local concentration of hydroxide ion in the vicinity of the substrate adsorbed onto the surface of the micelle. The activity of hydroxide ion must be constant throughout the system, so that the reduced activity coefficient in the vicinity of the micelle will result in an increased concentration of hydroxide ion in this region. The rate acceleration may be described more directly as the consequence of a decrease in the activity coefficient of the transition state of the reaction at the surface of the micelle, relative to the activity coefficients of the reactants in the bulk solution. This decrease is caused by hydrophobic interaction with nonpolar components and electrostatic interaction with the charged components of the transition state. This sort of bifunctional interaction with a small molecule, in which different parts of the molecule are stabilized by different mechanisms in their microenvironment on a macromolecule, provides a particularly close analogy to what must almost certainly occur in the interaction of substrates with the active sites of enzymes.

The changes in the pK of acids and bases which are adsorbed at the surface of micelles may be explained in a similar manner. The pK of 7 for example is increased from 6.55 in water to 7.02 in

[39] T. C. Bruice, J. Katzhendler, and L. R. Fedor, *J. Phys. Chem.* 71, 1961 (1967).

$$\text{(CH}_3)_3\overset{+}{\text{C}}\text{N} \doteq \overset{\overset{\displaystyle H}{|}}{\text{C}} - \hspace{-0.5em}\left\langle\!\!\!\!\!\overline{}\!\!\!\!\!\right\rangle$$

with H on the nitrogen as well.

7

an anionic micelle of sodium lauryl sulfate, and is decreased to 4.96 in a cationic micelle of cetyltrimethylammonium bromide and to about 5.0 in an uncharged micelle of a nonionic detergent.[40] These shifts reflect the influences of simple electrostatic stabilization and destabilization of the cationic acid species of this compound and the destabilization of this charged species by the relatively poor ion-solvating medium of the hydrophobic region of the micelle. They provide a model for the analogous changes in the pK of side-chain groups or adsorbed molecules on enzymes and other proteins.

A particularly interesting example of catalysis by micelles, which may require a more complex explanation and bear a closer analogy to the rate accelerations induced by enzymes, is found in the acceleration of the hydrolysis of the p-nitrophenyl esters of acetate and octanoate by mixed micelles of cetyltrimethylammonium bromide and N-α-tetradecanoyl-L-histidine.[41] The rate accelerations observed in dilute solutions of the reactants and catalyst at pH 7.2 are approximately 30-fold for the acetate ester and 1,000-fold for the caprylate ester, as compared with the activity of free imidazole molecules in solution. Some specific structural feature of the mixed micelle is required for catalytic effectiveness because micelles composed of either the cationic or anionic components alone are catalytically inactive. The high catalytic activity is presumably caused in large part by an approximation of the substrate and the imidazole groups of the catalyst which is brought about by hydrophobic interactions; however, the requirement for both components of the micelle suggests that there may be additional stabilization of the transition state by electrostatic interaction or other more specific structural effects.

6. CLATHRATES—INCLUSION COMPOUNDS

These terms refer to a class of compounds in which one of the components is "enclosed or protected by a bar or grating" of the other component. Such compounds have a definite composition, but gen-

[40] M. T. A. Behme, and E. H. Cordes, *J. Am. Chem. Soc.* **87**, 260 (1965).
[41] A. Ochoa-Solano, G. Romero, and C. Gitler, *Science* **156**, 1243 (1967).

erally do not exhibit an integral stoichiometry and are known mostly in the crystalline state. Suppose a polar molecule can exist in two crystalline states, A and B, of which B is less dense and is ordinarily of higher energy. If a "guest" molecule is of the proper size and shape to fit into the vacancies of the more open structure B, even a small amount of stabilization resulting from a weak van der Waals interaction of the guest and host molecules may be sufficient to stabilize B relative to A, so that a solid inclusion compound containing the guest compound may be isolated. Many examples of this type of behavior are known, of which two of the most dramatic are the formation of solid water-hydrocarbon clathrates well above the freezing point of water in natural-gas transmission lines (which may obstruct the pipeline if sufficient water vapor leaks into the system) and the stereospecific formation of linear, all-*trans* polymers when butadienes are polymerized while contained as guest molecules in the interior of long, tubular urea or thiourea clathrates.[42]

The loss of entropy upon clathrate formation is ordinarily too large to permit the formation of separate clathrate units in solution, but there is evidence for the formation of stable inclusion compounds in solution from cyclodextrins, in which the host molecules are covalently bonded to each other in a ring so that there is little loss of entropy upon complex formation (Fig. 3). The solubility of benzoic acid in water increases linearly as the concentration of cyclodextrin in the solution is increased.[43] The molar ratio of the increase in solubility to the concentration of cyclodextrin is close to 1.0, which demonstrates that the increase in solubility is the result of the formation of a 1:1 inclusion compound of the cyclodextrin and benzoic acid. The cyclodextrin-induced increase in the solubility of long-chain aliphatic carboxylic acids containing 7 to 10 carbon atoms shows a specificity with respect to the relative size of the host and guest molecules: the C_7 acid is solubilized most effectively by α-cyclodextrin, which is composed of six glucose units and has a cavity diameter of approximately 6 Å, whereas the C_{11} acid is solubilized most effectively by β-cyclodextrin, which is composed of seven glucose units and has a cavity diameter of 8 Å. The binding of the acid is accompanied by a change in the optical rotation of the cyclodextrin, which might be taken as another model for a substrate-induced change in conformation.

[42] J. F. Brown, Jr. and D. M. White, *J. Am. Chem. Soc.* **82**, 5671 (1960); D. M. White, *Ibid.*, p. 5678.

[43] H. Schlenk and D. M. Sand, *J. Am. Chem. Soc.* **83**, 2312 (1961).

Fig 3. A molecular model of α-cyclodextrin (cyclohexaamylose).[44]

The binding to α-cyclodextrin of colored substances, such as p-nitrophenolate ion and azo dyes, may be followed spectrophotometrically because there is a shift in the spectra of these compounds upon binding; this shift is 15 mμ to longer wavelength in the case of the p-nitrophenolate anion.[44] The equilibrium constant for complex formation with p-nitrophenolate ion is 2,800 M^{-1}, which corresponds to the considerable free energy of binding of -4.7 kcal/mole and is associated with an enthalpy of binding of -7.2 kcal/mole; the binding of free p-nitrophenol is tenfold less. Small molecules such as p-nitrophenol combine with the cyclodextrin with a rate constant of about 10^8 M^{-1} sec^{-1}, measured by the temperature-jump technique, which is close to a diffusion-controlled rate. However, dyes with

[44] F. Cramer, W. Saenger, and H-Ch. Spatz, *J. Am. Chem. Soc.* **89**, 14 (1967).

substituents in the 3' position, which interfere with the threading of the guest molecule into the cyclodextrin cavity (Fig. 4, R = methyl or ethyl), combine more than seven orders of magnitude more slowly, in spite of the fact that they exhibit equilibrium constants very similar to those for unhindered dye molecules. Thus, the interfering substituents decrease the rate of the combination and the separation steps by similar amounts. This system provides an interesting model to show how the combination of an enzyme with its substrate may occur at a less than diffusion-controlled rate even if no changes in covalent bonding take place.

Some examples of the manifestation of specificity in the acylation or phosphorylation of cyclodextrins by "substrates" of different structure are described in Chap. 1.

B. EXPLANATIONS

Given the experimental fact that nonpolar, hydrophobic, or almost any organic molecules in water have a tendency to come together, the scientific world is divided rather sharply between those who assume that this interaction is the result of a positive attraction caused by van der Waals–London dispersion forces and those who assume that it is the result of "hydrophobic" interaction, a negative sort of force which results from the strong attraction of water molecules for each other and which is often associated with changes in the "structure" of water in the neighborhood of the solute molecules. It is unusual for an author to make a serious attempt to distinguish between these mechanisms; manifestations of these interactions are usually ascribed to van der Waals interactions, hydrophobic bonds or changes in water structure, ignoring other possibilities, and frequently no attempt is made to demonstrate a clear cause-and-effect relationship between the observed phenomenon and, for example, changes in water structure. This state of affairs is indicative of the obvious: that is, that no definitive criteria exist to distinguish among these mechanistic possibilities. In fact, it is certain that no description of this type of interaction can be complete unless *both* the attractive forces between the solute molecules and the changes in the

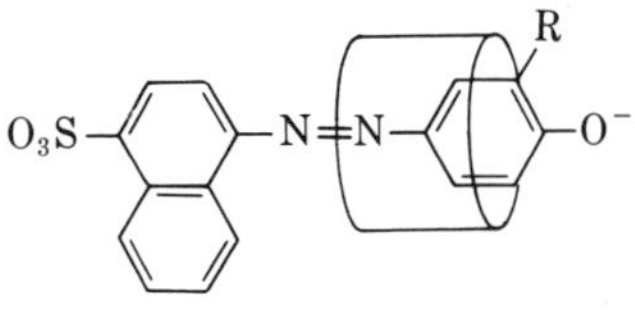

Fig 4. An azo dye with a substituent in the 3' position fitted into the cavity of α-cyclodextrin.[44]

bonding and distribution of solvent water molecules are taken into account.

Some aspects of these problems which are not too far removed from experimental observations will be described in a qualitative or semiquantitative way in this section. Detailed, quantitative treatments are helpful in providing a way of thinking about these subjects, but the author believes that too little is known at the present time about the nature of water and its interaction with solutes to accept the quantitative application of such models to aqueous solutions with any confidence.

1. VAN DER WAALS-LONDON DISPERSION FORCES

The weak interactions which occur between molecules in the gas phase are described collectively as van der Waals forces and include dipole-dipole, charge-dipole, charge–induced-dipole, dipole–induced-dipole, and induced-dipole–induced-dipole interactions. The electron distribution at any instant in a molecule with no permanent dipole is not likely to be perfectly uniform, so that the charge distribution at that moment may be described in terms of a transient dipole. This transient dipole will induce a complementary dipole in a neighboring molecule, which will in turn stabilize the original dipole; an instant later the dipoles in the two molecules are likely to be reversed (Fig. 5). These oscillating dipoles give rise to a net attractive force, the London dispersion interaction.

The energy E of the dispersion interaction between two nonpolar molecules is given by equation 1, in which α is the polarizabil-

$$E = -\frac{3\alpha_1\alpha_2(h\nu_1)(h\nu_2)}{2d^6(h\nu_1 + h\nu_2)} \tag{1}$$

ity, $h\nu$ is the average excitation energy, and d is the distance between the two molecules designated by the subscripts 1 and 2. This equation was modified by London to equation 2, in which ionization

$$E = -\frac{3\alpha_1\alpha_2}{2d^6}\frac{I_1 I_2}{I_1 + I_2} \tag{2}$$

potentials I have been substituted for excitation energies. This equation predicts interaction energies which are smaller than those which are found experimentally in the gas phase, so that various

Fig 5. The alternation of induced dipoles in a nonpolar molecule which gives rise to dispersion forces.

modifications have been proposed in which the vibration frequency of the induced oscillating dipole, ν, is changed. A discussion of these modifications and their application is given by Webb.[45] A rough estimate of the energy of such interactions may be obtained from equation 3, in which Z is the number of electrons, bonding and un-

$$E = -238.6\sqrt{Z}\,\frac{\alpha_1\alpha_2}{d^6} \tag{3}$$

bonded, in the outer shells of the atoms of the interacting molecules or groups and is in the range of 8 to 16 for many small molecules and substituent groups.

The characteristic features of dispersion interactions are their proportionality to the polarizability of the interacting molecules and their dependence on the sixth power of the intermolecular separation d. However, for molecules in close contact, the approximation that the distance over which the interaction occurs is large compared with the length of the dipole no longer holds, and calculation of the strength of the interaction becomes more difficult. Such calculations for interacting polyenes[46] and paraffinic hydrocarbons[47] suggest that the interaction energy is proportional to a smaller power of d as the molecules approach each other.

Especially for large molecules at short separation distances it may be preferable to follow London's original suggestion and treat the interaction in terms of monopoles rather than dipoles. This procedure has been followed in an important paper by Grunwald and Price, which has helped to reawaken interest in the importance of dispersion interactions in solution.[48] As the solvent is changed from water to methanol to ethanol the acidity of picric acid relative to that of trichloroacetic acid increases by almost two orders of magnitude. The charge in the picrate ion is generally believed to be delocalized to a considerable extent onto the oxygen atoms of the

[45] J. L. Webb, "Enzyme and Metabolic Inhibitors," vol. I, Academic Press Inc., New York, 1963.

[46] C. A. Coulson and P. L. Davies, *Trans. Faraday Soc.* **48**, 777 (1957).

[47] L. Salem, *J. Chem. Phys.* **37**, 2100 (1962).

[48] E. Grunwald and E. Price, *J. Am. Chem. Soc.* **86**, 4517 (1964).

nitro groups by resonance, whereas the charge in the trichloracetate ion is largely on the two oxygen atoms of the carboxylate group. If it is assumed that the two acids have approximately the same stability in the different solvents, the observed difference in relative acidity may be ascribed either to a greater stabilization of the delocalized charge of the picrate ion in alcohol or to the greater relative stabilization of the more localized charge of trichloroacetate ion in water, a good solvent for localized charges. Grunwald and Price evaluate the former interpretation and show that the delocalization of charge in the picrate ion is expected to give rise to a considerable increase in the strength of the dispersion interaction with the solvent. They argue further that dispersion interactions with the solvent will be stronger in alcohol than in water because the solvent atoms can interact more effectively with the solute if they are linked by covalent bonds than they can in water, in which a larger fraction of the region surrounding the solute will be taken up by spaces between the individual solvent molecules. Such a stabilization of the picrate ion in ethanol through dispersion forces should contribute to the observed increase in the relative strength of picric acid in this solvent. Similarly, the relatively greater stability of trimethylammonium picrate compared with ammonium picrate ion pairs may be ascribed to dispersion interactions with the alkyl groups of the trimethylammonium ion, and calculations suggest that the strength of the interaction is of the magnitude required to account for the observed difference; this effect may be one factor which contributes to the changes in the base strength of amines upon the addition of alkyl substituents.

It is often assumed that the special mobility of π electrons will result in an enhanced polarizability and interaction energy of unsaturated molecules compared with their saturated analogs. This assumption is probably correct, but calculations of the magnitude of this effect are difficult, and the few experimental indications that such a special interaction exists suggest that it is small. It is true that π electrons have an exalted polarizability, but the hydrogen atoms which are added when an unsaturated is converted to a saturated hydrocarbon cause a compensating increase in polarizability, and the total polarizability of a saturated hydrocarbon is very similar to that of the corresponding unsaturated molecule. Detailed calculations suggest that there is an enhanced dispersion interaction of parallel unsaturated hydrocarbon chains, but the interaction energy is small and is reduced further if electron-correlation effects (the influence of one electron on the position of another) are taken into account.[46, 49] The calculated energy of the dispersion interaction, in terms of the heat of sublimation, is very similar for conjugated polyenes with equivalent bonds and for the corresponding saturated hydrocarbons, as are the observed polarizabilities and heats of sublimation of cyclohexane and benzene.

The heats of mixing of aromatic with aliphatic hydrocarbons indicate that the removal of a benzene molecule, for example, from an environment of other benzene molecules followed by its insertion into an environment of saturated hydrocarbon molecules is energetically unfavorable to an extent ranging up to about 1 kcal/mole. This suggests that the average of the energies for the interaction of like molecules with each other is slightly larger than the energy of the benzene-hydrocarbon interaction. The difference could be accounted for if the interaction of the aromatic benzene molecules with each other were made slightly more favorable by π electron interactions.[31, 50]

The "stacking interactions" of nucleic acid bases with each other in aqueous solution may involve the π electron systems of the aromatic bases, but the extra stabilization provided by this effect does not appear to be large in view of the fact that purines also interact with steroids in water, largely on the α side of the saturated D and C rings, to give complexes with formation constants in the range of 10 to 50 M^{-1}. Thus, the free energies of interaction are similar for the interaction of a purine with a saturated and an unsaturated system, as are also the enthalpies of interaction, which are negative in both cases.[51, 52] The interaction of aromatic substrates with chymotrypsin also does not involve any large contribution from π electron interactions, since (1) the kinetic constants for the hydrolysis of N-acetyl-L-phenylalaninamide are very similar to those for the saturated analog, N-acetyl-L-hexahydrophenylalaninamide,[53] and (2) the binding of hydrophobic inhibitors to chymotrypsin, which occurs with negative enthalpies and entropies of binding, can be correlated with a simple model of extraction into a nonaqueous medium and is not significantly larger for aromatic molecules.[18]

[49] H. Sternlicht, J. Chem. Phys. **40**, 1175 (1964).

[50] A. E. P. Watson, I. A. McLure, J. E. Bennett, and G. C. Benson, J. Phys. Chem. **69**, 2753 (1965).

[51] A. Munck, J. F. Scott, and L. L. Engel, Biochim. Biophys. Acta **26**, 397 (1957).

[52] P. R. Stoesser and S. J. Gill, J. Phys. Chem. **71**, 564 (1967); S. J. Gill, M. Downing, and G. F. Sheats, Biochemistry **6**, 272 (1967).

[53] R. R. Jennings and C. Niemann, J. Am. Chem. Soc. **75**, 4687 (1953).

From a practical point of view, one goal of studies on dispersion interactions is the calculation of the energies which may be expected from the action of forces between solutes in aqueous solution. In the opinion of the author, it is not possible to carry out reliable calculations of this kind at the present time. It is only recently that detailed calculations have been carried out on the much simpler problem of the interaction energies to be expected for saturated and unsaturated molecules of known geometry and mutual orientation in the absence of water, and even these calculations are at a stage at which experimental measurements are used to assess the validity of the calculations, rather than the stage at which calculations can reliably predict the strength of interaction to be expected between two molecules. In water the problem becomes far more difficult because it is now necessary to estimate the relatively small *difference* between the energies of solute-water interactions, on the one hand, and of solute-solute and water-water interactions on the other. The problem is compounded by the fact that the water molecule is neither a sphere nor a nonpolar molecule and the probability that the orientation and interaction energy of solute and water molecules will be different for solutes of differing geometry and polarity. The situation at the present time is illustrated by a comparison of the conclusion that dispersion interactions will not make a significant contribution to the energy of interaction of hydrocarbons in water, because the polarizability per unit of volume is very similar for water and for hexane,[54] with the previously mentioned conclusion that dispersion forces will contribute significantly to the interaction energy of solutes with each other or with solvent molecules which are larger than water, because of the greater area of effective interaction with these molecules compared with water.[48]

It is apparent that one of the most important aspects of this type of interaction, and one which provides a particularly serious barrier to any quantitative theoretical treatment, is the detailed *geometry* of the interaction. In addition to the dependence of the dispersion energy on the size and average interatomic spacing of the solute and solvent molecules, it is important to consider the direction of the polarizability upon which the strength of the dispersion interaction depends. The polarizability is ordinarily measured by the molar refraction, which is a measure of the total polarizability of the molecule. However, the polarizability is usually different along different axes, so that the energy of the dispersion interaction is

[54] N. C. Deno and H. E. Berkheimer, *J. Org. Chem.* **28**, 2143 (1963).

likely to be different, depending on the orientation and geometry of the interacting molecules. This effect may be especially important in comparing aromatic and aliphatic molecules of similar overall polarizability if the aromatic system has a geometry such that it can interact efficiently with an adjacent aromatic system. Planar molecules can interact in a variety of relative configurations, whereas the chair form of a substituted cyclohexane derivative, for example, is likely to have a less favorable entropy for aggregation because of the small number of orientations which can provide maximum contact between aggregating molecules. The introduction of interfering alkyl substituents often decreases or prevents the aggregation of dyes, steroids, and other molecules.

The relative orientation of the reactants is of particular importance in determining the strength of the interaction of molecules which have large permanent dipoles, such as nucleic acid bases. It is probable that dipole-dipole interactions do not provide the principal driving force for the interaction of these bases in aqueous solution because water is itself an excellent solvent for charges and strong dipoles, so that the net strength of a simple dipole-dipole bond in water should be small. In fact, the solubility of the bases is increased and polynucleotides are denatured upon the addition of relatively nonpolar materials to water, which should decrease the strength of dipole-dipole interactions with the solvent and increase the strength of dipole-dipole interactions of bases with each other. The self-association of nucleosides increases with increasing size and polarizability of the base, but shows no correlation with either the dipole moment or hydrogen-bonding ability.[55] Nevertheless, dipole-dipole and other electrostatic interactions in an aggregate or helix will make a large contribution to the total energy of the system, which can be either favorable or unfavorable depending on the exact relative orientation of the bases,[56] so that no calculation of the interaction energy, from studies on the aggregation of model compounds, for example, can be complete unless this geometry-dependent contribution is included.

2. HYDROPHOBIC BONDING

Aside from direct van der Waals–London interactions, there are

[55] A. D. Broom, M. P. Schweizer, and P. O. P. Ts'o, *J. Am. Chem. Soc.* **89**, 3612 (1967).

[56] H. Devoe and I. Tinoco, Jr., *J. Mol. Biol.* **4**, 500 (1962); B. Pullman, P. Claverie, and J. Caillet, *Proc. Natl. Acad. Sci. U.S.* **55**, 904 (1966); H. A. Nash and D. F. Bradley, *J. Chem. Phys.* **45**, 1380 (1966).

two principal approaches to the description of the solution of hydrophobic molecules in water and the hydrophobic bond. The first approach emphasizes the requirement for the separation of strongly interacting water molecules in order to insert a weakly interacting molecule into the solution.[13, 54, 57, 58] The second emphasizes the restrictions to free movement or increase in "structure" of the solvent which can give rise to a negative change in entropy when a nonpolar molecule is placed in an aqueous solution.[31, 59-61] The following qualitative description of the hydrophobic bond is based on both of these approaches, which are by no means mutually exclusive.

The model is based on two postulates: first, that the special properties of water arise *primarily* from the very strong mutual interaction of water molecules and, second, that mutually compensating changes in the entropy and enthalpy of aqueous solutions may occur with little or no change in free energy.

a) **The solution of nonpolar and moderately polar solutes in water**. The strong mutual interaction of small, strongly dipolar water molecules through hydrogen bonds and other dipolar interactions is manifested in the large cohesive energy density and internal pressure of liquid water, which are considerably larger than for almost any other solvent (with a few rather special exceptions such as liquid mercury and hydrogen peroxide). This large cohesive energy density is manifested in the large surface tension of water. The first step in the solution of a nonpolar solute in water may be regarded as the formation of a cavity into which the solute will fit (Fig. 6). In the case of water, the free energy required for the formation of such a cavity will be large because it requires the separation of strongly interacting solvent molecules, and the favorable free energy of interaction of the nonpolar solute molecule with water will be too small to compensate for this unfavorable free energy. This internal cohesion is probably the ultimate source of the low solubility of relatively nonpolar solutes in water and of the strength of the "hydrophobic bond." Calculations of the energy changes which are involved in the insertion of nucleic

[57] D. D. Eley, *Trans. Faraday Soc.* **35**, 1281 (1939).
[58] O. Sinanoglu and S. Abdulnur, *Photochem. Photobiol.* **3**, 333 (1964); *Fed. Proc.* **24**, II. S-12 (1965).
[59] H. S. Frank and M. W. Evans, *J. Chem. Phys.* **13**, 507 (1945).
[60] R. E. Powell and W. M. Latimer, *J. Chem. Phys.* **19**, 1139 (1951).
[61] G. Némethy and H. A. Scheraga, *J. Chem. Phys.* **36**, 3401 (1962).

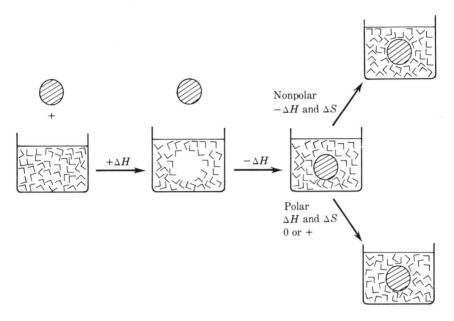

Fig 6. The solution of a nonpolar or polar molecule in water with the intermediate formation of a cavity. After the solute is placed in the cavity the solvent may rearrange to a greater degree of structure and hydrogen bonding (nonpolar solute), may undergo no change, or may decrease in structure and hydrogen bonding (polar, structure-breaking solute).

acid bases in water indicate that the free energy of cavity formation is the most important contributor to the overall energy of the process.[58]

Once a cavity is formed and the solute is placed in the cavity, the solvent will undergo any further changes which reduce the free energy of the system. Water-water hydrogen bonds were broken in order to form the cavity and, in the case of a nonpolar solute, no compensatory hydrogen bonding to the solute is possible. Consequently, there will be a tendency for the water molecules surrounding the solute to reorient themselves in such a way as to form the maximum possible number of hydrogen bonds, especially at low temperature. This tendency may be reinforced by the desirability of presenting a regular surface close to the solute to permit the maximum possible dispersion interaction with the solvent molecules. In liquid water there are many possible orientations that a given water molecule may assume and still maintain energetically favorable interactions with surrounding molecules. In the presence of a nonpolar solute no hydrogen bonding is possible in one direction, but the water molecule can be fully hydrogen-bonded to neighboring water molecules with a coordination number of four if it exists in one of a small number of specific orientations with respect to its neighbors. This leads to the formation of a region around the solute in which the number of energetically favorable orientations of the water molecule is restricted, resulting in a decrease in the entropy and an increase in the "structure" of the system. This decrease in entropy is offset by a more favorable enthalpy resulting from the formation of new hydrogen bonds. The total number of hydrogen bonds in the system at equilibrium may be as large as in the absence of the solute, or even larger. Thus, the initially unfavorable enthalpy for cavity formation has been compensated for by the formation of hydrogen bonds around the solute, so that the unfavorable free energy appears as an unfavorable *entropy* of solution. The limiting case of this process is seen in the gas hydrates, a series of crystalline inclusion compounds of inert gases surrounded by water molecules arranged in a rigid structure corresponding to a form of ice.

Now consider a solute with either an appreciable overall dipole moment or localized dipoles in its substituent groups, such as a dye or a nucleic acid base. For most such solutes the interaction of these dipoles with water will not be sufficient to overcome the unfavorable free energy of cavity formation, so that the same barrier to solution will exist as in the case of nonpolar compounds, albeit to a reduced extent. However, there will be a difference in the rearrangement of the system after the solute has been introduced into the cavity because the polar solute will perturb the surrounding water molecules. It was pointed out in the previous chapter that there is evidence that the relatively weak electric field around an ion of moderate size or beyond the immediate hydration shell of a small ion competes with the interactions of water molecules with each other in such a way as to decrease the degree of order or structure of the solution. A similar structure-breaking effect would be expected from the weak field in the neighborhood of the dipole of a polar solute. This will decrease or prevent the formation of an organized water structure around the solute, so that the unfavorable free energy of solution of such a solute will be reflected directly in an unfavorable enthalpy of solution.

In both of these cases the ultimate cause of the unfavorable free energy of solution of the solute is the difficulty of separating water molecules from each other because of their large internal cohesion; i.e., it reflects both the large strength and the large number of hydrogen bonds in a given volume of water. This unfavorable free energy may appear in either the enthalpy or entropy of solution, depending on the secondary consideration of the way in which the solute interacts with the solvent. Many instances have been pointed out in this volume of the ease with which water can undergo a decrease in entropy accompanied by a compensating increase in enthalpy, and vice versa, with little or no net change in free energy. A number of further examples of this behavior are found in measurements of the thermodynamic parameters for rate and equilibrium processes in water containing increasing amounts of t-butanol or related compounds. The solution of organic solutes, salts, and transition states in such solvents occurs with extraordinarily large changes in enthalpy and entropy, with little or no change in free energy, as the concentration of t-butanol is increased up to about 20%.[62] This must mean that the loss of entropy which occurs when water molecules become more structured is almost entirely offset by a compensating favorable enthalpy change resulting from the increased amount of hydrogen bonding which is made possible by the increase in structure. The important point, then, is that the existence of such a facile and mutually compensatory relationship between entropy and enthalpy changes in water means that changes in these thermodynamic quantities may occur easily as *secondary* effects and it may be misleading to ascribe a fundamental, causal role to them; the first property which should be explained is the free energy of the process under consideration.

At this point it may be helpful to consider the concrete example of the transfer of a molecule of methane from solution in some inert liquid, such as carbon tetrachloride or ether, to water. This process may be examined directly or through the intermediate formation of gaseous methane (Fig. 7).[63] The most important fact, that methane has a very low solubility in water (which is sometimes lost sight of in the heat of arguments about the detail-

[62] E. M. Arnett and D. R. McKelvey, *Record Chem. Progr.* **26**, 185 (1965); E. M. Arnett, in F. Franks (ed.), "Physico-Chemical Processes in Mixed Aqueous Solvents," p. 105, Elsevier Publishing Company, Amsterdam, 1967.

[63] The values shown in Figs. 7 and 8 are based on data in the recent compilation of Némethy and Scheraga[61] for hydrocarbons in the series from methane to butane. Earlier data on a wider series of compounds are in rough agreement with these; however, the increment in ΔH for transfer of a methylene group from the gas phase to water based on aliphatic alcohols is -1.6 kcal/mole, and the increment in ΔF, from a larger series of compounds, is $+0.16$ kcal/mole.[13]

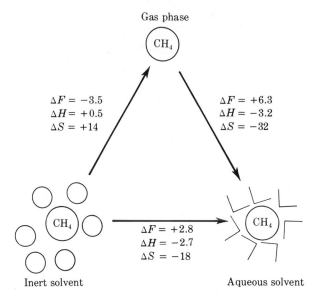

Fig 7. The transfer of a molecule of methane from an inert solvent to water, either directly or through the gas phase.

ed mechanism of these processes), is reflected in the unfavorable free energies of transfer of methane to water from solution in an inert solvent and from the gas phase of +2.8 and +6.3 kcal/mole, respectively, at 25°. These and subsequent numbers are based on a mole fraction standard state in order to avoid contributions of the entropy of dilution to the entropy and free-energy values. The enthalpy of transfer of methane from an inert solvent to the gas phase of about +0.5 kcal/mole reflects the loss of the van der Waals interaction energy of methane with the solvent; this value is of the expected sign and magnitude. Now, there can hardly be a much larger van der Waals interaction energy of methane with water than with an inert solvent, so the observed favorable enthalpies of transfer to water from an inert solvent and from the gas phase of −2.7 and −3.2 kcal/mole, respectively, must represent a change in the enthalpy of the solvent, i.e., an *increase* in the bonding of water molecules to each other. The amount of hydrogen bonding in liquid water is certainly not the maximum possible, as in ice; the less than maximal hydrogen bonding is compensated for by the disorder—the large number of possible orientations for each molecule—in the liquid. Therefore it is possible for the amount of hydrogen bonding to increase upon the introduction of a nonpolar solute.

The most dramatic changes occur in the entropy of solution: the value of -18 e.u. for transfer from an inert solvent to water corresponds to $+5.5$ kcal/mole. This decrease in entropy overbalances the favorable enthalpy change of -2.7 kcal/mole to give the overall unfavorable free-energy change of $+2.8$ kcal/mole. The entropy of transfer of methane from solution in an inert solvent to the gas phase of $+14$ e.u. reflects the expected increase in the freedom of a molecule in the gas compared with the liquid phase; the larger value of -32 e.u. for transfer from the vapor to aqueous solution and the negative entropy of transfer from an inert solvent to water must then reflect a restriction to the freedom of the solvent molecules, i.e., a degree of ordering or structuring of the solvent. This ordering is partially, but not entirely, compensated for by the increase in solvent bonding which is reflected in the favorable enthalpy of methane transfer to aqueous solution; the difference between the $T \Delta S$ and ΔH contributions is the unfavorable free energy of $+2.8$ kcal/mole for transfer from an inert solvent to water.

The behavior of larger hydrocarbons may be considered in the same manner by examining the consequences of the successive additions of methylene groups in the series methane, ethane, propane, and butane (Fig. 8).[63] Again, the most important point is that the free energy of transfer from an inert solvent or the liquid hydrocarbon to water increases by an increment of 0.7 to 1.0 kcal/mole for each additional methylene group. However, the enthalpy change for this process is *positive*, with a value of $+0.6$ kcal/mole. The overall enthalpy is the resultant of an enthalpy of transfer to the gas phase of $+1.5$ kcal/mole and for transfer from the gas phase to water of -0.9 kcal/mole. The positive enthalpy of transfer to the gas phase reflects principally the loss of van der Waals interactions in the liquid. The fact that this quantity is smaller for the transfer to water and the overall positive enthalpy of solution suggest that there is no large increase in the amount of bonding in the solvent when the hydrocarbon is introduced; in fact, there must be either some breaking of solvent hydrogen bonds or the van der Waals interaction of the hydrocarbon with water must be weaker than with other hydrocarbon molecules (see the discussion of van der Waals interactions above). The negative entropy change of about -1.4 e.u. for transfer from an inert medium to water is much smaller than that found for methane and presumably reflects only a small additional amount of structure formation in water as the size of

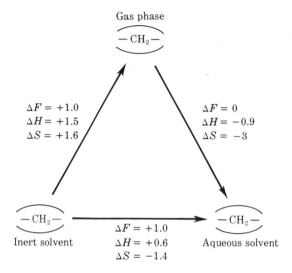

Gas phase

$\Delta F = +1.0$
$\Delta H = +1.5$
$\Delta S = +1.6$

$\Delta F = 0$
$\Delta H = -0.9$
$\Delta S = -3$

Inert solvent $\Delta F = +1.0$ Aqueous solvent
                                 $\Delta H = +0.6$
                                 $\Delta S = -1.4$

Fig 8. The effect of increasing the number of methylene groups on the thermodynamic parameters for the
transfer of a hydrocarbon from an inert solvent to
water, either directly or through the gas phase.

the hydrocarbon is increased. It is of interest that the overall
free-energy change appears mainly in the transfer of the hydrocarbon from an inert medium to the gas phase, whereas there is
little or no effect of the size of the hydrocarbon on the free energy
of transfer from the gas phase to water; i.e., there is not a large
decrease in solubility with increasing size at a constant vapor
pressure. The effect on the transfer to the gas phase may be
attributed to the loss of van der Waals interactions, which is manifested in the enthalpy of vaporization; the small or negligible
change in the free energy of transfer from the gas phase to water
suggests that the van der Waals interaction with water and any
additional hydrogen bonding of water in the immediate vicinity of
the solute are cancelled by an increase in the difficulty of cavity
formation for the larger solute.

An increase in chain length to that of butane, which might be
regarded as a more or less average hydrophobic group, results
in an overall free energy of transfer from liquid butane to water
of $+5.9$ kcal/mole and an entropy of transfer of -22 e.u., which
is not very different from that of methane. The opposite values of
ΔH for methane and for each methylene increment have almost
cancelled each other out in butane and there is left only a small

value of -0.8 kcal/mole, which may reflect a small net increase in hydrogen bonding in the neighborhood of the hydrocarbon compared to the bulk solvent. A similar disappearance of the favorable enthalpy term is observed for aromatic molecules; the enthalpy of transfer of a benzene molecule from benzene to water is $+0.6$ kcal/ mole at 25°. The thermodynamic parameters for the solution of longer-chain hydrocarbons in water have been examined with alcohols and nonionic detergents, which have sufficient solubility to permit relatively easy experimental measurements. The solution of these compounds exhibits an increment of about 0.6 kcal per additional methylene group in ΔH, similar to that for short-chain alkanes, for chain lengths of up to 12 carbon atoms.[21,64] However, for the short-chain compounds, there is little change or a decrease in ΔH with increasing chain length (up to four carbon atoms), in contrast to the alkane series, suggesting that the thermodynamic parameters for solution of hydrocarbons may be altered by adjacent polar groups. The unfavorable ΔH for the longer-chain compounds may be interpreted in terms of an increased difficulty of cavity formation with increasing chain length, in the same way as for the alkane series. However, a detailed interpretation of the behavior of the longer-chain compounds is difficult because of the many factors involved, one of the most important of which is the tendency of such a hydrocarbon in water to curl up into a hydrocarbon globule in order to present a minimum surface to the solvent.

b) The hydrophobic bond. The difficulty of placing a relatively nonpolar solute in water provides the driving force for the formation of the "hydrophobic bond." It generally requires less work to make one large cavity than two small cavities, so that there will be a tendency for two large hydrophobic solute molecules in water to come together in a single cavity, just as oil droplets in water tend to coalesce. The properties of the hydrophobic bond follow from the properties of the solutes in water, described above. In the case of molecules that are largely or entirely hydrocarbon in nature, some of the structured solvent molecules surrounding each solute molecule will be transferred to the bulk solvent when the two solute molecules come together (Fig. 9), so that the formation of the hydrophobic bond will be accompanied by an increase in entropy and may be accompanied by a positive enthalpy change, if there is a net decrease in the amount of hydrogen bonding in the system. The

[64] J. M. Corkill, J. F. Goodman, and J. R. Tate, *Trans. Faraday Soc.* **63**, 773 (1967).

Nonpolar

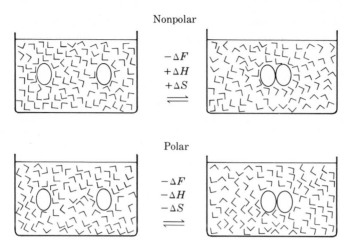

Polar

Fig 9. The formation of a hydrophobic bond between two non-polar (upper) or two moderately polar (lower) molecules in water.

cavity model may be less directly applicable to small nonpolar groups, such as the methyl group, since these groups may fit into interstices or cavities with a specific structure; however, for most purposes the same general principles may be applied to large and small groups.

This positive enthalpy of interaction is responsible for the characteristic increase in stability of many hydrophobic bonds with increasing temperature up to about 60°.[31, 65] In addition to the transfer processes and other examples which have already been mentioned, this type of "classical" hydrophobic bond is seen in the binding of ethane, propane, and butane to several proteins, which occurs with a ΔH near zero,[66] in the polymerization of tobacco mosaic virus protein, which occurs with the large positive ΔH of 190,000 cal/mole and ΔS of 682 e.u., corresponding to the release of a large number of water molecules into the bulk solvent,[67] and in the aggregation of molecules of nonionic detergents into micelles, which occurs with a positive ΔH of approximately +5 kcal/mole and ΔS of +30 e.u.[23, 68]

On the other hand, solutes of moderate polarity, which are surrounded by solvent molecules with a similar or smaller amount of

[65] G. Némethy and H. A. Scheraga, *J. Phys. Chem.* **66**, 1773 (1962).

[66] A. Wishnia, *Proc. Natl. Acad. Sci. U.S.* **48**, 2200 (1962).

[67] M. A. Lauffer, *Biochemistry* **5**, 2440 (1966).

[68] M. J. Schick, *J. Phys. Chem.* **67**, 1796 (1963).

structure compared with water molecules in the bulk solvent, also have a tendency to associate, but will do so with no change or a negative change in the entropy of the solvent (Fig. 9). Since solution of these molecules in water is manifested in an unfavorable enthalpy, there will be a negative, favorable enthalpy change when they aggregate. According to this picture then, a major driving force for the aggregation of both nonpolar molecules and molecules of moderate polarity is the overwhelmingly strong mutual adhesion of the water molecules; in the latter case this driving force appears directly as a favorable enthalpy of aggregation, whereas in the former case it is manifested indirectly as a favorable entropy of aggregation.

There are a number of examples of intermolecular association which cannot easily be accounted for by electrostatic, hydrogen-bonding, or charge transfer interactions, but which occur with a negative enthalpy change and, usually, a negative entropy change. These interactions probably represent this type of "nonclassical" hydrophobic bond; attractive van der Waals–London dispersion forces may contribute an additional driving force for their formation. The examples include the dimerization of thionine, a cationic dye ($\Delta H = -6.8$ kcal/mole),[6] the association of other dyes which can exhibit values of ΔH as large as -25 kcal/mole and ΔS of -40 to 60 e.u.,[7] the association of purines ($\Delta H = -2$ to -6 kcal/mole and $\Delta S = -6$ to -16 e.u.),[52] and even the association of purines with relatively nonpolar steroid molecules ($\Delta H = -6$ kcal/mole).[51] The favorable enthalpy for the stacking of nucleic acid bases is the principal factor which contributes to the enthalpy of the heat denaturation of DNA. It should be emphasized that a favorable enthalpy of association may be caused by changes in the solvent, rather than by the net attraction of the associating molecules, which is often invoked to explain an observed negative enthalpy of association. It is of interest that the association which gives rise to the metachromasia of dyes in water does not occur in formamide or a number of other solvents which have dielectric constants both higher and lower than that of water.[69]

c) **Water "structure."** The decrease in the freedom of movement of water molecules in the neighborhood of a nonpolar group which is reflected in negative entropy changes has often been referred to as "iceberg" formation. This is a useful, but potentially misleading, descriptive term for a situation in which much of the driving force

[69] R. B. McKay and P. J. Hillson, *Trans. Faraday Soc.* **63**, 777 (1967).

for the restriction to free movement of water molecules is simply that they cannot undergo libration and rotation in the region which is occupied by the solute molecule to the same extent that they can in the bulk solvent. Furthermore, the "iceberg" is exceedingly unstable with respect to time: no separate species of ice-like structured water in the presence of nonpolar solutes can be detected by measurements of dielectric relaxation, so the lifetime of any such species must be less than the dielectric relaxation time of water of 10^{-10} to 10^{-11} seconds. For this reason, the "structured" water may be more appropriately referred to as a "flickering cluster."[70] Finally, the structured water around a hydrocarbon such as methane is certainly not the same as that in a solid methane-water clathrate. The enthalpy of formation of such a clathrate from gaseous methane and liquid water is -12.8 kcal/mole, which is far larger than the value of -4.6 kcal/mole for the transfer of gaseous methane to liquid water at $0°$. The difference of -8.2 kcal/mole must reflect an increase in the amount of structured hydrogen-bonded water upon formation of the clathrate from an aqueous solution of methane. Division of this number by 1.4 kcal/mole, the heat of fusion of liquid water, gives 5.8, which corresponds closely to the number of water molecules per methane molecule in the solid clathrate.[71]

Another term about which there has been much confusion is the hydrogen bond of liquid water. There is wide disagreement regarding the extent to which water molecules are hydrogen-bonded at a given temperature, depending on the method used for estimation of the degree of hydrogen bonding.[72, 73] On the one hand, it is certain that water molecules in the liquid state at ordinary temperatures interact with each other very strongly indeed and do not resemble water molecules in the gas phase.[74] On the other hand, it is equally certain that liquid water molecules, even at low temperatures, are different from completely hydrogen-bonded water molecules in ice or clathrates; we have seen that such liquid water molecules can undergo what appears to be an increase in hydrogen bonding at the expense of a decrease in entropy with very little change in free energy. The nature of these water molecules that are not completely hydrogen bonded and yet are very different from gaseous water is still not clearly defined. They may be

[70] H. S. Frank and W-Y. Wen, *Discussions Faraday Soc.* **24**, 133 (1957).

[71] D. N. Glew, *J. Phys. Chem.* **66**, 605 (1962).

[72] K. A. Hartman, Jr., *J. Phys. Chem.* **70**, 270 (1966).

[73] B. E. Conway, *Ann. Rev. Phys. Chem.* **17**, 481 (1966).

[74] D. P. Stevenson, *J. Phys. Chem.* **69**, 2145 (1965).

stabilized electrostatically by dipole-dipole interactions or by "bent" hydrogen bonds. The problem is partly semantic: a hydrogen bond is largely or entirely an electrostatic interaction between two dipoles which includes a hydrogen atom as a part of one dipole, so that it is difficult to make a meaningful distinction between a hydrogen bond and a dipole-dipole interaction. One might attempt to distinguish between covalent hydrogen bonds on the one hand and electrostatic hydrogen bonds on the other, but such a distinction is not clear-cut even in theory, and there does not appear to be definitive evidence that the hydrogen bonds of water have any covalent character in any case.

For these reasons, it may be misleading to put too literal an interpretation on the common statement that there is a breaking of hydrogen bonds and of ice-like structure as the temperature of liquid water is increased. Heating will certainly increase the disorder of the solution with, on the average, some weakening of hydrogen bonds as the molecules take up orientations which are less favorable for the formation of hydrogen bonds of optimal stability. This may increase the number of "bent" hydrogen bonds.[75] If there is some covalent or cooperative character to the hydrogen bonds of water, with relatively strict requirements for a linear O—H—O geometry for maximum stability, heating or "structure-breaking" solutes may decrease the importance of this contribution and leave an electrostatic hydrogen bond with less demanding steric requirements. It is difficult to give a more detailed description than this with any assurance with our present limited understanding of liquids in general and of liquid water in particular.

The notion that there is some increase in water "structure," or at least a limitation to the free movement and vibration of solvent molecules in the neighborhood of a nonpolar or "hydrophobic" solute molecule in water, is one of the few interpretations of the properties of aqueous solutions for which there is strong evidence from a number of different experimental approaches and an agreement among most (but not quite all) students of this difficult subject.[76] In addition to the negative entropies of solution of nonpolar solutes, there are two relatively simple types of experimental evidence for such structure formation based on the effects of solutes on the viscosity and on the dielectric relaxation of water. The addition of increasing amounts of dimethylformamide to water

[75] J. A. Pople, *Proc. Roy. Soc.* (*London*) **205A**, 163 (1951).

[76] J. L. Kavanau, "Water and Solute-Water Interactions," Holden-Day, Inc., San Francisco, 1964.

causes an increase in the viscosity of the solution to several times
that of water itself (Fig. 10).[77] As the mole fraction of dimethylformamide is increased, the viscosity rises to a maximum and then
falls to a value not unlike that of pure water for pure dimethylformamide. Similar behavior is observed for N-methylformamide,
and for both compounds there is a decrease in diffusion coefficient
corresponding to the increased viscosity. The very similar behavior
of mixtures of water with dioxane, alcohols of different chain
lengths, and other relatively nonpolar solutes [78,79] suggests that
this is a quite general phenomenon for molecules which do not interact with water as strongly as does another water molecule and
that it is not caused by the high dipole moment of dimethylformamide. This increase in viscosity means that the movement of
molecules past each other in a mixture is more difficult than in

[77] A. Fratiello, *J. Mol. Phys.* **7**, 565 (1964).

[78] J. A. Geddes, *J. Am. Chem. Soc.* **55**, 4832 (1933).

[79] F. Franks and D. J. G. Ives, *Quart. Rev.* **20**, 1 (1966).

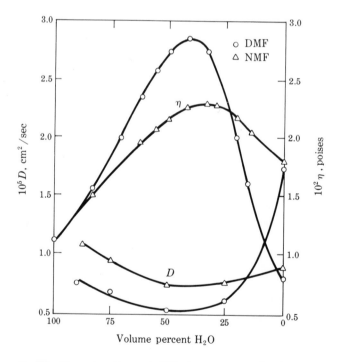

Fig 10. The viscosity and diffusion constant of mixtures of
dimethylformamide and water.[77]

either of the pure liquid components of the mixture; i.e., there is a restriction to free motion, implying the existence of an increase in the "structure" of the mixed solvent relative to that of the components.

The effects of a series of salts and organic solvents on the dielectric relaxation time of water are shown in Table III.[80] The addition of these substances up to a concentration c of approximately 1 M causes a nearly linear change in the dielectric relaxation time of water according to equation 4, in which $\delta\lambda_s$ is a measure of the effectiveness of a compound in changing this parameter, and the

$$\lambda_s = \lambda_{sH_2O} + c\delta\lambda_s \tag{4}$$

sign of $\delta\lambda_s$ indicates whether the compound causes an increase or a decrease in relaxation time. The dielectric relaxation time of a solution is a measure of the average speed with which the dipoles of the solution can orient themselves in response to an applied alternating electric field. The fact that this relaxation time is *increased* upon the addition of a relatively nonpolar solute to water, in spite of the fact that the overall strength of the mutual interaction or cohesion of the water molecules with each other should be decreased by the introduction of a weakly interacting solute, must mean that there is a restriction to the free movement and alignment of the water molecules, i.e., an increase in "structure" of the solvent. Evidently, the water molecules in the neighborhood of the hydro-

[80] G. H. Haggis, J. B. Hasted, and T. J. Buchanan, *J. Chem. Phys.* **20**, 1452 (1952).

Table III   Effect of solutes on the dielectric relaxation time of water[80]

Solute	$\delta\lambda_s$ ($\times 100$)
Dioxane	+20
n-Propanol	+35
Alanine	0
NaF	−5
NaCl	−20
NaI	−25
Na Propionate	+15
EtNH$_3$Cl	+15
Et$_4$NCl	+30

carbon surface of hydrophobic solutes cannot reorient themselves as easily or quickly as those in the bulk solvent. This effect may be opposed to a greater or lesser extent by polar groups on the solute. The addition of dioxane to water, for example, also gives rise to a new, shorter relaxation time, which may be interpreted as evidence for a local disruption of the normal water structure by the oxygen atoms at each end of the dioxane molecule.[81]

Simple salts, such as the alkali halides, cause a *decrease* in the dielectric relaxation time of water (Table III). This is one of the most straightforward lines of evidence for the "structure-breaking" effect of such salts on water. The decreased relaxation time reflects the increased freedom of movement of the water molecules in the presence of these ions. However, in the presence of small, highly charged ions there will also be some water molecules in the first-layer hydration shell which are so strongly oriented by the intense electric field of the ion that they are not free to reorient themselves in an applied electric field at all. These water molecules, which may be designated as "irrotationally bound," will cause a decrease in the observed dielectric constant of the solution. If some assumptions are made with respect to a model for the solution, the number of water molecules which are "irrotationally bound" to each ion may be calculated from the observed dielectric constant.[80, 82] Because of this "structure-forming" tendency, such small ions cause a smaller decrease in dielectric relaxation time than medium-sized ions, as is evident for sodium fluoride in Table III. The fact that the dielectric relaxation time passes through a minimum as the salt concentration is increased and may eventually reach a value higher than that for pure water is in accord with this general picture: as the salt concentration is increased, there is a decrease in the number of interstitial water molecules which have an increased freedom and which account for the decreased dielectric relaxation time. Eventually, the salt concentration reaches a point at which all the water molecules are in the immediate vicinity of ions and have their freedom of movement restricted by the field of the ion.[83]

If the size of the ion is increased sufficiently, the charge will be effectively shielded from water, and the strength of the interaction of the ion with a water molecule will become even less than that of another water molecule. For such ions the electrostriction

[81] S. K. Garg and C. P. Smyth, *J. Chem. Phys.* **43**, 2959 (1965).

[82] E. Glueckauf, *Trans. Faraday Soc.* **60**, 1637 (1964).

[83] F. E. Harris and C. T. O'Konski, *J. Phys. Chem.* **61**, 310 (1957).

and even the structure-breaking effect associated with most ions disappear and the behavior of the ion approaches that of a nonpolar solute. This effect is seen in dielectric relaxation measurements in the *increase* in dielectric relaxation time which is observed with tetraethylammonium chloride; i.e., this salt is "structure-making" according to this and other criteria. The similar increases observed with sodium propionate and ethylammonium chloride may reflect an effect of this kind or may result from the hydrocarbon substituent adjacent to the charged group of these ions.

It is frequently found that the partial molar volumes of relatively nonpolar solutes in water are considerably smaller than the volume of the pure solute; almost everyone is familiar with the decrease in volume which is observed upon mixing alcohol and water. This may be explained by the open, loose character of liquid water, which permits the introduction of weakly interacting solutes into the interstices of the system with relatively little increase in total volume. The strong, geometry-dependent dipolar interactions between water molecules give rise to a liquid in which the lowest free-energy state is of much less than maximal density in order that maximum stabilization may be obtained from the dipole-dipole interactions; the observed molar volume of water of 18.1 ml/mole is half again as large as the estimated molar volume of tightly packed water of 12.5 ml/ml.[84] The large molar volume of completely hydrogen-bonded water is, of course, manifested in the low density of ice and provides an attractive explanation for the temperature of maximum density of water a few degrees above the freezing point. The increase in volume as the temperature is lowered from this temperature to the freezing point reflects an increase in hydrogen bonding and in the amount of water structure as the completely hydrogen-bonded state is approached. We will not enter here into the controversy over whether or not liquid water may be accurately described as a two-state system composed of low-density regions of structured water and high-density regions of disordered water, but the details of this controversy do not affect the usefulness of the qualitative concept that an increase in the overall degree of "structure" or in the number of linear hydrogen bonds is accompanied by an increase in the amount of low-density water. This process occurs to a greater extent in the presence of nonpolar groups which favor the formation of more "structured" water molecules and fit into the interstices between them.

[84] J. E. Desnoyers, R. E. Verrall, and B. E. Conway, *J. Chem. Phys.* **43**, 243 (1965).

These volume changes introduce a serious complication into quantitative attempts to relate water-solute interactions directly to the internal cohesion of water. It was indicated in the previous chapter that the order, the direction, and the approximate magnitude of the effects of different salts on nonpolar solutes in water could be correlated with the cohesive energy density of the salt solution, as estimated from the electrostriction upon solution of the salt in water. Salts, such as tetraalkylammonium ions, which cause an increase in volume upon solution increase the solubility of hydrophobic solutes. The same criterion cannot be applied to the addition of nonionic materials to water because such materials have a negative volume of solution in spite of the fact that they decrease the internal cohesion of water and increase the solubility of hydrophobic solutes.

The very large heat capacities of solutions of hydrophobic solutes in water are still another consequence of the "structured" water around such solutes; as the temperature is increased, these structured areas are broken up and the solution becomes more normal in its properties. This breaking of a required sheath of structured solvent around the solute provides an explanation for the decreased solubility of many hydrophobic solutes with increasing temperature. This may lead to the separation of a new phase at high temperature of liquids, such as alkyl substituted pyridines, that are miscible with water at lower temperatures.

As in the interpretation of the effects of salts on aqueous systems, the primary effect of the addition of uncharged substances to aqueous solutions must be sought in their effect on the free energy of the system; it may be misleading to interpret these phenomena directly in terms of the structural model. Thus, the structural model provides an attractive explanation of the solubilizing influence of relatively nonpolar molecules, such as alcohols and alkyl substituted amides and ureas, on other hydrophobic molecules. If one solute increases the average "structure" of the solution, it might be thought that it would be easier to insert another solute molecule which requires a high degree of structure in its vicinity. On the other hand, it is not necessary that a material be "structure-forming" in order that it may increase the solubility of a hydrophobic molecule in water. It has already been pointed out that one of the mechanisms by which urea causes denaturation of proteins and nucleic acids is by increasing the stability of hydrophobic side chains of amino acids and nucleic acid bases upon exposure to the solvent, as shown by the increase in solubility and decrease in the activity coefficient of these groups in the presence of urea.[31,32,35] Alcohols, acetone, and similar molecules break hydrophobic bonds of the polymer and favor the denatured state in the same manner. However, it is almost certain that urea is not a structure-forming agent, at least in the same sense as relatively nonpolar molecules; urea has very little effect on many of the properties of water and either fits into the aqueous solution with little change in water "structure" or, according to measurements of ultrasonic attenuation, tends to break the normal water "structure."[85] Measurements of the enthalpy and heat capacity for the solution of hydrophobic groups and of the ultrasonic relaxation spectrum of polyethylene glycol in water and urea solutions suggest that the energetically more favorable interaction of hydrophobic groups with the urea solution as compared with water is accompanied by a *decrease* in the amount of water structure around the hydrophobic groups.[85,86] Thus, the breaking of hydrophobic bonds by urea and by alcohols cannot be accounted for by the same detailed mechanism in terms of solvent structure, although the effects of the two types of compounds are similar in terms of free energy. It is possible that urea provides a more favorable environment for the fitting of hydrophobic solute groups into interstitial regions of the solvent structure.[87] It would be expected that there would be less loss of entropy in the restriction of movement of a urea molecule adjacent to a hydrophobic group than in the restriction of movement of the several water molecules which would be required to occupy the same space. An even simpler explanation is based on the fact that the urea molecule is considerably larger than water; it might be expected that it would take less work to break the hydrogen bonds to the urea molecules and create a cavity in a given volume of urea solution than to break the larger number of hydrogen bonds in the same volume of pure water in spite of the fact that the dipole moment of urea is larger than that of water. Therefore, aqueous urea should be a better solvent for hydrophobic groups than is water and should tend to break hydrophobic bonds. Finally, the possibility should be kept in mind that aqueous urea may interact more strongly than water with nonpolar groups through van der Waals forces. This hypothesis receives some support from the fact that the addition of urea de-

[85] G. C. Hammes and P. R. Schimmel, *J. Am. Chem. Soc.* **89**, 442 (1967); G. C. Hammes and J. C. Swann, *Biochemistry* **6**, 1591 (1967).

[86] G. C. Kresheck and L. Benjamin, *J. Phys. Chem.* **68**, 2476 (1964).

[87] M. Abu-Hamdiyyah, *J. Phys. Chem.* **69**, 2720 (1965).

creases the interfacial tension between water and n-decane, which is in contrast to the increase in the surface tension of water upon the addition of urea.[88]

Some of the conclusions which have been reached in this chapter may be briefly summarized as follows. There is abundant experimental evidence that relatively nonpolar molecules have a favorable net free energy of interaction with each other in water and that this interaction is of primary importance in providing the driving force for intermolecular interactions in aqueous solution. There is strong evidence that the much greater affinity of water molecules for each other than for most solutes is ultimately responsible for a major part of this free energy of interaction. Attractive van der Waals–London dispersion forces may well provide a further contribution to the observed free energy of interaction, but a quantitative evaluation of the importance of such forces is difficult or impossible for most systems at the present time. There is strong evidence that the water molecules surrounding nonpolar solutes in aqueous solution are more "structured" than in the bulk solvent and that a decrease in this structure occurs when contact with the solvent is reduced by association or aggregation of the solutes. However, such structural changes are not a necessary consequence of the solution or association of solutes which interact with water less strongly than do water molecules with each other, and it may be misleading to assign a primary role to structural changes in the solvent in explaining intermolecular association in water.

[88] J. M. Corkill, J. F. Goodman, S. P. Harrold, and J. R. Tate, *Trans. Faraday Soc.* **63**, 240 (1967).

9
Donor-Acceptor and Charge Transfer Interactions[1]

The widespread confusion regarding the nature and significance of "charge transfer," "molecular complex," and "donor-acceptor" interactions stems in part from the difficulties inherent in the subject, but is in large part simply a semantic problem which has arisen because different groups of investigators with differing interests have approached the problem from different directions and sufficient time has not yet elapsed for a common language to develop. Spectroscopists and organic chemists, for example, are likely to be referring to quite different things when they speak of "charge transfer" phenomena.

---

[1] For further reading see L. J. Andrews and R. M. Keefer, "Molecular Complexes in Organic Chemistry," Holden-Day, Inc., San Francisco, 1964; G. Briegleb, "Elektronen-Donator Acceptor-Komplexe," Springer-Verlag, Berlin, 1961; and E. M. Kosower, *Progr. Phys. Org. Chem.* **3**, 81 (1965).

A. MANIFESTATIONS OF THE INTERACTIONS

There are many familiar chemical phenomena which may be described with a greater or lesser degree of precision by the approaches outlined in this chapter, although there is probably no chemist who would regard all of them as manifestations of a single mechanism of interaction. These phenomena include the precipitation of aromatic compounds as solid complexes with nitro-aromatic compounds, such as picric acid; the formation of complexes in solution and in the solid state which exhibit a new, charge transfer absorption band; the formation of complexes of carbonyl compounds and acceptor molecules, such as amide-iodine adducts; the existence of I_3^- and several different types of pyridine-iodine compounds; the blue color of starch-iodine complexes; olefin-silver ion complexes; the interaction of flavins with indole derivatives in solution and in the solid state; the appearance of unpaired electrons and electrical conductivity in certain complexes, such as those of tetramethylphenylenediamine and chloroanil; the existence of coordinate bonds in amine oxides, tertiary amine-boron trifluoride adducts, and related compounds; and even the hydrogen bond. All these phenomena have been described in terms of "charge transfer," "donor-acceptor," or "molecular" complex formation, and they are all, in some sense, related.

The importance of charge transfer complexes in catalysis and in interactions involving biologically significant macromolecules is probably rather limited, although the existence of such complexes has been demonstrated in a few instances. The combination of 2,4-dinitrotoluene with antibodies directed toward the dinitrophenyl group causes a decrease in the extinction coefficient of the dinitrotoluene absorption band and the appearance of a new absorption band at 300 mμ which may represent the formation of a charge transfer complex.[2] Charge transfer complexes involving pyridinium and flavin groups, which are the active centers of coenzymes involved in biological oxidation-reduction processes, have been shown to exist under rather special conditions and may be involved in oxidation-reduction reactions of these compounds.[3] Some sort of donor-acceptor interaction may be involved in determining the spectroscopic properties and structures of interacting nucleotide bases and other conjugated groups in biologically important macromolecules.

---

[2] H. N. Eisen and G. W. Siskind, *Biochemistry* **3**, 996 (1964).

[3] E. M. Kosower, "The Enzymes," vol. 3, p. 171, 1960; *Progr. Phys. Org. Chem.* **3**, 81 (1965); Q. H. Gibson, V. Massey, and N. M. Atherton, *Biochem. J.* **85**, 369 (1962).

There is evidence in a model reaction that catalysis by electron donors involves stabilization of a transition state by charge transfer interaction. The rate of solvolysis of 2,4,7-trinitrofluorenyl p-toluenesulfonate (1) in acetic acid is increased in the presence of phenan-

1

threne, hexamethylbenzene, napthalenes, and other aromatic compounds which can act as π electron donors.[4] This rate enhancement is associated with the formation of a complex between the substrate and the catalyst, as shown by the fact that the rate levels off with increasing concentration of catalyst. A double reciprocal plot of the rate increase against catalyst concentration, analogous to the Lineweaver-Burk plot familiar to enzymologists, for the 1,5-dimethoxynaphthalene catalyzed reaction at 85°, gives an extrapolated maximal rate of solvolysis of the substrate-catalyst complex which is 1,900 times larger than that of the uncomplexed substrate and an equilibrium constant of 1.0 M^{-1} for formation of the complex. Complex formation is accompanied by a change in the visible absorption of the fluorenyl compound, and an equilibrium constant of 3 M^{-1} determined spectrophotometrically for complex formation with phenanthrene agrees well with a value of 2.8 M^{-1} obtained from a double reciprocal plot of the increase in rate constants against the concentration of this catalyst. The spectral changes generally consist of the appearance of a shoulder or an increase in absorption at longer wavelengths, but discrete charge transfer absorption bands are observed in the analogous complexes with trinitrofluorene. Furthermore, the catalytic activity, measured by the logarithm of the product of the equilibrium constant for complex formation and the rate constant for reaction of the complex, is proportional to the electron-donating ability of a series of donor molecules, estimated from the calculated energy of the highest filled molecular orbital or the charge transfer absorption maximum for complexes with tetracyanoethylene and chloranil.

[4] A. K. Colter and S. S. Wang, *J. Am. Chem. Soc.* **85**, 114 (1963); A. K. Colter, S. S. Wang, G. H. Megerle, and P. S. Ossip, *Ibid.* **86**, 3106 (1964); A. K. Colter and S. H. Hui, *J. Org. Chem.*, **33**, 1935 (1968); A. K. Colter, personal communication.

The second-order rate constant for the nucleophilic aromatic substitution reaction of 2,4-dinitrochlorobenzene with aniline in ethanol exhibits a progressive decrease with increasing aniline concentration, which is associated with the development of the yellow color of a complex.[5] The equilibrium constants for complex formation are 0.46 and 0.29 to 0.34 from kinetic and spectrophotometric measurements, respectively, which are probably in agreement within experimental error. No complex formation or rate perturbation is observed in the less polar solvent, ethyl acetate. There is little doubt that the changes in the rate constant are caused by the formation of a complex, which may be of the charge transfer type. However, in interpreting this result one is faced with the recurring problem of deciding whether the reaction involves attack of free aniline on dinitrochlorobenzene (DNCB), the rate of which is *decreased* by the formation of an unreactive complex at high reactant concentrations, or whether the complex is the reactive species and complex formation serves to *increase* the rate over that which would be observed in the absence of complex formation. These two possibilities are illustrated schematically in Fig. 1. The rate laws for these two situations are shown in equation 1. These

$$\text{Rate} = k[\text{aniline}][\text{DNCB}] = k'[\text{complex}] = k'K[\text{aniline}][\text{DNCB}] \qquad (1)$$

rate laws are kinetically indistinguishable because the transition states for both mechanisms have the same stoichiometric composition, and [aniline][DNCB] is related to [complex] by the equilibrium constant $K = [\text{complex}]/[\text{aniline}][\text{DNCB}]$, so that $k = k'K$. A choice between these interpretations requires the use of other chemical information, the most useful of which is a structure-reactivity correlation. If enough is known about the dependence of reactivity on structure for reactants which do not undergo complex formation to permit an estimate of the "normal" rate of reaction, then if the observed rate for compounds in which complex formation takes place is much faster than this one can conclude that complex formation leads to a rate increase, i.e., that the forces which provide stability to the complex also provide stabilization for the transition state. If the rate in dilute solution is normal for those compounds which undergo complex formation, one may conclude that the free reactants undergo reaction and that the observed complex formation consists largely of one or more nonproductive complexes. Insuffici-

[5] S. D. Ross and I. Kuntz, *J. Am. Chem. Soc.* **76**, 3000 (1954).

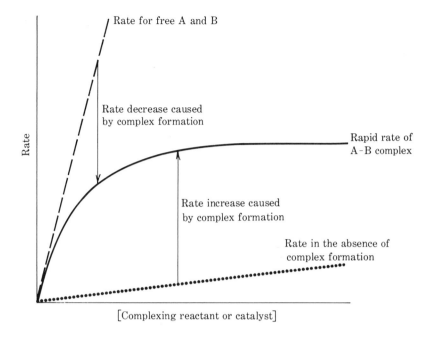

Fig 1. Diagram to show how a leveling off of the rate associated with complex formation may represent either a decrease in the rate of a bimolecular reaction (dashed line), which is caused by the formation of an unreactive complex, or an increase in rate over that in the absence of complex formation (dotted line), which is caused by the formation of a reactive complex which is on the reaction path (solid line).

ent data are available to resolve this question in the case of the aniline-dinitrochlorobenzene reaction.

B. CLASSICAL CHARGE TRANSFER
COMPLEXES IN SPECTROSCOPY

Solutions of iodine in benzene are reddish brown instead of violet in color, because of the shift in the position of the normal iodine absorption band caused by interaction with benzene. However, there is no large change in the intensity or shape of this band, and a far more striking spectroscopic change is the appearance of a strong *new* absorption band with a maximum at 297 mμ upon mixing iodine and benzene, which is associated with the formation of an iodine-benzene complex (2). The equilibrium constant for the formation of this complex may be determined from the dependence of the intensity of this new absorption band on the concentrations of the reac-

tants; it is 1.72 M^{-1} in carbon tetrachloride.[6]   A similar phenomenon
is seen with charged reactants in the salts of pyridinium derivatives.

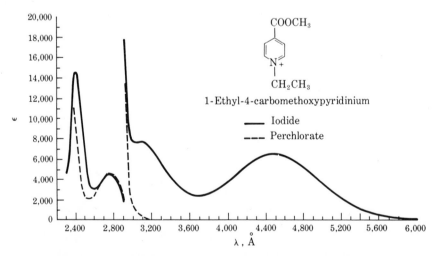

1-Ethyl-4-carbomethoxypyridinium perchlorate in ethylene dichloride
shows no absorption above 320 mμ, but the iodide salt shows a
strong, broad absorption with a maximum near 440 mμ and a second
peak near 310 mμ (Fig. 2). These new absorption peaks are not
present in the separated compounds and increase in intensity as the
concentration of the salt is increased in the manner which is expected if the species responsible for this new absorption is a pyridinium-
iodide complex, **3**.[8]

[6] H. A. Benesi and J. H. Hildebrand, *J. Am. Chem. Soc.* **71**, 2703 (1949).

[7] E. M. Kosower, "Molecular Biochemistry," p. 185, McGraw-Hill Book Company,
New York, 1962.

[8] E. M. Kosower, *J. Am. Chem. Soc.* **80**, 3253 (1958).

Fig 2.   Spectra of 1-ethyl-4-carbomethoxypyridinium iodide and perchlorate in ethylene
dichloride, showing the charge transfer absorption bands of the iodide salt.[7]

The appearance of a *new* absorption band associated with the formation of a complex under conditions in which the chemical identity of the reacting species is maintained, as shown by the retention of the characteristic absorption bands of the reactants, is evidence for the formation of a classical charge transfer complex, as defined by spectroscopists. This is the most precise operational definition of a charge transfer interaction. Although a number of other phenomena have closely related properties, both theoretically and experimentally, it is important to keep this basic criterion in mind, and it is probably desirable to restrict the term "charge transfer complex" to interactions which exhibit these spectroscopic properties.

The theory of charge transfer complexes and absorption is described in a classical paper by Mulliken.[9] Consider a molecule D which is easily able to donate electrons and an acceptor molecule A. When these two molecules come together there will be a tendency for the donor molecule to donate electrons to the acceptor molecule, so that the system in the ground state may be described as a resonance hybrid of the forms D,A and D^+—A^-. In the dative structure D^+—A^- there is a bond between D and A, so that the small contribution of this structure to the complex means that there is a *small* amount of bonding between D and A in the complex. This may be regarded as a form of "no-bond" resonance, and the ground state may be described according to equation 2, in which a,

$$\Psi_{ES} = a\Psi_0(D,A) + b\Psi_1(D^+ - A^-) \tag{2}$$

the coefficient for the contribution of the unbonded form D,A, is much larger than b, for the contribution of the bonded structure D^+—A^-. It should be noted that while there is some degree of electron transfer from D to A associated with the formation of a weak bond, there is no unpairing of electrons, and if electron donation occurs from a free electron pair on D, there is no suggestion that these electrons are distinguishable or that only one of them is transferred.

Now, if this complex absorbs light, it is possible for one of these electrons, which was localized predominantly on D, to be excited to a new orbital of the complex in which the electron is localized predominantly on the acceptor A. This state is described by equation 3, in which the coefficient a^* for the contribution of the

[9] R. S. Mulliken, *J. Am. Chem. Soc.* **74**, 811 (1952).

$$\Psi^* = -b^*\Psi_0(D,A) + a^*\Psi_1(D^+ - A^-) \tag{3}$$

charge transfer form $D^+ - A^-$ in the excited state is much larger than that for the corresponding form in the ground state, b. (It is the magnitudes and not the signs of these coefficients that should be compared, since the electron distribution depends on the square of these terms.) In the benzene-iodine complex the coefficients a and b in the ground state are approximately 0.97 and 0.17, whereas b^* and a^* in the excited state are 0.27 and 0.99, respectively. The excitation is called a charge transfer process simply because the charge distribution of the excited state is very different from that of the ground state.

Although charge transfer complexes must, by definition, exhibit charge transfer absorption bands, the converse is not true, and charge transfer absorption may occur in the absence of complex formation. In any moderately concentrated solution there will be a finite probability that a donor molecule will be near to an acceptor, so that if the donor absorbs light an electron may be excited to a charge transfer orbital of $D^+ - A^-$ even if the charge transfer complex has no stability in the ground state; this is called *contact charge transfer absorption*.[10] The equilibrium constants for charge transfer complex formation and the extinction coefficient of the complex are commonly estimated from the abscissa and ordinate intercepts, respectively, of double reciprocal plots of the change in absorption caused by complex formation against the concentration of one of the reactants which is present in large excess[6]; in the case of contact charge transfer such plots pass through the origin.

It is important to keep in mind that any measured equilibrium constant for complex formation in solution is actually the sum of the equilibrium constants for the formation of all the different types of 1:1 complexes which can be formed between the reactants, and only if one of these complexes is much more stable than the others will the observed equilibrium constant be equal to the equilibrium constant for the formation of the complex. The observed equilibrium constant for complex formation in solution may, therefore, be larger than the equilibrium constant for the formation of the complex which gives rise to the charge transfer absorption band if other complexes are formed which do not exhibit charge transfer absorption. This situation is especially likely to arise if the energy of interaction in the charge transfer complex is small, as is often the

[10] L. E. Orgel and R. S. Mulliken, *J. Am. Chem. Soc.* **79**, 4839 (1957).

case. If only a fraction of the complexes which are formed exhibit charge transfer absorption, the experimentally determined extinction coefficient for the absorption of the charge transfer complex will be erroneously small because this extinction coefficient is based on all of the complexes which are formed, not just the absorbing ones. In fact, in cases in which the interaction is very weak much of the observed charge transfer absorption may arise from contact charge transfer rather than from the formation of a charge transfer complex. These situations are manifested experimentally by variations in the experimentally determined extinction coefficient of the complex under different conditions, depending on the fraction of the complexes which are active. The situation is entirely analogous to the formation of nonproductive complexes of substrates with enzymes, which leads to anomalously low dissociation constants and maximum velocities for the enzyme-substrate complex (Chap. 5, Sec. B, Part 2).

If donor and acceptor groups are incorporated into the same molecule, a charge transfer excitation may occur intramolecularly. For example, the $n \rightarrow \pi^*$ excitation of aniline may be regarded as a charge transfer excitation in which the electron distribution in the excited state corresponds to the partial transfer of an electron from nitrogen to the aromatic ring in the excited state (equation 4). It is

$$\ddot{N}H_2 \qquad \dot{N}H_2 \quad (+)$$

$$(4)$$

difficult to draw a sharp line between intramolecular charge transfer excitations of this kind, in which an electron is transferred from a donor group D to an acceptor A, and any excitation in which there is a considerable difference in the distribution of charge in the ground and excited states. The use of the term "charge transfer" in this sense by spectroscopists is perfectly correct, but it has contributed to the confusion and misunderstanding surrounding the term.

There is no difference in principle between the situation in which the reacting molecules are uncharged and that in which they are charged in the ground state, as in the case of pyridinium iodide complexes. In these complexes the transfer of charge upon excitation is from the iodide ion to the pyridinium ring, so that the effect of the charge transfer is to reduce rather than to increase the amount of charge separation in the complex upon excitation (equation

5). Because of this large difference in the charge distribution of the ground and excited states, there will be a large difference in the energy of these states in different solvents, depending on the

$$\tag{5}$$

charge-solvating ability of the solvent, with a consequent change in the energy of the excitation and in the absorption maximum of the charge transfer band. The position of the charge transfer absorption band, therefore, serves as a sensitive indicator of the charge-solvating ability of the solvent, and this relationship has been utilized by Kosower to define a scale of Z values for this solvent property, based upon the excitation energy of the charge transfer complex in each solvent.[8] The Z values generally agree well with Winstein's Y values, which are based upon the rate of solvolysis of t-butyl chloride and are a measure of the difference in energy between the nonpolar ground state and the ionic, carbonium-ion-like transition state 4 for this reaction in different solvents.[11] The quite

4

general absence of a close correlation between the macroscopic dielectric constant and the charge-solvating ability of solvents over more than a very limited range of solvent variation is demonstrated especially clearly by the large amount of scatter which is evident in a plot of Z against the usual dielectric constant function, $(D-1)/(2D+1)$ (Fig. 3).

Since a classical charge transfer absorption band may be approximately described, in an uncomplicated case, as the result of

[11] S. G. Smith, A. H. Fainberg, and S. Winstein, *J. Am. Chem. Soc.* **83**, 618 (1961); A. H. Fainberg and S. Winstein, *Ibid.* **78**, 2770 (1956) and references therein.

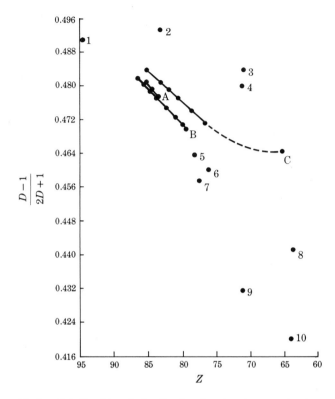

Fig 3. Relationship of the Z value for the charge-solvating power to the dielectric constant function $(D-1)/(2D+1)$ for a series of solvents. The lines A, B, and C are for methanol-water, ethanol-water and acetone-water mixtures, respectively. The other points are (1) water; (2) formamide; (3) dimethyl-sulfoxide; (4) acetonitrile; (5) 1-propanol; (6) isopropyl alcohol; (7) 1-butanol; (8) pyridine; (9) t-butyl alcohol; (10) methylene dichloride.[8]

the excitation of an electron from the highest filled orbital of the donor to the lowest empty orbital of the acceptor, the difference between these energies and, hence, the energy of the transition and the position of the absorption band should depend on the ionization potential of the donor, I_p, and the electron affinity of the acceptor, E_A. The expected relationship has been found for a number of series of complexes with a constant acceptor and a varying donor. In some of these series there is a linear relationship between the frequency of the charge transfer absorption band, $h\nu_{CT}$, and the

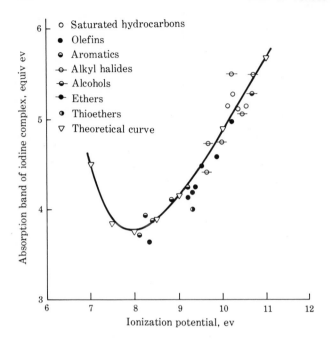

Fig 4. Energy of the charge transfer absorption band of iodine complexes as a function of the ionization potential of the donor.[12]

ionization potential of the donor, but closer examination of larger series reveals the relationship to be more complicated. The energy of the charge transfer band for iodine complexes has a parabolic relationship to the ionization potential of the donor (Fig. 4) and follows equation 6, in which C and β are approximately constant for

$$h\nu_{CT} = I_p - C + \frac{2\beta^2}{I_p - C} \tag{6}$$

a given series.[12]   Less information is available regarding the effect of the electron affinity of the acceptor on the position of the absorption band, but the available data support the expected relationship. Similar correlations of the calculated energies of the highest filled molecular orbital of D and of the lowest empty orbital of A show

[12] S. H. Hastings, J. L. Franklin, J. C. Schiller, and F. A. Matsen, *J. Am. Chem. Soc.* **75**, 2900 (1953).

good linear correlations with the energies of the observed charge transfer absorption bands.[13]

C. RELATED PHENOMENA AND LONG, ELECTRON-DEFICIENT BONDS

In the classical charge transfer complexes usually referred to by spectroscopists the contribution of the charge transfer form $D^+ - A^-$, i.e., the coefficient b in equation 2, to the structure of the ground state is very small, so that there is little bond formation between A and D as a result of the charge transfer phenomenon in the ground state. This has led to the frequent statement that *classical* charge transfer does not make an appreciable contribution to the stability of charge transfer complexes and that these complexes are held together largely by van der Waals and London dispersion forces (among which quadrupole-induced dipole interactions appear to be especially significant[14]) and, in hydroxylic solvents, by hydrophobic bonds rather than by the charge transfer forces themselves. However, Mulliken pointed out clearly that charge transfer *could* be at least as important as London forces in stabilizing intermolecular interactions and that an extension of the concept beyond that reserved for weak, spectroscopically identifiable complexes could describe situations in which there is strong bonding.[9] The inevitable difficulty in drawing a sharp dividing line between these related phenomena has contributed to much of the confusion in this field. In this section we shall consider some of these situations in which significant bonding energy arises from charge transfer or "donor-acceptor" interactions or in which the classical spectroscopic criteria of charge transfer interactions may not be satisfied. The equilibrium constants for the formation of some (but not all) charge transfer complexes increase with increasing electron-donating ability of the donor and exhibit negative ρ values in $\rho\sigma$ correlations with substituted donor molecules.[15] Since these equilibrium constants show no apparent dependence on the polarizability of the substituents, it must be concluded that electron donation from the donor may contribute directly to the stability of even classical charge transfer complexes.

---

[13] M. J. S. Dewar and A. R. Lepley, *J. Am. Chem. Soc.* **83**, 4560 (1961); M. J. S. Dewar and H. Rogers, *Ibid.* **84**, 395 (1962); A. R. Lepley, *Ibid.*, p. 3577.

[14] M. W. Hanna, *J. Am. Chem. Soc.* **90**, 285 (1968).

[15] L. J. Andrews and R. M. Keefer, "Molecular Complexes in Organic Chemistry," p. 102, Holden-Day, Inc., San Francisco, 1964; M. Charton, *J. Org. Chem.* **31**, 2991, 2996 (1966).

An instructive example of a complex or compound of intermediate character is found in the immediate product of the reaction of pyridines with iodine (equation 7). This product in the case of 4-

5   6

7   (7)

methylpyridine has been shown by chemical and x-ray analysis to have the structure **5**. The length of the I—I bond of 2.83 Å is increased by 0.17 Å over that in I_2, and the length of the N—I bond is 2.31 Å, which is significantly longer than the normal N—I covalent bond distance of 2.03 Å but is much shorter than the sum of the van der Waal's radii of N and I of 3.65 Å. Thus, the compound may be regarded as a perturbed complex of 4-methylpyridine and iodine, in which the I—I bond has been somewhat weakened and stretched and a long, weak N—I bond has been formed. It meets the spectroscopic criterion for charge transfer complexes in that it has a new absorption band at 235 mμ which is not present in either of the starting materials. However, the complex has considerable stability; the equilibrium constant for its formation is 290 M^{-1} in heptane[17] and that for the diethylamine-iodine complex in dioxane has been reported[18] to be 146,000 M^{-1}. The stability of the complexes increases with increasing electron-donating power of the donor atom: the stability of pyridine complexes is proportional to the basicity of the pyridine and follows the $\rho\sigma$ correlation with a ρ value of −2.34.[19] The water-insoluble compound **5** is to be distinguished from the water-soluble, ionic complex **7**, which is formed on prolonged standing of pyridines and iodine. The formation of this salt may take place through the intermediate **6**, which differs

[16] O. Hassel, C. Rømming, and T. Tufte, *Acta Chem. Scand.* **15**, 967 (1961).

[17] C. Reid and R. S. Mulliken, *J. Am. Chem. Soc.* **76**, 3869 (1954).

[18] S. Kobinata and S. Nagakura, *J. Am. Chem. Soc.* **88**, 3905 (1966).

[19] G. Aloisi, G. Cauzzo, and U. Mazzucato, *Trans. Faraday Soc.* **63**, 1858 (1967).

from **5** in that a strong N—I bond has been formed and the I—I bond has been broken.

The triiodide ion, $(I$—I—$I)^-$, which is generally regarded as a stable compound, is the same type of complex as the pyridine-iodine complexes, except that an iodine anion has been substituted for pyridine. It is sometimes assumed that charge transfer interactions with second-row or heavier elements as acceptors involve electron donation to an empty d orbital on the acceptor. However, this does not have to be the case in order for a significant interaction to occur, and the stability of the triiodide ion may be accounted for without invoking participation of the high-energy d orbitals by a simple molecular orbital model[20] similar to that already described for the hydrogen bond. Consider three iodine atoms with one p orbital from each atom which is available for bond formation. These three atomic orbitals may be used to construct the three molecular orbitals shown in equation 8, into which may be placed the four electrons of

$$
\begin{array}{ccc}
I & I & I \\
p_1 & p_2 & p_3
\end{array}
$$

$$\Psi_3 = \frac{N'}{\sqrt{2}}\,(p_1 + p_3) + \lambda' p_2 \qquad \text{antibonding} \;\text{—}\qquad \text{unoccupied}$$

$$\Psi_2 = \frac{1}{\sqrt{2}}\,(p_1 - p_3) \qquad \text{nonbonding} \;\overset{\cdots}{\;}\qquad \overset{(\cdot\cdot)}{I}\;\; I \;\; \overset{(\cdot\cdot)}{I}$$

$$\Psi_1 = \frac{N}{\sqrt{2}}\,(p_1 + p_3) - N\lambda p_2 \qquad \text{bonding} \;\overset{\cdots}{\;}\qquad I\overset{\cdot}{-}I\overset{\cdot}{-}I \tag{8}$$

the triiodide ion. The first two electrons will be in the lowest-energy bonding orbital, which extends over all three iodine atoms and provides a relatively long, weak, electron-deficient bond involving two electrons and three atoms. The next electron pair will fill the intermediate, nonbonding orbital, in which they will be localized on the terminal two atoms, and the highest, antibonding orbital will be unoccupied. The localization of the nonbonding electrons on the outer atoms accounts for the enhanced stability of complexes such as $(Cl$—I—$Cl)^-$, in which the outer atoms have an increased electronegativity.

[20] R. E. Rundle, *Record Chem. Progr.* **23**, 195 (1962); *Surv. Progr. Chem.* **1**, 81 (1963); E. H. Wiebenga, E. E. Havinga, and K. H. Boswijk, *Advan. Inorg. Chem. Radiochem.* **3**, 133 (1961).

The same type of interaction provides an explanation for the bonding in larger polyhalide ions, such as I_5^-, and also accounts for the peculiar geometry of these compounds. The well known starch-iodine complexes with their characteristic blue color are formed from long, negatively charged polyhalide chains which reside in the center of a coil or helix of the starch molecule and probably represent the same or a similar type of interaction.[21]

Still another application of this important general method of describing compounds in which the usual valence numbers are exceeded is to compounds of the PCl_5 class. Earlier attempts to describe such molecules utilized the d orbitals of phosphorus to account for the extra bonding. The structure of the PCl_5 molecule is a trigonal bipyramid in which the two P—Cl bonds at the apices are longer than the three at the equator. The structure of such molecules may be reasonably accounted for without invoking d-orbital participation by constructing three normal P—Cl bonds extending outward from the phosphorus atom at the base of the pyramid and a long, electron-deficient, three-atom–two-electron bond, similar to that of I_3^-, from the phosphorus to the chlorine atoms at the two apices of the bipyramid. The structure of a number of other compounds, including PF_5, SF_6, ICl_4, and the rare gas halides XeF_2 and XeF_4, may be described in a similar manner.[20, 22]

It is apparent that there is no essential difference between this description of a charge transfer complex and the molecular orbital description of the covalent nature of a hydrogen bond in Chap. 6, Sec. C, except for the symmetries of the orbitals involved. In both cases long, rather weak electron-deficient bonds are formed over three atoms with two electrons and a second electron pair is distributed between the terminal atoms of the system in a nonbonding orbital. In both cases, too, the major contribution to bonding in the system is likely to arise from other interactions, for example, from electrostatic interaction in the hydrogen bond and from London dispersion or hydrophobic forces in the charge transfer complex, but the possibility exists in both cases that the covalent bond may become strong and may even make a major contribution to the strength of the bond if the donor and acceptor molecules have a favorable composition and geometry.

[21] R. E. Rundle, *J. Am. Chem. Soc.* **69**, 1769 (1947); R. S. Stein and R. E. Rundle, *J. Chem. Phys.* **16**, 195 (1948); J. A. Thoma and D. French, *J. Am. Chem. Soc.* **82**, 4144 (1960).

[22] R. E. Rundle, *J. Am. Chem. Soc.* **85**, 112 (1963).

Particularly interesting examples of donor-acceptor complexes are found in the series of carbonyl or acyl interactions with Lewis acids and other acceptors. Interaction of amides and other carbonyl compounds with a proton, with Lewis acids such as boron trifluoride and aluminum chloride, and with "charge transfer" acceptors such as iodine and bromine generally occurs by donation of the lone pair electrons of the carbonyl oxygen atom to the acceptor. This results in a lengthening of the $>C=O$ bond and a shortening of the bond to an adjacent electron donor atom, such as the nitrogen of an amide, and increases the susceptibility of the carbonyl group to nucleophilic attack. The lengthening of the $>C=O$ bond is manifested in a decrease of 43 cm^{-1} in the carbonyl stretching frequency of N,N-dimethylacetamide in its complex with iodine.[23] These complexes are generally weak, with equilibrium constants within a few orders of magnitude of unity; the equilibrium constants for the formation of N,N-dimethylbenzamide–iodine complexes in carbon tetrachloride are approximately 4 M^{-1}, for example.[24] The complexes show the expected increase in stability with electron-donating substituents: the value of ρ for the formation of iodine complexes of substituted N,N-dimethylbenzamides is -0.7,[24] and complexes of amides are more stable than those of simple carbonyl compounds, such as acetone, in which electron donation by adjacent atoms to the carbonyl group is much less important than in amides. The structure of a representative member of this group, the bromine-acetone complex in the solid state, has been determined by x-ray diffraction and has been found to involve bonding of each carbonyl oxygen atom to *two* bromine molecules to form a zigzag network of cross-linked groups (8).[25] The bonding in compounds of this type can be re-

8

garded as either the result of donation of an electron pair from oxy-

[23] C. D. Schmulbach and R. S. Drago, *J. Am. Chem. Soc.* **82**, 4484 (1960).

[24] R. L. Carlson and R. S. Drago, *J. Am. Chem. Soc.* **85**, 505 (1963).

[25] O. Hassel and K. O. Strømme, *Acta Chem. Scand.* **13**, 275 (1959).

gen to an empty orbital of the acceptor—the s orbital of a proton, the vacant bonding orbital of a Lewis acid, a vacant d orbital of bromine, or an antibonding orbital of an aromatic molecule—or as the result of the formation of a new hybrid orbital which does not require the utilization of d orbitals for bonding, as described above for I_3^-. Both of these types of interaction are probably significant, depending on the nature of the reacting atoms.

Complexes of metals with unsaturated systems are of two types. In the first the metal adds to one or the other of the carbon atoms of the system to form a new σ bond. This type of interaction is found with mercuric ions and in most products of proton addition (9). The best known example of the other class is the silver ion–olefin complex in which the silver ion does not add to either of the carbon atoms, but rather interacts with the π electrons of the double bond in a form of donor-acceptor complex (10). It is probable

that complexes of this kind receive a significant amount of additional stabilization from back-donation of electrons from a d orbital of the metal ion to an antibonding π orbital of the olefin or aromatic system.

D. UNPAIRED ELECTRONS AND RADICALS

One aspect of this problem which has been particularly difficult to clarify and which is still not entirely clear is the question of the role of unpaired electrons and radical-like states in donor-acceptor and charge transfer complexes.[26] As noted above, there is no implication that electrons *must* be separated or unpaired when such complexes are formed. As the strength of the interaction becomes stronger in a series of compounds, several quite different things may happen depending on the structure of the donor and acceptor (Fig. 5). If the coefficient b corresponding to the contribution to the ground state of the charge transfer form $D^+—A^-$ of equation 2 increases and the structure of the donor and acceptor are such that

[26] E. M. Kosower, *Progr. Phys. Org. Chem.* **3**, 113 (1965).

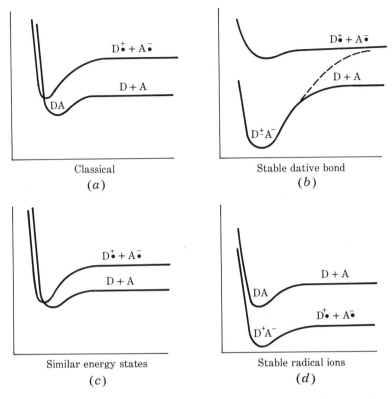

Fig 5. Potential-energy curves for ground and excited states of donor and acceptor molecules and their radical ions.

a stable compound rather than a pair of radical ions is formed, the ground state of the system corresponds to an ordinary covalent "dative" bond and the excited state may not be readily accessible, so that no charge transfer absorption band is observed (Fig. 5b). This is the situation in trialkylamine–boron trifluoride complexes, R_3NBF_3, and amine oxides, $\geqslant N^+\!\!-\!\!O^-$, for example.

If the ionization potential of the electron donor decreases and the electron affinity of the electron acceptor increases in a pair of reactants which form stable radical ions, both complexed and separated ions may be formed (Figs. 5c, 5d). One possibility is that the DA and $D^+\!\!-\!\!A^-$ states of the charge transfer complex become of similar equilibrium energies, so that the complex may exist at ordinary temperatures as an equilibrium mixture of D,A and $D^+\!\!-\!\!A^-$ (Fig. 5c). The most stable state of the $D^+\!\!-\!\!A^-$ complex is probably that in which the electrons are paired, i.e., a singlet state, and the formation of such a complex will not give rise directly to unpaired electrons unless a significant fraction of the complex exists in a triplet state. A more likely source of unpaired electrons in such a system is the separate radical ions $D^+ \cdot$ and $A^- \cdot$, which can exist as such in solution upon dissociation of the $D^+ - A^-$ complex (Fig. 5d). The difference between $D^+ - A^-$ complexes of this type and the ordinary dative or coordinate bond is not in the degree of charge transfer in the ground state, which is large in both cases, but in the stability of the bond between the donor and acceptor, i.e., the relative stabilities of the compound and the separate radical ions.

The complexes of phenylenediamine and its methyl substituted derivatives with chloranil (tetrachlorobenzoquinone) or tetracyanoethylene illustrate several of the possible types of interaction (equations 9 and 10). In nonpolar solvents, such as cyclohexane, these molecules interact to form a normal charge transfer complex with a characteristic charge transfer absorption band (11; equation 9). As the charge-solvating power of the solvent is increased in the series cyclohexane-acetonitrile-water, or as ethanol is added to chloroform, the charge transfer band disappears and the characteristic visible absorption bands of the radical ions corresponding to the loss of an electron from the donor and the addition of an electron to the acceptor appear and finally become predominant, accompanied by the appearance of an electron spin resonance signal indicating the presence of unpaired electrons.[27, 28] This new prod-

(9)

[27] R. Foster and T. J. Thomson, *Trans. Faraday Soc.* **58**, 860 (1962); I. Isenberg and S. L. Baird, Jr., *J. Am. Chem. Soc.* **84**, 3803 (1962).

[28] W. Liptay, G. Briegleb, and K. Schindler, *Z. Elektrochem.* **66**, 331 (1962).

$$\text{(10)}$$

uct may exist as a complex or ion pair (12) or may diffuse apart
into the separate radical ions (13), which, in the case of the phenylenediamine-chloranil system, correspond to the well known Wurster's
blue radical cation and the chloranil radical anion. In the case of
the tetramethylphenylenediamine-tetracyanoethylene system the
equilibrium constants for the separate steps of reaction 9 have been
estimated by ultraviolet spectroscopy in several solvents; the value
of K_2 is reported to be small in ether, 0.17 in tetrahydrofuran, and
large in acetonitrile, in which conversion to the charged forms is
almost complete.[28]

This type of system is shown schematically in equation 11. Al-

$$D + A \;\rightleftharpoons\; D,A \;\rightleftharpoons\; D^+ - A^- \;\rightleftharpoons\; D^{+\cdot} + A^{-\cdot} \qquad (11)$$

though this scheme is reasonable and attractive, it has not yet been
examined experimentally with as much care as would be desirable.
In particular, the different experimental manifestations, such as the
visible and ultraviolet spectra of the reactants and products, the
concentration of unpaired electrons on the separated radical ions,
and the properties of the ion pair $D^+ - A^-$ in equilibrium with the
radical ions have not been examined for a single system in one
solvent. What is quite clear is that the complexes D,A and $D^+ - A^-$
are distinct species with altogether different spectral properties,
and it appears that both of these species can exist in the same
solution at the same time. Thus, 12 is *not* simply the D,A species
11 in which the coefficient b corresponding to the charge transfer
form $D^+ - A^-$ has become large. It is important to keep in mind
the difference between contributing resonance structures and differ-

ent electronic states of these complexes: the D,A complex is a single species or state which may be regarded as composed of the contributing resonance structures D,A and D^+—A^-, of which the first is ordinarily much the more important. Conversely, the D^+—A^- complex is a different single species, to which the resonance structures D,A and D^+—A^- contribute in the opposite order of importance. The latter complex has not been carefully examined experimentally, but some of its properties may be inferred from the properties of other radical dimers in solution.[29] As two relatively stable radicals come together, there will be a tendency for the formation of a (weak) bond between them, implying that they exist with paired electrons in a singlet state; this means that the complex should exhibit no significant electron spin resonance signal. A new absorption band, resulting from the interaction of the two components in a manner similar to the charge transfer band of the D,A complex, may be detectable.

One might ask how it is that the D,A and D^+—A^- complexes may exist in thermal equilibrium, i.e., with similar energies, and at the same time a charge transfer band may be observed upon excitation of an electron from D,A to the D^+—A^- state, implying that these two states have different energies. This apparent anomaly is a result of the Franck-Condon requirement that the electronic excitation take place more rapidly than the atoms of the complex and the surrounding solvent can undergo rearrangement to their most stable configurations (Kosower[1]). Thus, the excitation takes place to an energy level at which the geometries of the complex and the surrounding solvent are the same as those of the starting material, and this energy is higher than the equilibrium energy for the solvated D^+—A^- complex.

The existence of solid charge transfer complexes which exhibit a small amount of conductivity and a small number of unpaired electrons has led to considerable speculation about a possible role of solid charge transfer complexes, conductivity, and solid-state electrical behavior in biological systems. In a number of cases, such complexes exhibit the characteristic infrared and electronic spectra of the $D^+\cdot$ and $A^-\cdot$ ions and therefore might be regarded as having a structure analogous to that of D^+—A^- complexes in solution. For example, phenylenediamine-chloranil complexes in the solid state exhibit the characteristic visible and infrared spectra of

[29] E. M. Kosower and Y. Ikegami, *J. Am. Chem. Soc.* **89**, 461 (1967); M. Itoh and E. M. Kosower, *Ibid.*, p. 3655; M. Itoh and S. Nagakura, *Ibid.*, p. 3959; R. H. Boyd and W. D. Phillips, *J. Chem. Phys.* **43**, 2927 (1965).

the Wurster's blue cation and the semiquinone anion, so that some sort of electron transfer to give a state similar to **12** has certainly occurred.[30] The mechanism of the electrical conduction and formation of unpaired electrons in these solids is still imperfectly understood, but it is certain that they result from impurities and lattice imperfections in some cases, and it is probable that they arise from the unpaired electrons of a small concentration of triplet states which are in thermal equilibrium with the more stable singlet state.[31, 32] Interaction between the electrons of the D^+ and A^- ions in the solid presumably results in a weak bonding interaction and the formation of an electron-paired, singlet state. There does not appear to be any clear indication that non-ionic solid complexes of the D,A type contain a significant amount of excited ionic states at ordinary temperatures, or that such solid complexes provide unpaired electrons or conductivity which is significant in biological systems.

E. CHARGE TRANSFER AND DONOR-ACCEPTOR INTERACTIONS IN BIOCHEMISTRY; FLAVIN COMPLEXES

The majority of the examples of "charge transfer interactions" which have been reported in biological systems have not been proved to be classical charge transfer complexes and, in fact, almost certainly do not represent such complexes. The primary criterion for the identification of such complexes is the demonstration of a *new* charge transfer absorption band, and this criterion has been satisfied in only a few instances. In addition, it is desirable to show (1) that this band changes its absorption maximum in the expected direction with changing solvent polarity and (2) that the position of the band shifts in the expected direction with changing energy of the highest filled molecular orbital of the donor and the lowest empty orbital of the acceptor molecule in the presumed complex. If the charge transfer interaction contributes to the stability of the complex in the ground state, it should also be shown that this stability changes in the expected direction with changes in the energies of these orbitals.

[30] Y. Matsunaga, *J. Chem. Phys.* **41**, 1609 (1964); B. G. Anex and E. B. Hill, Jr., *J. Am. Chem. Soc.* **88**, 3648 (1966).

[31] D. B. Chesnut and W. D. Phillips, *J. Chem. Phys.* **35**, 1002 (1961).

[32] P. L. Nordio, Z. G. Soos, and H. M. McConnell, *Ann. Rev. Phys. Chem.* **17**, 237 (1966).

On the other hand, there is suggestive evidence that some sort of donor-acceptor interaction may be important in systems which do not exhibit a classical charge transfer absorption band. The hard pressed proponent of such interactions can always retreat to the hydrogen bond as an example of a significant donor-acceptor interaction in biology. There are several examples of complex formation in aqueous solution in which there appears to be a rough correlation between complex stability and the energy of donor or acceptor orbitals, which cannot be easily explained in terms of hydrophobic or dispersion forces. These examples include the denaturation of myoglobin by a series of aromatic compounds, probably through an interaction with the heme prosthetic group,[33] the formation of riboflavin-nucleoside complexes,[34] and the formation of complexes between aromatic molecules and methyl cinnamate, which causes a strong inhibition of the hydrolysis of this ester.[35] Much more extensive data on systems of this kind are needed before an estimate can be made of the amount of driving force, if any, which can be obtained from donor-acceptor interactions in aqueous solution.

The most extensively studied examples of these types of interactions in biochemically significant molecules are flavin complexes. The complexes which are formed between phenols or hydroxynaphthalenes and *protonated* flavins in acid solutions are classical charge transfer complexes which exhibit a charge transfer absorption band, the position of which is correlated with the ionization potential of the donor molecule.[36] The equilibrium constants for the formation of these complexes are quite respectable, in the range of 1 to 160 M^{-1}. However, the equilibrium constants bear no relationship to the ionization potential of the donor or the position of the charge transfer band, so that forces other than the charge transfer interaction must be responsible for the stability of the complexes.

The complexes formed from reduced flavin mononucleotide ($FMNH_2$) and the pyridinium ring of a series of nicotinamide adenine dinucleotide analogs are of more direct biochemical interest. These complexes exhibit formation constants in the range 1 to 10 M^{-1} and new absorption bands at a position which is correlated with the electron affinity of the pyridinium acceptor molecule.[37] Complexes of flavins with indole-containing compounds exhibit a "tail" of in-

[33] J. R. Cann, *Biochemistry* **6**, 3427, 3435 (1967).

[34] J. C. M. Tsibris, D. B. McCormick, and L. D. Wright, *Biochemistry* **4**, 507 (1965).

[35] J. A. Mollica, Jr. and K. A. Connors, *J. Am. Chem. Soc.* **89**, 308 (1967).

[36] D. E. Fleischman and G. Tollin, *Proc. Natl. Acad. Sci. U.S.* **53**, 38 (1965).

[37] V. Massey and G. Palmer, *J. Biol. Chem.* **237**, 2347 (1962); T. Sakurai and H. Hosoya, *Biochim. Biophys. Acta* **112**, 459 (1966).

creased absorption at long wavelengths, which may represent a charge transfer band, but complexes with purines and other aromatic molecules exhibit only a small shift of the original absorption band, without the appearance of a new absorption band, and are almost certainly not classical charge transfer complexes.[37,38,39]

Flavin complexes may be involved in the oxidation-reduction reactions of these compounds.[3] Flavin mononucleotide (FMN) is reduced nonenzymatically by reduced nicotinamide adenine dinucleotide (NADH) to give a mixture of fully reduced flavin and partly reduced flavin semiquinone radicals at intermediate times.[40] That the reduction is a two-electron process followed by dismutation to radicals, rather than a one-electron process to give radicals as the primary product, is shown by the fact that the appearance of radicals, measured by electron spin resonance absorption, is slower than that of fully reduced flavin and shows a lag period (equation 12).[41] Direct measurements on the partly reduced flavin system by

$$
\left.
\begin{array}{l}
\text{FMN} + \text{NADH} \xrightarrow{-\text{NAD}} \text{FMNH}_2 \\[2mm]
\qquad \text{fast} \left\|\right. \pm \text{FMN} \\[2mm]
\qquad \text{FMNH}_2 \cdot \text{FMN} \\[2mm]
\qquad\quad 900\,\text{m}\mu
\end{array}
\right\}
\;\;\begin{array}{l}\text{slow}\\ \rightleftharpoons\end{array}\;\;
\begin{array}{l}2\,\text{FMN}\cdot\\ 570\,\text{m}\mu\end{array}
\tag{12}
$$

the temperature-jump technique have shown that FMN and FNMH_2 react at a rate that is close to diffusion-controlled to form a dimer with maximum absorption at 900 mμ, which is generally believed to be a charge transfer complex, and that the dismutation to two molecules of semiquinone, with maximum absorption at 570 mμ, occurs much more slowly.[42]

The solubility of the model peptide, acetyltetraglycine ethyl ester, is increased by salts which contain an aromatic group, such as benzoate and benzylammonium ions, whereas related salts which do not contain an aromatic group, such as trimethylacetate and cyclohexylammonium chloride, have much less effect or cause a

[38] H. A. Harbury, K. F. LaNoue, P. A. Loach, and R. M. Amick, *Proc. Natl. Acad. Sci. U.S.* **45**, 1708 (1959); H. A. Harbury and K. A. Foley, *Ibid.* **44**, 662 (1958).

[39] J. E. Wilson, *Biochemistry* **5**, 1351 (1966).

[40] C. H. Suelter and D. E. Metzler, *Biochim. Biophys. Acta* **44**, 23 (1960).

[41] J. L. Fox and G. Tollin, *Biochemistry* **5**, 3865 (1966).

[42] J. H. Swinehart, *J. Am. Chem. Soc.* **87**, 904 (1965).

decrease in the solubility of the peptide.[43] Similarly, 0.5 M phenol causes nearly a twofold increase in the solubility of the peptide, whereas dioxane and tetrahydrofuran have almost no effect. This suggests that there is an interaction between aromatic systems and the peptide group which is not a simple "hydrophobic" effect. This is presumably the same interaction which is largely responsible for the well known denaturing and solubilizing action of phenol on proteins and which makes possible the separation of proteins from nucleic acids by phenol extraction.[44] The nature of the interaction is not known, but the requirement for aromaticity suggests that it may be either some form of "molecular complex" or "donor-acceptor" interaction or a van der Waals–London dispersion interaction involving the π orbital system of the aromatic compound and either the n or π orbitals of the amide.

[43] D. R. Robinson and W. P. Jencks, *J. Am. Chem. Soc.* **87**, 2470 (1965).

[44] F. C. Bawden and N. W. Pirie, *Biochem. J.* **34**, 1258, 1278 (1940); W. Grassmann and G. Deffner, *Z. Physiol. Chem.* **293**, 89 (1953); G. R. Shepherd and P. A. Hopkins, *Biochem. Biophys. Res. Commun.* **10**, 103 (1963).

part three

10
Carbonyl- and Acyl-group
Reactions[1]

A. METHODS FOR THE DIAGNOSIS OF MECHANISM

Not all chemical and biochemical reactions involve the carbonyl group or its derivatives, but a surprisingly large fraction of them do. Because of the special importance of these compounds and the usefulness of the techniques which have been utilized for their investigation in the examination of other reactions, some aspects of the mechanism and catalysis of carbonyl- and acyl-group reactions in nonenzymatic systems are summarized in this chapter from the points of view which have been described in previous chapters. Although these reactions are still far from understood, especially at the acyl level of oxidation, a few generalizations about their mechanism are now beginning to emerge and there is a reasonable pros-

[1] For further reading, see M. L. Bender, *Chem Rev.* **60**, 53 (1960); W. P. Jencks, *Progr. Phys. Org. Chem.* **2**, 63 (1964); T. C. Bruice and S. Benkovic, "Bioorganic Mechanisms," vol. 1, W. A. Benjamin, Inc., New York, 1966; R. B. Martin, *J. Phys. Chem.* **68**, 1369 (1964); S. Johnson, *Adv. Phys. Org. Chem.* **5**, 237 (1967).

pect that within the next few years it will be possible to fit the mechanisms of most of these reactions into a general scheme.

Some of the possible pathways for a "simple" acyl-group transfer reaction, the aminolysis of an ester, are shown in equation 1. The scheme shows steps for the formation and decomposition of

$$
\begin{array}{c}
\overset{O}{\underset{\displaystyle RCN}{\parallel}}\overset{H^+}{\diagdown} + {}^-OR \;\rightleftharpoons\; \overset{O}{\underset{\displaystyle RC-N}{\parallel}}\diagup + {}^-OR \\[4pt]
\overset{O^-}{\underset{\displaystyle RC-OR}{\mid}} \;\rightleftharpoons\; \overset{{}^-O}{\underset{\displaystyle RC-OR}{\mid}}\;H^+ \\[2pt]
\underset{\displaystyle N}{\mid} \qquad\qquad \underset{\displaystyle N}{\mid} \\[6pt]
\overset{H}{\underset{\displaystyle O}{}} \\
RC-OR \\
\mid \\
N
\end{array}
$$

$$
\begin{array}{c}
\overset{O}{\underset{\displaystyle RCOR}{\parallel}} \;\rightleftharpoons\; \overset{O^-}{\underset{\displaystyle RC-OR}{\mid}} \qquad \overset{O}{\underset{\displaystyle RC-OR}{\mid}} \qquad \overset{O}{\underset{\displaystyle RC-N}{\parallel}}\diagup + HOR \\
{}^-NH \qquad\quad {}^{-+}NH \qquad\quad N \\
\mid \qquad\qquad \mid \\[6pt]
\overset{OH}{\underset{\displaystyle RC-OR}{\mid}} \;\rightleftharpoons\; \overset{OH}{\underset{\displaystyle RC-OR}{\mid}}\;H^+ \\
{}^-NH \qquad\qquad N \\
\mid
\end{array}
$$

$$
\begin{array}{c}
H^+ \\
O \\
\parallel \\
RCOR \;\rightleftharpoons \\
N^- \\
\parallel \qquad\qquad \text{etc.} \\
O \\
\parallel H^+ \\
RCOR \;\rightleftharpoons \\
N^-
\end{array}
\tag{1}
$$

a tetrahedral addition intermediate and for the associated proton transfers. This scheme is, in fact, *oversimplified* because it considers only one of the several possible kinetically equivalent ionic forms of the starting materials and because it omits the molecules of acid and base catalysts that are involved in the proton transfer steps. Furthermore, it is possible that some, or even all, of the steps may be concerted and that no intermediates of significant lifetime exist. It is apparent that this apparently simple reaction is, in fact, complicated and that a complete specification of its mechanism is no easy task.

The problems of mechanism and catalysis of reactions of this kind are centered around two areas: the tetrahedral intermediate and proton transfers. Addition to the carbonyl group of a compound H_2X can be followed by elimination of the group Y, to give an acyl transfer reaction (equation 2, *a*), by elimination of the attacking group X to reform starting materials (equation 2, *b*), or by protonation and elimination of the oxygen atom, as in the formation of nitrogen derivatives of carbonyl compounds (equation 2, *c*) and the exchange of labeled oxygen from water into the carbonyl group of acyl compounds (equation 2, *c*, X = O). All these reactions could

$$
\begin{array}{c}
\text{O} \\
\| \\
R-C-Y \\
+ \\
H_2X
\end{array}
\underset{}{\overset{b}{\rightleftharpoons}}
\left[
\begin{array}{ccc}
\overset{\textstyle \cdot\text{O}}{\underset{\textstyle H_2}{\overset{\textstyle |}{\underset{\textstyle +X}{R-C-Y}}}}
&
\rightleftharpoons
&
\overset{\textstyle \cdot\text{OH}}{\underset{\textstyle H}{\underset{\textstyle X}{R-C-Y}}}
\end{array}
\right]
\begin{array}{l}
\quad\overset{\textstyle O}{\overset{\textstyle \|}{R-C-X}} + HY \quad a \\[4pt]
\nearrow \\
\searrow \\
\quad\overset{\textstyle X}{\overset{\textstyle \|}{R-C-Y}} + H_2O \quad c \quad (2)
\end{array}
$$

conceivably proceed without the formation of a discrete tetrahedral addition intermediate of appreciable stability, and the initial problems in the determination of mechanism are to determine whether or not such an intermediate is formed on the reaction pathway and, if it is formed, whether the rate-determining step of the reaction involves the formation or the breakdown of the intermediate.

Tetrahedral addition compounds of aldehydes and ketones are well known, and if there is little resonance stabilization of an aldehyde or if the carbonyl group is attached to strongly electron-withdrawing substituents, the compound exists predominantly as the hydrate even in water. Acetaldehyde in water exists in approximately equal parts as the hydrate and as the free carbonyl compound, while formaldehyde and chloral are almost completely hydrated in water.[2] Tetrahedral addition intermediates are formed from acyl compounds much less readily because of the resonance stabilization of the carbonyl group by the group X (**1**), and the for-

$$
\begin{array}{ccc}
\overset{\textstyle O}{\overset{\textstyle \|}{\underset{\textstyle X}{\diagup C \diagdown}}}
&
\longleftrightarrow
&
\overset{\textstyle O^-}{\overset{\textstyle |}{\underset{\textstyle X^+}{\diagup C \equiv}}}
\\
\mathbf{1} & &
\end{array}
$$

[2] R. P. Bell, *Advan. Phys. Org. Chem.* **4**, 1 (1966).

mation of thermodynamically stable addition compounds is observed only with acyl compounds in which the addition reaction is favored by strongly electron-withdrawing substituents or ring structures. Ethoxide ion adds to ethyl trifluoroacetate to form a stable addition compound in dibutyl ether under conditions in which breakdown to hydrolytic products is not possible[3] (equation 3), and a number of

$$
CF_3COC_2H_5 + {}^-OC_2H_5 \rightleftharpoons CF_3\overset{\displaystyle O^-}{\underset{\displaystyle OC_2H_5}{C}} - OC_2H_5 \tag{3}
$$

cyclic tetrahedral addition adducts, such as 2, are stable compounds,

2

even when $R = H$.[4] Thus, there is no question but that tetrahedral addition compounds exist, and the problems in acyl transfer reactions are to determine whether or not they are formed under the conditions of the reaction, whether they lie on the principal reaction path, and whether they have a lifetime which is sufficient to make them kinetically significant and deserving of the name "intermediate." Kinetic methods appear to offer the best means of resolving these questions at the present time.

The second principal problem in these reactions is that of proton transfer: where, when, and how it takes place. This problem, which is of particular importance with regard to mechanisms of catalysis, has been discussed in Chap. 3, and the discussion in this chapter will be limited to application to specific reactions of the methods for approaching these questions.

Examples of the kinetic consequences of the occurrence of tetrahedral addition intermediates in a reaction path will be described first, and the properties of a number of carbonyl- and acyl-group reactions will be summarized in the latter part of the chapter. The

[3] M. L. Bender, *J. Am. Chem. Soc.* **75**, 5986 (1953).

[4] H. E. Zaugg, V. Papendick, and R. J. Michaels, *J. Am. Chem. Soc.* **86**, 1399 (1964).

reactions are arranged according to the composition of the transition state around the reacting carbon atom. For example, the hydrolysis of amides, the aminolysis of esters, and the hydrolysis of imidates all involve transition states in which two oxygen atoms and one nitrogen atom interact with the central acyl carbon atom, and a comparison of the mechanisms of these reactions can be helpful in elucidating the mechanism of any one of them.

1. TETRAHEDRAL INTERMEDIATES AND THE RATE- DETERMINING STEP

Before discussing the mechanism and catalysis of reactions of compounds at the acyl level of oxidation it is desirable to consider simpler carbonyl-group reactions in which a tetrahedral addition intermediate can be observed directly. The rate-determining step of such reactions can be specified with certainty, and the mechanism of catalysis can frequently be diagnosed by one or more of the methods outlined in Chap. 3. The methods for investigation of mechanism and any generalizations regarding mechanism and catalysis which are developed for these simpler reactions may then be applied to the more complex acyl transfer reactions.

The reaction of hydroxylamine with an aldehyde provides an example of the application of a kinetic technique for the demonstration of an addition intermediate in a reaction in which the intermediate can be observed directly.[5] At neutral pH, hydroxylamine adds to the carbonyl compound in a fast reaction and the loss of water from the addition intermediate is the rate-determining step of oxime formation (equation 4). The addition can be observed directly

$$NH_2OH + {>}C=O \underset{\underset{k_{-2}[H^+]}{k_{-1}}}{\overset{\overset{k_1}{k_2[H^+]}}{\rightleftharpoons}} {>}C{\overset{NHOH}{\underset{OH}{<}}} \xrightarrow{k_3[H^+]} {>}C=NOH + H_2O$$

$$\Big\Updownarrow \pm H^+ \qquad\qquad \text{Intermediate}$$

$$^+NH_3OH \tag{4}$$

at high concentrations of hydroxylamine by the disappearance of the ultraviolet and infrared absorption peaks of the carbonyl group. By measuring the amount of the decrease in carbonyl-group absorption at different concentrations of hydroxylamine, the equilibrium constant for the formation of the intermediate may be calculated. Near neutral pH the rate of the reaction is directly proportional to

[5] W. P. Jencks, *J. Am. Chem. Soc.* **81**, 475 (1959).

the hydrogen ion activity, which shows that the dehydration step is acid catalyzed. Under these conditions the rate is dependent on the equilibrium concentration of addition compound and the hydrogen ion activity and is given by the rate law of equation 5. As the pH

$$\text{Rate} = k_3[\text{Int}][\text{H}^+] = k_3 \frac{k_1}{k_{-1}}[\text{NH}_2\text{OH}][\text{>C=O}][\text{H}^+] \tag{5}$$

is decreased the rate of acid catalyzed dehydration continues to increase, but, as the free hydroxylamine becomes protonated, the equilibrium concentration of the addition compound decreases until, at pH values below the pK of hydroxylamine, these two effects exactly offset each other and the calculated rate becomes independent of pH (Fig. 1, dashed line). The experimental points agree well with this theoretical line down to pH 5.

As the pH is lowered below 5, however, the observed rate constants fall *below* those predicted by the rate law which is followed at higher pH values. Now, an increase in rate above that predicted by a given rate law can be accounted for simply by adding a new term, corresponding to a new reaction path, to the rate law. However, a *decrease* in rate below that predicted by a rate law means that some other step in the reaction sequence must have become rate-determining, so that the reaction now follows a new rate law corresponding to this other step. The assignment of this other step is straightforward in the case of oxime formation: as the rate of acid catalyzed dehydration becomes very fast, the rate of formation of the addition intermediate from the aldehyde and free hydroxylamine can no longer keep up with the rate of its dehydration and the attack of hydroxylamine on the aldehyde becomes rate-determining. The rate of this reaction is proportional to the concentration of hydroxylamine present as the free base which, at these low pH values, is directly proportional to the hydroxide ion activity, so that the rate of this step increases with increasing pH as shown by the dotted line in Fig. 1. At very low pH values the rate again becomes independent of pH because of the existence of an acid catalyzed addition reaction, but this is not important for the purposes of the present discussion. The rate law describing this step of the reaction is given in equation (6).

$$\text{Rate} = k_1[\text{NH}_2\text{OH}][\text{>C=O}] + k_2[\text{NH}_2\text{OH}][\text{>C=O}][\text{H}^+] \tag{6}$$

The rate can be described over the entire range of pH by the

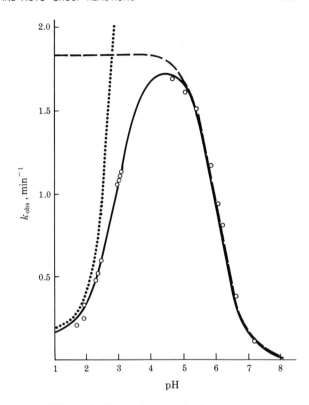

Fig 1. Effect of pH on the pseudo first-order rate constant for the reaction of 5×10^{-4} M acetone with 0.0167 M total hydroxylamine, showing the change in rate-determining step with changing pH.[5] Dotted line: rate of attack of free hydroxylamine on acetone. Dashed line: rate under conditions in which acid catalyzed dehydration is rate-determining. Solid line: calculated, from the steady-state rate equation 7.

steady-state rate equation 7 (see Chap. 11, Sec. C), which takes into

$$\text{Rate} = \frac{k_3(k_1 + k_2 a_{\text{H}^+})}{(k_{-1}/a_{\text{H}^+}) + k_{-2} + k_3} \; [\text{NH}_2\text{OH}][\underset{}{>}\text{C}=\text{O}] \tag{7}$$

account the rate laws for both the addition and the dehydration steps. The solid line in Fig. 1 is a theoretical line based on this rate law.

The important point in this system is that there is a change in rate-determining step in a sequential reaction as the reaction conditions are varied. Such a change in rate-determining step requires that there be at least two sequential steps in the reaction, one or the other of which is rate-determining under different reaction conditions, and the existence of two sequential steps demands that there be an intermediate in the reaction. The formation of the intermediate may be observed directly in the hydroxylamine reaction at high pH values, but the same technique may be used to demonstrate the existence of an intermediate in other reactions in which the accumulation of an intermediate is not detectable. The most probable structure for this intermediate in carbonyl- and acyl-group reactions is that of a tetrahedral addition compound, but the possibility exists that proton transfer steps may become rate-determining in the reaction sequence and that the kinetically significant intermediate may be an ionic form of the reactants or intermediate which undergoes rate-determining proton transfer under certain conditions.

In order for this technique to be valid, it is essential to show that a rate decrease which is observed under a particular set of experimental conditions does, in fact, represent a change in the rate-determining step of the reaction and not simply a decrease in the concentration of one of the reactants or catalysts which is caused by the change in reaction conditions. For example, when the pH is changed, the ionization of the reactants must be taken into account and only a decrease in rate which does not correspond to the ionization of one of the reactants is evidence for a change in rate-determining step and an intermediate in the reaction. Similarly, if a change in rate-determining step is suspected because of a nonlinear increase of the rate with increasing catalyst concentration, it must be shown that the catalyst is not forming a complex with the substrate or some other component of the reaction mixture which would account for the leveling off of the rate. The rate of the reaction of dinitrochlorobenzene with aniline, for example, shows a leveling off with increasing aniline concentration which is caused by the formation of a complex between the reactants rather than by a change in rate-determining step.[6] Borate buffers are particularly troublesome in this respect because borates undergo polymerization in aqueous solution[7] so that a linear relationship of rate to the concentration of borate buffer is not to be expected.

There are four experimental situations in which an intermediate on the reaction path, which does not accumulate in detectable

[6] S. D. Ross and I. Kuntz, *J. Am. Chem. Soc.* **76**, 3000 (1954).

[7] N. Ingri, *Acta Chem. Scand.* **17**, 573 (1963).

concentrations, gives rise to characteristic kinetic behavior. The first three of these involve nonlinear rate relationships in which a negative deviation in a rate may be caused by a change in rate-determining step.

1. Negative deviations in pH–rate behavior which are not caused by ionization of one of the reactants.
2. Negative deviations in the relationship of rate to catalyst concentration which are not caused by complexing of reactants or catalyst.
3. Breaks in structure-reactivity correlations.
4. Partitioning of an intermediate after the rate-determining step to give different products, without a change in the observed rate of disappearance of starting material.

Examples of each of these will be described before proceeding to a summary of the behavior of individual carbonyl- and acyl-group reactions.

2. CHANGE IN RATE-DETERMINING STEP WITH CHANGING pH

The change from rate-determining acid catalyzed breakdown of the addition intermediate to rate-determining attack of free hydroxylamine with decreasing pH in oxime formation has just been described. An example of the same kind of behavior at the acyl level of oxidation, in a reaction in which the tetrahedral intermediate does not accumulate in detectable amounts, is the reaction of imidates with amines to form amidines (equation 8).[8] The observed rate

$$\tag{8}$$

constants for the reactions of a series of amines with ethyl benzimi-

[8] E. Hand and W. P. Jencks, *J. Am. Chem. Soc.* 84, 3505 (1962).

date and ethyl m-nitrobenzimidate follow a series of bell-shaped curves as a function of pH (Fig. 2). In every case, one or both of the limbs of the pH curves do not correspond to the ionization of the reactants; i.e., as the pH is changed, the rate drops below that predicted by the rate law which is followed at higher or lower pH, indicating that there is a change in the rate-determining step. This is shown in greater detail for the reaction of ammonia with ethyl benzimidate in Fig. 3. In this figure, the dashed line corresponds to the expected pH-dependence of a reaction with a transition state containing the elements of an imidate, an amine and a proton. As the pH is decreased, the rate decreases below that expected for this transition state and follows that for a reaction with a transition state containing the elements of free imidate and amine. The solid line is calculated from the steady-state rate equation for a

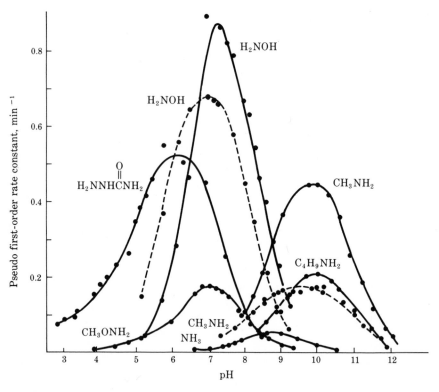

Fig 2. Dependence on pH of the reactions of ethyl benzimidate (solid line) and ethyl m-nitrobenzimidate (dashed line) with amines at 25° and ionic strength 1.0 (n-butyl-amine at ionic strength 2.0).[8]

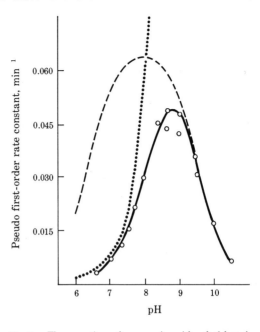

Fig 3. The reaction of ammonia with ethyl benzimidate at 25°: dashed line, calculated for rate-determining amine attack; dotted line, calculated for rate-determining addition compound decomposition; solid line, calculated from steady-state rate equation.[8]

reaction which undergoes a change in rate-determining step between those represented by these two transition states.

Although the kinetic results show that there is a change in rate-determining step and, hence, an intermediate on the reaction pathway, as shown in equation 8, they do not establish which step is rate-determining in each pH region. In this reaction this can be established by the use of an exchange reaction, as follows. Consider the reaction of ethyl N-methylbenzimidate with a large excess of ammonia (equation 8, $R = CH_3$, $R' = H$). On the side of the pH-rate curve in which the first step is rate-determining and the second step is fast, each molecule of addition intermediate that is formed will immediately break down to products and the only product will be the monomethyl amidine. At pH values in which the first step is fast and the second step is rate-determining, the intermediate will expel ammonia and return to starting materials several times in the reversible first step before it breaks down to products. However, sometimes the reversal of the first step will result in the expulsion of methylamine instead of ammonia, to form a new, unsubstituted imidate. This unsubstituted imidate will react with ammonia to form a new tetrahedral intermediate and finally will give an unsubstituted amidine as product. Thus, under conditions in which the second step is rate-determining, an unsubstituted imidate should be formed in a rapid reaction and the principal final product should be the unsubstituted amidine. This is found to be the case in the pH region of the lower limb of the pH–rate profile, while in the region of the upper limb only the substituted amidine is formed, showing that the first step is rate-determining at the higher pH values. This situation is analogous to the well known exchange of ^{18}O from solvent into starting materials in the course of hydrolysis of acyl compounds, except that in the imidate reaction a methyl-labeled amine replaces isotopically labeled oxygen. In the imidate reaction the disappearance of the exchange reaction at high pH values permits a definite assignment of the nature of the change in rate-determining step with changing pH.

A particularly useful way of thinking about the nature of the rate-determining step of a reaction is to consider the preferred way in which an intermediate will break down under various conditions (Fig. 4). If the free-energy barrier for breakdown of the intermediate in one direction is significantly higher than for breakdown in

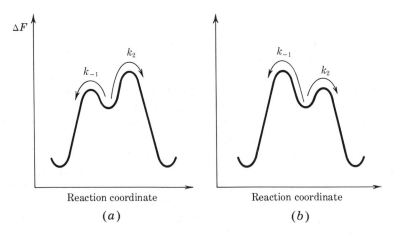

Fig 4. Reaction-coordinate diagram to show how the ratio of k_2/k_{-1} determines the rate-determining step. (a) Second step rate-determining, first step at equilibrium, $k_2 \ll k_{-1}$. (b) First step rate-determining, second step at equilibrium, $k_2 \gg k_{-1}$.

the other direction, breakdown will occur many times by the lower-energy path for each time that it occurs by the high-energy path. In other words, the intermediate is at equilibrium with respect to the low-energy path and the high-energy path is the rate-determining step of the overall reaction in either direction (equation 9).

$$A + B \underset{k_{-1}}{\overset{\overset{\text{fast}}{k_1}}{\rightleftharpoons}} \text{Int} \underset{k_{-2}}{\overset{\overset{\text{slow}}{k_2}}{\rightleftharpoons}} C + D \tag{9}$$

If the higher free-energy barrier is changed, there will be a change in the observed rate of the overall reaction, while if the lower-energy barrier is changed, there will be no change in rate unless the distance from the starting materials to the higher barrier is also changed. It is important to note that the energy barrier for the formation of the intermediate from starting materials may be larger than that for conversion of the intermediate to products in the rate-determining step; i.e., it is the highest point on the overall free-energy profile, not the highest-energy barrier for an individual step that determines which step is rate-determining. Thus, under steady-state conditions in which the intermediate does not accumulate, the critical factor in determining which step of a reaction is rate-determining is the relative rate of breakdown of the unstable intermediate in the forward and reverse directions, i.e., the ratio k_2/k_{-1} rather than the relative rates of formation and breakdown of the intermediate k_1/k_2. As in many kinetic descriptions, it is important to make a clear distinction between a *rate constant* and the absolute *rate* for a particular step; the latter quantity is a function of the rate constant for that step, the rate and equilibrium constants for preceding steps, and the concentrations of the reactants. This point may seem obvious, but uncertainty regarding the meaning of "rate-determining step" has repeatedly led to confusion in description of reaction mechanisms. From this point of view it is more rigorous to attribute the change in rate-determining step in oxime formation with decreasing pH to an increase in the rate of the acid catalyzed k_2 step compared with the uncatalyzed k_{-1} step, rather than to a change in the relative rates of the k_1 and k_2 steps.

In the aminolysis of imidates at low pH the expulsion of alcohol through a transition state with no net charge is slow and the acid catalyzed addition and loss of amine is fast, so that the second step is rate-determining and the energy-profile diagram for the reaction is that of Fig. 4a. At high pH the attack of amine on the protonated imidate is rate-determining and the expulsion of alcohol is fast, so that the intermediate decomposes to products more often than it reverts to starting materials and the reaction-coordinate diagram is that of Fig. 4b. There is a transition between these two types of reaction coordinate at the pH at which the change in rate-determining step occurs, at about pH 8. Thus, we can set up a scale of pH (Diagram 1) and say that for the tetrahedral interme-

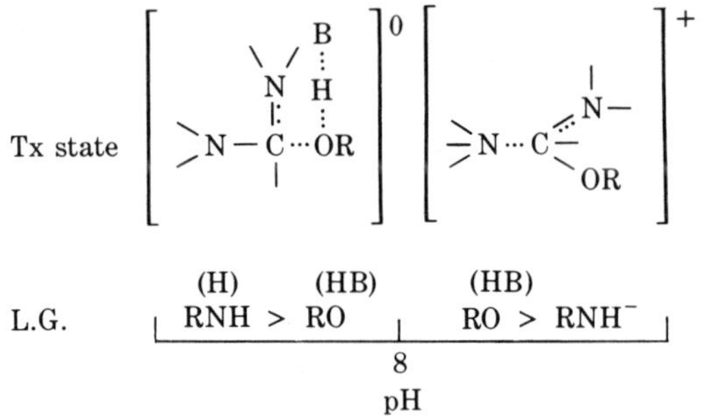

Diagram 1

diate in the aminolysis of imidates the protonation of nitrogen and expulsion of free amine is favored over the protonation of oxygen and expulsion of free alcohol below pH 8 and that the expulsion of alcoholate ion is favored over that of amine anion above pH 8. This is in accord with what might be expected from chemical intuition.

Diagrams of this kind are useful to indicate the preferred leaving group (L.G.) and the change in rate-determining step of a reaction as a function of pH. A proton or (BH) in parenthesis indicates that a proton must be added to the group in question for its expulsion at the indicated pH, so that the rate of departure of the group will depend on its ease of protonation as well as its leaving ability. The transition state (Tx state) for the rate-determining step is indicated above the region of pH in which that transition state represents the predominant pathway for the rate-determining step. The overall charge of the transition state compared with that of the reactants determines the dependence on pH of the reaction in each pH region: if the reactants have a net charge of zero and the transition state has a positive charge, the reaction will be acid catalyzed; whereas if the reactants and transition state are both positively charged, the observed rate will be independent of pH. The vertical lines in the pH scale indicate a change in rate-determining step accompanying a change in the charge of the transition state. This will give a downward deflection in the pH–rate profile. Upward deflections in the pH–rate profile are caused by *additional* pathways for a given step and occur when there are transition states with different net charges for that step. If a scale of this sort could be set up for every reaction of acyl compounds, the nature and the change of rate-determining step at different pH values would be described and generalizations regarding the mechanisms of these reactions should appear. While this cannot be done at the present time, a beginning can be made and the prospect for a more comlete table is promising.

3. CHANGE IN RATE-DETERMINING STEP WITH CHANGING CONCENTRATION OF GENERAL ACID OR BASE CATALYST

An example of this behavior in a simple reaction is found in the formation of semicarbazones from semicarbazide and carbonyl compounds (equation 10).[9] The attack of free amine on the carbonyl

$$
RNH_2 \; \searrow C = O \xrightarrow[\; k_{-1}[HA] \;]{\; k_1[HA] \;} RN - \overset{H}{\underset{|}{C}} - OH \xrightarrow{\; k_2[H^+] \;} RN = C \diagdown + H_2O \tag{10}
$$

group in this reaction is subject to general acid catalysis, while the dehydration step is not significantly catalyzed by general acids (that is, α is near 1.0 for this step). The assignment of rate-determining steps may be made unambiguously because the accumulation of the addition intermediate may be observed directly near neutral pH values, at which the rate of the dehydration step is slow. At low pH values the general acid catalyzed attack of amine on the carbonyl group is rate-determining and the reaction rate at pH 3.27 increases linearly with increasing concentration of formic acid catalyst (Fig. 5a). At the higher pH value of 4.10, near the pH region in which the change in rate-determining step occurs, the rate increases with increasing propionic acid concentration at low concentrations of catalyst, but then levels off as the catalyst causes the rate of the first step to become so fast that the dehydration step cannot keep up and the second step becomes rate-determining. The observed rate then approaches the rate of the dehydration step, shown by the dashed line in Fig. 5b.

[9] E. H. Cordes and W. P. Jencks, *J. Am. Chem. Soc.* 84, 4319 (1962).

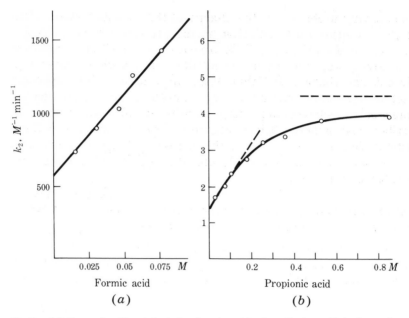

Fig 5. (a) General acid catalysis by formic acid of p-nitrobenzaldehyde semi-carbazone formation at pH 3.27. (b) General acid catalysis by propionic acid of acetophenone semicarbazone formation at pH 4.10. The horizontal dashed line is the rate of the carbinolamine dehydration step at this pH.[9]

An example of the same phenomenon in a reaction at the acyl level of oxidation, in which accumulation of the addition intermediate cannot be observed, is found in the reaction of amines with hydroxyl-amine to give hydroxamic acids[10] (equation 11). This reaction is

$$\underset{\substack{}}{NH_2OH} + \underset{\substack{\parallel \\ O}}{R\overset{}{C}NH_2} \underset{k_{-1}[HA]}{\overset{k_1[HA]}{\rightleftharpoons}} \underset{\substack{| \\ R}}{HON-\overset{\overset{OH}{|}}{\underset{\overset{|}{H}}{C}}-NH_2} \xrightarrow[k_3[HA]]{k_2} \underset{\substack{\parallel \\ O}}{R\overset{}{C}NHOH} + NH_3$$

(11)

subject to general acid catalysis by hydroxylammonium ion, so that the rate increases with increasing hydroxylamine buffer concentration more rapidly than the first power of the hydroxylamine concentration and exhibits a pH–rate maximum near the pK of hydroxyl-amine. The dependence of the experimental second-order rate constant (k_{obs} / [NH_2OH]) on the buffer concentration is shown in

[10] W. P. Jencks and M. Gilchrist, *J. Am. Chem. Soc.* **86**, 5616 (1964).

Fig. 6. The increase in catalysis with decreasing pH reflects the fact that the active catalytic species is the hydroxylammonium ion. At low buffer concentrations there is a sharp increase in rate with increasing catalyst concentration, but as the catalyst concentration is increased, there is a break in the curves and the rate continues to increase with a much smaller dependence on the concentration of catalyst. This is evidence for a transition from a rate-determining step which is strongly dependent to one which is weakly dependent on catalyst concentration as the concentration of catalyst is increased. More precisely, there is a significant uncatalyzed or water catalyzed

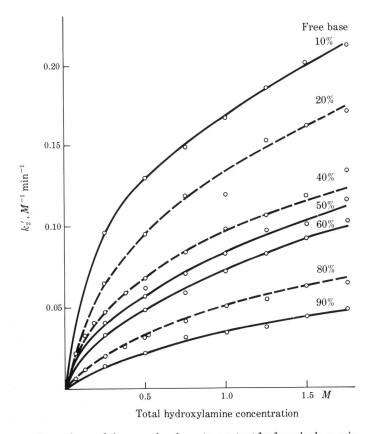

Fig 6. Dependence of the second-order rate constant for formohydroxamic acid formation ($k_2' = k_{obs}' / [\,NH_2OH\,]$) on hydroxylamine concentration at different fractions of hydroxylamine neutralization at 39°, ionic strength 2.0. The dashed lines were calculated from the steady-state rate equation.[10]

term in the rate law for the step which becomes rate-determining at high catalyst concentrations. The dashed lines in the figure are theoretical lines for a reaction which undergoes such a change in rate-determining step, calculated from the steady-state rate equation for this system.

The kinetic data show that there is a change in rate-determining step, but they do not show which step is rate-determining at the different concentrations of catalyst. One possible assignment, in which the attack of hydroxylamine is subject to general acid catalysis (α is large) and the departure and addition of the more basic amine is less sensitive to acid catalysis, so that there is a significant water reaction as well (α is smaller), is shown in equation 11. However, the kinetics are satisfied equally well by a mechanism in which the attack step proceeds with both catalyzed and uncatalyzed terms and the second step has only a significant acid catalyzed term.

4. CHANGE IN RATE-DETERMINING STEP WITH CHANGING STRUCTURE OF THE REACTANTS

A change in rate-determining step with changing pH or catalyst concentration requires two sequential steps with different rate laws, i.e., transition states with different stoichiometric compositions, and provides strong evidence that there must be an intermediate between these two steps. A downward deflection in a nonlinear structure-reactivity correlation may be caused by a change in rate-determining step of a two-step reaction in which the two steps have different dependencies on structure, but it may also be the consequence of a continuous change in the nature of the transition state with changing structure of the reactants in a reaction in which there is no discrete intermediate.

Semicarbazone formation is a simple two-step reaction in which the nature of the rate-determining step under various conditions is known from other criteria. In the reaction of semicarbazide with a series of substituted benzaldehydes at low pH, at which the attack of semicarbazide on the aldehyde is rate-determining, the rate increases as electron-withdrawing substitutents are added to the aldehyde and shows a linear correlation with Hammett's σ values as shown in Fig. 7.[11] At neutral pH, at which the dehydration step is rate-determining, the observed rate is almost independent of the nature of the substituents (Fig. 8, horizontal line). This is because the favorable effect of electron-donating substituents on the rate

---

[11] B. M. Anderson and W. P. Jencks, *J. Am. Chem. Soc.* **82**, 1773 (1960).

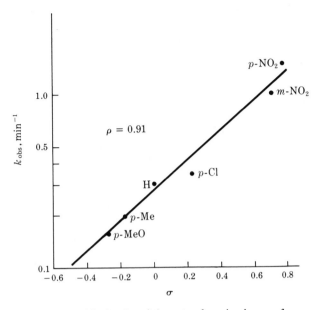

Fig 7. Logarithmic plot of the rate of semicarbazone formation from a series of substituted benzaldehydes in 25% ethanol at pH 1.75 against Hammett's σ function.[11]

of acid catalyzed dehydration of the addition intermediate ($\rho = -1.74$) is almost entirely cancelled by the unfavorable effect of these substituents on the equilibrium concentration of the addition intermediate ($\rho = 1.81$), so that the observed rate, which depends on both of these steps, is almost independent of σ. At an intermediate pH value of 3.9, in the region at which the change in rate-determining step occurs, there is a break in the structure-reactivity correlation because the attack step with its large dependence on structure is rate-determining for aldehydes with electron-donating substituents, while the dehydration step is rate-determining for aldehydes with electron-withdrawing substituents, which undergo the attack step relatively rapidly (Fig. 9).

This type of interpretation must be applied with caution to reactions in which the changes in observed rate are small because small downward deflections in $\rho - \sigma$ correlations can result from reasons other than a change in the nature of the rate-determining step. One reason for such a deviation is an incomplete cancellation of substituent effects on the two steps of a reaction in which the second step is rate-determining. In the formation of nitrogen derivatives of carbonyl compounds under conditions in which the dehy-

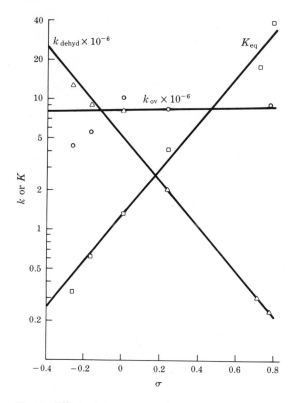

Fig 8. Effect of structure on the separate steps of semi-carbazone formation from substituted benzaldehydes in 25% ethanol at neutral pH. Equilibrium constants for addition compound formation, □ ; rate constants for acid catalyzed dehydration, △ ; horizontal line: rate of the overall reaction, ○.[11]

dration step is rate-determining, for example, the rate of the dehydration step follows σ, but the equilibrium constants for the addition step deviate in the direction of the σ^+ scale. The σ^+ scale describes reactions in which electron donation by resonance to the reaction center is important, and this is the case for aldehydes, which are stabilized by such resonance (3). The deviation from the $\sigma\rho$ plot

$$X-\!\!\!\bigcirc\!\!\!-C\overset{O}{\underset{H}{<}} \quad\longleftrightarrow\quad \overset{+}{X}=\!\!\!\bigcirc\!\!\!=C\overset{\bar{O}}{\underset{H}{<}}$$

3

caused by this behavior does not appear to be very significant for

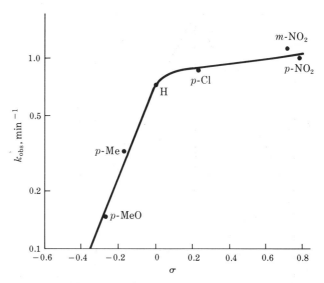

Fig 9. Logarithmic plot of the rate of semicarbazone formation from a series of substituted benzaldehydes in 25% ethanol at pH 3.9, showing the break in the $\sigma\rho$ plot due to a change in rate-determining step.[11]

the addition equilibrium of the first step because of the steep slope of the plot and the fact that the scale for the equilibrium constants covers several orders of magnitude. However, the observed overall rate constants vary only slightly with substituents because of the cancellation of substituent effects on the two steps, and when these rate constants are plotted on an expanded scale there is a more noticeable negative deviation of the points for compounds with electron-donating substituents, which is caused by a larger effect of these substituents on the equilibrium than on the dehydration step. This situation, which is shown diagrammatically in Fig. 10, might be mistakenly identified as evidence for a change in rate-determining step if the situation is not analyzed with sufficient care. It, along with some experimental scatter, accounts for the negative deviation of the overall rate constants for p-methyl- and p-methoxybenzaldehyde in Fig. 8 (open circles).

    An example of a change in the nature of the rate-determining step with changing structure at the acyl level of oxidation is found in the nucleophilic reaction of imidazole with a series of acetate esters.[12] It is reasonable to assume that the reaction of hydroxide

---

[12] J. F. Kirsch and W. P. Jencks, *J. Am. Chem. Soc.* **86**, 837 (1964).

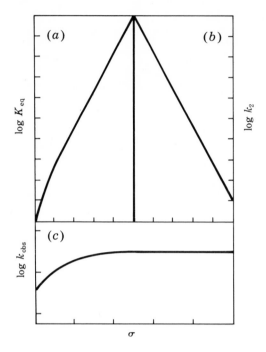

Fig 10. Illustration showing how a small deviation from linearity in the $\sigma\rho$ plot for one step of a two-step reaction causes a downward deflection in the $\sigma\rho$ plot for k_{obs}, which is dependent on both K_{eq} and k_2. Note that the scales of the ordinate and abscissa are increased twofold for k_{obs}.[36]

ion with a series of such esters proceeds by the same mechanism, in which the attack step is largely or entirely rate-determining, so that the rate constant for the hydroxide ion reaction is a measure of the reactivity of the ester toward nucleophilic attack. Now, if the rates of the nucleophilic reactions of imidazole with the same esters are plotted logarithmically against the rate of the hydroxide ion reaction, there is a linear correlation for compounds which have a good leaving group, such as acetic anhydride, 2,4-dinitrophenyl acetate, and p-nitrophenyl acetate (Fig. 11). With these compounds the expulsion of the leaving group is easy, so that the rate-determining step might be expected to involve attack of imidazole on the ester (equation 12, k_1). As the leaving group becomes worse in the series of substituted phenyl acetates, the rates of the imidazole reactions

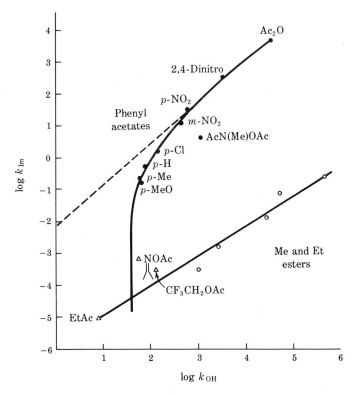

Fig 11. Rates of imidazole catalyzed ester hydrolysis as a function of the rate of alkaline hydrolysis: nucleophilic reactions of acetates, ●; general base catalysis of acetates, Δ; general base catalysis of methyl and ethyl esters, O (ionic strength 1.0; 25°). Trifluoroethyl acetate rate measured with N-methylimidazole.[12]

$$
HN \overset{\frown}{\underset{\smile}{N}} + RCOR' \underset{k_{-1}}{\overset{k_1}{\rightleftharpoons}} \left[\begin{array}{c} R-C-OR' \\ \end{array} \right] \overset{k_2}{\longrightarrow} RCN \overset{\frown}{\underset{\smile}{N}} + HOR'
$$

$$(12)$$

deviate downward from the line obtained with the more reactive compounds; and for esters with still worse leaving groups, such as trifluoroethyl acetate and ethyl acetate, there is a still larger negative deviation of several orders of magnitude. In fact, the deviation is even larger than is indicated by the points in the figure because the observed rates of the reaction of imidazole with these compounds represent general base catalysis, rather than a nucleophilic reaction with imidazole. These points fall close to the lower line in the figure, which represents the rates of the imidazole catalyzed hydrolysis of a series of acyl-substituted ethyl and methyl esters in which imidazole is acting as a general base catalyst. This negative deviation shows that there is a change in the nature of the rate-determining step when the leaving group becomes sufficiently poor and might be interpreted in terms of a change to a rate-determining step similar to that expected for the breakdown of a tetrahedral addition intermediate (equation 12, k_2).

This correlation for nucleophilic reactions of imidazole may be regarded as a more or less quantitative expression of the fact that poor nucleophiles are not able to displace poor leaving groups. When the leaving group is made sufficiently bad, the addition intermediate, if it is formed, will break down to expel imidazole instead of the leaving group and will then give back starting materials instead of forming products, resulting in a break in the structure-reactivity correlation. Results of this kind demonstrate a large change in the nature of the transition state with changing structure of the reactants, but they can be interpreted in terms of either a two-step reaction or a concerted reaction with an asymmetric transition state. If there is a discrete intermediate, the reactions could be described by the curves of Fig. 12a, in which the dashed and solid lines represent compounds with good and bad leaving groups, respectively. However, they could also be described by the curves of Fig. 12b, which describe asymmetric transition states rather than

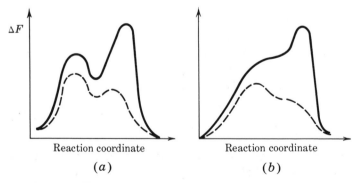

Fig 12. Transition-state diagrams (a) for reactions with an unstable intermediate and (b) for reactions with no intermediate.[12]

discrete intermediates. In other words, the tetrahedral addition compound of equation 12 could be close to a transition state rather than a discrete intermediate. Because of this possible interpretation of nonlinear structure-reactivity correlations in terms of changes in the symmetry of transition states as well as in terms of a discrete intermediate, such correlations do not provide definite evidence for the existence of an intermediate on the reaction coordinate.

5. PARTITIONING OF AN INTERMEDIATE AFTER THE RATE-DETERMINING STEP

A different type of evidence for the existence of an intermediate on the reaction path is the demonstration that the nature of the products can be changed by changing the reaction conditions without changing the rate of the reaction. An example is the hydrolysis of the N-phenyliminolactone 4 (equation 13), which has been discussed

in Chap. 3, Sec. D, Part 5. The *rate* of hydrolysis of this compound follows a single rate law near neutrality, but the *products* are the anilide above pH 7 and the lactone and aniline below pH 7; the yield of lactone can also be increased by increasing the concentration of bifunctional acid-base catalysts in the transition region of pH.[13] Thus, the composition of the transition state for at least one of the product-forming reactions must be different from that of the rate-determining step, and there must be an intermediate, **5**, on the reaction path which can partition to two different products, depending on the reaction conditions, without affecting the overall rate of reaction.

[13] G. L. Schmir and B. A. Cunningham, *J. Am. Chem. Soc.* **87**, 5692 (1964); B. A. Cunningham and G. L. Schmir, *Ibid.* **88**, 551 (1966).

A particularly important consequence of this kind of result is that it shows how a tetrahedral intermediate decomposes under different reaction conditions and therefore makes it possible to define the rate-determining step in an acyl transfer reaction which gives the same tetrahedral intermediate. The bottom reaction of equation 13, read from left to right, is the aminolysis of an ester by aniline. The products obtained from the hydrolysis of the phenyliminolactone show that below pH 7 the energy barrier for the breakdown of the addition intermediate **5** to lactone and aniline is smaller than that for breakdown to anilide (Fig. 13a). Thus, if the same intermediate is formed in the aminolysis of the lactone, it will break down to starting materials more often than it decomposes to products and the decomposition to products will be rate-determining. Above pH 7 the energy barrier for the breakdown of the intermediate **5** to anilide is smaller than that for breakdown to lactone, as shown by the products formed from phenyliminolactone hydrolysis under these conditions, so that the same intermediate will break down to products more often than it reverts to starting materials in the aminolysis reaction, and the first step of this reaction will be rate-determining (Fig. 13b). The great usefulness of this type of experiment for the interpretation of the role of addition intermediates in acyl transfer reactions is that it permits the generation of the intermediate from a compound which is not on the normal reaction path and thus per-

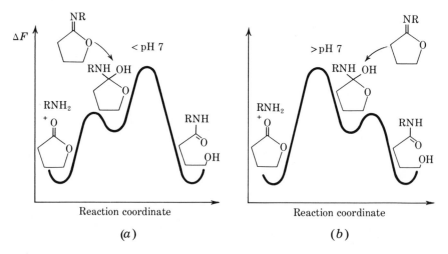

Fig 13. Diagram to show how the decomposition of an imidate generates the same tetrahedral intermediate as would be formed in an aminolysis reaction and can be used to determine the rate-determining step of the aminolysis reaction.

mits a definition of the behavior of this intermediate simply by an analysis of its breakdown products under various reaction conditions. From the results of the N-phenyliminolactone decomposition we can describe the modes of breakdown of another tetrahedral intermediate on a scale of pH as shown in Diagram 2. This division is not

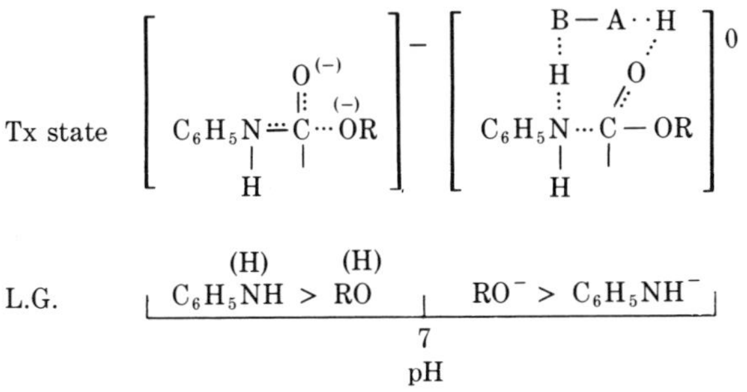

$$
\text{Tx state} \quad \left[\begin{array}{c} O^{(-)} \\ \| \ \ ^{(-)} \\ C_6H_5N\!=\!\!\!=\!\!C\cdots OR \\ | \quad | \\ H \end{array} \right]^{-} \left[\begin{array}{c} B-A\cdots H \\ \vdots \quad \ \vdots \\ H \quad \ O \\ \vdots \quad \ \text{\textit{k}} \\ C_6H_5N\cdots C - OR \\ | \quad | \\ H \end{array} \right]^{0}
$$

$$
\text{L.G.} \quad \underbrace{\overset{(H)}{C_6H_5NH} > \overset{(H)}{RO}}_{} \quad \underbrace{RO^- > C_6H_5NH^-}_{}
$$

$$
\begin{array}{c} 7 \\ pH \end{array}
$$

Diagram 2

very different from that for the intermediate in the aminolysis of imidates, in spite of the differences in the structures of the intermediates and the basicity of the amine in the two reactions.

One important assumption which is implicit in this argument and which may not hold in all reactions is that *proton transfer occurs more rapidly than the breakdown of the addition intermediate*, so that the different ionic forms of the intermediate are in rapid equilibrium. If this is not so, and it appears not to be so in some reactions, the same ionic form of the intermediate may not be formed in the different reactions, so that a common intermediate may not exist, and the observed behavior of the intermediate in one reaction may not reflect the behavior of a different ionic form of the same intermediate in another reaction. Conversely, the demonstration of a difference in the behavior of the intermediate in the two reactions may provide evidence that the proton transfer steps are slow.

The direct observation that a tetrahedral addition compound is formed from an acyl compound is not conclusive evidence that this or related intermediates are on the reaction path for a particular acyl transfer reaction of the compound because the addition compound may represent a side-reaction. The kinetic criteria have the advantage that they indicate that the intermediate is on the normal reaction path and is not a side-reaction, since the occurrence of a side-reaction would not have an effect on the kinetics unless it resulted in a depletion of the concentration of starting material by the formation of a large and easily detectable amount of side product.

The fact that bell-shaped pH−rate profiles and other breaks in pH−rate curves can result from changes in rate-determining step as well as from ionization of the reactants means that every such curve cannot be assigned to the ionization of the reactants. This conclusion is of particular significance in enzymatic reactions, in which the inflection points of bell-shaped pH−rate profiles are commonly assigned to the ionization of groups in the active site of the enzyme, if they cannot be assigned to ionization of the reactants. The decrease with decreasing pH of the rate of phosphate ester hydrolysis catalyzed by the alkaline phosphatase from *E. coli* might have been ascribed to the ionization of a group in the active site with a pK near 7, but is actually caused by a change in rate-determining step from rate-determining phosphorylation of the enzyme at high pH to rate-determining dephosphorylation at lower pH.[14] It is probable that other enzymatic reactions will be found which show changes in rate with pH which are caused by a change in rate-determining step rather than by ionization; this is made particularly probable by the multistep nature of enzymatic reactions.

B. SPECIFIC REACTIONS

The known behavior of a number of carbonyl- and acyl-group reactions with respect to the role of a tetrahedral intermediate, the rate-determining step, and the mechanism of general acid base catalysis is summarized in this section. The criteria for the diagnosis of the mechanism of these reactions have been described in greater detail in the preceding section and in Chap. 3. Most of the conclusions are summarized according to diagrams similar to Diagrams 1 and 2 and in tabular form at the end of the chapter. Carbonyl-group reactions will be considered first because of their relative simplicity and because they may serve as models for the more complicated acyl-group reactions.

1. $>$C$=$O AND RNH$_2$

The formation and hydrolysis of nitrogen derivatives of carbonyl compounds may be divided into reactions which involve strongly basic amines, such as aliphatic amines and hydroxylamine, and those which involve weakly basic amines, such as semicarbazide and aniline. The change in rate-determining step in the former

---

[14] H. N. Fernley and P. G. Walker, *Nature* 212, 1435 (1966); W. N. Aldridge, T. E. Barman, and H. Gutfreund, *Biochem. J.* 92, 23C (1964).

class generally occurs between pH 2 and 5.[5,15-17] Below this pH
the attack and loss of water is fast and the attack and loss of free
amine is rate-determining (equation 14). Above this pH the attack

$$(14)$$

and loss of free amine is fast and the attack and loss of water or
hydroxide ion is rate-determining. The protonated or cationic imine
is the reactive species. The transition pH decreases with increasingly electron-withdrawing substituents on the carbonyl group because
electron withdrawal inhibits the protonation and expulsion of OH
from the intermediate, through a positively charged transition
state, more than the expulsion of amine, through a transition state
with no net charge.

The attack of water on the cationic imine is subject to true
general base catalysis and the departure of hydroxide ion from the
intermediate to general acid catalysis, as shown by the fact that catalysis is observed with cationic and completely protonated imines
(Chap. 3, Sec. C, Parts 1 and 2). The value of β is about 0.25 and
that of α is about 0.75; that is, the proton is near the oxygen atom
in the transition state.[16,18] The rate constant for the attack of
hydroxide ion on the cationic imine falls well above the Brønsted plot
for general base catalysis,[18] which indicates that the reaction with
hydroxide ion is a direct nucleophilic attack (equation 15) rather

$$(15)$$

[15] E. H. Cordes and W. P. Jencks, *J. Am. Chem. Soc.* **85**, 2843 (1963).

[16] J. E. Reimann and W. P. Jencks, *J. Am. Chem. Soc.* **88**, 3973 (1966).

[17] L. do Amaral, W. A. Sandstrom, and E. H. Cordes, *J. Am. Chem. Soc.* **88**, 2225
(1966).

[18] K. Koehler, W. Sandstrom, and E. H. Cordes, *J. Am. Chem. Soc.* **86**, 2413 (1964).

than an attack of water which is catalyzed by hydroxide ion. A similar pH–independent reaction is found in the formation of oximes and nitrones from aliphatic aldehydes and acetone, but has not been detected in reactions of hydroxylamine with aromatic carbonyl compounds.[19],[20] The fact that general acid-base catalysis of this reaction shows the same characteristics if the hydrogen atom on the nitrogen is replaced by an alkyl group means that cyclic or concerted mechanisms which involve proton transfer to or from this nitrogen atom are not important for these reactions. There is no significant rate of attack of water or hydroxide ion on the free imine. The attack of all but such highly reactive nucleophiles as borohydride ion on the imine group requires prior protonation to give a cationic imine. However, in the reaction of the less basic hydroxylamine, there is a base catalyzed dehydration pathway, which must represent the specific or general base catalyzed expulsion of hydroxide ion.[11]

The attack and expulsion of substituted oxygen, as in the hydrolysis of the morpholine adduct of equation 16, may be explained

$$(16)$$

according to the same mechanism with a neutral transition state. The peculiar pH–rate profile of this reaction at low pH[21] may be

[19] A. Williams and M. L. Bender, *J. Am. Chem. Soc.* **88**, 2508 (1966).

[20] M. Masui and C. Yijima, *J. Chem. Soc.*, **1966 B**, 56.

[21] M. L. Bender, J. A. Reinstein, M. S. Silver, and R. Mikulak, *J. Am. Chem. Soc.* **87**, 4545 (1965).

attributed to an enhanced rate of hydrolysis of the imine through an attack of water in a cationic transition state and to an acid inhibition caused by the requirement for a dipolar transition state for amine expulsion, although this explanation has not been proved.

Proton transfer in the intermediate to form the zwitterion (equation 14) must be intramolecular and extremely fast; a stepwise proton transfer would not occur rapidly enough to account for the observed reaction rate.[16] This proton transfer may be concerted with the attack of amine on the carbonyl group. However, the attack of alkylamines is not subject to catalysis by added acids or bases; that is, $\alpha = 0$ for the attack of these and other strongly basic nucleophiles on the carbonyl group. The attack of the less basic hydroxylamine molecule does show a very small acid catalyzed term,[5, 22, 23] but general acid catalysis has not yet been detected for this reaction. Conversely, the absence of an acid catalyzed pathway for amine expulsion in the reverse reaction accounts for the inhibition of the rate of imine hydrolysis in acid solution. The electron pair on

neutral oxygen in the species $R_3\overset{+}{N}{-}\overset{|}{\underset{|}{C}}{-}OH$ does not provide sufficient driving force to expel a strongly basic amine, and breakdown of the intermediate takes place only through the dipolar form,

$R_3\overset{+}{N}{-}\overset{|}{\underset{|}{C}}{-}O^-$. Inhibition occurs in acid solution because the concentration of the dipolar intermediate, which is in equilibrium with the cationic imine $>C = NHR^+$, decreases with increasing acidity.

The reactions of *weakly basic amines* such as semicarbazide and anilines with the carbonyl group proceed by additional pathways which reflect the effect of electron withdrawal by substituents on the amine. The change in rate-determining step is of the same kind and occurs at the same or at slightly higher pH compared with the reactions of the more basic amines.[5, 9, 24-26] This means that electron-withdrawing substituents on the amine inhibit the protonation and expulsion of oxygen and of nitrogen from the addition intermediate to approximately the same extent (equation 17).

[22] E. Barrett and A. Lapworth, *J. Chem. Soc.* **93**, 85 (1908).

[23] R. B. Martin, *J. Phys. Chem.* **68**, 1369 (1964).

[24] A. V. Willi, *Helv. Chim. Acta* **39**, 1193 (1956).

[25] E. H. Cordes and W. P. Jencks, *J. Am. Chem. Soc.* **84**, 832 (1962).

[26] R. L. Reeves, *J. Am. Chem. Soc.* **84**, 3332 (1962).

$$B \frown H - O \overset{\backslash}{\underset{H}{\overset{|}{\diagup}}} C \overset{H}{\underset{R}{\overset{|}{=}}} N^+ \underset{\beta \sim 0}{\rightleftharpoons} B\overset{+}{H} \overset{\frown}{O} - \overset{H}{\underset{H}{\overset{|}{C}}} - \overset{|}{N} \diagdown R \rightleftharpoons B \frown H - O - \overset{H}{\underset{H}{\overset{|}{C}}} - \overset{H}{\underset{H}{\overset{|+}{N}R}}$$

$$\beta \sim 0.8 \Big\Vert$$

$$B\overset{+}{H} \overset{\frown}{O} = \overset{|}{\underset{|}{C}} \frown NH_2R$$

$$(17)$$

The addition and loss of water occurs by the same mechanism as with more basic amines, but associated with the smaller driving force of the less basic nitrogen atom there is more acid catalysis of the dehydration step (α approaches 1.0, $\beta \approx 0$ in the reverse direction). Accordingly, general acid-base catalysis of this step is not very important, although it has been detected in the hydrolysis of benzylideneanilines under conditions in which the attack of water is largely rate-determining.[25,27] There is little or no detectable general acid catalysis of the dehydration step of semicarbazone formation or of the hydrolysis of alkoxymethylureas.[5,11,28] This is in agreement with the predictions of structure-reactivity relationships for this mechanism of acid-base catalysis (Chap. 3, Sec. C, Part 4).

As the amine becomes more acidic, a base catalyzed pathway of water attack and expulsion becomes significant. This step is subject to base catalysis in reactions of hydroxylamine, semicarbazide, and anilines with carbonyl compounds.[11,19,22,29,30] Possible mechanisms are shown in equations 18 to 20; a concerted or "one-

$$HO^- \frown \overset{\backslash}{\diagup} C = N - \rightleftharpoons HO - \overset{|}{\underset{|}{C}} - \overset{\frown}{N} -$$

$$(18)$$

$$B \frown H - O \overset{\backslash}{\underset{H}{\overset{|}{\diagup}}} C = N - \rightleftharpoons \overset{+}{B} - H \overset{\frown}{O} - \overset{|}{\underset{H}{\overset{|}{C}}} - \overset{\frown}{N} -$$

$$(19)$$

[27] A. V. Willi and R. E. Robertson, *Can. J. Chem.* **31**, 361 (1953).

[28] F. Nordhøy and J. Ugelstad, *Acta Chem. Scand.* **13**, 864 (1959).

[29] E. H. Cordes and W. P. Jencks, *J. Am. Chem. Soc.* **84**, 832 (1962).

[30] B. Kastening, L. Holleck, and G. A. Melkonian, *Z. Electrochem.* **60**, 130 (1956).

$$HO^- \overset{\frown}{\searrow} C \overset{\frown}{=} N \overset{\displaystyle H}{\underset{|}{}} \overset{\overset{+}{\frown}{B}}{} \quad \rightleftharpoons \quad HO \overset{\frown}{\underset{|}{-}} \overset{|}{\underset{|}{C}} \overset{\frown}{-} N \overset{|}{\underset{|}{-}} H \overset{\frown}{} B \tag{20}$$

encounter" mechanism is also possible. (Note that B = OH⁻ according to the experimental results which are available at this time.) It is not known whether the catalysis represents specific or general base catalysis. The inverse isotope effect, $k_{OD^-}/k_{OH^-} = 1.4$, for the base catalyzed formation of benzaldehyde oxime under conditions in which the dehydration is rate-determining, has been cited as evidence that the dehydration step is specific base catalyzed,[19] but both experimental and theoretical uncertainties regarding the magnitude of isotope effects in reactions which involve proton transfers of this kind make this interpretation inconclusive.

The fact that the attack of weakly basic amines on the carbonyl group is subject to general acid catalysis, with a value of α of about 0.25,[29,31] is also in accord with the expected structure-reactivity relationship. Conversely, the expulsion of the more electrophilic amine from the addition compound does not require the full driving force of an alkoxide ion, but occurs with general base catalysis with a value of β of about 0.75. The value of α for the attack of the still less basic urea molecule on acetaldehyde is 0.45.[17,32] An alternative mechanism for this step which involves preequilibrium protonation of the carbonyl group would require the attack of amine to occur with a rate constant which is larger than that of a diffusion-controlled reaction (Chap. 3, Sec. C, Part 3). The possibility remains that catalysis of this step may occur by a concerted or "one-encounter" mechanism, especially with very weakly basic amines.

Amines with electron-withdrawing substituents, such as amides, urea, and thiourea, attack carbonyl compounds through a general base catalyzed mechanism.[33] A similar pathway is probably important in other condensation reactions of relatively acidic amines, but is obscured by the fact that the rate-determining step of the reaction under conditions in which base catalysis would be significant is the dehydration step. The reaction could occur by the mechanisms

[31] E. H. Cordes and W. P. Jencks, *J. Am. Chem. Soc.* 84, 4319 (1962).

[32] Y. Ogata, A. Kawasaki, and N. Okumura, *Tetrahedron* 22, 1731 (1966).

[33] G. A. Crowe, Jr., and C. C. Lynch, *J. Am. Chem. Soc.* 71, 3731 (1949); J. Koskikallio, *Acta Chem. Scand.* 10, 1267 (1956); J. Ugelstad and J. De Jonge, *Rec. Trav. Chim.* 76, 919 (1957); K. Dušek, *Collection Czech. Chem. Commun.* 25, 108 (1960); J. I. De Jong and J. De Jonge, *Rec. Trav. Chim.* 71, 643, 661 (1952); M. Imoto and M. Kobayashi, *Bull. Chem. Soc. Japan* 33, 1651 (1960).

shown in equations 21 and 22 or by concerted or "one-encounter"

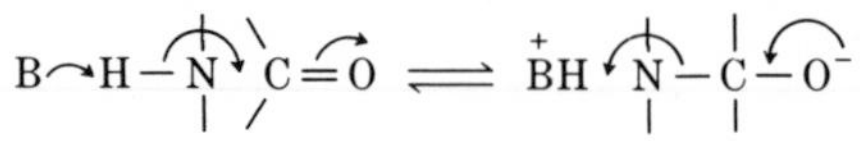

$$B \frown H - \overset{\scriptstyle|}{\underset{\scriptstyle|}{N}} \overset{\scriptstyle\searrow}{\underset{\scriptstyle/}{C}} = \overset{\frown}{O} \quad \rightleftharpoons \quad \overset{\scriptstyle+}{B}H \frown \overset{\scriptstyle|}{\underset{\scriptstyle|}{N}} - \overset{\scriptstyle|}{\underset{\scriptstyle|}{C}} \overset{\scriptstyle\frown}{-} O^- \tag{21}$$

$$\overset{\scriptstyle\diagdown}{\underset{\scriptstyle\diagup}{N}} \frown \overset{\scriptstyle\diagdown}{\underset{\scriptstyle\diagup}{C}} = \overset{\frown}{O} \, H - B^+ \quad \rightleftharpoons \quad \overset{\scriptstyle\diagdown}{\underset{\scriptstyle\diagup}{N}} - \overset{\scriptstyle|}{\underset{\scriptstyle|}{C}} \overset{\scriptstyle\frown}{-} O \frown H \frown B \tag{22}$$

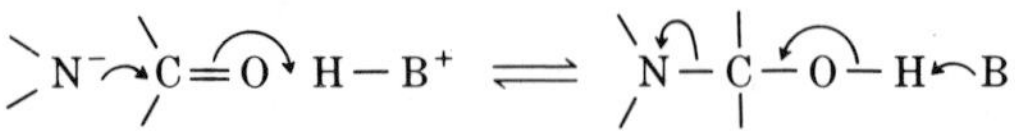

mechanisms. The fact that general acid catalysis is not seen for the attack of nucleophiles that are less basic than amide anions, such as cyanide, sulfite, and free amines, suggests that the mechanism of equation 22 is unlikely, in accord with the expectation from structure-reactivity correlations (Chap. 3, Sec. C, Part 4).

The preferred mode of breakdown of the addition intermediate in these reactions at different pH values, which determines the rate-determining step, is shown in Diagram 3. It should be noted that

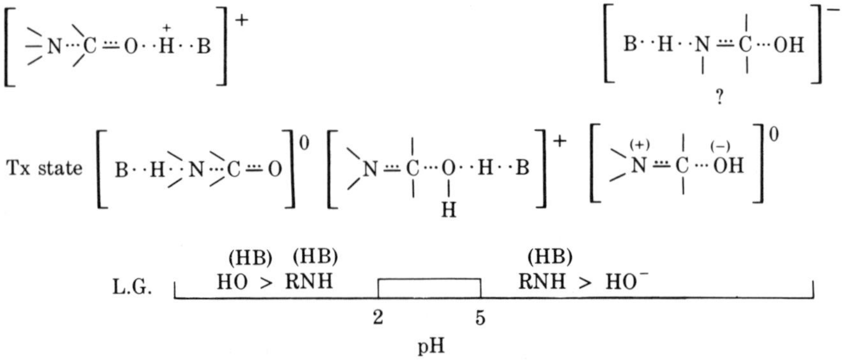

$$\left[\overset{\scriptstyle\diagdown}{\underset{\scriptstyle\diagup}{N}} \cdots \overset{\scriptstyle\diagdown}{\underset{\scriptstyle\diagup}{C}} = O \cdots \overset{\scriptstyle+}{H} \cdots B \right]^+ \qquad\qquad\qquad \left[B \cdots H \cdots N \overset{\scriptstyle|}{=\!=} \overset{\scriptstyle|}{C} \cdots OH \right]^-$$
$$?$$

Tx state $\left[B \cdots H \overset{\scriptstyle\diagdown}{\underset{\scriptstyle\diagup}{N}} \overset{\scriptstyle\diagdown}{\underset{\scriptstyle\diagup}{N}} \overset{\scriptstyle\diagdown}{\underset{\scriptstyle\diagup}{C}} =\!= O \right]^0$ $\left[\overset{\scriptstyle\diagdown}{\underset{\scriptstyle\diagup}{N}} =\!= \overset{\scriptstyle|}{\underset{\scriptstyle|}{C}} \cdots O \cdots H \cdots B \right]^+$ $\left[\overset{\scriptstyle\diagdown}{\underset{\scriptstyle\diagup}{N}} \overset{(+)}{=\!=} \overset{\scriptstyle|}{\underset{\scriptstyle|}{C}} \overset{(-)}{\cdots} OH \right]^0$
                                                                              H

	(HB) (HB)		(HB)
L.G.	HO > RNH		RNH > HO⁻
	2	5	
	pH	

Diagram 3

the driving force for expulsion of oxygen is the free electron pair on the amine, and vice versa, and that the equilibrium constant for isomerization of the neutral intermediate to the dipolar form may influence the direction of breakdown, so that the direction of breakdown does not involve only the relative leaving ability of the possible leaving groups. For this reason, the modes of breakdown of these addition intermediates cannot be used directly to predict the modes of breakdown of tetrahedral addition intermediates in reactions of acyl compounds.

2. $>$C$=$O AND ROH

The reversible hydration of carbonyl compounds occurs by both general acid and general base catalyzed pathways.[2] As discussed in Chap. 3, it is probable that both of these pathways involve concerted or "one-encounter" mechanisms, so that the energetically unfavorable formation of a free oxonium ion or oxygen anion intermediate is not required. The addition and loss of alcohols and related compounds are also subject to general acid-base catalysis and probably proceed by similar mechanisms.[34,35] The acid catalyzed hydrolysis of acetals shows no water reaction and little or no detectable general acid catalysis (equation 23); that is, α is about

$$(23)$$

1.0.[36,37] Protonation of the leaving oxygen atom is required in order that the lone pair electrons of the other oxygen atom should have sufficient driving force to bring about expulsion of alcohol. However, if the leaving oxygen atom is made more electrophilic by an adjacent electron-withdrawing carbonyl group, it can be expelled without acid catalysis. In the lactone **6** the lone pair electrons

6

$$(24)$$

of the ethereal oxygen atom provide sufficient driving force for the unassisted expulsion of the carboxylate ion.[38] This situation is closely analogous to the hydrolysis of phosphate monoester anions. Hydrolysis of the monoanion presumably involves protonation of the leaving alcohol and its expulsion from a dipolar intermediate (**7**),

---

[34] G. W. Meadows and B. de B. Darwent, *Trans. Faraday Soc.* **48**, 1015 (1952); R. P. Bell and E. C. Baughan, *J. Chem. Soc.* **1937**, 1947.

[35] E. G. Sander and W. P. Jencks, *J. Am. Chem. Soc.* **90**, 4377 (1968).

[36] W. P. Jencks, *Progr. Phys. Org. Chem.* **2**, 63 (1964).

[37] E. H. Cordes, *Progr. Phys. Org. Chem.* **4**, 1 (1967).

[38] P. Salomaa, *Acta Chem. Scand.* **19**, 1663 (1965).

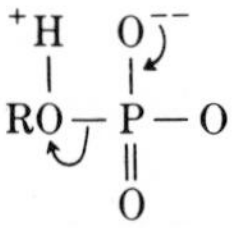

$$\overset{+}{H} \quad \overset{--}{O}$$
$$RO-P-O$$
$$\overset{\parallel}{O}$$

7

whereas hydrolysis of the dianion involves direct expulsion of the oxygen anion (8) and becomes important only with good leaving

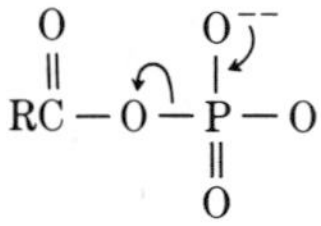

$$\overset{O}{\underset{RC-O-P-O}{\parallel}}$$

8

groups, such as the carboxylate group of acyl phosphates.[39]

The formation and breakdown of the addition compound of hydrogen peroxide and the carbonyl group is subject to general acid and general base catalysis and presumably proceeds by mechanisms similar to those for the analogous reactions of water.[35] The values of α and β for general acid and base catalysis are close to 1.0 and 0.66, respectively; general acid catalysis is detectable because of a negative deviation of the catalytic constant for water. These values are both larger than the corresponding values for hydration, presumably because of the much smaller basicity of hydrogen peroxide compared to water. The rapid rate required for a stepwise mechanism and the negative deviation of the catalytic constant for the solvated proton suggest that the reaction catalyzed by carboxylic acids and related compounds may proceed through a cyclic mechanism such as that of equation 25. In addition, there is an

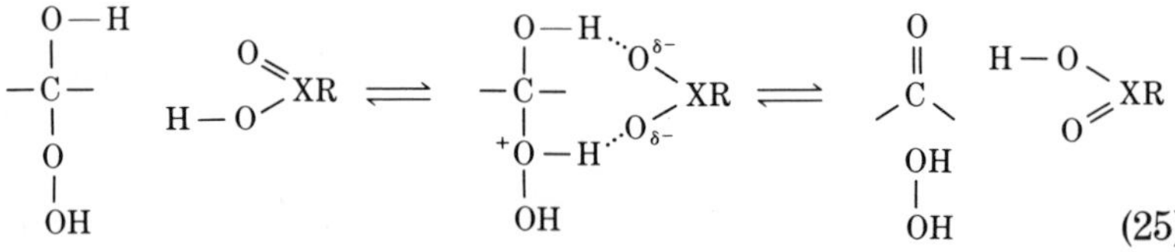

$$(25)$$

uncatalyzed addition and expulsion of hydroperoxide anion (equation 26). This reaction appears as a positive deviation of the point for

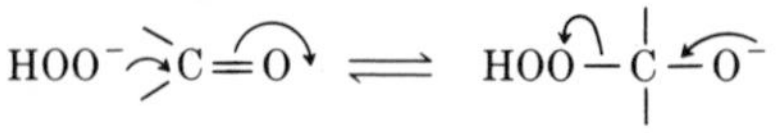

$$HOO^- \, C=O \rightleftharpoons HOO-C-O^-$$

$$(26)$$

[39] W. P. Jencks, *Brookhaven Symp. Biol.* **15**, 134 (1962).

hydroxide ion catalysis of the reaction (i.e., specific base catalysis). The occurrence of such a reaction is difficult to explain if the general base catalyzed reactions occurred by mechanism 27 because it

$$HOO^-\!\!\underset{/}{\overset{\searrow}{C}}\!=\!O^{\curvearrowright}H-A \;\;\rightleftharpoons\;\; HOO\!-\!\underset{|}{\overset{|}{C}}\!-\!O\!-\!H\,{}^{\curvearrowleft}A^- \tag{27}$$

should then appear as a water catalyzed attack $(H\!-\!A = H_2O)$ and should fall on the same Brønsted plot as other catalysts. This provides some further evidence in favor of the mechanism of equation 28 (or the corresponding one-encounter mechanism) for the

$$A^-\!\!\curvearrowright\!H\!\overset{\curvearrowright}{-}\!\underset{\underset{HO}{|/}}{O}\!\!\overset{\searrow}{}\!C\!\overset{\curvearrowright}{=}\!O \;\;\rightleftharpoons\;\; A\!\overset{\frown}{-}\!H\,{}^{\curvearrowleft}\underset{\underset{OH}{|}}{O}\!-\!\underset{|}{\overset{|}{C}}\!\overset{\curvearrowleft}{-}\!O^- \tag{28}$$

general base catalyzed reactions. The high equilibrium affinity of hydrogen peroxide for the carbonyl group is reflected also in transition-state stabilities: both free hydrogen peroxide and its anion attack the carbonyl group at an unusually rapid rate.

3. $\searrow\!C\!=\!O$ AND RSH

Hemithioacetal formation occurs by the direct addition of the strongly nucleophilic thiol anion to the carbonyl group (equation 29) and by

$$RS^-\!\!\curvearrowright\!\!\underset{/}{\overset{\searrow}{C}}\!\overset{\curvearrowright}{=}\!O \;\;\rightleftharpoons\;\; RS\!-\!\underset{|}{\overset{|}{C}}\!\overset{\curvearrowleft}{-}\!O^- \tag{29}$$

a general acid catalyzed addition of free thiol to the carbonyl group (equation 30).[40] There is no detectable water or general base cata-

$$RS\!\underset{\underset{H}{|}}{\overset{\searrow}{C}}\!=\!O^{\curvearrowright}H\overset{\curvearrowright}{-}A \;\;\rightleftharpoons\;\; RS^+\!\underset{\underset{H}{|}}{\overset{|}{-}}\!\!\underset{|}{\overset{|}{C}}\!\overset{\curvearrowleft}{-}\!O\!-\!H\,{}^{\curvearrowleft}A^-$$

$$\Big\Updownarrow\text{fast}$$

$$RS\!-\!\underset{|}{\overset{|}{C}}\!-\!O\!-\!H \;+\; H^+ \;+\; A^- \tag{30}$$

lyzed addition of weakly acidic thiols, probably because the rapid rate of addition of the anion is fast enough to mask any such mechanism. Structure-reactivity correlations favor the mechanism of equation 30 as the kinetically significant mechanism of general acid catalysis,

[40] G. E. Lienhard and W. P. Jencks, *J. Am. Chem. Soc.* 88, 3982 (1966).

but the strong possibility of a concerted or "one-encounter" mechanism exists for this reaction, as for the hydration of aldehydes.

The decomposition of hemithioacetals of more acidic thiols, such as thioacetic acid and thiophenols, occurs with general base catalysis with a β value of 0.8; the reverse, attack step involves general acid catalysis of attack of the anion with $\alpha = 0.2$ (equation 31).[41] The kinetically equivalent mechanism involving general base

$$RS^- \overset{\displaystyle }{\underset{\displaystyle }{{\overset{\frown}{>}}C {=} O}} \, H {-} A \;\rightleftharpoons\; RS {-} \underset{|}{\overset{|}{C}} {-} O {-} H \, A^- \tag{31}$$

catalysis of the attack of the free thiol is ruled out because catalysis is observed under conditions in which the thiol is 98% in the form of the anion. The appearance of general base catalysis for the breakdown of these adducts presumably reflects the ease of expulsion of the relatively good leaving group; more basic thiols require complete removal of a proton from the hydroxyl group ($\beta = 1.0$) to give an alkoxide ion which has sufficient driving force to expel the leaving group. Conversely, strongly basic thiol anions attack the carbonyl group without assistance ($\alpha = 0$), whereas weakly basic anions require assistance by general acid catalysis. The rate of hydroxide ion catalyzed breakdown of the adducts of weakly basic thiols is so fast that the observed rate constant is the rate of diffusion-controlled encounter of the reactants.

As in the case of hydrogen peroxide adducts, the high thermodynamic stability of hemithioacetals is paralleled by their rapid rate of formation. The large nucleophilic reactivities of both the free thiol and the thiol anion are shown by the facts that the rate of the acid catalyzed addition of ethanethiol to acetaldehyde is about the same as that of water, in spite of its approximately 10^5 smaller basicity, and that the anion of methyl mercaptoacetate adds to acetaldehyde more rapidly than hydroxide ion in spite of its 10^8 smaller basicity.[40]

From the rate and equilibrium constants for the addition of water and thiols to acetaldehyde, the rates of breakdown of hemithioacetals and hydrates may be calculated and compared. The acid catalyzed loss of thiol from the hemithioacetal of acetaldehyde and ethanethiol is some 2,500 times slower than the acid catalyzed dehydration of acetaldehyde hydrate, a difference which is similar to the differences in the equilibrium constants for the formation of the two compounds. Thus, its low basicity and its large affinity

[41] R. Barnett and W. P. Jencks, *J. Am. Chem. Soc.* **89**, 5963 (1967).

for the carbonyl group make the thiol group a poorer leaving group than the hydroxyl group in acid catalyzed reactions. The rate of base catalyzed breakdown of the hemithioacetal of ethanethiol and acetaldehyde is 2,000 times faster than that of acetaldehyde hydrate, according to the rate law of equation 32. The interpretation of this

$$v = k\,[\text{OH}^-]\,[\text{HO}\overset{|}{\underset{|}{\text{C}}}\text{XH}] \tag{32}$$

result is clouded by possible differences in the acidities of the hemithioacetal and the hydrate, but it suggests that the thiol anion is a better leaving group than hydroxide ion. These relative leaving abilities of sulfur and oxygen compounds from a tetrahedral addition intermediate through acid and base catalyzed pathways may be useful in attempting to predict the rate-determining step of acyl-group reactions.

4. $>$C=O AND HC$\leqslant$

The addition to the carbonyl group of cyanide ion, a strong nucleophile, occurs without appreciable general or specific acid catalysis (equation 33).[42] Under conditions in which addition to the carbonyl

$$\underset{/}{\overset{\backslash}{\text{C}}}^-\ \underset{/}{\overset{\backslash}{\text{C}}}=\overset{\frown}{\text{O}} \;\rightleftharpoons\; \underset{/}{\overset{\backslash}{\text{C}}}{-}\overset{|}{\underset{|}{\text{C}}}{\cdot}\overset{\curvearrowleft}{\text{O}}^- \tag{33}$$

group, rather than ionization or enolization of the carbon compound, is the rate-determining step, general acid-base catalysis of the addition of a carbon compound has not been detected under either basic or acidic (equation 34) conditions, but further exploration of

$$\tag{34}$$

this point would be desirable.

---

[42] A. Lapworth, *J. Chem. Soc.* **83**, 995 (1903); W. J. Svirbely and J. F. Roth, *J. Am. Chem. Soc.* **75**, 3106 (1953).

The relative ease of addition and expulsion of carbon as the carbanion in *base* catalyzed reactions is responsible for the fact that in two-step carbonyl addition reactions to form unsaturated products (equation 35) the dehydration step is more likely to be rate-

$$
\begin{array}{cccc}
\text{X} & & \text{X} & \\
| & & | & \\
\text{C} & k_1[\text{OH}^-] & \text{C} & k_3[\text{OH}^-] \\
| & k_2[\text{H}^+] & | \quad | & k_4[\text{H}^+] \quad \text{XC} \\
\text{H}-\text{C}-\text{H} + {>}\text{C}{=}\text{O} \rightleftharpoons \text{H}-\text{C}-\text{C}-\text{OH} \rightleftharpoons {>}\text{C}{=}\text{C}{<} \\
| & k_{-1}[\text{OH}^-] & | \quad | & k_{-3}[\text{OH}^-] \\
& k_{-2}[\text{H}^+] & & k_{-4}[\text{H}^+]
\end{array}
\tag{35}
$$

determining in base than in acid. The intermediate addition compounds formed by the addition of methylalkylketones to benzaldehyde undergo dehydration and expulsion of the carbanion at similar rates in basic solution, which means that in the overall reaction in either direction both steps are partly rate-determining.[43,44] Changes in structure change the ratio of these rates and can therefore change the nature of the rate-determining step. In acid solution dehydration of the intermediate is faster than expulsion of carbon, so that the rate-determining step in either direction is the attack and departure of the carbon compound (equation 35, k_2, k_{-2}). Under these conditions substituents on the aldehyde have little influence on the rate because the favorable effect of electron-withdrawing substituents on the condensation step is cancelled by an unfavorable effect on the protonation of the aldehyde. It is well known that the intermediate addition compound may often be isolated from the reaction mixture of an aldol condensation which is carried out under alkaline conditions (i.e., dehydration is rate-determining for the overall reaction), while dehydration takes place rapidly under acidic conditions.[45]

The hydration-dehydration process is itself a two-step reaction with carbon compounds because of the slow rates of proton transfer to and from carbon. The addition and loss of water is faster than the protonation of carbon in the acid catalyzed reactions of benzalacetophenones, which undergo *cis-trans* isomerization more rapidly than hydrogen exchange α to the carbonyl group (equation 36).[44]

[43] D. S. Noyce and W. L. Reed, *J. Am. Chem. Soc.* 81, 624 (1959); D. S. Noyce and L. R. Snyder, *Ibid.*, p. 620; D. S. Noyce and W. A. Pryor, *Ibid.*, p. 618.

[44] M. Stiles, D. Wolf, and G. V. Hudson, *J. Am. Chem. Soc.* 81, 628 (1959).

[45] S. Winstein and H. J. Lucas, *J. Am. Chem. Soc.* 59, 1461 (1937).

$$\underset{XC_6H_4}{\overset{H}{>}}C=C\underset{\overset{\|}{\underset{\overset{|}{H}}{O^+}}CC_6H_5}{\overset{H}{<}} \overset{H_2O}{\rightleftharpoons} XC_6H_4-\underset{HO}{\overset{\overset{H}{|}}{C}}-C\underset{\overset{|}{OH}}{\overset{H}{<}}CC_6H_5 \rightleftharpoons \underset{H}{\overset{XC_6H_4}{>}}C=C\underset{\overset{\|}{\underset{\overset{|}{H}}{O^+}}CC_6H_5}{\overset{H}{<}}$$

$$\Big\Updownarrow \text{slow}$$

$$XC_6H_4-\underset{HO}{\overset{H}{\underset{|}{C}}}-\underset{H}{\overset{H}{\underset{|}{C}}}-\overset{O}{\overset{\|}{C}}C_6H_5 \qquad (36)$$

With compounds which contain electron-donating substituents a carbonium ion mechanism of dehydration becomes predominant (equation 37).[46]

$$\underset{CH_3OC_6H_4}{\overset{H}{>}}C=C\underset{\overset{\|}{O}}{\overset{H}{<}}CC_6H_5 \overset{H^+}{\rightleftharpoons} \underset{CH_3OC_6H_4}{\overset{H}{>}}\overset{+}{\underset{\overset{|}{H}}{C}}-\overset{\overset{H}{|}}{C}-\overset{O}{\overset{\|}{C}}-C_6H_5$$

$$\Big\Updownarrow$$

$$CH_3OC_6H_4-\underset{HO}{\overset{H}{\underset{|}{C}}}-\underset{H}{\overset{H}{\underset{|}{C}}}-\overset{O}{\overset{\|}{C}}C_6H_5 \qquad (37)$$

The addition of alcohol (and presumably the expulsion of alcohol or water in the reverse reaction) to dibenzoylethylenes[47] and ethyl-*cis*-α-cyano-β-*o*-methoxyphenylacrylate[48] occurs through pH–independent and specific base catalyzed pathways. The reaction with the latter compound results in a *cis-trans* isomerization, which is also brought about by other nucleophilic reagents (equation 38). The

[46] D. S. Noyce and M. J. Jorgenson, *J. Am. Chem. Soc.* **83**, 2525 (1961).

[47] T. I. Crowell, G. C. Helsley, R. E. Lutz, and W. L. Scott, *J. Am. Chem. Soc.* **85**, 443 (1963).

[48] S. Patai and Z. Rappoport, *J. Chem. Soc.* **1962**, 396.

$$\left.\begin{array}{c} RO^- + \quad \underset{H}{\overset{C_6H_5}{\diagdown}}C=C\underset{\diagdown COOEt}{\overset{\diagup CN}{}} \\[2em] \Big\Updownarrow \pm H^+ \\[2em] ROH + \quad \underset{H}{\overset{C_6H_5}{\diagdown}}C=C\underset{\diagdown COOEt}{\overset{\diagup CN}{}} \end{array}\right\} \rightleftharpoons \left[\begin{array}{c} \overset{C_6H_5}{\underset{H}{RO-\overset{|}{\underset{|}{C}}-\bar{C}}}\overset{\diagup CN}{\diagdown COOEt} \\[2em] \Big\Updownarrow \pm H^+ \\[2em] RO-\overset{C_6H_5}{\underset{|}{\underset{H}{C}}}-\overset{H}{\underset{|}{\underset{COOEt}{C}}}-CN \end{array}\right]$$

$$\Big\Updownarrow$$

$$\underset{H}{\overset{C_6H_5}{\diagdown}}C=C\underset{\diagdown CN}{\overset{\diagup COOEt}{}} \qquad\qquad (38)$$

mechanism of alkoxide addition is straightforward, but the mechanism of the neutral reaction is not known. In the hydrolysis of nitrostyrenes to benzaldehydes and nitroalkanes, an intermediate, which is presumably the addition compound **9** or **10** (equation 39) is formed

$$Ar-CH=CHNO_2 \underset{-H^+}{\overset{+H_2O}{\rightleftharpoons}} \underset{\underset{OH}{|}\quad \mathbf{9}}{ArCH-CH=NO_2} \overset{(-)\quad HA}{\rightleftharpoons} \underset{\underset{OH}{|}\quad \mathbf{10}}{ArCH-CH_2NO_2}$$

$$\Big\Updownarrow \text{fast}$$

$$ArCHO + CH_2\bar{N}O_2 \rightleftharpoons \underset{\underset{O^-}{|}}{ArCH-CH_2NO_2} \qquad\qquad (39)$$

in a fast step under both acid and alkaline conditions, so that dehydration of the intermediate is apparently faster than expulsion of the carbanion or enol.[49,50] The hydrolysis of the styrene formed from piperonal and nitromethane undergoes changes in rate-determining step with changing pH and with changing buffer concentration. The decomposition of the intermediate can be observed directly and occurs by both pH-independent and hydroxide ion catalyzed pathways. The detailed assignment of the steps in this reaction is not certain, but by analogy with other reactions it appears probable

[49] R. Stewart, *J. Am. Chem. Soc.* **74**, 4531 (1952).

[50] T. I. Crowell and A. W. Francis, Jr., *J. Am. Chem. Soc.* **83**, 591 (1961); T. I. Crowell and T. R. Kim, Doctoral Dissertation, University of Virginia, Charlottesville, Va., 1965.

that the buffer catalyzed step represents a general acid catalyzed protonation of the carbanion, which is kinetically indistinguishable from a general base catalyzed reaction of a neutral species. The fact that the nitrostyrene can be regenerated if the addition intermediate formed in alkaline solution is immediately treated with acid, but not after standing, suggests that the protonation of carbon is slow relative to the rate of addition and loss of hydroxide ion,[49,50] as in the case of the acid catalyzed reactions of benzalacetophenones. The condensation of dimedone with benzaldehydes also undergoes a change in rate-determining step with changing pH, but does not show buffer catalysis.[51]

5. $\diagup$C=N— AND RNH$_2$

The reaction of amines with imines (trans-imination, or "trans-Schiffization") occurs predominantly by attack on the protonated or cationic imine, as is the case with other additions to this group (equation 40).[17,18,52] With hydroxylamine as the nucleophile and

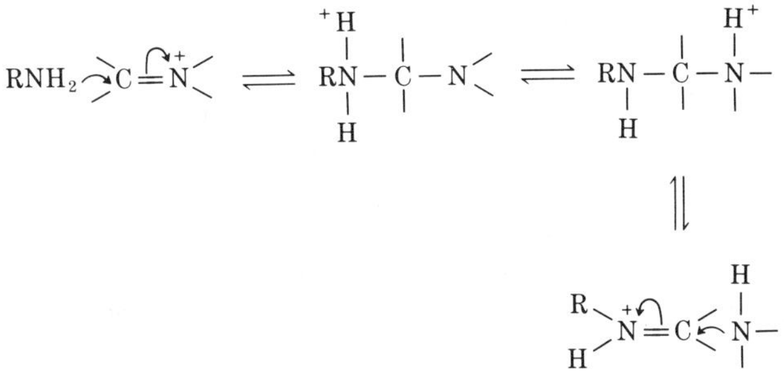

(40)

dimethylamine as the leaving group, the reaction of the cationic imine is subject to general base catalysis by a second molecule of hydroxylamine.[18] This catalysis could occur by mechanisms 11, 12, or 13. Since, in the general case, the reaction is symmetrical, 11

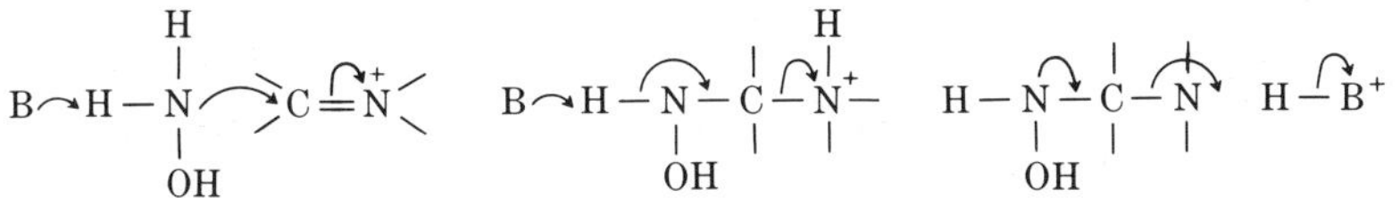

11   12   13

[51] B. E. Dawson and T. Henshall, *J. Phys. Chem.* **67**, 1187 (1963).
[52] E. H. Cordes and W. P. Jencks, *J. Am. Chem. Soc.* **84**, 826 (1962).

and **13** represent the same mechanism of catalysis for the reaction in the two directions. In this particular reaction, mechanism **13** is improbable because the basicity of the free amine is sufficient that the intermediate should become protonated without the help of a catalyst at the pH value at which the experiments were carried out. The most unstable intermediate in the reaction, the conjugate acid of the oxime, would be avoided by catalysis according to mechanism **12**. However, it has been suggested that the effects of structure on the reaction rate favor a mechanism in which the attack of hydroxylamine is rate-determining.[18]

Hydroxylamine also reacts with benzhydrylidenemethylamine at higher pH values at a rate proportional to the concentrations of the basic species of the reactants.[18] The great instability of amine anions, which would be necessary intermediates in an uncatalyzed mechanism (equations 41 and 42) suggests that this reaction pathway

$$-\overset{\displaystyle |}{\underset{\displaystyle H}{N}}\overset{\frown}{>}C=\overset{\frown}{N}- \;\;\rightleftharpoons\;\; \overset{\pm}{\underset{\displaystyle H}{N}}\overset{\frown}{\underset{|}{-}}\overset{|}{C}\overset{\frown}{\underset{|}{-}}\overset{\frown}{N}- \tag{41}$$

$$-\overset{\displaystyle |}{N}\overset{-}{>}C\overset{\frown}{=}\overset{+}{N}\overset{H}{<} \;\;\rightleftharpoons\;\; >\overset{\frown}{N}\overset{\frown}{\underset{|}{-}}\overset{|}{C}\overset{\frown}{-}NH \tag{42}$$

either involves general acid catalysis or proceeds with concerted intramolecular proton transfer.

6. $>$C=N— AND HC$\leqslant$

The mechanism of the addition of carbon compounds to imines, best known as the second step of the Mannich reaction, is not firmly established. The fact that the addition of cyanide to an adduct formed from acetone and a secondary amine occurs at a rate which is independent of the concentration of cyanide (or cyanide donor) shows that the attack of cyanide does not occur in the rate-determining step, so that the reaction must proceed through the rate-determining formation of the cationic imine, **15**, rather than by direct displacement of hydroxide ion by cyanide in the intermediate **14** (equation 43).[53] It is difficult to interpret the results of kinetic studies of the

[53] T. D. Stewart and C-H. Li, *J. Am. Chem. Soc.* **80**, 2782 (1938).

$$\text{>NH} + \text{>C=O} \ \rightleftharpoons \ \text{>C}\begin{smallmatrix}\text{OH}\\ \diagdown \\ \text{N}-\\ |\end{smallmatrix} \ \rightleftharpoons \ \text{>C=}\overset{+}{\text{N}}\text{<} \ \xrightarrow[\text{CN}^-]{\text{fast}} \ \text{>C}\begin{smallmatrix}\text{N}-\\ \diagup \\ \diagdown \\ \text{CN}\end{smallmatrix}$$

14   15   (43)

Mannich reaction[54, 55] because of uncertainties regarding the nature of the rate-determining step and the reactive ionic species under the conditions of the kinetic experiments. The pH–independent and base catalyzed third-order terms in the rate law for the condensation of dimethylamine, formaldehyde, and cyclohexanone at pH values at which the amine is protonated (equation 44)[55] may be

$$\text{Rate} = k_1[\text{R}\overset{+}{\text{N}}\text{H}_3][\text{HCHO}][\text{H}-\text{C}\overset{\diagdown}{\diagup}] + k_2[\text{RNH}_2][\text{HCHO}][\text{H}-\text{C}\overset{\diagdown}{\diagup}] \qquad (44)$$

interpreted in terms of attack on the cationic imine formed from formaldehyde and dimethylamine of the enol and enolate of cyclohexanone, respectively (equations 45 and 46). A mechanism analog-

$$\text{H}-\text{O}-\text{C}\overset{|}{=}\overset{|}{\text{C}} \quad \text{>C}\overset{+}{=}\text{N}\text{<} \ \rightleftharpoons \ \overset{+}{\text{HO}}\text{>C}-\overset{|}{\text{C}}-\overset{|}{\text{C}}-\text{N}\text{<} \qquad (45)$$

$$\text{}^-\text{O}-\text{C}\overset{|}{=}\overset{|}{\text{C}} \quad \text{>C}\overset{+}{=}\text{N}\text{<} \ \rightleftharpoons \ \text{O}\text{>C}-\overset{|}{\text{C}}-\overset{|}{\text{C}}-\text{N}\text{<} \qquad (46)$$

ous to that of equation 46 is probably involved in the condensation step of the ammonium acetate catalyzed reaction of vanillin with nitromethane (Chap. 2, Sec. C, Part 3).

The addition of hydroxymethyl and alkoxymethyl adducts of piperidine to acid solutions of antipyrene gives a good yield of the Mannich condensation product under conditions in which the overall reaction of piperidine, formaldehyde, and antipyrene proceeds quite poorly.[56] This qualitative observation provides strong evidence (1) that the final condensation step involves the cationic imine formed

[54] E. R. Alexander and E. J. Underhill, *J. Am. Chem. Soc.* 71, 4014 (1949).

[55] T. F. Cummings and J. R. Shelton, *J. Org. Chem.* 25, 419 (1960).

[56] H. Hellmann and G. Opitz, *Ber.* 89, 81 (1956).

by elimination from the piperidine adduct and (2) that the rate-determining step of the overall reaction under these conditions is the reaction of free piperidine with formaldehyde (equation 47).

$$\text{HCHO} + \text{HN}\!\!<\;\; \underset{\text{acid}}{\overset{\substack{\text{slow}\\\text{in}}}{\rightleftharpoons}}\;\; \text{HOCH}_2\text{N}\!\!<\;\; \overset{\text{H}^+}{\rightleftharpoons}\;\; \text{H}_2\text{C}\!=\!\overset{+}{\text{N}}\!\!<$$

$$\Big\Updownarrow \pm\text{H}^+ \qquad\qquad\qquad\qquad\qquad \Big\downarrow \text{HC}\!\lessgtr$$

$$\overset{+}{\text{H}_2\text{N}}\!\!< \qquad\qquad\qquad\qquad \substack{>\\ >}\text{C}\!-\!\text{CH}_2\!-\!\text{N}\!\!< \qquad\qquad (47)$$

The elimination of a lag period in the condensation of ethylmalonic acid, formaldehyde, and dimethylamine by prior incubation of formaldehyde and dimethylamine suggests that the reaction of amine with formaldehyde can be rate-determining under acidic conditions in this reaction also.[54]

$$\overset{\text{O}}{\overset{\|}{}}$$

7. RCOR' AND HOR''

The hydrolysis and alcoholysis of esters and anhydrides occur through base catalyzed, pH-independent, and acid catalyzed reaction pathways. Of these, the base catalyzed pathway is by far the easiest to understand because of its symmetry and the relatively few possible mechanisms of catalysis of proton transfer. A tetrahedral addition intermediate may be observed directly upon the addition of ethoxide ion to ethyl trifluoroacetate in a nonpolar solvent, under conditions in which a net acyl transfer reaction is impossible (equation 48).[3] The alkaline hydrolysis of esters with relatively poor

$$\overset{\text{O}}{\overset{\|}{\text{CF}_3\text{COC}_2\text{H}_5}} + {}^-\text{OC}_2\text{H}_5 \;\rightleftharpoons\; \text{CF}_3-\overset{\overset{\displaystyle {}^-\text{O}}{|}}{\underset{\underset{\displaystyle \text{OC}_2\text{H}_5}{|}}{\text{C}}}-\text{OC}_2\text{H}_5 \qquad\qquad (48)$$

leaving groups shows a small amount of exchange of the carbonyl oxygen atom with labeled solvent oxygen atoms, which probably proceeds through a tetrahedral addition intermediate (equation 49),[57]

[57] M. L. Bender, *J. Am. Chem. Soc.* **73**, 1626 (1951); *Chem. Rev.* **60**, 53 (1960).

$$
\underset{\substack{\parallel \\ RCOR' + {}^-\overset{*}{O}H}}{O} \underset{k_{-1}}{\overset{k_1}{\rightleftarrows}} R-\underset{\substack{\downarrow \\ {}^*OH}}{\overset{\overline{}O}{\underset{|}{C}}}OR' \xrightarrow{k_2} \underset{\parallel *}{\overset{O*}{RCOH}} + HOR'
$$

$$k_3 \updownarrow\updownarrow k_{-3}$$

$$
\underset{\substack{\parallel \\ RCOR' + {}^-OH}}{O*} \underset{k_{-1}}{\overset{k_1}{\rightleftarrows}} R-\underset{\substack{| \\ *O^-}}{\overset{\uparrow OH}{\underset{|}{C}}}OR' \xrightarrow{k_2} \underset{\parallel *}{\overset{O*}{RCOH}} + HOR' \tag{49}
$$

but could conceivably proceed by a concerted mechanism if several proton transfers can occur during the reaction at a rate which is fast compared with the lifetime that one decides an intermediate must have in order to merit the name "intermediate" (e.g., equation 50).[58] The observation that an addition intermediate can be formed

$$ \tag{50}$$

and the observed exchange of oxygen suggest, but do not prove, that a tetrahedral intermediate is formed in the course of the alkaline hydrolysis and alcoholysis of esters. Because of the symmetrical nature of the reaction and because the less basic alkoxide ion will certainly be expelled preferentially from an addition intermediate, the rate-determining step for both reactions will be that which involves the attack or departure of the more basic alkoxide ion.

The only reaction of this kind in which exchange is faster than hydrolysis is the alkaline hydrolysis of $\underset{\parallel}{\overset{O}{Co(NH_3)_5OCCF_3}}{}^{++}$ with C—O cleavage; $Co^{++}(NH_3)_5O^-$ is evidently the worst oxygen leaving group known.[59] The rate of this hydrolytic reaction is second order with respect to hydroxide ion, and the exchange reaction is observed only at low hydroxide ion concentrations, at which the rate of hydrolysis is relatively slow. Assuming that the exchange does occur through a tetrahedral intermediate, this behavior may be explained by the mechanism of equation 51. It is a quite general phenomenon that the hydrolysis of compounds with poor leaving groups occurs

[58] C. A. Bunton, *Ann. Rep. Chem. Soc.* 55, 186 (1958).

[59] R. B. Jordan and H. Taube, *J. Am. Chem. Soc.* 88, 4406 (1966).

through a process which is second order with respect to hydroxide ion. A single hydroxide ion does not have sufficient driving force to expel the leaving group, but expulsion of hydroxide ion, after proton transfer, does lead to oxygen exchange, and a significant amount of oxygen exchange usually occurs in such reactions. It is assumed in the mechanism of equation 51 that the second molecule

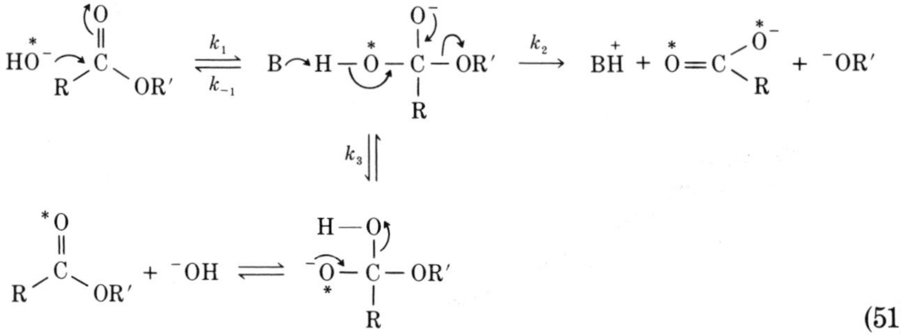

$$
\text{(51)}
$$

of hydroxide ion acts as a general base catalyst, but this has not been proved. An alternative mode of breakdown of the intermediate is shown in equation 52. In either case, the breakdown of the

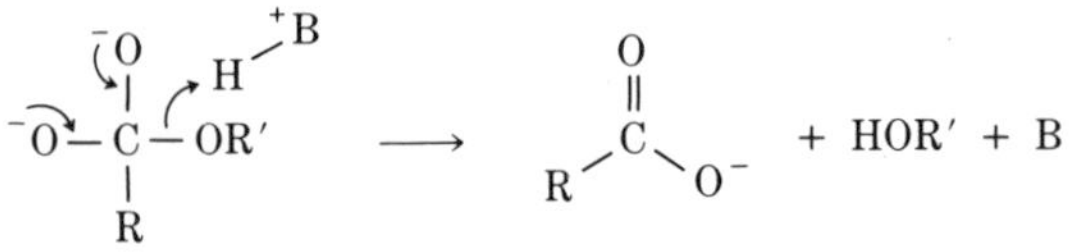

$$
\text{(52)}
$$

intermediate to products is slow at low hydroxide ion concentrations, so that proton transfer, hydroxide ion expulsion, and oxygen exchange with the medium are fast. At high hydroxide ion concentration, the breakdown of the intermediate is fast, attack of hydroxide ion becomes relatively slow, and oxygen exchange is not observed.

Over a limited range of structural variation the rates of nucleophilic reactions of oxygen anions with esters are well behaved and show linear structure-reactivity correlations with different esters. For the attack of strongly basic oxygen anions on esters with good leaving groups, such as substituted phenyl esters, the rate constants for a series of esters are directly proportional to the rate constants for the reactions with hydroxide ion (Fig. 14, upper lines). The rate constants increase with increasing pK of the nucleophile and with

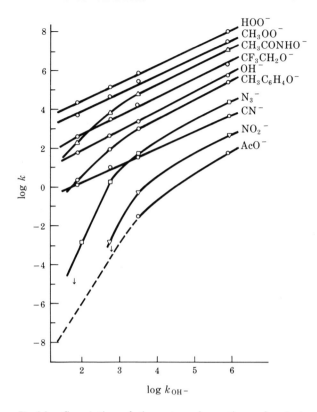

Fig 14. Correlation of the rates of reactions of anionic nucleophiles with substituted phenyl acetates and 1-acetoxy-4-methoxypyridinium ion, showing the break in the structure-reactivity correlation as the attacking group becomes less basic than the leaving group.[60]

decreasing pK of the leaving group, with Br∮nsted slopes of about 0.3.[60] For these reactions, the transition state occurs early along the reaction coordinate. As the leaving group becomes worse or the nucleophile becomes weaker, curvature appears in structure-reactivity correlations and the rate shows a sharper dependence on the basicity of the nucleophile and of the leaving group. Eventually, as in the reactions of imidazole with esters, the nucleophile does not displace the leaving group directly at all, but rather acts as a general base catalyst for hydrolysis of the ester. With oxygen nucleophiles the transition occurs in the reaction of acetate (pK 4.7) with

[60] W. P. Jencks and M. Gilchrist, *J. Am. Chem. Soc.* **90**, 2622 (1968).

p-nitrophenyl acetate (pK of the leaving group = 7.0); this reaction occurs partly by nucleophilic attack and partly by general base catalysis.[61] The increased dependence on the pK of the leaving group is apparent in the downward deflection of the lower lines in Fig. 14. Logarithmic plots of the rate of the nucleophilic reaction against the pK of the nucleophile also display a downward curvature, as shown in Fig. 15, in which the arrows represent the rates of general base catalyzed hydrolysis and, hence, an upper limit for the rate of the nucleophilic reaction. With poor leaving groups and weak nucleophiles the values of β are near 1.0 for both the attacking and leaving groups. This means that the transition state occurs

[61] D. G. Oakenfull, T. Riley, and V. Gold, *Chem. Comm.* **1966**, 385; V. Gold, D. G. Oakenfull, and T. Riley, *J. Chem. Soc.* **1968B**, 515.

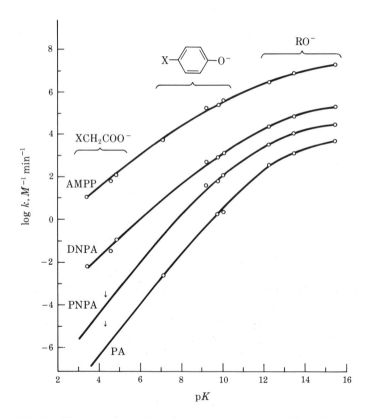

Fig 15. The rate of reaction of anionic oxygen nucleophiles with substituted phenyl acetates and 1-acetoxy-4-methoxypyridinium ion (AMPP) as a function of the basicity of the nucleophile.[60]

far along the reaction coordinate if the attacking group is much less basic than the leaving group and that it resembles what might be expected for rate-determining decomposition of a tetrahedral addition intermediate. It is apparent that there is a change in the nature of the rate-determining step as the attacking and leaving groups are varied, but it cannot be definitely decided from these results whether this represents a discontinuous change from rate-determining formation to rate-determining breakdown of a discrete intermediate or a continuous change in a concerted reaction in which there is no intermediate (Fig. 12).

The reactions of esters and anhydrides with neutral oxygen nucleophiles, such as water and alcohols, are subject to general base catalysis.[62,63] The fact that the rate constants of the water reaction itself fall on the same Brønsted plot of slope 0.47 as the rate constants for other general base catalysts suggests that the water reaction involves general base catalysis of the attack of water by water. However, the rate constant of the hydroxide ion hydrolysis shows a positive deviation from this Brønsted line, which suggests that the hydroxide reaction occurs by a different mechanism, i.e., that it is a direct nucleophilic attack of hydroxide ion.[63] The rates of the water reactions, expressed as second-order rate constants, are 10^7 to 10^{11} slower than those of the hydroxide ion hydrolysis and show a greater sensitivity to the structure of the ester. A plot of log k_{H_2O} against log k_{OH^-} has a slope of 2.1 for a series of esters in which the leaving group is varied and a slope of 1.4 for a series in which the acyl group is varied.[12]

The water reactions of esters and anhydrides have several characteristic properties. The entropies and volumes of activation have extraordinarily large negative values, on the order of -20 to -50 entropy units and -19 to -22 cc/mole, respectively.[63,64] These quantities presumably reflect a transition state in which a large number of solvent molecules are immobilized and subjected to electrostriction associated with the solvation of developing charges and the transfer of protons (which the observation of general base catalysis indicates must occur). The solvent deuterium isotope effects, k_{H_2O}/k_{D_2O}, are generally in the range of 2.0 to 4.0.[63,65,66]

[62] M. Kilpatrick, Jr., *J. Am. Chem. Soc.* 50, 2891 (1928).

[63] W. P. Jencks and J. Carriuolo, *J. Am. Chem. Soc.* 83, 1743 (1961).

[64] J. Koskikallio, D. Pouli, and E. Whalley, *Can. J. Chem.* 37. 1360 (1959); G. DiSabato, W. P. Jencks, and E. Whalley, *Ibid.* 40, 1220 (1962).

[65] M. L. Bender, E. J. Pollock, and M. C. Neveu, *J. Am. Chem. Soc.* 84, 595 (1962).

[66] S. Johnson, *Advan. Phys. Org. Chem.* 5, 237 (1967).

The rates of these reactions and of the hydrolysis of the acetylimidazolium cation are greatly retarded by concentrated solutions of certain salts and (provided there is no acid catalysis) acids.[63,67,68] A striking example of this phenomenon is the 500-fold decrease in the rate of acetylimidazolium hydrolysis which is caused by 8 M sodium perchlorate.[67] This inhibition cannot be entirely accounted for by the decrease in the activity of water in concentrated salt solutions and is probably another manifestation of the interaction of salts with polar carbonyl compounds, which shows a special sensitivity to the nature of the anion of the salt.

The problem of the mechanism of general base catalysis of the alcoholysis and hydrolysis of esters is simplified but not solved by the symmetry of the reaction. If the attacking and leaving groups have similar properties, the reverse reaction is simply the mirror image of the forward reaction and, according to microscopic reversibility, must be subject to the same mechanism of catalysis. The symmetrical nature of the reaction is supported by the fact that the ratio k_{hydrol}/k_{exch} is 2 for the neutral hydrolysis of ethyl trifluoroacetate,[69] which means that the expulsion of ethanol occurs at a similar rate to the proton transfer and expulsion of water which are required for the exchange reaction. The simplest mechanism, which is written to include a tetrahedral addition intermediate, involves a more or less concerted proton removal by the general base from the hydroxyl compound as it attacks the carbonyl group, converting the weakly nucleophilic hydroxyl group into some sort of a partial or potential alkoxide or hydroxide ion (equation 53).

$$
B\!-\!H\!-\!\underset{\underset{R}{|}}{O}\quad \underset{\underset{R''}{|}}{\overset{R'}{\underset{|}{O}}}C\!=\!O \;\rightleftharpoons\; RO\!-\!\underset{\underset{\underset{R''}{|}}{\overset{H}{O}}}{\overset{R'}{\underset{|}{C}}}\!-\!O^- \;\rightleftharpoons\; RO\!-\!C\!\!\underset{\underset{R''}{\overset{}{}}}{\overset{R'}{\diagup}}\!\!\diagdown O
\tag{53}
$$

This is the same minimal mechanism as for the addition of hydroxylic compounds to simple carbonyl compounds. The mechanism may be modified to a "one-encounter" mechanism, in which the conjugate acid of the catalyst donates a proton transitorily to the car-

[67] S. Marburg and W. P. Jencks, *J. Am. Chem. Soc.* **84**, 232 (1962).

[68] C. A. Bunton, N. A. Fuller, S. G. Perry, and I. H. Pitman, *J. Chem. Soc.* **1962**, 4478.

[69] M. L. Bender and H. d'A. Heck, *J. Am. Chem. Soc.* **89**, 1211 (1967).

bonyl group as it develops a negative charge, but the absence of a special catalytic effectiveness of polyfunctional catalysts, such as phosphate, suggests that it is not true concerted acid-base catalysis. An alternative mechanism in which an alkoxide ion is formed in a prior equilibrium step and attacks the carbonyl group with aid from general acid catalysis (equation 54) is made unlikely for the

$$RO^- \overset{R'}{\underset{R''O}{>}}C\!=\!\overset{+}{O}\; H\!-\!\overset{+}{B} \;\rightleftharpoons\; RO\!-\!\underset{R''O}{\overset{R'}{\underset{|}{C}}}\!-\!OH\frown B \;\rightleftharpoons\; RO\!-\!C\overset{R'}{\underset{R''O^-}{<}}_O\; H\!-\!\overset{+}{B} \qquad (54)$$

pyridine catalyzed alcoholysis of ethyl trifluoroacetate by the fact that it would require a rate constant of more than $7.4 \times 10^9\ M^{-1}$ sec^{-1} for the attack of alkoxide ion on a hydrogen-bonded complex of ester and catalyst in order to account for the observed overall reaction rate. If this conclusion is accepted, arguments based on the symmetry of the reaction suggest that an addition intermediate must be formed. The mechanism of equation 54 is improbable, and if there were no intermediate, symmetry demands that there be catalysis of *both* the attack and leaving of alcohol; this would require a term in the rate law which is second order with respect to catalyst for a concerted reaction.[66,70]

The amount of oxygen exchange during the pH-independent hydrolysis of ethyl trifluoroacetate is decreased two- to threefold in deuterium oxide solution.[69] This could be explained by a decreased rate of decomposition of the intermediate to starting materials relative to the rate of decomposition to products in deuterium oxide (the rate of formation of the intermediate is known to be decreased in deuterium oxide), or by a decrease in the rate of the proton transfer step which is required in order that oxygen exchange may occur, or by both of these factors.

Very little is known about the mechanism of acid catalyzed ester hydrolysis and alcoholysis. The fact that the exchange of labeled oxygen with the solvent occurs at a rate about one-third that of hydrolysis suggests that an addition intermediate probably exists, with a lifetime which is sufficient for the proton transfers required for such exchange to take place (equation 55).[71] The very small basicity of esters (the pK of the conjugate acid of ethyl ben-

[70] S. L. Johnson, *J. Am. Chem. Soc.* **86**, 3819 (1964).
[71] M. L. Bender, R. D. Ginger, and J. P. Unik, *J. Am. Chem. Soc.* **80**, 1044 (1958).

$$
\begin{array}{c}
RO-C\underset{OH}{\overset{R'}{\underset{+}{\diagup}}} \\
H-O \\
| \\
R''
\end{array}
$$

$$
\underset{\substack{| \\ H \\ | \\ R''}}{RO}\overset{R'}{\underset{O}{\diagdown}}C=\overset{+}{O}H
\rightleftharpoons
\left[\begin{array}{ccc}
R' & & R' \\
| & & | \\
R^+O-C-OH & \rightleftharpoons & RO-C-OH \\
| \quad | & & | \\
H \quad O & & H-O^+ \\
| & & | \\
R'' & & R''
\end{array}\right.
$$

$$
\overset{+}{RO}=C\underset{OR''}{\overset{R'}{\diagdown}} \quad O\underset{H}{\overset{H}{\diagdown}}
\rightleftharpoons
\left.\begin{array}{c}
R' \\
| \\
RO-C-\overset{+}{O}H \\
| \quad | \\
O \quad H \\
| \\
R''
\end{array}\right]
$$

exchange reaction (R = H)   (55)

zoate is -7.4)[72] means that the conjugate acid of the ester is an extremely unstable intermediate and suggests that a general acid catalyzed reaction path, which would avoid the formation of such an intermediate, would be energetically advantageous. The hydrolysis of ortho esters is subject to general acid catalysis[73] which must occur by the mechanism of equation 56. The reverse of this reaction in-

$$
\underset{\substack{| \\ RO \quad R}}{\overset{\substack{RO \\ |}}{R'-C-O}}HA \rightleftharpoons R'-\overset{+}{C}\underset{\substack{| \\ R}}{\overset{\diagup O}{\diagdown O}} \quad \underset{\substack{| \\ R}}{O}-H\frown A
$$

$$\Big\downarrow H_2O$$

$$
\overset{O}{\overset{\|}{R'COR}}
$$

                                                              (56)

volves general base catalysis of the attack of alcohol (or water) on an O-alkylated ester, which is a model for a protonated ester (equation 57). This provides a reasonable mechanism for general

[72] J. Hine and R. P. Bayer, J. Am. Chem. Soc. 84, 1989 (1962).

[73] J. N. Brønsted and W. F. K. Wynne-Jones, Trans. Faraday Soc. 25, 59 (1929).

$$
\begin{array}{ccc}
\underset{\substack{|\\RO}}{\overset{\substack{OH\\|}}{R'-C-O}}\ \underset{\substack{|\\R''}}{\ }\ HA & \longleftarrow & R'-C\overset{\overset{H}{\overset{|}{+}}_{\nwarrow O}}{\underset{\underset{R}{\overset{|}{O}}}{}}\ \overset{}{O-H\curvearrowleft A^-}
\end{array}
\tag{57}
$$

acid catalysis of ester hydrolysis or alcoholysis and suggests that such catalysis should take place. However, in the case of the ester reactions the possibility of concerted or one-encounter mechanisms, in which the acid catalyst donates a proton to the ester carbonyl group, should also be considered. There is evidence for general acid catalysis of the esterification of acids in alcohol solution.[74]

As the leaving group is made better, the ratio of ^{18}O exchange with the solvent to hydrolysis decreases in base catalyzed reactions because an addition intermediate will always expel a good leaving group, to give hydrolysis, rather than hydroxide ion, to give exchange. No exchange is observed in the alkaline hydrolysis of phenyl benzoate, for example.[75] However, protonation of the leaving group is required in acid catalyzed reactions, and the inhibitory effect of electron-withdrawing substituents on such protonation would tend to inhibit the expulsion of the alcohol. Thus, if proton transfer in the intermediate is fast, the ratio of exchange to hydrolysis should be maintained or even increased in acid catalyzed reactions as electron-withdrawing substituents are added to the leaving group.

8. $\overset{O}{\overset{||}{R C S R'}}$ AND HOR''

The equilibrium for the transfer of an acyl group between thiol and hydroxyl groups (equation 58) favors transfer to the oxygen com-

$$
\overset{O}{\overset{||}{RCSR'}} + HOR'' \rightleftharpoons \overset{O}{\overset{||}{RCOR''}} + HSR'
\tag{58}
$$

pound by a factor of about 50.[76] This is presumably caused in large part by the relatively small stabilization of thiol esters by the resonance forms 16 and 17 compared with the stabilization of oxygen

[74] C. N. Hinshelwood and A. R. Legard, J. Chem. Soc. 1935, 587.
[75] C. A. Bunton and D. N. Spatcher, J. Chem. Soc. 1956, 1079.
[76] W. P. Jencks, S. Cordes, and J. Carriuolo, J. Biol. Chem. 235, 3608 (1960).

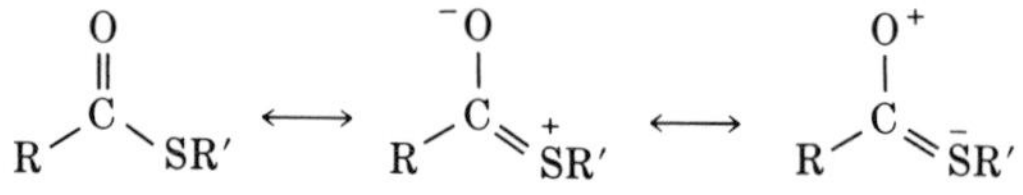

16   **17**

esters by the resonance form **18**. It is difficult for the electrons of

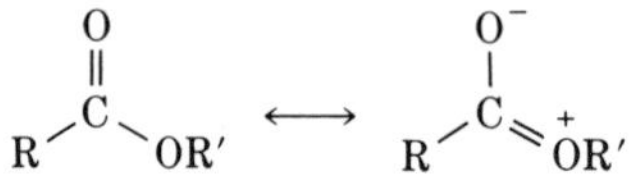

18

the large sulfur atom to overlap effectively with the adjacent carbonyl group to form a double bond (**16**). However sulfur can accept
electrons in empty d orbitals (**17**), which oxygen cannot, and the low
carbonyl stretching frequency and the small basicity of thiol esters
suggest that **17** makes a significant contribution to the ground-state
structure of thiol esters.[77] The small contribution of **16** leaves the
carbonyl group of a thiol ester relatively unperturbed, so that it
displays many of the properties of a simple ketone and provides
resonance stabilization to account for the well known ease of formation of carbanions adjacent to the thiol ester group in both chemical
and enzymatic reactions (**19**).

19

The important characteristics of the mechanism of thiol ester
hydrolysis have been elucidated by the use of a combination of oxygen exchange and kinetic experiments. The pH–rate profile for
the hydrolysis of ethyl trifluorothiolacetate is sigmoid (Fig. 16) and
the *decrease* in rate below pH 2 must represent a change from a
rate-determining step with a neutral transition state at neutral pH
to one with an anionic transition state below pH 2.[78] In addition
there is an *increase* in rate at high pH values, which shows that the
step which is rate-determining at neutral pH values can proceed
through an anionic as well as a neutral transition state. The neu-

[77] A. W. Baker and G. H. Harris, *J. Am. Chem. Soc.* **82**, 1923 (1960).

[78] L. R. Fedor and T. C. Bruice, *J. Am. Chem. Soc.* **87**, 4138 (1965).

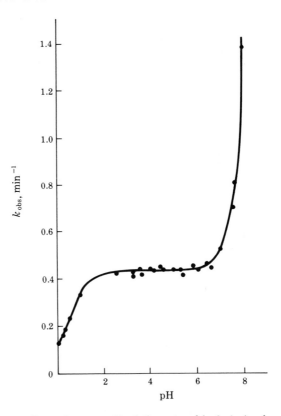

Fig 16. Dependence on pH of the rate of hydrolysis of ethyl trifluorothiolacetate at 30° in water.[78]

tral transition state of the pH-independent reaction could represent the attack of water on the thiol ester (equation 59, k_1) or the kinet-

$$(59)$$

ically equivalent breakdown of a tetrahedral intermediate through a transition state with no net charge (equation 60, k_2'). In the former

$$\underset{R}{\overset{HO^-}{\longrightarrow}}\overset{O}{\underset{SR'}{\parallel}}\underset{k'_{-1}}{\overset{\substack{slow < pH\ 2 \\ fast > pH\ 2 \\ k'_1 \\ \rightleftharpoons}}}\ H-O-\underset{R}{\overset{^-O}{\underset{|}{\overset{|}{C}}}}-SR'\ \overset{\pm H^+}{\rightleftharpoons}\ H-O-\underset{R}{\overset{O-H}{\underset{|}{\overset{|}{C}}}}-SR'$$

$$\Big\downarrow k_2'\ \substack{fast < pH\ 2 \\ slow > pH\ 2}$$

$$H-O-\overset{O}{\overset{\parallel}{C}}\diagdown_R\ +\ HSR' \tag{60}$$

case, the acid inhibited step at low pH would be the base catalyzed breakdown of the tetrahedral intermediate (equation 59, k_2), while in the latter case it would be the attack of hydroxide ion on the ester (equation 60, k_1'). The mechanisms of equations 59 and 60 give rate laws of the same form, as would be expected from the identical stoichiometric compositions of their transition states, and cannot be distinguished by any ordinary kinetic test. However, the mechanism of equation 60 is effectively ruled out by the fact that the observed rate of the reaction in the low pH region (in which the attack of hydroxide ion would be rate-determining) requires that the value of k_1' in the rate law for this step be $2.5 \times 10^{11}\ M^{-1}$ sec^{-1}, which is faster than the rate of a diffusion-controlled reaction. That the mechanism of equation 59 is correct is confirmed by the fact that below pH 2, in the region in which the breakdown of the intermediate is rate-determining, the ester undergoes exchange of ^{18}O with the solvent, whereas above pH 2, in the region in which expulsion of the thiol anion is fast, no oxygen exchange is observed.[69]

Furthermore, the mechanisms of the individual steps of this reaction may be specified in some detail and turn out to be the same as those for the corresponding reactions of simple carbonyl compounds. The attack of water on the thiol ester is subject to general base catalysis, and the rate constant for the water reaction falls on the same Brønsted line that is followed by other general base catalysts. This suggests that the water reaction represents base catalysis of the attack of water by water, as in the hydrolysis of oxygen esters.[78] This catalysis could occur by the removal of a proton from attacking water (equation 61) to avoid the formation of an unstable oxonium ion as the initial product of the addition reac-

$$B{\frown}H{-}\underset{\underset{H}{|}}{O} \quad \underset{R}{\overset{\overset{O}{\|}}{C}}{\diagdown}_{SR'} \quad \rightleftharpoons \quad B^+H \, {}^{\prime}\underset{\underset{H}{|}}{O}{-}\underset{\underset{R}{|}}{\overset{\overset{O^-}{|}}{C}}{-}SR' \tag{61}$$

tion or by general acid catalysis of the addition of hydroxide ion (equation 62) to avoid the formation of the alkoxide ion of the addi-

$$HO^-{\frown}\underset{R'S}{\overset{R}{\diagdown}}C{\xlongequal{}}O {\,}^{\bullet}H{-}\overset{+}{B} \quad \rightleftharpoons \quad H{-}O{-}\underset{\underset{\underset{R'}{|}}{\overset{|}{S}}}{\overset{\overset{R}{|}}{C}}{-}O{-}H{\frown}B \tag{62}$$

tion compound. According to the latter mechanism, the water reaction would represent hydronium ion catalysis of the attack of hydroxide ion and would require a rate constant of $6.6 \times 10^{11} \, M^{-2}$ sec^{-1}, which is large enough to effectively rule out this mechanism. Thus the mechanism of the hydration step appears to be that of equation 61 (or the corresponding concerted or one-encounter mechanism), as for the general base catalyzed hydration of carbonyl compounds.

The expulsion of the thiol anion in the breakdown of the addition intermediate of equation 59 is a simple base catalyzed reaction and corresponds to the reverse of the unassisted addition of the thiol anion to simple carbonyl compounds. The fact that the addition of thiol groups also occurs by a general acid catalyzed pathway at low pH values suggests that such a mechanism might become significant for the breakdown of the tetrahedral intermediate at low pH values. The observed rate constants of 0.076 and 0.043 min^{-1} for the hydrolysis of ethyl trifluorothiolacetate in 2 M and 6 M hydrochloric acid, respectively,[78] are 2.6 and 37 times larger than predicted by the rate law for hydrolysis in more dilute acid and the H_0 function,[79] which suggests that breakdown of the intermediate may also occur by a pH–independent or acid catalyzed mechanism.

The rate of breakdown of the anionic intermediate of equation 59 must be extremely fast. The rate constant for this reaction is given by equation 63, in which K_A is the equilibrium constant for

[79] M. A. Paul and F. A. Long, *Chem. Rev.* **57**, 1 (1957).

$$k_2 = \frac{k_{obs}(k_2/k_{-1} + [H^+])}{K_A K_B} = \frac{2.5 \times 10^{-3}}{K_A K_B} \qquad (63)$$

formation of the addition compound and K_B is the ionization constant of the intermediate. Since no evidence for the accumulation of the addition compound has been reported, K_A is probably less than 0.1.

$$K_A = \frac{\left[\begin{array}{c} >C<^{OH}_{SR} \end{array} \right]}{[\text{ester}][H_2O]} \qquad K_B = \frac{\left[\begin{array}{c} >C<^{O^-}_{SR} \end{array} \right] [H^+]}{\left[\begin{array}{c} >C<^{OH}_{SR} \end{array} \right]}$$

If K_B is taken as 10^{-10}, k_2 is larger than 2.5×10^8 sec^{-1}; smaller estimates for K_A and K_B would give an even larger number. If k_2 is this large for the addition intermediate formed from an ester with a strongly electron-withdrawing acyl group and a relatively basic thiol anion as the leaving group, the intermediate formed from other thiol esters will be even less stable and will break down even faster. Since the rate constant for the breakdown of the intermediate in the ethyl trifluorothiolacetate reaction is already close to the diffusion-controlled limit for the separation of the products of the reaction, a diffusion-controlled or proton transfer step, rather than a step in which bonds to carbon are made or broken, may become rate-determining in these reactions. The diffusion-controlled removal of a proton by hydroxide ion is the rate-determining step in the decomposition of hemithioacetals, a reaction which is analogous to the breakdown of the addition compound in thiol ester hydrolysis.[41]

The nature of the rate-determining step below pH 2 shows that the protonation and expulsion of a hydroxyl group from the addition intermediate occurs more readily than the protonation and expulsion of the thiol group. This is in accord with the relative rates of acid catalyzed breakdown of hemithioacetals and aldehyde hydrates. The change in rate-determining step occurs because above pH 2 the intermediate breaks down in a rapid base catalyzed reaction to expel the thiol anion more readily than hydroxide ion (20), which is also in accord with the behavior of the simple carbonyl

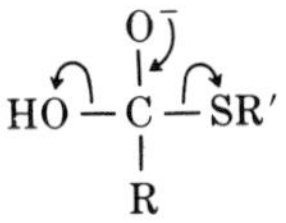

$$HO-\overset{\overset{O^-}{|}}{\underset{\underset{R}{|}}{C}}-SR'$$

20

adducts. The same conclusion with respect to the preferred mode of breakdown of an addition intermediate may be reached from the equilibrium constant and some estimated rate constants for the individual steps of the base catalyzed S to O transfer reaction of S-acetylmercaptoethanol.[80] The preferred modes of breakdown of the intermediate in thiol ester hydrolysis are summarized in Diagram 4. Note that expulsion of the thiol anion is preferred to expulsion

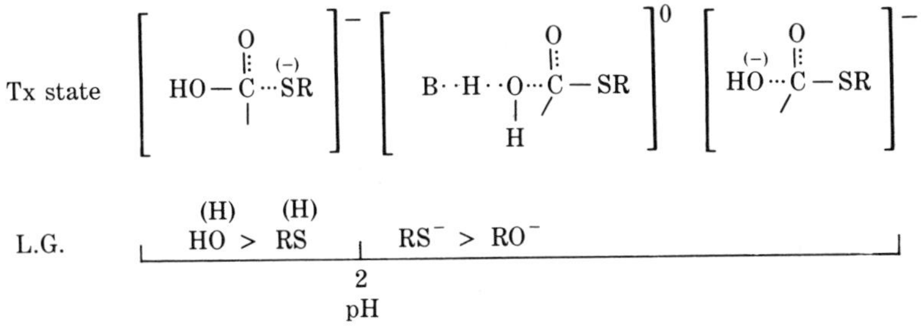

Tx state
$$\left[HO-\overset{\overset{O}{\|}}{\underset{|}{C}}\cdots\overset{(-)}{SR} \right]^{-} \left[B\cdots H\cdots O\cdots\overset{\overset{O}{\|}}{\underset{\underset{H}{|}}{C}}-SR \right]^{0} \left[\overset{(-)}{HO}\cdots\overset{\overset{O}{\|}}{C}-SR \right]^{-}$$

L.G.
$$\underset{\underset{pH}{2}}{\overset{(H)\quad(H)}{HO > RS \quad | \quad RS^- > RO^-}}$$

Diagram 4

of the hydroxyl group, by any mechanism, at all pH values above 2.0.

$$\overset{O}{\underset{\|}{}}$$
9. RCNR$_2'$ + HOR''

The most completely understood reaction of amides is the alkaline hydrolysis of anilides. The rate law for this reaction contains a term second order with respect to hydroxide ion.[81] Since it is unlikely that the attack of hydroxide ion could be catalyzed by hydroxide ion (equation 64), this term must represent a rate-determining

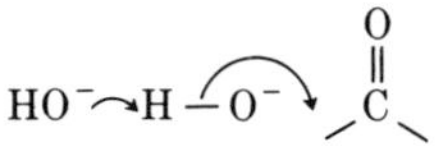

$$HO^-\frown H-O^-\searrow\overset{\overset{O}{\|}}{C}\diagdown \qquad (64)$$

[80] R. B. Martin and R. I. Hedrick *J. Am. Chem. Soc.* **84**, 106 (1962).
[81] S. S. Biechler and R. W. Taft, Jr., *J. Am. Chem. Soc.* **79**, 4927 (1957).

base catalyzed expulsion of aniline from an anionic tetrahedral addition intermediate, one possible mechanism for which is shown in equation 65. The hydrolysis of diacylamines (the nitrogen analog

$$ \text{HO}^- \underset{R}{\overset{O}{\underset{C}{\|}}}_{NR_2'} \;\rightleftharpoons\; B\frown H \frown O \overset{O^-}{\underset{R}{\underset{C}{\|}}} NR_2' \;\longrightarrow\; \overset{+}{B}H \quad O = C\underset{R}{\overset{O^-}{\diagdown}} {}^-NR_2' \tag{65} $$

of anhydrides) also exhibits a term second order with respect to hydroxide ion in the rate law and may be interpreted in the same manner.[82] It has been reported that the hydrolysis of anilides is subject to general base catalysis,[83–85] which suggests that the term in the rate law which is second order with respect to hydroxide ion may also represent general base catalysis. General base catalysis could occur according to the mechanism of equation 65 or according to the kinetically equivalent mechanism of equation 66. The latter

$$ \text{HO}^- \underset{R}{\overset{O}{\underset{C}{\|}}}_{NR_2'} \;\rightleftharpoons\; \text{HO}-\underset{R}{\overset{O^-}{\underset{C}{|}}}-NR_2' \;\rightleftharpoons\; {}^-O\overset{O}{\underset{R}{\underset{C}{|}}} \overset{H \overset{+}{B}}{NR_2} \;\longrightarrow\; O=C\underset{R}{\overset{O^-}{\diagdown}} $$

$$ HNR_2 + B \tag{66} $$

mechanism is more probable because it avoids the formation of the aniline anion (pK_a ca. 27),[86] which is so unstable that it almost certainly does not occur as a free intermediate in aqueous solution.

This is one of the few reactions in which the exchange of ^{18}O with the solvent occurs more rapidly than hydrolysis,[87] as would be expected if the breakdown of the tetrahedral addition intermediate to products is the rate-determining step. The mechanism is further supported by kinetic evidence for a change in rate-determining step with increasing hydroxide ion concentration.[83–85] As the hydroxide ion concentration is increased, the second step, which is

[82] M. T. Behme and E. H. Cordes, *J. Org. Chem.* **29**, 1255 (1964).

[83] P. M. Mader, *J. Am. Chem. Soc.* **87**, 3191 (1965).

[84] R. L. Schowen, H. Jayaraman, and L. Kershner, *J. Am. Chem. Soc.* **88**, 3373 (1966).

[85] S. O. Eriksson and C. Holst, *Acta Chem. Scand.* **20**, 1892 (1966); S. O. Eriksson and L. Bratt, *Ibid.* **21**, 1812 (1967).

[86] D. Dolman and R. Stewart, *Can. J. Chem.* **45**, 911 (1967).

[87] M. L. Bender and R. J. Thomas, *J. Am. Chem. Soc.* **83**, 4183 (1961).

second order with respect to hydroxide ion, becomes so fast that the first step, the first-order attack of hydroxide ion, becomes rate-determining and the observed rate also becomes first order with respect to hydroxide ion.

Hydrolysis also occurs in a reaction which is first order with respect to hydroxide ion under conditions in which breakdown of the intermediate is largely rate-determining. According to the mechanisms of equations 65 and 66 this term represents a "water reaction" in which water is the base which removes a proton from oxygen in the tetrahedral intermediate (equation 65) or the solvated proton donates a proton to the leaving aniline anion (equation 66). The effect of substituents in the aniline on the rate favors the second mechanism. The overall rate shows almost no sensitivity to substituents in the aniline group ($\rho = 0.1$), as might be expected if the favorable effect of electron-donating substituents on protonation of the nitrogen atom cancelled out the unfavorable effect of such substituents on the equilibrium concentration of addition intermediate and the leaving ability of the aniline.[87] The importance of this electron donation is further shown by the fact that electron-donating substituents in the aniline cause an increase in the ratio of hydrolysis to oxygen exchange ($\rho = -1$) by favoring the protonation and expulsion of aniline, rather than hydroxide ion, from the addition intermediate. The point is almost, but not quite, reached at which a change in rate-determining step with changing substituent should occur. At high concentrations of hydroxide ion the rate of expulsion of aniline by the pathway which is second order with respect to hydroxide ion becomes fast, so that the ratio of hydrolysis to exchange is increased.[87]

The preferred modes of breakdown of the tetrahedral intermediate in these reactions are summarized in Diagram 5.

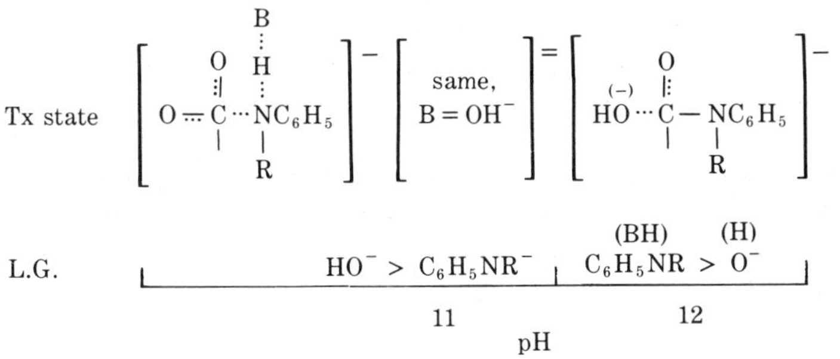

Diagram 5

The ratio of ^{18}O exchange to hydrolysis also decreases with increasing hydroxide ion concentration in the hydrolysis of benzamide. N-Methylbenzamide exhibits relatively less exchange than benzamide, and no exchange at all is observed with N,N-dimethylbenzamide.[88] One of several possible explanations for this behavior is that increasing substitution on the nitrogen atom leads to increased crowding in the tetrahedral intermediate, with a resulting increase in the tendency to expel amine (without exchange) rather than hydroxide ion (to give exchange). It is of interest that the ratio of exchange to hydrolysis is *increased* nearly twofold in deuterium oxide solution, compared with water, in spite of the requirement for proton transfer in order that exchange may take place. This may reflect a slower protonation and expulsion of the amine in deuterium oxide solution (equation 66). The overall rate of hydrolysis of benzamide, for which the amide expulsion step is largely rate-determining, is slower in deuterium oxide, whereas the hydrolysis of dimethylbenzamide, which shows no exchange, is slightly faster in deuterium oxide.[88]

The aminolysis of esters presents a more difficult mechanistic problem (equation 1), but this problem has been resolved, at least in its main features, by the use of (1) kinetic evidence for a change in rate-determining step, to demonstrate the existence of an intermediate and the charge of the transition state in different regions of pH and (2) identification of the rate-determining step, by generating this intermediate from the appropriate imidate and determining its preferred mode of breakdown to products at different pH values. From the effects of pH and catalysts on the partitioning of the tetrahedral intermediate which is formed in the hydrolysis of N-phenyliminolactones to the different possible products, for example, we can conclude that if the same intermediate is formed in the aminolysis of the lactone by aniline, the rate-determining step of aminolysis below pH 7 is the expulsion of alkoxide anion (equation 13, Fig. 13). At high pH the rate-determining step is the attack of aniline on the lactone, which is subject to concerted general acid-base catalysis. Although this aminolysis reaction has not been studied directly, the reverse reaction, the intramolecular alcoholysis of the anilide (equation 13 from right to left), has been examined and shows the change in rate-determining step with changing catalyst concentration that is predicted from the effects of catalysts on the products of imidate hydrolysis.[89]

[88] C. A. Bunton, B. Nayak, and C. O'Connor, *J. Org. Chem.* **33**, 572 (1968).

[89] B. A. Cunningham and G. L. Schmir, *J. Am. Chem. Soc.* **89**, 917 (1967).

The dependence on pH of the rate of intramolecular aminolysis of ethanolamine acetate shows that there is a change in rate-determining step at a pH of about 8 and, hence, an intermediate in the reaction.[90] Changes in the rate-determining step in the reaction of methyl formate with a number of amines show that intermediates are also formed in these intermolecular reactions. The nature of the rate-determining step may be diagnosed from the nature of the products obtained upon hydrolysis of the imidate 21, at different pH values.[91] The complete mechanism for these reactions is shown in equation 67, and a pH–rate curve for the reaction of methyl for-

(67)

[90] B. Hansen, *Acta Chem. Scand.* **17**, 1307 (1963).

[91] G. M. Blackburn and W. P. Jencks, *J. Am. Chem. Soc.* **90**, 2638 (1968).

mate with hydrazine, which serves to illustrate the most important pathways of the reaction, is shown in Fig. 17. At high pH the rate of the reaction is proportional to the concentration of ester and free amine and is independent of pH, according to the rate law of equation 68. Under these conditions the rate-determining step is the

$$v = k_1 [\,\rangle\!NH]\,[HCOOR]\tag{68}$$

attack of amine on the ester (k_1, equation 67), and the transition state has no net charge. (The rate of attack of certain amines shows a further increase in basic solution because of catalysis by hydroxide ion. This is a special case of general base catalysis of the attack step.) As the pH is lowered, the rate constants decrease

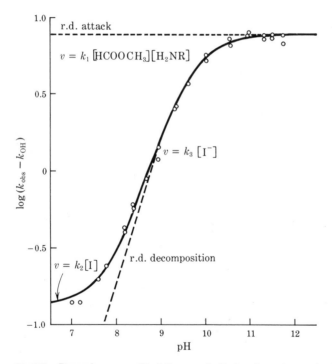

Fig 17. Dependence on pH of the pseudo first-order rate constants for the reaction of 0.2 M hydrazine as the free base with methyl formate at 25°, ionic strength 1.5. The solid line is calculated from the steady-state rate expression for this reaction.[91]

and become directly proportional to the hydroxide ion concentration. This represents a transition in rate-determining step to base cata- lyzed breakdown of the tetrahedral addition intermediate (k_3, equa- tion 67). In this region the transition state has a charge of -1, and the reaction follows the rate law of equation 69. As the pH is

$$v = k_3 \, [\text{I}^-] = k_3 \, \frac{k_1 K_{\text{I}}}{k_{-1} K_w} \, [\, >\!\text{NH}\,] \, [\,\text{NCOOR}\,] \, [\,\text{OH}^-\,] \tag{69}$$

decreased still further, the rate again levels off as a pH-indepen- dent breakdown of the intermediate becomes significant (k_2, equation 69). In this region the transition state is again neutral, and the reaction follows the rate law of equation 70. In intermediate re-

$$v = k_2 \, [\,\text{I}\,] = k_2 \, \frac{k_1}{k_{-1}} \, [\, >\!\text{NH}\,] \, [\,\text{HCOOR}\,] \tag{70}$$

gions of pH or for compounds in which the different regions are not well separated, the rate must be described by a steady-state rate equation. Other amines show similar behavior, although it is not possible for technical reasons to demonstrate all the possible types of transition states with each amine.

The assignment of these rate-determining steps to rate-deter- mining attack at high pH and to rate-determining breakdown at low pH is made possible by the fact that the imidate 21 breaks down to give amide and alcohol at high pH and to ester and amine at low pH. This shows which direction of breakdown has the low- est energy for the addition intermediate which is formed from the imidate or from morpholine and the ester at different pH values. The change in rate-determining step in the aminolysis of methyl formate by morpholine occurs at the same pH, approximately 7.6, as the change in product formation from the imidate. This assign- ment is further supported by earlier reports that N-substituted imidates undergo hydrolysis to esters in acid and to amides in base.[92, 93] As the amine becomes more basic, the pH for the transi- tion in rate-determining step increases.[91] This reflects the over- riding importance of amine basicity in determining the mode of breakdown of the addition intermediate: a more basic amine is

[92] A. Pinner, "Die Imidoäther und ihre Derivate," Berlin, 1892; R. Roger and D. G. Neilson, *Chem. Rev.* **61**, 179 (1961).

[93] D. F. Elliott, *Biochem. J.* **45**, 429 (1949); I. Brown and O. E. Edwards, *Can. J. Chem.* **43**, 1266 (1965); K. D. Berlin and M. A. R. Khayat, *Tetrahedron* **22**, 975 (1966).

protonated and expelled more easily, so that alkoxide expulsion is rate-determining over a larger range of pH than in a reaction of a less basic amine. (This trend cannot be extrapolated to the much bulkier aniline molecule, which is expelled in preference to alkoxide ion at pH values up to 7.)[13] The preferred pathways for breakdown of the tetrahedral intermediate and the mechanism of aminolysis of aliphatic esters are summarized by Diagram 6.

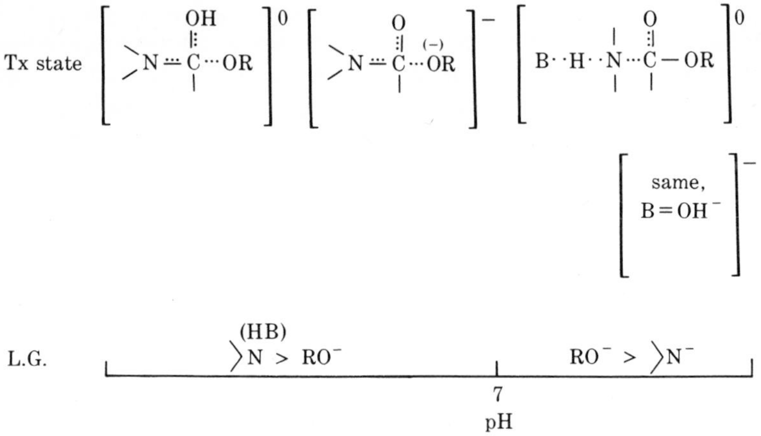

Diagram 6

The fact that ester aminolysis is subject to acid catalysis[94, 95] means that there is also a path for the formation and breakdown of the tetrahedral intermediate through a cationic transition state, shown by $k_1^+ - k_{-1}^+$ in equation 67 (no distinction between general and specific acid or base catalysis has been made in equation 67). All these pathways are significant for the breakdown of the inter-mediate formed from the imidate **22**.[60, 96] Above pH 7 this com-

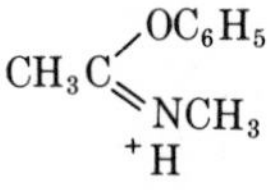

22

pound breaks down exclusively with phenol expulsion, presumably through a base catalyzed k_3 pathway. Between pH 2 and 5 it

[94] W. P. Jencks and J. Carriuolo, *J. Am. Chem. Soc.* **82**, 675 (1960).

[95] T. C. Bruice, A. Donzel, R. W. Huffman, and A. R. Butler, *J. Am. Chem. Soc.* **89**, 2106 (1967).

[96] M. Kandel and E. H. Cordes, *J. Org. Chem.* **32**, 3061 (1967).

breaks down predominantly with phenol expulsion through a neutral transition state (k_2), but also gives about 10% amine expulsion through a different neutral transition state (k_{-1}). The lower pH for the transition from the anionic to the neutral transition state, compared with the breakdown of **21**, and the predominance of the k_2 rather than the k_{-1} pathway in the neutral breakdown, reflect the fact that phenolate ion is a better leaving group than methoxide ion. Below pH 2, breakdown of **22** occurs predominantly to give ester through the acid catalyzed pathway and a cationic transition state ($k_1{}^+-k_{-1}^+$). The identification of these preferred modes of breakdown indicates that if a tetrahedral intermediate is formed, amine attack will be almost or entirely rate-determining for the aminolysis of phenyl acetate over the pH range in which aminolysis is ordinarily observed. However, it has not yet been demonstrated that a tetrahedral intermediate is formed in phenyl acetate aminolysis, and it is possible that the reaction occurs in a concerted manner. The fact that phenyl acetates react rapidly with tertiary amines means that removal of a proton from the nitrogen atom of an attacking amine is not a necessary step in these reactions. The preferred leaving groups for the hydrolysis of phenyl imidates as a function of pH are shown in Diagram 7. This scheme may also

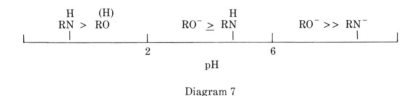

Diagram 7

apply to the aminolysis of phenyl esters, but this has not yet been established.

The increased tendency for oxygen rather than nitrogen expulsion from a tetrahedral addition intermediate as the oxygen becomes less basic is further illustrated by the breakdown of picrate and benzenesulfonate imidates to the corresponding amide[97] and the breakdown of the stable tetrahedral intermediate addition compound **23** with expulsion of phenol rather than of amine under both acidic and basic conditions.[4] However, the interpretation of the latter example is clouded by the fact that ionization of the oxygen atoms of **23** is not possible.

[97] P. Oxley and W. F. Short, *J. Chem. Soc.* **1948**, 1514.

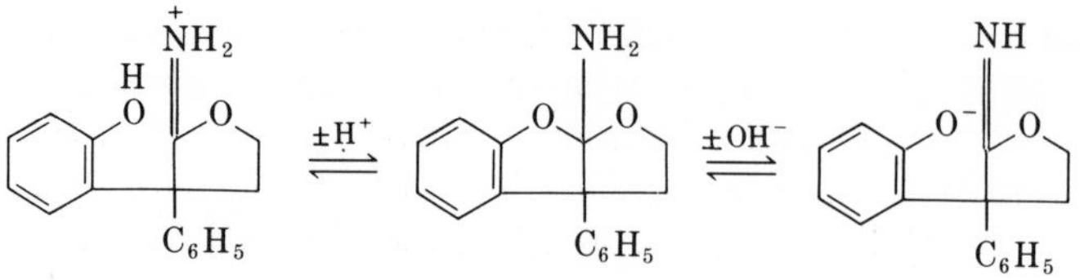

23

The rate constants for ester aminolysis under conditions in which the rate-determining step involves amine attack show a large dependence on the basicity of the amine, with a Brønsted slope β of approximately 0.8 for logarithmic plots of reaction rate against basicity.[60,98,99] A series of such curves for reactions with a series of phenyl acetates and related compounds is shown in Fig. 18. There is little dependence of this slope on the nature of the leaving group with leaving groups ranging from pK 10 to 2 and similar lines are followed for primary, secondary, and tertiary amines. However, the rate constants for the reactions of the most basic amines with the most reactive esters exhibit a rather sharp leveling off of the dependence on basicity. There is a similar large dependence of the rate constants on the pK of the leaving group of different esters (β about 1.0), with a break to a smaller dependence with the most reactive compounds. The large sensitivity to the basicity of the attacking and leaving groups means that there has been a considerable amount of change in the charge of the attacking and leaving atoms in the transition state. The transition state may be formulated as **24**, without specifying whether it breaks down to a

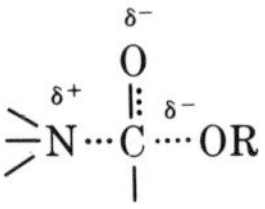

24

tetrahedral addition intermediate or directly to products in a concerted reaction.[60] This transition state is different from that for the attack of basic oxygen anions on esters, in which there is much less sensitivity to basicity and change in the charge of the attacking and leaving groups. For the strongly basic amines and reactive

[98] T. C. Bruice and R. Lapinski, *J. Am. Chem. Soc.* **80**, 2265 (1958).
[99] W. P. Jencks and J. Carriuolo, *J. Am. Chem. Soc.* **82**, 1778 (1960).

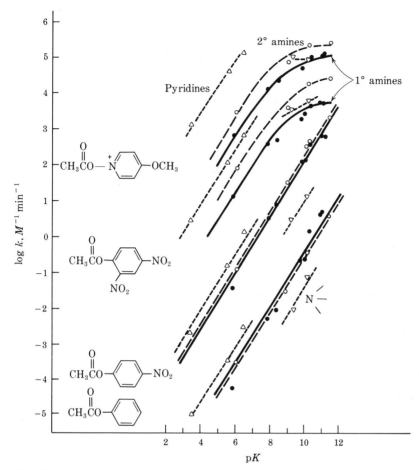

Fig 18. The rates of reactions of amines with substituted phenyl acetates and 1-acetoxy-4-methoxypyridinium ion as a function of the basicity of the nucleophile.[60]

esters there is a change in the nature of the transition state such that there is relatively little change in the charge of the attacking and leaving groups and a correspondingly small sensitivity to their basicity; however, it appears that the rate-determining step involves attack of the amine for both strongly and weakly basic amines.

The much larger sensitivity with respect to the leaving group of the attack step in aminolysis as compared with hydrolysis is also responsible for the fact that thiol esters, with their relatively good leaving group, are more reactive toward amines than oxygen esters, although the rates of alkaline hydrolysis of the two types of esters are very similar.[100,101]

The aminolysis of esters is subject to both general base and general acid catalysis.[94,102,103] The assignment of the rate-determining steps for the aminolysis of methyl formate[91] makes possible an assignment of the mechanism of catalysis because the kinetics of the catalyzed reactions have been measured under experimental conditions in which attack of amine on the ester is occurring in the rate-determining, catalyzed step. The mechanism for general base catalysis must be that shown in 25, since the alternative mechanism of 26 requires the formation of the unstable amine anion (pK_a about

$$
\begin{array}{cc}
\text{B} \to \text{H} - \underset{|}{\overset{|}{\text{N}}} \curvearrowright \underset{\text{OR}}{\overset{\text{O}}{\underset{\|}{\text{C}}}} & \overset{>}{\underset{>}{}}\text{N}^- \curvearrowright \underset{\text{OR}}{\overset{\text{O} \cdots \text{H}-\overset{+}{\text{B}}}{\underset{\|}{\text{C}}}} \\
\\
25 & 26
\end{array}
$$

30) in a prior equilibrium step, and such an unstable intermediate would have to react with the ester with a rate constant much faster than that of a diffusion-controlled reaction in order to account for the observed rate of aminolysis. The pH−independent and hydroxide ion catalyzed terms in the rate law for the attack step presumably represent general base catalysis by water and hydroxide ion, respectively. Concerted acid-base catalysis (27) provides additional stabili-

$$
\begin{array}{c}
\text{O} \\
\|\\
\text{O} - \text{P} - \text{O} \\
|\quad\quad| \\
\text{O}\quad\text{H} \\
\text{H}\quad\text{O} \\
|\quad\quad\| \\
- \text{N} \curvearrowright \text{C} - \text{OR} \\
|\quad\quad| \\
\\
27
\end{array}
$$

zation to the transition state for the attack step in some of these reactions.[13,91]

[100] K. A. Connors and M. L. Bender, *J. Org. Chem.* **26**, 2498 (1961).

[101] R. K. Chaturvedi, A. E. MacMahon, and G. L. Schmir, *J. Am. Chem. Soc.* **89**, 6984 (1967).

[102] J. F. Bunnett and G. T. Davis, *J. Am. Chem. Soc.* **82**, 665 (1960).

[103] T. L. Bruice and M. F. Mayahi, *J. Am. Chem. Soc.* **82**, 3067 (1960).

It is difficult to obtain a Brønsted slope for proton removal in general base catalyzed aminolysis because the fact that catalysis of these reactions is usually detected experimentally from the appearance of terms in the rate law which are second order with respect to the amine means that it is not possible to vary the catalyst and the nucleophile independently. However, Brønsted plots based on the water and amine catalyzed reactions give values of β which increase progressively with decreasing basicity of the amine from 0.19 for methylamine to 0.26 for glycine ethyl ester and 0.37 for hydroxylamine. Similarly, Brønsted plots based on the water and hydroxide ion catalyzed reactions give β values which increase with decreasing basicity of the secondary amine from 0.22 for piperidine to 0.27 with dimethylamine and 0.37 with morpholine.[104] These changes are in the expected direction for general base catalysis according to mechanism 25. The reaction of methoxyamine with p-nitrophenyl acetate is subject to general base catalysis by carboxylate ions, so that different catalysts can be examined with a single amine.[106] The value of β for catalysis of this reaction is 0.45.

General acid catalysis of the attack step may be formulated according to mechanisms 28 and 29; an alternative mechanism in

28   29

which a proton is donated to the alcoholic oxygen atom is a less probable alternative to 28. Mechanism 29 requires the formation of the unstable conjugate acid of the ester in a prior equilibrium step and can be ruled out because this intermediate would have to react with amine with a rate constant greater than that for a diffusion-controlled reaction in order to account for the observed rate of the overall reaction. For example, the general acid catalyzed hydrazinolysis of phenyl acetate would require a rate constant of 10^{15} M^{-2} sec^{-1} for this step, assuming a pK of -6 for the conjugate acid of the ester.[107]

[104] Calculated from the data of Jencks et al.[94, 105]

[105] W. P. Jencks and M. Gilchrist, *J. Am. Chem. Soc.* 88, 104 (1966).

[106] L. do Amaral, K. Koehler, D. Bartenbach, T. Pletcher, and E. H. Cordes, *J. Am. Chem. Soc.* 89, 3537 (1967).

[107] T. C. Bruice and S. J. Benkovic, *J. Am. Chem. Soc.* 86, 418 (1964).

The reaction of acetylimidazole with hydroxylic compounds, including water, alcohols, and hydroxamic acids, but not phosphate or carboxylate ions, is subject to general base catalysis.[108] The mechanism of this catalysis has not been established.

Breakdown of the tetrahedral intermediate takes place most rapidly through a hydroxide ion catalyzed reaction (for example, **30**).

$$
\begin{array}{c}
\overset{(-)}{O} \\
\|(-) \\
\text{>N}-\text{C}\cdots\text{OR} \\
| \\
H
\end{array}
$$

30

This step is also subject to general base catalysis, although catalysis is much less significant than for the attack step.[91] It is not yet possible to choose unequivocally between the minimal mechanisms **31** and **32** for this catalysis; one-encounter mechanisms are also possible.

$$
\begin{array}{cc}
\overset{(-)}{O} & O\cdots H\cdots B \\
\| & \|(-) \\
\text{>N}-\text{C}\cdots\text{O}\cdots\text{H}\cdots\text{B} & \text{>N}-\text{C}\cdots\text{OR} \\
|\ \ | & | \\
H\ R & H
\end{array}
$$

31   **32**

The hydroxide ion catalyzed decomposition may represent a special case of one of these mechanisms in which $B = OH^-$. A mechanism corresponding to **33** $(\overset{+}{BH} = HOH)$ presumably accounts for the

$$
\begin{array}{c}
\overset{(-)}{O} \\
\| \\
\overset{+}{\text{>N}}-\text{C}\cdots\text{O}\cdots\text{H}\cdots\overset{(+)}{\text{B}} \\
|\ \ | \\
H\ R
\end{array}
$$

33

reaction of tertiary amines with phenyl esters.

The hydrolysis of the conjugate acid of ethyl benzimidate and of an N-phenyliminolactone is subject to general base catalysis.[8,13] Since it is known that the attack of water is the rate-determining

[108] W. P. Jencks and J. Carriuolo, *J. Biol. Chem.* **234**, 1272, 1280 (1959).

step in N-phenyliminolactone hydrolysis and the substrate is protonated under the conditions in which catalysis is observed, the mechanism may be unambiguously assigned as shown in equation 71.

$$B\frown H\!-\!\overset{R'}{\underset{\overset{|}{O}}{\overset{|}{O}}}\!\!\diagdown C\!\equiv\!\overset{+}{N}\!\!\diagdown \;\rightleftharpoons\; B\!-\!\overset{+}{H}\,\overset{}{O}\!-\!\overset{|}{\underset{\overset{|}{R}}{C}}\!-\!\overset{|}{N}\!\!\diagdown$$

$$(71)$$

The reverse of this step provides a precedent for a mechanism of general acid catalyzed ester aminolysis, under conditions in which expulsion of the alcohol occurs in the rate-determining step. The mechanism is the same as for the attack and expulsion of water in simple carbonyl-group reactions.

$$\overset{O}{\overset{\|}{}}$$
10. RCSR AND H$_2$NR'

The intramolecular aminolysis of S-acetylmercaptoethylamine (equation 72, left to right) undergoes a change in rate-determining

$$(72)$$

step at about pH 3. Above this pH the reaction proceeds by pH-independent and base catalyzed pathways, whereas below pH 3 the reaction proceeds more slowly, at a rate which is again proportional to the concentration of hydroxide ion.[109] Above pH 3 there is also a nonlinear relationship of rate to buffer concentration, which is caused by a change from a rate-determining step that is subject to buffer catalysis to one which is not.[110] Thus, there must be at least two steps and one intermediate in this reaction.

[109] R. B. Martin and R. I. Hedrick, *J. Am. Chem. Soc.* **84**, 106 (1962).
[110] R. B. Martin, R. I. Hedrick , and A. Parcell, *J. Org. Chem.* **29**, 3197 (1964).

The reaction of thiol esters with hydroxylamine also undergoes a change in rate-determining step with changing hydrogen ion concentration and must involve an intermediate.[111] Both the formation and the breakdown of this intermediate are subject to general acid-base catalysis. The reaction of acetylimidazole with thiols and a number of other reactions of thiol esters with amines are also subject to general acid-base catalysis.[108, 112-114] Above neutrality the aminolysis of thiol esters follows the rate law of equation 73, so we

$$\text{Rate} = k_1 [\overset{\overset{\text{O}}{\|}}{\text{RCSR}'}][\text{RNH}_2] + k_2[\overset{\overset{\text{O}}{\|}}{\text{RCSR}'}][\text{RNH}_2][\text{B}] \tag{73}$$

· can conclude that the transition state for whatever step is rate-determining in this region has a net charge of zero (except in the special case when $B = OH^-$). At lower pH values the kinetics become more complicated.

The assignment of the nature of the rate-determining step may be made by determining the products of hydrolysis of an imidate which will generate the same tetrahedral addition intermediate that is formed in the aminolysis reaction, as described above for the aminolysis of oxygen esters. From early qualitative results it is known that thioimidates ordinarily break down to thiol esters in acid solution, but in some cases decomposition to amides is observed in alkali if elimination to the nitrile is not possible; for example, the hydrolysis of 34 occurs with expulsion of thiolate in alkali to give

$$\text{C}_6\text{H}_5\text{C}\underset{\overset{+}{\text{N}(\text{CH}_3)_2}}{\overset{\text{SCH}_3}{\diagup}}$$

34

N-dimethylbenzamide.[115] A detailed, quantitative study has shown that the transition region for several different imidates is near pH 2 to 3; below this pH the lowest-energy pathway for decomposition of the tetrahedral intermediate formed from the imidate involves

[111] T. C. Bruice and L. R. Fedor, *J. Am. Chem. Soc.* **86**, 4886 (1964).

[112] J. Th. G. Overbeek and V. V. Koningsberger, *Proc. Koninkl. Nedl. Akad. Wetenschap. (Amsterdam)* **B57**, 311 (1954).

[113] T. C. Bruice, J. J. Bruno, and W-S. Chou, *J. Am. Chem. Soc.* **85**, 1659 (1963).

[114] L. R. Fedor and T. C. Bruice, *J. Am. Chem. Soc.* **86**, 4117 (1964).

[115] R. Roger and D. G. Neilson, *Chem. Rev.* **61**, 179 (1961); R. N. Hurd and G. DeLamater, *Ibid.*, p. 45.

expulsion of amine to give the ester, whereas above pH 4 the low-est-energy pathway involves principally the expulsion of thiol to give amide.[101] In this region the expulsion of amine and the yield of ester are increased by general acid-base catalysts. The fact that the yield of products varies independently of the rate of imidate hydrolysis establishes that there must be an intermediate in the re-action.

These results suggest that in the high pH region the rate-determining step of the aminolysis reaction must involve the attack of amine and the formation of the intermediate, with a transition state of zero charge; once formed the intermediate breaks down rapidly with thiol expulsion, as shown by the products of imidate hydrolysis. At low pH the rate-determining step must be the de-composition of the tetrahedral intermediate with thiol expulsion, but the aminolysis reaction is not ordinarily studied in this region, in which the free amine is almost completely protonated. These conclusions may be described tentatively by the same scheme as for the aminolysis of oxygen esters, as shown in equation 67.

However, a serious inconsistency appears if this scheme is applied to the intramolecular aminolysis of S-acetylmercaptoethyl-amine.[80,110,116,117] The tetrahedral intermediate for this reaction is generated by the hydrolysis of 2-methyl-Δ^2-thiazoline (equation 72). This hydrolysis itself undergoes a change in rate-determining step with decreasing pH, which, in fact, represents the first reported example of the use of this kinetic criterion for the demonstration of the existence of an intermediate in a reaction at the acyl level of oxidation.[116] In acid solution the intermediate breaks down to ap-proximately equal amounts of thiol ester and amide, and these yields are independent of pH. The pH-dependence of the rate of the aminolysis reaction in this region corresponds to a neutral tran-sition state for the rate-determining step, and since both thiol and amine expulsion occur from the tetrahedral intermediate with ap-proximately equal facility, both steps of the S to N transfer must be partly rate-determining, with neutral transition states. The problem arises from the fact that there is a change in rate-determining step in the aminolysis reaction with increasing pH. This is accompanied by a decrease in the yield of thiol ester from hydrolysis of the thiazoline with increasing pH (this is not caused by a secondary transacylation reaction); i.e., there is a decrease in the rate of

[116] R. B. Martin, S. Lowey, E. L. Elson, and J. T. Edsall, *J. Am. Chem. Soc.* **81**, 5089 (1959).

[117] R. Barnett and W. P. Jencks, *J. Am. Chem. Soc.* **90**, 4199 (1968).

formation of the intermediate from the thiol ester, so that this step becomes rate-determining and the expulsion of thiol from the intermediate to give amide becomes relatively fast. This change in rate-determining step cannot be accounted for by a scheme such as that of equation 67 or 72, in which only the formation and breaking of bonds to carbon is rate-determining, because both of the pathways for breakdown of the intermediate involve transition states of the same charge and there is no reason that the rate should decrease below that expected for these steps as the pH is increased. The results demand that there be another step which becomes rate-determining with increasing pH, and this step must be a simple proton transfer step. The data may be explained by the scheme of equation 74, which includes such a step (k_A), that is, a proton

$$
\begin{array}{c}
S\diagdown\ \diagup NH^+ \\
\quad C \\
\quad | \\
k_{-T}[B]\ \Big\updownarrow\ \genfrac{}{}{0pt}{}{k_T[BH^+]}{\pm H_2O}
\end{array}
$$

$$
S\underset{O}{\diagdown}C\diagdown NH_2 \underset{k_{-2}}{\overset{k_2}{\rightleftharpoons}} S\underset{-O}{\diagdown}C\diagdown^+NH_2 \underset{k_{-A}[BH^+]}{\overset{k_A[BH^+]}{\rightleftharpoons}} S\underset{HO}{\diagdown}C\diagup NH \underset{k_{-N}}{\overset{k_N}{\rightleftharpoons}} HS\diagdown\ \diagup NH\ \ -C\diagdown_O
$$

$$(74)$$

transfer to the initially formed dipolar addition intermediate, followed by rapid proton loss from the nitrogen atom and expulsion of thiol. The two proton transfer steps may occur through a one-encounter mechanism or through a concerted reaction with bifunctional catalysis, but an acid catalyst is required to initate the process. The conclusion that proton transfer becomes rate-determining is supported by the fact that the value of α for general acid catalysis by carboxylic acids and phosphate monoanion according to the mechanism of equation 74 is 0.03. This value of α is equal, within experimental error, to the value of 0 which is expected for a simple diffusion-controlled proton transfer reaction.[117,118] Catalysis is detectable because the catalytic constant for the water reaction (the rate-determining step at high pH values) falls below the Brønsted line, as would be expected if proton transfer from this weak acid occurred with a rate constant smaller than the diffusion-controlled limit. Estimates of the absolute values of the rate constants for the

[118] M. Eigen, *Angew. Chem. Intern. Ed.* **3**, 1 (1964).

individual steps of this scheme are within reasonable limits, assuming a value of about 10^{10} M^{-1} sec^{-1} for k_A. It is possible that the general acid catalyzed methoxyaminolysis of phenyl acetate, which also exhibits an α value near zero for catalysis by carboxylic acids,[106] occurs with a similar rate-determining proton transfer step.

The important conclusion is that it is possible for general acid-base catalysis to involve only a simple diffusion-controlled proton transfer and that a change in rate-determining step may be brought about by a limiting rate for such proton transfer even in reactions with a slow overall rate. In this reaction the addition of amine to the thiol ester gives a dipolar intermediate which immediately reverts to starting material unless it is trapped by the addition of a proton to the oxygen anion to remove the driving force for amine expulsion.

The decrease in the yield of thiol ester from thiazoline hydrolysis with increasing pH is a consequence of the cationic transition state which is required for amine expulsion under conditions in which the transfer of a proton to the dipolar addition intermediate is rate-determining. A similar mechanism provides a reasonable, but unproved, explanation for the change in product ratio with pH in the hydrolysis of noncyclic imidates.

The first step of thiazoline hydrolysis (k_{-T}, equation 74) is subject to general base catalysis. Since thiazoline is protonated in the region in which catalysis is observed, the mechanism may be assigned unambiguously, as shown in equation 75. This is the same mecha-

$$B{\frown}H-\underset{\underset{R}{\overset{|}{\underset{H}{\overset{|}{O}}}}}{O}\quad \overset{\frown}{>}C\overset{\frown}{=}\overset{+}{NH} \;\rightleftharpoons\; \overset{+\frown}{B}H\overset{\frown}{O}\underset{\underset{SR}{\overset{|}{\underset{H}{\overset{|}{C}}}}}{-}\overset{|}{C}\overset{\frown}{-}NH \tag{75}$$

nism as for the hydration of imines and imidates.

The mechanisms of this class of reactions may be imperfectly summarized by Diagram 8; the change in the leaving group with

$$
\left[\underset{\diagup}{\overset{\diagdown}{N}}\cdots\underset{|}{\overset{\overset{O}{\|}}{C}}-SR\right]^{0}
$$

$$
\left[-\underset{|}{\overset{\overset{OH}{\|}}{N}}\overset{\cdots}{=}\underset{|}{C}\cdots SR\right]^{0}
\quad
\left[\underset{\diagup}{\overset{\diagdown}{\overset{+}{N}}}-\underset{|}{\overset{\overset{\overset{+}{BH}\cdots}{O^{-}}}{C}}-SR\right]^{+}
\quad
\left[\begin{array}{c}\text{same,}\\ B=OH^{-}\end{array}\right]^{0}
$$

$$\underbrace{\overset{(H)}{R_2N \geq RS^-}}_{} \quad | \quad \underbrace{RS^- > R_2N^-}_{}$$

3

pH

Diagram 8

changing pH is apparently the result of a rate-determining proton transfer step, at least in the intramolecular reactions.

11. $\overset{O}{\underset{\parallel}{R}}$CNHR' AND H$_2$NR''

The reaction of formamide with hydroxylamine to give formohydroxamic acid is subject to general acid catalysis by hydroxylammonium ion. There is a change in rate-determining step with increasing catalyst concentration at constant pH, which is evidence for the formation of an intermediate in the reaction (Sec. A, Part 3, equation 76). Both the formation and the breakdown of the intermediate are

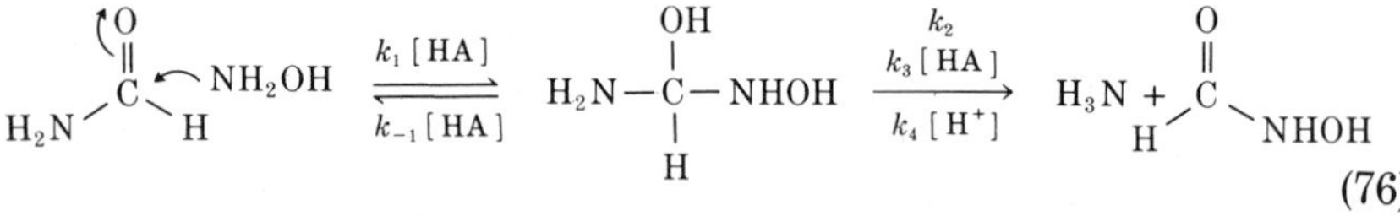

$$\underset{H_2N}{\overset{O}{\underset{\diagup}{\overset{\parallel}{C}}}}\diagdown_H \overset{}{\frown} NH_2OH \underset{k_{-1}[HA]}{\overset{k_1[HA]}{\rightleftharpoons}} H_2N-\underset{\underset{H}{|}}{\overset{\overset{OH}{|}}{C}}-NHOH \underset{k_4[H^+]}{\overset{k_2}{\underset{k_3[HA]}{\longrightarrow}}} H_3N + \underset{H}{\overset{O}{\underset{\diagup}{\overset{\parallel}{C}}}}\diagdown_{NHOH}$$

(76)

subject to catalysis, and the change in rate-determining step occurs because one step also occurs with a significant water reaction; i.e., it has a smaller value of α for general acid catalysis. The nature of the rate-determining step of this reaction at different catalyst concentrations is not established, but it can be argued from the behavior of analogous reactions and structure-reactivity correlations that the mechanism shown in equation 76 is more probable than the inverse assignment, in which the decomposition step is rate-determining at low, and the attack step at high, catalyst concentrations. The expulsion of nitrogen almost always requires addition of a proton, so that the leaving group is the free amine rather than the unstable amine anion. Because of this requirement, the basicity of nitrogen is generally of even greater importance than the leaving ability of the protonated nitrogen atom in determining the leaving ability of amines. For example, the hydrolysis of 5-10-methenyltetrahydrofolic acid takes place with the expulsion of the more basic N^5 nitrogen atom to give the N^{10} formyl compound as the product.[119] It

[119] D. R. Robinson and W. P. Jencks, *J. Am. Chem. Soc.* **89**, 7088, 7098 (1967).

might, therefore, be expected that the addition intermediate of equation 65 will break down preferentially to expel ammonia, so that the rate-determining step at low catalyst concentrations would be the general acid catalyzed attack of hydroxylamine. As the catalyst concentration is increased, the rate-determining step would then change to the expulsion of ammonia. For the mechanism of catalysis shown in equation 77, this assignment means that the attack and

$$\tag{77}$$

expulsion of the weakly basic hydroxylamine molecule occurs with a large α value (or smaller β value for the reverse reaction) than the attack and expulsion of ammonia (for which there is a significant water catalyzed reaction), as would be expected from structure-reactivity correlations. The alternative mechanism of catalysis shown in equation 78 is improbable because there is no general acid-

$$\tag{78}$$

base catalysis of the attack of hydroxylamine on ethyl benzimidate (equation 79), which is a model for this mechanism.[8]

$$\tag{79}$$

General acid-base catalysis is important for the reaction of hydroxylamine with esters and amides, whereas it is of little importance for the addition of hydroxylamine to aldehydes and ketones. The acyl-group reactions are more difficult because a large part of the resonance stabilization of the starting material must be destroyed in order to reach the transition state. Evidently general acid and base catalysis can provide a larger free energy of stabilization for these higher-energy transition states than for those of the simpler carbonyl-group reactions.

The rapid reactions of acetylimidazole and acetylimidazolium ion with amines are subject to general base catalysis,[108] but the mechanism of this catalysis has not been established.

The aminolysis of imido esters is a related reaction which proceeds through an addition intermediate with the same structure as that for the amide aminolysis, except that the formation of an oxygen anion is not possible in the case of the imidate. The change in rate-determining step and the partitioning of the addition intermediate in this reaction at different pH values have been discussed in Sec. A, Part 2, and it has just been pointed out that the attack of amine on the imido ester cation occurs without general acid or base catalysis. There is no detectable general acid or base catalysis of amidine formation from the intermediate obtained with strongly basic amines, but general base catalysis of the breakdown of the intermediate formed from the weaker bases hydroxylamine, methoxyamine, and semicarbazide is significant and follows the rate law of equation 80. This catalysis could occur by the kinetically equiva-

$$\text{Rate} = k[\text{imidate} \cdot \text{H}^+][\text{RNH}_2][\text{B}] \tag{80}$$

lent mechanisms of equations 81, 82, and 83. The mechanism of

$$\tag{81}$$

$$\tag{82}$$

$$\tag{83}$$

equation 81 is improbable because catalysis is observed under conditions in which an appreciable fraction of the intermediate must already be in the form of the free base, so that little is to be gained by proton removal, and the reverse reaction (e.g., hydrolysis) would require the addition of a proton to a cationic amidine. The mechanism of equation 82 is improbable because in the reverse reaction it requires the donation of a proton to amidine free base under experimental conditions in which the amidine is already protonated. The mechanism of equation 83, therefore, is the most likely, although it has not been rigorously proved to be correct. This mechanism is in accord with what would be expected from structure-reactivity relationships in that strongly basic amines can expel alkoxide ion without help from a catalyst (equation 84), whereas the more weakly

$$\text{(84)}$$

basic amines require the help of a general acid catalyst for alcohol expulsion. This is the same situation as is found for the dehydration step in simple carbonyl-group reactions, in which strongly basic amines can expel hydroxide ion directly, while for weakly basic amines the expulsion occurs predominantly with acid catalysis according to a mechanism (equation 17) analogous to that of equation 83.

The formation of a kinetically significant intermediate in formamidine hydrolysis is shown by the facts (1) that the hydrolysis of diphenylimidazolinium chloride (35) is second order with respect to

35

base, as is the case for a number of other hydrolysis reactions in which the expulsion of a poor leaving group from an addition intermediate is the rate-determining step, and (2) that the hydrolysis of methenyltetrahydrofolic acid shows a decrease in catalytic rate constant with increasing catalyst concentration, which is indicative of a change in rate-determining step.[119] The rate law for the former reaction is shown in equation 85, and the mechanism in equation 86. There is no evidence of a change in rate-determining step

$$\text{Rate} = k_1[S^+][OH^-][BH^+] + k_2[S^+][OH^-][B] \qquad (85)$$

$$\text{(86)}$$

with changing pH, so that breakdown of the intermediate to products must be rate-determining and the intermediate must decompose preferentially to expel hydroxide ion or water rather than amine or amine anion over the entire range of pH. This is in contrast to the situation with the similar intermediate in imidate aminolysis, in which the more basic nitrogen atom is protonated and expelled preferentially in acid solution. The trend toward lower pH values for the change in rate-determining step with less basic amines is already noticeable in the imido ester reactions with hydroxylamine and semicarbazide; in the diphenylformamidinium ion both nitrogen atoms are weakly basic, and the change in rate-determining step does not occur in the readily accessible pH range.

At low buffer concentrations the hydrolysis of 5-10-methenyl-tetrahydrofolic acid follows the same rate law as that of **35** and presumably has the same rate-determining step. As the buffer concentration is increased, there is a change to a new rate-determining step which is predominantly hydroxide ion catalyzed and for which buffer catalysis is less significant (β is larger). This step presumably represents rate-determining attack of hydroxide ion or water on the formamidinium ring (k_1', equation 86). This step is subject to general base catalysis, and the fact that the substrate is already cationic permits an unambiguous assignment of the mechanism, as shown in equation 87. This mechanism is the same as that

$$\tag{87}$$

for the second step of the aminolysis of imido esters (equation 83) and provides further support for the assignment of mechanism in that reaction.

The general base catalyzed breakdown of the addition intermediate in formamidinium hydrolysis could occur by the mechanisms of equations 88 and 89 or by a concerted or "one-encounter" mechanism, in which both types of catalysis occur (e.g., equation 90).

$$\tag{88}$$

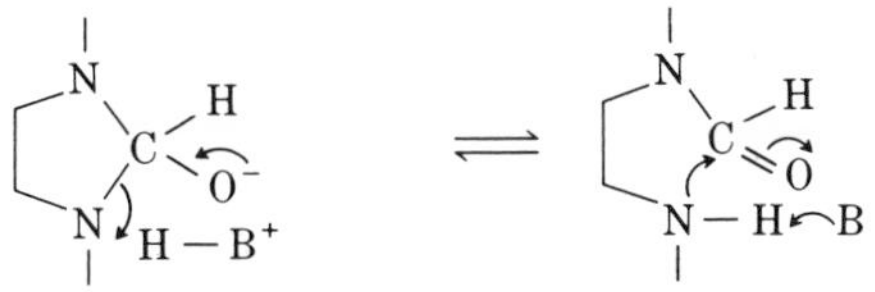

(89)

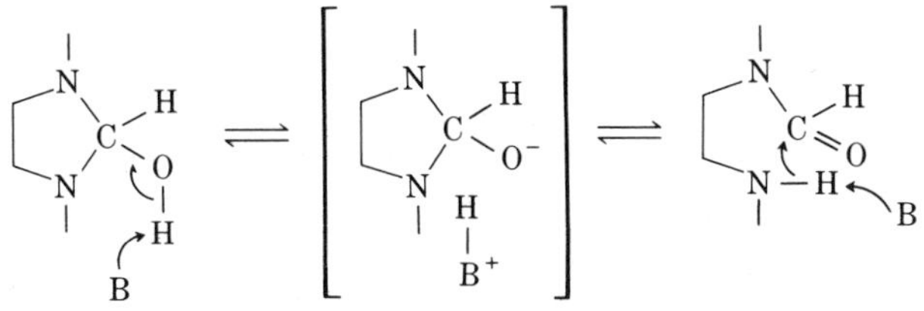

(90)

Mechanism 88 may be ruled out because it requires the formation of an aniline anion, which is too unstable an intermediate to permit the reaction to occur with the observed free energy of activation.[119] The enhanced catalytic activity of the bicarbonate ion and of phosphate dianion compared with methyl phosphate dianion suggests that bifunctional acid-base catalysis is slightly more efficient than monofunctional catalysis in these reactions. The mechanism might be regarded as analogous to that of equation 89 but with a small additional stabilization of the transition state by hydrogen bonding to the acidic group of a bifunctional catalyst (36).

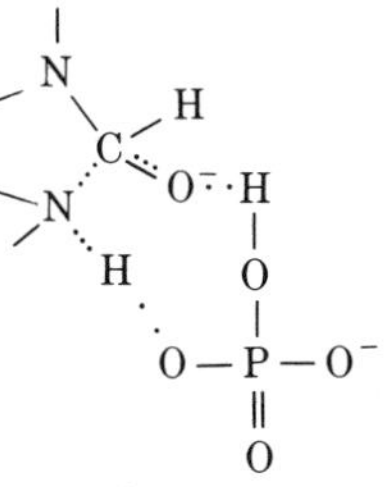

36

The general acid catalyzed breakdown of the intermediate may occur according to the mechanisms of equations 91 or 92. If this

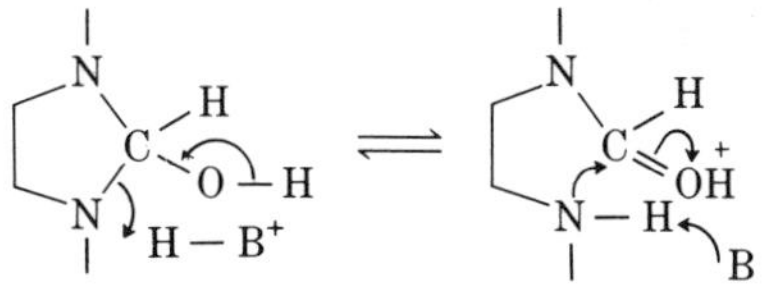

(91)

$$(92)$$

reaction is formulated as general base catalysis of the attack of an amine on a protonated amide (equation 91 in reverse) it exhibits a β value of 0.44. It is unreasonable that the value of β for attack on a protonated amide should be smaller than that for attack on a free amide, which occurs by the analogous mechanism of equation 89 with a β value of 0.26. This supports the mechanism of equation 92, which is the mechanism for other reactions in which an amine attacks the carbonyl group. This mechanism is further supported by the fact that the attack of amines on imido esters occurs by the mechanism of equation 91, with an alkyl group substituted for the proton of the hydroxyl group, but does not exhibit general acid-base catalysis; if the decomposition of the tetrahedral intermediate in amidinium hydrolysis occurred by the same mechanism, it should not show general acid-base catalysis either.

12. RCC $\stackrel{\nearrow}{\underset{\searrow}{}}$ AND HOR'

The hydrolysis of the acetyl group of diethyl acetylmalonate and diethyl acetylethylmalonate undergoes a change in rate-determining step with changing pH and with changing buffer concentration at constant pH, which indicates that an intermediate is formed in the reaction (equation 93).[120] The step which is rate-determining above

$$(93)$$

pH 5 is subject to general acid-base catalysis. Although the kinetic data alone do not permit assignment of the nature of the rate-determining steps at different pH values, an assignment of the rate-determining step at low pH to carbon-carbon bond cleavage and that at high pH to hydration of the carbonyl group is made possible by a comparison of the absolute values of the rate constants in the different pH regions to those of reactions of known mechanism and by

---

[120] G. E. Lienhard and W. P. Jencks, *J. Am. Chem. Soc.* 87, 3855 (1965).

the fact that the hydration of carbonyl compounds is known to be subject to general acid-base catalysis. The intermediate expels water preferentially in the low pH region and expels the carbon leaving group preferentially in the high pH region, as summarized in Diagram 9. The hydrolysis of acyl cyanides, RCOCN, occurs

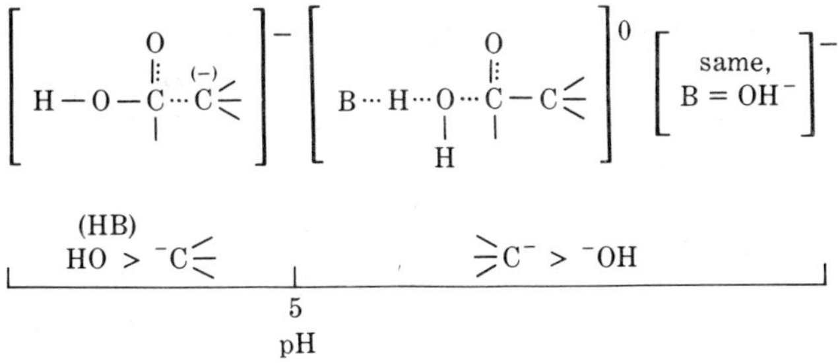

Diagram 9

with the same kinetic characteristics and mechanism.[121]

In the hydrolysis of the acetylthiazolium ion **37** the two steps

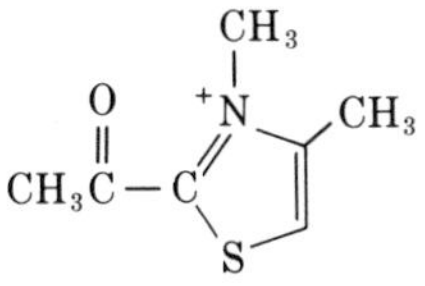

37

of the reaction may be followed directly because the intermediate addition compound accumulates to a significant extent. The hydration step occurs with catalysis by hydroxide ion, water, and general bases, and the breakdown step occurs only through a specific base catalyzed mechanism. In this reaction the rate of the breakdown step is always slower than that of the hydration step, so that there is no change in rate-determining step with changing pH.[122]

The detailed mechanism of the hydration step of these reactions is presumably the same as that of other hydration reactions of ketones. The expulsion of the carbanion from an anionic intermediate occurs without general acid-base catalysis and may be formulated as shown in equation 94. The mechanism of the pH–in-

[121] F. Hibbert and D. P. N. Satchell, *J. Chem. Soc.* **1967B**, 653.

[122] G. E. Lienhard, *J. Am. Chem. Soc.* **88**, 5642 (1966).

$$-O-\overset{\underset{|}{OR}}{C}-\overset{|}{C}- \;\; \rightleftharpoons \;\; O=\overset{\underset{|}{OR}}{C}-C\overset{\angle}{\;} \tag{94}$$

dependent expulsion of the carbon leaving group is not known.

As might be expected, a change in the nature of the carbon leaving group changes the nature of the rate-determining step as a function of pH. The alkaline hydrolysis of acetylacetone,[123] 2,6-dihalobenzaldehydes,[124] and chloral hydrate[125] occurs with terms second order with respect to base concentration, which means that in the hydrolysis of these compounds with relatively poor leaving groups the breakdown of the addition intermediate is rate-determining at alkaline pH and the driving force of an actual (equation 95) or potential (equation 96) dianion is required to force the expul-

$$-O-\overset{\underset{|}{O^-}}{C}-\overset{|}{C}- \;\; \longrightarrow \;\; O=\overset{\underset{|}{O^-}}{C} \quad {}^-C\overset{\angle}{\;} \tag{95}$$

$$B{\frown}H-O-\overset{\underset{|}{O^-}}{C}-\overset{|}{C}- \;\; \rightleftharpoons \;\; B\overset{+}{H} \quad O=\overset{\underset{|}{O^-}}{C} \quad {}^-C\overset{\angle}{\;} \quad \text{or} \quad {}^-O-\overset{\underset{|}{O^-}}{C}-\overset{|}{C}-\overset{|}{C}=X \; \overset{+}{H}B$$

$$\downarrow$$

$$O=\overset{\underset{|}{{}^-O}}{C} \quad \overset{|}{C}=\overset{|}{C}-XH + B \tag{96}$$

sion of the carbanion. The hydrolysis of 2-nitroacetophenone, nitroacetone, and thenoyltrifluoroacetone, which have better leaving groups, occurs with a change in rate-determining step with changing pH which is similar to that in the acetylmalonate series.[126]

[123] R. G. Pearson and E. A. Mayerle, J. Am. Chem. Soc. 73, 926 (1951).

[124] J. F. Bunnett, J. H. Miles, and K. V. Nahabedian, J. Am. Chem. Soc. 83, 2512 (1961).

[125] E. Pfeil, H. Stache, and F. Lömker, Ann. Chem. 623, 74 (1959).

[126] R. G. Pearson, D. H. Anderson, and L. L. Alt, J. Am. Chem. Soc. 77, 527 (1955); E. H. Cook and R. W. Taft, Jr., Ibid. 74, 6103 (1952).

13. $RCC \underset{\diagdown}{\overset{\diagup}{\underset{\parallel}{\overset{O}{}}}}$ AND HSR'

The ratio of the rate constants for the attack of thiol anion and of hydroxide ion, k_{RS^-}/k_{OH^-}, is some three orders of magnitude smaller for reactions with the acetyl group of diethyl acetylmalonate than for the reactions with p-nitrophenyl acetate or acetylimidazolium ion, in which the attack of both nucleophiles on the acyl group is almost certainly rate-determining.[127] Since it is known that the attack of hydroxide ion is the rate-determining step in the alkaline hydrolysis of diethyl acetylmalonate,[120] the low reactivity of thiol anion with this compound is probably caused by a change in rate-determining step to breakdown of the addition intermediate 38, which expels thiol anion (pK 9.95) more easily than diethyl malonate anion

$$\text{RSH} \qquad\qquad\qquad\qquad\qquad \text{HC} \underset{\diagup}{\overset{\diagdown}{}} \qquad (97)$$

(pK 15.2, equation 97). According to microscopic reversibility, the rate-determining step in the reverse direction must then be the attack of carbanion on the thiol ester. This situation is directly observable in the reaction of thiols with acetylthiazolium ion, in which the formation of the thiol addition compound occurs readily but breakdown to the thiol ester does not occur in aqueous solution. Evidently the additional driving force provided by the free electron pair of a second hydroxyl group is required for the expulsion of the carbon leaving group, since hydrolysis of the oxygen addition compound occurs readily. It is difficult to donate electrons from sulfur to form a partial double bond to carbon, so that the sulfur addition compound breaks down to expel thiol rather than the carbon leaving group.[122] Presumably with more acidic carbon compounds there will be a change in rate-determining step, and the attack and departure of the thiol anion will become rate-determining, but it is not known at what point this occurs. There is no evidence for general base catalysis of these reactions (under conditions in which the ionization of the carbon acid is not rate determining), and it is probable that they involve unassisted reactions of the free anions of the carbon compound and the thiol.

[127] G. E. Lienhard and W. P. Jencks, *J. Am. Chem. Soc.* 87, 3863 (1965).

SUMMARY OF MECHANISMS

The tabulation is divided into two parts: reactions in which the carbonyl group $>\!C = O$ is the immediate product or reactant and those in which the imine group $>\!C = N\!\!-$ is the immediate product or reactant. Two-step reactions often include one step in each of these categories. An "uncatalyzed" reaction may be one in which any necessary proton transfers take place in fast steps before or after the transition state (specific acid or base catalysis) or one in which true general acid or base catalysis occurs, but the value of α or β is too close to 0 or 1.0 to permit its detection. The abbreviations GAC and GBC are used for general acid catalysis and general base catalysis, respectively. The order of these terms corresponds to the forward and reverse directions of the indicated reaction; i.e., general acid catalysis in the forward direction generally requires general base catalysis in the reverse direction of the same reaction. Rapid equilibrium proton transfer steps (specific acid or base catalysis) are omitted. In some cases concerted or "one-encounter" mechanisms are also possible. The mechanisms of catalysis shown below are those which are thought to provide the principal stabilization of the transition state.

1. $>\!C = O$	Carbonyl derivatives	Acyl derivatives
"Uncatalyzed" ($\alpha = 0$, $\beta = 1.0$) 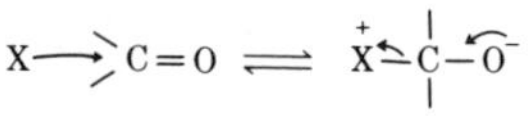 $X\!\longrightarrow\!>\!C = O \; \rightleftharpoons \; X\overset{+}{\frown}\overset{\shortmid}{C}\!-\!O^-$	Aliphatic amines Carbanions Sulfite Basic thiol anions Alkoxide and hydroxide ions Hydroperoxide anion	Alkoxide or hydroxide: esters thiol esters anilides Thiol anion: esters thiazoline hydrolysis thiol ester aminolysis acetylmalonates Carbanions: acids thiol esters
GAC-GBC 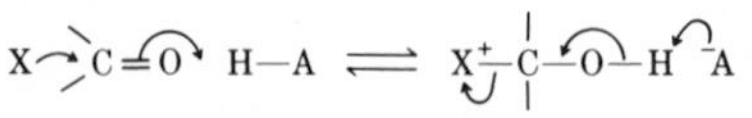 $X\!\frown\!C\!\stackrel{\frown}{=}\!O\!\cdot H\!-\!A \; \rightleftharpoons \; X\overset{+}{\frown}\overset{\shortmid}{C}\!-\!O\!\cdot\!H\!\frown\!A$	Weakly basic amines Free thiols Weakly basic thiol anions ROH ROOH (?)	Hydroxylamine-amides Amines-esters and thiol esters Amidine hydrolysis

GBC-GAC

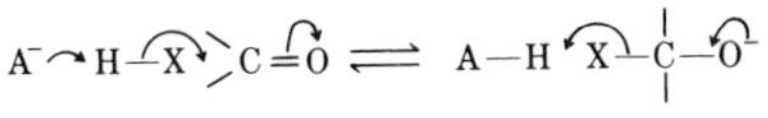

$$A^- \frown H \!\!-\!\! \widehat{X} \diagdown C =\!\! O \;\rightleftharpoons\; A\!\!-\!\!H \; \widehat{X}\!\!-\!\!\underset{|}{\overset{|}{C}}\!\!-\!\!O^-$$

ROH
ROOH
Amides

ROH – thiol esters
Amines – esters
ROH – ester (probable)
ROH – amides (?)
Amine – anilide
  (formamidine
  hydrolysis)

Concerted

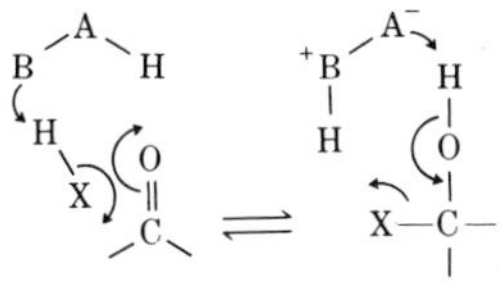

Aniline–lactone
Aniline–formanilide
  (probable in methenyl-
  tetrahydrofolate
  hydrolysis)
Anilide hydrolysis

"Uncatalyzed" ($\beta = 0$, $\alpha = 1.0$)

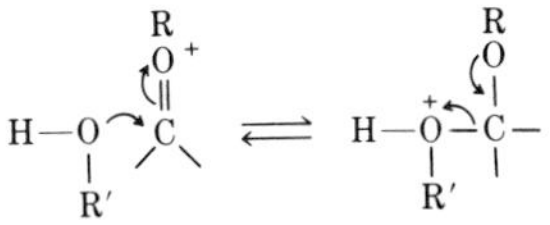

Ketal and acetal
hydrolysis

GBC-GAC

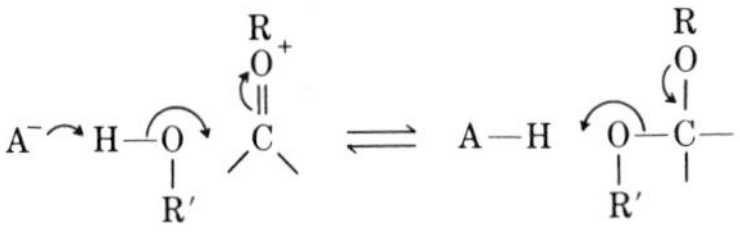

Ortho esters
  (large α)

Uncatalyzed

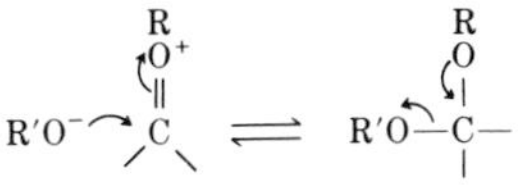

$R'O^-$ = carboxylate

GAC (kinetically GBC)

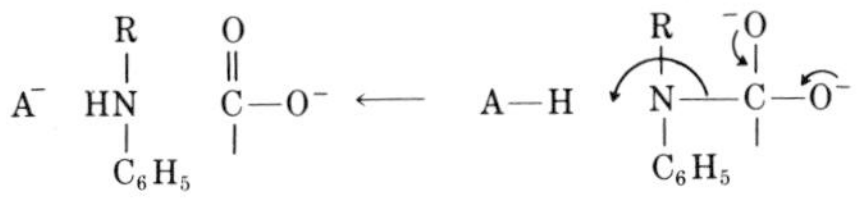

Hydrolysis of anilides

2. $\ce{>C=N-}$	Carbonyl derivatives	Acyl derivatives

"Uncatalyzed" ($\alpha = 1$ for free imine)

$X \rightharpoonup \ce{>C=\overset{+}{N}<}$

$\Updownarrow$

$\ce{^+X-\overset{|}{C}-N<}$

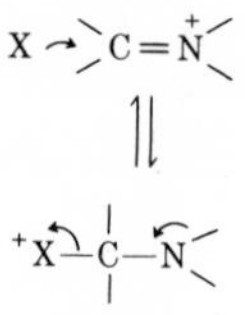	Alkoxide and hydroxide	Alkoxide expulsion in the reaction of imido esters with basic amines Amine attack–imidates Hydroxide attack–imidates

Uncatalyzed

$X \rightharpoonup \ce{>C=N-}$

$\Updownarrow$

$\ce{^+X-\overset{|}{C}-N-}$

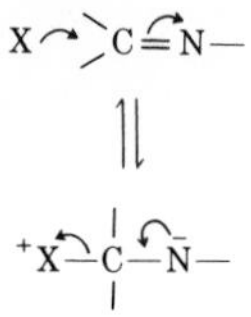	Imines and BH_4^- (probably) OH^- + benzylidene anilines, oximes (?)	

GAC-GBC

$X \rightharpoonup \ce{>C=N<} \quad H-A$

$\Updownarrow$

$\ce{^+X-\overset{|}{C}-\overset{|}{N}-H} \quad A$

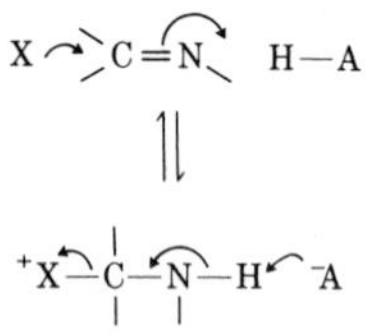	Thiosemicarbazones	

GBC-GAC

$A \rightharpoonup H - X \quad \ce{>C=\overset{+}{N}<}$

$\Updownarrow$

$A-H \quad X-\ce{\overset{|}{C}-N<}$

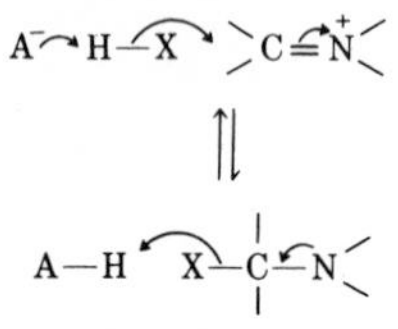	ROH Amines(?)	Alcohol expulsion in the reaction of imido esters with weakly basic amines ROH–amidinium ions ROH–imidates

11
Practical Kinetics

Kinetics may be approached either as a discipline unto itself or as a tool for the elucidation of reaction mechanism. The purpose of this chapter is to describe some elementary kinetic techniques and interpretations which are useful in the diagnosis of reaction mechanism. The author shares the healthy distrust of many students for proofs of reaction mechanism based on complicated kinetic equations which are difficult to understand in a concrete manner as a reflection of the observed behavior of a reaction. In fact, he has followed a rule of not finally accepting kinetic evidence for a proposed reaction mechanism unless he (1) can clearly see the relationship of the experimental observations to their kinetic description and presentation and (2) can understand the mechanistic significance of a particular type of kinetic behavior or equation in an intuitive, nonmathematical way. The consequences of this philosophy over a period of years have been that a few significant kinetic demonstrations of reaction mechanisms have not been accepted as soon as they deserved, but a far larger number, which later turned out to be incorrect, have been rightfully regarded with distrust because they failed to meet these criteria.

It is impossible to emphasize too strongly to the beginning experimentalist in this field the importance of obtaining and plotting data in such a way that the experimental manifestation of a particular kinetic observation is obvious and is of maximum size. For this reason, it is desirable to plot experimental results in a form as close to the raw data as possible in order to demonstrate a particular point. All too often, the use of mathematical functions of the observed rate constants, which are some distance removed from the experimental data, has led to incorrect conclusions based, perhaps, on some small systematic error which would have been obvious if the raw data had been plotted directly. In general, if one wishes to demonstrate the existence of a particular kinetic term in a reaction, it is desirable to choose experimental conditions such that at least a 50% change in observed rate is brought about by the variable which is being examined. The most convincing way to plot and present kinetic data is often in the form of uncorrected, experimental rate constants, with theoretical lines showing the calculated rate constants which would be expected in the presence and absence of this particular variable. Other types of linear plots are usually used to obtain numerical values of the rate constants, but even with these plots it is important to attempt to visualize the relationship of the experimental observations to the derived quantity which is being plotted.

For the application of kinetic techniques to the elucidation of reaction mechanism it is generally more useful to obtain five rate constants with an accuracy of ±5% than one point with an accuracy of ±1%. Experimental data obtained over a wide range of reaction conditions permit a clear-cut demonstration of the effect of a variable on the reaction rate and often reveal some unexpected result which leads to a more important conclusion than that which the experiment was originally intended to demonstrate.

The material in this chapter is elementary for any professional kineticist (which the author is not), but should provide enough background to understand and even to apply kinetic techniques for the elucidation of the mechanisms of a large number of reactions which take place in aqueous solution. The reader is referred elsewhere for more advanced experimental and theoretical treatments of reaction kinetics.[1]

[1] A. A. Frost and R.G. Pearson, "Kinetics and Mechanism," 2d ed., John Wiley & Sons, Inc., New York, 1961; L. P. Hammett, "Physical Organic Chemistry," chap. 4, p. 96, McGraw-Hill Book Company, New York, 1940; S. L. Friess, E. S. Lewis, and A. Weissberger (eds.), "Technique of Organic Chemistry," 2d ed., vol. VIII, parts I and II, Interscience Publishers, Inc., New York, 1963; K.B. Wiberg, "Physical Organic Chemistry," part 3, p. 305, John Wiley & Sons, Inc., New York, 1964; I. Amdur and G. G. Hammes, "Chemical Kinetics: Principles and Selected Topics," McGraw-Hill Book Company, New York, 1966; E. L. King's short book on "How Chemical Reactions Occur" (W. A. Benjamin, Inc., New York, 1964) is an excellent and readable introduction for those with no previous experience with the subject.

A. RATES, RATE CONSTANTS, AND REACTION ORDER

In the simplest case the rate of reaction of two molecules A and B to form a product P in solution (equation 1) is proportional to the num-

$$A + B \longrightarrow P \tag{1}$$

ber of collisions of the two molecules with each other and is, therefore, proportional to the concentration of each of the reactants. This relationship is described in equation 2, in which the second-

$$\text{Rate} = v = -\frac{dA}{dt} = -\frac{dB}{dt} = \frac{dP}{dt} = k[A][B] \tag{2}$$

order rate constant k describes the proportionality of the rate to the concentrations of the two reacting molecules. If the concentrations of the reactants are expressed on the molar scale, the units of this rate constant are M^{-1} time^{-1}. The rate of a first-order reaction (equation 3) is proportional to the concentration of a single species

$$A \longrightarrow P \tag{3}$$

and is described by a first-order rate constant with the dimensions of reciprocal time, such as sec^{-1} or min^{-1} (equation 4). Thus, the

$$v = k[A] \tag{4}$$

order of a reaction describes the number of molecules to which the reaction rate is proportional, as in equation 2 or 4, but it does not necessarily indicate the number of molecules involved in the reaction, because some molecules can react without affecting the rate (equations 5 and 6). A reaction is said to be zero order with respect to such a reactant.

$$A \xrightarrow[\text{slow}]{} A* \xrightarrow[\text{fast}]{+X+Y} P \tag{5}$$

$$v = k[A] \tag{6}$$

1. FIRST-ORDER REACTIONS

Equation 4 for a first-order reaction may be integrated from t_0 to the time of an experimental measurement according to equations 7 to 10, in which A_0 is the concentration of A at zero time. The

$$\int_{A_0}^{A} -\frac{d[A]}{[A]} = k \int_{t_0}^{t} dt \tag{7}$$

$$-\ln [A] + \ln A_0 = kt \tag{8}$$

$$\ln \frac{A_0}{[A]} = kt \tag{9}$$

$$[A] = A_0 e^{-kt} \tag{10}$$

variables in these equations are $[A]$ and t, so that the concentration of A decreases exponentially and a plot of $\log [A]$ against t is linear with a slope of $-k/2.303$ (Fig. 1). The half-time of the reaction is the time at which the concentration of A has decreased to half its initial value, $0.5A_0$. Substitution in equation 9 gives equation 11 and shows that the half-time of a first-order reaction is

$$\ln \frac{A_0}{0.5A_0} = kt_{1/2} = \ln 2 = 0.693 \tag{11}$$

directly related to the first-order rate constant as shown in equation 12.

$$k = \frac{0.693}{t_{1/2}} \tag{12}$$

In practice, it is convenient to plot $[A]$, or some experimental quantity which is directly proportional to $[A]$, on semilogarithmic graph paper as a function of time. The half-time can then be read directly off the plot by noting the amount of time required for the

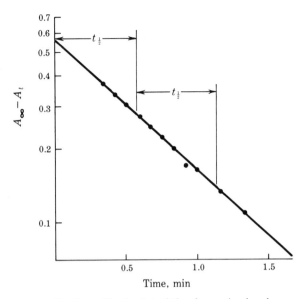

Fig 1. Semilogarithmic plot of the change in absorbance at 270 mμ caused by the release of phenol and phenolate ion in the reaction of 5×10^{-4} M phenyl acetate with 0.6 M ethylamine buffer, 40% free base, ionic strength maintained at $1.0 M$ with potassium chloride, at 5°. The reaction follows (pseudo) first-order kinetics with a half-time which is independent of the amount of reaction.

concentration of A to decrease to half its initial value. The first-order rate constant is then obtained from equation 12. Since the half-time (or any other fractional reaction time) is independent of the concentration of A, it can be read from any part of the plot, and in order to avoid errors it is important to check the half-time over at least one additional time period (Fig. 1).

One of the greatest practical advantages of first-order rate constants arises from the fact that the kinetic behavior of a first-order reaction is independent of the concentration of the reactant, so that the rate constant may be obtained from the half-time for the observed appearance or disappearance of a product or reactant without knowing its absolute concentration. Thus, instead of plotting log [A] against time, it is possible to plot the results of any experimental measurement which changes with the concentration of A (or P) in such a way that the concentration of A (or P) and the change in the experimental measurement have the same half-time. This is obvious if one plots the absorbance of A or of the product P which is formed from A in the absence of interfering absorbance from other species (Figs. 2a and 2b). It is less obvious, but equally true, if the absorbances due to both A and P are changing at the wavelength at which measurements are being carried out (Fig. 3). That the half-time for such a change in absorbance, 0.5 ΔA, is the same as for the disappearance of A or the appearance of P is apparent from the fact that the observed absorbance at the half-time

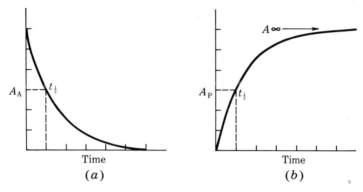

Fig 2. The change in the absorbance of a reactant A_A or a product A_P, with time in a first-order reaction when only the reactant or product gives absorbance at the wavelength of the experimental measurements.

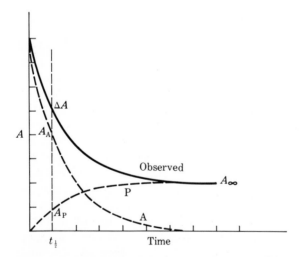

Fig 3. The observed change in absorbance and the changes in absorbance of the starting material and product when both of these species absorb, showing that the half-times for all absorbance changes are the same.

is that of half of the original concentration of A, $0.5A_0$, plus that of half the final concentration of P, $0.5\,P_\infty$, as shown in equation 13, in

$$0.5\,\Delta A_{tot} = A_0\,\epsilon_A - 0.5A_0\,\epsilon_A + 0.5P_\infty\epsilon_P = 0.5A_0\,\epsilon_A + 0.5P_\infty\epsilon_P \qquad (13)$$

which ϵ_A and ϵ_P refer to the molar extinction coefficients of A and P, respectively. Thus, the course of a first-order reaction may be followed by measurements of the half-time for changes in visible, ultraviolet, infrared, nuclear magnetic resonance, or infrared absorbance as well as changes in volume, conductivity, release of heat, optical rotation, refractive index, and hydrogen ion concentration, so long as the half-times for the changes in these quantities are the same as for the changes in the concentrations of A and P. This will be the case if the measured quantity is linearly related to the concentration of A, P, or A and P.

In practice, if the absorbance (or other quantity being measured) increases during an experiment, the quantity $A_\infty - A_t$ is plotted against time on semilogarithmic graph paper. If the absorbance is decreasing, the quantity $A_t - A_\infty$ is plotted. It is important to be certain that changes in absorbance caused by factors other than the reaction under consideration are not taking place during the experiment.

2. THE ENDPOINT

By far the most important experimental quantity which is required for the determination of first-order rate constants is the value of the absorbance, or whatever other quantity is being followed, at the end of the reaction, since each experimental reading must be subtracted from the time infinity value or the time infinity value must be subtracted from each experimental reading. The most common cause of deviations from first-order kinetics in reactions which are expected to be first order is an error in the value of this endpoint. The experimental readings near the end of a first-order experimental run show much smaller absolute changes than those near the beginning of the run and are especially susceptible to experimental error and to deviations caused by an incorrect endpoint. Experimental error usually appears as a scatter of the points, whereas an incorrect endpoint leads to an upward or downward curvature of the first-order plot near the end of the reaction.

Endpoints are usually obtained after about 10 half-times, when the reaction has proceeded 99.9% to completion. It may be desirable to make a preliminary estimate of the half-time and calculate the endpoint from the experimental measurement at seven half-times, at which the reaction is 99.2% complete, by adding a correction of 0.8% to the observed change in whatever property is being measured. In some cases it may be desirable to estimate the endpoint from a correction of this kind at even earlier times, but it is important to be certain beforehand that the reaction does, in fact, follow first-order kinetics. The amount of the reaction which has not yet taken place after different numbers of half-times is shown below:

Half-times	Percent of reaction not yet completed
4	6.25
5	3.1
6	1.5
7	0.8

Errors in endpoint determinations often arise from a slow secondary reaction, such as an oxidation of the products, which causes a change in the absorbance or other property which is being followed. It is sometimes useful to obtain endpoints from reaction mixtures in which the reaction of an identical amount of substrate has proceeded fast enough so that such secondary decomposition is insignificant. This may be done by adding a larger concentration of a second reactant, provided that a correction is made for any absorbance of this reactant, or by obtaining an artificial endpoint in a dummy reaction mixture. For example, the endpoint for the slow reaction of a phenyl ester with an amine, in which the reaction is followed by measuring the appearance of phenol spectrophotometrically, may be obtained by subjecting a known quantity of a relatively concentrated solution of phenyl acetate to alkaline hydrolysis, neutralizing it, and then adding it to a dummy reaction mixture containing amine to give the same final concentration as in the experimental run.

An alternative, but hazardous, method of obtaining a first-order rate constant when the endpoint is difficult to determine was described by Guggenheim.[2] When the value x of the property being measured is unknown at the endpoint x_∞, readings may be

[2] E. A. Guggenheim, *Phil. Mag.* 2, 538 (1926).

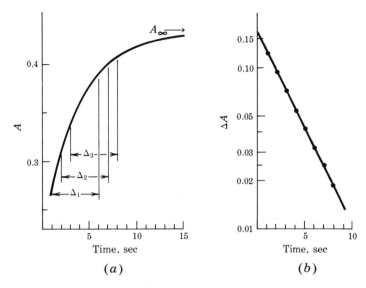

Fig 4. Application of the Guggenheim method to the reaction of 1-acetoxy-4-methoxypyridine cation with 5×10^{-4} M ethylenediamine in 0.01 M borate buffer at pH 8.36, ionic strength 1.0 M, 25°, followed with a recording spectrophotometer at 280 mμ. (a) Observed change in absorbance with time. (b) Semilogarithmic plot of the change in absorbance over successive 5-second time intervals.

taken at a series of times t and at a series of times which are a constant amount later, $t + \Delta$ (Fig. 4). The measurements should be carried to well over one half-life of the reaction in order to obtain accurate rate constants. The readings at each time, x_t, are expressed for a first-order reaction in equation 14, and the readings at $t + \Delta$, x_Δ, are given in the same way in equation 15.

$$x_t - x_\infty = (x_0 - x_\infty)\, e^{-kt} \tag{14}$$

$$x_\Delta - x_\infty = (x_0 - x_\infty) e^{-k(t + \Delta)} \tag{15}$$

Subtracting these two equations gives equation 16, which is con-

$$x_t - x_\Delta = (x_0 - x_\infty)\, e^{-kt}\,(1 + e^{-k\Delta}) \tag{16}$$

verted to logarithmic form in equation 17. Now, the last term of

$$\ln (x_t - x_\Delta) = -kt + \ln [(x_0 - x_\infty)(1 - e^{-k\Delta})] \qquad (17)$$

equation 17, which contains the unknown quantity x_∞, is a constant and does not have to be evaluated for a first-order reaction. The rate constant k is obtained in the usual manner by simply plotting log $(x_t - x_\Delta)$ [or log $(x_\Delta - x_t)$] against time (Fig. 4). The danger of this method is that it may give linear plots for reactions that do not accurately follow first-order kinetics. It is important to be certain before using this method that the reaction does follow first-order kinetics and that secondary reactions are not affecting the readings at $t + \Delta$.

The demonstration that a reaction accurately follows first-order kinetics for three or four half-times on a logarithmic plot is convincing evidence that the reaction is, in fact, first order. Accurate rate constants can generally be obtained by following the reaction for two half-times if a satisfactory endpoint can be obtained. In certain experimental situations a reasonably accurate rate constant may be obtained from a reaction which is followed for one half-time, provided that it is certain that the reaction follows first-order kinetics. However, deviations from first-order kinetics because of an inaccurate endpoint or for other reasons may not be apparent in plots over one or even two half-times, so that rate constants that are seriously in error may be obtained if it is not certain that the reaction follows first-order kinetics accurately.

3. SECOND-ORDER REACTIONS

The integrated rate expression for a second-order reaction (equation 1) which follows the rate law of equation 2 is given in equation 18,

$$\frac{1}{B_0 - A_0} \ln \frac{A_0(B_0 - x)}{B_0(A_0 - x)} = kt \qquad (18)$$

in which A_0 and B_0 refer to the concentrations of A and B at zero time and x refers to the amount of A and B which have reacted, which is equal to the amount of product. The rate constant k may be evaluated from a plot of $\ln [(B_0 - x)/(A_0 - x)]$ against time.

In the special case in which the concentrations of A and B at zero time are identical $(A_0 = B_0)$, the rate law is given by equations 19 and 20, in which C is the remaining concentration of A or B at any time. The rate constant k may then be obtained from a plot of $1/C$ against time.

$$-\frac{dC}{dt} = kC^2 \tag{19}$$

$$\frac{1}{C} - \frac{1}{C_0} = kt \tag{20}$$

In the special case in which the concentration of A is much larger than that of B, the concentration of A does not change appreciably during the reaction and may be treated as a constant. The rate law for such a situation is given in equation 21, in which

$$v = k[A](B_0 - x) = k_{obs}(B_0 - x) \tag{21}$$

k_{obs} is a first-order rate constant equal to $k[A]$. Such a reaction is said to be *pseudo* first order because any individual experimental run follows first-order kinetics, but the first-order rate constant k_{obs} is a function of the concentration of the second reactant A, rather than a true constant. The second-order rate constant is obtained from the slope of a plot of a number of values of k_{obs}, determined at different concentrations of A, against $[A]$. Pseudo first-order rate constants provide a particularly useful method for the kinetic evaluation of reaction mechanisms because they make possible a separation of the variables which affect the reaction rate in a controlled manner. The great danger of such rate constants is their sensitivity to impurities which may be present in low concentration in the reactant present in great excess, A. If such impurities are much more reactive than A itself, the observed pseudo first-order reaction may be a reaction with the impurity rather than with A. For example, piperidine is prepared by the reduction of pyridine, and the 0.1% remaining pyridine impurity is responsible for most of the observed reaction of a redistilled piperidine solution with reactive acylating agents at pH 6.[3] This impurity and other troublesome impurities in amines, such as the methyl-substituted pyridines, can often be removed by repeated recrystallization of the amine hydrochloride.

4. INITIAL RATES

The measurement of initial rates of reaction is particularly useful for obtaining the rate constants of slow reactions. The simplifying

[3] W. P. Jencks and M. Gilchrist, *J. Am. Chem. Soc.* **90**, 2622 (1968).

approximation of this method is that if a reaction is followed only 1 or 2% toward completion, the concentrations of all reactants are almost constant during the time of measurement, so that the rate constant may be evaluated directly from the rate of appearance of products and the concentrations of reactants, as shown for a second-order reaction in equation 22.

$$\frac{d\mathrm{P}}{dt} = k[\mathrm{A}][\mathrm{B}] \approx k\mathrm{A}_0\mathrm{B}_0$$

(22)

The experimental requirement for this technique is a method for the determination of small amounts of product in the presence of large amounts of starting materials. The concentrations of the reactants are ordinarily obtained from the amounts added to the reaction mixture or from analytical determinations of the concentrations in each reaction mixture. In experiments which are followed by spectrophotometry, it is often convenient to determine the concentration of that reactant which gives rise to the product being followed spectrophotometrically by forcing the reaction to completion in an aliquot of the reaction mixture and determining the absorbance after appropriate dilution. For example, the concentration of phenyl acetate in a reaction mixture may be determined by alkaline hydrolysis of the ester in an aliquot of the reaction mixture, followed by reneutralization to the pH of the reaction and spectrophotometric determination of the concentration of phenol after dilution. The advantage of this procedure is that it leads to the cancellation of any errors which might arise from uncertainty in the concentration or extinction coefficient of this component of the reaction mixture; it has the effect of treating the reaction of that component like a pseudo first-order reaction, which has a rate constant independent of the absolute concentration of the reactant. The dependence of rate constants obtained by measurements of initial rates of reaction upon the concentrations of the different reactants may be easily determined from experiments in which the concentrations of these reactants are varied separately. Small amounts of reactive impurities in the reactants may cause errors in kinetic measurements by the method of initial rates, as in pseudo first-order rate measurements.

5. REACTION ORDER

The order of a reaction is generally evident from the form of the rate law which is followed in a given experiment or, in the case of reactions in which pseudo first-order rate constants or initial rates are measured, from the dependence of the rate constants or rates obtained in individual experiments on changes in the concentrations of the reactants. An alternative method, which is useful when these criteria do not provide a clear-cut conclusion, gives the order of a reaction with respect to a particular reactant from the dependence of the half-time for its disappearance on its initial concentration. It is usually possible to determine the half-time for the disappearance of a given reactant regardless of the rate law which is followed for its disappearance. A logarithmic plot is made of the measured half-times of the reaction against the concentration of the reactant, as shown for the hydrolysis of phosphoramidate in the presence of formaldehyde in Fig. 5.[4] The order of the reaction is given by the negative slope of the resulting line plus 1.0. The half-time of phosphoramidate hydrolysis is independent of its concentration at low concentrations, as expected for a (pseudo) first-order reaction. As the concentration increases, the half-time decreases with a slope of -1 on the logarithmic plot as a term in the rate law which is second order with respect to phosphoramidate becomes significant. From this information, a minimal rate law may be written as shown in equation 23, in which the observed rate con-

$$-\frac{d[\text{PA}]}{dt} = k_1[\text{PA}] + k_2[\text{PA}]^2 \tag{23}$$

stants $k_1{}^*$ and k_2 are themselves dependent on the concentration of the other reactants. An alternative method of obtaining the reaction order for reactions up to third order is based on a plot of f/t against t, according to the approximate equation 24, in which f is the fraction to which the reaction has proceeded to completion, n is

$$\frac{t}{f} = \frac{1}{k\text{A}_0} + \frac{nt}{2} \tag{24}$$

the reaction order, A_0 is the initial concentration of the reactant, and k is the rate constant. The slope of such a plot is equal to one-half the reaction order, and the rate constant may be obtained from the intercept.[5]

[4] W. P. Jencks and M. Gilchrist, *J. Am. Chem. Soc.* **86**, 1410 (1964).

[5] R. W. Wilkinson, *Chem. Ind.* (*London*) **1961**, 1395.

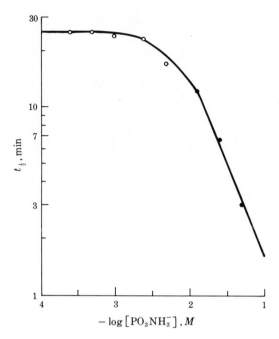

Fig 5. Logarithmic plot of the half-times for formaldehyde catalyzed hydrolysis of phosphoramidate against the concentration of phosphoramidate at 39°, ionic strength 1.0 M, pH 4.5. Solid circles: rates determined by automatic titration. Open circles: rates determined by measurement of the appearance of inorganic phosphate.[4]

B. THE UTILIZATION OF PSEUDO FIRST-ORDER RATE CONSTANTS

Pseudo first-order rate constants, obtained in the presence of a large excess of all the reactants except the one which gives rise to the change in whatever property of the solution is being followed, provide the most generally useful kinetic method for the elucidation of reaction mechanism, in the author's opinion. In the first place, it is often relatively easy to obtain a series of pseudo first-order rate constants for the disappearance of a substrate or the appearance of a product by spectrophotometry or by some other relatively simple analytical or physical measurement. Secondly, it is not necessary to know the exact concentration of the reactant or product which appears or disappears in a first-order reaction. The most important property of such rate constants, however, is that they make possible a facile separation of the variables that are involved in a given reaction, which is often difficult or impossible if the reaction is followed with the reactants at similar or equal concentrations. Some of the ways in which this can be done will be described in this section.

1. PARALLEL FIRST-ORDER REACTIONS

This separation of (pseudo) first-order rate constants is made possible by their additivity in parallel first-order reactions. If a substrate disappears by more than one concurrent first-order pathway, such as by hydrolysis and aminolysis of an ester in the presence of a large excess of amine (equation 25), the first-order rate constants for the reaction are additive (equations 26 and 27) so that the pseudo

$$
\text{ester}
\begin{cases}
\xrightarrow{k_{hyd}} & \overset{\overset{\text{O}}{\|}}{\text{RCOH}} + \text{HOR}' \\
\xrightarrow{k_{am}[R''NH_2]} & \overset{\overset{\text{O}}{\|}}{\text{RCNHR}''} + \text{HOR}'
\end{cases}
\tag{25}
$$

$$
v = \frac{-d[A]}{dt} = \frac{d[R'OH]}{dt} = k_{hyd}\,[\text{ester}] + k_{am}\,[R''NH_2][\text{ester}]
$$

$$
= (k_{hyd} + k_{am}[R''NH_2])[\text{ester}]
\tag{26}
$$

$$
k_{obs} = \frac{v}{[\text{ester}]} = k_{hyd} + k_{am}\,[R''NH_2] = k_{hyd} + k'_{am}
\tag{27}
$$

first-order rate constant for aminolysis k'_{am} may be obtained simply by subtracting that for hydrolysis, which can usually be measured in a separate experiment. The second-order rate constant for aminolysis may then be obtained by dividing the observed pseudo first-order rate constant for aminolysis by the concentration of free amine, *provided* that it is certain that the reaction with amine is first order with respect to amine concentration (i.e., is second order overall). It is usually desirable to plot the observed pseudo first-order rate constants against the concentration of the second reactant. The intercept of such a plot gives k_{hydrol}, and the slope, if the plot is linear, gives the second-order rate constant for aminolysis (Fig. 6).

Another way to separate the component parts of an observed pseudo first-order rate constant is to determine the products at the

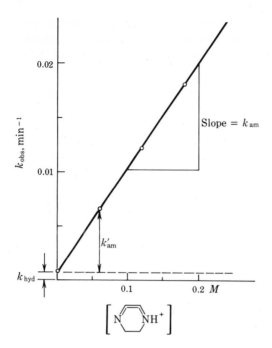

Fig 6. Pseudo first-order rate constants for the reaction of 2,4-dinitrophenyl acetate with triethylenediamine monocation in a buffer of 60% monocation-40% dication, pH 3.57, at an ionic strength maintained at 1.0 M with potassium chloride and 25°.

end of the reaction. Since all the pathways for the disappearance of the substrate are first order, the fraction of the substrate which disappears by each pathway during the course of the reaction is constant, as is the ratio of products from the different pathways. Consequently, the ratio of products at the end of the reaction is equal to the ratio of the pseudo first-order rate constants for the pathways from which they were derived. Thus, for the concurrent aminolysis and hydrolysis of an ester, the ratio and the absolute values of the pseudo first-order rate constants for aminolysis and hydrolysis can be obtained from the ratio of amide to acid product and k_{obs} (equations 27 and 28). However, in order to apply this

$$\frac{k_{hyd}}{k'_{am}} = \frac{[RCOOH]_{final}}{[RCONHR'']_{final}} \qquad (28)$$

technique to the evaluation of rate constants, it is necessary to be certain that the reactions are what they are assumed to be. For example, an amine might cause ester disappearance by general base catalysis of ester hydrolysis as well as by aminolysis, so that not all of the kinetic term containing the amine concentration would represent aminolysis. In practice, determinations of products and product ratios are most often carried out to identify the chemical nature of a kinetic term, such as whether a reaction with an amine represents aminolysis, amine catalyzed hydrolysis, or both. It is, of course, necessary to be certain in any determination of products that the product being measured is stable under the conditions of the experiment.

Students are nearly always surprised to learn that the half-time or the observed rate constant for a reaction which proceeds by several concurrent first-order pathways is the same, regardless of what is being measured. Thus, for the concurrent hydrolysis and aminolysis of an ester (Fig. 7) the half-times are the same for ester disappearance and for appearance of the amide and of the acid (although the *absolute* rates, in units of moles per minute, are of course different). The pseudo first-order rate constant for the overall reaction may be determined just as well from the half-time for the small fraction of the reaction which gives hydrolysis as from any other measurement. This can be useful for the measurement of reactions which do not give an easily measurable change in the properties of reactants or products. If an additional first-order reaction which is easily measured is introduced into the system, this can serve as an indicator of the overall rate of substrate disappearance and, after correction for the known rate of the indicator reaction, as a means for the determination of the desired rate constant. The reason for the identity of the half-time for the several concurrent reactions is apparent after some consideration: When half of the substrate has reacted, one-half of the maximum amount of each product must be formed, and the absolute rate of each of the concurrent reactions is just one-half the initial rate (Fig. 7).

2. NONLINEAR DEPENDENCE OF k_{obs} ON THE CONCENTRATION OF ANOTHER REACTANT

It is sometimes found that the plot of observed pseudo first-order rate constants against the concentration of a reactant present in great excess is not linear. This means that the reaction is not first order with respect to that reactant, and that the rate law is more complicated than that of equation 27. These deviations often provide the most interesting information about the mechanism of the reaction. The two possible types of deviations—downward deviations and upward deviations—have an altogether different significance and are considered separately.

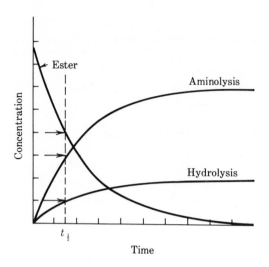

Fig 7. The time course of ester disappearance and of amide and acid appearance for concurrent aminolysis and hydrolysis of an ester by pseudo first-order reactions. The half-times for disappearance of the ester and for appearance of the two products are identical.

A downward deviation means that the reaction is proceeding more slowly than would be expected from the dependence on the concentration of the reactant at low concentrations; i.e., something is causing the reaction to proceed more slowly than predicted by a rate law of the form of equation 27. This may be caused either by some sort of complex formation of the reactants or by a change in rate-determining step. These possibilities are familiar to enzymologists in the leveling off of the rate of an enzymatic reaction with increasing substrate concentration, which can be caused either by formation of an enzyme-substrate complex at high substrate concentration (Michaelis complex, equation 29) or by a change in rate-

$$E + S \underset{}{\overset{K}{\rightleftharpoons}} ES \overset{k}{\longrightarrow} \text{products} \tag{29}$$

determining step from bimolecular formation of the complex to rate-determining monomolecular breakdown of the complex (Haldane interpretation, equation 30). An example of complex formation in a chemical reaction, the formation of an oxime from hydroxylamine

$$E + S \overset{k_1}{\longrightarrow} ES \overset{k_2}{\longrightarrow} \text{products} \tag{30}$$

and pyruvate, is shown in Fig. 8. At the pH of this experiment, 6.9, the dehydration of the addition compound I is rate determining, and the formation of this intermediate occurs in a rapid prior equilibrium step (equation 31). At low hydroxylamine concentrations a

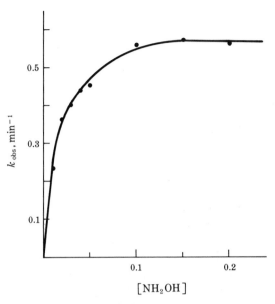

Fig 8. The leveling off of the rate of oxime formation from pyruvate in the presence of excess hydroxylamine caused by complete conversion of pyruvate to a hydroxylamine addition compound at pH 6.9, 25°, ionic strength maintained at 1.0 M with potassium chloride.[6]

$$\text{NH}_2\text{OH} + {\Large >}\text{C}{=}\text{O} \underset{}{\overset{K}{\rightleftharpoons}} {\Large >}\text{C}\underset{\text{NHOH}}{\overset{\text{OH}}{\big<}} \overset{k_2}{\longrightarrow} {\Large >}\text{C}{=}\text{NOH} + \text{H}_2\text{O} \tag{31}$$
$$\qquad\qquad\qquad\qquad\qquad\text{I}$$

negligible fraction of pyruvate is present as the addition intermediate, so that the concentration of intermediate and the overall rate are directly proportional to the hydroxylamine concentration. At high hydroxylamine concentration all the pyruvate is converted to the addition compound, so that a further increase in hydroxylamine concentration does not increase the rate and the observed rate is simply the rate of breakdown of the intermediate.[6] The observed rate constant at any amine concentration is given by equation 32,

$$k_\text{obs} = \frac{v}{[\text{C}{=}\text{O}]_\text{tot}} = k_2 [\text{NH}_2\text{OH}] \left(\frac{K}{1 + K[\text{NH}_2\text{OH}]} \right) \tag{32}$$

which is derived from the fact that the rate is equal to the rate of breakdown of the intermediate (equation 33), the equilibrium constant

[6] W. P. Jencks, *Progr. Phys. Org. Chem.* **2**, 63 (1964).

for formation of the intermediate (equation 34), and the conservation equation for the total added carbonyl compound $[C=O]_{tot}$ (equation 35). The equilibrium constant K may be obtained from the

$$v = k_2 [I] \tag{33}$$

$$K = \frac{[I]}{[C=O][NH_2OH]} \tag{34}$$

$$[C=O]_{tot} = [C=O]_{free} + [I] \tag{35}$$

negative abscissa intercept of a plot of $1/k_{obs}$ against $1/[NH_2OH]$, which is analogous to the Lineweaver-Burk plot for enzymatic reactions.[7] This example involves covalent association of the reactants, but similar behavior is observed with association from any cause. Pyridines, for example, exhibit a self-association or some self-interaction effect which results in a decrease in activity coefficient with increasing pyridine concentration as well as in nonlinear kinetic behavior.[8,9] Pyridines and other compounds with hydrophobic constituents also associate with esters and other substrates to cause nonlinear kinetic behavior.[3,10,11]

If association can be ruled out as a cause for a negative deviation in a plot of k_{obs} against the concentration of a reactant or catalyst, the change in the form of the rate law means that there is a change in the rate-determining step of the reaction. This is a useful technique for the demonstration of an intermediate on the reaction path. A number of examples are described in Chap. 10.

Positive deviations in such plots (Fig. 9) mean that the reaction proceeds faster than expected from the results at low concentration; i.e., the reaction is more than first order with respect to the concentration of the varying reactant and an *additional* term must be added to the rate law to account for the observed rate. The

[7] This procedure cannot be used if the reactant is a catalyst for the second step, so that the rate does not level off completely.

[8] A. J. Kirby and W. P. Jencks, *J. Am. Chem. Soc.* 87, 3209 (1965).

[9] R. J. L. Andon, J. D. Cox, and E. F. G. Herington, *J. Chem. Soc.* 1954, 3188; N. Ibl, G. Dändliker, and G. Trümpler, *Helv. Chim. Acta* 37, 1661 (1954).

[10] T. Higuchi and K. A. Connors, in C. N. Reilley (ed.), "Advances in Analytical Chemistry and Instrumentation," vol. IV, p. 117, Interscience Publishers, Inc., New York, 1965.

[11] J. A. Mollica, Jr. and K. A. Connors, *J. Am. Chem. Soc.* 89, 308 (1967).

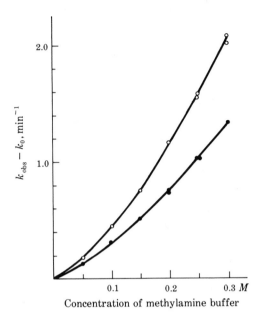

Fig 9. Pseudo first-order rate constants for the reaction of phenyl acetate with methylamine buffer, 40% free base, at 5°, ionic strength maintained at 1.0 with potassium chloride, showing the greater than first order dependence of the rate on the concentration of methylamine. Upper curve: in water. Lower curve: in deuterium oxide solution. k_0 is the rate of hydrolysis in the absence of amine.[12]

Ordinate: $k_{obs} - k_0$, min^{-1}

Abscissa: Concentration of methylamine buffer

simplest way to evaluate this term is to calculate an apparent second-order rate constant $k_{2\,app}$ by dividing each observed rate constant by the concentration of the reactive species of the reactant (equation 36). The increase in $k_{2\,app}$ with increasing amine concen-

$$k_{2\,app} = \frac{k_{obs} - k_0}{[RNH_2]} \tag{36}$$

tration in ester aminolysis represents catalysis of the reaction by a second mole of amine. Consequently $k_{2\,app}$ is plotted against the concentration of amine (Fig. 10). The ordinate intercept of this plot gives the second-order rate constant for the uncatalyzed (or solvent catalyzed) aminolysis k_1, and the slope is the third-order constant for the amine catalyzed reaction k_{RNH_2}, according to the rate law of equation 37. If there is no intercept, all of the reaction is catalyzed;

$$\frac{v}{[Ester]} = k_{obs} = k_{hyd} + k_1[RNH_2] + k_{RNH_2}[RNH_2][RNH_2]$$
$$+ k_{OH^-}[RNH_2][OH^-] \tag{37}$$

i.e., there is no measurable second-order term, k_1.

If the reaction contains more than one third-order term, it is necessary to extrapolate each apparent second-order rate constant to zero concentration of the other reactants before plotting it against the concentration of the reactant in question. This proce-

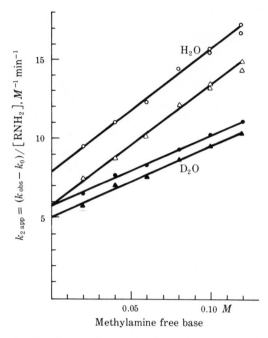

Fig 10. Apparent second-order rate constants for the reaction of phenyl acetate with methylamine in water (open symbols) and deuterium oxide (closed symbols) as a function of the concentration of methylamine. Circles: uncorrected rate constants. Triangles: corrected for hydroxide ion catalysis of aminolysis.[12]

dure, while laborious, makes possible the elucidation of the kinetics of reactions which would be difficult or impossible to evaluate by other techniques. The simplest procedure, if it is practicable, is to carry out the reaction at a sufficiently low concentration of the other reactants that only the first-order terms for these reactants are significant. The aminolysis of phenyl acetate is catalyzed by hydroxide ion as well as by a second molecule of amine (equation 37, k_{OH^-}). The observed rate constants may be separated into the contributions from k_{RNH_2} and k_{OH^-} by utilizing data obtained under conditions in which one of these terms makes the major contribution to the observed rate or change in rate and correcting for the contribution of the other, as shown in Figs. 10 and 11; the corrections may be made by successive approximations, if necessary, to obtain final values of the rate constants.[12]

[12] W. P. Jencks and M. Gilchrist, *J. Am. Chem. Soc.* 88, 104 (1966).

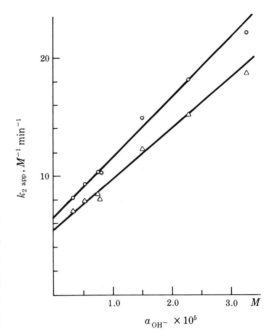

Fig 11. Apparent second-order rate constants, $k_{2\,app} = (k_{obs} - k_0)/[RNH_2]$, for the reaction of methylamine at a total buffer concentration of 0.05 M with phenyl acetate as a function of hydroxide ion activity. Circles: uncorrected values. Triangles: corrected for amine catalysis.[12]

3. EFFECT OF pH AND IONIZATION OF THE REACTANTS

Ester hydrolysis occurs through acid catalyzed, pH–independent, and hydroxide ion catalyzed terms according to equation 38, although one or more of these terms may not be significant for a given ester. The dependence on pH of the rate of hydrolysis of the phenyl ester moiety of methyl o-carboxyphenyl acetate (**1**) is shown in the *lower*

$$
\begin{array}{c}
\text{O} \\
\parallel \\
\text{OCCH}_3
\end{array}
$$

COCH₃

1

curve of Fig. 12 as an example.[13] At low and high pH the rate constants increase with slopes of 1.0 in this logarithmic plot, cor-

[13] T. St. Pierre and W. P. Jencks, *J. Am. Chem. Soc.* **90**, 3817 (1968).

responding to acid and base catalyzed terms which are first order

$$\frac{v}{[\text{Ester}]} = k_{\text{obs}} = k_0 + k_{\text{H}^+}[\text{H}^+] + k_{\text{OH}^-}[\text{OH}^-] \tag{38}$$

with respect to hydrogen ion and hydroxide ion, respectively (k_{H^+} and k_{OH^-}, equation 38). The dashed line is the sum of the acid and base catalyzed reactions in the intermediate pH region. The increase in the observed rate above this dashed line corresponds to the pH-independent, "water" reaction. The kinetic constants are

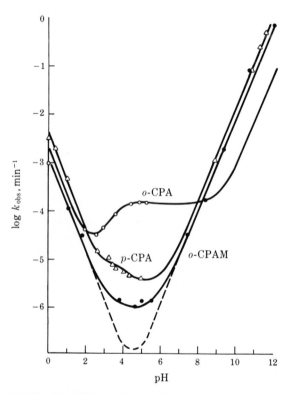

Fig 12. Logarithmic plots of the rate constants for the hydrolysis of aspirin (*o*-CPA), *p*-carboxyphenyl acetate (*p*-CPA), and methyl *o*-carboxyphenyl acetate (*o*-CPAM) as a function of pH. The dashed line shows the rate of hydrolysis of *o*-CPAM if hydrolysis proceeded with acid and base catalysis, but no pH-independent water reaction.[13]

evaluated from (linear) plots of k_{obs} against the concentration of hydrogen ion and hydroxide ion. (If the hydrolysis is catalyzed by buffers, the rate constants must first be determined at different buffer concentrations at each pH value and then extrapolated to zero buffer concentration.) The slopes of these plots give the second-order rate constants for the hydrogen and hydroxide ion catalyzed reaction, respectively, and the intercept of both plots is the pseudo first-order rate constant for the pH–independent, "water" reaction.

It is not possible to determine the order of a reaction with respect to solvent molecules by ordinary kinetic techniques because the concentration of solvent cannot be varied without changing the nature of the solvent in a manner for which it is difficult or impossible to make a suitable correction. If the "water" hydrolysis is known or assumed to represent a second-order attack by water, it may be desirable to convert the experimental first-order constant to a second-order constant by dividing it by the concentration of water, 55.5 M. If both the acid and the base catalyzed reactions contribute significantly to the rate at a given pH value, it is necessary to correct each observed rate constant for the contribution of the base catalyzed reaction before plotting it against acid concentration, and vice versa, through a series of successive approximations. This is usually not difficult, since accurate rate constants may be evaluated from the observed rates at high acid and base concentrations, at which other reactions are not significant.

Kinetic results are ordinarily expressed in terms of the *concentrations* of the reactants. This presents no problem for acid and base catalyzed reactions which are measured in the presence of known concentrations of added acid or hydroxide ion. However, a rate measurement based on a measured pH gives a rate constant for an acid or base catalyzed reaction which is based on *activity*, not concentration. The pH is, or very nearly is, a measure of the hydrogen ion activity and K_w, the ionization constant of water, is a true constant at finite ionic strengths only for activities (equation 39). If a_{OH^-} is to be calculated from the measured pH and K_w, the

$$K_w = a_{H^+} \cdot a_{OH^-} = 10^{-14} \text{ at } 25° \tag{39}$$

values of pH and K_w used must, of course, refer to the same temperature as the kinetic measurements. Rate constants which are based on activities should be so identified. They may be converted to a concentration basis by multiplication by the appropriate activity coefficients. For this purpose, the desired activity coefficients are most easily estimated from the measured pH of solutions containing a known concentration of hydrogen or hydroxide ion in the presence of the salt used to maintain the ionic strength of the reaction mixtures.

The complete rate law for a reaction of an ionizable reactant must refer to the rate of reaction of a particular ionic species of the reactant. It is desirable to convert observed rate constants to rate constants based on a particular ionic species of each reactant at an early stage in the evaluation of kinetic data. (It will be shown later that, because of the kinetic ambiguity of rate laws, it is generally not possible to decide by ordinary kinetic techniques whether a given ionic species is actually the species which is undergoing reaction, but it is still necessary to describe the rate of the reaction in terms of one or the other ionic species of each reactant; these may later be converted to kinetically equivalent forms if necessary.) The easiest way to do this is to divide the observed rate constant by the fraction of the material in a given ionic form. This fraction may be obtained from the Henderson-Hasselbalch equation 40, in which α is the fraction of the reactant in the basic

$$\text{pH} = \text{p}K_a' + \log \frac{[\text{base}]}{[\text{acid}]} = \text{p}K_a' + \log \frac{\alpha}{1-\alpha} \tag{40}$$

form, and from the measured pH of the reaction mixture. The sensitivity of apparent ionization constants to variations in ionic strength, temperature, and other reaction conditions makes it essential that the pH value be measured for each kinetic run and that the $\text{p}K_a'$ be determined under the exact experimental conditions of the kinetic run. It is not uncommon to obtain incorrect rate constants and even spurious additional terms in the rate law by calculating the value of α from measurements made under one set of experimental conditions and $\text{p}K_a'$ values, perhaps taken from a table, which were measured under different conditions. For the same reason it is important to report the $\text{p}K_a'$ values which are used for such calculations. For a reactant which is present in large excess, such as a buffer, it is far simpler and more accurate to obtain α from the stoichiometric composition of the buffer added to the reaction mixture; this avoids the possibility of error in measurements of both the pH and the pK_a'.[14]

If a constant value is not obtained by dividing the observed rate constants by α (or $1 - \alpha$) for each reactant, there is either an additional hydrogen or hydroxide ion term in the rate law or both ionic forms of the substrate react at significant rates and terms must be included in the rate law for each of them. The most straightforward way to evaluate these terms is to plot the observed rate constant against α. The ordinate intercept is the rate constant for the reaction of the acidic form of this reactant and the intercept at 1.0 is the rate constant for the basic form. If more than a single reactant undergoes ionization in the pH region under observation, k_{obs} should be divided by α for one reactant (or, if the reactant is present in large excess, by the concentration of a given ionic species) before plotting against α for the other reactant.

The curve with the open circles of Fig. 12 shows the dependence on pH of the rate of hydrolysis of aspirin, o–CPA. (2) The striking

feature of this curve is the rapid pH–independent hydrolysis of aspirin anion between pH 5 and 8.[15] The rate constant for hydrolysis of the anion may be obtained from any point on this plateau without interference from the acid or base catalyzed hydrolysis reactions. The rate constant for the pH–independent hydrolysis of the acidic, uncharged species of aspirin is not large enough to account for most of the observed rate at any pH value and must be obtained

---

[14] This procedure is not valid at high and low pH values at which a significant fraction of the acidic or basic component of the added buffer must give off or take up a proton to attain the final pH of the solution. For example, to reach a pH of 2.0 the buffer must supply about 0.01 M hydrogen ion, which would cause a significant decrease in the acid component and a corresponding increase in the basic component of a half-neutralized 0.05 M buffer of pK 2.0. The simplest way to correct for this dissociation is probably to: (1) measure the pH of the solution; (2) calculate the concentration of hydrogen ion from the pH and the activity coefficient of hydrogen ion or from an empirical calibration curve of pH against hydrogen ion concentration under the conditions of the experiment; and (3) subtract this concentration from the acidic and add it to the basic component of the buffer. Alternatively, a series of buffer solutions of increasing concentration may be brought to a constant pH by the addition of strong acid to each reaction mixture.

[15] L. J. Edwards, *Trans. Faraday Soc.* **46**, 723 (1950).

from a plot against α of the observed rate constants, corrected for the rate of acid catalyzed hydrolysis. The hydrolysis of p-carboxyphenyl acetate, p–CPA, does not show the rapid monoanion reaction characteristic of the *ortho* carboxylate group of aspirin (Fig. 12), so that the observed rate constants must be corrected for both acid and base catalyzed hydrolysis and then plotted against α to obtain the rate constants for the pH–independent hydrolysis of the acidic and anionic species. The solid lines in Fig. 12 are calculated from rate constants obtained in this way according to the overall rate law of equation 41, in which the superscripts refer to the charge of

$$\text{Rate} = k_{H^+}[SH]a_{H^+} + k_a[SH] + k_b[S^-] + k_{OH^-}[S^-]a_{OH^-} \tag{41}$$

the various ionic species of the reactants and k_a and k_b are the rate constants for the uncatalyzed hydrolysis of the acidic and basic species of the reactant, respectively.

The rate constants for the reactions of the acidic and anionic forms of aspirin with semicarbazide, which undergoes protonation to the unreactive cation in the same pH region that aspirin undergoes dissociation to the anion, may be evaluated as shown in Fig. 13

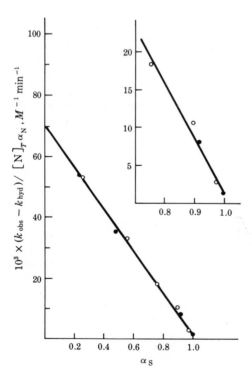

Fig 13. Apparent second-order rate constants for the reaction of semicarbazide with aspirin as a function of the fraction of aspirin present as the anion, α_S. $[N]_T$ and α_N refer to the total concentration of semicarbazide and the fraction of semicarbazide as the free base, respectively.[13]

according to the rate law of equation 42. The observed rate con-

$$v = k_a[o\text{–CPA}^0] + k_b[o\text{–CPA}^-] + k_3[o\text{–CPA}^0][\text{RNH}_2]$$
$$+ k_4[o\text{–CPA}^-][\text{RNH}_2] \quad (42)$$

stants, after correction for hydrolysis, are divided by the concentration of free semicarbazide and are then plotted against the fraction
of aspirin as the anion at each pH. The fact that the ordinate intercept k_3 is much larger than the intercept at $\alpha = 1.0$, k_4, reflects the
much larger susceptibility of aspirin acid than of aspirin anion to
attack by semicarbazide.

In some instances the procedure may be reversed, and the
variation in rate with pH is used to determine the ionization constant
of a reactant. This is particularly useful if the compound is too unstable to permit determination of its pK by ordinary methods.
There are no assumptions in such a procedure, except that the
reaction does not undergo a change in rate-determining step in the
pH region in question. For a reaction in which the rate constants
at pH values well above and below the pK are accurately known
and there is no interference from additional kinetic terms, the pK
of the reactant may be simply read from the midpoint of the Δk,
the difference in the rates of the reactions of the two species, in a
plot of k_{obs} against pH. This is shown for the hydrolysis of acetyl
phosphate monoanion and dianion in Fig. 14.[16, 17]

Several more accurate methods are available for obtaining pK
values from kinetic data; they may also be applied to other types
of pK determination. If the rate constants k_a and k_b for the reaction of the acidic and basic species of the reactant (equation 41) are
known accurately, either by direct measurement or by correction of
k_{obs} for the contributions of k_{H^+} and k_{OH^-}, the pK can be obtained
from a plot of $\log [k_{obs} - k_a)/(k_b - k_{obs})$ or $\log [(k_a - k_{obs})/(k_{obs} -
k_b)]$, against pH. The p$K$ is the pH at which this quantity equals
zero. This plot is simply an expression of the Henderson-Hasselbalch equation, modified to describe the dependence of k_{obs} on k_a,
k_b, and the pH according to equation 43. Curvature near the upper

$$k_{obs} = k_b\alpha + k_a(1 - \alpha) \quad (43)$$

and lower limits of such a plot, which should include data covering

[16] D. E. Koshland, Jr., *J. Am. Chem. Soc.* **74**, 2286 (1952).
[17] G. Di Sabato and W. P. Jencks, *J. Am. Chem. Soc.* **83**, 4400 (1961).

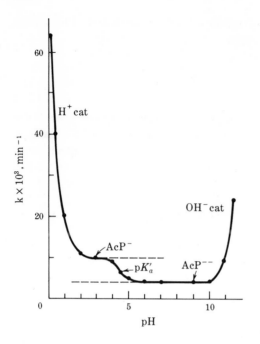

Fig 14. Dependence on pH of the hydrolysis of acetyl phosphate at 39°, showing the acid and base catalyzed reactions and the pH-independent hydrolyses of the acetyl phosphate mono-anion and dianion; the pK_a' for dissociation of the monanion to the dianion is at the midpoint between the two latter rates.[16,17]

about two logarithmic units, usually means that the value of k_a or k_b is inaccurate. The slope of this plot *must* be 1.0 if only a single ionization is involved.

If only one ionic species reacts, but it is impossible to obtain an accurate rate constant in the pH region in which the reactant is entirely converted to the reactive form, it is necessary to obtain the pK and the desired rate constant by an extrapolation procedure. The most satisfactory procedure for this, if the basic form of the substrate is reacting, is to plot k_{obs}' against $k_{obs}a_{H^+}$ (equation 44).

$$k_{obs} = k_b - \frac{k_{obs}a_{H^+}}{K_a} \tag{44}$$

The values of k_b and the ionization constant are obtained from the ordinate intercept and the negative reciprocal of the slope, respectively, of this plot. If the acidic form is reactive, k_{obs} is plotted against k_{obs}/a_{H^+}, the ordinate intercept is k_a, and the slope is equal to $-K_a$ (equation 45). These equations are derived from the

$$k_{obs} = k_a - \frac{k_{obs}K_a}{a_{H^+}} \tag{45}$$

expression for the ionization constant of the reactant and the proportionality of k_{obs} to the amount of substrate in the reactive form.[18] In an alternate procedure, $1/k_{obs}$ is plotted against $1/a_{H^+}$, if the acidic species reacts, or against a_{H^+}, if the basic species reacts. The ordinate intercept is the reciprocal of k_a (or k_b) and the abscissa intercept is the negative of $1/K_a$ (or K_a). Double reciprocal plots of this kind, like the analogous Lineweaver-Burk plots for enzyme kinetics, have the disadvantage that the points near k_b (or k_a) are clustered near the ordinate, whereas the slower rate constants are spread out. They should be utilized with caution and with understanding of this characteristic. If both ionic species react, either of these types of plot may be utilized by subtracting the rate constant for the slower reacting species from k_{obs} before making the plot. The ordinate intercept will then give $k_b - k_a$ or $k_a - k_b$, instead of k_a or k_b. These extrapolation methods are also useful for the determination of pK values by the usual methods— by plotting changes in absorbance or the amount of added acid or base instead of the rate constant.

The effect of the concentration of hydrogen or hydroxide ion on the reaction rate should be interpreted in the same way as for other reactants: an increase in reaction rate that is not accounted for by the ionization of a reactant is ascribed to an additional term in the rate law containing hydrogen or hydroxide ion. A decrease in the rate which cannot be accounted for by ionization of a reactant means that there is a change in rate-determining step and an intermediate in the reaction, as described for a number of reactions in Chap. 10.

4. SALT AND SOLVENT EFFECTS

In order to avoid unnecessary changes in the reaction medium in a series of experiments, it is usually desirable to carry out reactions at a constant ionic strength and solvent composition. A standard set of experimental conditions should be chosen before undertaking any large series of experimental measurements. If it is necessary to increase a reactant or buffer to a high concentration, the substance itself will change the nature of the solvent in a manner for which it may be difficult to make a valid correction. The various theoretical equations for the effects of salts and solvents on reaction rates are subject to so many exceptions in practice as to be almost useless for making corrections to observed reaction rates in the

[18] B. H. J. Hofstee, *Science* **131**, 39, 1068 (1960).

absence of direct experimental data demonstrating their validity for the reaction in question. It is, therefore, desirable to make a direct experimental evaluation of the effect of unavoidable changes in reaction conditions if this is possible. Correction to a constant ionic strength will effectively eliminate electrostatic effects which follow the simple Debye-Hückel equation, but in even moderately concentrated solutions specific ion effects and solvent effects on the activity coefficients of the reactants and transition state (Chaps. 7 and 8) are likely to become much larger than the Debye-Hückel effect and may conceal or exaggerate important types of kinetic behavior. For example, general base and general acid catalysis of the aminolysis of phenyl acetate by alkylamines may be difficult to detect if the ionic strength is maintained constant with potassium chloride, which, in contrast to tetramethylammonium chloride, has a specific rate accelerating effect on the reaction.[12, 19] The effects of other changes in the nature of the solvent caused by reactants and buffers may be evaluated by examination of the effects of appropriate model compounds. For example, dioxane may be used as a model to evaluate the effect of the hydrocarbon-ether ring of morpholine. The fact that such model compounds and salts can never be entirely appropriate models for the reactant requires that one should regard small changes in rate constants, such as small catalytic terms which are obtained at high reactant concentrations, with considerable reserve, especially if the reaction is known to be sensitive to salt and solvent effects. The large sensitivity of some reactions of uncharged molecules to solvent effects is illustrated by the 50% decrease in the rate of hydrolysis of acetylsalicylic acid anhydride in the presence of 10% dioxane.[20]

5. REVERSIBLE REACTIONS

The kinetic equation for a reaction which proceeds to an equilibrium position instead of to completion is complicated if the reaction is more than first order in either direction. It is desirable, therefore, (1) to pull the reaction to completion by adding some second reaction which shifts the equilibrium (this could involve protonating, hydrolyzing, or trapping a product, for example), (2) to measure initial rates under conditions in which the reverse reaction is not significant, or (3) to examine the reaction under conditions in which it is (pseudo) first order in each direction.

[19] T. C. Bruice, A. Donzel, R. W. Huffman, and A. R. Butler, *J. Am. Chem. Soc.* **89**, 2106 (1967).

[20] E. R. Garrett, *J. Am. Chem. Soc.* **82**, 711 (1960).

It is initially surprising that the observed rate constant for a first-order reaction proceeding to equilibrium is *larger* than the first-order rate constant for the reaction in either the forward or reverse directions; in fact, it is equal to the sum of these rate constants (equation 46). The reason for this becomes clear from an

$$k_{obs} = k_f + k_r \tag{46}$$

inspection of the course of the reaction (Fig. 15) under conditions in which it is pulled to completion by a trapping reaction (upper curve) and conditions in which it proceeds to an equilibrium position (lower curve). The upper curve gives the half-time and the rate constant for the forward reaction without interference from the reverse reaction. The lower curve begins with the same initial rate of product formation, but the rate of product formation is soon slowed as the product accumulates and the back-reaction becomes significant. The necessary consequence is that both the endpoint and the half-time will be smaller (and the observed rate constant larger) for the reaction proceeding to equilibrium compared with the reaction proceeding to completion. This is one of several instances in which it is easy to become confused if a careful distinction is not made between the absolute rate (in moles per minute) and the rate *constant* of a reaction.

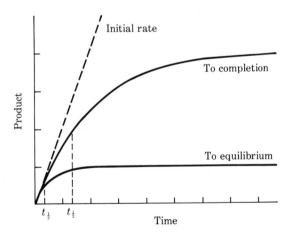

Fig 15. The course of a first-order reversible reaction which is forced to completion (upper curve) and which proceeds to equilibrium (lower curve).

The rate of a reversible first-order reaction is described by equation 47. If the apparent equilibrium constant K_{app} for a given

$$\ln\left(\frac{A_0 - [A]_{eq}}{[A] - [A]_{eq}}\right) = (k_f + k_r)t = k_{obs}(t) \tag{47}$$

set of experimental conditions is known, the rate constants for the reaction in each direction are easily obtained from the observed rate constant for approach to equilibrium and equations 46 and 48. It

$$K_{app} = \frac{k_f}{k_r} \tag{48}$$

is often possible to measure the equilibrium constant for a reaction of the form of equation 49 with a nonabsorbing component B present in large excess simply by comparing the change in absorbance observed for the reaction proceeding to equilibrium with that observed when it goes to completion at a much higher concentration of B (equation 50); this does not require a knowledge of either the con-

$$A + B \rightleftharpoons C \tag{49}$$

$$K = \frac{[C]}{[A][B]} = \frac{\Delta A_{eq}}{\Delta A_{max} - \Delta A_{eq}} \frac{1}{[B]} = K_{app} \frac{1}{[B]} \tag{50}$$

centration or the extinction coefficient of the product. In equation 50 ΔA_{eq} and ΔA_{max} refer to the absorbance of the product at equilibrium and when the reaction is forced to completion, respectively. If necessary, the values of ΔA_{max} and K_{app} may be obtained from the reciprocal ordinate intercept and negative abscissa intercept, respectively, of a plot of $1/\Delta A$ against $1/[B]$, or from the ordinate intercept and negative reciprocal of the slope, respectively, of a plot of ΔA against $\Delta A/[B]$. These are the same type of plots as for the evaluation of acid dissociation constants (Part 3). Once the values of k_f, k_r, and K_{app} have been evaluated for the (pseudo) first-order reaction at various concentrations of the reactant which is present in large excess, it is a simple matter to plot (for example) k_f against $[B]$ to obtain the second-order rate constant for the forward reaction of equation 49, based on the relationship $k_f = k_1[B]$. Alternatively, the constants may be obtained graphically from a plot of k_{obs} against $[B]$, which gives k_f as the ordinate intercept and $-1/K$ as the abscissa intercept.[21]

6. ISOTOPE EXCHANGE AT EQUILIBRIUM

It is frequently useful to measure the rate of a reaction under conditions in which there is no net change in the concentrations of the reactants by measuring the time required for a small quantity of an isotopically labeled reactant to give a labeled product. The change in the amount of label in the starting material or product always follows first-order kinetics, regardless of the order of the overall reaction.[22] What is desired, however, is not the rate of exchange of isotope, but the absolute rate, flux, or turnover of both the labeled and unlabeled reactant molecules to give the product. This rate R may be determined by measuring only the initial rate of incorporation or by multiplying the first-order rate constant for isotope incorporation, obtained in the usual way, by the factor $ab/(a+b)$, according to equation 51, which describes the first-order

$$-\ln\left(\frac{x_{\infty} - x}{x_{\infty}}\right) = R\,\frac{(a+b)}{ab}\,t = kt \tag{51}$$

exchange of labeled BX* to give labeled AX* according to equation 52. The terms are defined by equations 53 to 55. The kinetics of the overall reaction can usually be determined from the dependence of R on the concentrations of the reactants. The presence of a

$$BX^* + AX \;\rightleftharpoons\; AX^* + BX \tag{52}$$

$$[AX^*] = x \tag{53}$$

$$[AX] + [AX^*] = a \tag{54}$$

$$[BX] + [BX^*] = b \tag{55}$$

[21] I. W. Sizer and W. T. Jenkins, in E. E. Snell, P. M. Fasella, A. Braunstein, and A. Rossi Fanelli (eds.), "Chemical and Biological Aspects of Pyridoxal Catalysis," p. 123, Pergamon Press, New York, 1963.

[22] R. B. Duffield and M. Calvin, *J. Am. Chem. Soc.* **68**, 557 (1946).

significant isotope effect, of course, will mean that the flux of isotope exchange is not an exact measure of the flux of the unlabeled molecules.

C. STEADY-STATE RATE EQUATIONS

The rate equation for a reaction which proceeds through several steps is usually derived by application of the steady-state assumption to the intermediates in a proposed mechanism for the reaction. This is best described by an example, for which we will take the reaction of an aldehyde with hydroxylamine to give an oxime through the intermediate formation of an addition compound, as described in Chap. 10. Near neutral pH, the addition of hydroxylamine to the aldehyde is rapid and reversible and is followed by a slow, rate-determining, acid catalyzed dehydration of the addition compound (equation 56). At low pH, as the concentration of free

$$
NH_2OH + {>}C{=}O \underset{\substack{k_{-1} \\ k_{-2}[H^+]}}{\overset{\substack{k_1 \\ k_2[H^+]}}{\rightleftharpoons}} \overset{\substack{H \\ |}}{HON} - \overset{|}{C} - OH \overset{k_3[H^+]}{\longrightarrow} {>}C{=}NOH + H_2O
$$

$$
N \qquad\qquad C \qquad\qquad\qquad I \qquad\qquad\qquad\qquad P \qquad\qquad (56)
$$

amine decreases and the rate of acid catalyzed dehydration becomes very fast, the attack of amine on the aldehyde becomes rate-determining and the rate drops below that predicted from the rate law which holds at higher pH; i.e., there is a change in rate-determining step. At very low pH the rate again levels off and becomes independent of pH as an acid catalyzed attack of free amine on the aldehyde becomes significant; the decrease in the concentration of free amine is exactly cancelled by the increase in the rate of acid catalyzed amine attack with increasing acidity. These steps of the mechanism are designated by appropriate rate constants in equation 56 and the concentrations of amine, carbonyl compound, and product will be indicated by N, C, and P, respectively.

The steady-state derivation is based on the assumption that the rate of change of the concentration of an intermediate is zero or insignificant compared with changes in other reactants and products (equation 57). This assumption has given rise to some confu-

$$
\frac{dI}{dt} \approx 0
$$

$$
(57)
$$

sion because the *flux* or turnover of the intermediate must be as

fast as the accumulation of product, and the first-order rate constant for the change in the concentration of an intermediate in a
reaction which follows overall first-order kinetics can be as large
as that for the overall reaction. The point is that the *absolute*
rate of change of the concentration of an intermediate which does
not accumulate to a significant extent, in moles per liter per minute,
is very small compared with that of the reactants and products.
For the hydroxylamine reaction, the steady-state treatment may
be applied to rate measurements at low pH, at which most of the
hydroxylamine is protonated and there is no significant accumulation of the addition intermediate, but it cannot be applied to experimental data obtained at higher pH in the presence of concentrations of free hydroxylamine which are high enough to convert a
significant fraction of the carbonyl compound to the addition intermediate.

Now, the change in concentration of the intermediate with time
is equal to its rate of formation minus its rate of disappearance by
the pathways of equation 56, the proposed mechanism, so that
equation 57 can be extended to give equation 58. This equation is
solved for the unknown, the concentration of intermediate I, to give
equation 59.

$$\frac{dI}{dt} = 0 = (k_1 + k_2\,a_{H^+})NC - (k_{-1} + k_{-2}a_{H^+} + k_3 a_{H^+})I \tag{58}$$

$$I = \frac{(k_1 + k_2 a_{H^+})NC}{k_{-1} + k_{-2}a_{H^+} + k_3 a_{H^+}} \tag{59}$$

For a reaction in which the formation of product is essentially
irreversible under the conditions of measurement, the rate of product appearance is a function of the only possible path for product
appearance from the intermediate I according to equation 60. The
relationship of I to the rate constants for its formation and disappearance is known from equation 59, and substitution gives the
complete steady-state rate equation 60. This equation can be eval-

$$v = \frac{dP}{dt} = k_3 a_{H^+}\,I = \frac{k_3 a_{H^+}(k_1 + k_2 a_{H^+})NC}{k_{-1} + k_{-2}a_{H^+} + k_3 a_{H^+}} \tag{60}$$

uated from the experimental data. It is usually convenient to remove one or both of the variables N and C from the right-hand
side of the equation and describe the experimental results in terms

of apparent first- or second-order rate constants. If the reaction is carried out in the presence of a large excess of N, the pseudo first-order rate constant is given by dividing both sides of the equation by C; the apparent second-order rate constant k' is given by dividing both sides of the equation by both N and C (equation 61). It is possible to include terms in the steady-state rate equation to correct

$$\frac{v}{NC} = k' = \frac{k_{obs}}{N} = \frac{k_3 a_{H^+}(k_1 + k_2 a_{H^+})}{k_{-1} + k_{-2} a_{H^+} + k_3 a_{H^+}} \tag{61}$$

for the ionization of each reactant, but this leads to an unnecessarily complicated equation and, in general, it is preferable to correct the observed rate constants to a reaction of one or the other ionic form of each reactant by dividing by the fraction of the reactant in the desired ionic form at each pH value.

The next step is to evaluate the meaning of equation 61 under limiting conditions, so that one can understand its mechanistic significance and be certain that it describes the important mechanistic features of the rate law from which it was derived (equation 56); this procedure also is useful in detecting errors in the derivation. The following limiting regions of pH are significant for oxime formation.

a) **Low a_{H^+} (high pH).** The terms in parenthesis and in the denominator of equation 61 which contain a_{H^+} become insignificant compared with other terms and may be neglected. Consequently, equation 61 reduces to the simple form of equation 62, in which K_1 is the equilibrium constant for the first step of the reaction. This equation, then, describes the reaction at high pH, at which hydroxylamine addition occurs in a rapid equilibrium step and the observed rate depends on the equilibrium concentration of addition compound and the rate of its acid catalyzed breakdown. The numerical value of $k_1 k_3/k_{-1}$ may be evaluated from the observed rate in this pH region (provided that the steady-state approximation is valid, i.e.,

$$\frac{k_{obs}}{N} = \frac{k_1}{k_{-1}} k_3 a_{H^+} = K_1 k_3 a_{H^+} \tag{62}$$

from experimental data obtained at sufficiently low hydroxylamine concentration that there is no significant accumulation of the intermediate).

b) **Intermediate** a_{H^+} **and pH.**   In this region there is a change to rate-determining attack of amine on the carbonyl compound, which is equivalent to the statements: $k_3 a_{H^+} \gg k_{-1}$ and $k_3 a_{H^+} \gg k_{-2} a_{H^+}$. If an intermediate goes back to starting materials much faster than it goes on to products, it is in equilibrium with respect to starting materials and a subsequent step must be rate-determining; if it goes on to products much faster than it goes back to starting materials, every molecule of intermediate that is formed goes on to products and the rate of formation of intermediate is the rate-determining step of the overall reaction. It is important to understand this situation and remember that for a reaction under steady-state conditions it is not the absolute value of the rate constants for the two forward steps (for example, k_1 and $k_2 a_{H^+}$) that determines which step is rate-determining. It is perfectly possible (and not unusual) for the rate *constant* for the second step to be much larger than that for the first step when the second step is rate-determining. The *only* determinant of which step is rate-determining is the relative magnitude of the rates of breakdown of the intermediate to starting materials and products under a given set of experimental conditions (Fig. 4, Chap. 10). With the above inequalities and when $k_1 \gg k_2 a_{H^+}$ the rate equation for the hydroxylamine reaction reduces to equation 63. This is the expected equation for rate-determining attack of free amine, and the value of k_1 may be determined from the observed rates under conditions in which this step is rate-determining.

$$k_{obs} = \frac{k_3 a_{H^+} k_1 N}{k_3 a_{H^+}} = k_1 N \tag{63}$$

c) **High** a_{H^+} **(low pH).**   At high acidity the acid catalyzed attack of free amine will become rate determining as $k_2 a_{H^+}$ becomes larger than k_1. The same inequalities with respect to k_3 hold as in the previous case, and the rate equation reduces to equation 64. Since

$$k_{obs} = k_2 a_{H^+} N \tag{64}$$

both the k_1 and $k_2 a_{H^+}$ terms are likely to contribute significantly to the observed rate of attack under most experimental conditions, their magnitude is best estimated by plotting k_{obs}/N against a_{H^+} to give k_2 and k_1 as the slope and intercept, respectively.

These limiting cases give numerical values for k_1, k_2, and, since k_1 is known, for k_3/k_{-1}. The equilibrium constant for the first step is the same regardless of which path is used to reach equilibrium, so that the value of k_3/k_{-2} may be evaluated from equation 65 and the known value of k_2. These rate constants—the

$$K_1 k_3 = \frac{k_1}{k_{-1}} k_3 = \frac{k_2}{k_{-2}} k_3 \tag{65}$$

constants for the first step and for the partitioning of the intermediate to starting materials and products—are all that can be obtained from a steady-state treatment. Steady-state experiments do not give information which can be used to obtain a value of K_1, the equilibrium constant for formation of the intermediate, or the absolute value of k_3, the rate constant for its breakdown.

With these rate constants it is possible to calculate the value of k_{obs} at any pH, and this should next be done in order to see if the steady-state rate equation provides an accurate description of the experimental results at intermediate pH values, at which more than a single step is rate-determining. For this purpose it is useful to recast equation 61 in the form of equation 66, in which all the quantities on the right side are known. The solid line in Fig. 1 of

$$k_{obs} = \frac{(k_1 + k_2 a_{H^+}) a_{H^+} N}{k_{-1}/k_3 + k_{-2} a_{H^+}/k_3 + a_{H^+}} \tag{66}$$

Chap. 10 is calculated from the steady-state rate equation 66; the rates for acid catalyzed dehydration of an equilibrium concentration of the addition intermediate and for hydroxylamine attack through uncatalyzed and acid catalyzed reactions are shown as dashed lines and dotted lines, respectively.[23]

The description to this point has been based on the assumption that the differences in the magnitudes of the various rate constants are large enough so that one or the other step of the reaction becomes almost completely rate-determining under the conditions of the experiments, and the rate constants for that step can be evaluated directly from the experimental rate constants. In practice, however, this is often not the case and both steps contribute to the observed rate under all experimentally attainable conditions. This is particularly likely to be the case if there are two kinetic terms with the same dependence on acidity, such as the k_2 and k_3 terms of equations 56 and 60; unless k_3 is much larger than k_2, for ex-

[23] W. P. Jencks, J. Am. Chem. Soc. 81, 475 (1959).

ample, the dehydration step will be partially rate-determining even in strong acid solution. If preliminary calculations indicate that this is the case, the correct values of the rate constants must be obtained either by successive approximations or by calculation. Substitution of preliminary values of the rate constants in the steady-state rate equation will usually give an indication of what changes are necessary to take account of the fact that other steps are partially rate-determining, so that the numerical values may be adjusted until a satisfactory fit to the experimental data is obtained.

It is often possible to invert the steady-state rate equation and separate the variables so that the values of the rate constants may be obtained in a more elegant manner by reciprocal plots of the experimental data. For example, the reaction of protonated imido esters (IEH^+) with amines (N) to give amidines (P) proceeds according to the mechanism of equation 67, with a change from rate-determining amine attack at high pH (k_1) to rate-determining breakdown

$$IEH^+ + N \; \underset{k_{-1}}{\overset{k_1}{\rightleftharpoons}} \; IH^+ \; \overset{K_{IH^+}}{\rightleftharpoons} \; I + H^+$$

$$\downarrow k_3 \qquad\qquad \downarrow k_2$$

$$PH^+ \qquad\quad P \tag{67}$$

of an addition intermediate (I and IH^+) through uncharged (k_2) and positively charged (k_3) transition states at low pH.[24] The steady-state equation for this system (equation 68), in which f_{IEH^+} is the fraction of imido ester in the protonated form, may be con-

$$\frac{d(P + PH^+)}{dt} = \frac{k_{obs}}{N f_{IEH^+}} = \frac{k_1(k_3 + k_2 K_{IH^+}/a_{H^+})}{k_{-1} + k_3 + k_2 K_{IH^+}/a_{H^+}} \tag{68}$$

verted to the reciprocal form (equation 69) to separate the rate con-

$$\frac{1}{k_{obs}/N f_{IEH^+}} = \frac{k_{-1} a_{H^+}}{k_1 k_3 a_{H^+} + k_1 k_2 K_{IH^+}} + \frac{1}{k_1} \tag{69}$$

stants. A reciprocal plot of $k_{obs}/N f_{IEH^+}$ against a_{H^+} gives an initially straight line with an intercept equal to $1/k_1$ at $a_{H^+} = 0$ and

[24] E. Hand and W. P. Jencks, *J. Am. Chem. Soc.* **84**, 3505 (1962).

slope $k_{-1}/k_1 k_2 K_{IH^+}$. At higher acidity the $k_1 k_3 a_{H^+}$ term becomes dominant, and the line levels off to the value $k_{-1}/k_1 k_3 + 1/k_1$. A third alternative is to evaluate the rate constants by either an iterative procedure or by direct calculation with a computer, but it often takes longer to derive or locate the appropriate computer program than to utilize more primitive methods.

It is worth emphasizing that steady-state kinetics reveals nothing about the nature of an intermediate except the charge, stoichiometry, and *relative* free energies of the transition states for its breakdown to starting materials and to products. It has already been pointed out that kinetics cannot provide information which determines the equilibrium constant for the formation or the absolute rate constants for the breakdown of an intermediate which is present only in steady-state concentrations. It is also not possible to determine the predominant state of ionization or the ionization constant of such an intermediate, so long as it does not accumulate in significant amounts. Consequently, it makes no difference whether a rate law is formulated as an acid catalyzed reaction of a neutral intermediate or as a reaction of the conjugate acid of the intermediate; the same applies to base catalysis. For example, the mechanism of imido ester aminolysis of equation 67 could equally well be formulated in terms of equation 70, in which a neutral intermediate breaks down by uncatalyzed and acid catalyzed pathways. Note that the transition states for the forward and the corresponding reverse steps must always have the same charge and composition, so that the k'_{-1} step, the reverse of the k'_1 step in this mechanism, must contain a proton to balance the proton in IEH^+. The steady-state expression for the mechanism of equation 70 is given in equation 71. This has precisely the same form and is kinetically indis-

$$IEH^+ + N \underset{k'_{-1} H^+}{\overset{k'_1}{\rightleftharpoons}} I \overset{\overset{k'_2}{\underset{k'_3 H^+}{}}}{\longrightarrow} P \tag{70}$$

$$\frac{k_{obs}}{Nf_{IEH^+}} = \frac{k'_1 (k'_3 + k'_2/a_{H^+})}{k'_{-1} + k'_3 + k'_2/a_{H^+}} \tag{71}$$

tinguishable from equation 68; the only difference is that k'_2 is substituted for $k_2 K_{IH^+}$. A third formulation could be written with a protonated intermediate which breaks down by uncatalyzed and hydroxide ion catalyzed pathways. All these formulations are perfectly equivalent and indistinguishable kinetically, so that use of one or the other implies nothing about the detailed mechanism of the reaction.

It is important to keep in mind that equilibrium requirements and microscopic reversibility must be satisfied in the application or simplification of steady-state rate equations for ordinary thermal reactions. For example, under conditions in which $k_1 \gg k_2[H^+]$ in equations 56 and 61, it is also necessary that $k_{-1} \gg k_{-2}[H^+]$. The relative importance of two pathways for a given reaction must be identical for the reaction in both directions. Thus, if it is decided that a particular kinetic term is insignificant for a reaction in one direction, the corresponding term for the opposite direction must also be insignificant.

In general, a requirement for steady-state kinetic treatment provides important evidence for the two-step nature and, hence, the existence of an intermediate in a reaction, but the kinetics do not give any indication of *which* step is rate-determining under a given set of conditions, and an equivalent mechanism can nearly always be written in which the assignment of rate-determining steps is reversed. For example, a kinetically equivalent mechanism for oxime formation could be written in which acid catalyzed formation of the addition intermediate is rate-determining at high pH and decomposition of the intermediate through neutral and cationic transition states is rate-determining at low pH. A choice between such kinetically indistinguishable assignments can sometimes be made on the basis of chemical reasonableness or analogy to the mechanism of related reactions, but usually the distinction is made by obtaining direct proof that formation of the intermediate is a fast step under a given set of conditions. This may be done by demonstrating its accumulation, as in the hydroxylamine reaction at high pH,[23] or by demonstrating exchange reactions which proceed through the intermediate, as in the exchange of amines into imido esters[24] or the exchange of labeled oxygen from water into thiol esters[25] at low pH. A number of examples are discussed in Chap. 10.

1. INHIBITION BY AN INITIAL PRODUCT IN A TWO-STEP REACTION

The 4-methylpyridine catalyzed hydrolysis of p-nitrophenyl acetate proceeds through the initial formation of an acetylpyridinium ion intermediate, which then undergoes hydrolysis at a rate which is too fast to measure by ordinary techniques (equation 72). However,

[25] M. L. Bender and H. d'A. Heck, *J. Am. Chem. Soc.* **89**, 1211 (1967).

$$CH_3COR + N\overset{/}{\underset{\searrow}{}} \underset{k_{-1}}{\overset{k_1}{\rightleftharpoons}} CH_3\overset{O}{\overset{\|}{C}}N\overset{+/}{\underset{\searrow}{}} + {}^-OR$$

$$H_2O \downarrow k_2$$

$$CH_3\overset{O}{\overset{\|}{C}}OH + N\overset{/}{\underset{\searrow}{}} \tag{72}$$

the p-nitrophenolate ion which is released in the first step may react with the intermediate to regenerate starting material faster than water reacts with the intermediate to give hydrolysis products.[3] This back-reaction causes an inhibition of the observed rate of hydrolysis. As shown in Fig. 16, the inhibition becomes significant at a low concentration of product because of the very high reactivity of p-nitrophenolate compared to water. The inhibition by this back-reaction causes a deviation from (pseudo) first-order kinetics, but this deviation may not be easily noticeable.

This type of inhibition is useful for two reasons. First, it shows that there must be an intermediate in the reaction when the intermediate cannot be observed directly. This is a method of demonstrating that the above reaction proceeds by nucleophilic rather

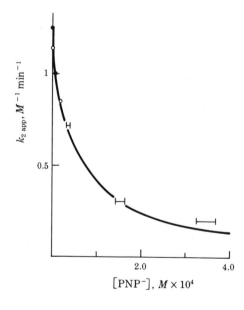

Fig 16. Inhibition of the 4-methylpyridine catalyzed hydrolysis of p-nitrophenyl acetate by added p-nitrophenolate ion PNP$^-$ at 25°, ionic strength 1.0 M. Open circles: 50% free base. Solid symbols: 90% free base amine. The bars show the range of variation of the concentration of p-nitrophenolate ion during the experiment.[3]

than by general base catalysis and that carbonium ions are formed in reactions which are inhibited by the initial leaving group, for example. Second, it provides a simple method for determining the *relative* nucleophilic reactivities of the leaving group and of solvent toward the reactive intermediate. This provides a means for setting up a scale of relative reactivities. The mechanism of equation 72 is described by the steady-state equation 73. The value of k_{-1}/k_2 for a

$$k_{obs} = \frac{k_1 k_2}{k_2 + k_{-1}[RO^-]} \tag{73}$$

reaction of this kind may be evaluated from a plot of $1/k_{obs}$ against $[RO^-]$ (equation 74), based on a series of values of k_{obs} obtained

$$\frac{1}{k_{obs}} = \frac{1}{k_1} + \frac{k_{-1}[RO^-]}{k_1 k_2} \tag{74}$$

under conditions in which the concentration of added RO^- is essentially constant.

D. APPLICATIONS OF TRANSITION-STATE THEORY

The transfer of an atom or group B from A—B to C can occur by the complete dissociation of B from A to give a radical which adds to C in a second step (equation 75), but often occurs by a more or

$$A\!-\!B \underset{\pm A}{\rightleftharpoons} B\cdot \underset{\pm C}{\rightleftharpoons} B\!-\!C \tag{75}$$

less concerted path in which some bond formation develops between B and C before the bond to A is completely broken (equation 76).

$$A\!-\!B + C \rightleftharpoons [A\cdots B\cdots C]^{\ddagger} \rightleftharpoons A + B\!-\!C \tag{76}$$

The two-step pathway follows the energy curves for the dissociation of A—B and B—C, whereas the concerted reaction follows a lower-energy path which might be regarded as a composite of the separate A—B and B—C energy curves and is defined in terms of a "reaction coordinate," a function of the A—B and B—C distances (Fig. 17). The highest-energy point between A—B and

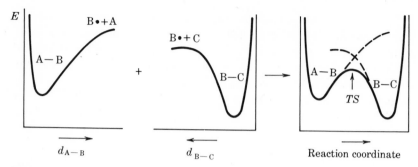

Fig 17. Energy curves for the dissociation of the molecules A—B and B—C and for the reaction of A—B with C to give B—C without complete dissociation.

B—C on this energy diagram is the transition state. The meaning of the reaction coordinate is apparent from an inspection of Fig. 18, in which the reaction coordinate, shown as the dashed line, represents the lowest-energy pathway from A—B to B—C as a function of changing A—B and B—C distances. This contour diagram shows that the B—C distance decreases considerably, as bond formation to C takes place, before the A—B distance has increased beyond that in which effective bonding can exist. If the reaction

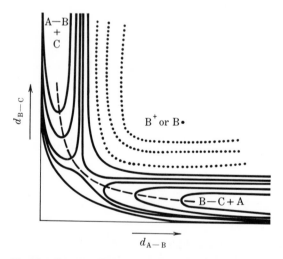

Fig 18. Contour diagram to show that the reaction coordinate (dashed line) is the lowest-energy pathway from A—B to B—C. The dotted lines represent the energy contours for a metastable intermediate carbonium ion or radical.

occurred through a carbonium ion or radical mechanism in which B separates completely from A before it reacts with C (equation 75 or 77), the reaction coordinate would pass through the energy hollow

$$A—B \underset{\pm A^-}{\rightleftharpoons} B^+ \underset{\pm C^-}{\rightleftharpoons} B—C \tag{77}$$

for a carbonium ion or radical, shown by the dotted lines in Fig. 18. Such a reaction would show a dip in the transition-state diagram corresponding to the metastable intermediate (Fig. 19).

The great conceptual advantage of the transition-state treatment is that it permits the application to reaction rates of nearly all the considerations that are applied to reaction equilibria by treating the transition state as a chemical species which exists in a sort of pseudo equilibrium with the starting materials (equation 76). The rate of reaction depends on the "concentration" (not the activity) of transition states, almost all of which decompose to products with a transmission coefficient κ, close to 1.0. The observed rate constant k can then be described in terms of a pseudo equilibrium constant, $K^{\ddagger}$, for the formation of the transition state from the reactants according to equation 78, in which k_B is Boltzmann's constant and h is Planck's constant.

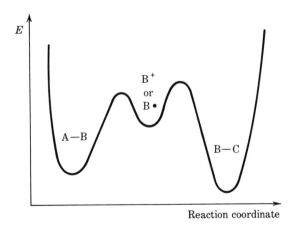

Fig 19. Reaction coordinate for a reaction which proceeds through a metastable carbonium ion or radical intermediate.

$$k = \kappa \, \frac{k_B T}{h} K^{\ddagger} \tag{78}$$

The pseudo equilibrium constant $K^{\ddagger}$ is, like other equilibrium constants, the ratio of the *activity* of the product (the transition state) to the activities of the reactants (equation 79). Since the rate depends on the *concentration* of the transition state and rate measurements are expressed in terms of rate laws based on the

$$K^{\ddagger} = \frac{a_{TS}}{a_A a_B} = \frac{C_{TS}}{C_A C_B} \frac{f_{TS}}{f_A f_B} \tag{79}$$

concentrations of the reactants, the rate may be expressed by equation 80, in which the activity-coefficient ratio $f_A f_B / f_{TS}$ describes the deviation from ideality of the transition state relative to the

$$\text{Rate} \sim C_{TS} = K^{\ddagger} C_A C_B \frac{f_A f_B}{f_{TS}} \tag{80}$$

reactants. This relationship permits an enormous simplification of considerations of solvent, salt, and other activity-coefficient effects on reaction rates. It is often possible to predict or rationalize such effects simply by inspection of the nature of the reactants and a proposed transition state and a knowledge of the expected stabilizing or destabilizing effects of salts and solvents on the *difference* in structure and charge between the reactants and the transition state. Any such consideration must be based on the predominant ionic species of the reactants in solution, upon which the observed rate constant is based.

Consider, for example, the well known reaction of ammonium and cyanate ions to give urea (equation 81). The mechanism of this

$$\text{NH}_4^+ + \text{NCO}^- \longrightarrow \text{H}_2\text{N}\overset{\overset{\displaystyle O}{\parallel}}{\text{C}}\text{NH}_2 \tag{81}$$

reaction was the subject of extended controversy among physical chemists regarding whether it proceeds by a direct reaction of cyanate and ammonium ions or whether it proceeds by a preliminary pair of proton transfers to give free ammonia and cyanic acid, which then react with a rate constant k' to give urea (equation 82). It is

$$NH_4^+ \quad NCO^-$$

$$\pm H^+ \Big\Vert \quad \pm H^+ \Big\Vert$$

$$NH_3 + HNCO \ \rightleftharpoons \ \begin{bmatrix} \overset{\delta+}{H} & \overset{\delta-}{O} \\ | & |: \\ H-N\cdots C \\ | & |: \\ H & N \\ & | \\ & H \end{bmatrix}^{\ddagger} \ \longrightarrow \ \overset{O}{\underset{H_2NCNH_2}{\overset{\Vert}{}}} \tag{82}$$

easily shown algebraically that the rate laws for these two mechanisms are identical, with rate constants which are interrelated by the ionization constants of the reactants (equations 83 and 84).

$$\text{Rate} = k[NH_4^+][NCO^-] = k'[NH_3][HNCO]$$

$$= k' \frac{K_{NH_4^+}}{K_{HNCO}} [NH_4^+][NCO^-] \tag{83}$$

$$k = k' \frac{K_{NH_4^+}}{K_{HNCO}} \tag{84}$$

However, this conclusion may be reached more rapidly by simple inspection, which reveals that the stoichiometric composition and charge of the transition states for the two mechanisms are identical, so that the two mechanisms must follow the same rate law and be kinetically indistinguishable.

The effects of salts and solvents on this reaction may be evaluated for the two mechanisms by considering separately the effects on the starting materials, on the equilibria for the two ionization steps, and on each rate step, and a number of attempts were made to distinguish the two mechanisms by examination of the effects of salts and solvents on the observed rate.[26] However, the transition-state theory makes it possible to state immediately upon inspection that salt and solvent effects will be the same for these two mechanisms and cannot provide a means of distingushing them. In both cases the starting materials are charged and any reasonable transition state for either mechanism (for example, equation 82) will have either a similar charge or, more probably, a smaller charge than the starting materials. Therefore, the addition of a salt will probably stabilize (decrease the activity coefficient) of the starting materials more than the transition state and give a rate decrease,

[26] A. A. Frost and R. G. Pearson, "Kinetics and Mechanisms," part B, p. 307 2nd ed., John Wiley & Sons, Inc., New York, 1961.

as is found experimentally, for either mechanism. The addition of most organic solvents will destabilize (increase the activity coefficient) of the starting materials compared with the transition state and give a rate increase, as is found experimentally, for either mechanism. The utility of the transition-state approach is that it permits one to ignore all the steps between the starting materials and the transition state.[27] Instead of considering the effect of a variation in reaction conditions on each individual equilibrium and rate step and then attempting to add these to predict the effects on the overall rate, one need only consider effects on the predominant ionic species of the reactants, according to which the observed rate constant is expressed, and on the transition state.

The same simplification applies to considerations of the effects of substituents on reaction rates. Consider, for example, the reaction of acetylimidazole with a series of substituted amines (equation 85).[28] The predominant species in solution near neutral pH are the

$$
\begin{array}{c}
\overset{+}{\text{RNH}}_3 \; + \; \text{CH}_3\overset{\overset{\displaystyle O}{\displaystyle \|}}{\text{CN}}\underset{}{\overset{}{\diagup\!\!\diagdown}}\text{N}\\[4mm]
\pm\text{H}^+\Big\Updownarrow \qquad\qquad \pm\text{H}^+\Big\Updownarrow\\[4mm]
\text{RNH}_2 \; + \; \text{CH}_3\overset{\overset{\displaystyle O}{\displaystyle \|}}{\text{CN}}\underset{}{\overset{}{\diagup\!\!\overset{+}{\diagdown}}}\text{NH} \;\; \rightleftharpoons \;\; \left[\begin{array}{c} \overset{\delta+}{}\;\;\;\overset{\delta-}{}\\ \text{H}\quad\text{O}\\ |\quad\;\; |:\\ \text{RN}\cdots\text{C}-\text{N}\underset{}{\overset{}{\diagup\!\!\overset{+}{\diagdown}}}\text{NH}\\ |\quad\;\; |\\ \text{H}\quad\text{CH}_3 \end{array} \right]^{\ddagger}\\[4mm]
\mathbf{3}\\[3mm]
\Big\downarrow\\[3mm]
\text{CH}_3\overset{\overset{\displaystyle O}{\displaystyle \|}}{\text{C}}\text{NHR} \; + \; \text{HN}\underset{}{\overset{}{\diagup\!\!\overset{+}{\diagdown}}}\text{NH} \qquad\qquad (85)
\end{array}
$$

protonated amine and uncharged acetylimidazole, but the reactive species are the kinetically indistinguishable free amine and protonated acetylimidazole. The effect of adding an electron-withdrawing

[27] One cannot ignore any "intermediate" which is so unstable as to require a greater than diffusion-controlled rate for its further reaction in order to account for the observed rate of the overall reaction; such an "intermediate" cannot exist on the reaction path.

[28] W. P. Jencks and J. Carriuolo, *J. Biol. Chem.* **234**, 1272, 1280 (1959); *J. Am. Chem. Soc.* **82**, 1778 (1960).

substituent to the amine is to increase the observed rate. This may be accounted for by a consideration of each of the two steps of the reaction: an increased concentration of the reactive free amine will be brought about by the decrease in pK of the substituted amine, and this increase must be larger than the decrease in the reactivity of the free amine caused by its decreased basicity. Alternatively, one may simply note that the electron-withdrawing substituent destabilizes the starting material more than the transition state, **3**, which will almost certainly have less charge on the nitrogen atom than the starting protonated amine. For more complicated reaction schemes the transition state approach can provide an even greater simplification.

1. THERMODYNAMIC ACTIVATION PARAMETERS

The dependence of observed reaction rates on temperature frequently follows the exponential equations 86 and 87, in which E_a is

$$k = PZe^{-E_a/RT} = Ae^{-E_a/RT} \tag{86}$$

$$\ln k = -E_a/RT + \ln PZ \tag{87}$$

the Arrhenius activation energy and PZ or A represents a "collision factor." The activation energy is given by equation 88, and is

$$\frac{d \ln k}{dT} = -\frac{E_a}{RT^2} \tag{88}$$

usually evaluated from the integrated equation 89 or from the slope

$$\log \frac{k_2}{k_1} = -\frac{E_a}{4.575}\left(\frac{1}{T_2} - \frac{1}{T_1}\right) \tag{89}$$

of a plot of $\log k$ against $1/T$ (in degrees Kelvin), which gives $-E_a/2.303R$. If this plot is nonlinear or if equation 89 does not give constant values of the activation energy over different temperature ranges, the reaction has a significant heat capacity of activation or there is a change in the nature of the rate-determining step with changing temperature.

The "collision factor" PZ (or A) is the so-called temperature-independent factor (although it is not altogether independent of temperature) and has a normal value of about 3×10^{11} M^{-1} sec^{-1} for a second-order reaction according to collision theory. According to this theory the collision frequency Z is given by equation 90, in which

$$Z = N_A N_B \left(\frac{d_A + d_B}{2}\right)^2 \sqrt{8\pi k_B T \left(\frac{1}{m_a} + \frac{1}{m_b}\right)} \tag{90}$$

the subscripts A and B refer to two reacting molecules A and B, N is the number of molecules per cubic centimeter, d is the diameter, and m is the mass of the reacting molecules. The probability factor P is an adjustable parameter which in the simplest possible case might be a steric factor describing the fraction of collisions between A and B which occur with the proper orientation of A and B to lead to reaction. The difficulty with this nomenclature for reactions in solution is that this adjustable parameter must include many variables other than steric factors and may even have a value greater than 1. An extreme case is the denaturation of egg albumin, which has a frequency factor of 10^{72}.

The pseudo equilibrium for formation of the transition state according to transition-state theory makes possible the application to reaction rates of the same thermodynamic parameters that are used to describe ordinary equilibria. The free energy of activation is a direct logarithmic expression of the magnitude of the observed rate constant because of the direct relationship of the rate constant to the equilibrium constant for formation of the activated complex (equation 91). At 25°, $\Delta F^{\ddagger} = -1360 \log k + 17,400$ cal/mole, for

$$\Delta F^{\ddagger} = -RT \ln K^{\ddagger} = -RT \ln \frac{kh}{k_B T} \tag{91}$$

rate constants expressed in units of time of sec^{-1}. The free energy of activation has the usual relationship to the heat of activation $\Delta H^{\ddagger}$ and the entropy of activation $\Delta S^{\ddagger}$ (equation 92). The relationship of $\Delta H^{\ddagger}$ to the Arrhenius activation energy is slightly different for different types of reactions, but for reactions in solution it differs

$$\Delta F^{\ddagger} = \Delta H^{\ddagger} - T \Delta S^{\ddagger} \tag{92}$$

only by the factor RT (equation 93). The entropy of activation cor-

$$\Delta H^{\ddagger} = E_a - RT \tag{93}$$

responds to a logarithmic measure of the frequency factor PZ or A and may be calculated from equation 94 or 95, as well as from equa-

$$\Delta S^{\ddagger} = R \ln k - R \ln \left(\frac{ek_B T}{h} \right) + \frac{E_a}{T} \tag{94}$$

$$\Delta S^{\ddagger} = 4.576 \log \frac{PZ}{T} - 49.203 \tag{95}$$

tions 91 and 92.

In calculating thermodynamic activation properties, particular care must be taken to take account of any rapid equilibrium steps, especially ionizations, which occur before the rate constant which is being examined. For example, a rate constant based on a_{OH^-} or on the free base species of a nucleophile at pH values below its pK must refer to each of these quantities at each temperature examined, so that pH measurements, values of K_w, and the ionization constant of each reactant must be obtained at each temperature in order to calculate the concentration of the reacting species at each temperature.

The physical meaning of the entropy of activation provides an intriguing subject for interpretation (and overinterpretation). In terms of the transition-state diagram of Fig. 18 the entropy of activation may be regarded as a measure of the *width* of the saddle point of energy over which reacting molecules must pass as activated complexes. The enthalpy of activation is a measure of the energy barrier which must be overcome by reacting molecules, whereas the entropy of activation is a measure of how many of the molecules which have this much energy can actually react. The activation entropy includes steric and orientation requirements, the entropy of dilution, concentration effects which result from the choice of some standard state in which to express equilibrium and rate constants, and solvent effects. Other things being equal, monomolecular reactions will have entropies of activation near zero because no concentration or orientation requirements ordinarily exist for such reactions. Bimolecular reactions which are described by rate constants with units of M^{-1} will have a negative entropy of activation simply as a result of the entropy requirement for bringing together two molecules from a 1 M solution to a single activated complex, and are likely to have still more negative entropies from steric and orientation requirements, including losses of translational and rotational degrees of freedom in the transition state. The entropy for the equilibrium hydration of an aldehyde, which might be regarded as a model for the combination of water and a carbonyl compound to give a transition state, is on the order of -18 e.u.[29] This is considerably more negative than the value of about -8 e.u. which would be required to bring a molecule of a reactant from a standard 1 M solution to a site adjacent to another molecule in preference to a molecule of solvent water.

In spite of uncertainties of quantitative interpretation, the entropy of activation provides a useful criterion to distinguish monomolecular from bimolecular (or polymolecular) reactions when the reaction order cannot be determined directly from the kinetics, as in the case of reactions which involve an unknown number of solvent molecules.[29] For example, the entropy of activation for the hydrolysis of the acetyl phosphate dianion is $+3.7$ e.u. This is consistent with a monomolecular mechanism in which acetate ion is expelled in the rate-determining step to give monomeric metaphosphate monoanion, which reacts with water in a subsequent fast step (equation 96). This mechanism is not available to acetyl phenyl phosphate,

$$\underset{\underset{O}{\overset{\displaystyle O}{\|}}}{CH_3C}-O-\underset{\overset{\displaystyle O}{\|}}{\overset{\displaystyle O^{--}}{P}}-O \xrightarrow{slow} \underset{\overset{\displaystyle O}{\|}}{CH_3CO^-} + \left[\underset{O\,\diagdown\,P\,\diagup\,O}{\overset{\displaystyle O}{\overset{\displaystyle \vdots}{}}}\right]^- \xrightarrow[fast]{H_2O} H_2PO_4^- \tag{96}$$

which decomposes more slowly with an entropy of activation of -28.8 e.u. This large negative entropy probably reflects a requirement for the orientation of several water molecules for nucleophilic attack on the *carbonyl* group with assistance by proton transfer (equation 97).[17] The same criteria may be used to interpret the

$$CH_3C-O-P-OR \longrightarrow CH_3CO^- + HOPOR \tag{97}$$

[29] L. L. Schaleger and F. A. Long, *Advan. Phys. Org. Chem.* 1, 1 (1963).

mechanism of reactions which involve an equilibrium proton transfer before the rate-determining step, such as the hydrolysis of sucrose (equations 98 and 99). However, the observed entropy of activation

$$S + H_{solv}^+ \;\; \underset{K_a}{\rightleftharpoons} \;\; SH^+ \tag{98}$$

$$SH^+ \;\xrightarrow{\;k\;}\; products \tag{99}$$

for such reactions includes the entropy for the preliminary proton transfer (equation 98) as well as for the decomposition of the proton-ated intermediate (equation 99), which makes interpretation difficult unless the entropy of the proton transfer step can be measured directly or estimated. Nevertheless, there is an empirical correlation between entropy of activation and reaction order for a number of acid catalyzed reactions: monomolecular A_1 reactions have $\Delta S^{\ddagger}$ values which are near zero or positive; bimolecular A_2 reactions of acyl compounds have $\Delta S^{\ddagger}$ values which are usually more negative than -15 e.u., and other bimolecular reactions have $\Delta S^{\ddagger}$ values in the range -5 to -15 e.u., with overlap among these categories in a few cases.[29]

The *volume* of activation may provide a more direct approach to the estimation of reaction order.[30,31] The volumes of activation for the preliminary proton transfers in acid catalyzed reactions (for example, equation 98) are generally constant for a given type of ionization so that the observed volume of activation may easily be correlated with that for the rate-determining step. A monomolecu-lar reaction is likely to have a transition state which is similar in size or is larger than the starting material, so that the volume of activation is zero or positive. The transition state for a bimolecular reaction is expected to be smaller than the starting materials because the reacting molecules are coming together to form a partial bond, so that the volume of activation is negative. The volume of activation[32] for the hydrolysis of acetyl phosphate dianion (equation 96) is 1.0 ± 1.0 cc/mole, whereas that for the hydrolysis of acetyl phenyl phosphate (equation 97) is -19 ± 2 cc/mole.

Both the volume and the entropy of activation are extremely sensitive to *solvent effects*. The orientation of solvent molecules around charges or developing charges results in a negative entropy

[30] E. Whalley, *Trans. Faraday Soc.* **55**, 798 (1959).

[31] W. J. Le Noble, *Progr. Phys. Org. Chem.* **5**, 207 (1967).

[32] G. Di Sabato, W. P. Jencks, and E. Whalley, *Can. J. Chem.* **40**, 1220 (1962).

change, and the accompanying electrostriction will give a negative volume change. These effects may be as large or larger than those resulting from the molecularity of a reaction, so that the entropy and volume of activation may be used as criteria for molecularity only if it is reasonably certain that there is no large difference in charge between the reactants and the transition state. Conversely, if the order of the reaction is known, the entropy and volume of activation can provide an indication of whether the transition state requires more or less charge and solvent orientation than the starting materials.

Since ions can have a structure-breaking as well as a structure-making effect on water, it might be expected that polar transition states might exist with a positive entropy of activation. This does not appear to be a common phenomenon, perhaps because ordered water molecules around the developing charge have a specific catalytic or solvating role, but this possibility and the general difficulty of clearly defining "structural" effects in water suggest that detailed interpretations of reaction mechanisms based on thermodynamic activation parameters should be made with caution.

In considering reaction mechanisms in aqueous solution it is often more useful to evaluate the free energy of activation than the enthalpy of activation because of the difficulties of interpretation of the latter parameter, for reasons which have been noted at a number of points in this volume. Two-dimensional transition-state–reaction-coordinate diagrams may be drawn based on the free energy rather than the enthalpy of activation, and changes in these diagrams with changing reaction conditions or reactants may be useful in interpreting reaction mechanisms. However, it is important to keep in mind that the free energy of activation includes concentration-dependent terms, so that it is easy to make misleading interpretations for steps of different reaction order or for experimental situations in which the concentration of a reactant is varied. Furthermore, the absolute value of the standard free energy of activation is dependent on the concentration scale in which the rate constants are expressed. These concentration effects reflect the contribution of entropies of dilution or concentration to the free energy. The free energy of activation usually refers to a standard state of 1 M concentration for the reactants and products given in the rate laws for the forward and reverse reactions upon which the transition-state diagram is based, including hydrogen and hydroxide ions.

For some purposes it is useful to construct a transition-state diagram based on the free energy of activation for an *observed* rate constant, which changes with changing reaction conditions. For example, the nucleophilic displacement of phosphate from p-nitrophenyl phosphate by dimethylamine is a two-step reaction with the intermediate formation of a tetrahedral addition compound. The second step is subject to catalysis by hydroxide ion, so that there is a change in rate-determining step from rate-determining attack on the aromatic ring in strong base to rate-determining breakdown of the addition intermediate as the hydroxide ion concentration is decreased (Fig. 20).[33] When diagrams of this kind are used to compare the relative importance of different reaction pathways, it is important to be certain that the order of the reaction and the units of the rate constants are the same for the different pathways that are being compared. For the diagram of Fig. 20 the standard state is taken as 1 M for all reactants *except* hydroxide ion. Free-energy–reaction-coordinate diagrams cannot be drawn for irreversible processes, which have an infinitely large free energy. For this reason it is easy to be misled by reaction-coordinate diagrams for reactions which are studied under conditions in which one of the steps is essentially irreversible under the conditions of measurement. This is the case, for example, in enzymatic reactions in which two products are given off in different steps, so that both steps are irreversible under the conditions of initial rate measurements.

2. SUMMARY OF RULES FOR INTERPRETATION

Some of the principles which should be kept in mind when transition-state terminology and free-energy–reaction-coordinate diagrams are utilized for the interpretation of reaction kinetics and mechanism may be summarized as follows:

1. Ordinary kinetic techniques can determine the overall charge and stoichiometric composition of the transition state, but cannot determine the charge distribution or arrangement of atoms in the transition state. The demonstration that the rate of a reaction follows a particular rate law is consistent with a reaction which involves the reactants included in that rate law, but is also consistent with any chemically reasonable mechanism involving other reactants which are in a rapid equilibrium with those in the rate law, if they have the same total composition and charge.
2. It is permissible and often desirable to consider only the reactants in solution and the transition state, ignoring all metastable in-

[33] A. J. Kirby and W. P. Jencks, *J. Am. Chem. Soc.* 87, 3217 (1965).

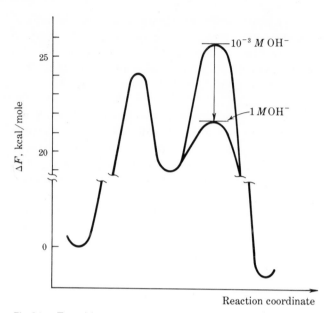

Fig 20. Transition-state diagram for the reaction of dimethyl-amine with p-nitrophenyl phosphate, based on observed second-order rate constants at 10^{-3} and $1.0\ M$ hydroxide ion concentrations. The free energies of activation are based upon the observed rate constants, but the depth of the valley between the energy barriers for the two steps is arbitrary.[33]

termediates, in interpreting the significance of changes in solvents, salts, substituents, and thermodynamic activation parameters. However, it is essential to know what the reactants are; i.e., their state of ionization and whether a significant fraction of one or more reactants exists in some complexed form or intermediate. It is impossible to distinguish between transition states of identical composition and similar charge distribution by examining the effects of changes in any of the above variables.

3. The rate-determining step is the highest point on the reaction-coordinate diagram. If there is a steady-state intermediate in the reaction, the rate-determining step is determined by the relative rates of breakdown of the intermediate to starting materials and to products, not by the relative rates of its formation and breakdown (Fig. 4, Chap. 10).

4. If there is an unstable intermediate on the reaction path it is likely, but not certain, that this intermediate will resemble the

transition state for the overall reaction and that factors which influence the stability of the intermediate will have a similar effect on the transition state.

5. The more unstable a starting material is relative to the products, the more the transition state is likely to occur early along the reaction coordinate and resemble the starting material. The converse holds for the transition state and products (Figs. 9, 10, and 12, Chap. 3). Points (4) and (5) provide the basis for many useful correlations of reaction rates with equilibra for overall or partial reactions.[34]

6. Free-energy diagrams are based on particular standard states, and free-energy barriers should be compared only for comparable standard states. For example, the energy barrier for an uncatalyzed reaction may be compared with that for an acid catalyzed reaction at the standard state of 1 M hydrogen ion. However, arbitrary standard states may be set up and used for comparisons; for example, an acid catalyzed reaction may be considered as a pseudo first-order reaction at some specified pH and compared with an uncatalyzed reaction at the same pH.

7. The baseline of transition-state–reaction-coordinate diagrams is arbitrary. If comparisons are made between related reactions, as in interpreting the effect of substituents on reaction rates, it is permissible to start from equal energies for all starting materials, transition states, or products, depending on the particular effect which is to be compared, because it is only the energy *differences* between starting materials, transition states, and products that are experimentally meaningful. For example, it is formally equally acceptable to speak of a substituent stabilizing the transition state (relative to the reactants) or destabilizing the starting materials (relative to the transition state) if it causes a rate acceleration; chemical intuition will usually lead to a preference for one or the other of these descriptions.

8. Reversible reactions must pass through the same transition state in both directions, so that the rate laws for the forward and reverse reactions must have the same stoichiometric composition and charge. If several reaction pathways are important, the energies of the different transition states and the fraction of the overall reaction that goes through each transition state are the

[34] J. E. Leffler, *Science* 117, 340 (1953); G. S. Hammond, *J. Am. Chem. Soc.* 77, 334 (1955); J. E. Leffler and E. Grunwald, "Rates and Equilibria of Organic Reactions," John Wiley & Sons, Inc., New York, 1963.

same for the forward and reverse reactions. It is not uncommon to reach incorrect conclusions about reaction mechanisms by postulating that a certain pathway is important under a particular set of experimental conditions for a reaction in one direction only and that the reverse reaction proceeds by a different mechanism. These requirements arise from the principle of microscopic reversibility or detailed balance.

Name Index

Subject Index

Chymotrypsin:
  interaction of aromatic substrates with, 415
  trimethylacetyl-, 47
Cinnamic acid dibromide, 118
Cis-trans isomerization, 74-76, 502-504
Citrate condensing enzyme, 276-277, 279
Clathrates, 39, 408-411, 428
Cobalt, catalysis by, 115
Coenzyme Q, 160
Cohesive energy, 374-384, 391, 394, 418, 434
Collagen, 359
Collision factor, 605-607
Compensation, 315, 316
Complex formation, 402, 471, 572-574
Compressibility of water, 378
Concentration effect, 18
Concerted catalysis, 199-217, 534, 547
Concerted reactions, 235
Conductance, 370
"Conducted-tour" mechanism, 204
Conformation changes, 277-278, 403
  of cyclodextrin, 409
  rate determining, 51
Contact charge transfer, 444
Control mechanisms, 308-310, 319
Cooperative interactions, 319
Coordinate bond, 456
Covalent bond strength, 88
Critical micelle concentration, 404
Crystal-lattice energy, 366-371
Cyanate ion, 601-602
Cyanide, 101, 119, 124, 130-132, 158
  addition to imines, 506-507
  reaction with aldehydes, 496, 501
Cyanine dyes, 396
Cyanohydrin, 37, 132, 158
Cyanoketene dimethylacetal, 271
Cyclodextrins, 39, 409-411
Cycloheptatriene, 273
Cyclohexaamylose, 40
Cyclohexanone, 507
Cyclopentanediolmonoacetates, 324
Cyclopentyl tosylate, solvolysis of, 254, 256
Cyclopropanedicarboxylic acid, 272
Cystathionine, 139, 144, 150
Cysteine, 139, 150
Cytochrome b_5 reductase, 275

Dative bond, 455, 456
Dealdolization, 121-122, 124, 129, 130
Debye-Hückel theory, 379, 586
Decarboxylases, 43
Decarboxylation, 116-120, 124, 127-129, 139, 142, 143, 145, 146, 150, 244
Dehydrogenases, 275
5-Dehydroquinate, 152
Denaturation:
  of DNA, 359, 361, 379-380, 382, 397-399, 427, 434
  of proteins, 335-337, 358-362, 379-385, 404-405, 434, 606
Deoxyribonucleic acid (see Nucleic acids)
Detailed balance, 614
Deuterium oxide solutions, acidity of, 276
Deuteromethanol, 338
Deuteroxide ion, 272
Diacetone alcohol, 121
Diacylamines, hydrolysis of, 524
Dialkylsuccinic acid, 272
Dibenzoylethylenes, 503
  2,3-Di-t-butylsuccinic acid, 329
Dicarboxylic acids, hydrogen bonding in, 327-332
  proton abstraction from, 272, 330
Dichloramine, 151
sym-Dichlorophenylpyrophosphates, 39
Dielectric constant, 315, 328, 370, 375, 376, 405, 432, 446
  of water and deuterium oxide, 258
Dielectric relaxation, 388, 428-433
Dielectric saturation, 370
Diethyl acetylethylmalonate, 548-549
Diethyl acetylmalonate, 548-549, 551
Diethylamine-iodine complex, 450
Diethyl aminomalonate, 142, 143
Diethyl malonate, 132
Diffusion, 389-390
Diffusion coefficient, 430
Diffusion-controlled proton transfers, 207-213, 272, 332, 540
Diffusion-controlled reactions, 51, 190-193, 233-236, 264-267, 410-411
2,6-Dihalobenzaldehydes, 550
9,10-Dihydro-3,4; 5,6-dibenzophenanthrene, 307
9,10-Dihydro-4,5-dimethylphenanthrene, 257
Dihydrolipoic acid, 130, 170
Dihydroxyacetone phosphate, 121, 124

TEA WITH DEMONS

Tea With Demons

BY
CAROL ALLEN

WITH
HERBERT S. LUSTIG, M.D.

WILLIAM MORROW AND COMPANY, INC. NEW YORK

To protect the privacy of those involved, the names of all persons mentioned in this book have been changed, with the exception of Dr. Herbert S. Lustig, Dr. Milton Erickson, and the author's friends Elaine, Mimi, Carol, and Sally.

Library of Congress Cataloging in Publication Data

Allen, Carol.
  Tea with demons.

  1. Allen, Carol.   2. Psychotherapy patients—
United States—Biography.   I. Lustig, Herbert S.
II. Title.
RC464.A39A35   1985   616.89'14'0924 [B]   85-5066
ISBN 0-688-05093-X

Printed in the United States of America

First Edition

1 2 3 4 5 6 7 8 9 10

BOOK DESIGN BY JAYE ZIMET

To my children and my family for their sustaining love

C.A.

For the young child to whom I made that special promise many years ago

H.S.L.

AUTHOR'S NOTE

While this is a personal account, written from my point of view, Dr. Herbert Lustig, my psychiatrist during the time of these events, played an invaluable collaborative role in helping me reconstruct portions of the therapy conversations presented. I was able to remember our interactions in broad outline, with highlights and conclusions firmly etched in my mind. When my memory grew dim over details, Herb and I sat together with my notebooks and his clinical notes and re-created our conversations to recover the specifics, sequences, and flow that lend authenticity to the work. He also thoughtfully and methodically reviewed the manuscript. I am most deeply indebted to him, however, for vigilantly directing me toward sanity and self-respect throughout the course of my therapy, and for his enthusiasm in working on this project as a friend.

—CAROL ALLEN

ACKNOWLEDGMENTS

For reading the work in progress and offering encouragement and insights that added immeasurably to the finished work, Dr. Lustig and I wish to thank Lindy and David High, Dick and Judy High, Nancy and John Zelnick, Mort Maimon, Margaret Maule, Carol J. Agnew, Mary Mercurio Scheip, Michael Scheip, Michi Ishida Rose, Dick Rose, Barrie Van Dyck, Claire Fitzgerald, and Martin Goldberg, M.D. For their support and thoroughgoing critique of the final draft, we are especially grateful to Patrick S. Pasquariello, Jr., M.D., and Paul J. Fink, M.D.

Our special thanks to our editor, Maria Guarnaschelli, for the spirit and enthusiasm she brought to this project and for her critical insights, which guided our revisions of the manuscript.

Our thanks also to Renee Davis, for the professionalism, care, and patience she displayed in preparing the manuscript. We would also like to thank Minerva Rosa for her early help in this respect.

For their support, we are indebted to many friends and colleagues in our private and professional lives. We would particularly like to acknowledge Nathaniel Branden, Gerard

McCauley, Sharon Lustig, Dan and Margo Polett, Gordon Wyner, Linda Kurtz, Sandra Schultz Newman, Sid Waldman, and Kay Reed. I would also like to thank Susan Schwartz McDonald for teaching me the discipline of writing in the workplace.

For their unhesitating acceptance and many kindnesses during the time of this story, I will always remain grateful to my friends and neighbors, Mimi Mortimer, Martha Wintner, JoAnne Zanin, Margo Cairns, Judy Goldberg, Wendy Gollub, Jerry Gollub, Earlene Sloan, Marty Dickson, Madeline Gutwirth, Sylvia Glickman, and Eleanor and Sam Gubins.

Finally, my special thanks to Elaine Maimon for her unerring critical judgment and illumination of the craft of writing, and for her unqualified loyalty and friendship throughout the past fifteen years.

—CAROL ALLEN

CONTENTS

THE CAVE

Plato tells a story about how we are all prisoners in a cave under the ground. We are bound and shackled and stand facing a wall of the cave, so that we can see only what is directly in front of us on that wall. Behind us is a rampart upon which puppets move—not just wooden dancing men, but figures of rivers and rainbows, and trees, and all the other things in the world.

Behind the figures is a fire that casts its light onto the figures, projecting their shadows onto the wall. It is these shadows that we see; it is these shadows that we think are real. We have fun and debates over these shadows. We play shadow games and have contests over them, and praise or blame the prisoner who can pick out this or that shadow quicker or better than the rest of us.

Plato asks us to imagine that someone frees us from our shackles and turns us around, so that we now face the fire. At first our eyes would be so confused by the light that we could discern objects only dimly. But as our eyes grew stronger and accustomed themselves to the light, we would begin to pick out the puppets and then the fire, and thereby know the shadows for what they are.

What if, Plato asks us, a wise person was to lead us on a journey up the tunnel and out of the cave? The journey would be difficult, with much prodding and stumbling. And if we succeeded, and came out into the sunlight, we would once again be blinded, but even more strongly this time. Our eyes would be so filled with light that we would see nothing. In order to adjust our eyes, we would first have to look at the objects in the light of the moon or look at their gentle reflections in the water, until our eyes became so accustomed to the sunlight that we could finally look directly at the things themselves. Then we would know that the shadows in the cave are actually copies of puppets, which are copies of reflections, which are copies of real things in the world above.

If we should come so far, Plato says, we would want to remain in the sunlight and nevermore enter the darkness of the cave. But it would be our task and our obligation to go back, in the hope of leading others out. But if we should enter the tunnel to the cave once more, our eyes would again be confounded by the darkness.

Plato says that our eyes become confused in two ways: by going from darkness to light, and by going from light to darkness. And if we should return to the prisoners below and begin to tell them what we have seen, they would not understand us, for how can one tell shadow people that their shadows are not real?

If we should return to the cave and compete in the games once again, we would be clumsy and awkward, and ridiculed as fools. Then, says Plato, we would fall silent, unable to speak about our different vision. We cannot put sight into blind eyes, or knowledge into people's heads. We can only turn the prisoners around, so that they look in a different direction. Or so Plato says.

Part 1

BLINDED BY THE FIRE

CHAPTER ONE

NOVEMBER 18, 1974

I sat for the first time on a hard deacon's bench in the doctor's narrow waiting room. Opposite me, too high to give me back my own image, was a large oval mirror with a polished black frame. It reflected the framed photograph hung above my head, a picture of the world, whose cloud cover formed the shape of an embryo. I stared at the disturbing reflection for some time until the world gave up its image. Now dancing demons marched mockingly around a pond of mirrored ice. Splinters of nightmare broke off and pierced me. Waves of pain stripped me of my strength.

Dr. Lustig came out of the inner office, and I saw his lips move as he motioned me to come in. I walked quickly past him, too caught up to notice him. When I did look at him, I was startled to see him looking back. We were like two shopkeepers on opposite sides of the street, who one day simultaneously lift the shades of their shops, only to as quickly drop them back into place.

Then I was past him and into the room, where browns and oranges and golds formed lines and straight angles.

Raw mineral crystals with sharp contours through muted colors—pale gold and purple and rose—stood on a table to my right. On the opposite wall a prehistoric fish fossil, solidly placed in its rock, seemed certain of its own history.

In the center of the room, near one wall, were two comfortably upholstered armchairs facing each other. Between them was an upholstered ottoman. Around the perimeter of the room were a few smaller, movable chairs. Dr. Lustig sat down in one of the armchairs and motioned me to sit in the other.

I sat down without words, pressing my hands together to insist on a unity, to join the pieces.

"Would you like to get yourself together before you begin?"

I nodded and fumbled for the pieces of myself. It took several minutes.

"My reality problem" was what I gathered to present. "I have a reality problem, and it has been denied for a long time. . . ." I stopped there. My words were frightening me. I took a deep breath and for the first time spoke the worst.

"I think I'm crazy."

I waited for the barely perceptible intake of breath, the composed and serious expression of concern, the carefully modulated voice probing my childhood.

"Congratulations! Some of the most creative people in the world think they're crazy . . . and sometimes they're right. What's your claim to craziness?"

I was too startled to reply. Somewhat defensively I finally answered, "'When I was a child I had this way of knowing things, this power . . ." My voice gave out and I could not go on.

He asked me what sort of things. I didn't know how to talk about the odd experiences that I had had of late or of the demons in the mirror. I began talking about intuition.

"Many people have intuition of the heart," I said, "which allows them to know what other people feel. But other people have intuition of the eyes, which lets them see what other people can't see." I talked at random now, groping for common ground.

"And which is it that you have?"

"I have them both," I said with some drama. "It is a terrible thing to know too much."

"That's been a problem of artists throughout the ages. In which creative medium do you use it?"

I was again taken aback and thought the question over for some minutes.

"I don't know how to use it," I finally said, and I was very sorry as I said it. "I just feel that I am being overwhelmed with information that I don't know what to do with."

"You probably are," he said softly. "There's no other thing that I can think of that will so rapidly . . . *immobilize* a functioning person."

I felt the suggestion of hope. "What shall I do?"

"What did you do here today, after you sat down and before you began to speak? Because when you sat down you were very distraught, but by the time you spoke you were much more collected. What did you do then?"

"I don't know."

"Fair enough. Even though you don't know what it was that you did, could you do it again?"

I said I didn't know, but I would try.

"Fine indeed. Will you try now?"

I nodded tentatively.

"Let yourself get a *little* overwhelmed. Not too overwhelmed, not so overwhelmed that it really becomes burdensome, but just a little overwhelmed." He paused a moment until his eye caught the lamp on the table near his chair. "Perhaps about the lamp over there. You know, it comes from driftwood. As a matter of fact it is constructed of pieces of driftwood. Now I don't know its history, except that it is made of driftwood. But perhaps intuition of the eyes gives you some information about its origin and travels that I don't have. So could you get a little overwhelmed about this lamp, and then do whatever it was that you did at the beginning of today's session to get yourself collected and functioning?"

I tried, but after a few minutes I was getting more than a little overwhelmed, so I stopped.

"The lamp is falling apart," I said.

"As a matter of fact the lamp *is* falling apart, if it were not for two or three *very real facts* of nature." He took his time over the words "very real facts," stretching them out, giving them time to seep in.

"Those facts are nails. You can see one of them right from where you are sitting."

I looked, but couldn't see anything holding it together. I didn't say anything.

"The thing about this lamp is that if it were not for those nails, gravity would cause the whole thing to fall down."

"In other words, the laws of nature?"

"You might say that. From the imposition of a minimal amount of order caused by the rigidity of the nails comes a beautiful structure."

"What are the nails that hold a person together?" He seemed to understand so well that I could afford to be direct.

"The thing that holds us together is not nails," he slowly replied. "It's more like . . . an invisible shield. A skintight invisible shield that envelops us, that keeps the outside out and the inside in. Except when we want an interchange between the two."

I felt the lump of fear diminish in my stomach and the pain in my limbs ease, and I took a deep breath. We sat for some time in silence of the comfortable kind, until my hands could finally rest quietly together on my lap.

The familiar image of Plato's cave came into my mind.

I was one of the prisoners chained in the half-light, watching shadows move on the rough wall. I looked at Dr. Lustig again, and for a moment he was the wise person who would lead me out of the cave into the sun.

"I am going to take a long journey and you will be my guide," I told him. "I can see the beginning of the journey and the end, but not the middle."

"Where are we going?"

"I had a dream a few days ago that I was bitten by a mad calf—by madness. That's how it begins. Two days later I had a second dream. I was standing with a psychiatrist in his office and he was holding me by the shoulders and gently rocking me back and forth. Everything bad had come out. I was filled with an indescribable peace, the kind that I've never had in my life. That's how it ends."

"That's certainly a dream worth having again," he replied.

Then the magic began to crowd in on me again. It came like a sorcerer out of nowhere, keeping to the shadows, everywhere making its presence felt. It cast its spell over the ordinary and mundane, so that background leaped forward into sudden prominence, insignificance caught in a sudden light. I thought of the items on my grocery list, even the dust on a bowl of rose leaves, and they were no longer indifferent, would not stay in place. I was defenseless against so much surplus significance. So I fastened it onto Dr. Lustig, that it should be less terrifying, that it should have a place.

"There's one thing I need to know before I start," I said. I was still talking about the journey, but the focus had shifted, and the wise man had become the sorcerer.

"I know you'll deceive me along the way," I said, "but will it be the deception of the thrush?"

He asked me what that was, so I began to quote T. S. Eliot. I wanted him to know I really did have something in mind, that I was not making it up.

"Footfalls echo in the memory," I began and went on until I came to the question:

"Round the corner. Through the first gate,
Into our first world, shall we follow
The deception of the thrush?"

I finished and waited expectantly, not realizing that the meaning of my quotation was obscure. Dr. Lustig, however, did not seem uncomfortable with my strange literary reference.

"Ahh ... *that* kind of deception," he said. "Yes, I can promise you it won't be anything more than that."

"I know you are going to use magic," I went on insistently. "Will it be good or bad magic?"

"I *only* use good magic. Bad magic gives me headaches." I laughed.

"Yes," he said with satisfaction, "it will be one hundred percent organic good magic—no artificial preservatives."

It was almost time to go, but I had one last question.

"At home my children have a small blue puzzle that's shaped like a cube. It's made up of smaller shapes joined together in different combinations and angles, and the idea is to form the pieces into one large cube. But I don't know how to put the pieces back together."

He was thoughtful for a moment.

"The first thing we're going to do *here* is to put the cube back together any which way. It won't matter if the pieces are in the wrong place. Then, after the cube is stuck back together again, we'll take the pieces off one by one, and put each one back into its proper place."

I smiled and he smiled back.

We talked several minutes more. Then Dr. Lustig wrote down some background information, gave me a regular appointment time, and saw me out the door with a warm handshake. I left reluctantly.

I pulled my collar up against the wind and felt the warmth on my back. Neither the gray November day outside nor the magic within could have their way with me now. I had found an ally who could sit down to tea with demons in the afternoon, and still sleep soundly at night.

CHAPTER TWO

NOVEMBER 10–14, 1974

It had begun suddenly eight days before I saw Dr. Lustig. That was the strangest thing of all. One moment I was who I was—a thirty-year-old wife, mother, and part-time philosophy professor at a Philadelphia college. The next moment I was spinning through a dreamlike void, swept into some primordial chaos whose dimensions made me very small, whose currents gave me a different name.

It began with a dream. I remember it clearly. It was the night of November 10, and it was the first dream I had remembered in twenty-five years.

I am in a modern, many-angled house that sits on a hill overlooking the ocean. It is light and airy with ceiling-high windows looking out on the water. In this house I am about to be remarried to my husband, Stan, and my relatives have gathered to prepare a wedding feast. I wander through the house looking for Stan. I cannot find him. I begin to run. I

*run faster and faster. I am out of the house, running down
a ramp from the door of the house to the roadway in front.*

*I cross the road and find myself in a country fair-
ground, such as those I remember from the late summers of
my childhood. Directly in front of me is a wooden fair
booth, the kind that you would expect women to sell pies
from. In this booth, a play is being performed. The grass in
front of the booth is divided by an aisle into two sections. All
of the audience members sit rigidly in stiff-backed chairs
arranged neatly in rows on the right-hand side. I cross over
to the left-hand side of the grass, assuming a reclining position to watch the play.*

*On the right side of the booth, to the back, stands a
king, the central character of the play. He is beating time
with two sticks. On the left side of the booth, to the front, is
a small platform where a jester stands. He is also beating
time with sticks, mimicking the rhythm of the king. Although the jester is supposed to maintain the tempo by following the king, I begin to realize that he is slowly and
subtly shifting the rhythm. Finally the two are in discord.
The jester is undermining the king. No one else in the audience notices this. I am the only one who understands.*

*I leave the fairground and wander through some des-
ert grass, until I come to a corral where beautiful wild
horses are galloping around the perimeter. As I approach
the fence, I notice a number of cowboys crowded around.
Leery of them, I step back and keep my distance. Suddenly
the men shout, the corral door bursts open, and all the wild
horses gallop out and away. The cowboys yell and wave to
me frantically to get out of the horses' way. I am not frightened. I do not move, and in a kind of trance watch the
horses sweep by.*

*Through the cloud of dust raised by the horses I see a
small calf following the horses out of the corral. It stands
between me and the fence. Once again, but even more frantically this time, the men wave to me to get out of its way. I*

pay no attention, however, because it seems so harmless. Suddenly the calf lunges at me and bites me on the right hand with a jagged tooth. Pain shoots down my left side and I realize that the calf is rabid and that I am dying. Bitten by madness, I stagger back toward the road that I have crossed, where a stranger, a kindly man, comes to my assistance. He takes my wounded arm and helps me back to the house.

I run through the rooms, looking for someone, until I find my friend Marion. We are standing at the door of a totally dark room. I point to the room and say in terror, "I must interpret my dream." She makes no reply.

I enter the pitch-black room alone and redream the dream. As I am leaving the room, Stan appears and we dance the last wedding dance. Stan then disappears. I leave the house and go to the shore of the ocean. I stand at the bottom of a hill of sand that is strewn with baby blankets. I struggle through the sand trying to get to the top of the hill, where my mother stands with a wedding cake.

I lay in bed in the dark, holding my breath, frozen in that instant before full consciousness returns. Beside me I could hear the steady breathing of my husband, Stan, and I wondered that his sleep should be undisturbed. For me the dream images filled the room, driving out my rationality and the safety it had brought all these years. I could feel again the bite of the calf. My fear was as dark as the room in my dream.

Some time passed, I could not tell how long, and then I reached out and switched on the bedside lamp. The sudden light brought me back to the present, but my body still shook from the memory of the dream. As if compelled, I began to look for a pencil and paper, for I felt I must record my dream. After living so long without a dream dimension, I felt the importance of what had happened, even as I did not grasp its sense.

My hands shook as I wrote. When I looked down I could not recognize my own writing. The marks resembled chicken scratchings in the dust, as if mysterious forces were at play with a private language and script all their own.

By an effort of will I finished. Gingerly, I put the paper away in a drawer, awed by the magic now trapped in the words. Then quietly, without waking my husband, I gathered a blanket around myself and trailed through the house. I turned on every light as I passed it. I got to the living room and sat on the couch, huddled over, with my feet pulled up under me in a posture of defense. So I sat through the night.

I must have looked tired the next morning, because Stan said to me over breakfast, "Were you up last night?"

"I had a bad dream," I answered noncommittally. I didn't tell Stan about the jester or the mad calf or dancing our last wedding dance. I didn't tell him how frightened and fragmented I felt, how my world was suddenly crumbling like a stale cookie, how I couldn't find the batter to make a new batch.

"Oh," he replied distractedly, as he shuffled his lecture notes for the day's economics classes. He went back to his reading and made no further comment.

Why is this happening to me, I wondered, just when I thought everything was safe? I have a husband, far from perfect but still a source of stability; I have two beautiful children and a profession. Why, then, do I feel this confusion surrounding me, blanketing me, clouding my mind and my judgment? Is it a diversionary tactic of the self, designed, perhaps, to smother the failure I feel in so many directions; failure not of acting, for I have always been responsible, but failure of focus, as if in trying to do too many things at once (and each, of course, perfectly) I am inevitably confronted with partial results, lingering and sometimes totally preoccupying uncertainties—how to be a good mother when all of my time is not devoted to my children, how to be a professional when my children take energy away from my work, what to do with a husband who tolerates but does not love me, what to do with myself when I fail to meet my own expectations? I am always running out of time, I thought, and now time is running out on me.

If the children noticed anything unusual about me that morning, they didn't indicate it. My three-and-a-half-year-old daughter, Elizabeth, carried on her usual morning chatter. My son, Daniel, who was nearly one, contributed a combination of words and noises. Our routine of breakfast, baths, and dressing went slowly, but otherwise much as usual.

As soon as possible after Stan left for the day and the children were settled, I called Marion, who had been next to the black room in my dream. I told her the dream, expecting her to interpret it. She was baffled but suggested that I call her therapist for a consultation.

Am I crazy? I wondered, as I dialed her therapist's number. I had never considered a psychiatrist before—nobody in my family ever had. We solved our own problems. Marion had said a "consultation." That was only going once. Maybe that will be enough. Yes, I'll go and just get my dream interpreted. That won't mean anything; there's no stigma in that. I rested comfortably on that thought for several minutes, before the worry intruded again. But what if I really am going crazy? Is this the kind of thing you are the last to know?

I dialed her therapist's number and made the appointment. Then it all just seemed to slip out of my mind. In its place came tears shed throughout the day. I no longer thought of reasons why I should be crying, and the tears mostly slipped unnoticed down.

Elizabeth looked at me inquiringly several times during our walk to the duck pond that day, and as we painted watercolors while Daniel napped. But she did not question me.

Daniel followed my footsteps more closely than usual. Once he patted my arm in a gesture of comfort.

At around five Stan arrived back home, and I became aware that the tears had stopped. There remained a shadowy haze, as if a filter had slipped between me and the world, lending an air of unreality to all that I experienced. When my children and my husband spoke to me, I found it hard to concentrate on what they said. I answered them absently. They did not seem to notice my distraction. Trying to focus my attention on them, I idly wondered why they were talking, or should want to disturb the stillness with their words.

I tied my daughter's shoes automatically, then warmed up the food for my baby's meal. But I kept returning to the window, as if the answer lay in that direction. Finally forcing myself back to the kitchen, I turned my attention to the kitchen clock. I was fascinated by its measured sounds, and searched its face for secrets. But it ticked on regularly, despite my scrutiny.

Unsatisfied by my encounter with the kitchen clock, I wandered slowly through the house, staring at the faces of all the others. It was then I noticed that all the clocks had gone awry. First they moved faster, then they stood still. Or perhaps, I thought, it is I who have stopped in the middle of a new dimension, where no clocks can be trusted, where proportion is as absent as in a clock without hands.

I shook myself and grasped the dining room table. I wanted the reassurance of hard smooth wood, that the real was real and could not be dispelled by my unruly imagination.

Chills swept over me and then I burned, but I managed to keep my hold on the mahogany. The urgency with which I needed to be steadied underscored the danger and made me afraid. I had read about people who had lost their grip on reality. I *am* going crazy, I thought. I grasped the table even harder. Some time went by and then, just as suddenly, it was over. The air in the room seemed to clear and I was out of the fog. I took some deep breaths and then shakily went to prepare dinner.

So it went that day and the next. I stumbled through the tasks of the hours alternately weeping, foggy, or frightened, confounded by the power of this visitation. Then, on the night of the second day, I had another dream.

NIGHT OF NOVEMBER 12, 1974

I am with a psychiatrist in his office. I am aware that he is a young man, although his face is indistinct. We are standing, and he is holding me by the shoulders and gently rocking me back and forth. I know everything that was hidden has come out; all the fear is over. I can hear him talking softly to me, but I cannot distinguish his precise words. I am exhausted. Lulled by his voice, I am filled with an indescribable peace of the kind I have never had in my life.

The next morning I tried to tell Stan about my dreams and my need to interpret them.

"I don't understand," Stan said when I was finished. "What exactly is the problem?" He spoke irritably, as if I were trying to confound him.

I sighed. It had become my response to most everything that Stan said. I really do want Stan to understand, I thought. Then, with more candor, I admitted that it might not be so.

The next day I saw the consulting psychotherapist. He did not interpret my dreams. He told me I needed therapy. He referred me to a young psychiatrist, Herbert Lustig. As he wrote down the name on the card for me, he noted how conveniently located Dr. Lustig's office was—only a block and a half's walk from my home, the first-floor apartment in an old stone house on Philadelphia's Main Line.

I phoned Dr. Lustig's office when I got home, but he was out. It was nearing five o'clock when Dr. Lustig returned my call. I remember because I was again preparing dinner. "This is Dr. Lustig," he said. "How can I help you?" Shock went through me when I heard his voice. Then a calm descended. It was exactly the voice of the psychiatrist in my second dream.

CHAPTER THREE

NOVEMBER 18–19, 1974

The sense of security I had found following my first meeting with Dr. Lustig was still with me when Stan returned home that evening. I rushed eagerly to the door to meet Stan, excited by my strange encounter with Dr. Lustig and the relief it had generated. "Oh, Stan," I began, and then in a rush of words told him about my meeting that afternoon, how Dr. Lustig had seemed to know what I was thinking, how he had seemed to understand.

Stan looked vexed at what I said. "Calm down," he told me. "I can't follow you. Now, *exactly* what happened?" He spoke slowly and methodically and somewhat impatiently.

My enthusiasm dried up at his tone of voice. "Never mind!" I said with irritation, and gathering up the children, left the room.

But Stan was not finished with the topic. Later, at the dinner table, he asked me again how my therapy session had gone, curiosity and suspicion mingling in his voice.

My reply was brief and noncommittal. "It was helpful"

was all that I said, feeling suddenly too tired to explain to anyone.

"Is that all you can say about it?" Stan prodded his food, exasperated.

"Yes," I answered softly, avoiding his eyes.

Neither of us spoke for several minutes. We continued pushing our food around, without much evidence of appetite. It seemed to me that Stan sat at a great distance that could not be traversed with simple words. But as the silence between us deepened, it seemed to shout at us with a third voice.

"It's too hard to explain," I finally began, wanting to rob the silence of its alienating power. But my words did not break the barrier that Stan and I had so unwittingly built.

"Well, are you going to continue or what?" Stan's words were doing no better at reaching me.

"Yes," I replied, suddenly knowing I was committed to therapy with Dr. Lustig.

"Okay," Stan replied, sensing my determination. Then, focusing on the financial issue, he added, "How much did he say it would cost?"

"I don't know," I said, feeling foolish. "I forgot to ask."

"Well, you'd better find out. Let's just be clear," he continued deliberately, "that *you* will have to pay for most of this out of your teaching money. We can't afford it out of my paycheck." So saying, he turned his attention to the children.

After dinner I washed the dishes and cleaned up the kitchen, then bathed the children and readied them for bed. Stan, meanwhile, retired as usual to the study immediately following dinner, to work on the book that was to assure his academic future at the college where he taught. He generally worked until about midnight, so it was not unusual that at bedtime I should find myself in the bedroom alone.

It was about 11 P.M., as I prepared for bed, that I sensed

another presence in the room with me. I froze, and then, as if directed, slowly turned my head toward the closet door. No one was near it that I could see, so it was with horror that I watched it slowly creak open. The secrets must go back into the closet, I told myself. I cannot bear this. Then the invading forces gathered in my head. Terrifying disconnected thoughts intruded, pounding out a pulsating, portentous rhythm, swirling through my brain with recurring urgency. Round and round.

Madness.

Death.

What I know is terrible.

Extra Y chromosome.

A childhood house on Eleventh Avenue East. Basement of the house, playing house, blankets draped like houses, something wrong. Did I do it?

"Mommy, Mommy, you've got to help me!"

My sweet baby brother. Did I do something terrible to him?

"He went after me with a butcher knife. I really must have made him mad."

Our dog Vicky, gentle and kind, in my dream turning into a rabid animal with yellow and green stripes and foaming mouth.

I am going mad.

My mother saying, "Your brother Daniel was born kind."

My son Daniel's eyes, looking at me.

Thirty-one months between my brother Daniel and me.

Twenty-seven months between my children.

The numbers must mean something.

I must stop this, or I will die.

Stan came in while these thoughts were whirling, but we did not speak. It was then that I began the pattern that was to last me for some time. Unwilling to confirm my madness before audiences, I dissembled and pretended to be perfectly all right. I learned that I could shroud my turmoil in a cloak of normalcy, and few would be the wiser except for me.

Although we did not speak, I was reassured as always by Stan's physical presence. Perhaps he is petty about details, I thought. At least he is grounded in the real world. Devils would not dare disrupt his dreams.

"I need a hug," I said coaxingly. Stan came over to the bed and put his arms around me.

"I really have been afraid," I confided softly.

"Of what?" he asked calmly, secure as always when I showed my need. Then, seeing the look on my face, he tried to be comforting.

"Don't worry," he said. "It'll be all right, honey." He got up from the bed and finished undressing for the night.

"Now," he said, climbing into his side of the bed, "let's get some rest, okay?" Clearly he thought everything was settled. Reluctantly I switched off the bedside light.

"Good night, Stan," I said. His answering "Good night" was muffled, for he was already half asleep.

"Good night," he muttered again, reaching over to pat my shoulder.

"Good night, Stan," I whispered.

I lay still in the bed for many minutes, listening to the steady sound of Stan's breathing. I was now alone in the dark with the forces of my mind. The terror began to overwhelm me again. I kept a lonely vigil, born out of desperation. If I kept my eyes open and my senses alert, no harm could come to me or entirely have its way.

As the hours passed I thought about Dr. Lustig, and he seemed to be my only recourse. He had given me his home number the day before, and I considered carefully how early in the morning I could call him. The hours ticked on. It was 4:30 or 5 A.M., at that hour known to the diseased and desperate and lonely, when the will to continue begins to atrophy and the clowns have a cup of coffee in the kitchen, that I determined that I could call him at 7 A.M. Then it was just a matter of counting out the minutes, second by second, for I had put an arbitrary time limit on my undoctored pain.

CHAPTER FOUR

NOVEMBER 19, 1974

At seven o'clock on the dot I dialed Dr. Lustig's number. I could hear him answer groggily, then almost instantly snap to attention. Afterward, I could not remember exactly what he had said. I remembered only his tone of voice and the way he had spoken. He was not sympathetic. Rather, he spoke tersely, in a decisive, commanding tone—in a voice that imposed control and demanded order and coherence. He told me to write down my terrifying thoughts. When I hung up the phone, I felt an enormous sense of relief. He has told me what to do, I thought. He has told me how I must talk to myself, what tone of voice to use.

I wrote the words down and then practiced speaking to myself firmly. I found that this exercise shored me up. Enough, anyway, to go about the business of my day, which, that Tuesday, was teaching my two midday philosophy classes. I prepared breakfast for the children, and got them and myself dressed. Then at ten o'clock the babysitter came to my house to watch the children, so that I could go to work. Driving to the nearby college, I steeled myself for the ordeal of facing my students. I concentrated my attention on behaving as normally as possible.

Walking up the hill that led from the parking lot to the main campus, I regarded the near perfection of this picture-postcard scene. The sun beamed down brightly on the colored tapestry of fall. The academic spires and towers that rose in the distance seemed to point heavenward, as if they had direct access to some higher authority and were never plagued by confusion or troubled by doubt.

The faces on the passing students were equally confident, revealing burdens no greater than late term papers or poor exams. Most of them were laughing, their faces alternately playful and earnest, suggesting preoccupation with the latest basketball score or the proper dress for an upcoming dance. They communicated health and life and happiness. Or so I romanticized them, as we are apt to romanticize those younger than ourselves. They seemed to be at home in this academic sphere, accepting the gifts of the mind as naturally as they accepted a plate of supper—some out of hunger and some because it was there and had been offered. Not here, tormented intellects or Heideggerian angst.

I arrived at my classroom and reluctantly opened my text to begin the class. In what seemed to me like an enormous irony, I was teaching the philosopher Descartes that day. I turned the pages of my book to the first meditation, "Concerning the Things That Can Be Doubted," in which Descartes, using doubt as a philosophical method for arriving at the truth, determines to "make a serious and unimpeded effort to destroy all my former opinions," and to "abstain from belief in things which are not entirely certain and indubitable."

I tried to teach my first class with my usual objectivity but I found my mind racing out of control or going blank over certain passages, as I interpreted these abstract hypothetical statements literally.

"Nevertheless, I must remember that I am a man, and that consequently I am accustomed to sleep and in my dreams to imagine the same things that lunatics imagine when awake...."

I flushed hot and then cold, and felt my face redden. They must know, I thought. It must be as obvious as the mark of Cain. I pushed the thoughts aside and kept on teaching.

"I realize so clearly that there are no conclusive indications by which waking life can be distinguished from sleep...."

My dream. The rabid calf. Mustn't think about the dream now. I continued reading in a literal way.

"How can I be sure that God has not brought it about that I am always mistaken when I add two and three or count the sides of a square...."

The numbers. What do they mean? Two—divided. The Pythagoreans said four was the number of justice.

"I will therefore suppose that, not a true God, but a certain evil spirit, no less clever and deceitful than powerful, has bent all his efforts to deceive me. I will suppose that the sky, the air, the earth, colors, shapes, sounds, and all other objective things that we see are nothing but illusions and dreams that he has used to trick my credulity. I will consider myself as having no hands, no eyes, no flesh, no blood, nor any senses, yet falsely believing that I have all these things...."

What did I just read? I can't remember. My mind's gone blank. Must continue, so nobody knows.

"Even though there may be a deceiver of some sort, very powerful and very tricky, who bends all his efforts to keep me perpetually deceived, there can be no slightest doubt that I exist, since he deceives me...."

Small consolation, I thought. Small solace in my present world.

* * *

I glanced at my watch and the hour was over. Somehow or other I had gotten through the class. I suppose I taught by habit, much as one sometimes drives a car, on a sort of mental automatic pilot. I was aware of little as I walked out of the classroom, but the students joining me suggested by their manner that all had gone as usual, so I guessed there had been nothing untoward in my conduct.

I taught a second class in the early afternoon in much the same fashion. Finished for the day, I started across campus to have my usual cup of coffee. As I walked, all the colors and sounds jumped out at me with double intensity, as if I was witnessing them with a heightened, unnatural clarity.

As I walked, I became aware of the intensity of the sun. It seemed to focus itself into a single narrow beam, targeted directly at the top of my head. I physically felt it pierce my skull. And then it happened. In a moment of blinding light and excruciatingly sharp pain, I felt my head split into two pieces, with the cut dividing the right side from the left. In that instant all the sights and sounds faded, and the scene became a black-and-white motion picture with the soundtrack switched off. I slipped out of the action and became an observer, located behind the movie camera that was filming the scene. I was separated from my surroundings as surely as a piece of film is separated from life.

I wasn't aware of what happened next. I just found myself walking robotlike in the direction of my car. My body obeyed the forces of long-standing habit and I found myself driving home. There, I dismissed the babysitter, and with the children trailing me, I moved unhesitatingly to the phone. I dialed Dr. Lustig's office number. When he answered, my internal soundtrack switched back on and I could hear clearly what he said. "I have a terrible headache," I murmured. "Is there any medicine I can take?"

He told me to come over at the beginning of the next

hour. I took Elizabeth by the hand and, carrying Daniel, walked directly to Dr. Lustig's office.

When he came out into the waiting room between appointments, I silently handed him a piece of paper on which I had written the thoughts of the night before. He closely regarded my face, then quickly read what was written. He took me and the children into the inner room and handed me a small bottle of medicine. Then he sat down and wrote out a prescription for me. He gave me the instructions for taking it, then told me to call him the next morning.

I was in a daze, so much so that when Daniel, my baby, grabbed at one of the crystals on the side table, I did not move. Dr. Lustig intervened and pulled Daniel's hand back. Then he asked me how much help I had with the children. I told him my schedule and how I could not focus my attention on them. He asked me for Stan's number and said that he would phone him. Then he spoke sharply and decisively to me.

"You must get all the babysitting help that you need, but when you're with the children, you must focus your attention on them, even if it's only for one half hour a day. When you're with them, you must be there for them."

I nodded mutely. Something else was weighing on my mind. Finally, my thoughts coalesced.

"I'm terrified of remembering something now," I said, my voice cracking. "Something that I just can't bear." My hands tore at one another as I spoke. And then with seeming irrelevance, but utter conviction, I voiced an idea that just seemed to materialize out of nowhere.

"You must hypnotize me," I said. It was the first magical solution that occurred to me.

I made the suggestion with no knowledge that Dr. Lustig had, in fact, studied hypnosis with one of its foremost practitioners, Dr. Milton Erickson. I had always doubted the legitimacy of hypnosis and had certainly never expected to plead for its use with me. But some uncanny instinct guided me in making my request, some primitive knowledge of how the healing should occur.

Dr. Lustig did not appear particularly surprised at my strange request. He told me later that patients often came to him knowing what they needed. "Sometimes a person will carry a book under their arm with the diagnosis of their problem in the title," he said as if awestruck by the wonder of the human mind. "Very little surprises me anymore," he added, "especially about the capability of the human heart and mind to get itself into trouble and then to find a perfect solution for it."

So when I made my impulsive request for hypnosis that day, he gave a brief nod. "I'll be glad to use hypnosis with you, but there's something I'd like to know first. Will whatever it is that you're afraid of remembering stay locked inside you, until after you've taken the children home and have returned to this office."

"I think so," I replied hesitantly, thinking to myself, I've kept myself from remembering so far. I guess I can continue for a little while longer.

Dr. Lustig instructed me to take the children home and let Stan watch them, and to return to the office at the next hour, between his regular appointments.

I did as he suggested. When I returned at 6 P.M., he had us both sit in our usual chairs. He told me that he was going to teach me hypnosis.

"Carol," he said, "here's what I want you to do. Sit back comfortably in the chair, get your body and feet and arms relaxed, and pick a spot on the ceiling to look toward. It can be any spot, in front of you or even slightly in back of you on the ceiling, and keep on looking right toward it and pay *close attention* to my words. It's not necessary that you *hear* all of my words, nor is it necessary that you *see* the spot very clearly . . . but just *do* the best you can in paying attention to the sound of my voice, and at paying attention to the precise area of the ceiling where the spot is located." The tempo of his speech slowed and his voice deepened.

"Focus all of your attention on the sound of my voice and on the spot on the ceiling, so that you can enter into the state of altered consciousness that we commonly call hypnosis." He paused, waiting expectantly.

"That's right . . . just let your eyelids close . . . and become familiar with how *comfortable*, and *calm* . . . and *confident* you feel, and how *proud you are* with what you've been able to accomplish here today."

"Hypnosis is a *skill in focusing attention*, and because it is a skill, you can *practice* it and become better at using it. Hypnosis can serve for you, when you're outside this office, the same lovely function that it serves for you now . . . to give you a moment's healing, to allow you to have this period of peace and comfort and calm and restoration, in the midst of what has been a very hectic day."

When I was relaxed and fully aware of his words, but listening with more attentiveness than usual, he addressed my concerns.

"The mind is very powerful in each of us. It causes us to experience feelings of pain and pleasure; it causes us to remember events and to forget them; it causes us to create beauty and to unveil illusion.

"Now, there's something that a part of your mind, the front of your mind, does not want you to remember. The back of your mind will not allow you to remember anything that is terrifying or unpleasant, until your ordinary mind, the front of your mind, is ready to accept it and to deal with it comfortably. The back of your mind will just keep it locked safely inside, calmly waiting for its time."

He waited until the words had sunk in, and then added, "You have a very powerful mind, Carol. Are you willing to let it work for you?"

I nodded yes almost imperceptibly. "Then let it begin now," he intoned.

Slowly, I gathered my thoughts, blinked my eyes, and stirred in my chair. I felt as if an enormous burden had been removed from my shoulders. I breathed more easily.

He observed me closely and then spoke again gently. "If you have any more bad thoughts, write them down, and then let them go out of your mind. You don't have to remember them—the paper will. You can just let them go."

Then he smiled, as if to let me know that everything would be all right.

Fortified and reassured, I returned home, stopping by the pharmacy on my way to fill the prescription. I took the prescribed dosage that evening. About half an hour later, my head began to clear, and I found it was easier to focus my attention on my immediate surroundings. Some of the color had returned, although everything still had a grayish cast. But I was vastly reassured to be able, with considerable concentration, to hear my children and understand their words.

Stan came out of the kitchen just then, carrying a bunch of yellow and white mums that he sheepishly presented to me, as if he was afraid they might be too little, too late.

"I spoke to Dr. Lustig," he said, as I sniffed the flowers and smiled for the first time in days. "I'll take care of the children this evening," he continued. "You just get some rest."

"Thanks," I replied, starting toward the bedroom.

"Honey," he called after me. "I really am worried about you. I really do want you to be all right." He held out his arms to me and I walked into them, clinging to him, too weary to speak.

"I'll help you as much as I can," he whispered. "Now, get some rest."

He walked me to the bedroom. Wearier than I had ever been, I went to sleep.

CHAPTER FIVE

Something about the hypnosis calmed me at the deepest level. It had really seemed so simple—an inner state of intense concentration akin to meditation; peace and stillness seeping in, replacing fear and angst—but its effects were far-reaching. My deepest terror, the terror of remembering something, something so terrible that I would forever go insane—that terror was gone. I was still foggy from time to time, still confused and upset. But I was no longer in an irrevocable nightmare, a nightmare from which I could not wake up.

In the days following the hypnosis session, I found it easier to perform my daily tasks. Because it had relieved so much of my inner strain, some of the attention that I had turned inward could now be directed to events outside myself, providing me with the energy to play a more active role in the world.

As I continued to practice the skill of focusing my attention, I found that I could concentrate better, focus better on things other than myself. It showed in my interactions with the children, with Stan, with my friends. My mind was less apt to float away from them during a conversation. I focused more on what they said; I was more present in our daily activities. Strange as it might seem, hypnosis, an intensely inner state, acted like a glue to bind me to the world outside myself.

My children accepted my renewed focus as a matter of course. Although the difference in me was subtle, Stan appeared to notice it and to take comfort from it. I found him scrutinizing my face from time to time, trying to read there some clue to my recent mysteriousness, some evidence that I was still solid, that he could count on me, that he needn't be afraid.

The effects of the combination of medicine and hypnosis were also apparent the next time I saw Dr. Lustig. I found the walk from my home to Dr. Lustig's office, in a small shopping center, invigorating. I entered his office building, climbed the flight of stairs, and walked down the chilly corridor. Stepping from the sterile, harshly lit hallway into this thickly carpeted, softly lighted waiting room was like entering a cocoon where all the elements had been spun together to achieve a delicate warmth and balance. Something in me relaxed, as I sat there and waited for him to appear at the door.

By the time I sat down in the chair opposite him for my therapy session, I found myself noticing details about him and the room that had escaped my attention earlier. The room looked like a reflection of a real person, with small, odd personal touches, rather than some decorator's vision of office finery.

"Your room isn't what I expected," I said.

"What did you expect?" He spoke good-humoredly, as if he was pleased that he had avoided some stereotype.

"I don't know exactly," I answered hesitantly. What was a psychiatrist's office supposed to look like? "I guess I expected something more formal—a desk or an analyst's couch—something like that. I didn't expect it to be so homey and comfortable.

He nodded. "That was my purpose in choosing the decor," he told me. "I wanted it to be comfortable for me and for the people who visit me."

My attention fastened onto the rather large, square picture that hung on the wall between our chairs. It looked like a sun with multicolored rays emanating from it. In the center of the design stood a stylized American Indian figure surrounded by several Indian symbols.

"What's that?" I asked him, pointing to the picture.

"It's a Navajo sand painting, one that an Indian medicine man uses when he heals a sick child." His tone seemed to compliment me for having noticed it. "When I first picked it out, I didn't know anything at all about it. I just knew that I liked it. Later I learned what it's used for." He smiled to himself, as if pleased with the appropriateness of his instincts.

"What about the fish over there?" I asked, turning my attention to the fish fossil hanging on the wall opposite the sand painting.

"Oh, that's for me," he answered. "It helps me keep things in perspective. That fish is forty million years old. When I look at it, I can appreciate where people's problems fit into the overall scheme of things. And," he added, "it happens to be a very pretty fossil."

I didn't say anything more for a while. I just looked around the room, noticing again the table lamps whose bases were made out of gnarled driftwood, the subtle harmony of the multishaded beige chairs we sat on, the abundance of natural surfaces and textures: plants, stones, crystals, and woods. Finally, my examination of the surroundings completed, I turned my attention to Dr. Lustig himself.

I noticed for the first time how young Dr. Lustig

seemed. I guessed that he was no more than my age. How could anyone that young know what he was doing? I wondered.

"You look very *young!*" I said challengingly.

He nodded in agreement. "Compared to that fossil, we both are," he said. "I'm thirty-one," he added, answering my implied question.

"Exactly how much experience do you have?" I continued. "Have you been in practice long?"

"I've been in private practice here for a year and a half," he answered casually.

I retreated from my challenging tone and became apologetic. I was afraid I might have offended him by questioning his credentials. And if I offended him, maybe he would throw me out. "I'm *sorry* I have to ask you these questions," I said miserably. "It's just that . . ." I couldn't continue.

"It's perfectly all right," Dr. Lustig replied good-naturedly. "I'm glad that you *are* asking these questions, since *you're* the person who has to decide whether you can ultimately benefit from my services. What else would you like to know?"

I had trouble formulating my concerns.

"Well, where did you go to school?" I asked at last.

"Do you want me to start with grade school?" He was smiling. Perhaps it was the absurdity and unexpectedness of the question that made me laugh.

"Medical school will do," I said.

"I went to Albert Einstein College of Medicine in New York, and then interned in pediatrics at Montefiore Hospital."

"In New York too?"

"Yes," he replied. "Then, I trained in adult psychiatry at The Johns Hopkins Hospital in Baltimore, and finally came to Philadelphia to take my child psychiatry training at the Philadelphia Child Guidance Clinic. After that, I opened this office in July, 1973. It was a momentous day in my life," he continued. "It was the first time I was totally on my own."

I was glad to know about his professional credentials, but something else was still nagging at me. I tried to think how to express my real concern. "When I asked you about your schooling," I said at last, "I guess what I wanted to know was not about your professional training, although I am glad to know it. What I really want to know is whether you're any good at what you do and whether I should trust you."

"Good question." He nodded approvingly. "The truth is, you don't know whether you can trust me and you won't know that for a decent period of time. The only thing you do know, about me and my professional skills, is that you left here on the last two occasions feeling a heck of a lot better than when you walked in."

I nodded.

"The real question," he continued, "is whether it can be done again. That's the true test of my ability as a therapist. If it can't be done on a regular basis, then I'm not the one for you."

I stared impassively into the distance, feeling the fog slip over me again. I had to be certain that he was a good therapist—how could I turn my mind over to anyone who was less?

He regarded me in silence for a few moments and then continued, as if he was still thinking over my question and how to answer it.

"*I* know I'm a good therapist," he continued slowly, "and *you'll* be able to find that out in due time. For now, I'm glad that you're a person who trusts her intuition. But don't use that as the sole basis for making your decision about my professional skills. Combine your intuition with the facts of the results that you obtain from our appointments here. Then you'll be on solid ground."

His words flowed over me like the refreshing waters of

a mountain stream, startling me with their clarity and crispness. I tried to think. He seemed to be talking about "facts" and "results." The way he had said "solid ground" was like a command for me to focus my attention and come down to earth. I took a deep breath and focused my attention on his face.

"The ultimate determiner of my usefulness to you," he continued in a soothing voice, "is whether you improve in your ability to function effectively in the outside world, and improve in your ability to function comfortably inside your mind."

I continued staring straight ahead. I was intently trying to think. Even though I did not know how it would be accomplished, I could appreciate the goal that he had articulated.

"You know," I said musingly, thinking about my meetings with him, "I really did feel better after seeing you. It was amazing the way you could read my mind."

"Well," he said, "I'm glad you felt better. But I must admit that I flunked mind reading in medical school." He grinned, as if he thought the reply was very funny. But I wasn't convinced. There was something uncanny about the way he seemed to know what I was thinking.

"I *know* you're using magic," I insisted, remembering my earlier instinctive conviction that he was a sorcerer.

"No," he replied calmly. "I am *not* a magician. But there is something that I do very well. I pay very careful attention to all that people say and to all that people do and to all the meanings of their words and actions when they are in this office. Some people who are not accustomed to this kind of attentiveness might mistake it for mind reading."

"But how did you make it work, then?" I asked him. "Why did I feel better?"

"I don't know why you felt better because I can't read minds," he replied with just the faintest hint of irony. "But

I'll tell you what you accomplished while you were here. You practiced the skill called getting yourself back together. And anytime a person practices a skill, they get better at it. The skills that you practiced here, at our last two meetings, are probably the most fundamental of all the mental skills."

"What skills are you talking about?" I asked him, puzzled. I had always thought of skills as being things like playing baseball well, or being good at schoolwork, or being able to paint or play a musical instrument. And I had always been rather good at that sort of thing. I couldn't understand what other kinds of skills he meant.

"You learned and practiced *two* skills at these last two meetings—two ways to use altered states of consciousness for your own betterment. If you're in an altered state of consciousness that is not very comfortable and not very pleasant, your first session's skill teaches you how to *leave* it, so that you can function much more comfortably in the real world. And in the second session, with the hypnosis, you learned how to *enter* an altered state of consciousness, in which you can feel comfortable and relaxed and whole, despite what is going on in your real world.

"And I'm sure there'll be some other important, but probably lesser, skills that you'll also have to learn along the way, about how to get along in the real world, and possibly even how to get along in your own inner world. But you'll learn them as you encounter them."

I sat very still. I felt dazed. What he said was very reassuring. But another part of my mind clung to my former impressions of magic at work and was confused by this altogether practical slant on things.

Dr. Lustig seemed to sense the inner turmoil behind my passive facade, because when he spoke a few moments later, it was in a different vein.

"Last month," he said, "a third-grade boy was brought to me because he was misbehaving in the classroom and wasn't doing his schoolwork. Whenever the children were supposed to be working quietly at their desks, he was always jabbering to his neighbors.

"His parents said he was a bright boy and, in fact, he was. When I asked him about his jabbering, he said that his friends whispered to him during the silent work periods, and that he couldn't ignore them. So he would answer back, and then get caught by the teacher."

I was listening intently to Dr. Lustig while he talked, even though I couldn't understand why he was telling me about this particular boy.

"So," Dr. Lustig went on, "I asked the boy whether he knew how to turn his ears off. Of course, he said no. I told him that I would teach him. I took out a book, brought the boy into the waiting room, tuned the radio to a rock music station, and explained how he could turn his ears off. Then, I told him to start reading the book, which was an interesting one for boys his age, and to turn his ears off so that he couldn't hear the music. He practiced in the waiting room with louder and louder rock music, and he became very good at ignoring the radio. Before he went home with his parents, I instructed him to read for half an hour at bedtime every night, with loud rock music turned on and with his ears turned off."

Dr. Lustig paused for a moment in his story, registering in a glance my absorption in his words. "The next time, we played a game," he continued in the same even voice. "The boy was to read the book and ignore all of the distracting sounds that I made. While he was reading, I made all sorts of noises and grunts and clanged all sorts of things together, in order to distract him. He won the game, though. I was not able to divert his attention. The boy continued to practice at home, until he had mastered the skill of maintaining his concentration whenever *he* wanted to, and both he and his teacher were pleased with his new behavior at school."

By the time Dr. Lustig had finished the story, I was

beginning to grasp what he meant by skills. But it still seemed to me that this therapist had an uncanny ability to know what was wrong with people.

"How did you *know* that the boy didn't know how to turn his ears off?" I asked.

"That's very simple," he replied. "You think I knew *intuitively* what the problem was, don't you?"

"Of course," I said. "You're a psychiatrist, aren't you?"

"Well, I'm not as intuitive as you are," he replied. "So what I had to do was to *imagine* what it would be like for me to be a normal third-grader surrounded by talkative friends, and to not be able to concentrate on my schoolwork. Then I figured out what *skill* I needed to learn in order to allow me, as the third-grader, to get along better. And, of course, I had the advantage of being able to use my adult mind when I imagined my experience as a third-grader."

I decided that Dr. Lustig knew what he was doing. Something about the boy's story appealed to me, maybe because it didn't seem so strange, but was just an ordinary sort of problem.

"Then you don't just see crazy people here," I concluded.

"I see people who have problems and people who are falling apart and all those in between. They have one thing in common, though—they all have a problem that they don't know how to solve. *My* job is to provide them with a fact or a skill or an experience that will solve it. *Their* job is to practice the solution and become good at it."

"But I thought what was done in therapy was to probe the past, in order to uncover hidden traumas, that sort of thing." What he was saying did not seem to fit with everything I had ever heard before about therapy.

"Most people live in the present. And when they do have problems in the present, they want to be able to solve them in the present.

"That's what I help them to do. And the way that I

help them to solve their problems is to arrange for them to partially experience those problems in an altered state of consciousness. While they're in that altered state of consciousness, they can practice changing the situation, and therefore find a solution themselves. Then, when they're back in their real life in the present, they'll be able to take the steps that are necessary to implement the solution that they've already experienced and approved of. I usually leave the past for historians. I'm a healer, not a historian."

His focus on finding solutions in the present made me want to laugh in sheer relief. I stirred in my chair, as if shaking off my earlier confusion. What he said seemed so sensible—staying in the present, learning skills. I didn't feel so frightened about the craziness that took me over from time to time. I sat enjoying a more rational calm and the simple pleasure of being in his presence. As I sat there, I surreptitiously looked him over out of the corner of my eye, although I was careful that our eyes did not meet. I noticed his hands for the first time, and that he wore no wedding ring. Gathering up my courage, I looked him full in the face.

"Are you married?" I asked.

"No," he said. "Not yet."

I looked at him again, consciously registering for the first time how attractive he was. He was a trim, short man, about five foot six, two inches shorter than I. He had a beautiful short, full, reddish-brown beard and a slightly receding hairline of darker color. He was stylishly dressed in a conservative wool suit. I found that these elements, combined as they were with his large, brown, and exceedingly clear-sighted and direct eyes, carried substantial charm.

Well, well, I thought, and then, embarrassed by my thoughts, quickly turned my attention to more neutral subjects.

"How often should I see you?" I asked, looking down at my shoes.

"I think, for now, twice a week would be adequate," he said, "Later on, when you're functioning better, once a week should do just fine."

"How long do you think it will take?" I asked him, not knowing whether we were talking in terms of weeks or years.

"Two years ... maybe a little more" was his answer.

I thought over the estimate. It wasn't going to be an overnight cure. But then again, neither did two years sound like forever. I was satisfied with what seemed to me to be a realistic optimism.

"There's one thing we haven't talked about yet," he said, "and that's my fee."

"How much do you charge?" I asked quickly, realizing that I had forgotten about the money issue involved.

"Fifty dollars for each fifty-minute appointment," he replied.

"Isn't the standard fee forty dollars?" I asked. It wasn't that I wasn't willing to pay him; it was just that fifty dollars seemed like so much money to spend on a regular basis.

"Yes, it is, but I'm worth it."

"When do I pay you?" I asked him.

"At the end of each month. I'll give you a bill," he said, adding, "If you have insurance, I'll be glad to fill out the forms so that you can be reimbursed."

"What shall I tell my husband?" I asked, remembering Stan's resistance to the idea of therapy and to its cost.

"Tell him that you're fighting real hard to not have a nervous breakdown. Tell him that I'll do my best to see that you don't, and that he can contact me anytime he wants. I probably will want to see the two of you together sometime soon," he added.

"Okay," I said. The practical details arranged, I glanced at the clock, saw that my time was over, and stood up to go. He again gave me a warm handshake as I left. I did not feel the droplets of rain on my face as I made my way home, wrapped as I was for the moment in the protective cloak he had given my mind, focusing me on skills in the present, reining in bad memories until such time as I could comfortably recall them and understand their place.

CHAPTER SIX

That evening I talked to Stan again about my therapy and its cost. I explained its necessity for me, using Dr. Lustig's words. Even though Stan was initially reluctant to pay for the therapy out of his salary, I hoped he might be persuaded otherwise.

"I need your help, Stan," I said. "I just can't afford the therapy out of my part-time salary."

"All right," he agreed as if making a great concession. "I'll pay for it now, but don't expect me to pay forever."

I said thanks, realizing that this was the best I could do. I wasn't angry at Stan, but there was an edge to my gratitude. I knew he was doing the best he could, that even his grudging support was a concession, for it required him to admit that something might be wrong. He felt my mind drifting away from him, out windows he could not look through. He did not know how to reach out and bring me back. I knew that underneath somewhere he was as afraid as I was, that from his viewpoint controlling the money was a means of containing the situation. But I was angry at myself for having to ask. I wished again that we could recapture the camaraderie and understanding of our early marriage, the small details of kindness that had marked our days—a small love note left on my pillow, a bunch of roses picked from our back garden and carefully arranged in a rose bowl, the encouragement he had given me about my career, the charming way he could tell a story and make me laugh. Now the emptiness, the drawn-out silences, the alienation. I hoped my therapy would not turn into a new battleground.

Feeling unsettled in spite of our tentative accord, I went into the bathroom to apply a fresh coat of makeup to my face. I had adopted this form of protection lately, from the day of my first dream. Each day I would apply heavy facial makeup, whitish and icy in hue, complemented by a dark purple lipstick.

The effect of this makeup mask was a subtly exaggerated one, suggesting something between the disguise of a clown and the appearance of a Japanese courtesan. But it served to protect me in the most primitive sense, or so it seemed to me at the time. It stood like a sentinel at the gate, guaranteeing that no distorted thought should slip unnoticed through the door of my face and out into the larger world. I felt safe behind my second face because it helped me hold my anguish in as, at the same time, it effectively kept other people at bay. I could hide and, by hiding, rest from the constant monitoring of my inner distortions. My mask protected me from the world, and it from me, or so I thought.

As I stood before the mirror applying my makeup that late November day, I did not perceive how ashen and cold it made my face look. Although highly dramatic in its contrast of dark lipstick against pale skin, it must have hovered somewhere within the bounds of normal, because neither Stan nor any of my friends, whom I saw regularly during that time, mentioned much about it. One of my friends, our neighbor Mimi, the wife of one of Stan's colleagues, did look at me strangely one afternoon when we were having coffee in her kitchen.

"You look different," she commented, shaking her head slightly, as if she was perplexed by the elusiveness of her impression. "Did you get your hair cut or change your lipstick or something?"

"It's just that I haven't been feeling well lately," I replied.

"Well, I guess that explains it," she answered with less than total conviction. "You do look pale," she continued, clearly groping for an explanation that would put to rest the unease that still nagged at her.

Our children's squabbling in the living room interrupted us. By the time we had settled the dispute and gotten the children to play peacefully again, it was time for me to return home and get supper ready. By then, the topic of my changed appearance had been forgotten.

Only Dr. Lustig seemed to take my makeup into account.

I had been in therapy for about two weeks when he gave me the gift of a new face. One day, after I had sat down in my usual chair and we had talked for a few minutes until I was adjusted to being there, he told me that he had some homework for me to do.

"I want you to go out and buy some new makeup," he said, "in a warmer shade to match your skin. I also want you to buy a new lipstick in a pretty shade of pink or orange."

I sank down protectively into my chair, curving my shoulders inward and clutching my arms with my hands. "I can't," I whispered. "I just can't."

"But," he continued as if he hadn't heard, "first I want you to take this paper and pencil and write what I tell you." He handed me a pad of yellow, legal-sized notepaper and a pencil, and I obediently wrote as he dictated:

I, Carol Allen, do solemnly swear to buy a warm
shade of lipstick for my lips, only when I am
ready. I do further swear that I shall not wear the
new lipstick publicly until I have worn it privately
in Dr. Lustig's office.

CAROL ALLEN
December 2, 1974

I relaxed and we talked until the session was over. But Dr.
Lustig's simple command had its effects. Carrying all the
force of a legal contract between us, our agreement demanded that I assume a normal and healthy demeanor. At
the same time it quelled my fear of losing my protective covering, since I had been instructed to wear new makeup only
when I was ready. And I found myself ready sooner than I
had thought.

Only two days later I went out and bought new face
makeup and lipstick. I approached the cosmetics counter intent on my task. I carefully examined all the options, but I
found that my right hand, as if propelled by an outside force,
kept selecting lipsticks that were purplish or brown in tone.
The others, the pretty reds and pinks and oranges, looked
vulgar to me. Finally, in a gesture that was a triumph of
rationality over instinct, I utilized my knowledge of mixing
colors and grabbed a lipstick with my left hand. Reassured
by its name that it would count as a "pretty pink" lipstick, I
hastily bought it. Then, with the saleswoman's help, I established the correct shade of face makeup to match my skin
tones.

I took my new purchases home and hid them in a
drawer, frightened by the possibilities they represented. But
on the day of my next therapy session, I dutifully took them
out and carried them to Dr. Lustig.

He told me to go to the rest room down the corridor
and completely wash the old mask off my face. Then I was
to return to the therapy room without any makeup on. Only

years of being, first, a dutiful daughter and, then, a dutiful wife could have made me go through this painful exercise. I was so panicked that I could scarcely breathe. My face, stripped of its protective coating, looked naked and ugly to me. But I steeled myself to go back and face him without my integument. I opened the bathroom door a crack and, assured that no one was presently in the hall to see me, ran back to the safety of Dr. Lustig's office.

I walked back into the therapy room embarrassed. But Dr. Lustig acted as if nothing was wrong. In fact, he smiled and nodded approvingly, and told me how nice I looked. As I continued to endure our conversation, my discomfort grew by leaps and bounds. It became a kind of extreme mortification. Several times, with my body uncontrollably shaking, I had to sit on my hands to stop them from reaching up to cover my face. Dr. Lustig continued to behave as if everything was normal. I wondered how he could just sit there like that, seated across from such an ugly person.

Toward the end of the hour when my discomfort had become unbearable, Dr. Lustig told me to go back to the rest room and put on my new makeup. It was such a relief to have *any* protective coating for my psyche that I barely noticed the way in which the new makeup transformed me. This time when I returned, his face positively beamed, and he told me again how nice I looked. "And human," he added. Thus encouraged, I told him that I thought I would be able to wear my new makeup home, and I did.

On the way home I stopped off at the supermarket to buy some bread. As I stood in the express checkout line, the woman standing next to me glanced at me briefly, and then smiled. It was a simple, ordinary gesture. But it startled me and, at the same time, was greatly pleasing. I smiled back.

I discovered in the days ahead that my warmer complexion touched a responsive humanness in the people around me, and in these newfound and simple bonds, I experienced brief moments of connectedness and peace.

My friends, in particular, responded affirmatively to the newfound warmth in my face. A week or so after the makeup change, I was having lunch with one of my best friends, Elaine. We had taught together several years before, at the same small liberal-arts college—she in the English department and I in philosophy—and we had discovered in each other kindred spirits. Our friendship had continued, even after she left the college where we had met. Although she now lived about an hour's drive away, we still kept in frequent contact by phone and usually managed to arrange a monthly meeting. Lunch, that day, was the first occasion I had seen her since I had dreamed my dreams and begun therapy.

Over lunch, Elaine listened to my dreams with interest and some concern. But she accepted the fact of my therapy with pragmatism, and spontaneously commented on my appearance.

"That's a very pretty lipstick you're wearing," she said. "It really accents your attractiveness. I never noticed, till now, how pretty your mouth is."

"Thanks," I said. "It's a new color I've started wearing recently."

"Well, it does wonders for you," she confirmed.

I was very pleased by her comments and the progress that they seemed to indicate. Even Stan noticed I was looking better, although he did not acknowledge this as a positive effect of my therapy, but rather a confirmation of his original judgment that there was nothing really wrong with me.

In spite of these reassurances, however, sometimes the loss of my old protection was too much for me. Catching a glimpse of my new face in a passing mirror would send waves of pain sweeping through my limbs. Then I would be pulled down into the dark windswept places beyond loneliness, where the gods of my imagination demanded payment for my presumption in possessing a moment of ordinary happiness. Later the pain and nausea would ease, leaving me o protection at all. It's like the martial arts master who appears to be unarmed, even though he or she can immediately, correctly, and appropriately respond to any situation. So too can you present to the rest of the world the illusion that you have no protection, when, in fact, you can be constantly imposing protective actions and mechanisms on your own functioning and on the world's intrusion upon you. In this way you can ensure your functional integrity and well-being."

What he said calmed me somehow, but the idea was still a new one. Finally, I voiced my one remaining objection. "How will an ordinary, transparent face protect the world from *me*?"

"As a representative of the rest of the world, I want you to know how much I appreciate your concern," he replied in a parody of seriousness. I laughed.

"But it's not a humanitarian act on your part to wear icy makeup. It only serves to isolate you from the rest of the world, so that you're truly alone." He thought for a moment. "The concept is correct. You have to keep what's inside in, and maintain the boundary between inside and out. It even makes sense to coat yourself, so that you have a constant tactile and visual reminder of where that boundary is. But there's no law that says you have to coat yourself with something that's bizarre. You can protect yourself better with an ordinary covering. Yes," he continued, as if pleased with this image, "protect yourself so that you still can maintain contact with the rest of the world.

"Your humanitarian instinct to warn the world of the danger within Carol can be handled in another way. The world is not in any real danger. Carol may be, but the world is not. Life will be better for you if you stop trying to save the world, when all you really need to do is to start taking better care of Carol. I, as a representative of the rest of the world, will do all that I can to ensure that the dangers you perceive yourself to embody will become neutralized, or else

with a gray cloud that settled on my head, heavy with moisture, but unable to yield any portion of healing rain.

Meanwhile, in the weeks that followed, Dr. Lustig began teaching me new and "healthy protections" to use in place of my maladaptive mask. One such conversation with him took place several days after I had put on my new makeup. We were talking about protections, and I was telling him how naked and vulnerable and defenseless I felt without my old makeup on.

"Even though my new makeup sometimes makes me feel good," I was saying, "it often at the same time terrifies me, because I feel so transparent and vulnerable."

"That's absolutely correct," Dr. Lustig said. "That's how everybody feels when they don't have any self-protection. But how did your old makeup protect you, *really* protect you? How was it a protection against the unpleasantness that was occurring in your ordinary life, and the unpleasantness that was occurring inside of you? How was it protecting you—really?"

"It covered up the . . ." I paused, and then started over. "It made me feel safe, like I could hide, and what was bad about me inside wouldn't come out and harm anybody. People wouldn't be able to read my thoughts."

"The old makeup certainly did provide you with that illusion, didn't it?" he equally replied. "There are some things in life that are absolutely true. For instance, that our thoughts stay locked inside our heads until we communicate them, and that no one can read another person's mind. You don't need makeup to have them be true."

"But people must be able to see it in my face," I replied.

"You do have a very expressive face," he confirmed. "What it conveys is *your reaction* to what's going on in your everyday life and to what's going on inside of you. If what's going on is very pleasant, whether inside or out, then your face is a very relaxed one. But if what's going on inside or out is very unpleasant, then your face is a face that very dramatically demonstrates the distress."

"But don't you see," I said, "that's just what I'm afraid of. That I'm going to show that I'm crazy. And I just can't let people see that. How can I teach my classes if my students can see it? How can I care for my children if they can know?"

Dr. Lustig settled back in his chair a bit, as if his answer would not be a brief one. "Well, I'll tell you something," he finally said, drawing his words out very deliberately. "If you want to *really hide* behind something, then hide behind pleasantness and ordinariness, so that if another person were to glance at you briefly, they would not see anything unusual in your appearance or mannerisms. That would be a far more powerful protection for you, against whatever is going on inside, than bizarreness."

"You mean my old makeup was like a road map of my madness—the visible expression of it, rather than a protection?" I asked. "Is that what you're saying?"

"Your face makeup was a road sign that indicated that there was danger ahead," he replied, subtly adjusting the metaphor to his own satisfaction. "However, there's no need for there to be danger ahead. There's no need for that particular road sign. The danger can be contained. It can be contained inside you safely, and comfortably handled.

"You see," he continued, sinking even further into his chair, "the first order of business for people is to ensure their own physical safety, their actual physical survival. The second order of business is to ensure their mental or emotional well-being. You do whatever you have to do to make sure that your physical integrity and your mental integrity continue. If it's a thought or a book that disturbs you, put it away. If it's a movie that causes you distress, walk out. Even if it's a conversation or an interaction that becomes uncomfortable for you, remove it—not the person but the inter-

action. It's not 'if thine eye offends thee, pluck it out' sight offends thee, close thine eye, or move thy gaze

"But," I objected, "aren't defenses by definiti That's what everyone seems to think. All people tal nowadays is 'openness' and 'honesty,' about 'ex your feelings' and not being 'defensive.' "

"This attitude ignores the laws of survival, wh persede everything else," he answered. "The laws your continued healthy existence. Protection of bot physical and emotional integrity, therefore, becon first order of business. Communication becomes sec But once you're ready to communicate, you must how much to keep private and how much to make about what's going on inside of you. It's your right *private* as much as you want to."

Dr. Lustig paused for a moment, as if lost in tho also sat deeply absorbed, thinking over what he had had been listening intently to his words, and in the that followed they seemed to wash over me again, s into the furthest reaches of my mind. I have a right tect myself. I have a right to my privacy. Survival is th order of business. I felt my fears slipping away.

After a few minutes, Dr. Lustig resumed the con tion, as if he was rethinking the whole issue. "Let's g for a moment," he said. "There were two purposes tha icy makeup served for you. One was to make the ph distinction for you between your inside and your o worlds, and the other was to communicate the distres you were experiencing inside. Now that you have, ir communicated that distress, it's no longer necessary fo to use makeup to send that message to me anymore. I u stand that you're in distress. And I understand a bit abo magnitude and its character.

"Your purpose is different now. Now your purp to continue to protect yourself, but to do it in a more tive way. And the most effective protection is the illusi

channeled in such a way that they become functional and contributory rather than destructive."

I nodded, feeling better, sure now that I had a right, perhaps even an obligation, to effectively protect myself, more confident that I posed no danger to others.

In the days that followed I began to wear my new, more human face with greater ease and more satisfaction. I began, for brief moments, to feel better about myself, and the improvements in my casual interactions with other people only served to reinforce this newfound pleasure.

But there were still times of great price, when my infant, struggling liking for myself confronted other forces inside me that were less charitable, if no less resourceful, and certainly of longer habit. Then I instinctively knew that for every movement, however slight, toward a more positive conception of myself, my inner demons would extract an exorbitant fee. But I endured those times as best I could, and kept returning to Dr. Lustig. It was part of our implicit agreement that he would nurture and foster in me whatever was healthy and strong—that however much discomfort I experienced from trying on a new identity, he would help me fight my internal demons in such a way that the victory would be decisive and I would be whole.

For every forward movement, however, there was the occasional slipping back. But the direction in which I was proceeding was at least clear to me. Like an airplane that experiences trouble midway in its flight, I was now past the point of no return. I continued forward, hoping for a safe landing, in some unknown but friendly field of the future. Dr. Lustig was my navigator and copilot. In order to move forward I had to place my trust in him, because he was my only hope, and because it is always easier to do something when it is the only choice.

CHAPTER SEVEN

DECEMBER 18–25, 1974

One day I woke up and realized that Christmas was a week away. I had been so caught up in clinging to the edge of sanity, as a small child clings to the hem of its mother's skirt, that Christmas caught me quite by surprise. Forgotten were my usual ways of welcoming it—buying gifts for friends and family, lavishing thought and care on the details of giving, wrapping presents in bright bits of silver and red and green, mailing cards to people I had known in other times and in other places, decorating the house with sprigs of holly and berry and branches of long-needled pine. This year it was as if an unexpected death in the house had postponed the rituals of the living.

We were expecting guests. My parents were coming from Idaho to celebrate Christmas with us, and my sister and her husband from New York were joining us too. Also expected was a favorite friend of a favorite aunt. But even their imminent arrival could not spur me to activity or preparation. I could not fix my attention on any date. I drifted through the calendar days of late December much as a novice deep-sea diver drifts past underwater formations and creatures, caught off guard by the pressure of water on his body, more conscious of his limited time underwater and that it might run out than with the details of the passing scene. I drifted, I floated, I clung, I survived, but nowhere was there room for celebration. My sole gesture toward the season was to go out and buy a Christmas tree. It was a blue spruce, elegant and full-branched. I brought it home and, then otherwise absorbed, set it aside in a living room corner, where it stood leaning against the wall inconspicuously, as if it had settled in to wait for the day of its dress.

On December 19, the day before my guests were to arrive, I returned home from teaching to find an empty house and absent children. In the kitchen I found an urgent message from Stan to call him at the local hospital. Terrified, with my imagination leaping ahead to disaster, I dialed the hospital number. After being passed through several connections, I finally located Stan. Briefly he recounted what had happened.

Daniel had suddenly begun gasping for breath and choking. The frightened babysitter had phoned Stan, who was working nearby. He had raced home and rushed Daniel to the emergency room. A surgeon had been called in, and X rays were taken, which seemed to show a blockage in Daniel's throat. Before performing an emergency tracheotomy, however, the doctor had once again examined Daniel. Unable to feel any foreign object or obstruction, the doctor had ordered new X rays. These showed no blockage and the surgery had been canceled. Daniel was now thought to be having a severe asthma attack, and had been put, minutes before, in an oxygen tent.

I hung up the phone and stumbled blindly to the car, automatically turning the ignition and starting it up. I was numb; I was stunned. Although I thought I had left my early fundamentalist-Christian upbringing far behind, on that drive to the hospital, I bargained with God.

Please, God, let him live. Please make him safe. If I've brought this harm upon him because of my misdeeds, then punish me instead. I'll do anything, suffer anything. Only please, God, let him be all right.

I somehow made my way to Daniel's hospital room and found him standing wide-eyed in a hospital crib, surrounded by a transparent oxygen tent. His breathing was a bit raspy, but he appeared calm and unconcerned. When he saw me and put out his arms to me, I silently began to weep. The invisible cord that connects the flesh of mother to child at even ordinary times was intensified that day, cutting through the plastic wall that separated us. I asked the nurse if she could pull the oxygen tent aside for a moment, so that I could hold him. I needed to touch him to know that he was safe; I needed to touch him to make my love tangible. The nurse kindly complied.

Stan and I stayed with Daniel for some time. Then we were told to go. I asked to stay with him overnight, but for some reasons that I couldn't grasp, I was told that this was not allowed. Forced to leave his presence but unwilling to leave his proximity, I walked several corridors away and waited in the hospital waiting room. Stan returned home with Elizabeth.

It is strange how in times of crisis or intense emotion, odd, incidental details become etched in your mind. I still remember things about that waiting room (where I spent the better part of the next three days) that I do not remember about houses where I lived for years. I can still see the cover of the *Good Housekeeping* magazine, showing a smiling hostess beside a gaily decorated tree. I remember the funnel shape of the plastic coffee cups laid out beside the Christmas napkins that somebody had kindly brought. I can see the plastic holly of the nurses' corsages, standing out in stark contrast to the starched white of their uniforms. I remember the small Christmas tree standing by the window, gaudily wrapped in someone's idea of finery, looking slightly embarrassed at its overdress, its blinking colored lights reflecting eerily off the sterile white walls.

I was overwhelmed by a sense of unreality. Hospitals had always struck me as otherworldly enough, but on this occasion, I felt transported to another time zone. I would think about Daniel and my mind would recoil, unable to bear the thought that somehow it was my fault, that somehow or other I had brought this malady upon him.

The feeling was magnified by my sense of helplessness. This hospital domain clearly belonged to the doctors and nurses scurrying around in their brisk, professional way. It did not belong to the mothers, fathers, relatives, or friends who sat in the waiting room and loved and waited. I felt useless, except for the time I actually spent with Daniel, because then I could see that he liked my being there. Otherwise the task of waiting seemed futile and detached. Although one part of me knew that my son was in no danger, another part of me was filled with doom as I sat and waited.

I was also filled with memories of other times in other hospitals. How large and white everything had looked the first time I was brought to a hospital for minor knee surgery, when I was ten years old. How metallic and scary-sharp the instruments had seemed on that occasion, how the brush had sounded as it scrubbed inside the wound. My mind took me back three months, to the memory of my own recent hospital stay. Doubled over with abdominal pains about a year after Daniel's birth, I had been admitted to the hospital with a uterine infection caused by my IUD. For three days and nights a fever of 105 degrees had raged within me, until a new combination of antibiotics had finally worked. I remembered one night of delirium, when a nurse had sat beside me and bathed me in ice.

Thinking back on it as I sat and waited, it seemed to have been the beginning of my coming unhinged. I remembered the aberrant thoughts that had flickered across my mind, seeming to be apart and unconnected to me, tied instead to burning sensations, feeling on fire, fire—what was there about fire that was so disquieting? I remembered the nurse's soothing voice as I had rambled. What had I said? Disconnected, that was all I could recall. Fever ravaging the wholeness of my mind, so that what was left was random pieces, broken thoughts that made no sense. Had the fever and delirium sparked the madness, caused a chemical imbalance, uncloaked buried memories, uncovered an innate tendency hidden within my genetic structure, snapped some synapses, burned away the mental glue by which our ordinary perception of the world is held together? What after all do we really know of the mysterious connection of body and mind?

Death—I remembered I had thought about death. I had thought not that someone else but that *I* would die, and I remembered that I had not faced death bravely. Sitting there now in the waiting room, waiting to see Daniel, I recalled just how afraid I had been. Then I pushed the memory aside, wondering idly as I did so just why Roosevelt had said that there was nothing to fear but fear itself.

My relatives arrived on the second day of Daniel's hospital stay, but I saw very little of them. I left to them the task of overseeing Christmas, and they carried on as best they could. On December 23, the day before Christmas Eve, Daniel was discharged from the hospital. My joy at bringing him home was overwhelming and was shared by everyone who welcomed him.

On Christmas Eve, we sang carols and drank toasts and performed the usual holiday rituals. We were all happy that Daniel was well, but a pall hung over our celebration in spite of that, because of the less comprehensible nature of the illness that visited me. My parents felt the presence of the powers that had stolen my well-being and perspective. They saw the strain on my face and the terror in my eyes. And they did not know what to do. They stood helpless before the nature of my complaint, wanting to take away my pain like good parents, but stymied by the unfathomable regions into which my mind had wandered, away from them into places where they could not follow.

Later that evening, when the children were in bed, I tried to tell my parents of the strangeness that was surrounding me, of my sense of loss, of the unreality at work. My mother tried to listen, but her mind kept turning away from my words. The pain and guilt they caused her were evident because she kept interrupting, offering anxious reassurances, minimizing the difficulties of which I spoke.

"I'm sure it will pass, honey," she said. "There's no reason to worry—everything will be all right."

I spoke of my fever and how it might have thrown off my chemical balance. I tried to explain that they were not responsible, that my childhood had been good. But my words bounced off them like balls against a net, thrown back at me, untouched.

I looked across at my mother, wanting to touch her, but it seemed to me that she stood at a great distance, as far away from me as I was from the Great Depression, which had colored her youth. Like others of her generation who had suffered that indignity, she struggled to put a positive face on all things, believing as she did that the negative aspects of life were a matter of private sorrow, that to give them voice was to admit defeat. I knew that she could not accept what was happening to me. I knew that her understanding was what I most wanted. So we stood there, separated by different histories, love on both sides but a gap in between.

My father listened intently as I spoke, and when I had finished made no reply. His face showed bewilderment that such irrationality should so suddenly impinge on his rational world. He remained standing silently for a minute more, as if unsure what response to make. Then he quickly stepped up to me and put his encompassing arms around me, to let me know of his love in any case. My mother joined us and we silently embraced.

Later that evening, preparing for bed, I tried to break the silence between Stan and me, perhaps because it was Christmas, perhaps because of the ordeal we had shared with Daniel.

"I'm terrified," I said, "of what's happening to me."

Stan's response surprised me, for he seemed very angry. "Why do you keep staring out of windows?" he asked accusingly. "Why are you so distant and uncaring about me? Your lack of attention is really disturbing. Why can't you be yourself, for heaven's sake?"

I said nothing further. There was nothing more to say. What has happened to us? I wondered for the umpteenth time. We had started out so bright just six years before. We had loved each other, and we could talk. We had gone on for hours about philosophy, politics, literature, always leaving the conversation with something more to say. Stan had such a good sense of humor. I do believe I married him because he could make me laugh.

I thought about the Stan I knew now, foolish, irritating, ponderous Stan, who still charmed me in public with his wit and laughter, who lectured me in private as if I were one of his slower students who could never grasp the obvious. Stan, who was solid and sensible by his own lights, grounded. Stan, who defined me as his extension—or rather, I thought, perhaps I am his shadow. Somewhat defensive, somewhat pompous Stan, who gave me a public persona, who cast me in a particular light by the simple fact of wedlock, who made me half of a couple but not a whole anything.

Our first few years had been good, I thought, or so it seemed in retrospect—although they did not, for all that, bear close scrutiny, because of the other women I chose to ignore, because of the uncertainty Stan had about the whole "married" business, as if he regretted turning our harmonious living together into a union that weighed on his spirits like too many loads of dirty laundry, that robbed him of his lightness and private laughter. "Marriage," he repeatedly told me, "is nothing but responsibility." The way he said "responsibility" it could have been "death," because it had the same sense of possibility extinguished.

I remembered a couple we had visited at Yale University during our first year of marriage. The couple, whose names I had forgotten, had fought with each other like trained guerrillas throughout the evening, never willing to step out of the underbrush and show their weapons outright, firing random shots in the dark, as if the enemy were always just out of sight. "Just wait until you've been married seven years," they had said over dessert. "The seven-year itch, you know."

Stan and I had smiled politely, arrogant and secure in our sense of marital superiority, certain that our marriage would never come to this. But now I was left wondering. Was it as simple as the seven-year itch? Would we outgrow it, say, in the eighth or ninth year? Would our silences with the sharp edges soften into harmonious ones?

"It takes two to make a marriage," my parents always said, but now Stan and I added up to less than one.

On Christmas Day itself, we opened our presents, prepared and had dinner, struggled through the rest of the day, trying to behave as if it were an ordinary Christmas. There was one brief respite that made me feel less alone. My sister and I took a long walk together. I could talk to her. She was not shocked at what I said.

"You know," she said, when I had finished speaking, "maybe it's really better this way. I know it must seem funny, but I'm almost envious—to have something vital and dramatic happening, so that once and for all you can straighten things out. As for myself," she continued slowly and thoughtfully, "I just go along doing the best I can. But I sometimes wish that something drastic would happen to me, to shake me out of my lethargy and force me into action to make things better."

I listened carefully to what she said. I loved her for her understanding.

On the night of Christmas Day, everyone had become weary and retired early, so by ten o'clock I was alone. I walked through the house switching off the lights, knowing, despite the presence of loved ones, the special sorrow of a lonely Christmas. As I passed through the living room I glanced at the darkened corner where the silhouette of the Christmas tree could barely be discerned. There it stood, exactly as I had left it, naked and unadorned, leaning wearily against the wall. I stood and stared at it for a moment, then continued mechanically on my way through the house, turning off the lights as I went. No one decorated the Christmas tree, I thought absently, as I switched off the last remaining light.

CHAPTER EIGHT

JANUARY, 1975

The days following Christmas continued in much the same manner. As Stan, the children, and I returned to our daily routines, I found myself for the most part blanketed by fog and fear, eclipsed by moments of illumination in Dr. Lustig's office. I would feel, after each therapy session, more cohesive, less afraid. But during the days between visits, my psychic pain would reassert itself, and once again I would drown in confusion and unreality.

I discovered, during that time, that it wasn't enough to learn a therapeutic lesson once. Often I had to have the instruction repeated within a variety of contexts, so that slowly new habits were built up, strong enough to supplant the old dysfunctional ones.

The self-hypnosis I had learned helped me in this respect. Sometimes when I was alone, I would sit on the living room couch and go into a trance where I would stay for some time, experiencing a timeless moment of peace and comfort. This private time was restorative and, along with my therapy, reinforced my fledgling belief that I could like myself. But these moments were teacups within a tempest.

By early January, my struggle to keep functioning—to care for my children, coexist with Stan, and teach my classes—in the midst of so much upheaval had left me exhausted and robbed of almost all emotion. It was then that a new feeling, anger, rose to the surface.

The day of January 9 started out gray and dreary. It was one of those early January days when winter seems the permanent season, leaving the imprint of its ashen face in the grime of the windowpanes and in the weariness of the soul. A steady drizzle of rain had made slush out of the mounds of dirt-streaked snow. Even the children hid indoors, unwilling to confront an atmosphere that could so unfeelingly make their once proud snowman weep.

During breakfast, I searched the morning papers for some glimpse of good news that would lift my spirits out of this winter gloom. But the paper, as might be expected, had only troubles to tell. Not even the horoscope, which was my last resort, could say a good word about a single sign. The children and I finished breakfast, and then I bathed them and got them dressed. At nine o'clock they were comfortably settled in front of the television, preparing to watch their morning programs. Meanwhile, I busied myself with my daily chores.

I was standing in the kitchen about an hour later, when the pain began. It started very slowly, as a tight band around my head, and it didn't seem to be attached to any specific thought or event. I was just aware one moment that it was there, where it hadn't been before. It was so strong that I was sure it must be coming from the atmosphere. I looked out at the sky and then at my children to see if the pain was encircling them too. But they played on unconcernedly, caught up in their games, undisturbed by any atmospheric visitation.

Ten o'clock turned to eleven, then twelve, and the pain droned on. By one o'clock, following lunch, it had moved to my chest, where it formed a small, hard sliver of anger. The infant anger gathered the pain around itself and suckled on it, and in this way grew, until it had become a ball of rage, burning out a place for itself in my chest cavity about the size of a heart.

From its thoracic perch the anger began to move. It burned its way up, down, and outward through my body, freezing and burning like dry ice. I felt the muscles of my face become rigid in response and my eyes freeze over. At last it came to the walls of my flesh and pounded against them. But the walls of my body held fast, containing the enemy. So the alien inner growth turned back on itself to feed. But the only victim it could find was me.

Throughout the day, the anger continued to eat its way slowly through my psyche, but I vigilantly guarded against its escape. No visible expression of its presence passed through my face, although a trained observer might have sensed its presence from the rigid way that I held my body, or from the way that my hands periodically clenched and unclenched.

My dread was that I could not contain it, that this force would take me over and have its way. I stood clasping the latch of a Pandora's box, afraid that the slightest movement would unleash unimaginable forces and send them flying to wreak havoc across the world.

But my greatest fear was for my children. I could not pinpoint exactly what I was afraid of. It was more a kind of ungovernable anxiety that, somehow through contact with me, they would be harmed. What if my anger got loose and harmed them? What if I turned into a child abuser? But these thoughts were too terrible. I shoved them away.

By six o'clock I was exhausted from my guard duties. Stan, who would usually have been returning home by this time, was out of town at a conference. On this day particularly I wished he were home—to act as a buffer, or if necessary a safety zone. But instead I was alone with my children and my fears.

The evening dragged on, minute by minute. As I read Elizabeth and Daniel their bedtime stories, the mixture of anger and fear that I felt nearly choked off my voice. But I made myself continue reading. When the children begged for yet another story, it took all my strength to comply and push my anguish into the background.

Finally, it was bedtime. I had made it through the day. I tucked Elizabeth and Daniel into their beds and kissed them good night. As I bent over them, my fear for their safety was as large as my love.

Exhausted by the intensity of the day, I went to bed early, shortly after the children. But sleep, which often served me as an anesthetic, was elusive. I tossed and turned, fighting my internal battle. I still didn't know what to do about my anger. All I knew was that it terrified me. It made me feel evil.

After several hours of fitfully trying to sleep, I got up out of bed and began pacing throughout the house. Finally I stopped and stood in the middle of the living room. Unable to contain my anger any longer, I began to scream and scream.

Someone else might not have called it a scream, for the sound was a choked and garbled one. It did not flow out of me freely, cleanly, purely. But to me it was a scream, nonetheless—one long excruciating sound. It gathered together years of pent-up rage and gave them voice. I thought my cry must have been piercingly loud, because what I heard was the intensity behind it. I was surprised when it did not awaken the children.

When I was finished, I took several deep breaths. Some of the pain had gone, but left in its place was an even greater confusion. I was horrified at what I had done, at the enor-

mity of my anger, at my loss of control. If I can so lose control of myself, I thought, how can I ever trust myself again?
It was then that I knew what was even more terrible than
anger—losing control of my feelings; because then, I feared,
I would lose my mind.

CHAPTER NINE

JANUARY 10, 1975

I often asked myself afterward, and other people asked me, how I managed to continue functioning during that time. How did I care for my children, teach my classes, run my household in the grip of such anguish and emotional upheaval? I can only say that I led different lives. It was as if different persons inhabited one dwelling. Something in me seemed to know when it could rage and when it could not—when it could let go and slip into madness, and when it could not afford to give the slightest clue.

I would find myself switching, often within minutes, from one persona to another. I would, for instance, be talking normally to the children. Then I would put them down for a nap. During the ten-second walk from their room to my bedroom, another part of me would gain ascendency. Upon entering the bedroom, I would find my hands wringing each other and clutching after sanity, my mind so immobilized by fear that I could barely stand.

These aberrations, I found, would usually surface in moments when the context made it safe for them to appear—when I was alone, that is, or during the times when I saw Dr. Lustig. Some instinct for self-protection made me wait until these moments—even madness had to wait to have its time. When that time came, a part of me would watch, with fascination and horror, as another part would surface and completely hold sway. I found that the observing part of me, often helpless but ever present, could not stop the madness from gaining possession of me. But it could observe and record the onset of madness and struggle to limit its power.

It happened on the day after I screamed my midnight scream. I was switched into normal function during most of the day. I finished teaching my two classes at the college and drove directly to Dr. Lustig's office for a scheduled appointment at 3 P.M. But by the time I walked into his waiting room, another mental switch had been thrown. I found my anger and fear of the night before returning to my psyche and coagulating there, so that by the time Dr. Lustig came into the waiting room to greet me, I had no voice left in me to speak. I simply rose and walked stiffly past him, feeling the muscles of my face draw tightly, my cheekbones prominent, my eyes opaque. I sat down in the inner room and stared straight ahead of me, my eyes turned inward, unable to focus.

Dr. Lustig closely regarded me and then spoke. "Carol, what's going on?" he asked searchingly.

I sat motionless, making no response. I felt the sounds wash over me, but they were out of alignment and made no sense. Finally, in a kind of delayed reaction, they registered in my brain, and I understood that I had been addressed. I struggled to form a responding word, concentrating all my attention in an effort to answer his question. I took in a short breath and then struggled to open my mouth. I felt the tension in my jaw and in my neck as I tried to speak. But the power of speech eluded me. I found that I could not make a sound.

Dr. Lustig again broke the silence. "I don't know exactly what's going on with you, but I have some guesses about what it might be. For anyone to look the way you look here today, and to have made the effort to speak but to not have spoken as you did here today, usually means that the person is totally overwhelmed by some experience they are having at the moment or have just had. If, in fact, you are experiencing something like this now, I want you to understand that it will pass. And we'll just sit here together until it does. But if you had it earlier," he continued, "then you probably are feeling totally numb by now, which is a very safe thing to feel. Can you tell me which it is?" he asked.

I struggled to speak, this time with more success. In the barest cracking voice, I finally was able to articulate a few words. ". . . scream . . ." I whispered, and then, after another lengthy pause, ". . . last night . . ." I could go no further.

"Are you feeling safely numb now?" he asked. I made a slight movement of my head upward in assent. "Good," he said, seemingly glad of my response. "Keep on feeling that and use the numbness to *protect* you from the memory of last night's experience." He paused and then went on.

"And when all the feelings about last night's experience have been frozen by your numbness, could you tell me more about what happened last night?"

A feeling of safety slowly crept over me, the numbness forming a protective shield, encircling my fear and placing a limit on it.

Haltingly, I began trying to explain about my experience of the night before. ". . . angry . . . I was so angry. . . ." I stopped there; it was some time before I could say the worst. ". . . I am so evil. . . ."

When it was clear that I could not continue, Dr. Lustig spoke. "Did your scream last night let the evil out?" I nodded briefly. "All of it or just some of it?"

I tried to think. I was confused by the question and wondered why he asked it. I tried to answer anyway, because it had become my habit to follow his lead.

"I don't know," I finally answered. "Some of it, I guess."

"Then there might be some evil still left?" he asked. So horrifying was this possibility that I became mute and immobile again.

"Well, then," he continued heartily, "let's get it all out of you safely. Scream here for as long and as loud as you need, so that you can get all the evil safely out." I remained silent.

"But would you do me a favor?" he continued. "Could you please scream silently so that my ears won't be damaged? Would that be all right?"

I was relieved. This was easier to comply with than screaming out loud. It also made me curious. Will it really work to scream silently? I wondered. Then I imagined myself screaming a silent scream. "Will it work just as well?" I asked out loud.

"A scream is a scream," Dr. Lustig replied. "And the only thing that really matters is getting out of you whatever it is you don't want to keep. It's just a matter of expelling. It's as simple as coughing up a foreign substance that you've breathed in by mistake."

As I listened I was connecting his words with the sensation of relief I was beginning to feel. My earlier confusion seemed to have eased. Everything seemed simple again. I found I could talk more normally.

"It's funny," I said, "but I don't feel like I need to scream anymore. At least for right now," I qualified. I wasn't entirely convinced that my inner screams had been subdued. I was still concerned that the anger that had prompted my nocturnal outburst might reappear at any moment and once again, I might be at its mercy.

"Last night I felt so out of control," I explained. "I was so afraid."

"Afraid of what?" he asked.

"Afraid that if all that force were released, I would disintegrate. Explode into a million pieces."

"That sure would be messy, wouldn't it?" Dr. Lustig answered cheerfully. He looked over to the wall across from us, motioned toward it with his hand, and continued, "You—splattered over the whole universe."

I hadn't intended my remarks to be taken quite so literally. Wait a minute, I wanted to say. You don't have to get quite so carried away. It was just a metaphor.

"Well, not really that," I said. "It was more of a *feeling*, really. The feeling that I wouldn't be able to contain the anger."

"Oh . . ." he replied musically, as if he was understanding the issue in a new light. "Not able to *contain* it? Well," he said, "that's different.

"When a very young child becomes so angry that he cannot maintain control of himself, a good parent physically contains the child. The parent imposes control from the outside until the child can regain control of himself from the inside.

"Now," he continued, "when you, Carol, *as an adult* become so angry that you begin to fear a loss of self-control, I cannot always be present to impose control on you from the outside. So I'll tell you what to do."

He took out his wallet as he spoke, and removing a twenty-dollar bill, handed it to me. "I want you to take this money and go out and buy yourself a sweater." He glanced briefly at the navy-blue and red scarf that I had tied tightly around my head that day. "Buy either a dark blue or a red sweater. And make sure it fits very tightly. Get a sweater that fits so snuggly that you can feel the edges of yourself—your physical limts. Then, anytime you feel that you're about to lose control of your feelings, or even if you *fear* losing control, go immediately and put on the sweater. This will allow you to accurately perceive your outer limits and to comfortably contain any emotion that you are experiencing—even if the emotion is a very frightening and powerful one."

I accepted his gift, gratitude mingling with amazement. I didn't know psychiatrists made such personal gestures. But it's such a right one, I thought, to address the fears I'm feeling. I feel safer already, safer and protected. He really cares about me, or he wouldn't have given me the sweater. I tucked the bill into my purse, forgetting even to say thanks, except for the smile that slipped over my face.

Dr. Lustig and I sat together quietly for several minutes. I was soaking up the calm, enjoying a moment's rest. When he spoke again, it was in a different, more conceptual vein, as if he understood that he was addressing a different person from the one who had entered his office half an hour earlier.

"Sometimes, you know, intense anger is really a very useful emotion to have. It so powerfully attracts our attention, even if it's in an uncomfortable way, that it allows us to stay whole, rather than fall apart. Your anger last night might very well have served that purpose for you."

I listened intently to what he said, captivated by the originality of his suggestion. For the first time in my life, someone had said that anger might be good, might indeed even have some useful purpose. Relief flooded over me. Maybe, in fact, I was using a *good*, self-protecting mechanism. Maybe, and this thought was the most radical one I had yet had, maybe there was something *healthy* about me after all.

We continued to talk, and soon our time was over. I thanked Dr. Lustig for his gift of the sweater. I did in fact go out and buy a tight, navy-blue sweater several days later.

And on several occasions during the next month, I put it on to calm my alarm. But gradually I found that I didn't need it anymore. Dr. Lustig's words had given me some of the inner control that I sought. I no longer needed, for the moment at least, a symbolic container for my fears.

CHAPTER TEN

LATE JANUARY, 1975

As January marched to a conclusion, the reality of my collapsing marriage began to take its toll, even as I denied the extent of the difficulty between Stan and me. The brief flares of anger that occasionally surfaced between us had, by late January, turned to marital ashes. As the winter snows piled up endlessly outside, the home fires quietly one by one died. Passion was extinguished; anger was put out. Left in their place were cinders and cold.

I felt numb; the feeling in me froze. My marriage had become a fragile shell, as if someone had pricked a hole in an egg and sucked out the yolk and the white. I learned how empty a marriage without its insides can be, a hollow echo chamber. Stan and I called across the open space and heard in reply only the distorted sound of our own voices. Words that no longer touched or communicated piled on top of silences that no longer touched or spoke. Frozen tears that could not be wept. Ashes and ice.

It was as if all desire to act had died with the feelings. We did nothing. To have done something would have taken too much effort. Our wills had atrophied. We drifted along lonely and cold but, oddly enough, with great politeness, as if the social amenities had replaced real connection.

"How would you like your eggs this morning?"

"Whatever is easiest for you."

"Did you remember to call the garage about the car?"

"No, it slipped my mind. Thanks for reminding me."

"Would you like me to carry out the garbage for you?" The politeness of strangers. Polished and cold.

After weeks of alienation, I told Dr. Lustig of the ever growing dissatisfaction between Stan and me.

"It's like a death by ice."

"What does Stan say about it?" he asked me.

"I don't know," I said. "We don't talk much."

After discussion, Dr. Lustig suggested a course of marriage counseling for Stan and me. It seemed like a good idea to me, and Stan agreed. So one of my weekly therapy sessions, from then on, was given over to the concerns of my marriage.

In the beginning, both Stan and I felt a sense of relief. At least we're trying, we told ourselves, feeling a shade less guilty for our mutual failures. At least we aren't throwing away a marriage without some effort to salvage it. It felt good to be doing something tangible, to be taking specific measures. It also felt good to be learning how to talk about our dilemma, which, paradoxically, we found easier to do in the presence of another than by ourselves.

That was our first "homework" assignment. We were to set aside ten minutes each day and talk with one another. It was difficult at first, and I felt very foolish. More awkward than on a honeymoon, we sat opposite each other across a table and tried to communicate. "What shall we do now?" I wanted to know. "Let's just try to talk," Stan replied, pausing, and then added, "You go first." After some more talk about talking and a few further fumbled conversational attempts, we did manage to have our first conversation in months.

"Why do you always seem so angry with me?" I finally gathered the courage to ask. "I want to tell you what's happening to me, about my confusion, but you always seem to resent it when I talk about it."

"I'm sorry," Stan said with genuine regret. "I guess . . . I guess . . . well, I'm just . . . afraid . . . of what might happen to *you*, of what might happen to *us*, of what might happen to *me*." He spoke softly, and I knew it was a great concession on his part.

"I know," I whispered, wanting to reach out and touch him. But something in me held back from physical contact. We both sat in silence for a while.

Then Stan voiced what I suspected had been bothering him all along. "You care about Dr. Lustig more than me," he said in an accusing way, and I could see how deeply his pride was hurt.

I wanted to tell him no, it wasn't as simple as that, that Dr. Lustig was my chance for mental survival, not a substitute for a husband, but somehow the words dried up in my throat.

"You don't understand," I said hopelessly, feeling exasperated at the attempt to try to explain anything to Stan. Then I calmed myself and tried again. "I need you too, Stan," I said softly. "I want our marriage to work out. I want to be well, and that's what Dr. Lustig is helping me with, but I also want to have a real marriage."

Stan seemed to understand. We began to talk, and then we talked and talked. I remember our euphoria. We became drunk on talk. We had become so accustomed to our perfunctory contact that our first simple communication in many months was an enormous relief.

After a few more evenings of practice, we began talking with each other better, although we were still often very general and vague. Once we had begun to converse, however, Dr. Lustig added to his original directive. He told us to be more specific in what we said about our emotional responses.

But as the weeks progressed and the initial euphoria wore off, we found ourselves very often in conversational dead ends. Neither one of us was very direct, and we both had a tendency to overanalyze the other person. We often used the seemingly direct language of our own emotional responses to indirectly critique each other's motives.

During one counseling session, we were talking about my unfocused behavior and my habit of staring out of windows when I was upset.

"I feel you're behaving that way just to be spiteful to me," Stan said.

"No, I'm not," I had replied. "I'm trying my best to be focused. And when I am not, I can't help it."

"The hostility that I feel coming from you is definitely there," Stan countered.

"No, it isn't," I insisted, and then continued with an imputation of my own. "And anyway, for you to say that what I'm doing is hostile to *you*, is in fact very hostile to *me*."

"No, it's not," Stan countered. And so it often went. After listening to several conversations of this kind, Dr. Lustig intervened.

"The primary purpose of communication," he said, "is to transmit facts about events in the external world. By only talking about your emotional responses to those events, or by talking about your *interpretation* of the other person's motivation, the two of you effectively subvert any useful communication between you."

He considered for a moment as if in search of a concrete example. "Suppose," he finally said, "that you're both hungry and can share a gorgeous piece of steak. But instead of using the steak for its *primary purpose* as food, the two of you decide that you'll save it as a work of art. By not eating it, you both remain hungry. And ultimately, the steak becomes unavailable even for a secondary purpose, because it decomposes.

"The mistake you're both making is that you're not using conversation to communicate about external reality, about the facts of whatever actually happened. Stan might say, for example, that he *considers* the overdone eggs that Carol gave him at breakfast to have been a hostile act. An important fact is that the baby vomited on the floor while breakfast was being prepared, and Carol was pleased to have been able to serve Stan anything at all. If Stan asks instead, 'Why are these eggs overcooked?' then Carol can tell him the facts about what actually happened. The two of you could then discuss the eggs and the baby, rather than just Stan's interpretation of Carol's motivation. Talking about your emotional reponses to an external event or your interpretation of it, without any discussion of the actual event itself, is like not using the steak for food. It ignores the primary purpose of the communication."

Stan and I both listened to what he said in our own way, and, over the next few months, we did from time to time communicate better. The icy climate that existed between us during the winter months thawed somewhat, due in large part to our new communion. But the ice did not melt into pure clean water. It resembled more a melted mound of grimy slush. Angers and hurts were expressed, but the conflict that lay behind them remained unresolved.

It always, in the end, came back to one thing. Stan told me that he did not love me, although I knew how much he wanted to love. "I just can't love you," he would explain mournfully each time we talked, rendering all other communications empty of healing. I knew that he found loving difficult within the confines of marriage, easy outside its context. I knew that it was the perceived burden of marriage itself, and not loving, that thwarted his attempts to reestablish a relationship with me. But in spite of this recognition, I would feel diminished each time he denied his love, believing that if he did not love me, it was because I did not deserve to be loved.

Still, we tried to save our marriage. It represented to both of us a commitment, independent of our personal feelings at the time. And at least through our marriage counseling we were talking, even though the talk rarely nourished, but became an empty form by which we maintained superficial contact.

But the attempt to save our marriage was itself reassuring, postponing as it did any need for more irrevocable action. Like Hansel and Gretel, we wandered through the woods, not knowing that we had stumbled into the witch's house. For the moment, we drifted on in the hope of a reconciliation.

CHAPTER ELEVEN

FEBRUARY, 1975

It was shortly after Stan and I had embarked on our course of marriage counseling that I began to have dreams about a figure in black.

NIGHT OF FEBRUARY 1, 1975

A spritely figure draped all in black is bending over a baby in the bedroom. The figure reaches toward the baby. At first I am frightened, because I think the figure wants to hurt the baby. Then, watching the way the figure moves, I realize that it only wants to hold the baby. As it bends over the baby, the figure sees me and, startled, rushes past me and out of the house.

The first dream about the figure in black alarmed me; the second, to follow some eight days later, left me terrified.

NIGHT OF FEBRUARY 9, 1975

I am in the upstairs bathroom with a friend. I am worrying about teaching my philosophy courses, and she is reassuring me. I walk to the downstairs bathroom by myself. I am just standing near the bathroom sink when a figure draped in black, with a black hood over his head, lunges into the bathroom from the hallway. He grabs me. I try to scream but no sound comes out. I am terrified that he is going to do some violence to me—rape or kill me. He puts his hand over my mouth and pushes me down.

The black-draped dream figure haunted my waking hours. Especially disturbing was the implied violence in the second dream. I had been rudely confronted with a shadow. It reminded me of a plane trip that I had taken not long before. It had been a sunny day, and idly looking out of the window, I had been startled to see the outline of the plane pursuing a parallel, if uneven, course on the ground below. What struck me most, on that occasion, was the way that the shadow had become a detached reflection of the plane, an alter ego completely separate from its source. I watched it as it dipped into valleys and then elongated, as it pursued the contours of the earth that it was following. It seemed an independent spirit, although it had never completely lost its resemblance to its originator. As the plane began its descent, the shadow grew even larger, assuming awesome, detached proportions. I wondered, as I watched it, whether it would ever join the plane in a peaceful uneventful merging, or whether the price of togetherness would be a crash landing.

I instinctively recognized the figure in my dreams as the same sort of shadowy presence, a reflection of myself that held its own power, followed its own course. I was afraid of it and startled by its presence, in the way that an infant is afraid and startled the first time that it sees its own reflection in a mirror. I too reached out a hand to touch the stranger, only to be confronted with hard, cold glass.

Where did these shadowy figures come from? I wondered. Surely not from my past. I thought over those early years and all I saw was an all-American girl, raised in the West with its traditional values of self-reliance and hard work, with the love and guidance of an unusual family, good at school, popular with my classmates. I saw no shadows in the activities of my childhood—exploring caves, riding horses, taking explorations into the foothills near my grandparents' farm, pretending with my sister and other friends that we were pioneers exploring a new and untouched country. In winter we skied, in summer we played softball, and as the grade school years turned into adolescence, I felt myself becoming a lovely woman. I had many friends and I had many dates; I was president of my church club and was even elected junior prom queen. My academic performance won me a scholarship to Carleton College, a coeducational institution in Minnesota known for its fine academic traditions.

Here, perhaps, the shadows began? At least the smooth surface of my life knew some strain; here were the first rumblings of discontent. Attached as I was to my family, I felt transplanted, cut adrift from the bonds that had always steadied me. I chose philosophy as my academic discipline, reveling in its beauty and order and rationality, choosing it for itself and also because it pushed aside other gnawing fears that were so vague as to be nameless, reading philosophers like Kant who kept irrationality at bay—at least until I got to the existentialists.

Then, with Kierkegaard, I too saw the question of suicide as the ultimate philosophic question. I took the issue seriously, not just as an intellectual exercise, wanting so much to be good, and more than that wanting to have Truth with a capital *T* on my side, so that whatever I did would be justified. I found instead that I must take my chances like everybody else, though I wanted to die rather than be morally wrong. I finally decided that I would simply do the best I could and that no one, not even myself, could blame me for that.

I continued along the path of philosophy into graduate school at Bryn Mawr College, but even here the darker questions followed me. However, it was during these years that I met Stan, who was teaching at a nearby college where I was working as an editor for a major philosophic journal. I invested in him the same intensity and devotion that I had in philosophy. He was solid and steady and above all rational. He offered me safe haven from my darker side.

But now, it appeared, it could no longer be hidden. I found myself facing a dark figure in my dreams.

I didn't know what to do about my recent dreams, or about the haunting black figures in them. But the next time I saw Dr. Lustig, I told him about them. Terror was evident in my quavering voice, and in the difficulty I was having even saying the words.

Dr. Lustig listened intently to what I said, and then nodded. "I would like you to do something," he said. "I'd like you to go back over the second dream in your mind. Start from the beginning and imagine yourself in the up-stairs bathroom. Then imagine yourself going to the down-stairs bathroom, and the figure lunging at you. Go through the whole dream, recalling it in exquisite detail, until it is as vivid as when you dreamed it. Become completely immersed in the dream, so that you can feel the terror and all the other feelings that you felt then."

I looked at him askance. "You want me to imagine the dream again, to redream it here?" I asked. I couldn't believe it. "I don't think I can," I said. It was painful to even think about calling up such a terrible image—and purposefully at that.

"Yes, you can," he replied equably. "Just think yourself into the dream again—take your time and remember it from the beginning. When you come to the part about the figure in black lunging at you, when you can reexperience the terror, then stop and tell me."

So I began, feeling frightened and somewhat foolish. But I had trusted him before and he had helped me, so I took it on faith that there was a purpose to this exercise.

I focused my attention and slowly slipped back into the nightmare. I closed my eyes when I came to the part about the figure in black attacking me, as if I could ward off the image with this instinctive gesture.

Dr. Lustig must have been watching my face, because just as I was feeling the full extent of my terror, he spoke. "Can you see the figure coming at you now?" he asked.

"Yes," I replied.

"Now!" he said. "What are you going to *do* to him? How are you going to defend yourself?"

When I didn't reply, he continued, "Are you going to strike him, or maybe stab him?" I still didn't reply, but I sank lower in my chair.

"Perhaps you would rather just kick him in the balls!" he continued. I put my hands to my face to cover my embarrassment.

"No, no, I couldn't do that," I replied in a small voice. Then, deciding that I had better pick an action quickly, for who could tell what preposterous alternative Dr. Lustig might suggest next, I said haltingly that I thought, well, *perhaps*, I *could* kick him.

"Fine," said Dr. Lustig. "Kick him somewhere."

I didn't even like *imagining* such violence, but I complied as best I could. Although I did not have the nerve to imagine kicking him in the balls, I finally did summon up a brief image of kicking the figure in the leg. Then I stopped, exhausted and overwhelmed by my audacity.

"What happened?" Dr. Lustig asked.

"He turned and ran away," I answered incredulously. I was truly astonished. The world had not disintegrated when I fought back. In fact, nothing untoward had happened at all. No bolt of lightning, no sign of the gods' displeasure. And although I was still a bit shaken, I was no longer terrified as I had been before.

I smiled at Dr. Lustig in a sheepish sort of way. "I did it, didn't I?" I said. I was pleased with myself, with the assertiveness of my gesture.

"Yes," he replied, and he seemed pleased too. "There's nothing in your imagination that you can't learn to handle, to control. The imagination is wonderful in that way. If you can *imagine* a particular dream of yours or a particular terror, you can also, just as easily, imagine a way of *achieving* that dream or of *banishing* that terror. If a gigantic bear is pursuing you, you can turn him into a mouse with a wave of your hand. If a witch casts a spell over you, use a counterspell and turn her into a glass of milk. It just takes practice," he said. "You have to develop the skills in that realm just as you're learning to do in the everyday world. It just takes practice, that's all."

My fears eased. From the way that he talked, the realm of the imagination seemed a less hostile and scary place. I felt less afraid of walking there, more sure that it, like other frontiers, could be explored safely with the proper amount of preparation and guidance.

"Thanks," I said, and I really meant it.

I was to remember his words in the days ahead, and slowly and cautiously I learned to put one foot and then the other into the waters of the imagination. And as for the figure in black, he was vanquished.

I was surprised when the figure in black did not return, and for many days afterward I half expected to see him in other dreams. But when he did not reappear, I began to grasp the power of the skill that Dr. Lustig had taught me— the power of the imagination to heal. It was a lesson that I never forgot. Demons that sprang from one's own untutored mind, I found, could be quelled by equal forces of a trained imagination. Imagined problems could be solved in the imagination itself. Nothing in that realm was so dark that it could not be confronted or, by a conscious act of imagining, robbed of its power.

It was this lesson about the skillful use of the mind that I began to teach my children. But that was later, of course, when they were a bit older and I had more fully mastered the lesson myself.

The first time Daniel had a nightmare, when he was about eighteen months old, at that age when it is common for children to have bad dreams, I was not alarmed. I talked him back to sleep. The next night, before he went to bed, he expressed fear about the return of the "monster." I asked him what he wanted to *do* to it. He didn't know, so I suggested some alternatives.

"You can hit him," I said, "or you can just tell him to go away and leave Daniel alone." Then we practiced. I can still remember Daniel's chubby little hand making a pushing-away gesture, and his small voice repeating, "Go away, monster, and leave Daniel alone!" It worked for my children, as it had worked for me. Neither of them was disturbed with nightmares again.

Several months later, following these lessons, Elizabeth came to me one morning and said with satisfaction, "I had a dream last night, Mommy."

"What was it about?" I asked her.

"Well," she said, "I was walking along a road with two other little girls, and we met a *giant* dinosaur. It was really scary," she said.

"What did you do?" I asked her.

"Oh, I just said, 'Get out of my way, dinosaur!' And guess what, Mommy," she continued. "The dinosaur went poof, and disappeared just like magic! Then we went on down the road."

"That's a wonderful dream, honey," I told her. It left me smiling. I was glad that my children, unlike me, would grow up knowing how to move with ease and control in that timeless world where dragons can be conquered and fools can be king.

Part 2

JOURNEY OUT OF THE CAVE

CHAPTER ONE

FEBRUARY 23–MARCH, 1975

Looking back on it afterward, my first three months of therapy, from late November to my birthday in late February, had the quality and tone of a dream play—because they seemed to progress so effortlessly from confusion and chaos to some degree of order and control. As my marriage disintegrated into a shabby formality, my inner life blossomed and took on an exaggerated importance. My "cure" seemed to progress with lightning speed, confirming to me the nature and magnitude of the mystical dimension I had stumbled upon. Like Joseph, who was cast into the pit, I had been miraculously lifted up, and I did not yet know that a further and more devastating fall awaited me. That was to be later, when my marriage finally failed.

For the moment, I was caught up in the magic of therapy. So it scarcely surprised me when, on February 23, my thirty-first birthday, I woke to early sunlight. The gray psychic fog that I had been shrouded in since autumn had mysteriously lifted, giving way to simple sunshine and warming rays. Hope radiated from my chest and out across the otherwise unremarkable landscape. I felt like a fish that, beyond reason or expectation, had become unhooked. I darted about excitedly, marveling at my exceptional reprieve.

I jumped out of bed and called eagerly to the children. I smiled at Stan for the first time in months, and hummed through the preparation of the bacon and eggs. I felt light and airy and released from a great draining weight. I talked; I gestured; I positively danced. I found the small crack in the breakfast dish enchanting, and the dusty clock in the corner profound. It seemed fitting that this should happen on my birthday. It seemed a good omen, a lucky charm.

I was especially glad that I would see Dr. Lustig the next day. I couldn't wait to tell him the news. I was as grateful as I was happy. I vowed to never again take ordinary happiness for granted. Then I promptly ignored my resolution, because when one feels most alive one expects the best. Rebirth has no memory for former deaths.

"I feel so much better," I told Dr. Lustig when I saw him.

"I can tell," he said smiling, and I could see how pleased he was.

Then I just sat and looked around, seeing the familiar room through lighter eyes. I noticed colors and tones I had never noticed before, and each object seemed altogether several shades brighter. My gaze particularly fastened on some perky-looking plants resting on the shelf behind Dr. Lustig's head. They're dressed in a particularly optimistic green, I thought, and I wondered why I had never noticed them before.

"Well, what do we do now?" I asked when I was through looking. I wondered what my therapy session would be about if I was not feeling a great deal of pain.

"Why don't we just take a vacation today?" Dr. Lustig replied. "There's no need to do any more work at the moment. You deserve a rest. Let's just enjoy the day."

So that was what we did. He asked me if I would like a

cup of coffee, and then we sat back and drank our coffee together. We talked and laughed, and he told me silly jokes. Starved for laughter as I had been, I basked in its healing power.

It was good to laugh deep from within. The mood in the room was that of children playing, and I felt more carefree than I ever had as a child. My delight formed a mood halo that encircled the room, and compensated me a hundredfold for my former misery.

Next to the side table between our chairs was a crystal bowl of brightly polished, smooth stones. Because of my newfound lightness, they captured my attention that day, and I reached over and selected one that had a particular appeal for me. It was burnished red in color, small and oval in shape—which, for some reason, I identified with myself. Then I selected a second, larger stone of translucent gray and brown that was etched with delicate lines resembling a Japanese painting.

I held the two stones for a moment, charmed by their beauty and uniqueness. "This one is for me," I said, motioning with the red one. "And this one reminds me of you," I continued, holding up the other.

"May I see them?" Dr. Lustig asked as he reached out his hand for them. Then, closely regarding the gray one, he continued. "It's strange," he said, "that you would select this particular stone for me. Of all the stones in the bowl, this has always been my favorite. And my second favorite has been the red one here." As he spoke he placed the red stone close to his eye. I was struck by the gentle, almost tender way that he held it, turning it this way and that to better see all its aspects and reflections. "Yes," he said finally, after a thorough examination, "this *is* a *lovely* stone." Then he smiled at me and asked, "Would you like to keep it?"

"Yes," I replied. I watched with gratification as the small red stone was delicately placed in my palm.

I had always thought that love and concern were conveyed in grand gestures. I usually interpreted the intensity of feelings as their measure, and because I was a person of great intensity, I assumed that I knew all there was to know about loving. But I learned on that occasion, and on many others to follow, that love shows a gentler face—in the quiet smile that indicates confidence in your abilities, the offer of a tissue to wipe away your tears, the gift of a small oval stone, a cup of coffee comfortably shared.

Caught up for years in the drama of expansive gestures, I found that I had overlooked an altogether subtler art: that of according to another person a full measure of human dignity, of conveying in small, seemingly insignificant gestures, respect and affection and human concern.

I left the office that day in the warm glow of affirmation. Although the aura of that day did not last, it lingered in my memory, giving substantial shape to the goal I was striving toward, making me mindful once again of possibility. If contentment could happen once, I thought, it could happen again. Its memory served me better than any good luck charm.

Dr. Lustig's gestures, that day, had subtly changed my feelings about myself. At some deep level I did not feel lovable, and Stan had unwittingly confirmed this when he told me he did not love me. But in the days ahead, as I regarded my red stone and remembered Dr. Lustig's words about it, I began to question my long-held assumption. Perhaps I was, after all, lovable; perhaps, like the stone, I had some worth. If Stan did not love me, then perhaps that was not my fault. Perhaps I, Carol as an adult, really deserved to be loved.

These were startling new thoughts, and I often felt uncomfortable with them. But in the end, it was precisely these beliefs that led me to end a bad marriage.

As for that spring, it saw me take many small steps forward, interspersed with an occasional turning back. The relationship between Stan and me continued much the same. We stayed together, ignoring a deeper alienation. The children thrived like healthy young growing creatures, and did not appear to wear the burdens of their elders.

Slowly and with much hesitation, I began to feel somewhat more complete. The difficulties I encountered that early spring were at least more evident to me than my earlier trials had been. For a while I was clearer-sighted, less encumbered by fog. Spring offered me a brief respite, standing as it did between my earlier flirtation with madness and my later immersion in it. For a few months, at least, I enjoyed a reprieve.

CHAPTER TWO

APRIL, 1975

Altogether, spring found me carrying a lighter burden of madness. When I put my ear to the ground, I could almost hear the rumble of the quickening bulbs. Hope, which had visited me little of late, crept out of the sheltered doorway of my house to stand tall in the back garden, halfway between the crocus and magnolia.

My teaching prospered as confusion slipped away, and I was newly confident that my mind would remain steady. Hope also brought me smiles as I watched my children, taking delight in the inconsequential details of their growing up—the cleverness of their observations about the neighbor's cat, their muddy sneakers after a walk in the rain, their tight little arms around my neck, the trusting in their faces that reflected the hope in mine.

It was strange that I should dream about the necklace just then, with madness receding and promise so close beneath the surface. It was a simple dream, but an odd one.

NIGHT OF APRIL 9, 1975

A man is trying to steal a necklace away from me. Intent on getting it back, I flirt and coax and try womanly wiles to win it. Failing, I take more direct action, wrestling the man to the ground to take the necklace by force.

The necklace I dreamed about was a real one that I owned, although it had lain for some time undisturbed in a lesser bureau drawer. I woke and, uneasy about the dream, went to the drawer to have a closer look. The necklace was there where I had left it several years before, next to a discarded copper belt buckle and two mismatched socks. It was tarnished to be sure, but still the same silver cross of Alsace-Lorraine that my grandmother had given me on a day much like this one, when some passing thought of her own mortality, or perhaps a vaguer wish for demonstrable continuity, had prompted her to pass the necklace on.

The cross hung on a delicate silver chain made of flat filigreed ovals interspersed with oval faces. Although the necklace presented itself as a fine-crafted piece, something about the faces did not bear close scrutiny. The mouths were tunneled holes pierced straight through each head, while the eyes stared blindly at some inner scene. These faces belonged to a forgotten Roman gargoyle, and it was altogether mysterious how they had made their way into my delicate chain. But there they were, gaping at me, the faces of madness suddenly substantialized. I slammed the drawer shut and tightly closed my eyes. In a few minutes I was breathing normally.

Throughout the day, between classes and while I was tending my children, the faces would suddenly be there, compellingly present to my inner eye. Then the air would begin to press in on me, suffocating me as if I had been underwater twenty seconds too long. I remembered the attempted seduction and the wrestling of the dream, and they seemed to speak distressingly about my femininity. They somehow made me feel ashamed. Who was this man that I could overpower in one manner but not in another, and what and why was he stealing from me? The thought went round and round in my head like a record stuck in a negative groove. And the worst thought of all that flitted in and out—what terrible thing did it mean about me that I wanted the necklace, those mad faces, back?

I took the necklace with me when I went to see Dr. Lustig late that afternoon. By this time an inner switch had clicked on again, and an inner chorus had preempted my power of fluent speech. I simply handed the necklace to Dr. Lustig and murmured something about a dream.

He examined the necklace closely with special attention to the faces, and slowly nodded when he was finished.

"Tell me the dream you had last night."

I gathered my strength to make a voice and haltingly told him about my dream. "A man was trying to steal this necklace from me. . . . I tried to get it back by being feminine. . . . That didn't work. . . . I wrestled with him and finally took it back."

"How did you try to be feminine?" Dr. Lustig asked.

I was weeping now without making any sound. I was ashamed. "I just tried to be . . . charming, I guess . . . and . . . well . . . seductive. . . ."

Dr. Lustig spoke in a calm voice. "A man is robbing you of your necklace. Charm and feminine wiles don't work, are not enough to distract the robber, so you wrestle him to the ground and get your necklace back?"

I mumbled a barely audible yes.

"That was smart." He paused for a moment. "He didn't put up much of a fight?" I murmured again.

"He did? Then what did you do to subdue him, weak woman that you obviously were?"

I was shocked at his words.

"People usually use their strengths first," he explained. "You used your charm first. You obviously considered *that* your strength. When it didn't work you resorted to a lesser skill."

I was now weeping with abandon, my nose dripping along with my eyes, but I attempted a defense. "I think what happened at that point . . ."

"Why don't you wipe your nose?" he interrupted. "There's Kleenex over there."

I took a tissue, dried my nose, and continued my tearful defense. "I didn't care what happened at that point," I sobbed. "I just had to get the necklace back."

"So what did you do to him?" Dr. Lustig asked. "How did you restrain him and get your necklace back? What did you *do?*"

I was silent.

"He couldn't have been *too* strong, if you wrestled him to the ground and prevailed. He must have been a weakling."

I was getting angry at these implications. "He wasn't *very* weak," I insisted. "I was just angry."

"An intense emotion does not increase the number of your muscles nor your skill in using them," Dr. Lustig replied. "Either he was weak or you were strong." He paused for a moment and then added, "Or at least, a better wrestler."

I was getting very angry. "Why do you keep saying he had to be weak?" I retorted. "Why can't *I* be strong?"

"Because when *you* selected your charm and femininity first," he replied evenly, "*you* indicated how powerful *you* considered them to be. And your strength was chosen second."

"Why can't he be strong, and I be stronger?" I said in a much stronger voice.

"Well, then, if he was strong and you were stronger, why didn't you use *that* first? What are you using this feminine charm and seduction stuff for? Why don't you just say, 'Give me back my necklace, you creep—you can't have it'? The man's using a physical threat against you and you say, 'Well, I'll use what works best against a physical threat. I'll charm the little fucker.' Why don't you just say, 'Hey, you can't have my necklace—it's mine'?"

I reflected on this sobering thought for several minutes. Finally he spoke again, very low and confiding.

"Most people use their strengths first, and if your strength was being feminine and charming, then that's what you used first." He paused as if a new thought had just occurred to him. "Of course, it's also possible that you're feminine, charming, *and* strong. But . . ." his voice trailed off.

"I was feminine, charming, *and* stronger than he," I finished for him, feeling that I had finally proved my point.

We sat in silence for some moments then. He seemed comfortable and confident and so was I, until I remembered the eyes in the faces of the necklace and how they were mad. A cold sweat swept over me with this thought, and I could feel the pressure of the air closing in on my skin.

"The point about the dream is that I want the necklace back, and the faces are mad," I said. My voice was low and anguished and miserable.

Dr. Lustig picked up the necklace and once again looked it over carefully. "Yes," he acknowledged matter-of-factly, "they are mad." He paused for a moment and then added, "Would you like me to fix it for you?"

I agreed, so he got up and crossed to a door on the left-hand wall of the room. When he opened it, I saw that it was a closet full of all sorts of paraphernalia, medicines, toys, odds and ends. I had always wondered what was behind that door. I had imagined a hidden staircase or a secret chamber, but never a simple storage room. He took down a tool chest from one of the upper shelves at the back of the closet, and got out a pair of pliers. When he had reseated himself, he took up the necklace and slowly began removing the faces one by one, carefully connecting the chain at each link so that any gap would be no more than momentary, and the whole would still remain whole. While he worked we continued to talk.

"I'm afraid to lose the madness," I said, "because it's the only thing about me that makes me unique."

"No," he replied firmly. "Your uniqueness is not predicated upon madness. Your uniqueness is based on all of you—your dark side and your light side. All of you together. You don't have to inhabit one side of yourself and stay stuck there to be unique. You're unique no matter where you are inside." He was speaking slowly in a soft, soothing voice.

"You're very familiar with both sides of yourself at this point, so why not have a bit of both? Balance yourself and stay that way." He thought for a moment, then continued. "It's really like being on a seesaw. If you stand right at the center of the seesaw you can have it balanced, and a little bit of motion or effort from you can get one side or the other to move down or up. But if you're away from the fulcrum, it becomes more complicated to keep that balance. Well, then, stay at the center and use yourself to balance the light and the dark."

"Or else get a partner to sit at the other end of your seesaw," I said, brightening. I liked this image; it made sense.

"Or else get a partner to sit at the other end," he said with amusement. "And that will work as long as the partner ..."

"... sits there night and day ..."

"... never taking a break." He paused for a moment as if relishing the thought. "And totally selfless," he added, spinning it out. "The partner must be someone whose main job in life is to be the other end of your seesaw." He paused in the game and suddenly grew serious. "Some people, I think, try that for a while, but they discover that it doesn't work for very long. Either they try to find that partner or to *be* that partner for someone else. But it doesn't work."

"So everybody's got to stand at the middle and balance themselves out?" I suggested.

"Yes," he replied. "You can get some help temporarily; you can find somebody to be on the other end. But at some point you're going to have to move toward your own center, and become adept at keeping it balanced."

I found the conversation very reassuring. Being alone at the center of a seesaw didn't seem like such a bad sense of being alone.

"But many people aren't at the center," I went on. "Many people are at one end or the other."

"True," he said. "But the center's there just the same. People make their own choices. But the center's always there to reach if they want. It will take some effort and it can be precarious, especially if it's done alone. However," he continued, "some people prefer to just sit on the ground at one end of the seesaw. Then there's no movement in their life. Others prefer to move partway up the seesaw and stop. It may not be important to them to get the thing balanced."

He sat in silence for a few minutes, musing. "Yes, some people prefer to have very unstrained lives," he finally reiterated. "But if you're there at the center of the seesaw, you'll have all the pleasures of a dynamic balance. People who just sit on the seeasaw while it rests on the ground are in a static balance, and don't have the ability to adjust to the swing of events. They probably think that they're better off, but it's only an illusion. There can't be any movement at all from that situation."

"What about the people who are at the other end of the seesaw, the ones hanging precariously in the air?" I laughed nervously and put my hand to my throat. "What about them?"

"The people up in the air in that way *think* that they don't have any control, but they do. They choose not to exert it. They're in a more stable situation than they realize. All they have to do is slide down the seesaw. Yet they prefer to sit there trying to convince other people that they have no control. They claim that nothing can be done about it, and expect everybody to excuse them for what they do." He began flailing his arms about and mimicking a person out of control.

"Or they complain about the one on the ground who's keeping them there," I said, thinking somewhat shamefacedly about myself.

"Yes," he agreed, becoming himself again. "Rather than figuring out for themselves what they can do to change the situation."

We seemed to have come to the end of our conversation. By this time the half-light filtered through the half-closed curtains, streaking the walls with the palest burnished pink. Dr. Lustig and I were silent for some uncounted minutes, until he reached over and switched on the lamp.

I jumped at the sudden intensity of light, and felt that I was waking from a partial dream. When I had somewhat gathered my wits, I saw that the footstool between our chairs now held a heap of separate silver faces. All the while that we had been talking, Dr. Lustig had been removing the mad faces, one by one. I watched as he set the last face with the others and finished reconnecting the silver chain.

"There," he said with a sigh, handing me the necklace. "How does it feel now?"

I took the necklace and carefully weighed it in my hand, searching out its new acceptability. It seemed to me better than it had been before, but it also carried a new sadness, as if it were mourning the loss of too many friends. He must have read the uncertainty in my face, because, when I looked up, he was looking at me in a puzzled way. Then all of a sudden he leaned back and laughed.

"But of course," he said, as if that explained it. "Will you give the necklace back to me?"

I watched as he carefully selected a single mad face from the pile and, with the pliers, put it back into the necklace. When his task was completed, he handed the necklace to me and asked me again how it felt.

I took it in my hand and it seemed just right. Then I smiled, understanding. Ten mad faces are too much madness, I thought, but no mad faces are just another pretty necklace.

"We have to find just the right amount of madness," he said, smiling back.

CHAPTER THREE

As spring ripened into summer, I felt the efforts of earlier months gradually merge to shape the beginnings of a new self. On the eve of my daughter Elizabeth's fourth birthday, eight months after I had begun psychotherapy, I dreamed the first dream of a trilogy.

NIGHT OF JULY 14, 1975

I have just returned from a place far away. I am sitting on a low wall made of smooth round stones, swinging my legs and gazing into the garden facing me. In this "Garden of the Happy People" it is perpetually spring. Fountains burst to overflowing with pure, crystalline waters; children, with heads and arms bathed in warm sunlight, frolic and dance and play. As I look longingly into the Garden from my isolated position on the wall, I see Dr. Lustig enter from the opposite side and walk through the idyllic scene, until he ar-

rives at a place near the wall where I am seated. He motions me to follow him.

The wall where I am sitting separates the Garden from a terrace behind me. Dr. Lustig leaps over the wall onto the terrace, and sits down on the floor. The terrace is transformed into a therapy room. I jump down from the wall into the room, and sit down on the floor near Dr. Lustig. He talks and talks to me, until I feel strong and well.

Then Dr. Lustig takes my hand and points toward the Garden of the Happy People. I see that the wall that separated me from the Garden has fallen away. I enter the Garden.

I woke from this dream with delight. I remembered a saying attributed to the philosopher Wittgenstein: "The world of the happy person is a different world from the world of the unhappy person." For me to have had even a brief glimpse of the other, happier world was utterly enchanting. I spent a splendid day with the children, celebrating Elizabeth's birthday and my renewal with a simple joy.

That night, I dreamed two further dreams.

NIGHT OF JULY 15, 1975

I am expecting a child. Dr. Lustig is both the father of the child and the obstetrician. I am standing in the room where I live, getting dressed for a therapy appointment. I happen to look into the mirror and discover that I am able to see my baby through the transparent skin of my pregnant belly. The baby is fully formed, and I realize that I am about to deliver. I am surprised, because I did not realize that it was time for me to give birth.

I give birth standing before the mirror. A baby girl is born bloodlessly and painlessly. I wrap her carefully in a

*blanket and cradle her in my arms. I am afraid for her
safety because she seems so small and fragile. I closely regard
her to be sure that she is still breathing. She sleeps peacefully
on. I lay her on the bed.*

*Looking around, I think that I must find a present to
give Dr. Lustig in gratitude for this birth. Then I realize
that the birth of my child is the gift that he has labored for.*

I woke in the night from this dream, feeling a great
sense of accomplishment, as if the metaphorical birth of my
new self in the dream had actually been accomplished. I rose
and wrote the dream down, and then drifted back to sleep
filled with contentment and overall well-being. Later that
night, just before dawn, I dreamed a third dream that
seemed to complete the sequence.

MORNING OF JULY 16, 1975

*I am invited to a party at Dr. Lustig's house one evening.
When I arrive, I am struck by the enormity of his home—it
seems to go on for miles. It is beautifully decorated with
both old and new furniture, and there are Japanese prints
on the walls.*

*I wander from room to room for a while, fascinated by
the harmony of all the rooms, absorbed in the interplay of
color and texture and motif. Finally I sit down on a couch
next to a woman. She turns to me and asks, "Who are you?"*

I say, "Carol."

She asks, "Carol who?"

I reply, "Carol Allen."

*She says, "No! I mean, who are you?" I don't know
what to say. "I am a woman analyst," she continues importantly. "Are you an analyst too?"*

"No," I reply, "I'm Dr. Lustig's patient."

At that, she turns away scandalized. It is clear that she thinks a patient has no business being at a party for psychiatrists. I wander into the next room, where I see a woman crouched in a corner. She says, "Oh, why did he invite me? He knows I don't like to be seen with so many people around. What if one of my patients sees me!"

"There's a woman analyst in the next room whom you might enjoy talking with," I tell her.

I continue my journey through the house. I finally come to a large room where a buffet banquet is being served. I notice that there aren't any clean plates left, so I walk all the way back to the kitchen to get some more. The kitchen is a large square room, with a square butcher-block table set directly in the middle. I go over to the cupboards on the far wall to look for the plates, when I notice Dr. Lustig's fantastic garbage-disposal system. The walls of the kitchen sink are curved like a slide, so that garbage placed anywhere on them simply slides right down into the disposal and disappears.

I take clean plates back to the banquet room. Most of the people have gone by this time, but there is still food left. I fill my plate and begin to eat. Dr. Lustig is in the room too, talking and joking with some of the guests. He comes over to me when he sees me, and begins laughingly and playfully teasing me. I smile, knowing that we are friends.

Again I woke and, sitting on the edge of my bed in the first light of dawn, wrote out the last dream in the trilogy. I liked the progression of the dreams: from a happy garden, to a rebirth, to a friendship with Dr. Lustig. I instinctively knew that the child in my second dream was my new self, a fragile being whose growth into a strong woman would require all my care and nurturing. Only then, it seemed to me, would I be able to meet Dr. Lustig as a friend and equal.

I walked through the next month in the halo created by

these images. My dream metaphors became more real to me than my real life, casting a warm, rosy glow over all that I touched. I took these dreams very seriously. I also took them literally. I am happy, I thought. I am reborn, I thought. Herb and I are friends, I thought. I forgot an essential fact about dream timework—that to enter the world of dreams is to enter a timewarp, or, to put it another way, that dreams are timeless. They can reenact and point to the past. They can prophesy and point to the future. Rarely are they solely about the present. But I took my dreams at face value. I was enchanted with the view of myself that they portrayed.

All through late July and early August, I daydreamed about my dreams constantly. Caught up in the solipsism of my inner reality, I cast out of my mind the truth of my domestic situation. Although my marriage was steadily declining, I steadfastly ignored the signs of strain beneath the surface. I pretended that my marriage had only minor flaws, that the course of marriage counseling that Stan and I had entered on in January was providing the panacea that I desired.

But the truth kept seeping in at the edges of consciousness, destroying the purity of my daydreaming escapes. Suddenly, at odd moments, I would see the image of Stan's vacant face turning away from me during our conversational attempts. I would remember the lack of essential connection, the great void of our eggshell marriage, the aimless drifting of two partners apart. Finally, the illusion of a married state could no longer be maintained. Divorce, like an uninvited actor, made a stage entrance into our marriage play.

CHAPTER FOUR

AUGUST, 1975

Divorce. On an ordinary day in mid-August I finally thought the unthinkable. There it was in stark relief, the word that reverberated with brutal associations—fragmentation, division, failure, defeat. Divorce. It was something that happened to other people, to other families. It had no place in my tradition or in my conception of myself.

I had grown up in a small town in Idaho, a modest town at the center of a farming valley. My parents had the values I always associated with the West. They were straightforward, honest, and hardworking. They prized independence above all else and yet, ironically, clung to the extended family like barnacles to a ship's bottom. My paternal grandparents, my uncle and his wife, my father's cousins all lived nearby. There were always holidays and picnics with the larger family. My uncle and grandfather would stop over most mornings, to chat and have coffee, before starting the day's work. The family was my primary means of identification. "Oh, you're Dick's girl," or "This is Nina's granddaughter," they would say, and in this way I would find my place.

Marriages, my family believed, required effort. "It's your responsibility to make a marriage work," they always told me. "The things that are worth having are worth working for." The family was the source and guardian of all values, providing protection like some great sentinel beast at the gate, dispensing nurture and solace within its boundaries, providing refuge against the inconstancy of the larger world.

Divorce was anathema within the society of my childhood. When it was spoken about at all, it was in hushed tones, like the time the neighbors' daughter came home without her husband. "She's getting a divorce," the adults murmured as they shook their heads in disbelief. "Her husband left her," they said, as if she were tarnished like a worn brass plate.

I was only a child then, about ten or eleven, but I remember the next time I saw the subject of these conversations. I regarded her closely, trying to detect in her person some sign of the stigma that so surely had attached itself to her. I saw nothing exceptional about her on that occasion, except that she looked tired and a little drawn. But I secretly thanked my lucky stars that I would never stand in her place.

Now, twenty years later, this was precisely where I stood. The thought of divorce had finally intruded, pushing itself relentlessly and painfully into my consciousness. The word bespoke failure of the worst sort, an offense for which the individual is always held accountable. And worse, a betrayal of the entire tribe.

On that particular day in mid-August, with the word "divorce" resounding in my mind's ear, I took off my wedding ring and held it in my hand. It had been my maternal grandmother's wedding ring, and her grandmother's before her. I turned it around in my hand several times, rereading the dates that were inscribed inside: "December 14, 1864," and "August 11, 1911," and next to the dates the single word "Ours."

I remembered the day my grandmother had given it to me. I was a girl of about twelve or thirteen then. The ring hung on a black velvet ribbon, which she placed around my neck. As my grandmother slipped the ribbon over my head, she told me the history of the ring: how it had always passed through the women of the family; how her grandmother, as she lay dying, had placed it around her neck in a similar manner; how it was made of twenty-karat gold that came from the California Gold Rush of '49. Because I was the oldest daughter of her only daughter, my grandmother had passed the ring on to me. "You will be married someday in this ring," she told me, "just as I was, and my grandmother before me." And as she said it, I knew that this ring wed me to my tradition.

And so in due course, I had been married in it. Regarding my ring now in the late August afternoon, I wondered how I could even consider spoiling it with a divorce. I was also superstitious. Would I bring bad luck to my children and the generations to follow? What harm would come if I so dishonored the symbol of my familial bond? I put my wedding ring decisively back on my finger. It's out of the question; I'll never get divorced.

A week later, wedged between the drowsiness of summer and the headier tempo of fall, came that particular week in August when we made our annual pilgrimage to the ocean. We piled the children into the car and drove the seventy miles to the New Jersey shore. This year we had added the babysitter to our entourage, hoping for some hours of solitude and marital companionship. We had rented an apartment situated several houses from the beach, so that we could move easily back and forth from house to ocean with the children.

A week at the ocean in August had become our annual family ritual. We sought revitalization and sanctuary at summer's end. That particular year, I think, Stan and I had also hoped that the ocean might prove to have the curative powers that would bind our wounds and restore our marriage.

The greater part of each morning and early afternoon, that week, were spent playing with Elizabeth and Daniel on the beach. The late afternoon hours were given over to solitary walks up the coast. In the evening, Stan and I generally went out to dinner by ourselves, leaving the babysitter in charge of the children.

These dinners became the focal point of our marital isolation. Stan and I would sit across the table from each other, generally no more than three feet apart. Yet the space between us might have been interstellar, for it was just as lacking in oxygen. We sat as if encircled by transparent domes, able to breathe only within our own shells, suffocating on the carbon dioxide of our own breath. Only three feet separated us, but it was too great a distance to be bridged with outstretched hands. We sat in silence, sad and indignant that it should finally come to this.

It was during my solitary walks along the ocean, in the mellow light of the late August sun, that slowly there began to form in my mind a resolve, which gradually took the shape of a decision. Perhaps, after all, we would be better off alone. Perhaps a divorce is the only answer. The steadiness and constancy of the ocean became the rhythmic backdrop for these reflections. Its very vastness gave me perspective. It reminded me of the limited place that I and my problems occupied in the larger order of things. I found the thought of my insignificance vastly reassuring. The world would survive, I grasped with relief, even if Stan and I got a divorce.

During that week Stan must have come to a similar conclusion, although no word of divorce was spoken between us. But as the week drew to a close, he began to acquire the look of weary calm that often accompanies a secret resolve. The earlier tension between us had evaporated, leaving in its place an exhausted truce. Then it became only a matter of enacting the inevitable. We each secretly sighed in vast relief.

CHAPTER FIVE

Marriages are created and so are divorces. There comes a time when both parties know that it is only a matter of time before they part. It becomes, then, a matter of enacting a final drama, saying things that can never be unsaid, words that haunt at later points of hesitation, fortifying the will against the hours of loneliness, steeling the resolve to dissolve the bond.

Stan and I were walking to a marriage-counseling session at Dr. Lustig's when we made our divorce.

"I think we should get a divorce." I spoke the words for the first time, thinking about the months of laden silences opaque and heavy against an even deeper void. Our lying together at night painfully alone. Our children's faces puzzling over our faces, asking unspoken questions about what had gone wrong. Scattered conversations that became minor irritants, minor skirmishes that grated on the nerves. I remembered how the words had died one by one. How the power of speech had died with the words. How the feelings had died with the power of speech. To be sure, there had been brief firecrackers of anger, but even these sparks had trailed quickly into smoke, leaving both of us knowing as the wisps faded that it was our last Fourth of July.

"We can't go on like this," I added.

"I know," he said with pain cracking his voice. "I know," he repeated, "but we cannot get divorced. What about the children? Have you thought about what it would do to them?"

"Yes, I've thought about it," I replied very softly. "Yes, I've thought about it, but it's no good for them now. It's no good for any of us now." We walked on for a few minutes.

"It's out of the question," he said suddenly and emphatically. "Just think about what our friends would say. It would be so humiliating, a divorce. I have to work with these people, you know. How could I face them?" I didn't say anything.

"And also," he continued, "what about our parents? What about your family, your brothers and sisters? What do you think this would do to them?" I was silent because I knew it was the truth. We just kept walking. Finally, I marshaled my will to fight a fight I wanted no part of, to argue for a course that could only bring pain, in the belief, however foolish, that some good might come.

"Those aren't good enough reasons, Stan," I finally said. "They're all about other people. But what about us? You haven't said anything about us. Is there any reason between us why we should stay? Is there anything about me that you admire or value or want to keep?"

He didn't answer immediately. We had stopped walking by this time and were just standing there, radiating misery, as if all the pain and disintegration and loss of a marriage had to find some visible expression, some tangible proof, so that it could know itself.

Slowly and deliberately he looked at me and answered my question.

"No," he said. "No, there isn't."

CHAPTER SIX

On October 11, Stan left the house and the marriage. For me, our separation had the finality of divorce. Weeks before, we had decided that Stan would move to an apartment and that I would stay in our rented home with the children. The brilliance of the autumn plumage on that particular moving day belied the colorlessness of the occasion. I felt empty and blank. A cosmic eraser had wiped me clean.

I took the children away from the house. I did not want them to see the movers carrying out Stan's belongings. I was afraid that the image of clothes and rugs and chests being carted out might linger in their minds and haunt them. I supposed that it was better for children to have no clear visual impression of divorce's domestic displacement.

We had told the children about our decision two weeks before. Stan and I had decided that it would be better if we told the children together, so that in the act of disuniting as husband and wife, we could confirm our parental unity.

We had all gathered together in the living room after dinner. We sat in a circle on the floor—four-year-old Elizabeth sitting next to her two-year-old brother, and Stan and myself facing them. Neither Stan nor I knew how to tell young children about adult anguish. So, we talked about the divorce as if it were a matter of houses.

"You will live here in this house with Mommy. Daddy will live in another house just down the street."

"Why?" Elizabeth asked.

Stan looked at me and I looked at him. This was going to be harder than we thought.

"Daddy and I aren't happy living together anymore," I tried to explain. "Even though it makes us all sad now, we think it will be better for all of us later." I tried to say it in a positive tone.

"Why?" Elizabeth asked again, this time with more alarm, as if she was beginning to grasp the implications of what had been said.

At a loss for words, I sat her on my lap. If I could only have pointed to something specific—arguments or fights or abuse—something that would translate into a child's language. I was silent and so was Stan. But I could tell by his posture, as he sat leaning toward me with his hand supporting his weight in back of me, that he was silently willing me to find the proper explanation.

"Daddy and I don't want to be married anymore," I finally said. "We don't love each other anymore." I looked at her face and quickly added, "But, of course, we still love both *you and Daniel* just as much as ever, and we always will."

She looked perplexed, as if our logic escaped her. If the love for a spouse can change, why can't the love for a child? I watched her as she lowered her eyes, under the realization that love has its seasons, and that it can fade away. Her face closed up around an inexpressible sorrow. Love could no longer be taken for granted. Against all reason, her father must go.

Slowly, she raised her index finger to her mouth and made the sign for silence.

"Shhhhh . . ." she whispered. "It's a secret."

Her response was more terrible to me than the most piercing scream.

Daniel had not said anything throughout. He simply read our faces. In a gesture at once compassionate and matter-of-fact, he put his arms around my neck and kissed my cheek.

"Don't worry, Mommy," he said.

Then, turning to Stan, he repeated his action, as if he had looked into our sorrow and wanted to put the pain in its place.

Stan's eyes moistened and he audibly drew in his breath. I too struggled to hold back the tears.

"I love you kids," I said.

Then the four of us put our arms around each other and formed a circle of affection, knowing that it would never be the same again.

A year or so later, when Daniel was three and a half, a neighborhood girl asked him how many people he had in his family.

"Four," he answered without hesitation.

"But your dad doesn't live with you," she countered. "You only have three."

"No," Daniel insisted. "We have four. You can wear different clothes and be the same person," he explained, "so you can live in different houses and be the same family."

But that was later, and represented an understanding of the subtle force that continues to link a family, even after a divorce. For the moment we confronted a different reality, one where two houses represented fracture and defeat, two houses each of which felt like less than half a house, as if they had been created by wrenching one viable edifice apart, so that what was left was two rickety structures with sides torn out and roofs tottering. How could we, or the children, call either place home?

Stan and I did try to ease the transition for the children, by walking with them hand in hand from my house to Stan's new apartment down the road, thinking that if they could see for themselves the proximity, they would know that Stan, though gone, was still accessible.

When we arrived at Stan's new apartment that day, Elizabeth and Daniel looked it over very carefully, but quietly. They maintained the silence throughout their inspection, and during the beginning of our return walk home.

When we were about halfway back, Elizabeth finally spoke.

"Daddy, carry me," she implored.

Stan reached down and took her up into his arms, and carried her that way for several minutes.

Then she turned to me and said, "Mommy, carry me."

After I had held her for several more minutes' walking, she reached out her arms once again for her father. We continued to ceremoniously pass her between us as our procession made its way home. When we neared our front door, Elizabeth summed up the situation.

"I guess we'll just have to take turns now."

But in spite of the philosophical attitudes of our children, the details of a divorced life weighed heavily on them. The predinner hour, in particular, became for the children and me a painful confrontation with Stan's absence, tangible evidence of a family torn apart that no magical adhesive could mend or bind.

At that late-afternoon hour of the day, when the shadows had always signaled to the children that Stan would be coming home, a quiet listening crept over the house. I watched as anticipation interrupted the children's play and lighted their faces, when they heard adult male footsteps in the outer hallway. I watched the blank disappointment that followed, when the footsteps passed by our door and ascended the stairs to our neighbor's second-floor flat. Our daddy will not be coming home, their faces said. Their bodies wilted and their heads bowed a little. Then, sadly, they resumed their play.

I watched and at night, when they were asleep, I wept. Have Stan and I really done everything we can for the children? Perhaps there's a better way to navigate divorce. What about earlier in the day when I was angry with the children and hit out and yelled at them? Sometimes what I am is terrible. Why can't I be more sure myself of this separation, so that the hurt and confusion I feel will not also stalk my children's footsteps as I saw it doing today, the children both crying, bursting out with small explosions, smaller but no less angry than mine now that Stan has left? All of us angry, angry with each other, angry with Stan, or alternately subdued, retreating into private places to lick our wounds.

Do the children feel abandoned, even as I feel abandoned? How can they possibly understand what is happening to us, if I cannot? What more can I tell them, what more can I tell myself? The truth is that explanations do no good. It's the absence of Stan and a firm structure that we're all mourning.

And what about Stan and myself? Now at the end of my marriage to Stan, I thought about its beginning, how we had walked together when we first met, droplets of autumn rain clinging to the remaining orange-brown tapestry of leaves, sun occasionally peeking out from behind gray clouds that bore no thunder. As we walked, Stan had suddenly turned to me and pulled me into his arms. "I think I'm beginning to love you," he had said softly, as if he surprised even himself with his words. Why had that love on his part been possible under an open sky, but not within the confines of our marriage? Why did that early memory wash over me now like so many tears, suggesting as it did the promise that had marked our beginning, the confidence that our love would never end?

And now, Stan was gone. At first, it had been a relief, I admitted, but now I felt as if someone had jerked the carpet from under my feet and sent me sprawling. Along with Stan had gone the structure and steadiness that I had counted upon, taken for granted, that had gone unnoticed even, but was now apparent in its absence.

Why had Stan and I not prepared ourselves for this? Or was it a minor self-deception to think that any preparation was possible? What little we had done was directed toward the children. But what about ourselves? In jumping our own emotional hurdles, we had avoided the practical prerequisites of breaking apart. Who would care for the children, for example. We had never sat down and talked about sharing child care duties. We had simply assumed that we would continue the pattern set in our marriage, that responsibility for the children would be mine. Why did that seem so unfair to me now, when my greatest fear was that my children would be taken from me?

And the subject of money, that was sure to fuel the flames. But how was I to live, to survive financially? Why could Stan and I never seem to talk about that? Finding no answers to my musings, I finally slept.

The answers came later, as they are likely to do, and seemed apparent, after the fact. One aspect was shame, our paramount feeling at the time, which so distorted our good judgment, which stood between us and potential solutions. Caught up in the felt shame of our situation, and in the utter pain of dissolution, Stan and I did not confront the factors that would slowly undermine us. Rather we bore our divorce as a disgrace, a fiery brand that had to be hidden from the outside world. We covered our sorrow as best we could, as if the final indignity would be to have the truth known. Like children we pretended that it was not quite real, that if we avoided the words, it would not utterly fragment our lives.

As a result, Stan and I made no arrangements for him

to visit or care for the children on a regular basis. On most evenings, he would just drop over at the house a few minutes before the children's bedtime, after they had been bathed and were ready for the night. He would talk to them for a while, then kiss them good night and silently leave.

I had had no experience facing economic realities, so I simply ignored the economic quicksand in which I stood. Throwing off the mantle of the fifties, I had embraced the philosophy of the new woman. I would do everything—have a career, have a husband, have children. The fact that I was working made me think that I was independent. Work outside the home was, to me, the symbol of the newfound equality. It was my entrée into the larger world. "Self-realization" was the slogan of our times and I, like the other middle-class women whom I knew, expected to work for self-fulfillment. I had a husband to provide the primary support for the family. I had little experience in facing financial facts or in living with economic urgency.

"I'm going for my master's degree," my friends would say. "I'm taking a few courses, and then I'll decide what I'll do." These were the litanies we recited. Work, we all believed, was a gift to the self. Work was the path out of feminine bondage. We renounced the "volunteerism" of our mothers' generation, and yet often took up work with a similar lack of economic motive.

Separation, I found, undid many of these assumptions. Work became a serious economic fact. It was a brutal awakening. I could barely support the children and myself with the income from my part-time job. The eighty dollars a week that I was earning had to pay for almost everything but the rent.

Still, I was not willing to forfeit my responsibilities to my children. Trapped between the conflicting expectations of two generations, I simply closed my eyes. The burden of reality was too sudden and too great. It was easier to dream than to address the facts.

When Stan left, he had agreed to pay the rent and give me a small amount of money for the children. But he did so as a "favor" rather than a responsibility. We had no formal financial arrangement and, blind to reality, I failed to insist that we should have one. I did not demand that the burdens of our separation be more equitably distributed. I wanted to get out of the marriage and I wanted custody of the children: These were my overriding concerns.

Also I wanted to cope, and I did not appreciate until much later how this commendable instinct undid me. Perhaps it was because I defined "coping" in the best Stoic fashion. It meant surviving no matter how unreasonable the circumstances. It did not mean asking for help, seeking support, redefining responsibilities, redistributing wealth, reducing daily pressures—in short, changing the situation.

I must cope, I must cope, was my constant litany, by which I meant hanging on in any way I could, with any sacrifice of clear-sightedness, with any forfeiture of the truth. I am a failure because I could not stay married. If I fail to cope now, I am a failure two times over. People always say that women cannot cope, but I will prove them wrong. I will not let divorce defeat me. I will care for my children, I will work, I will be even more perfect; because one humiliation can go unnoticed, but two will surely strip me of all pride.

I will not let the weary, lonely hours of the day defeat me, nor little money, nor the children, for then I might lose them. I must prove that I am a success at divorce, to diminish the string of so many other failures. Being Superwoman before was nothing compared to this.

It became paramount to show Dr. Lustig, above all others, how well I was doing, just how well I could survive. When I told him weekly that I was doing fine, I believed my words, saw nothing of the dangers in them. My therapy sessions had become an escape for me from the humiliation attending the dissolution of my marriage, a chance to make up for my felt defeat. I failed to find the words that would have described my situation, that would have provided a clue to further intervention, that would have initiated a change. Wrapped in the indulgence of failed hopes and false pride, I failed to look for the solutions I needed.

Stan had broken off all contact with Dr. Lustig several months before, and I talked at my appointments only in the metaphors of my private world, forgetting in his presence the actual backdrop of my life. To have admitted my practical plight, even to Dr. Lustig, would have been, in my mind, the final defeat. I was disappointing everyone by ending my marriage. Failure to cope would have magnified the problem. I did not want to let them all down. I wanted to cope for the women's movement, for Dr. Lustig, for my family. To have looked closely at my real situation would have presented too clear an image of failure. So I pretended to myself that I was doing just fine, that there were no insurmountable obstacles facing me. I talked to Dr. Lustig about dreams and fantasies. I did not talk about diapers or money or my terrors in the night. I lived, more each day, on a diet of daydreams. I faced neither the day nor the night.

CHAPTER SEVEN

NOVEMBER, 1975

Slowly and insidiously my separation separated me not just from a man, but from myself. As the days of November grew colder and darker, I retreated further and further into myself. Some remnant of animal instinct made me want to withdraw—to spin a cocoon, to burrow into the ground, to hibernate in a cave, to protest the night. My fears hummed drowsily in the gray of day but awakened to full chorus with the encroaching darkness. Once the children were asleep, I would huddle in my bed, hearing the violence of the branches as they beat against the house, listening to the misery in the sounds of the wind.

During the days I began to daydream seriously. I needed fantasy. What else could make my situation tolerable, suggest hope, offer encouragement, give meaning to my present absurdity, give me the courage to face another day? Where else but in fantasy could I seek a center to hold on to? Please, God, I prayed even as I retreated from the world, give me a steady point against which I can orient myself, something to grasp and hold on to that will prevent my disintegration, that will hold the pieces together.

Because fantasy had not provided that center, had become increasingly a vortex within which my ego swirled, I had looked to three people in search of that steady point, that anchor. One was Marion, my best friend, the friend who had stood next to me at the dark door of my first dream; Marion, who had shared my therapy from its beginnings, who had over the past year become a closer and closer friend, gradually displacing most of my other women friends, so that by the time Stan left she was almost the only one. Marion and Robert, my former lover, who had quietly reentered my life when Stan left, and of course Dr. Lustig— my three moorings in an otherwise ungovernable sea.

Well, with Stan gone, at least I have Marion and Robert, I reflected one late November afternoon, as I sat sipping tea in the tomblike silence of my house. Dr. Lustig had told me that with the breakup of my marriage I could no longer expect to find everything in just one person, but would have to build a network of friends, and get a little bit from each of them. But in reality, there were so few of my friends I could talk to, not because they would not have listened, but because some hesitancy in me prevented it, as if my contact would tarnish them, rob them of their common sense.

With Marion, though, I could share the details of my therapy. Was that why she had assumed such a large place in my life lately, because my therapy was the center of my world, and she knew what that meant, because her therapy was also the center of her world? The two of us were like sisters in search of wholeness, or perhaps closer than sisters even, because we were spiritually attached, seeking refuge from a world whose men—our husbands, but not our therapists—had let us down, alike in concentrating our energy on our therapy, sharing its magic with each other.

She delighted in fantasy as much as I did, especially about our therapists' love for us, and as we talked for hours each day, we played out this theme in all its variations—Dr. Wainwright loved her and would marry her; Dr. Lustig loved me and, though I did not dare to say it out loud, would soon recognize the inevitability and correctness of our attachment. Our inferior husbands would be replaced by our superior mentors, who would provide us with true guidance in our lives, who with sensitivity and understanding would lead us to the land of milk and honey, where we would settle into a comfortable domesticity, where we would be forever loved, and never alone.

I broke off my reverie abruptly, remembering that I was due to meet Robert in an hour. I thought about Robert—how we had begun and how we now stood. Robert, who had come back into my life after Stan had left; Robert, who was so like me that it was almost painful, who dreamed the same dreams as I did, who lately had taken on a haggard look around the eyes, frequently meeting me unshaven, showing the wear of his own excruciating divorce battles in the shabby and torn clothes he wore.

I had met Robert at a party eight years earlier, a faculty party given by a professor at the college where I taught. It was the first party of that scholastic season, a party typical of the times and the intellectual life. I found myself standing to one side of the room, gazing at the dance floor that had been cleared in the center, rugs rolled up and plants pushed aside, as if readying the room for its focus on the dance. The lights were muted, the liquor and grass plentiful. The conversation was idle and intellectual, with a trace of the times in the earnestness of its tone. Beards were plentiful, as was longish hair, those outward and visible signs of an inward and spiritual purity, untainted by establishment values, Vietnam, crass commercialism, or gray flannel suits—people caught up in a time that allowed for righteousness, that provided a cause.

Several colleagues and I had been chatting idly about Bergman—the Kierkegaardian and Heideggerian themes of *The Seventh Seal*, the brilliance of the time imagery in *Wild Strawberries*. Just as I was tiring of the talk, and ready to depart, a feeling that I was being observed crept over me. I felt a tingle go down my spine, and suddenly and unaccountably I was alert.

Unobtrusively, for I did not like to be obvious, I glanced in the direction from which I felt the presence come. I was confronted by the unshuttered gaze of Robert Anderson, an English professor whom I knew of, but had not met. We looked at each other a fraction of a second longer than is common, and in that glance the room emptied and we found ourselves alone.

I watched him make his way toward me. With inevitability I saw his lips move as he asked me to dance. The stereo was playing "Ruby Tuesday." I heard the words through a filter as if cotton stuffed my ears. As we danced, Robert hopped around the makeshift dance floor as if his footsteps could not keep pace with the leap of his spirits. Then in one instant, with one further look, the dancing leaped from his feet to his eyes.

After that, we walked outside into the crisp autumn darkness partially illumined by a quarter moon and a smattering of stars. We did not hold hands, but as we walked, we brushed together, like magnets drawn to their complementary poles. Hungry for words to confirm our affinity, we talked of Plato and other realities, about growing up in the West (he was from Colorado) and how it had shaped us. I laughed for no reason and quoted Yeats. He laughed for no reason and quoted e. e. cummings.

So our love had begun, and so it had continued until our very alikeness had driven us apart. But the physical affinity between us had never entirely dissipated, could be reignited at any moment, we had found. And so it had not surprised me that now, years later, in the midst of our divorces, Robert had returned.

I silently compared Robert and Dr. Lustig in my mind. Though I loved Robert now and had loved him earlier, before my marriage, how could I find in him an anchor, adrift as he was in his own divorce? And our sexuality, which had always been a mix of lightning and velvet, why was it alarming me now? Whenever I met Robert, usually covertly because of his complicated divorce, I was left with a physical satisfaction, but also a sinking stomach, a vague nausea, a desire to flee, a tendency to wrap a layer of daydreams even tighter around me—perhaps because of the spiritual desperation and raw physicality of our union, the hope that our sexual blending would vanquish our darker demons, would drive out the daily world made up of bitterness and despair.

But the fantasy was no longer working. Real sexuality with Robert was no longer offering an escape, was itself becoming a reality that I needed to escape from. Better to daydream about Dr. Lustig, who presented a clearer illusion, whose eyes were not haggard from sleepless nights, children's tears, a vindictive spouse, or personal failures glimpsed through a magnifying glass.

My fantasies about Dr. Lustig, in contrast to the reality of Robert, offered me an appealing escape. Ensconced in it, I possessed virtues and powers beyond my expectations. I was whole; I was healthy; I was a healer. He and I would be true companions and spend our days together. I would paint watercolors and he would do therapy. These were intoxicating reveries, safer than the sexual reality I shared with Robert. Robert was a mirror that perfectly reflected my own plight. Better to drift along on dreams about Dr. Lustig, free from more tortuous truths and messier realities. I can't go on seeing Robert, I decided. I can't meet him today.

But I felt immobilized. I sat as I was for another hour, until the time of my rendezvous with Robert had passed. Finally he called me.

"I'm just too ill to see you," I said. "I'm sorry, but I just can't right now."

He seemed to understand immediately and I sensed relief in him as well. "Be good to yourself," he said as he hung up.

My thoughts drifted back to Dr. Lustig again, how he was my partner in magic, being endowed as he was with equal gifts. Together, we would read the hidden signs all around us and speak our private tongue. I had even tried it out. During each office visit lately, I would closely regard his crystal bowl full of polished stones. Sure enough, I could, upon close scrutiny, detect a shift in their arrangement—the brown one or the gray one had subtly changed its position since the last time we met. I would smile inwardly, full of satisfaction. It's as I thought, I said to myself. He's sending secret messages that only I can interpret.

Then there were the keys. Dr. Lustig had two bathroom keys in the waiting room—one saying "girls" on one side and "women" on the other, the second labeled "boys" and "men." When I entered the room, I would search out the exact angle at which the keys lay, confident that Dr. Lustig was telling me of his love by the way they were juxtaposed on the table. And sometimes I would rearrange them myself, in full confidence that he would be able to interpret my symbolic message to him.

Then there were the numbers. The dates and the times of my therapy appointments assumed special meaning. If the therapy session was particularly helpful, its date and time began to carry magical powers. Alternately, any pain associated with a date condemned that number forever. Eighteen, for example, was a good number, being a combination of 8 ("eternity") and 10 ("wisdom"). Likewise, 25 carried a positive effect, being 5 ("healing") multiplied by itself.

Twenty-nine, by contrast, filled me with dread. Nine was an upside-down 6, and 6 was the number of "sexuality." Twenty-nine compounded this omen by also carrying a 2, the number for "divided." And so it went. If I saw Dr. Lustig on 10/8/75 at 10 A.M., the auspicious numbers of that date and time could only ensure my well-being: 1 brought "unity," 10 "wisdom," 8 "eternity," 7 "comfort," and 5 "healing."

Since Dr. Lustig was my mentor in magic, the need for explaining anything to him directly was circumvented. His thoughts, it was apparent to me, were running along a course similar to mine. I had proved it with the stones and the keys. We could communicate through our mutual understanding of the signs. We had no need for words.

"How are thing going at home?" he would ask me.

"Fine," I would reply smiling. I knew we weren't talking about home, because it was ten o'clock in the morning and my red stone, which I had previously returned to Dr. Lustig's crystal bowl, was nestled close to Dr. Lustig's gray one.

"How are the children?" he continued, closely watching my face.

"They're doing well," I replied confidently, my face softening into a peaceful expression. "The children," I was thinking, obviously refers to himself and me.

"The children are happy and playful," I said aloud. "They're adjusting to the separation better than I had hoped." I waited expectantly, eager for him to grasp my secret message.

"Wonderful," he answered. Now I knew for sure that he understood. There could be no doubt, for we were both wearing brown that day—the color of earthiness or being down to earth. He loves me and is glad that I'm getting a divorce, I was thinking. Perhaps he's even thinking about marriage.

"How are the children getting along at nursery school?" Dr. Lustig continued.

"They like school," I replied. School must mean therapy, I was thinking. He's asking me how I like psychotherapy with him.

"How are they sleeping and eating?" his questions continued.

"Fine," I smilingly replied. Perhaps he's telling me he

wants to sleep with me, I thought rapturously. He must care about me more than I thought.

And so I continued, placing magical meanings on the most ordinary of Dr. Lustig's words, construing them to the satisfaction of my needy imagination.

My need for this fantasy following my separation from Stan might yet have been diminished, however, had not circumstances intervened that turned reality and fantasy upside down, so that what was increasingly a tenuous connection with the world and with Dr. Lustig as its spokesman was finally and forcibly severed.

CHAPTER EIGHT

NOVEMBER–DECEMBER, 1975

As I drifted on daydreams of my spiritual union with Dr. Lustig that late autumn, Marion's fantasies were taking on a new and unexpected reality. Gradually, it seemed, or so she confided in me, Dr. Wainwright, her therapist, had begun to fall in love with her. He was like a father to her, she told me, so it had begun by her sitting on his lap for comfort. Then one day he began stroking her breasts, all the while telling her what a lovely woman she was. He began to share confidences with her. He was writing a diary about her, he explained, using a secret code, for he wanted to write of his love for her, and still hide his growing feelings from his wife of twenty-five years.

Somehow, at the time, her confidences seemed only right. There was an inevitability about the direction of her therapy that fueled my own ideas of perfect love. Perhaps someday Dr. Lustig will feel the same way about me, I thought, alight with new passion. Love with a therapist had become a possibility.

Finally, the day came when she told me they had made love.

"In his office?" I asked, wondering about the mechanics of the situation. "On the floor, with his wife in the house nearby?" I elaborated, suddenly feeling shaken and alarmed that fantasies should come true. The good of them, I was thinking, is that they are the mind's solace, but their actual translation into physical reality seemed perilous to me.

"He wants to have a baby with me," she said, her face aglow with her recent lovemaking. "A boy," she continued. "It's our private dream."

"You shouldn't be telling me about this," I pleaded. "Please don't tell me any more."

"But it's the most important thing that's ever happened to me in my life," she persisted. "Would you deny me the pleasure of telling my best friend about it?" Her tone was coaxing and she was smiling happily. "I need to tell someone," she said.

I nodded, feeling panic slipping over me like a familiar gray fog.

"Please keep this secret for me," she asked earnestly. "Do you know what *they*, the establishment, would say if they knew about this? They just would never understand about our love."

So I carried her secret for many days, sworn by my loyalty to her to a silence that was deafening. My conscience warred with my need to confide what I knew to Dr. Lustig, for I wanted him to tell me that such things were not possible, that in spite of my fantasies about him, he would never betray me by succumbing to them. But my friendship held me back.

After each meeting with Dr. Wainwright, Marion would hurry to my house to give me a detailed account of their lovemaking. "Please don't say any more," I told her finally, when I could stand it no longer. "This is something between the two of you. Leave me out of it."

But she insisted that sharing it with me was the only way she could contain the joy of his presence and the loneliness she felt when they were apart.

My silence had another reason. I felt I owed a debt to Dr. Wainwright, because he was the psychotherapist who had sent me to Dr. Lustig.

I thought about Harding Wainwright on the one and only occasion when I had seen him. I remembered vividly how he, an older, established, and highly respected member of the Philadelphia psychiatric community, had been standing on his front lawn waiting for me, because I was late for my consultation, having lost my way to his house. As I drew up to his house, I had seen a white-haired gentleman, tall and distinguished looking, wearing a tweed suit and a very substantial pair of shoes, giving the overall impression of an Oxford don who specialized perhaps in Near Eastern studies. He had walked over to meet me, concern obviously registering on his face.

My meeting with him confirmed in my mind his kindness. He led me inside and offered me coffee, and when I had composed myself somewhat, we talked about my first dream. "What did you know that no one else knew?" he asked me, and with that question he gained my confidence. Now, more than a year later, I remembered how supportive he had been to me, how he had been intent on finding me just the right therapist, how I owed finding Dr. Lustig to him.

The weight of these loyalties, however, finally became unbearable. Unable to carry Marion's secret any longer, I finally spoke of it to Dr. Lustig, telling him the facts in the form of a story, as if this transparent ploy could somehow salve my conscience, make me less disloyal to my friend and her lover. But my simple story-telling expedient, employed to soothe my scruples, did not for a moment disguise Marion's identity or that of her therapist.

Shortly after I left that day, Dr. Lustig phoned Dr.

Wainwright to tell him what had been said, he told me later, supposing as he did that one of Dr. Wainwright's sicker patients was slandering his reputation. Dr. Wainwright denied the affair, implying that it was Dr. Lustig's patient, and not his, who was out of touch with reality.

Marion was waiting for me when I returned home that day. Dr. Wainwright had phoned her and instructed her to disavow the affair to me. When I realized that she knew I had betrayed her confidence, I shrank back, ready for her anger or censure. But she seemed strangely calm, pleased even, as if now, finally, the truth was out.

"I'm supposed to deny that we are having an affair," she said to me grinning. "So let's just say that I've denied it and leave it at that.

"You know what you'll have to do now," she continued. "You'll have to go and deny it to Dr. Lustig. He would never have believed your word, anyway," she concluded. "You know these therapists all stick together. They never believe a patient if it's her word against one of their own."

Feeling guilty about my betrayal of her confidence, and swayed by Marion's words, I dutifully went back to Dr. Lustig's office that afternoon, and told him that what I had said was not true.

"Are you sure?" he probed, sounding as if he was beginning to wonder about it after all. "Are you sure that this was something Marion was making up?"

"Yes," I replied, my voice dying in my throat. "Yes," I said again, repeating my lie. Finally, Dr. Lustig appeared to be convinced. "I never doubted that what *you* were telling me was what you believed to be true," he assured me. "I'm glad that Marion has now told you the truth." I said nothing, grimacing inwardly at the irony of his words.

I had never felt so tired or so sad, for with my lie I had broken my trust with Dr. Lustig. If I could not tell him the truth, if he could not believe the truth when I told it, then how could he ever again distinguish dreams and reality for me? With that one lie, the therapy room ceased to be a refuge, and Dr. Lustig ceased to be truth's arbiter.

I wondered often afterward why telling a lie is so much worse than being told one, why my lie to Dr. Lustig had finally severed an already fragile trust that had been partially rent by his betrayal of my confidence in the first place. Was it because with my lie I could no longer trust myself? Was it because I had chosen between my mentor and my friend, had been thrown irrevocably into Marion and Dr. Wainwright's camp, where truth and sanity could be sacrificed for the sake of a reputation? Was it because Marion had issued a command that in my guilt and in the absence of a countercommand I had obeyed, because it had at least clarified a clouded situation, dissolved the confusion of conflicting loyalties that ran in too many directions? Was it because my lie had been successful, had fooled even Dr. Lustig, who, by some omniscience, should have known the difference?

It wasn't until the following spring, when Marion married Dr. Wainwright, that Dr. Lustig finally knew the truth. "I'm very sorry. I just didn't know," he told me. He apologized for the way his not knowing had contributed to my blurring of illusion and truth. But by then it did not matter, for I had survived the ordeal that was to be its outcome.

For the moment, however, as I plodded home, I knew only that I was irrevocably alone. Stan was gone. Robert was gone. Marion was acting more and more strangely as her affair went on, wearing boys' clothing, talking to me about how bisexuality was really better, frightening me with her implicit hints and gestures, introducing a possible sexuality into our friendship. And Dr. Lustig, whom I had counted on most to tell me what was real, ignoring the very reality about Marion and her therapist that I knew to be true; my ultimate denial of it myself, my unforgivable lie to him that had broken the bond between us. How could I find in him an anchor anymore, when he did not believe what I knew to be true?

There was nowhere in the world left for me to stand. Even fantasies about Dr. Lustig, *most of all* fantasies about Dr. Lustig, had to be replaced. Magic was all that was left. My growing immersion in magical thinking brought me relief in the beginning, sheltering my mind against the harshness of my felt isolation. But gradually I became trapped there, in a magical kingdom that seemed totally beyond my control, where occult powers reigned unchecked, and where the best defense was a sorcerer's crystal ball. The magical signs began to gain supremacy, and the task of interpreting them correctly became an obsession that took more and more of my time.

When the numbers were bad, waves of pain would sweep over me. I felt like an octopus whose eight arms were shot through with burning fire. Terrified, I would try to get a grip on my mind, to lessen my anguish by an act of will. But my will was ineffective in the fight against the forces of chaos and caprice. My only chance for survival lay in anticipating their ravages, in order to steel myself for their onslaught. The outside forces impinging on me followed magical and mysterious laws that could not be calculated with reason alone. I continually tried to decipher the magical signs, and desperately sought to discern their rules of grammar, so that I might defend myself by harnessing an equally powerful counterforce.

Numbers, the seat of quantification, had lost their objectivity and no longer quantified. What had begun as innocent numerical play became a compulsion to record each and every number in my life. Ordinary time had collapsed. The present acquired vectors reaching into the past and into the future. What was happening *now* suddenly had magical import in all three time frames. Numbers came to represent the most potentially powerful weapon in my arsenal, because they could predict what might happen.

The grocery list presented the ultimate challenge. I taught my philosophy classes on Tuesday and Thursday.

On the alternate days, I would shop for groceries during the part of the morning when my children were in their preschool classes. I would drop the children off at 9:30 and pick them up at 11:30. In between, I would mindlessly race to the grocery store, intent on my larger purpose: to remember the name of the food item that was the referent for every price on the cash register slip, so that later I could connect the symbolic meaning of the foodstuff to the numbers in its price. I would speed home with my store-bought goods and frantically begin recording the food names on the grocery receipt, in the belief that the numbers would allow me to predict future happenings on the parallel dates and times, or at least anticipate those forces which might impinge upon me with violence at any moment.

If bread was eighty-nine cents, then I knew I could expect some sign of beauty or flowers (because bread is made with "flour") on the eighth of the month at nine o'clock. Lettuce ("let us") implied some permission at the hour and day of its price. Meat meant that I would "meet" someone, and so my associations raged. The exact time when I recorded the grocery numbers (usually 11 A.M.) also went into the magical calculation, along with the time and date of their purchase. Eleven o'clock became a terrible hour for me, made worse by the fact that 11 is two 1's that are standing apart, divided. If I worked very quickly, I had just enough time to complete the recording process before picking up the children at 11:30. By that time I was spent, exhausted by the staggering enormity of the surplus magical significance.

As the days of December deepened, the distinction between me and the magic of the outer world collapsed. I became one with it. I could not distinguish a separate self apart from it. I became disorder and the absence of reason. No ordinary laws of causality operated within me. I was pushed and shoved indiscriminately—a leaf torn from its tree, adrift at the mercy of an alien wind. I did not make events happen; they happened to me. The more I struggled against the magical forces, the more powerful they became. The less I struggled against those currents, the less fragmented my fantasy became.

But sometimes I would fight to assert my separate identity. I would record messages to myself—reminders that there still existed within me some remnant of control. "I am a professional," I would write down. "I am a woman," I would remind myself. Then, caught up in the magic once again, I would quickly forget that personhood involves *acting on* the world, rather than being acted upon by it.

Sometimes when I was most flooded by magic, I would sit down and do logic problems, to insist on some order, to defeat the magical numbers with ordinary quantification. I would feel soothed by these intellectual exercises, if only momentarily.

Sometimes I simply begged the forces to let me go. On occasion they consented, and I would have an hour's rest. But then they would reassert themselves and gather me up again into their chaos and confusion, robbing me of my place in the ordinary and ordered world.

What had begun as a simple divorce from a man ended as a profound divorce from reality. Madness, with its charms and the stuff of dreams, had lured me away. But its enchantment soon turned to nightmare, and I could not wake up. Like Orpheus, I had glanced back over my shoulder, and had lost both Eurydice and the world.

Part 3

BLINDED BY THE SUN

MADNESS

I stared into the light and knew what madness
was.
Caught in a terrible vision, neither great nor common,
Still without movement in a time unredeemably
present,
In a place without the solace of a touch, a human
moment,
Wounded without the grace of the artist's dance.

CHAPTER ONE

DECEMBER, 1975

They came on silent feet out of nowhere, visitors from another dimension. I knew them immediately when I saw them, and from the intent way that they stared back into my eyes, I knew that they also recognized me. At once alien and familiar, like a stranger on the street who is mistaken for a friend, they marched out of my imagination and assumed a visible shape. They were not surrounded by shadow or mist. They had the dimensions, colors, and sharp outlines by which we distinguish the real from the illusory. Only their eyes, and their sometimes bizarre dress, indicated that they belonged to a different reality, were manifestations of the surreal. They came as friends of my solipsism. They were terrible only because they made me mad.

The first time I saw one of them, I was sitting on the deacon's bench in Dr. Lustig's waiting room. It was nine o'clock in the morning on a rather dreary early December day, and I was waiting for my appointment, in a daze devoid of thought. All of a sudden, my attention was inexorably drawn toward the hallway door. I watched, fascinated, as the door slowly opened. A woman stood in the doorway dressed in a short flared red costume, such as those worn by cigarette girls in old movies. Her white blouse was ruffled at the neck, suggesting the collar of a clown. A tray of candies and other confections hung around her neck. She did not speak, but stared intently at my face. As she stood there regarding me, large tears slowly began to pour out of her eyes. Then, turning away sorrowfully, she stepped back into the hallway and gently closed the door on the larger world.

I was not frightened. Instead, I felt a curious kinship with her. She too belonged to the secret society of lonely magicians. She too understood the messages that were not of this world. It seemed only natural to me that she should appear as messenger and ministrant to my isolation.

I said nothing to Dr. Lustig about my strange encounter in his waiting room. But some of my confusion must have been apparent during the appointment, because he mentioned, for the first time, the possibility of hospitalization. The thought was so terrible to me that I promptly put it out of my mind. The next day, when "sunglasses people" began appearing, I did not tell Dr. Lustig about them, either.

I was sitting in a local eatery having lunch with my friend Mimi, when I saw the first one. I was seated facing the entrance to the restaurant, talking with Mimi, when I happened to glance up from the table. There he was, waiting in line to be seated. He wore the costume of a rhinestone cowboy, an elaborate exaggeration of the dress worn by real cowboys I had known in the West. He was suited in a mass of purple satin. Sequins on the costume caught traces of the bright December sunlight streaming in at the windows. Beige-colored buckskin fringe ran up and down his arms, contrasting strangely with the shiny surface of his attire.

But the strangest thing about him was his large sunglasses. They stood like two black voids aligned in his face. They were absolutely opaque. No glimmer of light passed through them; no reflected light bounced off them. Like black holes in space, they seemed to capture the light from every direction. The black eyes attracted my gaze like magnets. My eyes felt pulled inexorably toward them. I stared fixedly at the two black orbs, as if my eyes had been lassoed and were being roped in. Deeper and deeper my gaze was drawn in, until I had no will to free it. Seconds passed like hours. I forgot to breathe. I became terrified by my paralysis.

Finally, gathering together the remnant of energy left within me, I willed my eyes away from his face and back to the table where my friend sat. "I'm so excited about teaching there," she chatted on unconcernedly. "I hope the job comes through." I tried to concentrate on what she was saying, realizing that I had not heard most of what had gone before.

I had, during the preceding month, become increasingly isolated from my friends who, to that point, had always formed a ready support system. It had become painful and straining to be with them, for I could not tell them about my mental anguish, or about the magic that was enveloping me. With everyone except Marion and Dr. Lustig, I sought at all times to appear ordinary, so that no glimmer of my madness would shine through my armor, no clue of my desperation could show itself. I had to protect them from insanity's curse. I was afraid of my friends' instinctive recoil if they were to find out.

Sitting that day in the restaurant, I wanted to ask Mimi to turn around and look toward the door, to confirm whether a sunglassed cowboy was standing there or not. But fortunately my vocal cords did not respond, for if I had asked her to look and she had not seen him, then I knew she would know that I was mad.

I stared intently at her for some minutes, summoning my attention back to the conversation. "Maybe we can get the kids together this afternoon to play," she was saying. I nodded, consciously avoiding looking at the spot where the cowboy had stood, knowing even as I did so that I would eventually have to look again, if only to know for myself where my sanity stood.

I steadied myself, took a deep breath, and quickly glanced toward the spot where I had seen him. He was no longer there. Cautiously, I looked around the restaurant, afraid that he would be there, more afraid that he would not. But he had vanished as neatly as he had arrived.

The waitress brought our sandwiches. "It looks good," my friend said, as she began to eat. I picked up my hamburger automatically and took a bite. But I tasted only the bitterness of defeat. I am mad, I finally acknowledged to myself.

After that first encounter, I began seeing people in sunglasses wherever I looked. This was not odd in itself, since we were having a streak of brilliant December days, with the sun almost painfully reflecting off sidewalks and off mounds of leftover snow. It is beneficial and common for people to protect their eyes against the glare on this kind of day. So sunglasses, in themselves, were not odd. What was odd was my perception, my instinctive certainty, that some of the sunglasses people were not real, even though their visual image was as sharp and as clear as any normal sight.

Several days after seeing the cowboy, I was walking over to the neighborhood bank before its usual closing at three o'clock in the afternoon. On the way, I passed four people wearing sunglasses. Two of them, I suspected, were real and ordinary people. Two, I suspected, were not. The terrible thing was that I could never be sure who was coming toward me: which ones were ordinary people wearing sunglasses, and which were alien folk disguising themselves as ordinary people wearing sunglasses.

With the clear memory of the rhinestone cowboy fresh in my mind, I trembled as each figure in sunglasses passed. The first one I encountered had the suggestion of eyes behind his sunglasses. He did not seem to notice me. He is real,

I thought with some relief, reading his lack of interest as a sign of ordinary existence. My body, however, remained tense as I continued along the path to the bank. By now, any appearance of sunglasses provoked in me a serious alarm.

Farther down the street, about half a block from the bank, stood a second person in sunglasses. She appeared to be an elderly woman with white hair and stooped shoulders. She stood at the window of the neighborhood travel agency, as if she was looking at the vacation displays. I stepped up my pace to walk rapidly past her, but I could not prevent one brief glance in her direction.

As I did so, my terror exploded. Like the cowboy, she caught me with the dense black voids that were her eyes, and began to draw me into them. My feet kept walking, but my eyes became trapped in her gaze. As I passed directly by her, my head swung around unwillingly in her direction, as if my eyes were being pulled by a puppeteer's string. At the same time, her head pivoted toward me, so that she continued to track my movements as I walked past. For an instant we were fixed in an encounter of absolute recognition. The glare of the sun was blinding. We stood motionless, she wearing sunglasses to protect her eyes from too much light, while I was being helplessly exposed to its overpowering intensity. I knew that she knew—that her eyes sought mine in recognition of our common dilemma. She too knew the suffering of too much significance. She too knew what it was like to be isolated in the middle of an alien light.

Finally, after several seconds of extreme scrutiny, her eyes shifted away and let me go. I scurried past her down the street. I walked on a few hundred yards, and then glanced back over my shoulder. She was nowhere to be seen. She had looked completely real. Was she, in fact, an idle passerby who sought information about possible journeys, who had simply stepped into the travel agency? Or was she a product of my imagination? Was she—I finally said the word to myself—was she, dear God, a hallucination?

I stumbled into the bank and made my deposit. Then, still shaking, I walked toward the outside through the revolving glass door. Just as I exited, a man in sunglasses was entering through the door. My gaze went to his eyes. His head swung around as he looked toward me. Oh, my God, I thought. I cannot take any more of this. My feet stumbled forward, toward home. Two more people in sunglasses were crossing the street directly in front of me. They looked like an ordinary middle-aged couple. I glanced at them briefly and then quickly looked away. I was afraid to know whether they were real or not.

When I arrived home, the babysitter was there with the children. They came toward me, eager to tell about what they had been doing. But I couldn't focus on what they said. I heard their excited little voices, but the content of their words did not come through. I patted their heads absently, and then asked the babysitter if she could stay with them for an extra hour. "I don't feel well," I told her. "I need to lie down for a little while." She said that it would be no problem to stay. I walked to the bedroom, turned down the covers, and got into bed completely clothed. I lay on my side, curled my body into a ball, and pulled the covers up around my head. I quaked there for the next hour, until the babysitter came in and told me that she had to go home. Then I dragged my body out of bed and, summoning my last ounce of strength, went into the living room to watch the children. I simply sat down in a chair and let them come to me. I answered their questions automatically, and expressed interest in the pictures that they had drawn.

"Mommy, please come and play blocks with us," Elizabeth pleaded, pulling at my arm.

"All right, honey," I said dully and rose to my feet. I spent the next hour on the floor of the study, building houses and structures that were far steadier than I. The rest of the afternoon and evening passed with me, as often happened, on automatic pilot. Twice the image of the sunglasses people came into my mind, and I felt that I was on fire. Then the images faded, and my limbs turned to ice.

When darkness fell that night, it no longer had the power to frighten me. I had discovered, that day, the even more elemental terror of too much illumination. Somehow or other, the metaphor had reversed itself. I had started out being frightened by the black room of my dream. Now, I had discovered an even worse terror, a second realm of light—a double intensity of seeing that illuminated things that were not real, a clarity more terrible than the darkest dark.

The darkness, when I closed my eyes that night, was a comfort. I was glad to exchange the realm of seeing for the more concrete realm of touch. I was glad that my distorted sight had been taken away, if only momentarily; glad to touch the familiar bedroom objects around me in the dark.

My hand clung to the edge of the mattress as I fell asleep.

CHAPTER TWO

DECEMBER, 1975

To know oneself to be mad is the worst of all possible predicaments. Complete insanity offers sanctuary. It allows one to slip behind a limitless veil of illusion, without any self-conscious monitoring to acknowledge the extent of mental wastage. But to be mad and to simultaneously possess some fragment of consciousness, whereby one glimpses with horror one's true situation, is to slice the protective shield of illusion with a knife and turn up the center raw.

My days in December were filled with endless drownings; endless struggles to surface for air, before once again slipping beneath the sea of unreality. The sunglasses people continued to be my frequent visitors. They beckoned me from the driver's seats of passing cars, from crowded sidewalks, from any public place. Only at home was I safe from their scrutiny. The more I saw them, the more powerful they became. Turn away from your pain, their presence seemed to say. Follow us to a place that is safe and free. I longed to comply and definitively renounce the world. But something in me still resisted and clung to the earth.

Christmas came again. Elizabeth and Daniel had gone to the Midwest with Stan to visit his parents for the holidays. I was left with few obligations to the real world. One of them was to grade a handful of papers from the academic semester that had just ended. During the morning and afternoon, I sat before the study window with the blue books piled up before me, reading essay questions on Plato's cave and Descartes's *cogito ergo sum*, routinely using that disciplined part of my mind that could function virtually on its own. Another part of my mind, however, kept slipping out through the window into a nonrational dimension.

After grading some exams each day, I would go shopping. I shopped with compulsion, moving determinedly from store to store in search of the perfect gifts for those I loved. They had to be presents surrounded with all the proper magical symbols of completeness, to compensate for its lack in my life now. Nothing less than perfection would do. As I looked and bought, I scrupulously recorded the time of each purchase and its price, hoping to find in their numbers a reassurance of the fitness and propriety of my gifts. Because the stores were open late, I often shopped in the night.

One evening several days before Christmas, I drove to the nearby shopping center. I had seen a pair of Lalique swans in the window of one of the small jewelry stores there, and I felt compelled to return to look at them again. They were exactly like the crystal swan that I had given Dr. Lustig in November, on the anniversary of my first year in therapy. In one of my early therapy sessions, we had talked about fairy tales. I had told him that my story was *The Snow Queen* by Hans Christian Andersen. He had told me that his story was *The Ugly Duckling* by the same writer. So I had bought him a crystal swan at the first opportunity, to remind him of his beauty. The piece I stared at so intently now was the same, only doubled—two swans intertwined. I knew that I did not deserve such beauty, but I derived some comfort from standing in front of the window, and looking at the swans anyway.

As I drove near the thoroughfare of shops that was my destination, I noticed a group of grade-school-age children assembled in the middle of the street. There had been a snowfall the night before, and freshly fallen snow still covered the ground. The children formed a circle, as they crouched down on the deserted, lamplit street. From my car I could not see what was in the center of the circle, but from the children's rapt attention, I knew that it must be something at once fascinating and important. My attention was transfixed by the circle as my car neared the place where they were playing. Just as I drove slowly by them, I caught a glimpse of the children lighting matches, just like the little match girl of the fairy tale, in order to warm their hands and have some light. Matches were strewn all over the street. I drove on, profoundly moved. I lifted my hand to my cheek and felt the tears there, unsurprised but saddened by what I had seen.

I parked the car near the jewelry store where I had seen the swans. Reverentially walking to the window where they were displayed, I stood silently before them, as before a shrine. Maybe someday I can be one of the swans, I thought. It saddened me that I could not be one of them now.

I had been standing there for several minutes, completely unaware of the time, when I glanced around and saw a man in sunglasses about five feet away. He too stood silently on the sidewalk, staring into a neighboring store's window display. I quickly looked away, before my eyes could be drawn into his gaze, feeling the familiar terror rise in my gut. Is he real? I wondered, afraid to know the answer. But why would anyone be wearing sunglasses in the dark? I asked myself.

I ducked into the jewelry store and approached a store

clerk, a nice-looking young woman with an open, friendly, freckled face. "How much are the Lalique swans in the window?" I asked her. She went to look at the piece and returned with the price. "It's fifty-nine ninety-five," she told me. Too much, I thought, as I carefully recorded the price and the time next to it on my shopping list. "Swan— $59.95—6:49 P.M.—Monday, 12/22/75." Somehow the numbers will tell me what will happen, I thought, although I did not define to myself just exactly what it was that I expected.

I left the jewelry store and, worried about the reappearance of the man in sunglasses, glanced around me. Seeing no one, I walked automatically back to my car. I drove home to a darkened house. Dully switching on the lights inside, I realized how weary I was, as if my body had stolen some of the tiredness away from my mind.

I went directly to my bedroom, switched on the television, then got undressed and plopped into bed. My watch said it was only 7:32. Drowsily, I began to watch the flickering screen. An episode of *Star Trek* was playing. Then something happened that, in its simplicity, seemed stranger and more terrible than all the demons that had been gathering. I entered a timewarp. I was a teenager again, and my mind was perfectly normal. No madness, no Dr. Lustig, no dreams had ever happened. No therapy, no struggle, no pain, no twisted thoughts. An earlier, completely normal perspective had been restored. I had no recent history; the slate was wiped clean. Nothing that has happened to me during these last years has been real, I thought. The clarity of this perspective was frightening, abolishing as it did my recent past and, in so doing, annihilating *me*. It seemed the final irony, the final trick—that to be clear-eyed about reality, I must deny myself.

I turned off the TV and curled myself into a protective ball in my bed. I lay there for some time, feeling myself drowning. It felt as if I had been underwater for a very long time and my breath was almost spent. I wanted to struggle to the surface, but something unknown and unperceived seemed to hold me beneath the water against my will. I clawed my way about frantically, losing all sense of orientation and direction. Even if I had wanted to surface, I did not know which direction to follow. Where is up? I asked myself. Finally, I let a partial breath out, and watched carefully as the bubbles moved away from me. They shot out to my right. That must be the way to the surface, I thought, and started swimming furiously in that direction. Just as the blackness of asphyxia began to creep over my consciousness, I felt myself emerge from the water and break free. I took a deep breath, feeling an enormous gratitude for the air. I will survive, I thought, as I drifted into sleep.

CHAPTER THREE

JANUARY, 1976

On January 2, Stan's thirty-sixth birthday, the children returned home from their Midwest Christmas vacation with their father. When I saw them get off the plane, my heart lightened. I grabbed them and hugged them to me, grasping after their physical solidity and presence, as if they were two small planets of sanity in the midst of a chaotic solar system where the sun was falling apart. I held on to them and begged God to let me become a whole sphere myself, that they could depend on me, as children ought.

But my plea was not immediately granted. I found, in the days ahead, that even the children's presence at home, calling me back to the world of practical affairs, was not enough to defeat the army of illusion and unreality that had me fast in its grip. The sunglasses people continued to be my frequent and silent visitors, now on occasion even appearing when I was with my children. Those times were the worst, for then my visions posed a direct threat to my functioning as a mother. At those times, I would turn my eyes away from the alien beings, assiduously ignoring their intrusion. Since the children did not see them, we could continue as if nothing had happened. But inside I would know the nature of my peril, the power of that alien call. Each time I resisted them and turned my attention back to the children, I wondered whether the next time I would have the strength.

The turning point came in mid-January, when I attempted to resume my teaching responsibilities in addition to caring for the children. It was then that my functioning ultimately faltered and failed.

It was the first day of the new teaching semester, and I was scheduled to meet with two new classes. I was confused and nauseated and filled with dread. How could I stand up in front of a classroom of youthful, eager students and outline a rational program of philosophy for the semester? How could I tell my students about Plato, caught as I was in the blinding sunlight outside the cave?

Years of self-discipline came to the fore. I will go to my classes and get through them at whatever price, I told myself. So I dressed, made breakfast, and readied the children for the babysitter, all the while trying to steady myself. After what seemed an eternity, although it must have been only an hour, the babysitter arrived and I was free to leave the house. By 10:30 I was on the campus and walking toward my assigned classroom building. I had never taught in this building before, and everything about its modern appearance seemed sterile and strange. Bracing myself, I ordered my feet to march forward and up the three flights of stairs. They obeyed, and soon I had arrived at Room 303, where I was scheduled to teach an introductory course at 11:00 A.M.

I walked to the desk at the front of the room, and registered the look of surprise on the students' faces that I had come to expect. "She's younger and prettier than we thought," I could almost hear them murmur to themselves. I smiled automatically at the students, and then began shuffling through my papers and notes for the class.

Suddenly, the terror surfaced. Nausea swept over me. Fiery hands ran up and down my arms. It was time to begin, but I could not move. I glanced at the students. They looked at me expectantly. I looked away. I must go home, I thought. I am not well. I looked back at the students, who were beginning to rustle in their seats. I stood up and walked to the first row of chairs facing me. Making my voice as composed as possible, I spoke.

"I'm sorry," I told them, "but I'm feeling quite ill. I'm afraid I'll have to cancel class today." So saying, I hurried from the room.

Overwhelmed by a sense of failure, of having let everyone down, I stumbled down the hallway, through the doorway, and across campus to my car. With terror now compounded by guilt, I started the engine and shifted the transmission into drive.

Missing one class won't matter, I tried to persuade myself. I *will* be able to keep going. I *will* teach my classes. And so resolving, I drove directly to Dr. Lustig's office. As I drove I was aware of gliding through red traffic signals—three in all. I must stop, I told myself. The red lights are telling me to stop.

Arriving unscathed and unarrested at Dr. Lustig's office, I sat down in the waiting room and tried to compose myself. An ebb tide seemed to have caught me up, pushing me farther and farther out to sea. Dr. Lustig seemed to be the only person who noticed my fate. I saw him standing at the water's edge with a life preserver in his hands, alertly ready to throw me a line. Once or twice, I could almost hear him shout, "Carol, don't go too far out. I must be able to pull you back to shore."

I looked at my watch. It was 2:35. The door to his inner room was closed, indicating that he was seeing another patient. Five minutes, then ten minutes passed. I began to feel frightened at the thought of seeing him. He'll think badly of me, I worried. If he finds me here in the middle of the day, he'll know that I'm not doing what I'm supposed to. He'll be disappointed in me; he'll know that I'm a failure.

But he's here to help you, another side of me argued. Just tell him what happened, and he'll help you.

He'll be angry, something in me countered. He told me that he would try to keep me functioning and out of the hospital. I failed him this morning. If I go to the hospital, I make him a failure too.

Then my mind went blank. I must go, I thought. I fled Dr. Lustig's waiting room.

I got back into my car and drove the block and a half home. The babysitter was still out for a walk with the children. I went through the quiet house to the storage closet where we kept our suitcases, and grabbed one automatically. Carrying it, I walked directly to my bedroom. I began pulling out clothes and methodically placing them into the suitcase.

I must go to the hospital was my only thought. Once the suitcase was packed, I walked to the study, picked up the phone, and dialed Dr. Lustig's number.

"Dr. Lustig," I heard him say.

I was silent.

"Hello, Dr. Lustig speaking," he said. Still I could not speak. Dazed, and with infinite sorrow, I hung up the phone.

To ease my panic I reached for my medicine bottle. I had found myself taking more and more medicine lately, often at irregular intervals, when the numbers were auspicious or when they foreshadowed doom. But even these measures were not enough. The medicine itself had begun playing tricks on me. I couldn't be sure if I was taking the proper amount. Was I taking too little, or was I taking too much? Too little, and the terror and pain prevailed; too much, and the fog and confusion rolled in. So I played games with the medicine, worrying and guessing over each dose, but taking steadily more until I was so surrounded by fog that I could not remember how much I had taken. My confusion had become so great that I lost track of the number of pills that I was swallowing, although I knew I was taking several each time. But the fact remained that I could no longer trust even my medicine.

The babysitter soon returned with the children. I felt myself moving in slow motion as I prepared their supper, settled them in front of the television, and later got them ready for the night. At eight o'clock when Stan arrived to see the children, I asked him if he would put Elizabeth and Daniel to bed that evening. I gave him no explanation, just walked apathetically toward the bedroom and got into bed without undressing. Stan followed me into the bedroom, concern on his face.

"Is everything all right?" he asked worriedly.

"No, it's not," I answered wearily. "But I'm too tired to talk about it, okay?"

"Okay," Stan replied, and then, turning, uncertainly left the room. "I'll lock the door as I leave, after the children are asleep," he called to me as he left.

I simply buried my head in the pillow and slept.

The next day, Friday, I did not have to teach. I had an appointment with Dr. Lustig. I stumbled toward his office, my feet mechanically following one another across the shopping center and up the stairs. After I sat down in his waiting room, an indescribable tiredness crept over me. My head could not be held upright. Of its own accord, it fell down toward my chest. Gravity folded my body into a ball and my arms clutched one another in sympathy and support. I silently remained in this position until Dr. Lustig came to the door of his inner office and told me to come in. Slowly rising to my feet, I dully followed him into the inner office and sat down in my chair. My head still hung low; my hands still clutched my arms. I could not look at him.

Registering the extent of my distress, he did not begin the session in his usual manner.

"We're going to do something different today," he said. "Do you see that plant over there?" He paused, gesturing toward the large rubber plant that stood in the corner, behind my chair. I looked up at him with a dazed and confused expression, and nodded. What is he doing? I wondered. Still I did not speak.

"Will you help me care for that plant?" he asked gently.

I didn't move, so he continued, "I'd like you to help me clean and polish the leaves. Here, let me show you."

He got up, took some cloths from his closet, and approached the plant. Slowly and gently he began to wipe its leaves, one by one.

Still I did not move. I had turned my head just enough to observe out of the corner of my left eye what he was doing. I watched him as if he were a person from another planet whom I was observing on a television screen.

When I still did not move of my own accord, he gave me more explicit instructions.

"Come over here and stand by the plant," he said calmly.

I obediently got up from the chair and haltingly moved toward him, until I was standing just a few inches from him and the plant.

He extended the cloth toward me. "Now take this cloth," he said gently and firmly. "Take the cloth and wipe each leaf clean like this." As he spoke, he ever so carefully grasped one of the broad leaves with his left hand, while his right hand wiped the dust from its surface.

I followed his lead and began methodically wiping the leaves, one by one. I felt my movements to be jerky, as if my nerves and muscles were disconnected. Since it was a large plant that reached almost to my height, our cleaning continued silently for the next half hour.

Finally, we were finished. I had found our task very soothing. I felt that I, like the plant, had been dusted and cared for and wiped clean.

We returned to our seats and I found that I could talk quietly.

"I'm so tired," I sighed lifelessly.

"Of what?" he asked softly.

"Of fighting to stay together," I replied.

"If it's that exhausting," he said, "perhaps you should consider entering the hospital."

"No, not yet," I replied fiercely. Then I remembered the dream I had had last night, a voice that had urged me to go to the hospital to get away from Marion. I pushed the thought aside, wanting so much to prove that I could cope. "No, not yet," I repeated more softly.

"How much medicine are you taking?" he asked.

I told him that I couldn't remember.

He took one of his cards and scribbled briefly on it. "Take the medicine only as I've written it," he instructed, handing me the card.

I nodded dumbly.

After seeing Dr. Lustig, I went home and unpacked my bag. I'll make it without going to the hospital, I said to myself. Once again, I resolved to keep performing my duties. Once again I resolved to go the next Tuesday and teach my classes.

By Tuesday morning, January 20, however, the mental fog of confusion and unreality had again moved in. Struggling against the terror that the prospect of standing in front of a class now produced within me, I dressed and set out for the college.

Again, I made my way to the appointed classroom. A

few students were already at their places; others were ambling in. I sat down at the desk in the front of the classroom, bracing myself for the ordeal.

Today I'll be able to do it, I told myself. To be certain of that fact, I had brought the red stone that Dr. Lustig had given me on my last birthday, which I had reclaimed from his crystal bowl. It was a symbol that I had imbued with magical powers, a talisman that would not allow any other occult forces to take hold of me. So long as I can hold on to this stone, I told myself, no harm can come to me.

I took the stone out of my purse and, clutching it tightly in my right hand, stood up to begin the class. I began telling the students about philosophy—how it was a rigorous discipline with its own language, questions, issues, and fields of investigation. How, as a discipline, it little resembled "philosophy" in the common sense meaning of the term. I continued lecturing, outlining some of the philosophers and issues that we would be discussing.

For the first five minutes of my talk, all was well. My stone is protecting me, I thought as I proceeded. Then suddenly, the stone turned on me. It became hot, scorching the flesh of my right hand. I clutched it more tightly, and it became a piece of burning coal. The pain that had begun in my hand now began to travel up my arm. I was on fire.

I stopped speaking abruptly in midsentence, gulped, and tried to continue. But no more sounds came out of my mouth. I was paralyzed. I'm going crazy, I thought. The stone continued to eat into my flesh.

"I'm sorry," I found myself saying to the students. "I'm afraid that I am still feeling rather ill. If you'll excuse me, I must go."

I fled the room, still clutching the burning stone. The good magic has finally betrayed me, I thought. Once outside the door of the classroom, I opened my right hand and, prying it away with my left, threw the stone into my purse. The burning stopped abruptly.

I must go to the hospital, I said to myself as I drove home. There's no other choice. Suddenly I knew I must trust my dream. I would only escape the madness and Marion by going there. A calm came over me. I knew that my decision was correct and final. Finally, I would rest.

I may die there, I thought, but I was too tired to care. The thought of death was not an unpleasant one. Perhaps, after all, it's as Plato said in the *Phaedo*—death is but a sleep undisturbed by bad dreams. Arriving home, I walked resolutely to my bedroom and, one final time, packed my bag for the hospital. Then I called Dr. Lustig on the phone. I waited till the hour, so that I would not disturb him if he was with another patient.

"I must go to the hospital," I said calmly, with resolve in my voice. "I'm sorry, but I must go," I repeated.

"Yes," he said quietly. "I'll make the arrangements. Will Stan or someone else be able to drive you there, once everything is arranged?"

"Yes," I said flatly.

"I'll call you back, after everything is in order," he said.

"Thanks," I said, and carefully replaced the phone on the hook.

Next I called Stan. "I have to go to the hospital," I told him over the phone. "Will you come over and take me there?"

"I'll be right home," he said, as if he had momentarily forgotten that he no longer lived there.

I went into the living room and sat down on the couch to wait. The children were still outside with the babysitter. I knew that Stan would take care of them while I was gone. I pushed the thought of the children out of my mind. Leaving them was too painful to think about.

The phone rang jarringly. I moved tiredly toward it.

"Hello," I said in a tired semblance of my ordinary voice.

"It's Elaine," I heard my friend say. "Is everything all right? You don't sound like yourself."

"Elaine, I have to go to the hospital," I said flatly.

"I didn't realize you were sick," Elaine replied sympathetically. "Is it for tests, or what?"

I realized that she didn't understand the kind of hospital I meant.

"A psychiatric hospital," I muttered. "My doctor agrees that I have to go."

"Those damned psychiatrists," Elaine began angrily, and then stopped herself. I knew what she was thinking. I understood her total incredulity, since I had so assiduously kept the truth from her. But I was too tired now to dissemble. I wanted her to know the worst.

"I have to go, Elaine," I said quietly and calmly. "I was driving back from the college Thursday, and I ran three red lights. I know it's time for me to stop."

There was a considerable pause at the other end of the line, as if Elaine was suddenly realizing the extent and nature of the problem. "Were the kids in the car?" she asked quietly. I told her they were not.

"Well, maybe it *would* be a good idea for you to go into the hospital *for a rest*," she finally said.

"What will you do with the children?" she continued. "Can I help take care of them?"

"Thanks, Elaine, but no," I said. "Stan will take them."

"He certainly ought to take some responsibility at this point," Elaine retorted, and then, collecting herself, continued more mildly. "Please let me know if there's *anything* I can do," she told me. "I'll be in touch with Stan, and if you'd like, I'll visit you. Don't worry. Remember, we all love you."

"Thanks, Elaine," I said. "Goodbye." I set the receiver gently back on the hook, and reseated myself on the couch.

The phone rang again. It was Dr. Lustig. "I've arranged for you to go to the sanitarium," he said. "It's a private hospital, the best in the area. Dr. William Otto, a colleague that I know and trust, will treat you while you're there."

"Can't *you* take care of me there?" I asked.

"Only psychiatrists who are members of the staff can treat patients there," he replied. "And I'm not one of them. But I *will* visit you."

"But you're my doctor," I protested feebly, suddenly feeling abandoned.

"Carol, I've done everything I could to prevent your downward spiral, but nothing has worked recently. It would benefit both of us if a different doctor were to assess you *and* your treatment. Please allow it. I'll be in close contact with Dr. Otto, and will reserve your regular appointment times here, for when you return. Please understand."

"Okay," I assented sorrowfully.

"Thanks," he replied.

"Who will be taking you to the hospital?" he resumed after a moment's silence.

"Stan."

"Well, have him call me when he gets to the house," he said.

"I will," I answered with finality. "Goodbye."

"You'll be all right," he told me firmly.

"Yes," I replied, not really caring one way or the other. "Goodbye," I said again and hung up the phone.

A few minutes later, Stan arrived. He looked very distressed. He was also angry. Anger was the way he sometimes expressed his concern. Almost immediately after walking into the room, he began speaking in an irate tone.

"Have you thought about the insurance! You know, this could be very expensive. Have you made sure that our insurance policy covers this kind of thing?" He spoke as if I were an irresponsible child. When I did not immediately reply, he continued challengingly. "Well, have you thought about it?"

Stan and I were standing on opposite sides of the living room. As he was speaking, I looked into the large square mirror that hung over our fireplace mantel behind him. I saw a face in agony. Strain had furrowed its forehead; the cheeks were sunken; the eyes were glazed. It had the pallor of the walking dead.

Suddenly I could not endure it anymore. I looked again at the face in the mirror, then I looked at Stan. I became hysterical. I began screaming.

"I have to go to the hospital," I shrieked at him. "I have to leave my babies . . . I may die there . . . and you are talking to me about *insurance*?" I began to cry in great gasping sobs.

My outburst startled Stan. "Okay, okay," he said, trying to calm me down. "I'll take you to the hospital." He reached out to touch my arm, but I recoiled.

Stan and I both lapsed into silence, while we each composed ourselves. Finally, I felt my hysteria pass.

"What about the children?" I asked.

"I'll take care of everything," he replied sincerely. "You just take care of yourself."

Then he told me that he wanted to speak to Dr. Lustig. He walked into the study to place the call. I remained seated where I was, letting my mind go blank. I didn't even remember Dr. Lustig's instruction to have Stan call him.

About half an hour later we were ready to leave. Stan picked up my suitcase and led me out the front door. By 6 P.M., we were driving through the darkness to the sanitarium. Neither of us spoke on the way.

CHAPTER FOUR

JANUARY 20, 1976

Entering the lobby of the sanitarium was like stepping back a half century in time. Ornate chandeliers hung from the high ceiling; a grand curving staircase swept upward to the left. Finely crafted period furniture was placed elegantly and comfortably in discrete conversation areas throughout the large room. Potted plants brought a touch of green and life to the softly modulated color scheme, while elaborately carved moldings graced the walls and ceilings. All together, the impression was one of a grand hotel rather than a mental hospital.

Stan and I approached the receptionist. We were told to take a seat nearby, and wait for someone to come and receive us.

I looked around dazedly. The room was reassuring. No barred windows or other signs of imprisonment marred its beauty.

"You'll take care of the children?" I again asked Stan searchingly.

"Of course."

"Will you bring them to visit me?"

"Certainly. You're their mother."

We sat in silence until a brisk-looking young man, dressed in a business suit, approached us.

"Allen?" he asked.

"Yes," Stan and I both said at once.

"I'm Dr. Phillips," he said, shaking our hands. "Follow me, please."

He led us across the large lobby and down a corridor to the left. Soon we were seated in an office, he behind a desk, and we on a sofa to the side. Several comfortable chairs remained empty in front of his desk.

He shuffled through some papers and then addressed me. "Let's see," he said. "You are Dr. Otto's patient?"

"Yes," I mumbled.

"All right," he continued. "Now, can you tell me why you're here?"

I found it difficult to frame the words. Words had become slippery and would not stay still. A thought would flicker across my mind, but before my tongue could form its sound, the word's meaning would melt into another meaning, and from there to yet another thought. I tried to speak, but I knew I was rambling.

"I can't go on. . . ." I said in the barest whisper. "The children . . ." Guilt swept over me, and I began to cry. "I had to come to the hospital. . . ." I said pleadingly through my tears, trying to justify my action in leaving Elizabeth and Daniel. "I'm so tired and afraid. I had no choice." I fell silent. I could hear the doctor's pen scratching on his pad.

"Do you know where you are?" Dr. Phillips asked me, when I did not continue.

"Of course," I replied, affronted. "I'm at the sanitarium."

"Do you know what day it is?" he continued.

"Yes, it's Tuesday, January twentieth," I replied, collecting my thoughts.

"Then could you explain to me again the events that led up to your hospitalization?" the young doctor asked.

I remembered the eyes of the sunglasses people and how they stared. I remembered how I had run through three red lights, to tell myself that this madness must stop. There was so much to explain. "My mind is betraying me," I finally answered. "I can no longer trust it, and I am afraid I will die."

"Are you afraid you're going to kill yourself?" Dr. Phillips spoke impassively, as if bored with yet another admission.

"Of course not." I answered stiffly, wondering why this fact was not readily apparent to him.

After a few moments, a few more scratches on his note pad, Dr. Phillips shifted his line of inquiry.

"I'm going to tell you several sayings," he explained. "There isn't any one right meaning for them. Just tell me what they mean to you."

I nodded.

"Ready?" he asked. I nodded again.

"A rolling stone gathers no moss."

I tried to think. "I guess it means that everything changes," I said.

He nodded approvingly. "Okay, what about this one: People in glass houses shouldn't throw stones."

I looked at him intently. That one seemed so obvious. "Everything is so fragile," I said softly. "Everything is so likely to be broken."

"Fine," Dr. Phillips said, busily recording what I had said. "Now," he continued after a pause, "do you ever see things that you aren't sure are there, or perhaps hear voices near you, but when you look around nobody is there?"

"Yes," I confessed. "About seeing things, that is." I felt I had to clarify. "I never heard voices or anything like that."

"What did you see?" he continued matter-of-factly.

I froze. I couldn't tell him about the sunglasses people. My mind went blank. When I didn't reply, he didn't insist. He jotted down some more notes, and then, sifting through some papers, took one out and handed it to Stan.

"Will you sign her in?" he asked, addressing Stan.

"No!" I said emphatically. "I'll sign myself in." It was a matter of principle and pride. If I have to go to a hospital, I thought, then at least I'll do so voluntarily. I will have final control over what happens to me.

"I'll sign the papers," I repeated more calmly.

"All right," the young doctor said, and he handed me a form. "This will be for thirty days," he explained and pointed to the line where I was to sign my name.

The formalities completed, he called in an aide who took my suitcase.

"Why are you taking my suitcase?" I anxiously asked him.

"It's just part of our admission procedure," he answered imperturbably. "They'll check its contents and label your clothing, so that it doesn't get mixed up with anybody else's while you're here."

"But the swan," I said, "I must have my swan."

Over the Christmas holidays, I had found a glass swan, larger and less delicate than the crystal swan that I had given Dr. Lustig. It had cost three dollars. The swan had brought me comfort during these last weeks. I had carefully packed it in my suitcase, along with a picture of my children, when I readied myself for the hospital. These symbols were my only links to Dr. Lustig, my children, and the outside world.

"Please," I said to the young doctor, "I know it's glass, but please can I keep my swan?"

"All of your things that aren't dangerous to you will be brought to your room," he answered noncommittally.

I nodded and didn't say anything more.

Dr. Phillips rose from his chair. "You'll be staying on

the third floor," he said. "Follow me and I'll take you there."

Stan and I followed him down the corridor to an elevator at the end of the hall. We entered and he pushed the button for the third floor. The elevator hummed as it rose.

We stepped off the elevator into a small lobby. Directly in front of us, protruding into the lobby area, was a small sitting room with glass panels on the two adjacent sides facing us. "That's what we call the Fishbowl," the young doctor explained. "It's where we have group therapy sessions."

I nodded, wondering why group sessions should be held in glass rooms. To the right of the Fishbowl was a closed door with a glass peephole at eye level. Dr. Phillips pressed the buzzer to the left of the door, and an attendant unlocked it from the inside.

We walked through, into a large common room. Aside from the one locked door, there were no signs of security. Comfortable couches and chairs were placed in the sitting area. A few patients, of all ages and both sexes, were sitting and talking or walking around, mostly in groups of three or four. The room had bright modern furniture and a cheerful look, with light yellow walls and a number of windows looking out onto the night.

A pleasant-looking black woman, dressed in street clothing, approached us smiling.

"I'm Mrs. Jones," she said. "I'm the administrator for this floor." She smiled at me reassuringly, and then, putting her arm loosely around my shoulders, she added, "but you can call me Edith. Everyone does."

"I'll see to Carol now," she said turning to Stan. Stan looked like he didn't know quite what to do or say.

"I hope you feel better," he said hesitantly, as if he recognized the inadequacy of his words. Then, he leaned over and gave me a kiss on the cheek. He followed the young doctor out.

Mrs. Jones, Edith, led me across the large communal

room and down a hall. I looked into the rooms on each side of the corridor as we passed them. They looked pretty much like sparsely furnished hospital rooms, although ordinary beds took the place of high-railed hospital ones.

We came to a room near the end of the hallway, and Edith told me it was my room. It had a single bed, and a dresser with a mirror above it, although I had noticed that in some rooms we had passed, the mirrors had been removed. On the far side of my room, a door stood open leading to a small bathroom.

Edith sat down on the chair in front of the dresser and motioned me to sit on the bed.

"Now," she said brightly, "I have just a few questions to ask you. It's just part of our procedure," she explained somewhat apologetically. "It won't take long, and then you can get to sleep."

It was clear to me from the first question that she was administering some kind of psychological test.

"Which do you like best, cats or dogs?" she asked.

That's a question about male and female, I thought. "I like them both a lot," I answered carefully.

"What do you do when you're happy?" she asked.

"I laugh," I answered.

"What do you do when you're sad?" she continued.

"I cry."

Although the questions struck me as very transparent, I continued answering them patiently until she was through.

"I guess some of these questions are kind of silly," she said, as she finished the last question. I smiled reassuringly at her. I liked her.

"Your clothes probably won't be up until sometime to-morrow," she explained. "I'll get you a gown to wear for to-night."

"Thanks," I said. "I *am* very tired."

Just then, there was a commotion in the hall outside my

door. I glanced toward the door to see what was happening, but Edith took my arm and pulled me back gently.

"That's just Debbie," she said. "She has to be restrained sometimes. Unfortunately," she continued, "the seclusion room is the next one over. Ordinarily we don't put anyone back here in this room, but we're full. We'll move you to a room up front as soon as we can. For now," she said, "if you hear anything, just ignore it. Nobody will harm Debbie, but she may scream a bit. I hope it doesn't disturb your sleep."

I nodded dumbly, trying to ignore the muffled shrieks from the adjoining room. Through the uproar, I heard several voices talking patiently. Surprisingly, the ruckus did not particularly alarm me. Terror lay in the world outside; pain within, I could comprehend.

A few minutes after Edith left, another young doctor came by. He introduced himself as Dr. Sutton, the resident on the floor, and seated himself on the lone chair. He had a very friendly, open face, and seemed to take his job of reassuring me very seriously. We chatted pleasantly for quite a while, he asking me questions about how I felt, and nodding sympathetically to all that I said. Some of the sadness that I was feeling must have come through my somewhat rambling conversation, because he said at one point, "You're very sad, aren't you? I can really *feel* your sadness."

"Yes," I replied, warming to the calm concern and understanding in his voice.

After about half an hour, Edith reappeared with a hospital gown for me to wear, and Dr. Sutton said goodbye and left. Somewhere in my mind, I again registered the sounds of distress coming from the seclusion room. I hadn't heard them while I was talking with Dr. Sutton.

I put on the hospital gown and got into bed. I lay quietly, all feeling spent. I knew that I was finally alone. Alone and locked inside my mind. No place for people here.

No place for fears or human tears. Locked away. Locked away, alone.

"Sleep, my child, and peace attend thee, all through the night." The melody of the lullaby ran through my mind.

My neighbor was still screaming as I fell into an exhausted sleep.

CHAPTER FIVE

JANUARY 21, 1976

I woke early the next day. I lay still with my eyes closed for a few minutes, letting the memory of where I was seep slowly into my consciousness. The sanitarium. The place where I would go and die. I had always thought of it as the end of a story, the place where one went after final defeat. But, I reflected after my night's sleep, perhaps, after all, it's a place of rest and not death, a place of order and not defeat.

I opened my eyes and looked around the sparsely furnished room. No sounds were coming from the hall or the seclusion room next door. Either the woman there last night had been removed or she was asleep, I concluded. Either way, she was safe.

I rose slowly, feeling the familiar dull ache in my limbs. With careful attention, I got dressed in the same clothes I had worn the night before. I wondered when breakfast would be served, and whether the patients ate alone in their rooms as in a regular hospital, or whether there were communal meals.

I wandered out of my room in search of information.

As I passed the adjoining room, I glanced through the glass peephole of the closed door. I saw a girl of about fifteen wrapped up tightly and bound to the bed. Her face was turned toward me, so I could see that she slept. I remembered the screams of the night before, but I still felt no particular alarm.

I continued past the room into the long corridor. Nobody was about and the hallway was darkened, so I guessed that it was still very early. As I approached the large common room, a male attendant whom I had not seen before approached me. I asked him about breakfast and he pointed to the adjoining dining room, where, he said, all meals were served. Breakfast was at seven o'clock, he explained. By his watch it was now a quarter to six.

I sat down on one of the couches to wait. He sat down comfortably near me and started chatting with me about the weather and himself. He was on the night staff, he explained, and was due to be relieved soon. Then he planned to go home and get some sleep, and do a little shopping later in the day. His ordinary prattle put me quite at ease, although I said little, still feeling too dazed to talk.

Soon, other patients drifted out of their rooms, many shuffling sleepily, and assembled in the common room to await breakfast. Then a bell sounded and everyone went into the dining room to be served.

The dining room was filled with small square tables, each seating four people. I was placed at one of the tables near the door, with two other women. My first cursory glance at the woman on my right startled me somewhat, so I turned my full attention to the woman seated on my left. She seemed to be about my age and was casually dressed. She smiled pleasantly at me, and I returned her smile, wondering, as I looked at her perfectly ordinary demeanor, why she was here.

Then I glanced again at the woman on my right. She was disheveled in her loose-fitting white hospital gown, which barely concealed her sagging shape. Her hair was a tangled mass of gray. She had a look of total confusion and alarm, like that of some wild animal cornered in an unexpected trap, uncomprehending of the nature of its constraint.

From my glimpse, it was clear to me that she had lost the world—her tongue flickered in and out of her mouth; saliva dribbled down her chin; the power of ordinary speech escaped her. From time to time throughout the meal, she would ramble in her own invented language—punctuated with words like "doggy" and "wolf." She wore long, baggy, red wool socks that she would continuously roll down, take off, and then put on again, as if she was performing some ancient and private ceremony.

Oddly enough, I was little disturbed by this sight of madness *in extremis*. The sober reality of life here, with even such as this, was altogether less terrible than my own self-imposed tyranny. I had lived with invented, staring, black-eyed strangers. I had been governed by the magic of numbers and occult noncausal laws. This disheveled woman's countenance had no power to alarm me. January in this modern, humane mental hospital was benign compared to most of my December days.

In fact, it was a relief to see insanity surface so openly. When madness intrudes into a normal setting, it has the power to provoke panic in all but the stoutest heart. In the broad daylight of a well-governed midtown street, one instinctively recoils at raving street people, as if turning away from some minor, if private, embarrassment. But within the world of the asylum, where it was legitimate to be insane, I found it somehow also fitting that madness be displayed. Here its public appearance resembled a mirror held up to the darkness, bridging the division between what was outside myself and what was within. At last, madness, that most private of all experiences, had a public and easily discernible face.

Slowly, I turned my attention back to the ordinary-appearing woman on my left, who introduced herself as Ellen. Martha, she explained, indicating our dining companion, had been in the sanitarium for the last twenty years. Ellen spoke about Martha as if Martha weren't there, a custom that, I discovered, was commonplace at the sanitarium, where ordinary rules of politeness gave way to more direct statements of fact.

Just then Martha howled angrily, and in a single forceful gesture swept her cereal bowl off the table onto the floor. An attendant hurried over and cleared away the mess, all the while speaking calmingly to Martha. Then Martha was led away.

I watched and listened as these events took place, and found that my assessment of my own mental condition was rapidly gaining some perspective. I could see myself as located somewhere in the center of a continuum—as far away from Martha as I was from normal. I found that meeting Martha made me feel less mad.

Ellen and I chatted about hospital procedures as we continued to eat our meal. The patients, she told me, filled out menus for each day on the evening of the preceding day. There was a daily morning meeting after breakfast for all the patients and staff, at which attendance was required.

As we talked, I noticed the medications nurse making her rounds of all the dining room tables, stopping to chat with each person as she administered the medicine. Although her manner was casual, I noticed that she watched carefully to see that each patient swallowed the pills.

She approached our table and handed me three tablets, one of which I did not recognize. Stories of hospital patients being drugged or overmedicated flooded through my mind. I looked again at the three pills lying in her outstretched hand.

"I'm sorry," I told her, politely but firmly, "but I won't take any medicine that I don't recognize." She explained in a patient voice that the pill I did not recognize was just a side effect medication that my attending physician had ordered for me.

I wasn't convinced, and she did not insist. I obediently took the two recognizable tablets. She said that she would speak to my doctor about it, and suggested that I do the same. Then she moved calmly on to the next table.

After breakfast, I followed the other patients out of the dining room into the common room, where everyone was assembling for the daily meeting that Ellen had told me about. I saw patients and staff members alike pulling sofas and chairs together to form a large circle. Ellen and I sat down on one of the couches. Other people filed in and seated themselves. I recognized Edith, the floor supervisor who had gotten me settled the night before, and also the young resident, Dr. Sutton, who nodded and smiled at me from across the room.

Doctors, nurses, attendants, as well as patients, it appeared, all participated in the daily meeting. Feeling foggy and deadened inside, I simply sat passively and observed what was taking place.

As the meeting progressed, it became clear that various privileges were proffered to the patients within the hospital context—freedom to walk to the snack bar downstairs, freedom to walk outside on the grounds without an attendant. And, it became evident, it was the group as a whole—doctors, nurses, staff, and patients—who granted these privileges.

The first person to speak at the meeting was a youngish man—in his twenties, I guessed.

"I would like to ask for grounds privileges," he said, addressing the group. "I feel that I am now able to be responsible for myself. I've been doing real well all this last week. And Sue," he said, pointing to the woman sitting next to him, "Sue will tell you so too."

Sue spoke. "I have taken Bill around with me for the whole week," she said. "He didn't try to run away or anything. I think he should have grounds privileges." Several doctors, nurses, and patients nodded in affirmation.

"Shall we vote?" Dr. Sutton asked. He appeared to be leading the meeting. "All in favor of granting Bill grounds privileges raise their hands."

Almost all the hands went up, with the exception of several patients who seemed too dazed to comprehend.

"Bill is granted grounds privileges," Dr. Sutton said, smiling his approval. "Congratulations, Bill."

Several people shook Bill's hand. He beamed proudly.

The meeting progressed. There was some dispute among the patients over the hours for viewing television. Another patient claimed loudly and angrily that one of the nurses had given her the wrong medication.

I could see from their faces that the staff took this particular charge very seriously. An investigation would be conducted, it was agreed. A woman in her mid-thirties, short, dark-haired, and gaminlike in appearance, suddenly stood up on one of the coffee tables and began shouting obscenities. A nurse and a male attendant rose and, taking her by the arms, drew her down from the coffee table and back to her seat, all the while speaking quietly and soothingly to her. But she was not appeased. So the same two attendants led her out of the meeting and back to her room.

Another woman stood up and spent five minutes commending the sanitarium. "I've been to many hospitals," she said, "but this is definitely the best of them all." Everyone nodded and appeared gratified at her endorsement.

The meeting was dismissed shortly thereafter. Edith, the floor administrator, approached me and explained that there were various activities, such as art therapy, crafts, and sports, that I might sign up for. I thanked her and told her that, for the moment, I preferred to rest.

Edith nodded sympathetically. "Some of the staff physicians would like to talk with you for a while in the Fishbowl," she told me. "Let's say at about ten-thirty."

I nodded, wondering somewhat uneasily what they wanted to know.

My eyes were bothering me, and I found that I could not read the hands on my watch. I asked Edith to tell me when it was time for the interview. She cheerfully agreed, and then left.

I spent the remaining time in the common room, seated on the L-shaped couch, a spot that seemed to be a popular sitting place for many of the patients. On the coffee table placed at the center of the L was a radio tuned to station WMGK, popularly known as "Magic."

How appropriate, I thought to myself as I listened to the broadcast. A radio station called Magic at the center of a madhouse.

The couches were the focal points of much of the social activity in the large common room. People came and sat for a while and then wandered off, often within the course of several hours making a journey from one seating area to the next, until the entire room had been traversed. The L-shaped couch, however, was the hub of the room. A steady procession of patients vied for the seats there and, if successful, sat for a time, so that it was almost never empty.

As I sat at my station, I appraised my fellow patients. I noticed that there were both men and women on the floor, of all ages and degrees of distress. There was even a young boy, I noted, who appeared to be about nine or ten. The patients leafed through magazines, watched television, or talked quietly for the most part. Many of the women were crocheting, under the supervision of Edith.

I noticed that the patients' conversations were often punctuated by giggles or outright laughter. What can be so funny here? I wondered to myself, feeling too tired for any sort of humor.

At 10:30 Edith came over to me and led me through the locked ward door into the adjoining room called the Fishbowl, and departed with a brief goodbye. Somewhat apprehensively, I sat down. Five or six staff physicians, who appeared to be older and part of the establishment, were assembled to interview me. I looked for a familiar face among them, but found none.

After I had seated myself, one of the gentlemen, as distinguished looking as the others, spoke.

"Carol, we're here to find out some information about you, so that this hospital will be able to help you better."

He waited, and I nodded.

"What events led up to your being here in the hospital, Carol?" he continued in an evenly modulated voice.

I tried to think and be very honest, but somehow the question did not make much sense to me.

"I don't quite understand," I said earnestly. Another doctor to his left tried to explain.

"Why are you here, Carol?"

I thought again for a moment. "Because it is so terrible and I have been so afraid."

A psychiatrist on the opposite side of the room spoke up eagerly. "What was so terrible—why were you afraid?"

"I think I'm losing my mind," I answered, bowing my head.

"What makes you think so?" somebody else asked.

"My mind plays tricks on me," I responded.

"When did you notice that your mind was playing tricks on you?" came from somewhere.

"I'm not really sure. Around Christmastime, I guess."

"What sort of tricks were they?" Again I heard the slight edge of eagerness in the voice across the room.

"Hallucinations," I said.

"What kind of hallucinations and what were they like?" I heard from the right.

I felt panicked. Although they were speaking calmly, I felt that I was surrounded by questions being fired at me from all sides. I couldn't tell these strangers about the sunglasses people, either. What to do?

"I can't tell that to anyone but my own doctor," I said anxiously. "Please," I added, meaning, "Please understand." They immediately dropped that line of questioning and shifted to questions about my history.

"We'd like to find out something about your background," the most senior-looking doctor said. "Where did you grow up, Carol?"

"Idaho. In a small town," I answered.

"What was your father like?" another doctor inquired.

"He's a good man," I replied. "A rational man, who's very kindly, although somewhat authoritarian. He's somebody who I always felt safe with," I continued musingly.

"What about your mother?"

"She's a dietician who gave up her career to raise her children," I answered. "She's very intelligent, like my dad, and they both encouraged all the children to further their educations and learn all they could about the world."

"What about your brothers or sisters, then?" the doctor on the left asked. "Can you tell us about them?"

I was slowly growing more and more upset. What's wrong with my family and my past? I wondered. I had always thought that they were decent enough, before. Perhaps these doctors can look into my past and know something that I don't know about myself. My answers will only confirm my insanity to them, I thought, feeling even more panicked. If it's all a matter of the past, then there's no hope for me in the future.

"What about your brothers or sisters?" the doctor repeated. I could not speak. Slowly, tears rolled down my face.

"Why are you asking me all these questions?" I implored, crying fully now.

"We're just interested in finding out more about you, Carol," one of the more distinguished-looking doctors said. "Thank you for telling us. Perhaps you'd like to go and rest now?"

I nodded and slowly rose to go. I left, feeling assaulted

and stripped of any protecton. My foundation, which I had always taken for granted, had been impugned. If I could not count on the beneficence of the past, what was there left to trust? The doctors' questions only raised more questions in my mind. Perhaps, I thought, as I walked toward my room, perhaps I've always been crazy. And all these years I've only thought that I was sane. Am I doomed by my past to remain forever mad?

The perspective about myself that I had gained earlier that morning, by seeing the spectrum of madness around me, was quickly evaporating. I could no longer locate myself and my madness on a continuum in the present. The staff physicians had introduced a backward-looking measuring tape, and all its numbers pointed to the past. The immediate, the now, was eclipsed by their careful backward scrutiny. But like Lot's wife, when I looked back, I turned to stone. I was nothing now, because there was nothing *now* that I could do.

I arrived at my room and my mind went blank.

CHAPTER SIX

JANUARY 21, 1976

I didn't remember anything else until Edith, the floor supervisor, arrived at my room to announce lunch. My psychiatrist, Dr. William Otto, whom I had not yet seen, would visit me shortly after the meal, Edith informed me.

I ate my meal in a daze, feeling myself suspended on a wind current somewhere outside my body. I was not connected to anything, neither the activities nor the physical objects in my surroundings. I stared at my knife and fork. They seemed to be alien objects belonging to someone else. I noted absently that Ellen was again seated on my right, but it was as if a glass panel now separated her from me. Martha, the madwoman, was nowhere to be seen. I felt completely alone, having no sense that my isolation was self-imposed.

Following a silent lunch, I quietly seated myself on the central couch, from whose vantage I caught my first glimpse of Dr. Otto about a half hour later. I watched as a tall, attractive-looking man stopped at the front desk and then made his way toward me. He looked as though he was in his mid-forties and was casually dressed in slacks and a bulky turtleneck sweater. He had sharp, pointed features that gave him a slightly raffish look. He wore his hair long and swept to the right, covering his bald spot. However, what most caught my attention was his voice—deep, rich, and resonant. It was like a reverberant call back to the present. His was a voice that I instinctively trusted, although I was prepared to trust him anyway, because Dr. Lustig had told me that I could.

I looked around, wondering where we could hold my therapy session with any privacy. But Dr. Otto answered my question before it had been articulated. "We'll meet in your room," he informed me, motioning me to follow him. I walked a step or two behind him down the corridor, but halfway down he paused so that I could catch up. We walked in step the rest of the way.

Arriving at my room, Dr. Otto closed the door and seated himself on the lone chair, while I sat down yoga fashion on the bed. I looked at him again, and saw that he returned my direct gaze. Scattered thoughts raced through my mind until they coalesced around the Fishbowl interview. I began telling Dr. Otto about my experience with the staff physicians. My alarm poured out of me in a staccato of speech, punctuated by rapid breaths.

Dr. Otto listened attentively and shook his head several times during my narrative. "We'll have no more doctors interviewing you," he said emphatically in his deep bass voice. "I'll see to it. If anyone here starts probing and asking too many questions," he continued, "don't talk to them. Just tell me about it at once."

I took heart from his determination, feeling the strength of the protection he was offering me. I sat still for several minutes after that, just letting the newfound feeling of safety wash over me. Dr. Otto was silent himself, as if he was waiting for me to compose myself. Then, in a rush of words, I began to tell him what was happening to me. I just started in the middle, where I had left off with Dr. Lustig.

As I talked, I was vaguely aware that I wasn't making much sense, because my speech was disjointed and I was talking in symbols. I stopped talking abruptly.

"Well, I see that you're eager to do therapy," he said with a slightly raised eyebrow, registering just a hint of irony. Then he told me the first of many stories I was to hear from him during my stay at the sanitarium. That day his story was about a Sufi leader, a wise man, who suddenly one day left his followers without explanation. The Sufi master walked to the top of a mountain and entered a cave, where he stayed for some days. His followers, puzzled by this behavior, and taking it to be an omen, finally approached him and asked, "Master, what does it mean that you have come to this cave?"

The wise man regarded them in silence for some minutes. Then he spoke. "A Sufi must know when it is time to rest," he said.

I nodded and smiled to myself, glad that Dr. Otto understood so well my need for rest and my right to it. "Yes, I need to rest," I affirmed.

"We'll have plenty of time to do therapy," Dr. Otto continued. "But for now, there are a few practical matters we need to discuss. I understand that you have two children. Who's taking care of them?"

I explained that Stan had taken them.

"What about your job?" Dr. Otto continued. "What have you told them?"

"Nothing," I whispered, shrinking inside, feeling the burden of the outside world pressing in on me again. "I don't know what to do or say about being here."

"Well, you'll have to let them know you're in a hospital, so that they can get a substitute to teach your classes," he said matter-of-factly.

"What if I call and the head of my department wants to visit me?" I said panicking. "I can't let him see me here."

"Just call him and tell him you're in the hospital, and

that you can't have visitors right now," Dr. Otto advised. "You needn't mention which hospital it is. Tell him you'll let him know as soon as possible when you'll be returning to work. You can estimate that it will be probably from two to four weeks. If he wants further information, tell him he can call me."

So Dr. Otto thinks I'll be all right in that amount of time, I thought. He's talking as if this stay is only temporary, not permanent. It was a new thought and the beginning of a different perspective on my hospital experience: a rest within a defined time frame. Suddenly, it did not seem so bad.

Dr. Otto and I talked some more about being in the hospital, and how to use the experience in order to get well. He talked to me as if signing myself in was a very sensible and appropriate thing for me to have done, and that my being here, and working hard with him, would lead me out of the morass and back to even better functioning in the world. He also told me that Dr. Lustig would be visiting me at least once a week. I remembered Dr. Lustig's promise to visit me, and the gladness I felt made me realize the importance of this essential connection with sanity in the outside world.

Before leaving that day, Dr. Otto told me that he would see me as often as possible, and that he thought I could profit from daily therapy sessions.

"This is your chance to get yourself together, without having to cope with all your other responsibilities as well. We'll work together to get you back in shape."

I thanked him, feeling profoundly grateful. His visit left me feeling tired but relieved, reinforcing as it had the fragment of sanity that I possessed.

After Dr. Otto left, I went in search of a telephone to call my department chairman, as Dr. Otto had instructed. One of the male aides agreed to accompany me downstairs, since I was not yet allowed to go alone. As I dialed the number of my department chairman, I was filled with dread. I struggled to compose myself as I heard Father Michaels answer the phone. I told him I was ill and in a hospital, without mentioning which one. He was concerned and eager to help.

"I'll take your classes for you," he offered. "So don't worry about that. And, of course, I'll come and visit you."

"No!" I almost shouted, and then somewhat more calmly repeated. "It's very nice of you, but I'm not allowed any visitors."

"But I'm a priest," he persisted. "They always allow a doctor or priest to visit a hospital patient."

I panicked, wondering what to say. "I really think it would be best if I didn't have any visitors right now," I said. "But thanks anyway. It's very kind of you."

"Well, okay," he said as if he was puzzled and just beginning to feel alarmed.

"Which hospital did you say it was?" he asked.

I took a deep breath, deciding I could not lie to him, hoping he wouldn't have heard of it as I spoke its name.

"Okay," he said noncommittally, and I could not be sure whether he knew now or not. Suddenly, I didn't care.

"You can contact my doctor, if you have any further questions," I said dully. Then I assured him that I expected to be back to work in two to four weeks.

He asked me to call again when I knew more definitely when I would be back.

I hung up relieved. It had been one of the most difficult telephone calls I ever made.

I returned to the ward, accompanied by the aide, went directly to my room, and fell asleep. I must have slept for several hours, because when I woke the winter sky was darkening. I got up, washed my face in the small bathroom, and walked back to the lounge area to inquire about dinner. I was told it would be served at 5:30. I took my watch out, but my eyes were still too foggy to read the time. I asked a nearby patient what time it was. He looked at me blankly. Then I found an aide who told me that it was five to five. Just a half hour till dinner, I thought. I seated myself, once again, on the central couch near the radio. A man and two women were already seated there. I found myself listening to their conversation.

"There's a dance tonight on the second floor," the young man said. "Are you guys going?" As he spoke, he clutched his hands nervously together until his knuckles were white. Then he began wringing them.

"I don't know," said the small middle-aged woman seated to his right. Then she giggled like a schoolgirl.

"Stop doing that with your hands!" the second woman said, addressing the man who had spoken. "You're driving me crazy."

"Sorry," the young man replied sheepishly. He sat on his hands to prevent them from wringing.

Just then, a hulking teenaged boy walked by. He was dressed in shabby jeans and his eyes were opaque, as if he had been heavily medicated. "That's Don," the outspoken woman next to me said loudly, as if she were speaking about someone who wasn't there. "He has no family. His parents deserted him when he was a child. He's been in and out of mental hospitals ever since. Or correctional institutes," she added ominously.

Don started moaning like a dumb, hurting animal. He began flailing his arms around, as if fending off an attack.

"Settle down, Don," the outspoken woman said. "Or you know what will happen."

"What will happen?" I asked her softly.

"They'll give him more medicine," she replied matter-of-factly. "Or if that doesn't work, they'll put him in restraints."

I remembered the crying woman in the room next to

mine the night before. I'd better be careful, I admonished myself, without articulating exactly what I had to be careful about.

The dinner bell sounded. We all got up and took our places in the dining room. I sat down at the table that I had been assigned to earlier. Ellen was there. Martha, the woman who spoke her own private language, was still absent.

Ellen and I chatted quietly throughout dinner. After we had established some rapport, I asked her directly why she was there. She smiled somewhat enigmatically. "I tried to kill myself," she said. "They have to send you here if you do that. But I expect to be out in a week or so."

I wanted to ask her why she wanted to kill herself, but I was reluctant to broach what might be a sensitive subject. She continued, however, without further prompting.

"You know that man that visited me today," she said. I nodded. "Well, he's married. I've been seeing him for seven years. He kept promising me that he'd leave his wife and we'd get married. But something always came up to prevent it. I just couldn't stand it anymore. What are you to do?" she concluded philosophically.

"I'm sorry," I said.

"What about you?" she asked me.

"Oh, I was seeing things," I said somewhat vaguely, wondering how much to say. "I'm so tired," I added.

She nodded sympathetically. We didn't talk much for the remainder of the meal, but the silence between us was not unpleasant.

The evening passed much like the rest of the day. My head was foggy, so I didn't do much. I just sat on the couch and let the waves of conversation and interaction sweep over me.

I noticed the nice resident, Dr. Sutton, standing in one corner of the common room talking to several patients. I decided to go over to say hello.

"Hi," I said approaching him, suddenly feeling like an embarrassed schoolgirl.

He looked around nervously, and then spoke to me quickly. "I can't talk to you," he said in a lowered voice. "All the staff physicians have been given strict orders to leave you alone. I'm sorry," he continued, looking genuinely regretful, "but I'm not supposed to speak to you, at least not about anything of substance."

"That's okay," I said reassuringly, glad that Dr. Otto had kept his word so promptly about forbidding any hospital physicians from probing my psyche.

"I just wanted to say hello," I continued. "Maybe we can talk about the weather." It was a feeble sort of joke, but we both laughed anyway. So we stood there and chatted in a friendly manner, for five minutes or so, until Dr. Sutton was called away. Then I returned to the couch.

At around eight o'clock, trays of sandwiches, fruit, cakes, and buttered toast were brought out of the kitchen and placed on one of the dining room tables. "Our nightly snack," one of the patients explained.

I was too tired to eat anything more. I approached one of the staff members, a six-foot-tall black woman named Sally. "Is it all right if I go to bed now?" I asked her.

"Sure, honey," she said. "I'll get somebody to give you your nightly medication early. You go and get changed into your pajamas."

I did as she suggested and then returned to the common room. The medication nurse came over to me and handed me my pills. "I spoke to your doctor," she said. "He agreed to give you just what you're used to."

I looked at the pills in her hand, and sure enough, they were all the familiar ones. "Thanks," I said.

Then I retired to my room, where, curiously enough, I sat down at the dressing table and meticulously set my hair in curlers. I saw nothing absurd about this simple social act, even though I was in an environment that was totally estranged from society at large. It was part of my nightly routine and, without a thought, I continued it throughout my stay at the sanitarium.

In its own way, maintaining my appearance proved to be a means of asserting self-respect. Whereas before, in the outside world, maintaining the appearance of normalcy had been an enormous burden, a mask covering over a darker reality, here it was simply one option among many. Deviations in appearance and behavior were accepted, so that finally I could choose how to look and what to show.

That fact did not change what I did, for I continued to dress and behave within the norm. But it considerably changed how I felt about it. I could choose to present a normal countenance, but I was not *required* to do so. The choice made all the difference.

That night I slept soundly, lulled to sleep by the realization that, at last, I was free to rest.

CHAPTER SEVEN

JANUARY 23, 1976

The morning of the third day dawned cold and clear. As I opened my eyes, I could see a sunny blur of whiteness through the screened grating of my bedroom window. I sat up in bed, stretched, and looked intently through the window, trying to detect the almost invisible line where the opaque white of the snow-covered ground merged with the slightly more translucent white of the sky. I swung my legs off the bed and felt my stomach rumbling. It was a simple, pleasant feeling of bodily attachment. Once again, my stomach belonged to me.

I carefully got out some jeans and a blouse to put on. My clothes had arrived the day before, in the late afternoon. I had returned to my room to find them all there, neatly labeled with tags bearing my last name. The glass swan was missing, I noted, as I sorted through the clothing, but the glass in the framed picture of my children had been left in its place. Delighted with the picture, but puzzled by the seeming irrationality of the acceptability of one form of glass over another, I had set the photograph up on my dressing table. Now, the smiling faces of my children greeted me.

The children's picture reminded me that today would be an eventful day. Stan was bringing the children to see me shortly after lunch. Later in the afternoon, I was to have a therapy session with Dr. Otto. In addition, Edith had told me that the night before, Dr. Lustig had phoned and said that he would visit me at 6 P.M.

The thought of seeing Elizabeth and Daniel produced mixed feelings in me. Excitement at the prospect of seeing them and holding them near competed with twinges of failure and guilt at having left them behind. My feelings about Dr. Otto were simpler. I looked forward to talking with him. As for Dr. Lustig, he still represented my strongest tie with reality and the hope of health outside these hospital walls. I felt unqualified delight at the thought of seeing him.

At breakfast, I found out that another activity also awaited me that day. Edith told me that Dr. Otto had arranged for me to visit the art room following the morning meeting. I explained to her that I still felt too tired to do much of anything, but she assured me that I could just sit there if I liked, that it would be good for me to get off the ward.

At the appointed time, an accompanying staff member unlocked the front door to our ward and escorted me and several others to the building's first floor. We walked through several passages to the room at the end of the corridor.

Entering the art room was like entering a cathedral of light. One entire wall was composed of windows that were two stories high. Sunlight flooded the room. Workbenches were scattered about and the wall was lined with cubbyholes, where bits of handiwork peeked out. There were looms for weaving and, from behind a tall partition, the sound of hammers pounding could be heard. All together, the room was immense, cheerful, and reassuring.

We crossed the room and approached a young, pleasant-looking woman, who was introduced to me as Suzanne, the art therapist. She smiled at me, and suggested that I get a cup of coffee at the table to my left, and then come and sit by her and relax. I did as I was instructed, and found that just being in the room lifted my spirits. I seated myself on a tall stool next to Suzanne. She chatted with me quietly, asking me about my children and interests. I wondered if I was supposed to be doing something, but I didn't raise the subject, being so content just sitting there sipping coffee. We were interrupted from time to time by patients asking for Suzanne's assistance. But it was all very low key and calming.

After about a half hour, when I was feeling very relaxed and a bit better oriented, Suzanne asked me if I wanted to do something that would not be too straining. She suggested making moccasins. I had noticed other patients wearing them, and it seemed like a nice idea to me. Better than basket weaving, I thought with pleasurable irony. She handed me the precut leather pieces, a top and a bottom for each foot. The holes had already been punched out. All I had to do, it appeared, was to lace them up, joining the bottom leather to the top.

I began working intently. At first, I laced slowly, then faster and faster, as if some accelerating inner tempo was driving me onward. I pulled the leather laces tighter and tighter, intent on doing a perfect job.

"Stop being so compulsive—they're all right just as you have them," Suzanne's voice intruded. I looked up astonished, and then I blushed. Ashamed, I abruptly stopped tugging at the strings.

"They're all right as they are," Suzanne repeated in a softer voice. "You're doing just fine." She patted my arm reassuringly. "Don't try so hard," she added. I nodded and went back to work on the remaining moccasin, more slowly and surely, but still feeling embarrassed.

Presently, one of the aides from my floor appeared at the door to take us back. Our time in the art room was over for the day. I had not yet finished my second moccasin, but Suzanne said I could complete it the next time I visited her. Our group returned with the aide to our ward. Back in my room, I flopped down on the bed and rested until lunchtime.

At 1 P.M., just after lunch, another aide came to fetch me. She led me downstairs once again, but in a different direction—to the coffee shop. There I met Stan, Elizabeth, and Daniel. I greeted Stan with a nod and embraced the children excitedly. I took in their appearance at one glance. They looked fit and healthy, if a bit subdued. Elizabeth, particularly, showed uncertainty on her face. Guilt swept over me when I saw that look, but I quickly pushed the feeling aside.

Stan, the children, and I sat down at the Formica-topped table in the snack bar and ordered liquid refreshments for ourselves. I concentrated on talking normally, for I wanted the children to feel that I was all right. I frequently reached out to touch them during the conversation, to reassure myself that they were really there.

As we sat and made small talk, I wondered what Stan had told them about my hospitalization. I wondered if I should say something to them now. But since they asked me no questions and I did not know what to say, I took the easiest course and left the subject alone.

After we had finished our drinks, we got up and walked, hand in hand, toward the central lobby of the building. It appeared that as long as Stan was there with me, I was free to move about the grounds. We walked and chatted idly. As we returned toward the snack bar, I suddenly began to feel overwhelmed. And guilty. I left my babies, I thought. How could I do it? I'm a bad mother. A tear fell onto my cheek. I began to panic. What if I'm still harming them? I looked at them again, trying to compose myself. I stopped walking, and stooping down to their eye level I hugged them to me, as if for the last time.

"I have to go now," I said to Stan without explanation. Kissing the children one last time, I turned and fled back to the ward. The last thing I saw was Stan's startled face watching my retreat.

I went straight to my room and, flopping onto the bed, sobbed and sobbed. I reached out for the children's picture and clutched it to my breast, crying even harder.

The tears had finally dried when Dr. Otto arrived for my therapy session, but my eyes were still swollen and red, and my cheeks sunken. Hollow-eyed, I sat up and regarded him, as he seated himself on the single chair in the room.

"You saw Stan and the kids?" he inquired.

I nodded yes, and began weeping all over again. "My babies . . ." I cried.

"Your children are not being taken from you, nor you from them," Dr. Otto said. "You're just on vacation here for a while. You're here for the rest cure."

I nodded again, and sobbed out my fears. "I'm a bad mother. I'm harming my children."

Dr. Otto did not seem upset by this revelation. "How did they look?" he asked me. "Did they look well and all right?"

I murmured yes and stopped crying.

"Were *they* distressed at seeing you or at leaving you," he continued, "or was it *you* who was distressed?"

"It was me," I acknowledged. "They looked fine."

"Well, they *are* fine," he said firmly.

Suddenly I was very tired and sad.

"I miss them," I said softly, "but I also know that I must be here. I must rest and get myself together so that I can go back home."

"Yes," Dr. Otto confirmed. "That's right." He smiled

at me and I smiled back. "Now rest some more, and take it easy. I'll be back tomorrow," he said.

After Dr. Otto left, I lay down again and slept for the rest of the afternoon. I woke as it was getting dark outside. My eyes were still so blurred that I couldn't read the face of my watch. I felt the urge to record all the day's events and their numbers, in the way that I had throughout the last two months, but almost protectively my eyes prevented me. I went to the dresser drawer anyway and took out a sheet of paper. I picked up the pencil and tried to write, even though I could not read my words. Then, just as abruptly, I stopped. Yes, I thought, I must stop this recording. It really doesn't matter. I pushed the paper and pencil back into the drawer and shut it.

I changed to a nicer pair of slacks and put on new makeup. I was going to see Dr. Lustig soon.

I was still sitting at the dinner table when Dr. Lustig arrived. I saw him enter out of the corner of my eye. Hurriedly pushing my food aside, I got up and went to meet him.

He stood there in his winter coat, all bundled up, looking slightly uncomfortable and unsure of what to do. Then he leaned over and kissed me on the cheek, just as if he were greeting a friend. I was surprised and pleased. Then we went over to the lounge area and sat down on one of the sofas to talk.

He asked me how I was doing. "I feel *so* much better," I said, remembering the chaos that had imprisoned me on the outside. He regarded me carefully.

"Yes," he said, "I can see that this was the right thing for you." There was relief in his voice as he spoke. Hearing that relief, I believed as I never had before that he did care and that he had been worried about me. It was such a simple revelation of his humanity, but it touched me more deeply than any other thing he had done.

Just then, Martha, the crazy woman who spoke the unknown language, approached us. After two or three interactions we had become "friends," in the hospital sense of being
at ease with each other. She didn't alarm me and, with some
animal instinct, she knew it. When she indicated that she
wanted them, I would give her cigarettes. I had even become
familiar enough with her language and gestures to know a
little about what she meant.

She came up to us and stood right in front of me, with
her hand outstretched. I didn't have any cigarettes with me.
"Go over to Ellen," I told her firmly. "She'll give you a cigarette."

Martha nodded and shuffled over to Ellen.

I turned back to Dr. Lustig. "I'm getting along just fine
with the people here," I told him.

"Yes, I can see," he said, and he seemed impressed.

Dr. Lustig stayed and talked with me for about an
hour. Then he said he had to go, but that he would return
next week. I thanked him for his visit. He still stood at the
center of my universe, along with the children. Together,
they represented my most essential connection with the outside world.

After Dr. Lustig left, I seated myself on the central
couch again and visited with the other patients. One of the
aides, Sally, the strapping tall black woman, joined our conversation. Earlier she had told me proudly that she counted
as one of the "men" who had to be on the floor at all times,
due to her physical strength.

I had liked Sally from the beginning. She was direct
and kind and also a believer in astrology. She would guess
the patients' signs, and more often than not, she would be
right. She read a detailed horoscope each day, and when we
confided in her the events or feelings of our day, she would
nod knowingly and tell us, "Yes, it was bound to happen
that way. It's in the stars." There was something vastly

reassuring about Sally and her interpretations. The world, for all its strangeness, she seemed to say, did after all have some rhyme and reason.

That evening, she regarded me with clear observant eyes as she seated herself on the couch.

"Well, Carol," she said, "I've been watching you and I'll bet you're a Pisces."

"Yes," I replied, surprised at the accuracy of her perception.

"Well," Sally continued in a soft southern drawl, "Pisces are very sensitive and intuitive. But occasionally," she added, "occasionally, there's a Pisces that's a strong one too. You're one of those."

I didn't know what to say, but I was very pleased by her remarks.

Shortly after, she invited me to help her make the evening snacks in the kitchen. As a rule, the kitchen was off limits to patients. But I noticed that Sally often enlisted assistants, and that the patients regarded it as an honor to be invited by her to help with the preparations.

"Thanks," I said sincerely, in response to Sally's invitation. So, together, we went into the kitchen, and soon I was making toast and buttering it, and making sandwiches. The routine of this simple domestic duty was very soothing. So was Sally's calm, solid presence.

That evening, I stayed up and had some snacks. When I finally did retire at about ten o'clock, I felt more at peace than I had for a long time. The routine of the hospital—the regularity of the meals, medication, and sleep—had begun to nourish me. The sanitarium had organized my external world for me, so that I could contend better with my internal chaos. Freed from all responsibilities to my children and my job, I could focus all my energies on myself—and have the luxury and time to introduce order there, as well.

I drifted off into a restful sleep.

CHAPTER EIGHT

The next several days passed uneventfully. I continued to observe the ebb and flow of life at the sanitarium, too divorced from myself to be an active participant, but reassured nonetheless by the activity and camaraderie around me. I began to make friends with some of the patients. Like survivors on a lifeboat, we naturally clung to each other for support, finding the bond of our common situation a considerable adhesive. Although the patients were often blunt about deviations in behavior, they were remarkably reserved, respectful, and discrete about the psyches of their companions. I found that they accepted me, as they did most every newcomer, matter-of-factly and without intrusive questioning. Their manner conveyed that I was there and they were there. That was all there was to it.

And in their own way, many of the patients, except those who had totally lost the world, conveyed a certain human dignity, despite their inner turmoil and failures in functioning on the outside. A prime example was Geraldine. She was a tall, regal personage in her late fifties or early sixties. She had white-tinged gray hair, tied back severely in the fashion of an earlier time.

Geraldine was always meticulously and elegantly dressed, usually in tailored clothing, with a cameo brooch at her neck. But her uniqueness lay in her self-appointed task. Each day, for the entire length of the day, she would walk up and down the longest corridor, up and down, up and down. When she reached the end of the passageway, she didn't hesitate for a moment, but pivoted gracefully and began her return journey.

Geraldine walked like a queen surveying her troops, with a regal tilt to her head and direct proud eyes. She would nod and smile at the people whom she passed and, often as not, greet them by name. How she learned our names I never knew, but by the third day of my stay she was calling me Carol. Beyond her initial greeting, she never stopped or paused long enough to converse, and it was only if you joined her in her walk that you could hold a conversation with her.

Geraldine's husband was an elderly, solemn gentleman. On his frequent visits to the sanitarium, he would accompany his wife in her endless walk. They rarely spoke to one another as they traversed the length of the hall, but the very manner in which they fell into step suggested an understanding that had no need for words. They would walk in all solemnity for an hour or so, and then her husband would take his leave. When his visits were over, Geraldine would resume her walk alone.

One day, he came to the sanitarium and took Geraldine away. Probably the insurance money had run out, we speculated, and she had been taken to a state hospital. In any case, I never learned what happened to her after that, nor did I ever learn what inner force guided her steps. All I could see was the seeming endlessness of her journey. Like Sisyphus, the mythical hero whose fate for all eternity was to roll a rock up a mountain only to have it continually fall back down, Geraldine's pointless repetition seemed to speak of the absurdity of life. But how, I later wondered, must she have felt at the corridor's end, just before she began her journey back? Did she, like Sisyphus, scorn her fate, and thereby triumph over it with every smile?

Don, the unruly teenager who wore ragged jeans and the blank overmedicated look, perhaps the most unlikely candidate for dignity that I saw, had, I discovered, his own brand of courage. Wounded and frightened, with little left but animal instinct, he nonetheless illustrated the remnant of humanity hidden inside even the most troubled of us there. Don had received little education from any of the institutions that made up his life, but he would sit for hours over his third-grade text, trying to do his homework, trying to learn.

When he found out that I was a professor, he asked me humbly if I would help him with his schoolwork. His assignment that day was to transpose a simple statement of fact into a question, but in spite of my hour's worth of tutoring and counsel, he could not do it. Although he was often frustrated, I never saw him toss the book away in disdain. "I gotta do my work," he would say, as he continued to stare at the text.

I thought, at first, that Don was retarded and had somehow been misdiagnosed as mentally ill. But I soon discovered that Don was very smart in his own way, especially at poker. Seated at a table with cards before him, his whole being would brighten. "Come on," he would call to whatever group was assembled in the common room. "How about a game?" Usually he beat us all soundly.

But what most remained in my mind was the day that the social worker came to talk to Don. As I walked by, I saw the two of them seated on one of the couches, huddled over some papers.

"The State is your parent," I heard the social worker explaining. She was apparently trying to persuade Don to voluntarily transfer to some other institution.

"I don't have no parents," Don was insisting, as if at least on that one matter, he knew his facts. "My parents are dead."

"Yes, I know, I know," the social worker said. "That's why the State is your legal guardian—like a parent."

"I don't have no parents," Don insisted, again. The social worker was becoming exasperated.

"You just have to sign these papers," she was saying, "and then everything will be taken care of for you."

"I don't want to sign no more papers," Don insisted stubbornly.

"We're just trying to help you, Don," she said cajolingly. "Really, Don, there's nothing to be afraid of."

But Don stuck to his point, and finally she left in obvious chagrin.

"They want to send me back to Bradyville," Don said to me after she left. "The kids have knives there. I got beat up lots of times. Don't want to go back there. This is better," he added.

I wondered what kind of nightmare Don must have lived in for his fifteen years, that this was the best he had ever had. "Wanna play poker?" he asked me then, and no more was said that day about his possible transfer.

Another patient whom I particularly liked was Clara. She was a short, somewhat round woman in her fifties who was diabetic. She had short, unruly blond-gray hair and a cherubic smile and giggle. Her favorite task was crocheting an afghan throughout most of the day. All I discovered about Clara's situation was that her husband and five sons regularly beat her up when she was on the outside. But you would never have known it from her demeanor or constant smiles.

Clara was a devout Catholic, and each day at 6 A.M. she would meet her Catholic doctor. They would spend half of the hour praying together, Clara told me, and the rest talking. Clara derived considerable comfort from both. I respected her doctor for his commitment to her, and for his willingness to utilize their common set of beliefs as the framework for a treatment that Clara could most understand.

Clara was also absentminded, and frequently dropped stitches while crocheting. She would laugh good-naturedly when she did, and then rip out the row and start over again. "I can just see you standing at Saint Peter's gate," I joked with Clara one day. "You'll be dropping stitches in front of the angels too."

Clara giggled and smiled, pleased with the reference. The rest of us roared with laughter.

Clara was good-hearted—she prayed for all of us each day—and, as a sign of special liking, gave me a religious medal of the patron saint of mental illness.

Another patient was Ginny, a girl of about sixteen, slim and lithe, who had undone much of nature's bounty by bleaching her hair into straw pre-punk blond and masking her face with the greasepaint of clowns. I saw little of her, actually, except for the afternoon she approached the couch where I was sitting and withdrew a tiny gray toy mouse from her pocket. She stood silently in front of me, stroking it.

"That's a nice mouse," I said, opening the conversation.

"Do you think so?" she replied distractedly. "But I don't know whether it's a boy mouse or a girl mouse."

I asked her if I might hold it and she handed it over. I stroked it thoughtfully as she had done.

"I'm sure it's a girl mouse," I said, because it seemed so obvious to me.

"Oh," she whispered, as if she no longer cared. She drifted away.

A week later, I noticed her again, or rather we all noticed her with her new doctor. He was tall and slim, a handsome man, meticulously suited, almost too studied in his dress, with a penchant for silky ruffled shirts, in short a dandy—Dr. Dandy, we called him—not gay, but touched by a feminine sheen.

We regularly giggled as we saw Ginny and her doctor pass by, because they seemed such a comic pair; he positively strutting in his finery, one hand on her shoulder, lightly guiding; she shuffling along, disheveled, with her painted scarlet face.

Two weeks later, Ginny took off her clown's mask for good, revealing a strikingly beautiful adolescent woman's face underneath. We recognized it as a breakthrough, the first, after three years of institutionalization.

"You look wonderful, Ginny," we all chorused and she grinned, which she did more of lately.

I decided that dandy doctors are best for little gray mice who don't know whether to be a girl or boy mouse.

Then there was Ken, a quiet handsome man in his twenties, who usually sat in a corner chair, staring blankly into space, his mind, along with his demons, blown away by electroshock. That was about the only thing that really scared me at the sanitarium, the thought that electrical or surgical intrusion could reduce me to an idiot. That and two people I considered dangerous—one was a young male staff member with crazy eyes who seemed to relish putting patients in restraints, especially Debbie, the severely deranged patient whom he was assigned to most of the time and whom he enjoyed bathing behind closed doors. The only other dangerous person, I felt, was a fellow patient, a well-educated, articulate man who for some reason made me uneasy. I learned later that he had killed a number of his own men while an officer in the Israeli army, thinking them to be Syrians. I stayed out of the way of both these people.

Toward the end of my first week at the sanitarium, Marion came to visit me bringing flowers. She stayed for about an hour, talking the whole time about her mother and the problems she was having with her.

My mind kept blanking out as we talked, and by the

time she left I was engulfed in fog. Then the sobs began.
Throwing myself on my bed, I cried and cried. Finally, I
called one of the staff members and insisted on talking to Dr.
Otto. Although it was a Sunday and he was not scheduled
for a visit, the staff member, seeing my agitation, reached
him by phone.

Near hysteria, I mumbled to him about Marion's visit.
I couldn't explain to him the real story, knowing how my
first attempt at telling it to Dr. Lustig had turned out. I nevertheless communicated the extent of my distress.

"Stay away from her," Dr. Otto told me firmly, and
then continued with an irony that he could not appreciate,
"It takes a trained therapist to deal with someone like that."

"You must break off your relationship with Marion,"
he repeated the next day during our therapy session.

"But how?" I asked. "What can I say to her? What reason can I give?"

"Don't give any explanation," Dr. Otto recommended.
"Just don't see her anymore."

Sorrowfully and reluctantly I followed his advice. The
next time she called, I told her I could not see her anymore.

"I was afraid this would happen" was her comment. "I
wasn't sure you could keep your friends."

Heavy and at the same time light, I hung up the phone.

I continued to meet with Dr. Otto every weekday. Because the sunglasses people had not invaded the safety of the
sanitarium, I was willing to tell Dr. Otto about them. I spoke
about them in a small frightened voice, but he did not appear
to share my alarm.

"Have you seen any of them since you've been here at
the sanitarium?" he asked me.

"No," I admitted, although I still felt somewhat appre-
hensive that they might reappear.

"Well, then . . ." Dr. Otto said, letting his words drift
off into the air. It was clear that he was shrugging them off,
as if they were not the real issue.

Then Dr. Otto resumed the line of questioning that he had adopted since the second day.

"How do you feel this morning?" he would ask.

"Kind of foggy and confused," I would reply. "And the pain still runs down my arms and legs."

"Exactly what happened this morning?" he would continue. I couldn't understand why he was introducing such irrelevancies, but I would dutifully recite the events and feelings of the day.

"What happened after that?" he would ask. When I finished replying, he would continue in the same vein.

I was puzzled by this questioning, because I had lost all sense of myself as an active force in the world—myself as an agent *causing* events. My inner world worked by association, and was always subject to magic and myth.

Then on the seventh day, under Dr. Otto's sequential questioning, I finally made the connection.

"You mean that how I feel is related to things that are actually happening around me now?" I nearly shouted the question, delighted to find a rational explanation for my distress. How I feel and what I do are the result of *everyday* occurrences, I realized with astonishment. Magic is not ruling me or the universe. I am an actor and participant in the world. I am tied to other people and other events. I affect them and they affect me.

Dr. Otto nodded and smiled. "Yes," he said, "you're tied to people and events in the world."

It was a simple enough revelation—one that most people take for granted daily. But for me, it was like a lifeline. For the first time in months, I was again able to see myself as part of, not apart from, the world. I was once again placed in the mainstream of events—I had joined society again.

As if to note the essential nature of the connection that I had just made, I found that within hours my eyes had cleared up. They had become blurry during my first day at the sanitarium, conveniently preventing me from endlessly scribbling the events, dates, and numbers with which I meant to capture the future. This blurred vision, which appeared to be a physical impairment, was indeed, I realized now, a gift from my body to myself. By being prevented from compulsively recording, I was taken one step further from madness and one step closer to the real world. And by the time my eyes had cleared up, the dysfunctional habit of recording had been broken.

Superstitious as always, I took my improved vision to be a good omen, as well as a practical advantage. I could read the hands on my watch, which, for me, had always been the symbol of reality. I couldn't wait to tell Dr. Otto, and Dr. Lustig when I saw him, about the improvement in my eyes.

At my therapy session with Dr. Otto the next day, I eagerly told him the news.

Dr. Otto responded approvingly. "Yes," he said in a pleased tone, "your 'I' is indeed better."

"My *eyes* are better," I repeated, thinking he had misunderstood me.

"Your 'I' is better," he said again, this time writing the letter *I* in the air. "Your 'I,' your *self*," he explained.

"Oh, I see," I said, surprised and happy. "Yes, it's true, my 'I' is much better now."

Dr. Lustig was equally pleased that evening when I told him. "Having a self, an 'I,' " he said, "means that you are in charge of you—that you make things happen, even inside yourself. And," he continued, "being in charge of yourself, of your inner and outer worlds, means that you deny the power of magic."

I was reassured that the power of magic was gradually diminishing, that a sturdier "I" was being formed, that the veil of illusion had lifted at one edge.

"I *am* getting better, aren't I?" I asked Dr. Lustig with hopeful uncertainty.

"Yes," he said. "Yes, you are."

CHAPTER NINE

JANUARY 29–FEBRUARY 5, 1976

Of all the aspects of the sanitarium, perhaps the most wonderful was the matter-of-factness of its inner life. Madmen babbled and mirrors broke but somehow the voice of sanity also spoke. Whatever was bizarre was openly displayed, and whatever needed containing was openly contained.

At the sanitarium, there was little need for hiding the inner demons at work. Society at large disavows demons, but mental hospitals exist to provide them with a place. When I had been on the outside, in that larger society, the chaos within me had had to hide from my fellows, until at last, yearning to be acknowledged, it had demanded an outward, if illusory, face. But inside the hospital all this was reversed. Madness was everywhere apparent: in the eccentric behaviors, in the distorted postures, in the babbling of voices—speaking untold terrors, in unknown tongues. What need was there, in this place, of hallucinations? Here, my private demons had many a public address.

By the second week of my stay at the sanitarium, I was making substantial progress. The mental connectedness I was beginning to experience was continually reinforced by my newfound social bonds. I became an active participant in the events and social life of the hospital, and in doing so moved one step closer to connection with the outside world.

The world inside those walls was almost a microcosm of the larger society. Like a somewhat grimy mirror held up to the world's face, the hospital did not reflect perfectly, but still bore a resemblance to the society that was its model. We held poetry readings, and at one session I wrote a haiku. We made artificial flowers at the craft workshops, laughing good-naturedly at our ineptness and many false starts and stops. There were yoga classes where I experienced another way to enter an altered state of consciousness that was calm and restful, and that, the instructor noted at the end of the session, completely transformed my face. We assembled in the gymnasium for sports and played lively games of volleyball. We even danced one evening at a communal square dance.

These activities and social encounters acted like a further adhesive—tying me not only to others but to myself. Being in the society of real people who, in the midst of their pain and struggle, could laugh at the foolishness of it all eclipsed my need for imaginary companions. This society, combined with the new causal thinking that I was learning in my therapy, at last had the power to drive my visions away. The sunglasses people disappeared, and as the days went on and they did not resurface, I realized that they were gone for good. My world of myth and magic was gradually being replaced by a reality that, inchoate and halting as it was, was nevertheless of this world.

Paradoxically, I became profoundly sad when my hallucinations left. Mournfully, I watched my world of magic go. It was as if I had suffered a great loss, a death of that part of myself which had given them birth. A place in me was empty, and would remain so for some time, until the outer world could again step forward and assume its proper place. I wondered at my sadness and my sense of loss. Why, when they had been so terrible, was I so sad to see them go?

My question went unanswered, but I was left knowing that the loss of illusion is a real loss, that we are bonded to what we create, even when what we create is not real, that the death of illusion is akin to the death of hope, even when that hope is worn and walks the street.

We love what we labor for, be it a child or our mind's own invention, and as we sit at the deathbed of our smallest creation, we mourn its loss more than the imagined loss of our own life. So when the sunglasses people died in my mind, as I watched my invented world of magical connections go, I wept long and bitterly at their demise, knowing the special sorrow of a world without their blinded sight.

The sadness, in its way, may have filled the place that terror had occupied, as if the space that had been stretched within me to accommodate the demons would remain to be filled by other feelings, and would finally be the seat of an enlarged perspective. For the moment, however, the sadness prevailed.

But there were compensations. I discovered, in the art room, a new outlet for my need to create. From lacing moccasins two weeks earlier, I now found myself painting watercolors. One picture in particular I considered an achievement—a lavender and blue butterfly with touches of purple and rose, perched ready for flight on a purple-pink-blue hedge. To me, the butterfly was a symbol of my newfound metamorphosis, and I eagerly presented it to Dr. Lustig as a gift when he next visited me. I also showed him the haiku that I had written:

A butterfly pauses on a leaf
A moment of silence
Before the beat of the wings

He nodded several times, as if in wonder at my transformation. He beamed as he accepted my gift. "I'm going to
frame this and hang it in my home." He turned the picture
this and that way in the light. "It's really very lovely." He
continued studying the painting, then stopped abruptly
and asked, "Would you please write your haiku at the bottom of the painting, and sign your name under it?" I
proudly complied.

When I had finished, he considered the picture again,
as if he was even more pleased by these additions. Finishing
his appraisal, he looked down from the painting to my moc-
casined feet. "It's sure a gigantic leap from moccasins," he
joked. We laughed together.

It is one of the subtleties of giving that it rekindles the
giver's self-esteem. Perhaps I'm a healing, not a harmful,
person, I reflected. Perhaps there's something in me of value.

The other patients must have instinctively sensed my
changed perspective, for many of them began to seek me out
for company. It started with my daily morning walk within
the sanitarium courtyard before breakfast, after I had gained
grounds privileges. I began inviting other patients to walk
with me, and soon it became a social event. Within three
days, fifteen or twenty patients were assembling at 6 A.M. to
troop around the courtyard to enjoy the crisp winter air.

This daily parade of inmates may have seemed comi-
cal—a strangely costumed procession of unworldly clowns.
Some participants marched stiffly with near-military bearing; others straggled, barely keeping to the path. Some were
outspoken, joking or shouting encouragement to those
around them; others were silent and mechanical as they
stepped along. But to all who marched, there was a belonging in our queer assemblage and self-appointed task, a common purpose and companionship that soothed many an
individual isolation. For the first time, many felt, I now belong.

I gained credibility when it became known that I was a professor.

"Are you really a professor?" they would ask hesitantly, sometimes puzzled, sometimes amused that a "professor" shared their fate.

"Yes," I admitted, "I teach philosophy."

Most of them did not know precisely what philosophy was, but, as it was presumed to be learned and intellectual, I was sought out as an adviser on many practical matters.

"When I'm home, my husband does nothing but work on his cars. He completely ignores me, as if I don't exist. I don't know what to do," a young married woman confided.

"It sounds like he should have married a car, not a wife," I said jokingly, and we both laughed.

"I think that nurse on the morning shift is giving me too much medicine, because I feel terrible after I take it," another woman who was subject to constant headaches told me. "Would you talk to her for me?"

"I'll talk to her with you," I said. "But it's something you should really do for yourself."

"I want to ask for grounds privileges, but I'm too scared to talk in the group meeting," the youngest patient, a boy of twelve or thirteen, said to me shyly. "Will you ask for me?"

I told him he'd have to ask for himself, but that I would sit next to him.

"I'm afraid to go back home—it just seems so hopeless," Ellen, my dining companion, told me.

"When I feel powerless and hopeless, it makes me angry—very angry," I said.

"Yes, I guess I *am* angry," she agreed

"Well, maybe you can use that anger to hold yourself together and change the situation," I suggested. "It helped me."

Talking to the other patients was, in many ways, like talking to myself. I told them what I was trying to learn—to be in control of my own fate, to stop being a victim of real or imaginary forces. Saying these things to others strengthened my resolve to learn better survival skills for myself. It also made me realize that, in many ways, I already *knew* what to do—it was putting it into practice that was the hard part.

Toward the end of my first two weeks at the sanitarium, Dr. Lustig and Dr. Otto both encouraged me to return to my teaching. They wanted to reinforce my rational thinking processes. They also wanted to facilitate my reentry into the world with the gradual resumption of a portion of my former responsibilities.

It was agreed that beginning on Thursday, I would leave the sanitarium on my regular teaching day, go to the nearby college where I taught, teach my two classes, and then return to the sanitarium for the night. In that way, I could step into the world's waters one foot at a time, without experiencing the shock of total immersion. Even though the situation with the children and Stan had substantially changed during the two weeks of my hospital stay, I was not yet ready to take full responsibility for the children.

Not only had Stan been caring for the children on a daily basis, but he had begun to take pride in doing so. I could see the change in him when he brought the children to visit me that evening. He spoke about his care of them with an air of confidence that I had never seen before. "At first I wasn't sure exactly what to do," he confided, "but I'm learning. And I think you can see that the kids are doing as well as can be expected. They miss you, though." A twinge went through me.

Stan hesitated for a moment as if he was unsure whether to continue. Then he took a deep breath and went on. "Elizabeth painted a completely black picture at nursery school the other day," he said worriedly.

The image of that darkness swept over me, followed by waves of bodily pain. "I'm so sorry I'm causing this to happen to her," I said, feeling overwhelmed with defeat and guilt. "But at least you're there for them, Stan. That must mean something."

I wanted to weep and run away from the thought of Elizabeth's pain. Black upon black, that was all that I could see. Everything around me took on the heightened clarity of unreality.

"I must go now," I told Stan and the children abruptly, wanting to run from the image of Elizabeth's picture and what it might mean. I'm harming my children, I thought again, wanting only to hide from that black thought. But the image followed me back up the corridor and into the ward. There's no escape from the sight of so much pain, I cried inside, as I returned to my room and pulled the covers over my head, trying to blot out the conviction that I was a bad mother. Then another side of me spoke up. You must put all your effort now into getting well, so that you can return to your children, it said. I clung to that notion tenaciously, in order to drive the darkness back. But its forces submerged me again. My child's black picture, black upon black. A wellspring of pity poured forth. I was not sure whether it was for my daughter or for me.

It would take me some time to resolve my maternal conflict about guilt and inadequacy. But during it all, I could count on the love of my children, and the love of my extended family.

My mother, on first hearing from Stan that I was in the hospital, had immediately taken a plane from Idaho to be there to help me. She visited me in the hospital with words of love and encouragement, and homemade brownies, but most importantly she set about putting my home in order, and helping Stan with the children. "I cleaned out all the closets, and I'm getting the house in good order for when you come home," she told me. I felt the burdens attached to the outside world lighten considerably.

My father, sister, and brothers also called me with

words of reassurance, and my sister sent flowers to the sanitarium, as if it were a regular hospital and I had a regular sickness.

A day before I was scheduled to begin teaching, I spread out my class notes on the hospital bed and went over them. I found my mind clear and precise, and felt no doubt that I could teach the material. I was anxious about standing in front of a class once again, but, as much as possible, I put that unease aside. I was determined that I would return to the classroom. I needed to make it up to my students. I needed to know for myself that I was a competent and functioning person.

On the day that I was scheduled to teach, my mother picked me up at the hospital in my car, and set out to drive me to the nearby college. Our route lay through the middle of the urban slum that surrounded the sanitarium. As we slowly traveled past gutted, decaying buildings, with the smell of poverty and hopelessness in the air and sullen hostility on the faces of the residents, I began to panic. It was like stepping back into a nightmare, only this bad dream was the real world—peeling paint on crumbling walls, boarded windows, lifeless interiors, broken lives. The magnitude of ugliness and despair overwhelmed me. In a frightened voice, I begged my mother to hurry.

She picked up my alarm and agitation. But, unfamiliar with the city, she promptly got lost.

My panic was assuming gargantuan proportions.

"I've got to get to the college. Please," I begged my mother. I began to cry.

My mother, in panic, brought the car to an abrupt halt and, leaping out of the car, started running down the street to ask for directions.

"Come back," I yelled after her in terror, knowing that her interactions with her western, small-town neighbors had not schooled her for a chance encounter on an inner-city street. But she didn't hear me. I watched as she approached an idle man standing on a street corner. As if through a filter, I saw her hands gesturing and her mouth moving. Then she seemed to be thanking him, and came running back to the car.

"I got the directions," she said in a still-panicky voice. I quickly locked all the doors and we sped off toward the college. We arrived in one physical piece, but my mind was still reeling from the horror of that image of danger and defeat.

I got out of the car, patted my mother on the shoulder, and thanked her for driving me. I took several deep breaths and started up the steps from the parking lot to the classroom building where I was to teach.

I'll take a cab next time, I decided, sorry that my mother, who was trying so hard to be of help, had caught my panic from me.

The contrast between the college campus, with its green manicured lawns and its bright well-scrubbed faces, and the brick-and-concrete hell from which we had just emerged could not have been greater. I wiped the memory of our harrowing ride out of my mind and focused on the classes I was about to teach. I was still trembling, but my mind was clear. Plato, I thought, with relief. Plato, with his orderly, purposeful world—that's what I must think about now.

The chairman of my department, Father Michaels, met me at the door of my classroom. Knowing, as I suspected he did, about the nature of my recent collapse, he had obviously come to see whether I was well enough to teach.

"I'll just sit in on your class," he told me. Since he had also been my substitute for the first two weeks of the semester, I could not argue with him.

Father Michaels stood at the front of the classroom on the left; I stood on the right. He began the class with a few words of introduction, diplomatically stressing how happy he and the students were that I was back. Then he turned the class over to me and seated himself at one of the front desks.

With my heart pounding, I began. I started that day's lesson on Plato, hearing my voice talking in an even, coherent tone. I asked several simple questions about the assignment, but the blank looks on the faces of the students told me that they had not understood the material, even at an elementary level. The few who did try to answer seemed to be using abstract labels, without at all comprehending the ideas involved.

I realized that I would have to begin at the beginning of the semester. But Father Michael's presence in the classroom posed a dilemma. How could I reteach material he was supposed to have already taught?

"Perhaps it would be best if we just go back and *summarize* what you have learned about Plato to this point," I told the students. Then, beginning at the semester's beginning, with Plato's *Apology*, I began to teach.

"Why do you think this dialogue is called the *Apology*?"

"Why was Socrates being tried?"

"Is Socrates apologizing?"

"What were the charges against him?"

"What analogy does Plato use in this dialogue?"

"Who is the one true trainer of horses analogous to?"

"How does Socrates use this analogy as an argument in his defense?"

"Is it true that a person can't do evil intentionally?"

"How does Socrates use this argument to refute the charges against him?"

"Is it ever right to defend oneself against evil by doing evil?"

The questioning and answering continued.

As the class progressed and I watched the students begin to sit up in their seats, the dull look on their faces evaporating, I knew that it was going to be all right. I began to enjoy the class. Before I knew it, it was time to adjourn. Father Michaels came over to me and shook my hand. He looked relieved.

"I'm glad you're back," he told me.

"I'm glad to be back," I said. "Thanks so much for taking my classes while I was sick."

He nodded, as if it were nothing, and left.

I'm going to be all right, I thought joyously. I'm going to be all right.

CHAPTER TEN

FEBRUARY 7, 1976

But my reentry into the world was also rough-edged, as I learned on the following Saturday, when I returned home for a brief visit with my children. After experiencing the euphoria from my successful teaching, I had assumed that all my other duties could be as easily resumed. I was unprepared for the torrent of emotional uncertainty that swept over me at the sight of my "abandoned" children. As they ran toward me with outstretched arms, I began to cry uncontrollably. Joy at their presence quickly turned to guilt, and I felt the world tumbling down around me. I clutched the nearby table, and began to chant over and over, "I am a bad mother. I have failed my children."

Surprise and alarm registered on my children's faces, which only confirmed in my mind the truth of what I was saying. My mother immediately grasped that the situation was out of control. She gently but firmly led me by the hand, away from the children and into another room, all the while patting my arm and speaking soothingly to me.

"Why don't you go out with a friend for a little while?"

she suggested. "Or perhaps you should go and see Dr. Lustig."

I remembered that I had scheduled an appointment with Dr. Lustig for twelve noon. Although some forty-five minutes still remained until my scheduled visit, I knew I must leave the house. I could not remain with the children if I did not calm myself, which I was not yet able to do. I decided to go to Dr. Lustig's office and wait in the waiting room.

I was still sobbing, but with more composure, when Dr. Lustig opened the inner door at noon.

I sat down in my armchair opposite him, and immediately articulated the one thought that had been going round and round in my mind.

"I am a bad mother. I have failed my children."

"What did you do that was so terrible?" Dr. Lustig asked me offhandedly, as if it could not be that bad. When I didn't reply, he continued, "In what way have your children been failed?"

"They must know, *somehow*, about it," I said with conviction, certain that my hospital stay *must* have had some detrimental effect on them. I marshaled the one concrete bit of evidence I had for believing that they had been harmed by me.

"The other day, Elizabeth . . . Stan told me . . . Elizabeth painted a completely black picture!" I waited for Dr. Lustig to acknowledge the seriousness of this incontrovertible proof.

"If she had painted a completely *white* picture, what would your reaction have been?" He was not responding as I had expected.

I sat confused, thinking. "I would have thought a white picture was a bit strange," I admitted, "but I wouldn't have been so worried." Doesn't he understand the symbolism involved with black? I wondered.

"What if she had painted a completely *purple* picture?"

"It'd be all right," I admitted.

"What about a completely *pink* picture?"

This was getting ridiculous. I sensed that he was not going to give up on this line of questioning. I was rapidly getting the point.

"How *old* is this daughter of yours?" he asked, as if a new thought had occurred to him.

"Four and a half," I answered dully.

"It's okay if she paints a completely white picture, or a completely purple picture, or a completely pink picture," he summarized good-humoredly, "but it's *not* okay if this four-and-a-half-year-old girl paints a completely *black* picture. Is that right?"

I felt foolish, but I wasn't ready to concede the point. "Don't you *see*," I said, "that if she paints a completely *black* picture, she must know there's something wrong with me! Or she must be *very unhappy*," I amended.

"Good possibility!" Dr. Lustig replied. "What does she know when she paints a completely white picture?"

His constant shifts were confusing me. It had all seemed so simple before; my failures had seemed self-evident. But now, to my discomfort, it was all being turned around.

"What's so special about *black*?" Dr. Lustig resumed. "People wear it all the time. Women look particularly attractive in it when they're going out at night, more attractive than in some of the other colors."

"It's just so obvious that it's the color of doom," I replied.

"For *you* it may be the color of doom," he responded, "but did anyone *ask her* what the picture meant?"

I said that it had not even occurred to me. "Then," he continued with some indignation, "how can you be so presumptuous as to assume that *you* know its meaning, when *she* is the final authority on it?"

By this time, I was at a complete loss for words. I kept

trying to grab hold of my original thought about being a failure, but it was becoming more and more difficult to remember exactly what I had been thinking. It was as if Dr. Lustig's line of questioning had blocked the mental path of that earlier idea. I couldn't seem to remember what it was that I was trying to say.

I remained silent, straining to remember why I had been so worried. "There's something about her face. . . . I can see something in her face. . . ."

"Most people can, when they look at another human being. What did you see?"

"A terrible sadness."

Dr. Lustig sat forward in his chair.

"Do you think your children miss you?"

"Yes," I softly replied.

"Right!" he affirmed. "Do you think your kids are sad because you're not with them?"

"Yes."

"Right! Do you think your kids are going to be irrevocably harmed by your absence?"

"That's what I'm afraid of."

"Wrong!" he exclaimed. "A four-and-a-half-year-old girl . . . sure she's going to miss her mommy," he continued joshingly. "But to say she's a banana, no ma'am! To say her mommy's a banana, could be."

Laughter flooded over me, bringing relief. Dr. Lustig had articulated, and then dismissed, the thought that I could barely acknowledge to myself: If I was crazy, it would make my children crazy too.

We sat in silence for a few moments. I basked in the newfound relief I was feeling.

"I guess I'm *really* worried about going back home," I finally resumed, seeing the issue for the first time in a more rational and practical light, "that I won't be able to take care of the children very well."

"Good thing to worry about!" Dr. Lustig said approvingly. "Particularly since you haven't done it in a while . . . particularly since it was so difficult for you before you went into the hospital . . . so what are you going to *do*, to make sure you have it easier, when you *are* back home for good?"

"Well, my mother's going to stay on with me after I get out of the hospital."

"For how long?"

"She says as long as I need her . . . I would guess for another couple of weeks or a month."

"After that, what are you going to do? . . . Now that Stan's trained, how are you going to use him? The guy's a pro now, right? Two weeks with the kids?"

"He'll be much more helpful than he was before," I agreed, suddenly feeling better just remembering that Stan would be there to share the responsibility.

"He says, or you say?"

"Well, I really haven't talked to him about it."

"Think you might want to?"

"Yes. That's a good idea."

"When are you going to do it?"

I realized that I should talk to Stan immediately and formalize the child care arrangements, so that I would know what to count on from him and what I had to do for myself.

"As soon as I can," I answered, but that was not immediate enough for Dr. Lustig.

"Well, today's Saturday. . . ." he stated, giving me the clue.

"I'll try to talk to him today. Maybe we could set some . . . specific hours when he takes them, and I wouldn't feel quite so alone."

"Or burdened," he added.

I sat, reflecting on what had been said. Yes, it would be better when I got home, I realized. With Stan taking an active role with the children, it would be much better.

Then my mind shifted gears and I thought again about

my failures as a mother, how I was causing my children pain. "What about Elizabeth's black picture?" I repeated, again focusing all my concern on that one symbol.

"Do you think a four-and-a-half-year-old girl painting a totally black picture is rampant psychopathology?"

"It's what I worry about, I guess."

"Do you want to know what to do to make that concern disappear?"

I nodded vigorously, eager for a solution.

"Has she shown you the picture yet? No? Well, ask her to show you the picture, because her daddy had told you about it. And then tell her what a *lovely* picture of the heavens it is, but that she hasn't put the stars and the moon in it yet. And then you and she do that together."

I smiled to myself. It was another example of Dr. Lustig's ability to change a symbol, and then the meaning and feelings that went along with it. "Yes," I said, at last satisfied.

I sat contentedly, until Dr. Lustig again spoke.

"You know you can't do everything all at once," he said reflectively. "Some things you can teach your children *now*, and some things will have to wait till later. It is your obligation as a parent, at *some time*, to teach them what they need to know. What you can't do now, though, you can just do later."

I could see that he wasn't going to let me indulge in guilt and self-pity about my inadequacies as a mother, or allow me to think my children had been irrevocably harmed. It wouldn't be too late to help them later, when I was stronger, he seemed to be saying. But, in spite of madness, my responsibility to the children remained.

I returned home that day happier than I would ever have expected, calmed, knowing that it would be all right with the children. And two weeks later, when I returned home for good, Elizabeth and I took care of the completely black picture, by painting silver stars on it and a golden moon.

I don't know who felt better—Elizabeth or I—after we changed the picture. We hung it on the refrigerator, where Elizabeth proudly showed it to every friend and neighbor. The new picture represented for me a fundamental lesson about the powers of the imagination and how, by using them effectively, I could make them a healing force.

CHAPTER ELEVEN

FEBRUARY 9–20, 1976

My second two weeks in the sanitarium had a different texture. The mental cripple who had arrived there was gradually giving way to a somewhat unsteady, but better-functioning, person. The daily sessions with Dr. Otto still continued, centering more and more on the practical requisites of my return home.

"Who are you going to have to meet?"

"What are going to be their concerns about you?"

"What are going to be their reactions to you?"

"What will be their greatest fear about you?"

"Tell me what these people are like, so that we can figure out how you'll handle them."

"What will Stan's role be when you get back?"

"How long does your mother plan to stay?"

"What will you do for child care help when she leaves?"

Dr. Otto's questions demanded that I think realistically about the situation I would be confronting, and oriented me once more toward the larger world. In addition to Dr. Otto's practical advice, I once again had a professional identity to rely on. I was no longer just a crazy person, I was again a working professor. This simple fact further expanded my role within the social framework of the hospital.

The incident with the student psychiatric nurses was an example. It seemed that the student nurses were asking the patients a lot of probing personal questions. A number of tearful patients had talked to me about it.

"I feel like they're trying to analyze me all the time," Mary, a depressed young mother, told me. "They keep trying to talk to me about why I tried to kill myself. They ask me about my family, and about when I was a kid, and I get so upset." She burst into tears.

I heard the same story from several other people. It made me think about the healing process. Why were some of the staff so effortlessly helpful, while others sowed the seeds of further distress? I thought about it all day.

The concern of the patients became known to several of the doctors and staff members, as well as to the student nurses' instructor. Consequently, at the morning meeting the next day, all the student nurses had gathered, as well as several men whom I had not seen before, who appeared to be either doctors from other floors or hospital administrators. Everyone was upset, especially the nursing instructor. She was the first to speak about the issue at the meeting, and she spent her time capably defending her trainees. As she spoke, the patients began to sag into their chairs. The student nurses looked ashen.

After the nursing instructor had finished speaking, hot words began flying back and forth. "We want you out of here!" a patient shouted at the students. "They're just trying to do their jobs!" their protector countered.

I waited until the hubbub had subsided, so I could get the floor. Then I stood up.

"I would like to speak about what has been most helpful to me, personally, since I've been here." Half the audience quieted down and turned to listen to me.

"Most of us are here," I said, "because we have found it difficult to live and do well in the outside world. Many of us have been separated from that world by the disturbances in our minds. But we're trying, in whatever way we can, to get back to that world, to again find someplace for ourselves in it." I felt everyone listening intently now.

"This is where the staff, including the student nurses, can be such a valuable help to us. They're our link with that outside society. They can remind us of what it's like to be a normal and ordinary and competent person. They can form a bridge between the sanitarium and the places we've left behind.

"The people who have been the most helpful to me since I've been here"—I paused and mentioned a few names—"those people have been not only supportive and kind. They've been helpful to me precisely because they've treated me like an *ordinary* person, and talked to me in an *ordinary* way about *ordinary* things. It hasn't mattered whether we were talking about the weather, or about our knitting, or about what their child did in school that day. Their ordinary conversation helped me to be a little more ordinary myself.

"It may seem to you," I continued, turning to the student nurses, "if you have ordinary, seemingly insignificant conversations with us, that you're not doing anything special for us, that you're not doing your job. But just the opposite is true. Most of us have a doctor or other person whom we talk with about our personal dilemmas. They're intensely private problems and, therefore, cannot be talked about with everyone. What we patients have been trying to say to you is that this kind of probing of our psyches, by people whom we don't know well, is distressing and, in fact, makes us more upset than we already are.

"This doesn't mean that the student nurses, or the staff, don't have critically important roles in our healing process. They do. Please let us take advantage of what you have most to offer us—an antidote to the bizarre and disturbed and frightening inner worlds that we ourselves have created. Give us what we most need from you—a dose of the ordinary, so that we can remember how it is to be a person with an ordinary life." I finished and sat down.

The room was completely silent for a few seconds. Then everyone started talking at once. Patients turned to the nurses and apologized tearfully. Misty-eyed nurses apologized in return. The nursing instructor came over to me and shook my hand. Mary, who had first told me about the problem, came over and thanked me for explaining the patients' side of the situation. Edith, the floor supervisor, approached me and smiled. "We should hire you for the staff."

After that, life in the sanitarium was very different for me. I enjoyed a newfound status as an intermediary, carrying the concerns of the patients to the staff, and the concerns of the staff to the patients. My new role helped me feel that, soon, I would be able to take up my other responsibilities, and once again become a full-fledged member of the human community.

The following days melted into one another in relative comfort for me. I continued my teaching two days a week, and was otherwise engaged in the activities of the hospital and its society. Don, the semiretarded teenager whom I had befriended, was leaving in a few days to go back to the state institution that he so despised. I discussed with several other patients what we could do for him before he left. Since he had only one torn pair of jeans to his name, we decided to take up a collection, so that at least he might have a decent set of clothes. One by one, we went to the downstairs office, where our money and valuables were kept, and withdrew our contributions. When we had finished, thirty dollars had been collected. Ellen bought a card at the canteen and we all signed it. Then we presented the card, with the money inside, to Don.

Don's words of appreciation were incoherent, but his tear-streaked face showed the extent to which he was moved by our gift.

"Nobody gave me nothing before," he finally mumbled as he wiped his eyes. It was an eloquent speech.

During that time, I noticed one of the more interesting aspects of hospital life—the way the patients used humor to numb the cutting edge of their despair. We all took particular delight in "fooling" the outside world at any opportunity. On the first evening of my fourth week at the sanitarium, my chance finally came. A group of us had taken a foray into the larger world, and had walked, supervised by several staff members, to a nearby ice-skating rink for an evening's exercise. We had paid for our skates, and then spent several enjoyable hours skating and mingling with ordinary people in an ordinary setting.

Toward the end of the evening, one of the staff members, Judy, asked me if I would supervise Debbie while she took a turn on the ice. I was glad to comply. Debbie was the severely disturbed patient who had been my neighbor in the seclusion room on my first night at the sanitarium. She always had a vacant look in her eyes, and her head was perpetually bandaged from her frequent rhythmic beating of it against the walls.

While Debbie and I were sitting in the public dressing room, a man entered with his children. As they changed from their shoes and laced up their skates, I found him periodically looking from me to Debbie, and then back to me again. Apparently determining that we were together, he nodded toward Debbie and addressed me.

"What happened?" he whispered, as he gestured in Debbie's direction.

Without a moment's hesitation, I replied in an equally confidential whisper. "It was a terrible automobile accident." He nodded sympathetically. "The family likes her to get out," I further explained. Again he nodded sympathetically, and exiting the dressing room with his children, he wished us both well.

Later, when I repeated the story to some of my friends in the hospital, we all laughed uproariously. Underneath our laughter, however, there was a sadness at a world whose compassion extended to auto victims, but not to their psychiatric counterparts.

During my stay at the sanitarium, I had grown very fond of many of the patients and staff, so when it was time for me to go, I said a tearful goodbye. The sanitarium had been good to me. Like the nurture of a benignly uncritical family, the sanitarium had proved to be a safe haven, within which I could consolidate an identity. Like the child that I was when I had entered its halls, I had received a child's care. But now it was time for growing up. Like an ungainly adolescent at the threshold of adulthood, I reluctantly put this particular childhood behind me, and hesitantly stepped once again into the larger world.

The parting from my hospital friends was like telling childhood chums goodbye. We talked of writing and of meeting again, but I knew that it was a youthful illusion. They belonged to that time and to no other, like friends made at summer camp or on vacation in some foreign place. I knew I must choose between their society and that of the world, and for all its imperfection, I chose the world.

Part 4

JOURNEY BACK TO THE CAVE

JOURNEYS

There are many ways to travel and many places to travel to, but perhaps the most difficult and illuminating of all journeys are those that come round full circle, beginning and ending at the same place. My journey through madness had led me farther and farther away from the world, until I ended at a place where madness reigned. It was precisely there, at the sanitarium, that I turned around and once again faced the ordinary world.

My return to the world was marked by a significant shift in my perception of time. Under the influence of madness, persons, objects, and details stood out with sudden clarity, imbued with such significance and intensity that time itself seemed to slow under their burden. My return home witnessed a return to a more normal time sense. Most days flew by quickly on ordinary currents. Some days stood out with special meaning. I discovered how welcome a backdrop of insignificance can be, how necessary for perceiving the overall design of one's life. From that point on, my memory began to curl around events of importance, signposts of progress in the process of shaping a self. Against the gray and neutral background tones of the tapestry, what was vital and important began to stand out.

CHAPTER ONE

MARCH, 1976

Curiously, the spring of my return to the world was more difficult than my month of winter in the sanitarium. At the sanitarium there had been less life to cope with. There, I wore only the stigma of the deranged. At home, I had to don responsibility's dress.

The transition from hospital to home reminded me of a ride I had taken on the commuter elevated train. Detached, I had sat back in my seat and watched the blur of life go past my window. The inside of the car had become more real than what passed outside. I gazed idly at the overhead advertising placard: DOREEN'S DISCOUNT SHOES, $12.95, SHOES ON RACKS TO SIZE 12EEE. Then in a brief instant, as I glanced out the window, my gaze focused on the reality to which the placard referred. There, on the shabby street below, stood Doreen's Discount Shoes, an unprepossessing building badly in need of repair and a coat of paint.

In just such an abrupt fashion, I viewed the reality of my situation upon returning home. I was a woman alone with two small children. I had no one to rely on but myself.

I had little money. I had fewer illusions, and no invented comrades. Reality seemed shabby and bleak, like a house without laughter, like the impoverished outlet for discount shoes.

My mother's presence at home, during the first two weeks of my return from the sanitarium, softened somewhat my transition to adult society. Still, I often found myself floundering, like a child who had never been schooled in self-nurture and self-reliance. It took enormous effort for me to perform the most commonplace tasks. Driving a car again posed a serious strain; carrying keys and matches and medicine bottles again was a new demand. Above all else, I was conscious of my solemn duty to my children, at a time when I was not far from being a child myself.

Two feelings inexplicably intertwined during that time—anxiety and loneliness. My mother's care during the early weeks was like a tender cushion of love, standing between me and true aloneness. But she too had a life to return to. Many nights after my mother had gone back to Idaho, I stood over my children's beds when they were fast asleep, drinking in their physical presence, their steady warm breathing, their small bodies tousled under the covers, thinking of their innocence and trust in me. Why have I been given this gift, I wondered, when I know so little about living well myself? How can I teach my children to be strong and confident, when all I feel is a huge lump of fear that settles just under my stomach? Why do these two sleeping faces tug at my heart so, making me want to endure, as if my strength could infuse them with strength? Wanting for them, not just myself, the warmth of a man, the security of an authority for us all, someone who would feel confident about raising them, about decisions for them, as I could not. But the loneliness and anxiety I felt as I looked at them was far surpassed by the new and unreasonable apprehension I felt at work.

My anxiety that grew there daily made even the most

commonplace interactions monstrous. Before one recent class, I had been so frightened I had retired to a lavatory adjacent to my classroom and huddled there in a toilet stall. Time ticked away. My class was due to start. Still, I could not pry myself from the questionable safety of my isolated perch. Steeling myself, I finally entered the classroom. Several students approached me before the class began. I was terrified by these cursory social exchanges. Inner thoughts and sensory perceptions, random pains and searing flashes pushed aside public words, crowded out common sense, made a mockery of external conversation. Sick with dread, feeling physically faint, I struggled to keep my mind on the words being spoken. I concentrated. What are they saying? Why are they laughing? Did someone make a joke? I'd better laugh too, or they'll know I can't focus.

Somehow, by some discipline, I continued teaching the class. It was as if I was conscious at two distinct levels. I could hear and follow the classroom discussion, but another deeper part of my attention was directed inward, constantly monitoring and privately commenting on my inner states. Yes, you handled that question convincingly. Is fear showing on my face? Are the students, even now, registering my alarm? Look closely at their faces. Read their reactions there. They *look* normal, so perhaps my secret is safe. If they knew that I had been in the hospital, that kind of hospital, what would they think of me? Would I be forever consigned to the ranks of the damned? Keep teaching, that's right, only fifteen minutes left. Hold your hands steady so they won't see them trembling. Almost done now, five minutes to go.

An hour's worth of living at these two levels brought me close to exhaustion. With vast relief, I would close my text at the class's end.

I looked again at my sleeping children. How can I be sure that I'm not, after all, harming them? What if my fear is making them afraid? The bad dream Elizabeth had last night—why did she dream of monsters chasing her? Are my demons contagious, invading even the sanctuary of my children's dreams?

What am I afraid of? I wondered. Is it failure? Why then, does it seem to grow worse with every successful class I teach? Is it fear of failing my children? But Dr. Lustig had reassured me about that.

It must be teaching. How can I go on teaching in the midst of this anxiety? If I pray, standing here in my children's room, perhaps I can ward off the next attack, perhaps next time it will be different. Please, God, take away my fear. I can stand the loneliness, but not the fear. Take away the confusion that lies at the center of the fear. Let me trust my mind again.

It was only reluctantly that I admitted my fears to Dr. Lustig. All I knew was that the fear was there. All I wanted was for the fear to go away.

"What are you afraid of?" he asked me when I spoke of it, as if he was surprised that, after all I had been through, I should be fearful now.

When I didn't answer, he made the question more concrete: "*When* are you afraid?"

"Usually when I have to go and teach," I answered dully. "The days I have to teach, I wake up in the morning ... terrified."

"Of what?" he asked again, as if it still did not make sense.

I sat marshaling my thoughts. "That I'll go crazy in front of the class, I guess," I said tentatively. Although it did not seem quite right, it was the only reason I could think of.

"That's certainly something worth being concerned about," he confirmed. "Have you had any of the symptoms that you had before you went into the hospital?" When I told him that I had not, his eyes opened wide in mock disbelief.

"None of them?" he asked incredulously. "Not even at

home? Not even driving to work? Not even in the classroom? Not even after work? Not even in your dreams?"

"No," I repeated.

"Then you're in pretty good shape!"

I nodded, feeling some surprise and even a touch of
gratification at this lack of symptomatology that had escaped
my notice.

"So, what's the problem?" Dr. Lustig asked again, as if
it could not be all that serious.

"Even though nothing terrible has happened, *so far,*
I'm still afraid to stand in front of my classes." One can
never be too careful about the future, I thought.

"Still afraid of what?" Dr. Lustig persisted.

"That's the worst part," I admitted, "not knowing. I
think sometimes it's fear itself that frightens me. I get so
frightened that I can't focus my attention. It's like I blank
out, and then I'm even more frightened that I won't know
what's going on."

"If you could have some *control* over the fear," Dr.
Lustig asked, "would that make you feel better?"

"Yes," I said tentatively, wondering how this could be
accomplished.

"Well, how about having some of the fear here?" he
suggested. "Can you feel frightened here, now?"

I didn't answer immediately. On the one hand, I was
eager for a solution, but Dr. Lustig's request warred with
my conviction that my fear was ungovernable.

"I don't have any control over the fear," I answered
with finality. "When I feel frightened, it seems like I'll always feel frightened. But when I'm not frightened, like
being here with you now, I can't even imagine being frightened." I said all this by way of explanation, so that Dr. Lustig would know why it was impossible for me to feel the fear
on demand, as he had suggested.

"Right! That's the way it usually is with this kind of
feeling." Dr. Lustig spoke enthusiastically, as if he was un-

deterred by my skepticism. "You're reporting the facts exactly as they are. The same thing happens to people who are depressed. But could you do me a favor and *try* to feel frightened now?"

"Do you *really* want me to get frightened?" I asked, still feeling doubtful about the efficacy of such an approach. Something about it scared me a little.

"Just a *little* frightened," Dr. Lustig replied. "I'll tell you why. If you can get a little frightened now, and then let yourself return to neutral, you'll have learned how to control one of your feelings. And if you practice this skill enough, particularly if you practice it here, today, you'll be able to do the same thing on your own after you leave here. So if you practice going from frightened to neutral inside this office, you'll be able to use the same skill outside this office, when you're bothered by an uncontrollable feeling."

Something in me still rebelled against the idea. "I don't feel I have any control over it at all," I repeated insistently, shrinking from the idea that my fear was under my own control.

"I understand you don't *feel* that you have any control over it," Dr. Lustig replied equably. "But I *know* that you *do* have control over it. You're not exercising it, that's all. And I'd like you to learn how to control it today, just like you've learned how to control lots of other things about your own functioning . . . so that *you* can use it for your betterment, rather than it being used to your detriment. Now you might not be ready to learn about it *fully*, but you certainly can make a start. You don't have to get a Ph.D. in self-control right away, but you could take the introductory course, Self-control 101!"

I found myself chuckling in spite of myself. But my good humor rapidly faded. I still was not ready to accept his novel idea. I reverted, instead, to my earlier reasoning, once again trying to explain why the skill he was asking me to practice in his office was not feasible for me.

"When I'm with people and have to hide anything to do with madness, that's when I get afraid—afraid that somehow the madness is going to show. The difficulty about being frightened in this office is that, when I'm here, I don't have to be afraid of your knowing." I paused. "So," I concluded, "it's very difficult to be frightened here."

"That was well spoken, like a good professor!" he said heartily in mock approval. "But *pretend* . . . just pretend that I'm some undergraduate, waiting for pearls of wisdom to come out of your mouth. And instead you talk jabberwocky!"

I smiled at this apparent absurdity, and thus encouraged, Dr. Lustig continued, "And then I'd think that you must be truly learned, because I wouldn't understand a single thing you'd be saying. That's the mark of a good professor, isn't it, being unintelligible to the students?"

I laughed again. "Are you saying that they'd never know?" I translated in relief.

"I'm saying that students *expect* their professors to be incomprehensible."

"But I *do* make philosophy understandable to my students," I objected. "That's one of the things I pride myself on. I had a student come up to me after a class recently, and she said that she was really enjoying my course. 'And I can understand what's going on,' she even added. 'Last semester I had Professor Richards for philosophy. I think he must be a *genius*, because I didn't understand a single word he said.' "

Dr. Lustig and I both laughed.

"Well, when I took philosophy," he continued conversationally, "I didn't understand a darn thing about it. I had to memorize it all, because it didn't make any sense to me. After Descartes I was lost. You mean to tell me you can make that stuff understandable?"

I nodded, granting my professional competency. Why

the fear then? I wondered. Perhaps it's not really failure that I fear.

"I guess I'm not really afraid of going crazy again in front of my classes," I admitted, rethinking the whole issue. "But the amount of fear I feel there is so . . . intolerable. It's so painful that all I want to do is run away."

"Where would you like to run *to*?" Dr. Lustig replied cheerfully, reminding me that even running away has some destination.

I was confused for a moment. Where did I want to run to? To childhood, I realized. I would like to run away from my adult responsibilities. "I would just like to go home and be a child," I told him emphatically, knowing even as I said it that I was responding like a stubborn child. But I had to say it, anyway. "I would just like to have somebody take care of me."

"I don't blame you," Dr. Lustig answered heartily. "It's tough having to assume adult responsibilities when you're not sure of your own capabilities. It's a tough job to help three people to grow up, when only two of them are children!"

I laughed at this rather comic interpretation of my plight. "I *do* feel like a child," I resumed seriously. "But I feel I have to *act* like an adult."

"Well, in a way you *are* like a child," Dr. Lustig said gently. "There are lots of things about getting along in the real world that you don't know a lot about. And part of growing up is learning about those things, and becoming good at doing them. So in many ways you are like a child."

"But then I need to be *taken care of*." I felt I had finally proven my point.

"No, you just need to *learn*," he gently corrected. "You can take care of yourself, but you do need to learn. That's what children do—they learn. You don't have to live in fear. You don't have to feel like a child. You *can* be a good mother to your children, and teach them the things that they need to learn, and help them to learn the things that they want to learn. It's just a matter of learning yourself. And one of the things *you* need to learn is how to make yourself comfortable inside yourself—how you can create feelings inside of yourself and how you can control them. There's no need to live in fear. It's a terrible way to exist."

I sat and thought, still caught up in my feelings of being a vulnerable child.

"When I go home, I have two children there who need to be taken care of, and I'm like a third child," I repeated sorrowfully. "I *need* a family, and I don't have a family anymore. It's not a family without a man."

"Well, one of the things you can do is put an ad in some magazines for a mail-order husband," he replied promptly, not in the least discomfited by my imagined plight. "That way, there will at least be a man in the family." As he spoke, he pressed his fingertips together to form an arch, what we called a steeple as children. Then his fingers folded inward and intertwined, in a gesture that seemed to convey both thoughtfulness and unity. "Another way," he continued seriously, "is for *you* to acquire the skills that you think a man would have, so that you can do it for yourself."

I let my face go blank. The conversation was distressing to me. It was not going the way I liked. I was not getting the sympathy that I felt I so richly deserved.

As if he understood the turmoil behind my immobile face, Dr. Lustig, when he resumed a few minutes later, spoke cajolingly. "Now what could a man do for you that you couldn't do for yourself?" he inquired.

But I was not to be distracted from the sense of injury and anger that I was feeling. I was angry that I was alone. I was angry that I had no husband, when I so clearly deserved one. I was angry that Dr. Lustig was not more sympathetic to my situation. My face hardened. I was not going to be talked out of my plight.

Dr. Lustig, as if sensing this, or perhaps reading it from my face, said nothing further. I felt the tension in the room's silence, but my anger kept me from speaking. Five minutes turned into ten minutes. Still no word was spoken. I looked at the clock. There were only about twenty minutes of my appointment time left. Finally, unable to bear the silence and sense of estrangement from Dr. Lustig, I spoke.

"A man would take some of the responsibility," I said grudgingly, answering his earlier question about what a man could do that I couldn't do for myself. "I wouldn't have to have all of it!"

"Well, you still have a partner in raising your children," Dr. Lustig replied matter-of-factly. "Can you use Stan more?"

"Yes, but it's not the same," I said stubbornly.

"Right . . . it's not the same as having a live-in partner," he acknowledged. "But you do have a live-out partner. He can still do his part."

"How?" I asked, reluctantly.

"Tell him that he has to help more with the children. Even though you have chosen to assume the main responsibility for raising them, this is a time when it would profit all of you for Stan to do more. Tell him that you're still recovering and that you can't be expected to resume full activity immediately. It has to be gradual, otherwise you'll end up back in the hospital."

"He has been helping more," I said, defending Stan. "It's not just the care of the children that's difficult," I continued musingly. "It's the worrying about them."

"Well, let Stan worry about them. Why don't you just worry about you?

"You don't have to worry about your children," Dr. Lustig said more softly, when I remained silent. "You *do* have to do your job as a *parent*, but you *don't* have to worry about your *children*. You just worry about you."

"It's not any one thing I'm worried about," I replied, thinking again about the way that my anxiety seemed to generalize to many of the duties I was expected to perform. "I just feel like a failure at everything."

"Right!" Dr. Lustig agreed heartily. "And you can also feel that you're a success at everything, since all the emotions you have inside yourself come from you. That's the way it is in the world. Growing up means taking control of ourselves and our feelings. And we do that by learning about the mechanisms within ourselves that govern our actions and create our feelings."

"I thought being an adult was performing successfully in the world," I replied, again shying away from his insistence on personal control.

"No, it's more than that." He sat back in his chair and thought for a few moments before resuming. "Being an adult is performing competently in the world *and* being in control of oneself. People can fake performances. They cannot fake being in control of themselves. Many people are under the misconception that it's just the performance that counts. They fool other people into believing that they're self-possessed, but actually, they're scared to death inside, because they really don't know how to control their internal worlds. They'd be feeling a whole lot better about themselves if they had bothered to learn about their own inner workings, and if they had practiced the skills that would help them to take charge of themselves comfortably. It's really a very simple and straightforward process, like any other learning."

"I don't understand how you can do that," I said, finding my attention captivated in spite of myself.

"Well . . ." he said, "I asked you, before, whether you'd be willing to become a little fearful and then get back to neutral, and you adeptly sidestepped that request. You might want to go back and do it now, and practice going from fear to neutral. That's all you really have to do, be able to get back to neutral—from *any* feeling. You don't have to be totally in charge right away, but you do have to be able to get back to neutral if a feeling becomes unpleasant."

I decided to try to do as he suggested, but I found that I couldn't feel frightened in his presence. "I'm trying to get frightened, but I can't seem to do it now," I said apologetically.

"That's right—when you exercise control over your emotional functioning, you don't get frightened," he replied mildly. "But when you do not exercise that control, you get frightened. It's the absence of being in charge of yourself that causes you to feel frightened. So the more you're in charge of yourself, the more comfortable you're going to feel."

"Do you mean that, sometimes at least, I *am* in charge of myself?" At least I'm not afraid here in his office, I was thinking.

"Yes," he replied, "you're in charge of yourself when you're feeling fine. And the more you're in charge of yourself, the more often you're going to feel fine. And it *is* possible to feel fine most of the time, without medications. That's not to say you'll feel *happy* all the time, but you can feel fine!"

"Every time I don't feel fine, I assume that I'm crazy," I admitted, feeling a little foolish.

"Well, for a person who makes her living thinking, that's a lopsided thought!"

I laughed with relief. "I talked to my brother the other day," I continued reflectively. "I was telling him about the anxiety that I feel at work, how sometimes I'm so anxious that I can't tune in to what people are saying, or hear them very well, and that then I get even more frightened. He said, 'Oh, that happens to me all the time.' He's a lawyer, and he said, 'I try to avoid fading out when I'm with clients, but if it happens, I just say, "Could you please repeat that? I'm not sure that I quite understood your point." Then when they repeat it, *that time* I pay attention!' "

We both laughed. "Neat fellow, your brother," Dr. Lustig said.

"The other thing my brother said," I continued, "is that everybody has problems. They may be small problems, or they may be large problems, but everybody has some problems. Our family, though, has always assumed that we never ought to have problems or at least not show them. That's why they're denied all the time. But this assumption—that we're never supposed to show any problems—creates a very unrealistic expectation. And every time I have a problem, I think there's something wrong with *me*.

"So I don't want to expect that I'm going to be happy all the time," I concluded.

"Correct," Dr. Lustig replied. "But you can feel *fine* all the time."

When I remained silent, he added more gently, "You don't have to grow up *alone*, but you *do* have to grow up."

"I think I don't *want* to grow up," I said petulantly, feeling my anger returning.

"Well, the same thought crossed my mind too," Dr. Lustig said soothingly. "There's no need to make a decision now. But you might want to think about it, after you leave here, during the course of the next several days. Think about the price you've paid for *not* growing up, and what the rewards would be for *growing* up."

"The fear and panic that I feel lately . . ." I said reflectively, "is that the price of *not* growing up or the price of *growing* up?" I knew the answer, but I wanted to hear it anyway.

"It's the price of *not* growing up," Dr. Lustig answered without hesitation. "It's the price of *not* growing up, *not* being in charge of yourself, *not* being in control of what goes on inside of you. And it's the price you'll continue to pay. . . ." His voice trailed off into silence.

"I can tell you how to make it better," he resumed when I didn't reply, "but I can't make it better *for you*. And that's the problem in a nutshell. You've discovered the limits of Dr. Lustig's magic. It stops at your skin."

"You can't take away my fear," I said soberly, sorry that there were no magical solutions.

"Only you can do that," he affirmed. "When you did *not* get frightened and then return to neutral earlier, you tacitly indicated that you had grave doubts about learning a skill that would make you responsible for yourself. So the choice now is: *nobody* responsible for Carol, or *you* responsible for Carol. But it can no longer be: *someone else* responsible for Carol."

I was not enamored of that day's lessons. I felt the harshness of Dr. Lustig's truths. And I left without practicing the skill of self-control that Dr. Lustig had tried to teach me.

But on the next occasion when I stood before my class in a state of terror, I remembered what he had said about going from panic to neutral. Desperate, I grasped after any means of taking away the fear. I decided to try it.

I imagined "neutral" as a restful valley floor between the jagged ridges of two mountains that seemed to represent the edges of my fear. I imagined myself settled down in this valley, beside a golden river. Warm sunlight flooded over my shoulders. Wild flowers nodded in the breeze. I stretched out my arms and imagined myself taking a deep breath of the pristine air. The edges of the mountains blurred and smoothed out. They changed from deep brick-red to gentle blue. Another gulp of fresh air. The mountains receded into the distance, still present on the horizon but no longer paramount. I felt my anxiety ease. It was such a relief that I wanted to shout with joy. Instead, I quietly continued teaching my philosophy class.

During the days ahead, I continued to use my imagination as a weapon against my fear. Calling up a neutral state took effort and discipline. I had to insist to myself that I create positive images. Some days it worked better than others.

But I usually found that, with discipline, I could make my fears subside, although they rarely dissipated completely. Nonetheless I persisted with my exercises. It was not until May 27, some three months later, however, that I realized that my fear had gone. I found myself teaching that day with confidence and ease, and with a physical feeling of connectedness coursing through my body. I felt a simple pride. Even fear was no match for my imagination.

CHAPTER TWO

JUNE, 1976

As my springtime fears diminished, the loneliness that lay hiding behind them engulfed me. Stripped of a husband, I felt naked and reduced, like a wheel sliced through the middle that could not roll smoothly. Where is my other half that Plato spoke of? In the beginning, he said, people were joined at the shoulders, like so many pairs of Siamese twins. When they stretched out their limbs, they resembled the spokes of a wheel. From this position, they frolicked and played, turning cartwheels and spinning in circles. But the noise of their laughter angered the gods, who, in irritation, split all the pairs apart. Thus, we are destined to search the world over, looking for our other half.

I looked around me, but found no pairing. Only the feeling of loss, loss of a husband, which translated into loss of a family. Being married was believing that things would last. More than children, more than religion, it had given me a sense of continuity, a belief in the future, that there was a future. But now, divorce. It was as if the essence of all heartbreak had been poured into a thimble and placed before me. The fact that the portion was small and commonplace did not make it any less bitter to drink.

Saturdays, when the children went to Stan, were barely livable, in spite of distractions such as shopping or visiting with friends. But Sundays, "family days," were days of despair. I felt as if my face had been pressed into the dirt and ground down by an unkind cosmic boot, so that I had no breath left, so that life slipped out of me. Looking toward the phone in desperation, thinking, Whom can I call that will keep me alive? Knowing that friends would be busy with their own families. Loath to disrupt such a sacrosanct time. Thinking of my own family, my parents, my sister. Calling them, eagerly hearing their voices. Assuring them that yes, I was fine, because how could I impose my lifelessness on them? Wanting to hold on to their voices. Finally hanging up the phone. The sound of my heartbeat, deafening in the silence. Pulsating on, as if it had a life of its own, independent of my anguish. I thought about people in prisons and prisoners of war. Day after day, marking notches on blank walls. Why don't they die of loneliness? Perhaps they do.

Somehow I would stay alive until the children returned at six o'clock. Then, from sheer relief, I would collapse into bed just after they did, triumphant over another Sunday.

When the children were with me, my loneliness eased, but even our togetherness couldn't make our family feel whole. So we spent our weekdays seeking out the company of families that were still intact, as if the rupture in our own family life could be healed by osmosis. I would take the children by the hand, late each afternoon, and journey down our lane to the homes of neighbors who were also friends. There, the women and I would sit and sip coffee while our children played. Putting aside for a moment the faster rhythms of our professional working lives, we working mothers would sit idly discussing the commonplace events of our day, as the afternoon shadows lengthened, until the evening brought their husbands home. Then, reluctantly, I would gather up my children and make my way home, our footsteps heavy as we marched toward an empty house.

On the day that Elizabeth asked me, upon returning home, why her daddy did not come home at night anymore, I wondered, not for the first time, how I could go on.

When I told Dr. Lustig how alone and desperate I was feeling, he reacted as if it was to be expected. The loneliness, I explained, often made me want to die.

"As a matter of fact, that is what it's all about," he said. "Facing death, knowing that we're all alone. Looking death in the eye and deciding to go on living.

"I believe that some philosophers have written about it," he added. "I don't know what the philosophers have said, because I'm not a philosopher, but I do have some knowledge about looking death in the eye . . . and choosing to live."

"I've suffered too much," I moaned. "I just feel that I can't suffer anymore." It seemed such an enormous injustice to me, that I had had more than my fair share of pain.

"Well, whenever you decide to cash in your chips, just cash them in," he told me. "Meanwhile, go on living until you change your mind. You always have the option," he continued, and then added as if it was an afterthought, "but it's such a *permanent* option, killing yourself, that you might as well be very sure that you want to exercise it."

Yes, it is permanent, I thought. That's precisely the appeal, a final option when things seem so bad that death seems better. Then I thought of my children, how their faces would look, the dismay they would feel if I was gone. And later, the sense of desertion they would feel, the absence of love for them that such an act would imply.

"The one thing that keeps me going is my children," I said. "I think it would matter to them whether I live or die."

"That's an antidote to the loneliness you've been feeling," Dr. Lustig agreed with conviction. "It gives meaning and purpose to your life. Actually, sometimes I think that raising children is the most important job in the world."

I thought about my children and about raising them, and an unaccountable but now familiar guilt crept over me. "But I feel that I've failed at it," I said miserably.

"Well, what you feel is determined solely by you," he replied without sympathy, and I remembered again his emphasis on personal control. "But if you would like an *objective* opinion about your children, I would be glad to provide one."

After a long pause, my curiosity got the better of me. "Why do you think they're doing all right?" I could not help but ask.

"Because they're functioning adequately. And to have been through what you've been through, and to have children who are functioning adequately, is a *triumph!*"

I felt my face flush in spite of myself. Dr. Lustig's face showed just the trace of a smile.

"It *is* important to have meaning in your life . . . to have a purpose. Not only to raise your children, but to raise yourself. You have to be the best person you can be for as long as you possibly can . . . until, of course, you cash in your chips."

I listened to what he said, and found that death no longer seemed such an attractive alternative. It's not just my duty to my children. I also owe something to myself, I reflected. However, I was not prepared to discard the option of suicide altogether, not just yet.

"But the world seems so bleak to me," I said softly, mustering what further arguments I could on the side of despair.

"On cloudy days, that's the way it appears to *everyone*," Dr. Lustig replied without hesitation, making me less alone even in my despair.

"I just seem to go from one kind of pain to another kind

of pain, and there is no solace." I again let the feelings of suffering pass over me.

"When you're hopping from pain to pain, there isn't any," Dr. Lustig replied firmly. "I would suggest that you *stop* hopping from pain to pain . . . and maybe go from pain to pleasure."

When I didn't reply, he resumed, "Or . . . if you don't want to be so *outlandish*, how about just going from pain to neutral?"

I remembered what he had said before about going from fear to neutral, and I remembered practicing that lesson in front of my classes.

"The few times I *can* get to neutral," I said, "I feel so relieved—to be out of the pain—that it does seem good."

We sat together in silence as I considered life and death. I thought about a saying of Nietzsche's Zarathustra: "The thought of suicide is a great consolation: by means of it one gets successfully through many a bad night." Yes, that's it, I reflected. The appeal of suicide is simply that it gives one an option—something to *do*, some action to take if the pain and loneliness get unbearable. But perhaps there are other, less radical choices, I reflected. Perhaps a vacation, or a visit with my family in Idaho.

Then, in a rush, I remembered why it was that I felt so alone. Stan had left. I was no longer married. Anger rose up within me at the thought, anger that wanted to destroy something, even if that something was myself.

"I want to be married," I said with sudden intensity.

"I want to be a millionaire," Dr. Lustig replied with equal emphasis.

"I don't really want to go through a courtship . . ." I continued, as if I hadn't heard him, "I just want to *be* married!"

"I don't really want to work to become a millionaire either," he replied cheerfully. "I'd just sort of like it to fall into my lap!

"A man prays to God that he'll win the lottery," he continued anecdotally, when I did not deign to reply. "He prays night and day, 'Lord, I've been a good man and I've lived a good life. ... Please, Lord, grant my one wish.' The man repeats his prayer every day, imploring God to let him win the lottery. Finally, one night, as he's praying, he hears the voice of God in reply: 'Give me a break—buy a ticket.' "

I giggled, feeling more than a little foolish.

Again, we sat in silence for some time, until gradually I felt the sorrow envelop me again.

"I've lost everything," I said.

"Everything?" Dr. Lustig replied in mock seriousness. "Your health? Your children? Your friends? Your family?"

A wry smile crept over my face at this reminder. "I *do* love my children, and they love me," I said.

"Then, I guess you haven't lost *everything*, have you?

"You love your children and they love you," he continued, "but the more important question is, do you love Carol?"

"Not very much," I admitted in a low voice.

"Well, I think love is an all-or-none phenomenon," Dr. Lustig replied, which unaccountably made me laugh.

"You might want to get to know the *real* Carol, rather than the person she was supposed to have been. You might want to get to know the real Carol and then find out whether, in fact, you can first *like* her. Then, maybe later, you could love her. That's part of growing up too," he added. "For most people it happens when they're very young. For those people for whom it has not happened, it can certainly happen later on. It's the exact same process, earlier or later."

"Why is it so painful, then, to try to love yourself?" I implored.

"It's *not* painful when you love yourself," Dr. Lustig corrected. "It's painful when you *don't* love yourself. It's like being allergic to yourself."

"It seems like it should be so easy," I said sadly, "but it isn't."

"Well, you might have to unlearn some improper attitudes about yourself—having to do with things like perfection, having to do with things like other people's expectations, having to do with things like normal human motivations and normal human limitations."

"I guess I do think I have to be perfect or I don't deserve to be loved," I admitted with a nervous laugh. "It's an impossible standard." I could recognize the ironic nature of that particular bind.

"Yes, it certainly is," Dr. Lustig confirmed. "In order to function according to that standard, you'd have to be a god. That's a tough business to be in."

"It's not a human business, anyway," I acknowledged.

I let my thoughts roam freely for a little while, until they finally fastened on my unworthiness. I remembered my standing in front of my students, fearing that they would find me out.

"About my panic at standing in front of my classes," I resumed, "I think that's what I'm really afraid of. . . . If the students find out about me, they won't love me."

"They don't love you, anyway." Dr. Lustig replied emphatically. "To love someone means that you really *know* them. Half of your students don't even know your first name."

I was startled by what he said, but also relieved. I was not the center of the universe. My students were not judging me; they were merely indifferent.

"Who else besides family, then, really loves you?" I asked.

"Most importantly, when you're growing up, your mom and dad. And then they teach you to love yourself. Sometimes people don't get taught it; sometimes people don't learn it. But *you* have to love *you* most of all, and then it doesn't matter whether anyone else does. It's sort of nice if you can find somebody else who does later on, but it's no longer critical to your existence. But I can understand your desperation to have a man in your life," he continued, "if that man's love is what validates you as a person. Your validation really ought to be coming from *your* love, though, so that *his* love only supplements yours, but never displaces it."

Why is it so hard to love yourself? I wondered again. Why, when Stan left, did I feel so empty inside, so unsure of my judgment?

"It's not just that Stan is not there anymore," I said quietly. "It's that ..." I paused to think. "It's just that ... I *believed* in my marriage so much, I believed so much that it ˉwould *last*. Now, how can I ever believe in anything again? How can I believe in myself when my judgment was so bad?"

"Your judgment was good when you chose Stan. From the experience and knowledge that you had of the world at that time, you made a decent decision. And the two of you did your very best to make the marriage work. But the marriage didn't. That's the simple fact. It does not mean that either of you is defective or deficient. It does mean that the marriage didn't work out, and the two of you wisely decided to end it. And the next time you find somebody who interests you, and the next time you get to thinking seriously about marriage, you'll have more information and knowledge, more experience and wisdom to rely upon when you make the decision. But it will *still* require a great deal of effort on both of your parts. And there will still be no guarantee that it will last forever. But I do hope that both of you will have the hope that it will."

"You have to have the hope to stay alive," I muttered, thinking about the primitive hope that had brought me so far.

"You certainly do have to have the hope to keep going," he countered. "You have to *breathe* to stay alive."

I didn't say anything immediately. With disappointment, I began telling him how deceived I was feeling. Society had seemed to promise me that, if I followed its rules, my marriage would last forever. "I admit I may be responding with childish anger," I said in conclusion, "but that's how I feel."

"Well, it's never nice to find out that some of our beliefs from childhood are just myths," Dr. Lustig replied. "But on the other hand, it can be an incredible relief. Knowing them to be myths puts them in their place."

As my appointment drew to a close, I realized how difficult it is to have illusions stripped away. I was in shock at such a dose of realistic thinking.

"I'm so weary," I told Dr. Lustig, as I stood up to go.

"Well, then, get some rest," he said sympathetically. "This is not a marathon. Take it in small steps, in small doses."

And that was what I did over the next few months. I often left my conversations with him feeling confused, as if everything that I thought had been turned upside down. But gradually, I came to have a more realistic grasp of my current situation, and began to have more realistic expectations. I sought ways to avoid my Sunday isolation. I would call friends in advance, and arrange to see them on the weekends when the children were not at home. I joined an art class and began painting watercolors on a regular basis. Slowly, I learned the art of surviving on my own. And sometimes, even small pleasures would present themselves—a good movie, a good dinner with friends, sitting in the lovely summer twilight sipping wine. And best of all I could occasionally laugh at myself.

CHAPTER THREE

JULY, 1976

As my rampant anxiety faded into a more rational calm, and the loneliness of lost companions eased its hold on me, I found my thoughts turning to men. Men had found little place in the theater of the absurd that had been my playground. But in the mellow light of summer evenings, new possibilities of romance came to mind. One man, in particular, had recently caught my attention.

I had seen him several times in Dr. Lustig's waiting room. It was not his pleasing manner, or his impish grin, that first captured my notice—it was a kind of intensity in his light brown eyes, a ripple of energy that sent waves cascading over me. We found ourselves looking at each other, trying to frame words that would match the unspoken attraction. Our conversation was mundane, even as its effect was exhilarating.

"What's your sign?" he asked me.

"I'm a Pisces," I replied, amused at this stereotypical singles-scene gambit.

"I'm a Cancer," he announced. "Cancers and Pisces go well together."

The intensity of our mutual looking belied the banality of our words.

I watched for him after that, but it was not until the following Thursday that I saw him again. By then, he had come to be a romantic figure in my imagination, and I was ready to pursue our initial brief connection more vigorously. I learned at our second meeting that his name was Ted and that he was a producer at a local radio station, an occupation that only heightened his romantic stature in my eyes. He was ready for me too on that occasion, for almost immediately he asked me for a date. We settled on the following Saturday at eight o'clock. "A party with friends," he told me.

I dressed carefully that Saturday, trying to achieve an impression of casual elegance that conveyed an understated sexuality. I finally chose a soft-pastel flowered dress, open at the neck but not too daring. My mirror told me that it draped me in a becoming manner.

Ted obviously approved of my choice, for he was barely through the front door before he reached over to kiss me. I was flattered and excited.

After a few minutes, I took him by the hand and led him into the living room. "Would you like a glass of wine?" I asked a bit breathlessly, striving for just the appropriate nonchalance.

"That would be nice," he replied. I heard the huskiness in his voice, as he cleared his throat. As I got the wineglasses out of the cupboard and poured, they clinked in my shaking hands.

"Here we are," I announced as cooly as I could, as I handed him his drink. "To you," he said as our glasses met. We each took one sip and then, in unison, set our glasses down on the coffee table. His arms slipped around my shoulders and into an embrace.

It seemed only natural that we should melt into one another as we did. It was just like a story. Heroes and heroines have no need for sophisticated speech. He held my face between his hands as if I were an idol. I stroked his hair and nuzzled at his ears. His hands slipped down my dress and cupped my breasts. My hand traced the contours of his hips until they found the hardened outline of his masculinity.

I didn't think about what would happen next. I simply assumed that we would make love to each other. I had always been married when this had happened before. And when you are married, you do not wait. So I broke away gently, and thinking about the necessity of some contraception, said simply, "Wait here."

As I hurriedly left, I called back to him, "You can pull out the sofa. It makes into a bed."

I was too enchanted to see the startled look on his face as I left. I did not see how I had shattered the illusion.

When I returned to the room a few minutes later, I immediately saw that something was wrong. But I did not grasp what it was. He stood there, fidgeting. The sofa had not been opened.

"What's the matter?" I asked in genuine surprise. I could not understand how the mellowness of the mood some minutes before could have been so quickly transformed, why our embrace had not faded into instant fulfillment. Ted looked uncomfortable, like he didn't know what to say. "We really should be going to the party," he said nervously.

I felt hurt and rejected, but I didn't say anything immediately. Didn't he want to have sex? I wondered. Why this sudden change? I had no inkling that I was playing by married rules. I did not understand that I had moved too fast. I had skipped all the middle steps. I had not let a fledgling relationship flourish in its own time. And most unpardonably for a romantic heroine, I had taken the lead.

I looked at Ted quizzically, still not grasping what had

happened. I reached over to kiss him again, but he drew away. "We really must be going," he repeated again. By now, the earlier mood had been completely fractured. I felt robbed. I also felt embarrassed, as if I had committed a faux pas whose nature everyone else recognized, even as I did not.

"Okay," I said, as I rose to go. "I'm sure the party will be fun." I was trying to put on a cheerful countenance, hoping to redeem what I could of the evening. Perhaps later, after the party, I thought, we can recapture the mood. I took his arm as we walked out to the car. He still looked shaken, but he did not pull away.

The party was a disaster. No sooner had we arrived than Ted fled from me, seeking sanctuary with his friends. When I entered a room in search of him, he would immediately exit it. Hopes of redeeming the evening were quickly evaporating. I didn't know any of the people, but I tried to talk to some of them anyway. All the while, I was wondering what I had done wrong.

The party seemed to drag on interminably. Several times I suggested to Ted that we go, but he only looked alarmed at the prospect, and insisted that he did not wish to leave. Looking back on it later, I realized that he was afraid to return home with me at too early an hour, afraid of the advances that I might make.

Finally, we left. It was 2 A.M. Too late for sex. Too tired for sex. Too sudden for sex. I was finally beginning to understand. We spoke little on the way home. Ted accompanied me to the door. He kissed me, and for a moment our earlier passion was awakened. I clung to him, hoping that I could see him again, hoping that I had not spoiled everything. He seemed to be fighting with himself. I think he really liked me, but I had broken the rules. Finally, he pulled away from me and abruptly said good night. I knew I would not see him again.

Later I expressed my embarrassment and puzzlement

to Dr. Lustig. When I described our comedy of errors and my role as the clown, Dr. Lustig laughed so hard that tears formed in the corners of his eyes. Finally, when he could speak, he seemed to empathize as much with Ted as with me.

"Poor fellow," he commented. "He was probably frightened to death by your sexual directness. Take it easier on the next guy, will you? You tried to score a home run without getting past first base!

"It's great to be that straightforward," he continued more soberly, "but you can only be that candid with someone you've known a little longer."

And so, rather painfully, I learned that the rules of marriage do not translate to the single life. Nor could I rely on my experiences of being single at an earlier and simpler time. Social forces larger than myself were forging new expectations and shaping new dreams. One of those aspirations was for sexual freedom, in a context of equal partnership between men and women.

But the dreams, I learned that summer, were far from the social reality. We, my friends and I and the people I met, talked at length of the new order, but in practice, the old order imprisoned our feelings and beliefs.

I had worked in the women's movement before the currents of madness swept me up. Then it had seemed simple—a simple matter of equity. I took the lead on the education committee of our local NOW chapter, approaching the local school boards with demands for curriculum innovations. Our modest efforts had been successful, and we had delighted in our power to effect social change.

In spite of this advocacy, I did not see the women's movement first and foremost as a political force, perhaps because by nature I was not political. For me, it was more like the sounding of an inner bell. Not a call to arms, so much as a call to some long-lost recollection of what I was or what I might be. Its echo was profound in a way that I did not comprehend, then. It called me to consider the issue of my worth.

In this context, I saw my battle with madness as just another, perhaps more extreme, battle for a self-sufficient self. Now, as I stood at the door of society again, I somehow expected the ideals that were being articulated from every street corner to take substantial shape in the relationships at hand. What competence I had, had been forged in the fire. So I expected the men I met to see my worth in my own terms.

That they did not was a surprise to me, although perhaps it should not have been, since my own emotions lagged several steps behind my ideals. I told myself that I was a person of worth, but then was grateful if any man noticed me.

Nowhere, perhaps, was the shifting battleground more evident than at the singles events held at a nearby Unitarian church. There, survivors of divorce and separation assembled every Sunday evening, to participate in group discussions and mingle at a later "social."

The impact of the women's movement was felt in the early evening discussions. There, we talked about the new standards of our times. In order to be equal, should women pay for themselves on dates? Would women respect men if they expressed a gentler, feminine sensitivity? We talked earnestly of such matters and then retired to the drinks and dancing that followed.

But this "mixing" after our discussions suggested a goal more reminiscent of *Cosmopolitan* than *Ms.* magazine. The search for equality and sensitivity quickly evaporated into the search for sex. It was a climate of singleness in search of salvation. Since for many, the committed married order had resulted in a fall from grace, many "singles" sought redemption through uncommitted physicality. And the nature of the sexual search was not so far from the traditional sexual roles. I found that any reference to a doctoral degree sent would-be suitors running for cover. Alternately, sexual coyness and passive smiles brought numerous invitations to the one-night stand.

I concurred in all this because I was famished for sex. True intimacy and companionship seemed secondary; simple physical connection was paramount. The desire to be touched became the most pressing need. Committed or uncommitted, my sexual nature demanded fueling. I was willing to play by the new-old rules of the game.

It was at the Unitarian church social that I met Joe. He asked me to dance. After two dances, we retired to "someplace quieter," which turned out to be a vast church hall on the upper floor. We found a sofa there, tucked in one dimly lit corner, and Joe and I proceeded to carry sexual touching as far as was possible in a public room.

From the church hall we retired to his car, where we did not bother to start the engine. Moving shadows of people returning to their cars did not deter us from our explicit sexual goal. Finding the front seat too awkward and cramped, we promptly retired to the backseat, and there consummated our hastily contrived union.

Later we talked. Joe, it seemed, was an auditor, weary of the routine of his life. I thought about telling him of my travails and recent hospitalization, but decided that he would not understand. So we talked of the commonplace, in the absence of a more meaningful intellectual compatibility. But mostly, our relationship took a physical form.

I saw him several times after that, at his house and at mine. Although nothing had been explicitly stated, he seemed to assume that we were going together. It was on our third tryst, the first at my home, that he scared me badly.

He arrived that evening full of smiles, carrying a tote bag under his arm. I asked him what was in it, and he smiled a strange smile. I began to feel uneasy. "I'll show you later," he said mysteriously. I put my vague feeling of unease aside.

Although I had never brought a man to the house when my children were there, Joe began talking about the need for a lock on my bedroom door. He talked about it with a feverish intensity and a certain opaqueness of eye that suggested some deeper concern or meaning behind his words. Again, I felt uneasy. Again, I put it out of my mind.

Later, we retired to the bedroom. Only then did I learn what Joe had brought along in his mysterious bag. With considerable eagerness, he told me to wait in the bedroom while he got it. Reentering the room with the bag, he carefully withdrew its contents and set it on the bed.

It was an electric drill with a long, large bit. He displayed it with excitement, explaining that he had brought it to install a lock on the door.

I panicked. The drill was wicked looking and alarming. The rather crooked way that he smiled when he handled it gave me the oddest sensation that he wanted to use the drill on me.

"Please take it out to the living room," I insisted, the edge of my voice lifting in a newfound fear. "Please take it out of here."

Joe looked bemused and not altogether pleased, but reluctantly did as I requested. When he returned to the bedroom, he looked angry. He grabbed me roughly, as if he had finally put aside any pretense of concern. He pinched my breast as if he wanted to hurt me, and began to force me into anal intercourse.

I suddenly became terrified of the situation. I pushed him away, but that only seemed to make him angrier. No one else was around. I realized that I had to rely on my wits.

I began talking soothingly to Joe. "I really don't feel like having sex now," I said wheedlingly. "I guess I'm just not ready for a sexual relationship now—I'm just too confused."

I started telling him about the hospital and how I had so many problems. I hoped that if it seemed to be my own limitation, perhaps he might go willingly. I talked on and on, in the most calming voice I could muster.

After a while, Joe began to grasp what I was saying. He gathered up his clothes roughly, and slowly put them on. He seemed puzzled by what I said, but satisfied. I told him I was tired and, reluctantly, he said he would go.

As the door closed behind him, I stood shaking for some time. The slice of depravity I sensed in this supposedly normal man had scared me more than the voices of all the lunatics at the sanitarium.

Whereas Dr. Lustig had laughed about my absurd encounter with Ted, he was concerned and serious when I told him about Joe.

"How are you going to prevent that from happening again?" he asked earnestly. "What clues were there in the situation that, next time, you'll recognize sooner?"

"I guess the fact that we had nothing in common except our bodies and our loneliness," I replied.

"What else?" Dr. Lustig continued. "Was there a look in his eyes?"

"I don't know," I admitted, feeling inept. "I didn't notice until later."

"Most people give clues about themselves *before* something catastrophic happens," he said.

"I guess I'd better become a better observer," I acknowledged, understanding in a new way the necessity of a firm grasp of people and events outside myself, rather than so much inner absorption.

"You're ready to do that now," Dr. Lustig affirmed, "and now, as a single person, it's necessary for your well-being."

It wasn't until over a year later, when my divorce was finalized, that I was ready for love. In the meantime I avoided the singles scene, occupying myself instead with the day-to-day business of eking out a living, struggling to be a steady emotional source for Elizabeth and Daniel, trying to transform their tears and insecurities into well-being, encouraging them not to shrink from the world, but to meet it boldly, with confidence in their own worth, showing more confidence and perspective myself so that they could learn from me what they had not before. Especially showing Elizabeth, my deeply sensitive child, how to be sturdier and more matter-of-fact, explaining to her in detail the dynamics of many social situations that she did not naturally understand, how what other people did was not necessarily a response to or criticism of her, how she must make friends if she wanted to have them, how to walk up to other children and ask if they wanted to play, instead of cowering in the background, afraid of rejection. Learning that too much sympathy did not help her, that lessons about getting along in the world were what she needed most. And both of us learning from Daniel, who seemed to have an innate confidence and ability to get along, who seemed to have been born with an even temperament and practical outlook that little could disturb.

And of course, throughout, the business of lawyers, negotiations over child support and future financial obligations to the children for orthodontia, college, other unexpected expenses along the way, parceling out vacation days and holidays, distributing what little property there was, finally settling for fifteen hundred dollars, since Stan had cleaned out all the bank accounts prior to leaving and that was all there was left, and that going to cover my lawyer's fees. Becoming increasingly incensed at the legal system because of its handling of divorce, its adversarial insistence that cost the warring parties time and money, and discouraged compromise.

Somehow surviving it all, sometimes succeeding, sometimes failing, but growing stronger each day, learning to be more observant of what passed outside myself, finding that a self is not given, but must be made by the very attempts to face problems and solve them, by the daily struggle itself that is the fire that forges steel.

CHAPTER FOUR

MARCH, 1977

The afternoon, almost a year and a half after Stan had left, when I received my divorce papers was much like any other Saturday without the children, except perhaps for the slight twisting of my heart, the trace of sadness I felt that now it was over. I had expected to feel, at a minimum, a cataclysmic wrenching, but I discovered instead that my mourning was done.

I read through the legalities slowly, noting the transgressions I was supposed to have committed against Stan—how I had humiliated him in public—contrived violations that had allowed the divorce to go through. Our state had no provisions for no-fault divorce, and I had agreed to be the guilty party, just to see it done.

I didn't even feel angry as I read the lies. I just felt tired. Tired to the core after the months of legal wrangling, the distrust, the last savings slipping through my lawyer's hands, the final settlement of meager child support, the court hearing that I, as the guilty party, had not attended, and now these papers, so properly signed and sealed, saying that my marriage was nothing, defining me as a divorced woman.

I stuffed them back into their envelope and put them on the shelf. Later, I would put them in my safety deposit box at the bank, the same one that now held my engagement ring.

I dialed the number of a friend and invited her to join me for a drink. It was not a celebration exactly, but a ritual nonetheless, a public sanctioning of my new unmarried state, just as friends and family had sanctioned my marriage eight years earlier.

My friend, Carol, and I met and drank and talked about our divorces. "How does it feel to be a free woman?" she asked me.

"It feels fine," I said, brushing away the tears that unaccountably sprang up. "I'll manage," I continued, and just as unaccountably laughed heartily, feeling myself expand outward as if to fit the shape of the new freedom my divorce represented. "I'll survive," I summed up both weeping and laughing, knowing that, whatever else was true of me at that time, I would go on.

We drank and talked some more. She recounted the horrors of her marriage, such as the time her husband had thrown a wrench at her head during a marital dispute, missing her by inches and indenting her bedroom wall just above the bed.

As I listened, sadness settled over me. Memories of Stan holding my hand during labor when the children were born, memories of earlier carefree times filled my eyes to overflowing again. I must think about all the other things, I thought. I must remember the reasons why I got divorced. I tried to summon the negative recollections, to remember, to feel the icy disenchantment of the last year. But these thoughts were stubbornly unavailable.

"Why is it easier for me to remember the good times?" I asked Carol. "Why do my reasons for divorce seem now like so many shadows, flitting through the half-light? Why can't I reach out my hand and grab them, so that their presence would make my decision seem right? Why, after all my suffering, do I still wonder if I've done the right thing?"

I wept some more and, this time, Carol wept with me. Then, we got rip-roaring drunk. Near midnight, after short goodbyes, we stumbled back to our respective empty houses.

Stan returned the children the next day. He made no reference to the divorce papers, nor did I. After all, the legal formality seemed anticlimactic.

That day in particular, I scrutinized the children's faces, to see if I could find mirrored there any sign of psychic damage. I looked to them to find out how we were doing, to gauge whether I should view the divorce as our salvation or our defeat or, most probably, something quite different altogether.

Their faces provided no clues to answer my questions. What they showed me instead was the power of children to survive. For an hour or so, when they made the transition between Stan and me, they seemed unsettled, as if the changing of houses and parents required such an enormous adjustment of feelings and attitudes that their mental gears started slipping. For an hour or so, when they returned, they clung to me more than usual. For an hour or so, they cried and complained about small things. Then slowly, they returned to normal, accommodating to our household as if they had never left it for a weekend trip to another.

That day, when Stan brought the children back, I was reminded of the day he and I had brought Elizabeth home from the hospital. We had spread out a quilt on the living room floor, carefully placing her on it. She burbled and gurgled happily. We looked at her and then at each other. "What do we do now?" we asked simultaneously. Then we burst into laughter.

From that moment of shared ignorance, we had

achieved, via the circuitous route of divorce, a newfound shared comfort in our parental roles. Curiously, as divorced parents, we constituted a team. Now, more than ever, we were able to support one another, perhaps because, standing outside of marriage as we did now, our need for support from each other was so much more apparent.

During the year and a half since our separation, both Stan and I had learned much about being competent parents. He now had an ease about him, when he was with Elizabeth and Daniel, that spoke of routines and rituals, security and care. He and I had each become better at drawing the line, and making our expectations firmer and clearer. The children, in turn, had responded with gratitude and affection, had made pictures and signs constructed of "I love you's," hearts in pink and red crayon, rainbows in all the colors of the spectrum.

One critical child-rearing lesson I learned and began putting into practice was how to be the adult in charge, how to be the parent, and how to let the children be children. But confronting their literal-mindedness, from which exceptions to the rules sprang up like Hydra heads, was a Herculean task.

"Stop yelling!"

"I wasn't yelling, I was just talking loudly."

"Well, stop talking loudly!"

Humming ensues.

"Stop making that noise!"

"I'm just humming! You didn't say I couldn't hum!"

By simply turning it around, however, as Dr. Lustig suggested, by saying what I *wanted* them to do, rather than what I did *not want* them to do, this negative pattern was undercut and order was restored. I did not have to think of all the possible permutations of unacceptable behavior that can make the disciplining of youngsters so exhausting. Although it took effort to think clearly and articulate in advance how I wanted the children to behave, it eclipsed my tendency to react reflexively. I took charge. "Don't do this, don't do that" was replaced by positive commands and expectations.

"I expect you to behave yourselves properly when we go out. You will be polite and well-mannered. That means you will keep your hands to yourself and be considerate of others. Is that clear?"

The children thrived on the newfound order, and I thrived on the newfound simplicity.

I appreciated what Stan did for the children and the appreciation was mutual. Throughout our separation and divorce proceedings, in spite of the bitterness and battles over power, control, and money, we had both instinctively followed one basic rule of decency: We never spoke against each other in front of the children or undermined each other in more subtle nonverbal ways. So the children suffered less, were not pulled apart in their fundamental love or loyalty. Stan and I also benefited, because of all the things to be forgiven in the process of divorcing, the least likely is seeing yourself ridiculed by your ex-partner in your children's eyes.

Because of this fundamental decency Stan and I later could improve our relationship, becoming cooperative parents rather than warring ex-spouses.

AUGUST, 1977

A turning point for Stan and me in our relationship was a conversation we had about five months after our divorce became official. Stan had called me one day and asked if we could meet for dinner. He wanted to discuss the children and ourselves, he said. Seated across from each other at a neighborhood restaurant, we found that the words did not flow smoothly. After some hesitations and a few false starts, Stan began telling me how sorry he felt about my stay in the hospital, and what had happened to me. He regretted that he had not been more helpful, more sensitive to my needs during that time. A tone of guilt infused his words of apology; a note of sadness sounded in his voice. He lamented what we had lost, or perhaps never had, and tentatively suggested that we try again. Perhaps if we made another effort, we might recapture the marriage we had scarcely had.

I did not want Stan to feel guilty about the past—there was no need for that now. Nor did I want him to regret our mutual decision. To me there was no going backward, however appealing the past might appear, set against the backdrop of current loneliness.

As Stan talked, I considered the issue of our relationship.

"The divorce isn't your fault, Stan," I said. "We both contributed to it, so there's no reason for you to place all the blame on yourself. We did the best we could. It just didn't work out."

Stan nodded, but I could see that my words were not taking away the sorrow and regret he felt. I tried again, in a different vein, carefully considering my words.

"Even though we're divorced, Stan," I said, "we're still in a long-term relationship. It's not a married relationship anymore, but because we have children together, we're inevitably involved with one another. Divorce didn't turn you into a monster, nor into a casual acquaintance. You remain a person of importance in my life—what you do and what happens to you are matters of concern to me.

"Even though we're no longer married," I suggested, "we have a nonsuperficial relationship that demands work and effort on both of our parts. Rather than going over and over the past and our mistakes, I think our energy would be better spent in making our current relationship a mutually cooperative one—the best it can be, for both our sakes, as well as the children's."

Stan listened attentively to me, and nodded.

"Yes, you're right," he said. He reached across the table and, with the lightness of a butterfly, touched my hand.

I realized, then, how often I had been unfair to Stan in my thoughts, painting him and our relationship in the darkest colors, in order to justify so great a loss. I had repeatedly told myself that Stan had not helped with the children, forgetting the many times he had: the daily walks he took with Elizabeth during our nine months' stay in England in 1973, so that I, pregnant with Daniel, could rest in quiet in our tiny cramped flat; the many times he *had* bathed the children or read them bedtime stories; the way he listened to my concerns about them. And his love for Elizabeth and Daniel—that had never wavered.

Whether or not he had equally shared the child care no longer seemed the issue, for that had not been our bargain. I had chosen that role; he had worked full time to support us.

I told Stan what I was thinking, and he was glad of this more realistic reminder of his former role. Throughout the rest of the meal, our conversation shifted to shared concerns about the children. As we talked, I sensed relief in both of us. We were no longer married, but some continuity was preserved. "You're still like family to me," I concluded as we rose to go.

"I feel the same," Stan replied, as he helped me on with my coat.

From that occasion onward, our relationship was indeed marked by a newfound spirit of cooperation. We both strived to achieve the art of good will, to avoid two pitfalls—the bitterness of continued feuding and the nostalgia for our former married state. We began to direct our gaze away from the past, toward the present and future. We became comrades in the effort of raising our children well. Like an old and valued friend, Stan was there to take the children to the dentist, to ballet lessons, to soccer games. As they grew older, we went together to events at their school, met their teachers at report card conferences, rooted for them at their baseball games.

An ease accompanied our encounters that had never been there before. From the shattering of divorce, we finally moved to a different union—founded on a common commitment to the children we had conceived and continued to share. Our broken spirits slowly mended. Our divorced relationship became, ironically, more successful than our married one had been.

Part 5

LOOKING IN A
NEW DIRECTION

CHAPTER ONE

MAY, 1977

Love when it came was unexpected. I was sitting at the kitchen table, sipping coffee, on a May afternoon. From the softness and angle of the sun through the window, I judged that it was about four o'clock. Alone in the house again, on another Saturday, alone because it was Stan's weekend with the children, alone with only the sounds of the kitchen clock for company. I had just woken from a nap and felt thick and heavy. I stared at the clock absently, and then found myself watching it in earnest. I became absorbed by the second hand, methodically ticking away the time—time wasted, gone for good.

I wonder why people say, "Time heals all wounds." That makes no sense, because the wounds I feel are cumulative, an endless string of meaningless encounters with men whose names were forgotten after they never called again, no single one of whom was important enough to be called a wound, any one of whom I could have gotten over easily if he had been the only one. But the wound lay in the pattern of pointlessness—the chance encounters, the bundling into bed after an evening of attention and small favors. Dinner, wine, perhaps flowers. The sense of regret the morning after. Nonetheless, the waiting by the phone. The phone silent for days, just long enough to announce that it was over, without so much as a polite call or meeting to say so directly. Left feeling lonelier than when I was alone.

I would never have left Stan, I reflected, if I had known that freedom amounted to this. Better to be in a marriage, any marriage, however alienated, than alone like this, trailing a string of one- or two-night encounters that spoke of multiple meaninglessness.

I roused myself from the table to prepare a light supper, when there was a knock at the door. I opened it to find Robert standing there, in clean jeans and a pressed shirt, hair trimmed neatly, eyes alight with a smile.

Somehow I was not surprised that he was standing there. I was surprised at the change a year and a half had made. Gone was the haunted look, the desperation that did not lie quietly in the background, the pain of a previous time. He looked well to me in a way that he had not before, as if he had enjoyed the beneficence of some kindly power, or perhaps had himself wrung a new confidence out of the sweat of dismantling a worn-out marriage.

I was glad that he was here, because he was one of those people who make an indelible impression on your life, whether they be friends or lovers, mentors or strangers. They may stay for years, or, like Robert, they may go quickly, but their coming is always an unexpected gift. It matters little whether you have much in common with them or little in common, because you share a secret understanding when you meet.

So it was now, as always, with Robert. As we stood at the door grinning at each other, the year since we had last met dropped away like a shed skin. We resumed our conversation as easily as if it had been interrupted only yesterday.

"I've thought about you often," he said as he slipped his arms around me. "I never could get you out of my mind."

I traced his face slowly with one finger, wondering at my luck that he should have come back. Then we moved to the living room sofa and laughed and talked, again charmed by each other and by the connection that always connected. We spoke of our failed marriages, about his current custody battle for his daughter, about my hospitalization and why we could not have continued before. Later we moved in unison to the bedroom.

Whereas with madness, one feels timelessness as a great divider that isolates the instants and splinters the self, the timelessness of love is a gathering of temporal moments into one cohesive sphere, timeless in the sense of no mechanical division, as if even past and future lay in one another's arms. To love the night away, with no sense of tomorrow, free for the moment of yesterday's limitations, wrapped for the present in the smiles of a spring night, is to know the meaning of luck, or if luckier, of grace. To know the gentleness of a hand that traces the outline of your face, that smoothes away the lines that have worried your brow, outlining, still with gentleness, the curve of your breast, sliding down your body to find the places of secret pleasure, bodies stretching and straining in physical attunement, wanting the final release to be soon and in unison, to mirror the enchantment of a rare and instant understanding, to fit the body's pleasures to the ungrasped soul, and when all is accomplished, to lie together with time lifted, is to know for one moment the sweet laughter of the gods.

We made love to each other again and again that night, with a hunger that found no easy appeasement. As we loved each other, I suddenly felt the inadequacy of my physical beauty. I wanted to have a perfect body for him. When I told him my fears, he only smiled and continued his caresses. "You don't have the kind of body that they make statues out of," he said laughingly, "but how you can move!"

Later, in the early morning hours, we returned to the study, where I kept my stereo. Feeling the splendor of our mutual nakedness, we played "Lay Lady Lay" and danced, moving slowly and sensually, our nude bodies intertwining in the center of a room filled with books and other trappings of the intellectual life.

Later yet, just as dawn was breaking, we played Chopin nocturnes and settled on the sofa to watch the first rose-colored light filter through the windows. Robert draped me with a blanket so that I would not be cold.

Finally it was time for him to go. As he was dressing, he suddenly turned to me and said, "Did you notice that we have the same color eyes?" I nodded, and he continued musingly. "They're very unusual eyes," he said, "gray-green." He was quiet for a few moments. "Our kind of eyes are very sensitive to the light."

I smiled in acknowledgment.

Again and again, afterward, I thought of that night with Robert, and of those that followed, as a salutation from the Muses, who understood the simultaneous needs of the flesh and the spirit, the human frailty that can be so touched by its mirror image. Love with Robert was a compelling experience that pronounced the body good and the mind its servant, a step into the Garden of the Happy People that I had earlier only dared to dream. He loved in me what I most admired in myself—not beauty or intellect, but the power to survive, the courage to fight with demons and prevail.

What I remember most about that period with Robert was its beginning and its end, almost a year later. What passed in the middle—stolen hours carefully arranged, glimpses of each other within the confines of our restricted social situation, leisurely afternoons in the country lunching at quaint rustic inns—passed before my eyes with the inevitability of a dream play whose middle is dictated by the playwright's conception of the first scene and the last.

Because of Robert, I learned a little more about loving myself, because I loved him and he was my counterpart. We were both lovers of intensity, seeking the highs and tolerating the lows for the sake of the exercise of our imaginations. He was a person of high temperament, more drawn to the language of metaphor than to the practicalities of the daily round. Like children at play, we strove to be sensible, but our spirits often took the easier road to ecstasy. I told him the lessons that I was learning in my therapy, about how to live better in the middle ground. We would agree on all points, and then, caught up, feed once again on a diet of the senses.

I think Robert left me, finally, because in our alikeness we limited each other. He and I were twin violins, always straining to reach the ethereal timbre. We greeted each other with the same tone color, the union of our sounds echoing some dark and rich and primeval understanding, founded perhaps in the collective unconscious or, as the poet said, in the "wisdom of old stones." But, for all of that, the time came for us to part, to find better balance with more grounded partners.

I often thought afterward of our final meeting. We were sitting in the front seat of his car, having ventured out into the countryside for the afternoon. It was a rainy day in early March of the next year, completing the cycle of the seasons. The wipers of his car rhythmically pushed away the rain, but I could not smooth away the tears in my eyes and the lump in my throat.

As he sat telling me of the new love that he had found, I knew, although I had never met her, that she would be a cello, mellow and grounded. I knew that she would represent the earth and the business of getting along day by day. Even as I brushed aside my tears, I knew that he would be choosing wisely.

"I don't know why you came into my life," he told me as he started the engine to return home. "But I've always thought of you as a bit of grace." I gave him one last look and then asked him to drive me home quickly, because it was the only way I could go.

I knew that it might be months or years before I found another Robert, or better yet, a Robert with more grounding in the practical. But my fledgling sense of worth demanded nothing less. The elementary self-respect that I was building cried out that, first and foremost, I like myself. Better to be alone, than with someone who does not cherish me. Better to build a solid self by myself, than to chase its fleeting shadow in someone else's eyes. There is still much work to be done, I told myself, before you can count yourself among the strong. The foundation to build upon may be in place, but there are still many bricks to lay to build your own house.

CHAPTER TWO

OCTOBER, 1977–DECEMBER, 1978

One Sunday in October, I was sitting at the kitchen table, balancing my checkbook. The gray, threatening sky outside filtered a gloomy light over the pile of unpaid bills stacked neatly beside me. Two more weeks until the end of the month, and only fifty dollars left in my checking account. How am I going to get through this month, I wondered not for the first time, and all the months stretching out into the future? I took a sip of coffee, and sighed. Another month, another financial dead end. How to survive?

For years, it seemed, I had been on uncertain terms with existence. First there had been madness to conquer, then depression and divorce. Now the forces of economic insecurity pressed on me like gravity. When I had attempted to ignore them in the past, they had toppled me. I had depended on other people, particularly my family, to pick me up. It's time to stand on your own financially, I told myself firmly, like a football coach giving his team a pep talk. It's time to confront the economic realities. It's time to reconsider the issue of your work.

Somewhere in me, over the past few months had grown the resolve to address the issue of my economic survival. Ignoring this elemental force of nature was an indulgence I could no longer afford.

It's time to reassess your professional goals, I told myself. You started out as a fragmented blue cube. You found the means of sticking the pieces of the cube together. Now you must find the piece that represents your work, and put it into its proper place.

Academic career opportunities, so bright just a few years earlier, were rapidly fading. Tenured positions, the ultimate privilege of academe, were few within the geographical area where I lived, and getting fewer. The part-time teaching that I had done for the past five years was, at best, a stepchild compared to permanent academic work. Even though, this fall, I had been hired full time at a larger university, my position was a temporary one. I was replacing a tenured professor on sabbatical, with no prospects for the following year.

As I surveyed my situation, I regretfully concluded that I must consider an alternative career—one that would allow me to stay within the community where I lived, but would provide adequate financial support for me and my children.

But where to begin? My whole adult life had involved academics—I had worked there, lived there, married and brought my children up there. I knew virtually no one outside this sphere. How do you go about finding another profession, I wondered, when you don't even know what the alternatives are? The prospect of beginning an unstructured search was frightening. I was floundering in the water, wishing someone had thought to give me swimming lessons.

Perhaps because I was an academic by training, I started with a book. *What Color Is Your Parachute?* had been recommended to me as the "must" manual for changing careers. I bought it, absorbed it, and thus inspired, set out on my search for a new occupation. Guided by my self-help manual, I decided that I wanted a career, not simply a job, and that I must be prepared to devote at least six months to establishing it. I also decided that career changing called for a strategy. I would apply my intellectual skills to the problem-solving task at hand.

I began by thinking. What skills do I have that would be transferable to another occupation? What needs do I have that I would expect a new career to fulfill?

The first task, I concluded, is to decide what career I *want;* the second task is to go about getting it. But I could not know what I wanted to do unless I knew what options were available. And I knew no one who could tell me what they were.

I mused for weeks, wondering how to make a beginning. If I could just figure out some concrete step to take, then perhaps I could begin to master the art of survival. But before I could move forward, I had to hurdle a wall of anxiety and uncertainty. The world outside academe seemed so scary, because it called for a competence I was unsure I had. I wondered daily if I was made of strong enough stuff.

I must find a way to approach that world, I decided. With a logical approach I can make a beginning. I worried and thought, until I had a glimmer of an idea. I'll approach the outside world like an anthropologist confronting a foreign culture. First I'll learn what its values and language are. Then I'll try them on and see how they fit.

I picked up the newspaper and turned to the classified ads, not to find or apply for a job per se, but to discover the cultural values that I would be confronting. I scanned the newspaper for jobs paying annual salaries of fifty thousand dollars and upward. I noticed that, aside from experience, there were certain key skills that these jobs demanded— "problem-solving" abilities, "communication skills," "managerial" talents.

I have those abilities, I said to myself. I got out my

résumé and rewrote it, dwelling not on my teaching experience, but on the skills that becoming and being a philosopher had demanded. A common prejudice against academics, I reflected, is to assume they can *think*, but not *do*. So I chose my words carefully as I rewrote my résumé, ensuring that I articulated my abilities in terms of *action* words. Under the section I titled "areas of expertise," I wrote "analyzing, synthesizing, problem solving, communicating, managing."

Now that I had some grasp of my skills, I needed to find a job they would fit. But first, I reflected, I must decide which of my abilities *I want* to utilize from nine to five, what I want my career to do *for me*.

I thought about that for several days. My children demand my emotional and intuitive side. My artwork demands my creativity. What's lacking, I realized, is a strong analytic component. I primarily want to use my intellect in a career. Using my rationality there will provide me with the best balance in my life, especially in light of the way intuition earlier held sway.

So a rational, problem-solving job is what I need, I concluded. Now, how do I go about finding one? I could rule out certain occupations right away—social work and social services were too demanding on the emotions and too lacking, from my perspective, in an analytic focus. I crossed social services off my list of possibilities. Government and private industry remained. I must explore those spheres, I decided, to try to find my niche.

My book had recommended a procedure known as interviewing for information, as a way to match one's own skills with the skills demanded by particular professions. The idea was to find people doing interesting things, and to ask them not for a job, but about what they did, in order to match one's own skills against that job profile. While it seemed like a good idea, I didn't know anyone to interview.

I began asking around among my friends, "Do you

know *anybody* who does anything else besides teaching?" Finally, I found a friend of a friend who did. I had one name to start from. Unfortunately my contact worked in social services. But that did not deter me. At least it was a starting point that could lead me to others.

As I picked up the phone to dial the number of my first contact, fear paralyzed my throat. When I heard the voice on the other end of the line, I spoke with exaggerated boldness to cover my terror. I introduced myself and explained my interest in finding an alternative career.

The voice at the other end of the line was sympathetic and helpful. She would be glad to give me information about her agency's project. They wrote many grant proposals for federal funding. Perhaps they could use my skills. She would see me next Tuesday at one o'clock if that would be convenient. I hung up the phone grinning and leaped into the air, clapping my hands together in congratulation. I've done it, I thought. I've made a start!

My meeting with the social services woman began, despite my pounding heart and sinking stomach. It's just fear, I told myself. You've struggled with that before. Almost miraculously the interview went smoothly. I gave the woman my résumé, in case a job opening materialized in her agency. She gave me several other names to contact.

And so from one name, my "network" grew. I visited several other social-service agencies; I contacted government offices; I got names of potential leads in private enterprise. I told everyone I met, friends and acquaintances, what I was doing. I asked all those I met if they knew anyone else I might contact.

There were many dead ends. I was still teaching full time while conducting my search, so I had to set reasonable goals for myself. If I contacted two people a week, or wrote two letters, I considered that I had done my job. Slowly but methodically I would draw closer to my objective.

The most difficult part of all lay in giving up my professional identity, or rather in changing it for another that, as yet, had no definition. "How do I maintain my identity as a professional," I asked Dr. Lustig, "when I'm losing the only profession I have ever known, and have nothing to replace it with?" I was discouraged and, most of all, I felt very vulnerable.

"Do you remember the story of the Little Prince?" he asked me. "Do you remember the king without a kingdom? ... Well, that's what you are, right now," he continued. "You're a professional without a profession."

I clung to that idea in the discouraging days ahead, as I made my way from one interview to the next. I'm a professional, I repeatedly told myself, even though I don't know what my profession will be. I'll try on an identity at every opportunity. Surely, one of these days, I'll find a profession that suits me.

So I continued my search, from one contact to another. Nothing captured my imagination, however, until May 20, 1978, the day that I ran into my friend Carol at the local office-supply store. We chatted and I told her of my job search. She suggested that I visit her at her center-city office. She offered to introduce me to some people there. Carol worked for a marketing-research and consulting company, she told me, as a field supervisor. However, most of the professional staff were Ph.D.'s. "It's a good place to work," she said. "There's a good feeling about the place." It sounded promising, so I eagerly arranged to meet her there on the following Tuesday. "Wear a suit," she told me. "This is the business world."

I took my last bit of savings, and bought a navy-blue suit and a light-blue blouse for the meeting. As I surveyed myself in the mirror, it seemed a different person looked back at me. My new clothes felt uncomfortable. I felt too dressed up, like a child playacting. But what I saw in the mirror was an image of a bright young business professional. I found myself taking the suit off and then, later, putting it back on, letting the mirror tell me what I might be. I walked back and forth before the mirror, holding imaginary conversations with interviewers, telling them about my skills, trying to sound confident as I did so.

Tuesday arrived and my suit felt less uncomfortable. I met Carol at her office, résumé in hand, and she led me upstairs to meet with a member of the professional staff, a study director named Sally. As I walked through the strange halls past office after office, I felt excitement replace fear. Something about the place and the pleasant-looking people I passed made me feel at home. My meeting with Sally confirmed that feeling.

As she described the work, it seemed heaven-sent. "Marketing research," she explained, "is like a halfway house between business and academics. The clients, mostly large businesses, have specific marketing problems. Our company customizes research to meet their needs. That means designing a study, implementing it in the field, processing the data, and, finally, analyzing the data and writing the report. You need good analytic skills," she told me, "and you also must be able to write."

She was amused when I told her that my Ph.D. was in philosophy.

"We mostly hire Ph.D.'s in the social sciences," she explained, "but a Ph.D. is a Ph.D. What I think you need for a job here is further background in quantitative methods or marketing. Perhaps you should learn statistics," she suggested, "or take a computer or marketing course. Also try to get some research experience."

I left the meeting feeling that I had found my profession. It was not just the match between my skills and the work that intrigued me. It was the total feeling about the place. I want a job in marketing research, I decided on the way home. And in particular, I want a job at that firm. It seemed to have a social element that was missing from academics. These professionals worked together as a team. The efforts they made, it appeared to me, were cooperative as well as individual. Theirs was a society I felt I would enjoy.

I had a month left in my teaching job. I'll go on unemployment, I decided, and take some statistics courses and a computer course. Then I'll ask my academic friends if they have any quantitative research projects that I can do gratis. I'll get some research experience, and then go back to the company and apply for a job.

I promptly enrolled in the courses at the university where I had been teaching, and went on the unemployment rolls. It was a paradoxical summer. On the one hand, I was stimulated by the courses and what I was learning. On the other side, I had hit rock bottom financially. Standing in the unemployment line, I patiently waited for the surly clerk to process my unemployment check as if it were a personal beneficence that she somehow begrudged giving. At that moment the outer world mirrored the profound discouragement I would feel from time to time. That was when I relied on Dr. Lustig to keep me focused on the possibilities of a better future.

I saw him every two weeks during this period. He reduced his fees in light of my shaky financial situation, and, with some financial help from my parents and brother, my therapy could continue. I continued to take my medication, although at a much smaller dosage.

In August, when my courses were completed, my friend Elaine offered me the chance to do some data analysis for a research project in which she was involved. With three A's in my statistics and computer courses boosting my confidence, and with that bit of analytic experience behind me, I approached the marketing research firm again in October, 1978—this time to interview for a job, not simply information.

I was passed from one professional to the next, until an interview with the president of the company was arranged. Dressed once again in my sole blue suit, which now felt like it belonged on me, I entered his office. The interview was a most unusual one.

After scanning my résumé, he tossed it onto his large desk and exclaimed, "You don't have any of the experience we're looking for."

I started to speak up for myself, but he silenced me with a wave of his hand. I said nothing more, just sat there, staring straight back at him, while he looked at my résumé again. After what seemed like an eternity of silence, he finally spoke.

"I see that you have the problem-solving and statistical background," he said. "Do you, by any chance, write poetry?"

I was more than startled by his question, but I quickly replied that I did occasionally. "There's some evidence that people with a quantitative background who can also write poetry make excellent marketing-research professionals," he told me. "So I'm willing to consider you. But how do I know that you can do the work?" It almost seemed as if he was musing out loud.

"Give me a project to do," I suggested. "I'll do it for free. Give me a chance to show you what I can do."

"Perhaps," he replied as if he was still thinking. "I'll let you know if any project turns up that you can do." He shook my hand, and I was dismissed. I returned home and wept, sure that I had missed my opportunity.

I waited a full month, but heard nothing from him. In the meantime, I had done other interviewing and had been offered a job with a telecommunications firm. I decided not to go through intermediaries anymore. On impulse, I picked up the telephone and called the president of the marketing-research company that was my first choice.

"I haven't forgotten you," he told me. "You're high up on our list of potential candidates."

"I'm still interested in a position at your firm," I assured him, "although I do have a concrete job offer that I must decide on." He promised to get me a trial project right away. Two weeks later, I was writing my first marketing-research report.

Although my analysis was occasionally shaky, it must have shown promise, because I got the job. I agreed to take an entry-level position, with the understanding that I could work my way up rapidly within the company. We negotiated my salary, and it was done.

To celebrate my new career, I promptly bought a simple gold pinky ring as a present to myself, and as a reminder that I was wedded to a new way of life.

CHAPTER THREE

FALL, 1979

I spent the next year honing my competence at my new job and directing my children along the path of common sense. By the end of this time, my madness had become a memory, but one I remained on uneasy terms with. Alone at night, after a full day's activity, I would find myself wondering about it all.

Why had it happened, where had it sprung from? Was it an unspoken stigma that I would always carry with me? Not content to simply set it aside, I searched out a reason for that unspeakable, ultimate irrationality.

I found my thoughts turning to my past. Perhaps somewhere in my childhood lay the seeds of later sorrow; perhaps the madness had been mandated by my distant youth.

Images from my past flickered across my mind, slippery as shadows in Plato's cave, trying to speak and tell me where I had come from and what forces had made me, yet always elusive, first dark and then light. My past, which only recently had appeared fixed and irrevocable, was susceptible, I was finding, to countless interpretations. My memories changed like the colors of a chameleon, blending into the environment of thoughts they rested against.

Memories of my father had grown more compassionate lately. I had put aside my earliest recollections of feeling deserted because he had gone to war. Instead, I remembered the later, grade-school years—how he had helped me with my report about geysers in Yellowstone Park. Not content to use the encyclopedia, he had drawn me pictures of the geological stages by which geysers are born, from a crack in the ground to jets of shooting steam. When finally I had stood trembling in front of the class, drawing the pictures on the blackboard, I had remembered the look of confidence and pride on his face when we had worked together, and that memory had wiped away my fear.

What about my mother? My mind closed up around that thought, and then ever so carefully opened up again. Why do I find myself so often angry with my mother? Why is it easier to blame her than anyone else, to accuse her in my thoughts of having been unloving, when in spite of her faults, I know that she always did love me? Is it some part of me that doesn't love myself, that wants an excuse, wants to pretend that it was really someone else's fault? It's almost as if I *wish* that there were somebody to blame for what had happened to me. Why my mother? Because we're so alike? Because I feel her vulnerability more than anyone else's, and I despise that very same vulnerability in myself? Why do I have trouble seeing my mother as strong? Is it just that her strengths are of character and feeling, rather than worldly competence?

Why do I remember the trace of fear in her voice whenever she answered the telephone, as if she must be shielded from some alien and potent and potentially dangerous outsider? Why was it, is it, so important to me that she should not be afraid of the outside world? Is it because, somewhere in me, I believe that if her fear was gone, mine would go too? Do I want her to fight that particular battle for me?

Why do I keep remembering the time in my earliest childhood—I couldn't have been more than three or four years old—when I picked some flowers early one Sunday morning, flowers from a sprawling pink hedge of our neighbors' yard?

I had taken the flowers with delight to my mother, thinking them an especially auspicious gift of the early spring. But instead of being joyful, she had been angry and ashamed, angry that I had "stolen" the neighbors' flowers, ashamed that a child of hers could do such a misdeed. She insisted that I go immediately to the neighbors' house and apologize to them for my theft.

The memory of walking into their cheerful, wood-paneled kitchen is indelibly etched in my mind—the parents, the two twin girls a year or so older than I, another older girl finishing breakfast. Telling them shamefacedly, stumbling over the words, that I was sorry, hearing them laugh uproariously. I thought, of course, that they were laughing at me. Somehow or other, I exited the house.

Anger welled up in me as, once again, I remembered that day. Why had my mother shamed me so? Was it not, after all, a natural impulse toward beauty that had prompted my action? Why was my mother so fearful of social censure? Why had she not sided with me?

To make matters worse, when, later that day, I had told her I was angry, she had refused to hear of it. "No, you aren't angry," she had said. "You're my good girl, and good girls don't get angry."

A week later, another neighborhood friend and I pulled up an entire row of tulips skirting our neighbors' front drive. The punishment I got for that, I felt I deserved.

I talked about my anger at my mother with Dr. Lustig.

"If somebody says, 'You're not angry, dear,' when you know that you are, they're taking away your *power*," he said. Intrigued, I asked him to continue.

"We cannot always control what goes on outside of us," he went on to explain, "but what is *inside* of us, belongs to us—we *create* it; we *control* it. If I want to feel an emotion, I'm going to feel it, because I'm in charge of me. That's my way of exercising my personal power. But if somebody says that something I possess inside, something that I created, doesn't *exist*, denying my experience of my emotion, then I become the victim of the ultimate robbery—the loss of my personal power."

An enormous sadness welled up in me as I thought about that loss. "That's probably my single overwhelming feeling about my childhood," I said quietly. "Powerlessness." I stopped there, overawed by that single word. "I remember," I went on slowly, "I remember having the very strong sense from the time I was very small, maybe two or three, of wanting to control my own fate—wanting to decide for myself what I would do. I even remember saying to my father, who was a very impressive and imposing man, 'You can kill me if you want, but you can't *make* me do anything.' I was only about two or three when I said that—but that's how strongly I felt about it."

"If you're willing to say, 'I'd rather let myself die, because I'm going to be in charge of me and nobody else is; I'm going to keep my power and I'm not going to give it up'— when you're that *clear* about it, it makes a big difference in the world," Dr. Lustig said.

"But where did I lose it—that determination?" I asked miserably. "Somewhere along the way, I lost it."

"Well, you traded it for love," Dr. Lustig promptly replied.

"That's right," I answered, relieved that he should understand. "I felt that to stand up for myself, and to have self-respect and be self-determining, was to be denied love."

"Well, that's where you were had," Dr. Lustig replied. "You gave up your power in order to be . . ." There he paused and thought for a moment. ". . . *imperfectly* loved."

"In order to belong," I said.

"Yes, to belong," he replied.

We sat for a while, then, in silence, each thinking our own thoughts. Where is the line, I wondered, between proper parental control and autonomy for a child? Was it just that I had sought independence too early, or was it that I had sought it at all, being a girl, that is, in a time when self-determination of females was not the norm? I thought about all the girls I had known, and how many of us had so understandably, but so foolishly, given away something that was best about ourselves—how I had given up my self-determination, a part of my integrity, inch by inch, so that finally I didn't know that I had lost it. I didn't know what Dr. Lustig's thoughts were on that occasion, but the look of sadness on his face suggested that he also had some regrets of his own.

Finally, I broke the silence. "Yes," I said, thinking it out, "I can see how losing autonomy is losing personal power. But there's still something missing in the equation."

"Well," he said, "when you lose personal power you also become angry at the people who are telling you to give up your power, and at yourself. And if you're *angry* at yourself, you can do *mean* things, *destructive* things. And if you want to, you can even hide them, so that nobody will ever know. But inside you're constantly being flagellated in some way."

I thought about the way that my anger would devour me, and I understood the other price that I was paying for not acknowledging it.

"How do I stop, then?" I asked quietly.

"By acknowledging what's going on inside of you, by

letting yourself feel it, but still having enough self-control to use it only for the benefit of yourself and others."

I thought about the story of the flowers again, and I felt petty even as I felt angry. After all the wonderful things my mother had done for me, how could I blame her for such a minor thing? She made a mistake, that's all. I know I've made worse.

"I know how my mother felt," I said. "Her feeling was shame. She felt ashamed of me that I would take the flowers. She felt that it made her a bad mother—that is reflected badly on *her*."

"That's losing sight of the limitations of the child. Children need opportunities to learn. And every time a child does something to indicate some confusion about a rule, it means that the parent has to make sure that the child learns the rule correctly. It isn't a punishable misdeed. It's an opportunity for the child to learn some subtlety about the rule. However," he went on, "once the child knows the rule, has followed it, and then breaks it, that's a different story."

I didn't say anything. A tear rolled silently down my cheek. "I'm afraid I've done the same thing to my own children." I spoke quietly, as you do at those rare times when you trade an imagined fault for a real one. "My daughter will say to me, 'You said do so-and-so, and I did *exactly* what you said,' and I get angry at her and I say, 'Well, you knew perfectly well what I *meant!*'"

"No," Dr. Lustig said softly, "it's *your* obligation to tell your kids what you mean—not for them to attempt to figure it out. It's the obligation of the person communicating to communicate *exactly* what they intend."

We sat some more in silence. I felt a new empathy for my mother; I felt empathy for all mothers, including myself. Like my own mother and the chain of mothers stretching back before me, I regretted the distance between my desire to protect my children and my ability to do so, between my intentions and my actions, between my love and my limitations.

If the memory of the flowers was the worst memory from my childhood that I could summon up, I realized, then I'd been pretty lucky. Certainly here was no explanation of my illness. With a curious irony, it was almost as if my childhood had been too good—too protected and warm; too honest, loving, and kind. And my parents, although not society at large, *had* encouraged my autonomy at what they considered a reasonable age. So, I had been surprised and unprepared for the injustice I had found in the larger world, and had raged against the pain and unfairness of life. It would have been convenient to find something long buried that would have made sense of the madness I had endured, that would have provided an excuse, so that I need not blame myself. But perhaps there's no need to locate blame anywhere, I reflected. Perhaps madness remains a mystery to be survived, not explained.

And then, like an unexpected gift, another memory of my mother and flowers came to my mind. It was when I was in grade school, maybe nine or ten. Easter was coming soon, and my mother had not bought a new Easter hat. When my sister and I asked her about it, she said that she didn't need a new one. But we knew that the real reason was that she didn't have the money. So my sister and I pooled our allowance and the money we had earned from odd jobs, $9.56 in total, and walked to town one day to buy our mother a hat. We finally settled on a bonnet that was covered with pink and white flowers. It met our budget and our tastes, so we bought it and brought it home.

When we gave it to Mother, she almost wept. She immediately tried it on, pronounced it most becoming, and proudly wore it to church the next Sunday.

Many years later, Mother fondly recounted the story, telling us that she, of course, would have worn the hat to church no matter what it had looked like. "But how did you know it would look good on me?" she asked us. "Oh, I tried it on myself, and it looked good on me," I replied. We laughed about it, at my assumption that what looks good on a nine-year-old will suit her mother.

I smiled to myself as I thought about the Easter hat. Do the character of one's memories mark the stages of one's life? Is the secret of well-being to put painful memories in their place, and if possible to transform them or replace them with more kindly remembrances? Whenever I think of my mother and flowers, I decided, I'll think of her Easter hat.

CHAPTER FOUR

DECEMBER, 1979

So often, the best gifts are small, ordinary things. We may miss them amid the clutter of complexity; we may dismiss them because they are so near at hand. During that year I came to recognize them, one by one. My profession offered me order and rationality and the grounding of quantitative measures. Numbers were no longer mysterious and powerful and secret and contradictory. They were straightforward and ordinary, and could be dealt with.

My children became a pleasure rather than a burden, as they shared with me my growing up. My responsibility for them firmly fastened me to the world, so that I did not again drift into magical or mad waters. Family and friends offered real connection, banishing my former need for companions of the mind. And Dr. Lustig, my healer and adviser, continued to clear away the cobwebs from my psyche, replacing them with skills that solidified a new self.

My madness was gone, was put behind me, but I had yet to find a place for it in my thoughts, to discover how it would continue to define me, how to accept it but not as part of my current self. As I was pondering on its place and its effect on the rest of my life, I had a dream that pointed the way to a new acceptance. Even a crazy person, I discovered, may have gifts to give.

NIGHT OF DECEMBER 1, 1979

Dr. Lustig is sitting on a chair at the center of a large empty room, telling me a story about a crazy person. One day, he relates, a crazy person is standing on a hillside overlooking the ocean. A man appears. The crazy person points to the ocean and the vast expanse of horizon beyond. "For the price of five pence, which is healing," the crazy person says to the man, "I will give you a piece of the sky." The crazy person pauses and gestures toward the sky. "But for the price of ten pence, which is wisdom, I will give you a perfect sunset at the end of a perfect day." So saying, the hands of the crazy person frame the sunset, and offer it to the man. Dr. Lustig finishes telling the story and smiles.

My dream set me thinking, put madness in a new light. If the crazy person has gifts to offer, then perhaps I needn't feel shame at that just-passed portion of my life. Perhaps someday, I will be able to speak of it to others, if I myself can understand the nature and price of that journey: its illumination but also its humanlessness; its destination: a place enchanting but grudging of comfort, most terrible finally because of its nonhuman scale. Perhaps it is a place to bring something back from, I reflected, a source of gifts that can be given only by turning away, by returning to the cave and looking in a new direction, free of shackles, but warmed by a mortal fire.

I have been crazy, I said to myself, but I am still a

human being. I drew myself up just thinking of the dignity of it. Then joy possessed me and I smiled a rare smile.

A few days later, I redreamed my first dream.

NIGHT OF DECEMBER 15, 1979

I am back in the house on the hill overlooking the ocean, the house of my first dream with all the interesting windows and rooms. This time, however, I go directly to the lone dark room. I open the door. The room appears gray and gloomy and ominous, although it is no longer black and terrifying. I walk through the dimness of the room to the large window on the other side. I open the curtains. Light floods into the room. I see that it is empty, and that it is a perfectly ordinary room. There is nothing frightening about it anymore. I walk throughout the house. Light is everywhere. The heart of the house is no longer dark.

Several days later, as I was driving to see Dr. Lustig, eager to tell him the symbolism of my changed dream, I idly switched on the car radio. It was tuned to a station that I had never listened to before. Someone was speaking about the jester in literature. "The court jester was mad," I heard a man saying. "He was inappropriate, but considered by some to be divine. And he was exempt from the usual rules of the court, because he constantly reminded the king of his own humanity."

I remembered the jester of my first dream. It seemed natural that I should be reminded of the jester now. The king and the jester—two sides of myself—no longer at war, but reconciled. I knew with the certainty of attuned intuition that my earlier drama was now resolved—that peace lingered in that dream kingdom, that the king and the jester were now each more complete.

By the time I arrived at Dr. Lustig's, a smile was securely fastened on my face. An answering smile quickly appeared as I told Dr. Lustig the details of my new dreams.

"The dark room is now empty and light, calm and serene?" he reiterated in amazement. "Wonderful! . . . How long has it been since you dreamed that first dream?"

"Five years." I was struck with the symbolism. In my lexicon 5 was the number of healing.

"Perhaps that's what the dream about the crazy person's gifts is saying," I said. "Perhaps the dream is about the five years it has taken to achieve some degree of healing." Perhaps it will take ten years to muster some wisdom, I added to myself, although I did not presume to speak this thought out loud.

Dr. Lustig nodded. "I've come to greatly respect the timetable that each person has for his or her own life," he said softly, as if he was marveling at the ability of all people to guide their own healing. "It doesn't surprise me at all that it would have taken five years for you to come full circle in a healthy way."

I thought again about the dark room that had been transformed into light. Then I remembered that Dr. Lustig, in all those five years, had never interpreted my first dream.

"I've told you many dreams in these last five years," I continued musingly, "and you've never really interpreted them. I wonder why."

"Your dreams are *your* creations," Dr. Lustig answered. "My interpretation of your dreams would be imposing my forms on your creativity. And I'm reluctant to do that. But I'm very interested in what *you do* with your dreams, especially with the elements that are problematic. I'm interested in how you change those elements, so that they become productive and helpful."

Perhaps it's better to redream a dream, I reflected, than it is to interpret one. Whatever was dark, in that room in my first dream, has now been transformed into light. Better to achieve the light now than to continually delve into the infinite origins of the darkness.

"I do have the sense that many things have come together for me," I said, feeling a quiet sort of peace creep over me as I spoke. "Yesterday, for example, I had a day with a perfect sunset. It was a special, peaceful day with the children. We were a family together. I didn't feel the absence of anyone, not of a man or anyone else. We went out in the early morning and bought a Christmas tree, came back home, and put lights on it. Then the children strung popcorn and cranberries, just as I had so often done in my childhood. It seemed like an old-fashioned Christmas. For the remainder of the day, we all stayed together in the living room, around the tree. The children didn't quarrel, but played quietly. We just stayed in the room together, because we felt so comfortable and good there. It was the nicest day I can remember in a long time."

"That's lovely," Dr. Lustig said. "And it only cost ten pence? . . . There was a time when you feared that it would never happen."

I nodded in acknowledgment. "It seemed like the three of us were a family—whole together."

I sat quietly, steeped in the remembered sense of peaceful purpose. Life seemed good. Then I recalled those other days, also part of my current life, when nothing was easy, when I worried about my job and whether I did it well, when I felt less than adequate as a parent, when I felt alone and discouraged in spirit.

"That's not to say that I no longer have any anxieties or fears," I said aloud for Dr. Lustig's benefit, not wanting him to think that I had found a magic talisman. "The fact that I sometimes have those old feelings makes me wonder if I really *am* all right now, if I ever *can be* totally well."

"Are you talking about being well," he countered laughingly, "or are you talking about being *perfect*?"

I granted that I might be confusing the two, that I did now have more tools to cope with life's strains.

"Before you had *some* tools, but not *all* of them," he affirmed with his usual precision. "And the ones that you didn't have were costing you a great deal, in terms of what was happening to your mind and your life. But now you have all the ones you need. I certainly do hope, Carol, that you use them and enjoy them, because I'd much rather have you as a friend than a patient."

Friendship with him was something I had long coveted, but now that it was being introduced as a real possibility, I felt unaccountably unsure. What if I still needed Dr. Lustig as a therapist? What if I wasn't well enough yet to be his friend? He must have guessed some of my uncertainty from my awkward smile, because he quickly added, "Whenever you're ready, it's fine with me if we become friends. *You'll* be the person who decides that."

I sighed comfortably, glad that he had left the timetable for friendship to me, just as he had let me set my own course of healing. He never takes away a grain of my freedom, I realized, grateful that the price for a whole self had not been a loss of volition.

We sat in silence then, both occupied with our own thoughts. It seemed to me that we had arrived at a turning point, that something had changed, although I could not at that moment state precisely what it was.

"You know, Carol," he resumed musingly, "your story is almost a universal one. Look at all you've been through— marriage, getting divorced, going mad, being hospitalized, reorganizing yourself, keeping your family together, switching careers, and now succeeding in a way that you never expected. Have you ever considered writing about it?"

It was as if a half-formed idea at the back of my mind had suddenly jumped forward. I was surprised and flattered at his suggestion, while another part of me was hesitant.

"I wonder . . ." I said aloud. "I've kept journals

throughout the course of my therapy. I've written down many of our conversations."

"More than what you gave me?" he asked astonished. I had never mentioned the journals before. "You have more material than what I've seen? I still have a whole file full of writings that you gave me when you were going crazy."

"Yes, I have five notebooks," I replied with a smile, realizing that once again the 5 of healing had crept into our conversation.

But the thought of writing had its drawbacks. Wouldn't it be too painful to write, to have to go back over that experience again? Wouldn't it be better to stay solidly fastened in the present?

"It would be painful," I said.

"What would be painful about it?"

"Having to go back over the experience, having to relive it," I answered, thinking about the price that must always be paid for creativity.

"You don't have to go crazy again to write about going crazy," Dr. Lustig replied. "You'll be able to intimately examine the experiences of your past from your present perspective as a healthy, normal person. It might not be pleasant to examine them, but it certainly won't be dangerous. It could even be a final step in your process of healing. It would allow you to harness those elements in your past that had wounded you, had caused you to go mad. In writing about them, you could return to those old places and view them exactly as they were, but with the light of wholeness, just as you returned to the dark room of your original dream and found that it was no longer frightening, because you had let the light in."

His reference to a wound reminded me of "the wound and the bow," the literary theory that the artist is more wounded than other people, and that the wound is the source of creativity. I explained the view to Dr. Lustig.

"The people who write about that theory make one

mistake," he responded. "They look at the surface of things. The wound is not the issue. The issue is the fact that the wound has made an *opening* into another world, which the artist now has an opportunity to explore. The truly creative person is someone who has explored that world as *safely* as possible, and has become *familiar* with as much of it as possible. Then the other world is available to that person all the time, without it having to be costly. It is not necessary to be wounded in order to create. It is only necessary to establish a permanent safe passageway to the other world through your experiences, a *door* that only you can open. The other world is accessible to everyone. It is neither good nor bad—it's just dark, that's all."

We said no more on the subject of writing that day, beyond my statement that I would think about it. But an idea was left germinating in the back of my mind. Perhaps if we become friends, I thought, we might someday work together to write my story.

We fell into another comfortable silence. Soft strains of Christmas music from the nearby shopping center filtered into the room. The music recalled me somewhat, reminding me of the gift that I had brought for Dr. Lustig, partly because it was Christmas, but mostly because it marked our five years of work together. I drew a small gold-wrapped box from my sweater pocket and handed it to him. "For all you've done for me," I said.

He accepted the package with a smile and some eagerness. He quickly pulled aside the wrapping paper, drew out the enclosed velvet case, and opened it. Inside was the gold pocket watch I had chosen for him, because time to me had always been the symbol of reality, and reality was what he had given me. On the cover of the watch, I had had his initials, H.S.L., inscribed, and inside the words, "Because you made time golden."

As he read the inscription, it was clear that he was

moved. His eyes moistened and he seemed momentarily at a loss for words. His voice somewhat choked as he finally said thank you. He continued to hold the watch carefully in his hands, turning it this way and that in the light, opening the case again to reread the inscription.

"A lovely watercolor, a lovely haiku, and now a beautiful watch with a beautiful inscription," he said. "Are you sure that you haven't been shortchanged?"

Images from the last five years flickered past my mind's eye, as they are purported to do at the moment of death. But I am alive, I thought, alive and well. And it is only this man, and the determination in myself, that has made it possible. How do I say thank you for all of that?

"I don't know how to say thank you, except to say thank you," I said.

"I don't know how to say thank you, except to say thank you," he echoed.

We both smiled.

Sitting at my desk in my new office several days later, I was quietly greeting the morning with a fresh cup of coffee. Natural light from the winter sun streamed through the window to my left, casually defining my place. Sitting in the middle of my new beginning, I was thinking about my madness and its end. I did not waken from my nightmare in Emerald City. There can no longer be such transcendent realms for me. I have put aside wizards and magical red shoes. I must discover the comforts of dwelling in Kansas. Amid the problems and trials of everyday living, I will seek some grain of sanity, some sense of achievement, some impulse toward health. I will learn what the Greeks always knew—that to be well and do well is happiness.

This book is an accurate chronicle of Carol Allen's mental disintegration and reconstitution. It is also a testimony to her personal courage, faith, and determination.

Although each of us, during periods of intense mental stress in our lives, might have had one or some of the behavioral, cognitive, or sensory disturbances that Carol experienced, it does not mean that we have, or might develop, the same illness. It just means that we all share the condition of being human, and that our responses to an extreme situation are sometimes selected from the same menu of mental symptoms, but usually to a lesser degree.

In this book, we have purposely refrained from giving a clinical diagnosis of Carol's illness—although a mental health professional should be able to infer one—in order to avoid incorrect and agonizing attempts at self-diagnosis by our lay readers. Carol's symptoms indicate that her illness was severe, one that would have rendered most people nonfunctional. Surprisingly, Carol did function, albeit in a diminished manner sometimes, during the events of this book. This is due, I believe, to several factors. Carol kept voluminous and detailed notes about her daily activities, mental life, and therapy sessions. These allowed her to maintain a modest perspective, even during the active phase of her illness, and helped to form and order her chaotic experiences. Carol also used the intellectual discipline of philosophy, in which she had been thoroughly trained, to help balance the specter of intuition that was threatening to overwhelm her. And finally, Carol had a good family—one whose unity, solid values, and emotional stability served as a permanent anchor to the real world of loving people.

The psychiatric treatment that Carol received from me consisted of psychotherapy and the prescription of a standard psychotropic medication. Because we are all unique, the particular combination of mental symptoms that we might come to produce is very special. For this reason, Carol's psychotherapy was designed and customized specifically for her. The therapeutic style that I used with Carol evolved during this period, having had its roots in more traditional methods of intervention, and in my personal appreciation for the efficiency of altered states of consciousness and skill mastery in the healing process. A different psychiatrist might well have used a different approach.

Although Dr. Wainwright's sexual activity with Marion was professionally unethical and personally painful to me, Carol and I reluctantly deemed the inclusion of the episode necessary, in order to explain Carol's further deterioration and subsequent hospitalization.

This book publicly confirms my cherished belief that competent and compassionate psychiatric treatment of people with mental illness is a reality. It also confirms the reality of the mind's ability to restore itself, and of the power of healing with the spoken word. For this, I thank a former patient and current friend.

—HERBERT S. LUSTIG, M.D.